www.ingramcontent.com/pod-product-compliance
Lightning Source LLC
Chambersburg PA
CBHW081423210726
48464CB00020B/1370

six

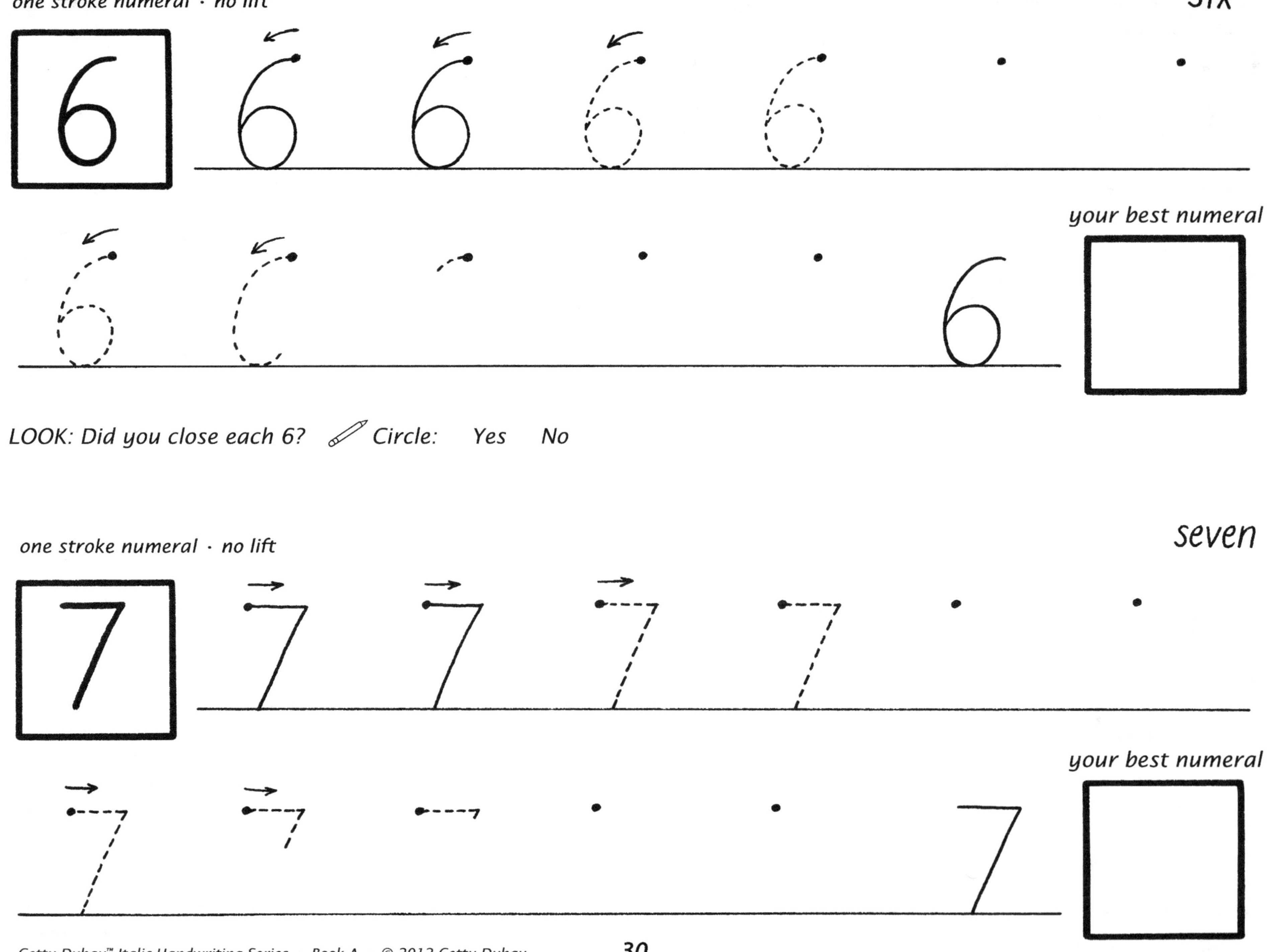

your best numeral

LOOK: Did you close each 6?   Circle: Yes   No

one stroke numeral · no lift

seven

your best numeral

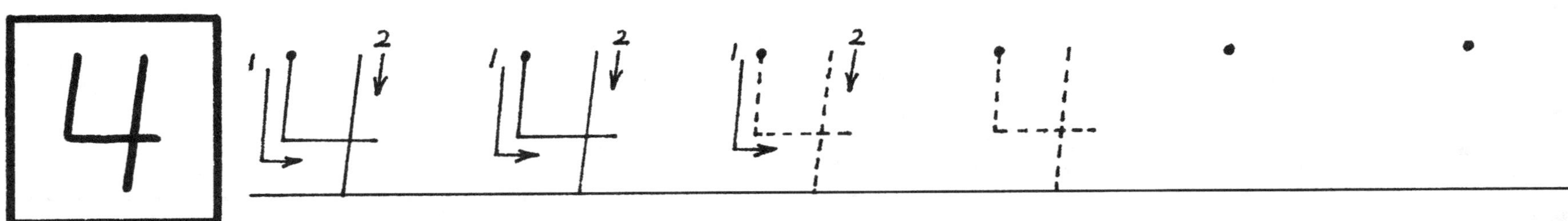

two stroke numeral · one lift
four
your best numeral

two stroke numeral · one lift
five
your best numeral

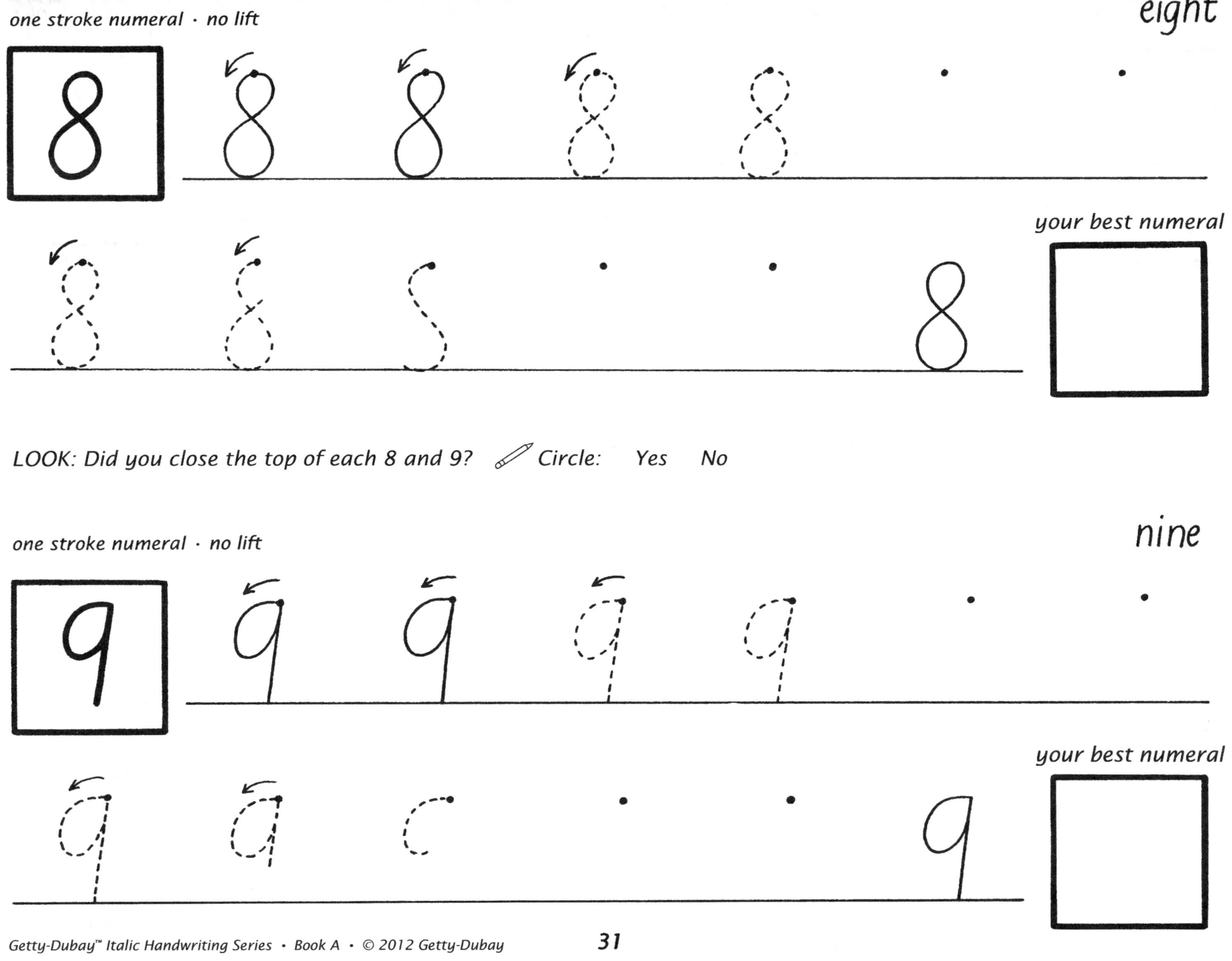

one stroke numeral · no lift
eight
your best numeral
LOOK: Did you close the top of each 8 and 9?   Circle: Yes   No
one stroke numeral · no lift
nine
your best numeral

one stroke numeral · no lift

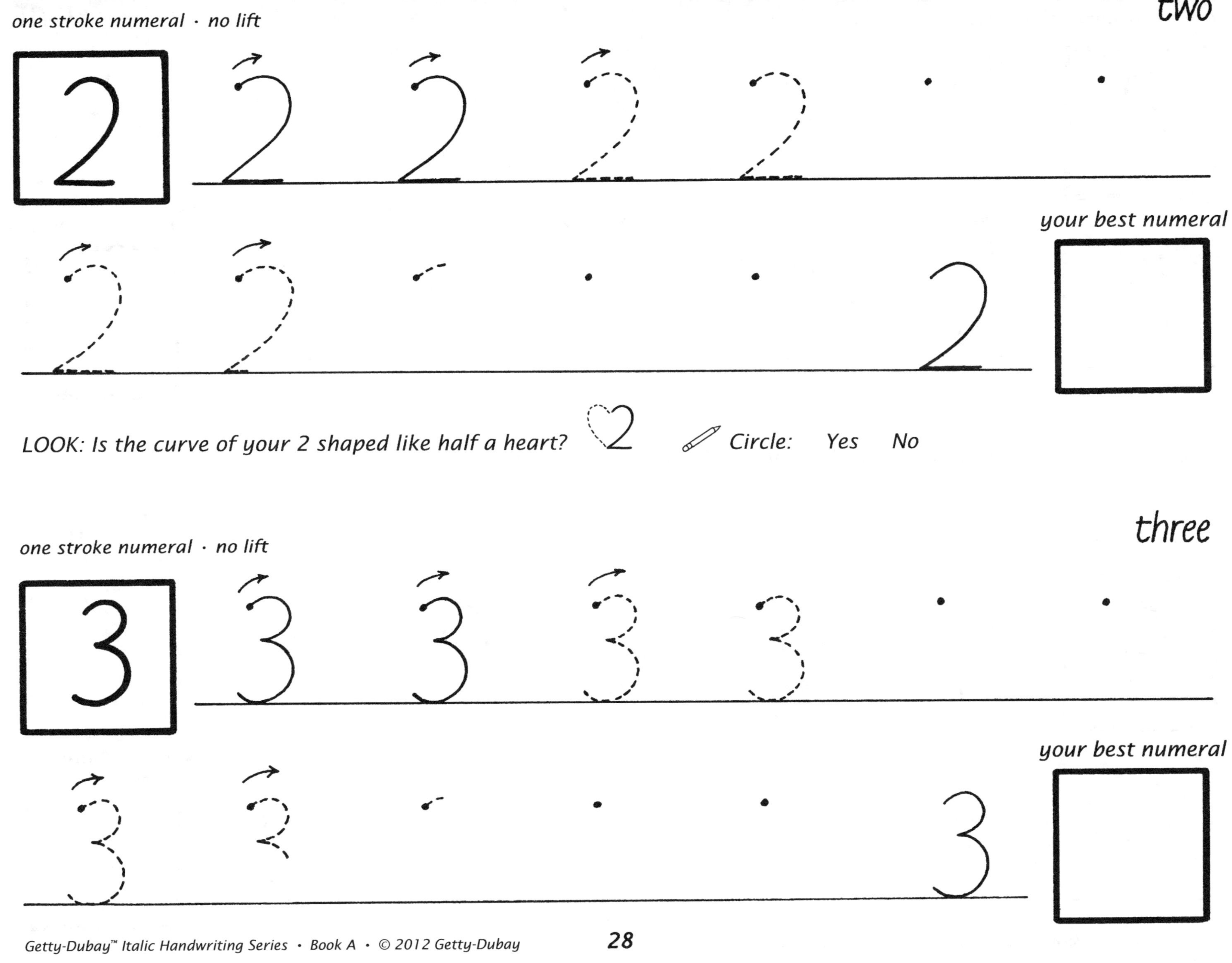

your best numeral

LOOK: Is the curve of your 2 shaped like half a heart?   Circle: Yes   No

three

one stroke numeral · no lift

your best numeral

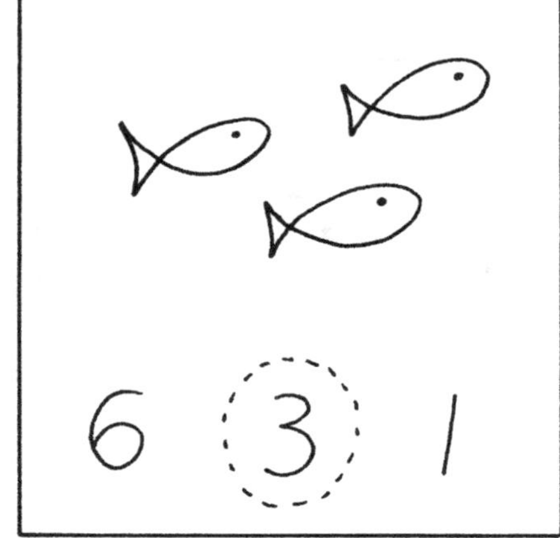

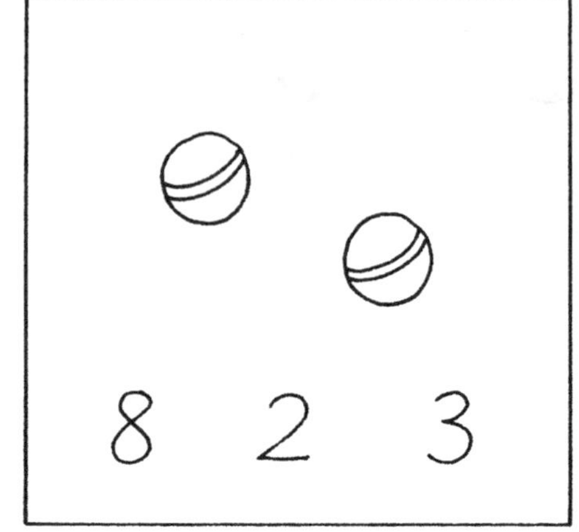

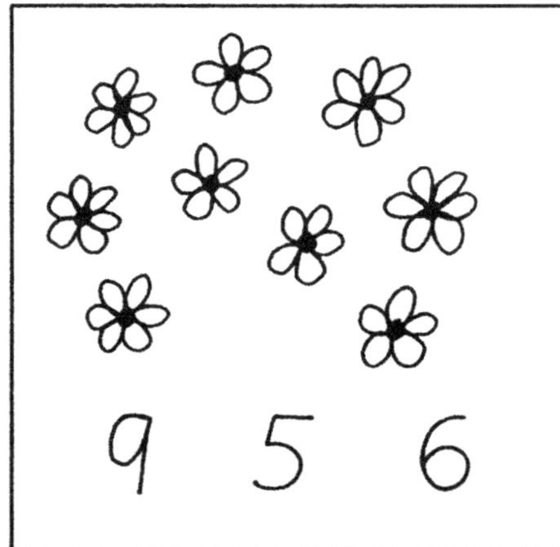

*Ask the student to circle the numeral
that stands for the number of objects in the box.*

one stroke numeral · no lift
zero
your best numeral
LOOK: Did you close the top of each zero?   Circle: Yes   No
one stroke numeral · no lift
one
your best numeral

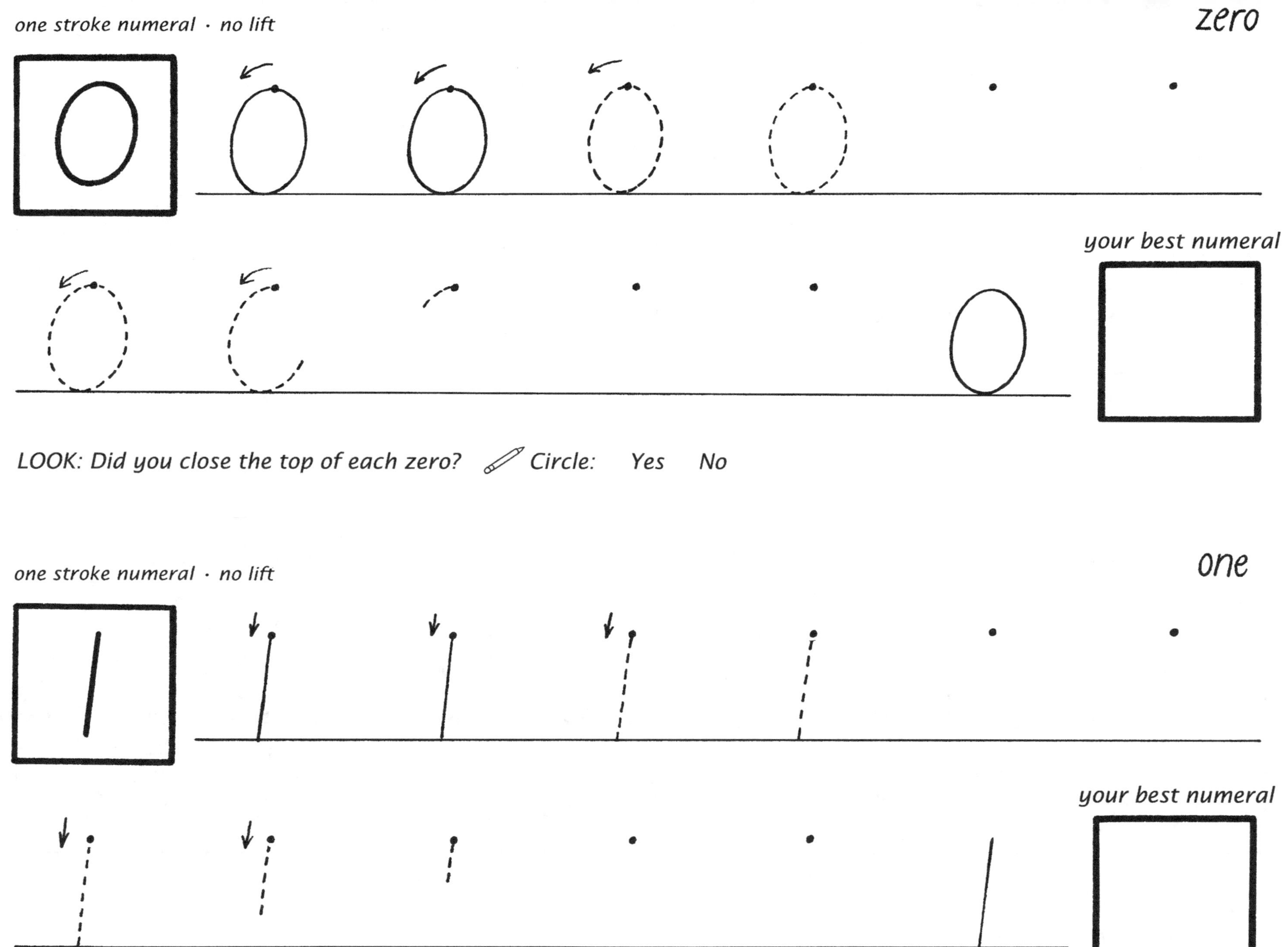

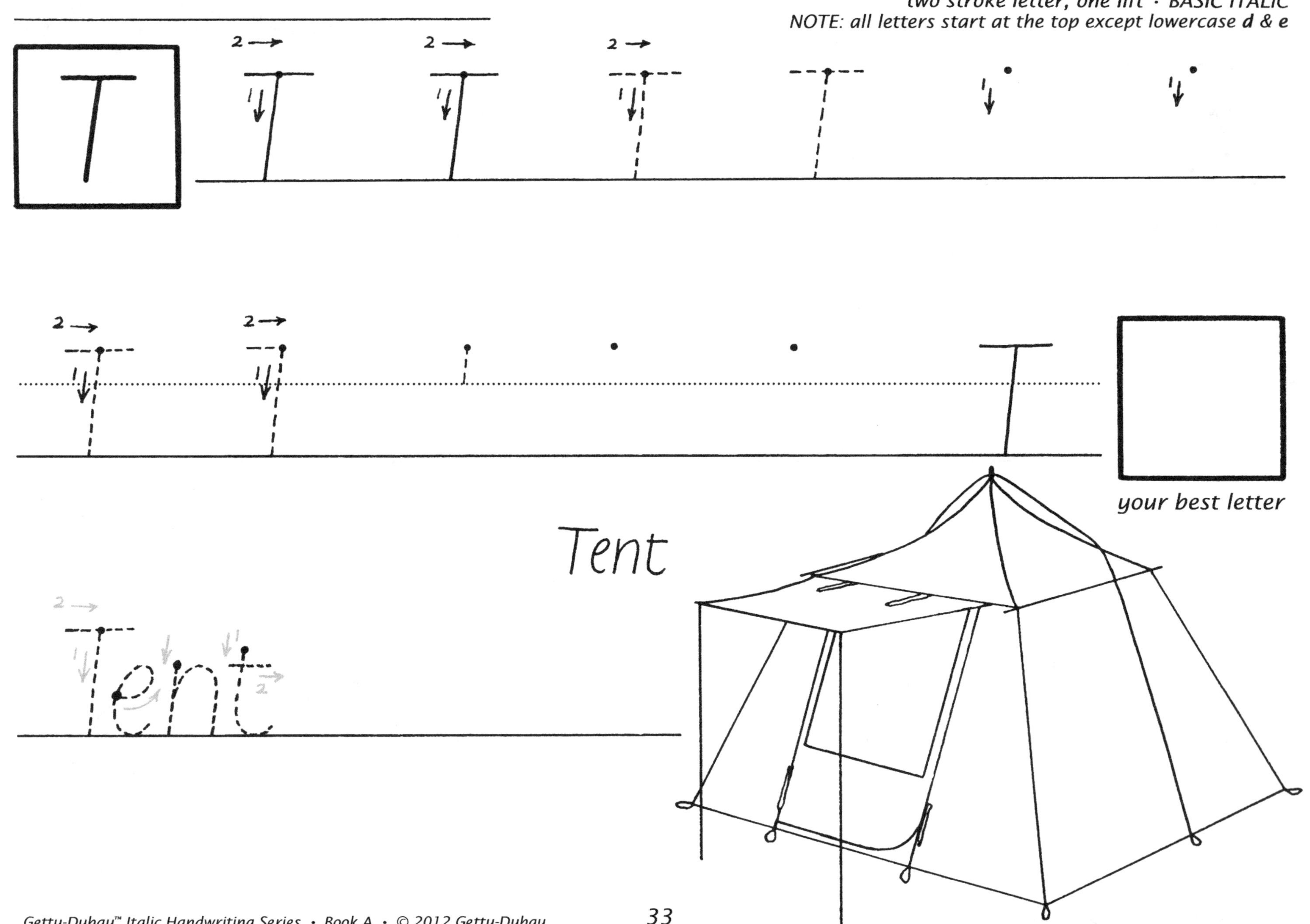

your best letter

Tent

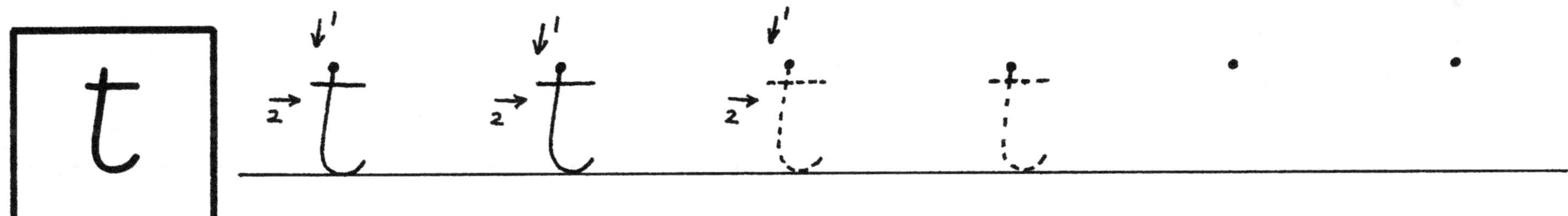

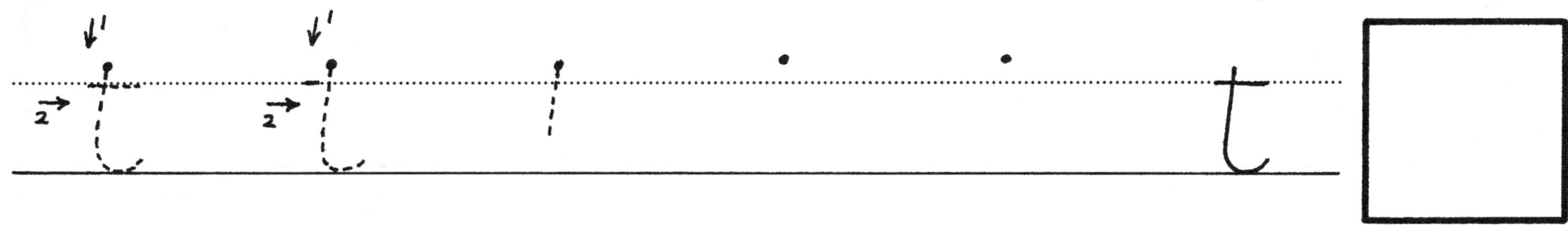

your best letter

turkey

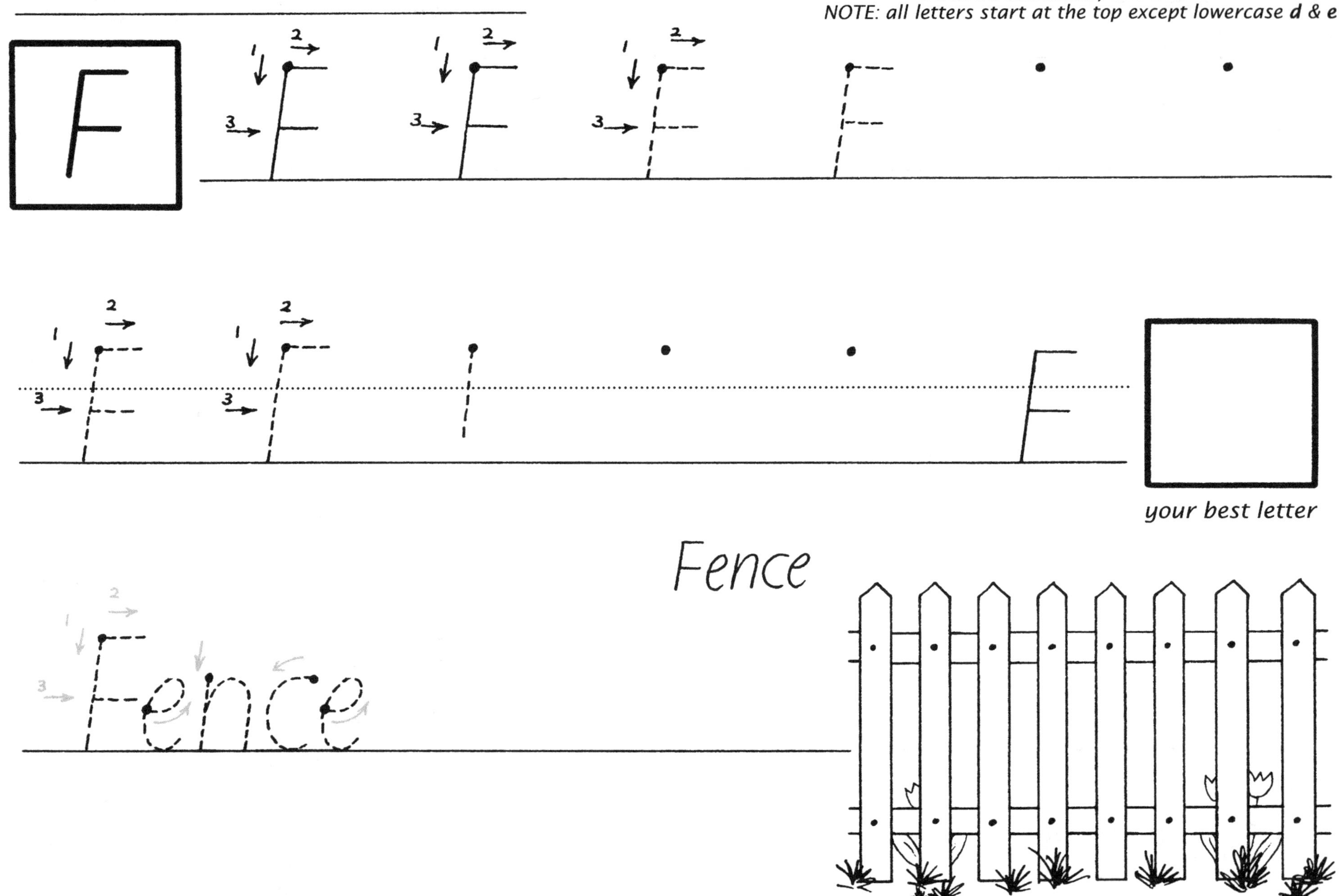

F
your best letter
Fence
Fence

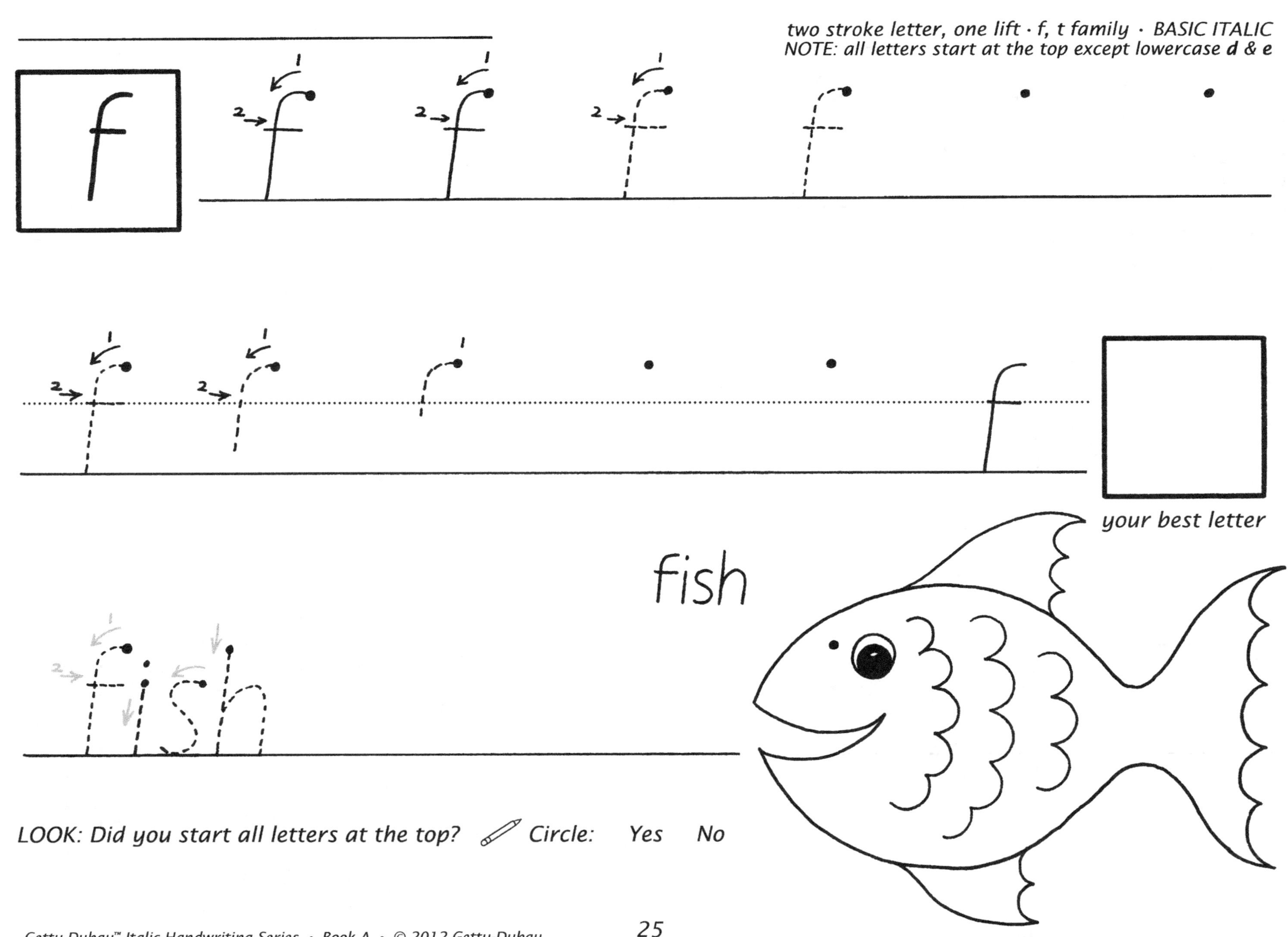

two stroke letter, one lift · f, t family · BASIC ITALIC
NOTE: all letters start at the top except lowercase d & e
f
1
2
your best letter
fish
fish
1
2
LOOK: Did you start all letters at the top?   Circle: Yes   No

your best letter
Sailboat
S

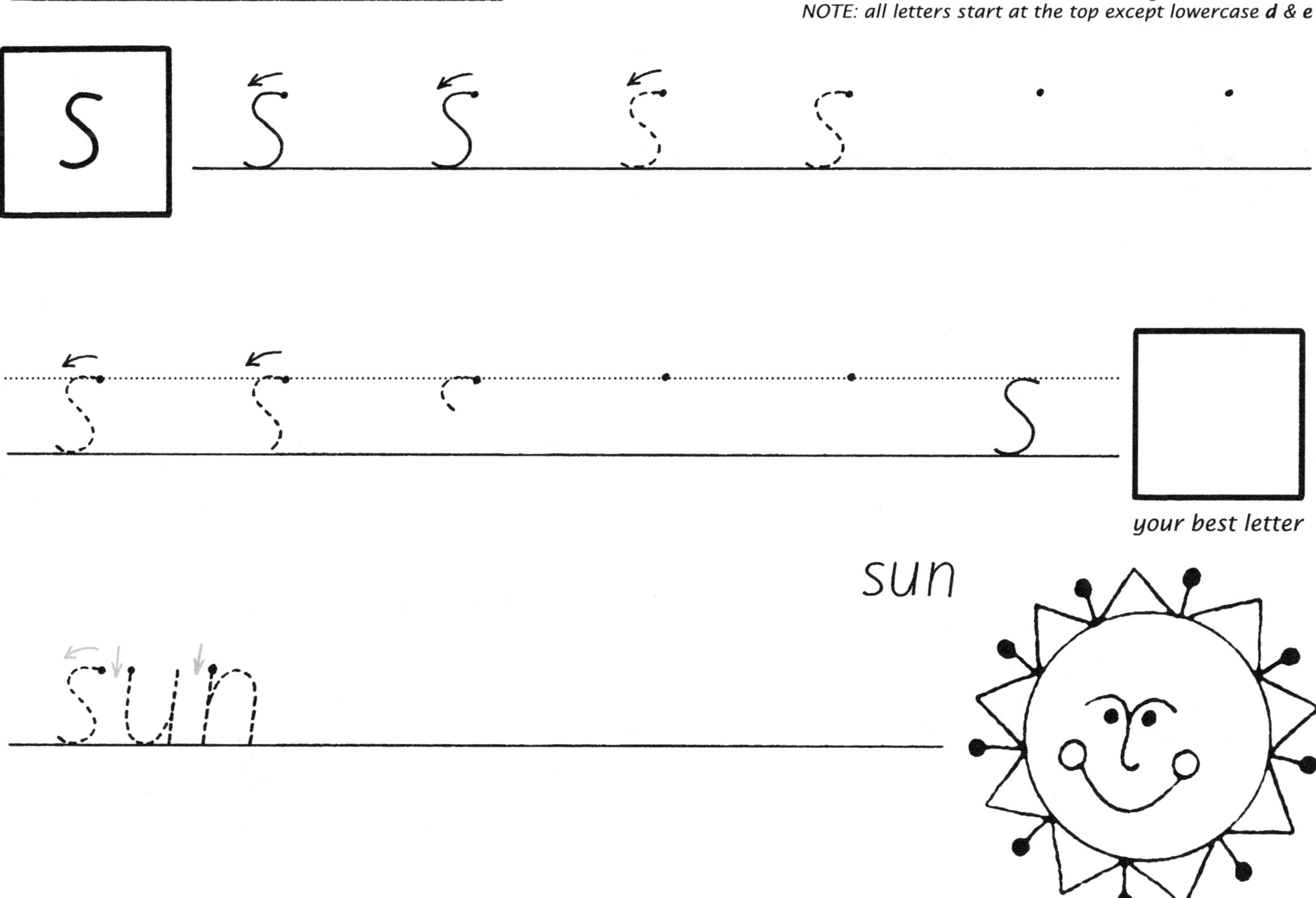

your best letter
sun

LOOK: Did you trace each letter before writing your own?

✐ Circle: Yes   No

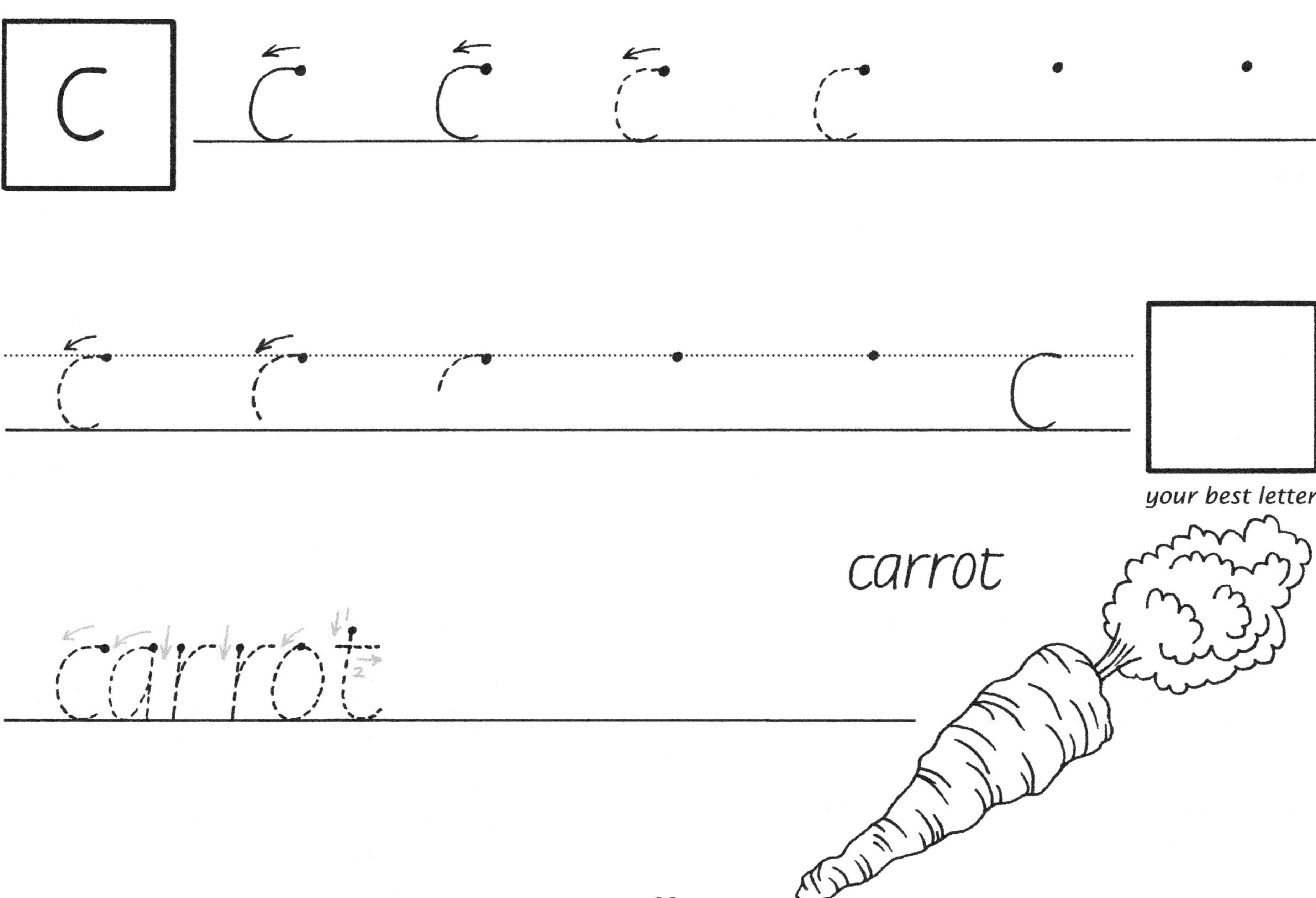

your best letter

carrot

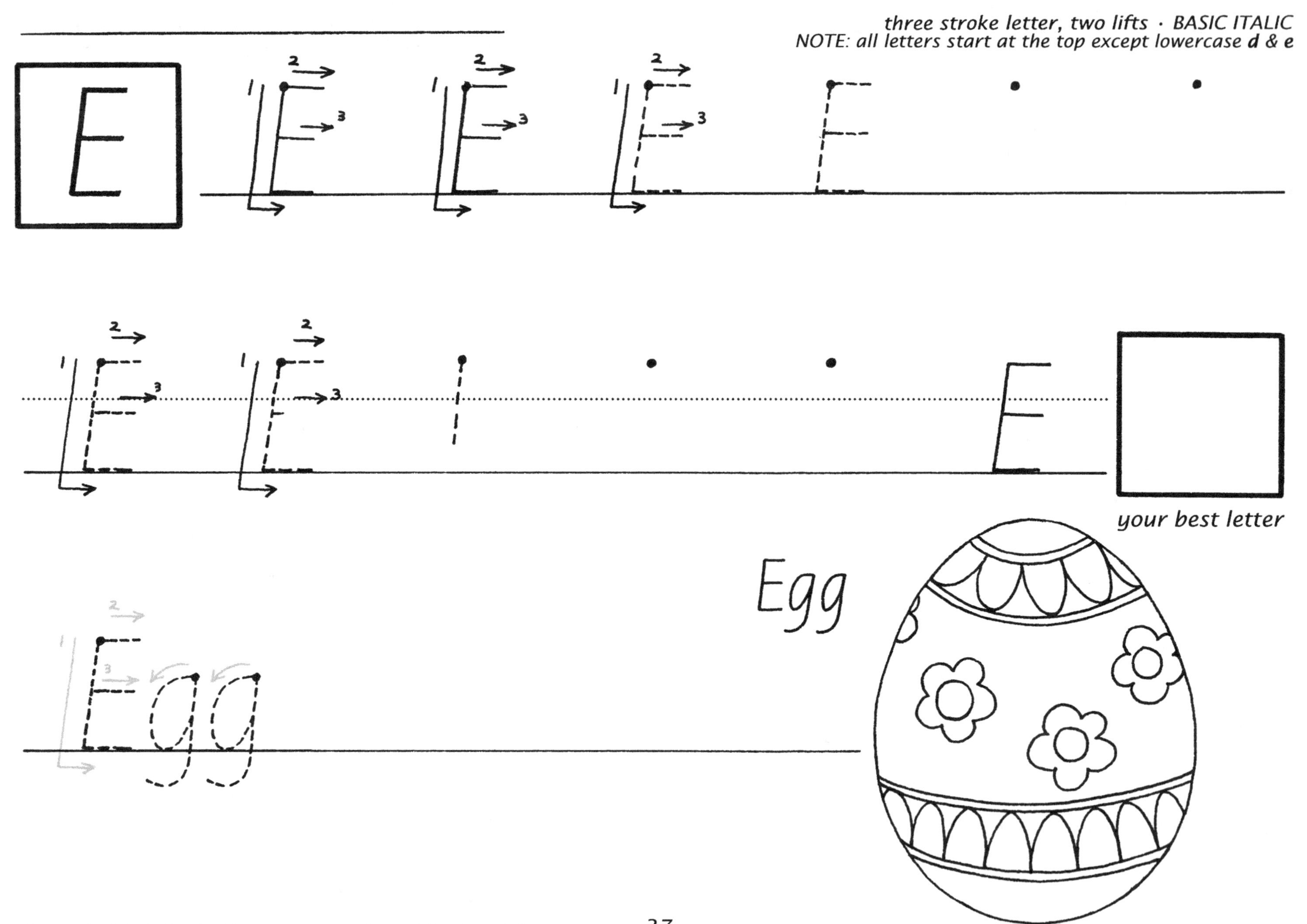

E
2
3
your best letter
Egg
Egg

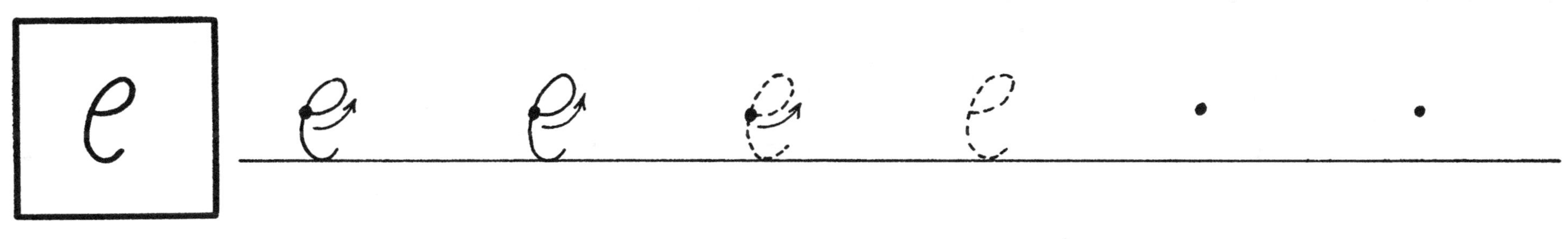

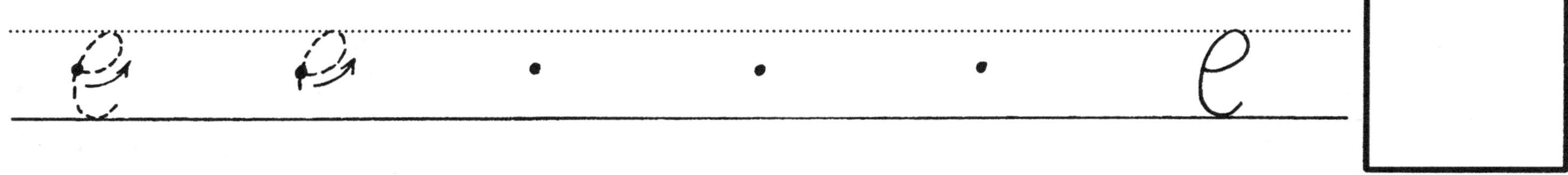

your best letter

elephant

LOOK: Did you trace each **e** before writing your own?

Circle: Yes   No

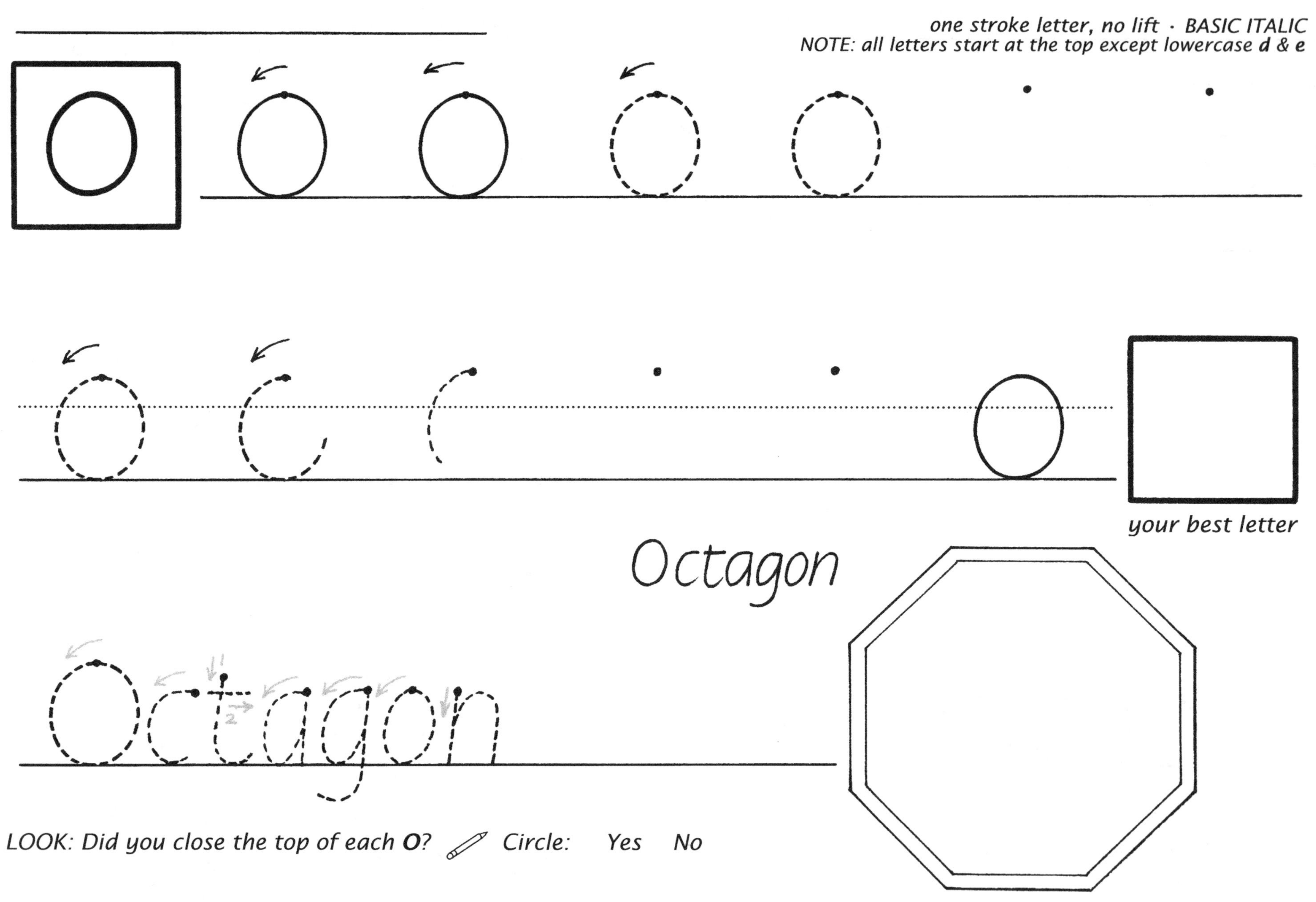

one stroke letter, no lift · BASIC ITALIC
NOTE: all letters start at the top except lowercase d & e
your best letter
Octagon
LOOK: Did you close the top of each O? Circle: Yes No

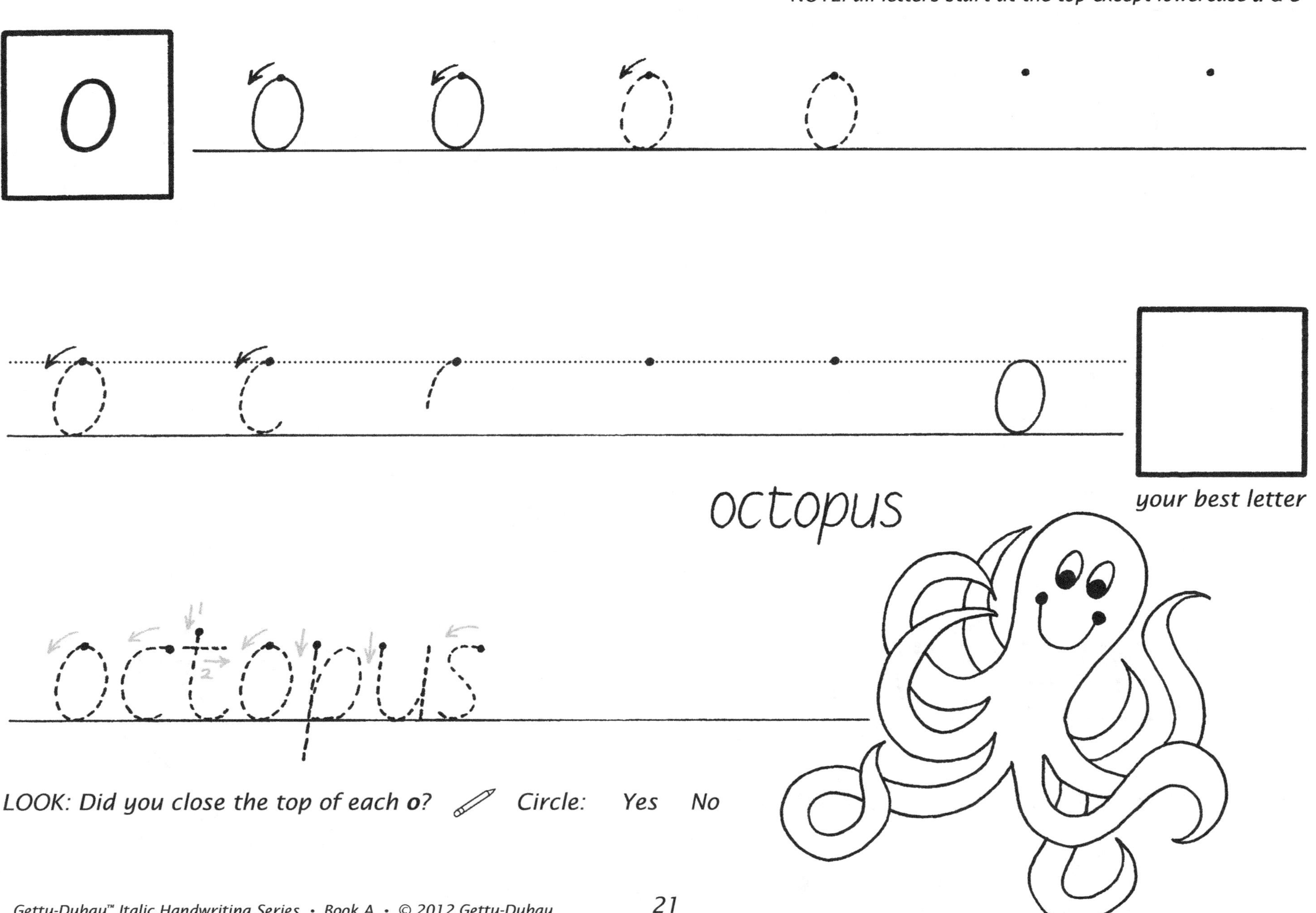

LOOK: Did you close the top of each **o**?   Circle: Yes   No

your best letter

Peacock

parrot
your best letter

B

B

Balloons

your best letter

Balloons

b
your best letter
butterfly

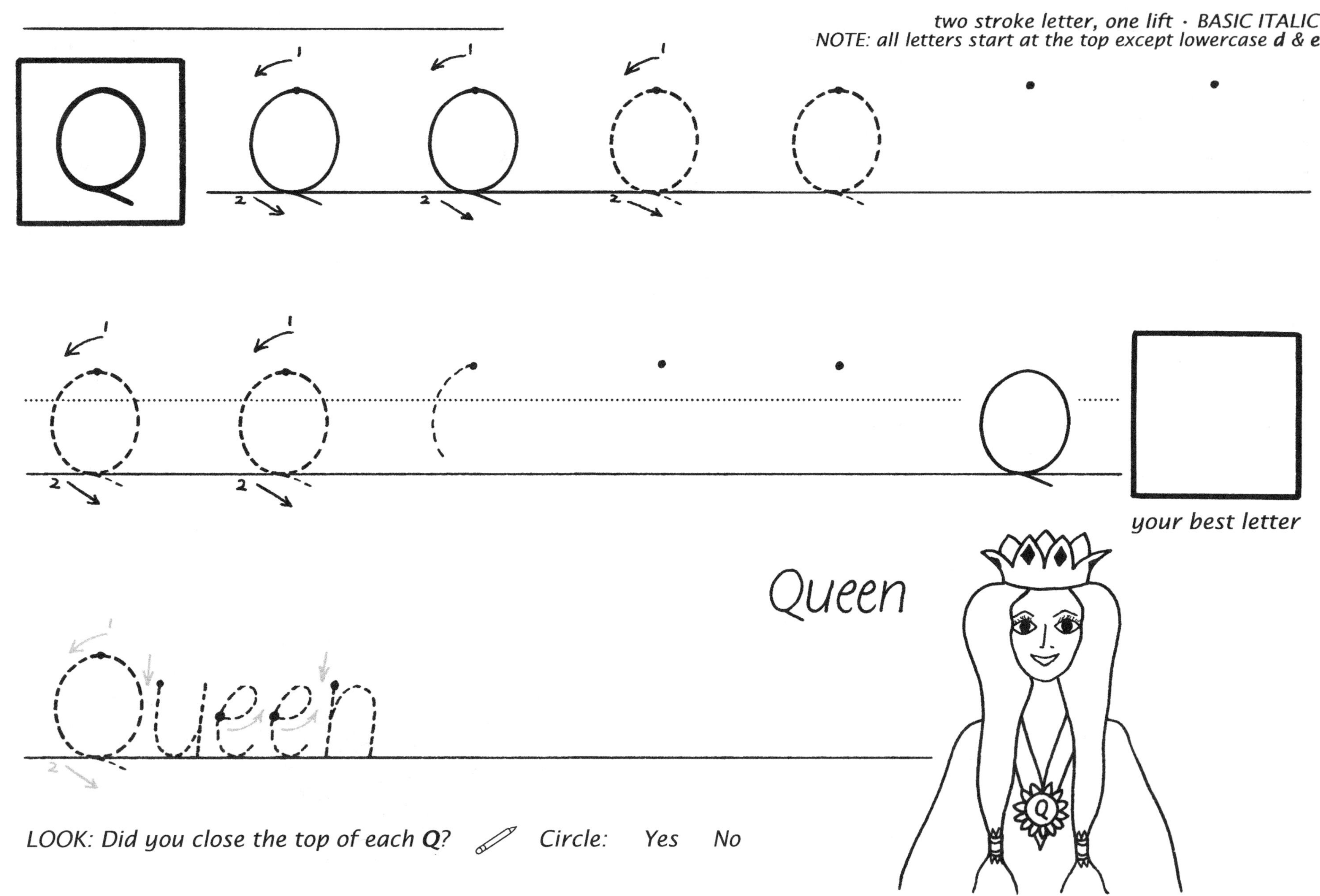

your best letter

Queen

LOOK: Did you close the top of each **Q**?   Circle: Yes   No

quilt

your best letter

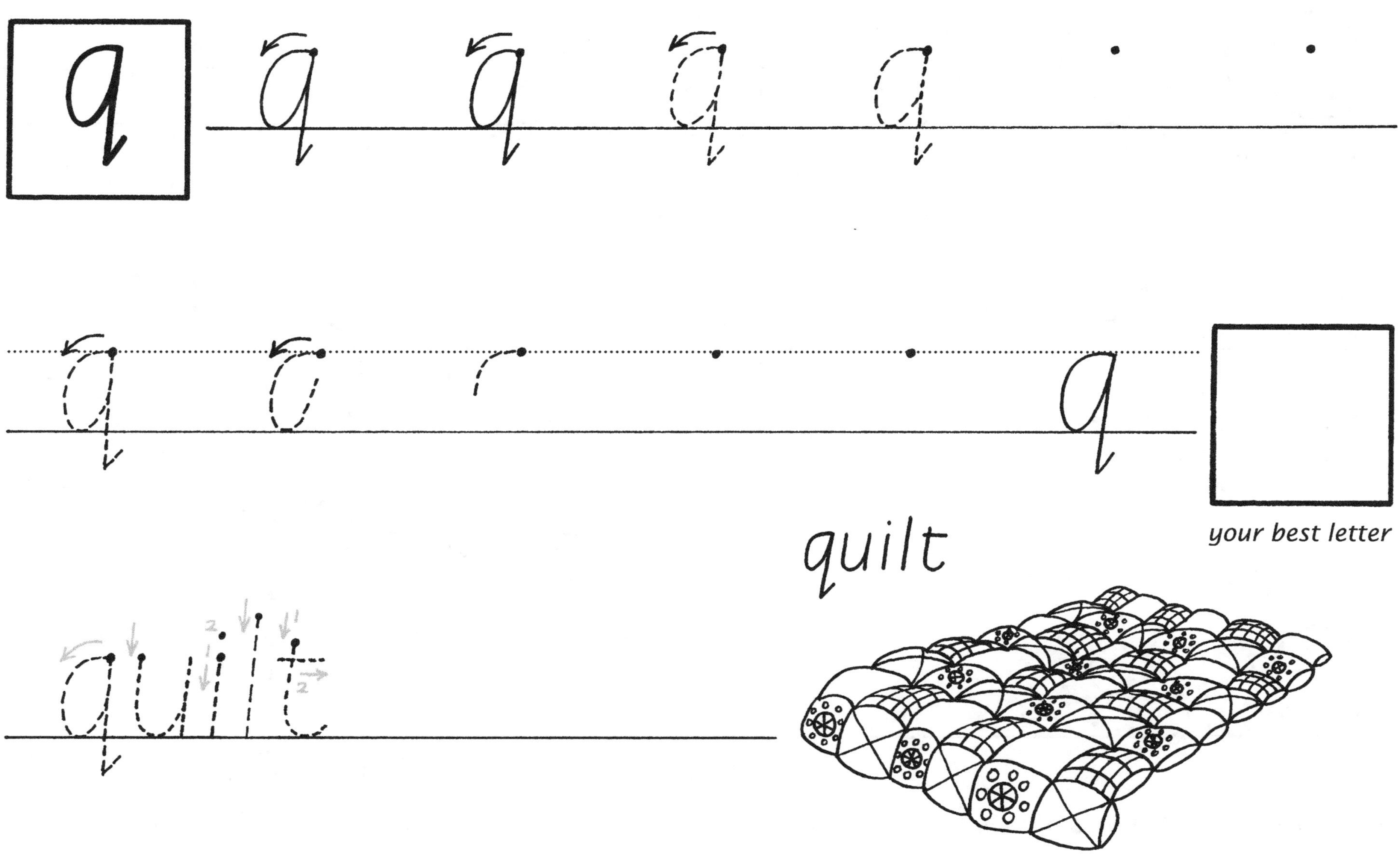

two stroke letter, one lift · BASIC ITALIC
NOTE: all letters start at the top except lowercase d & e

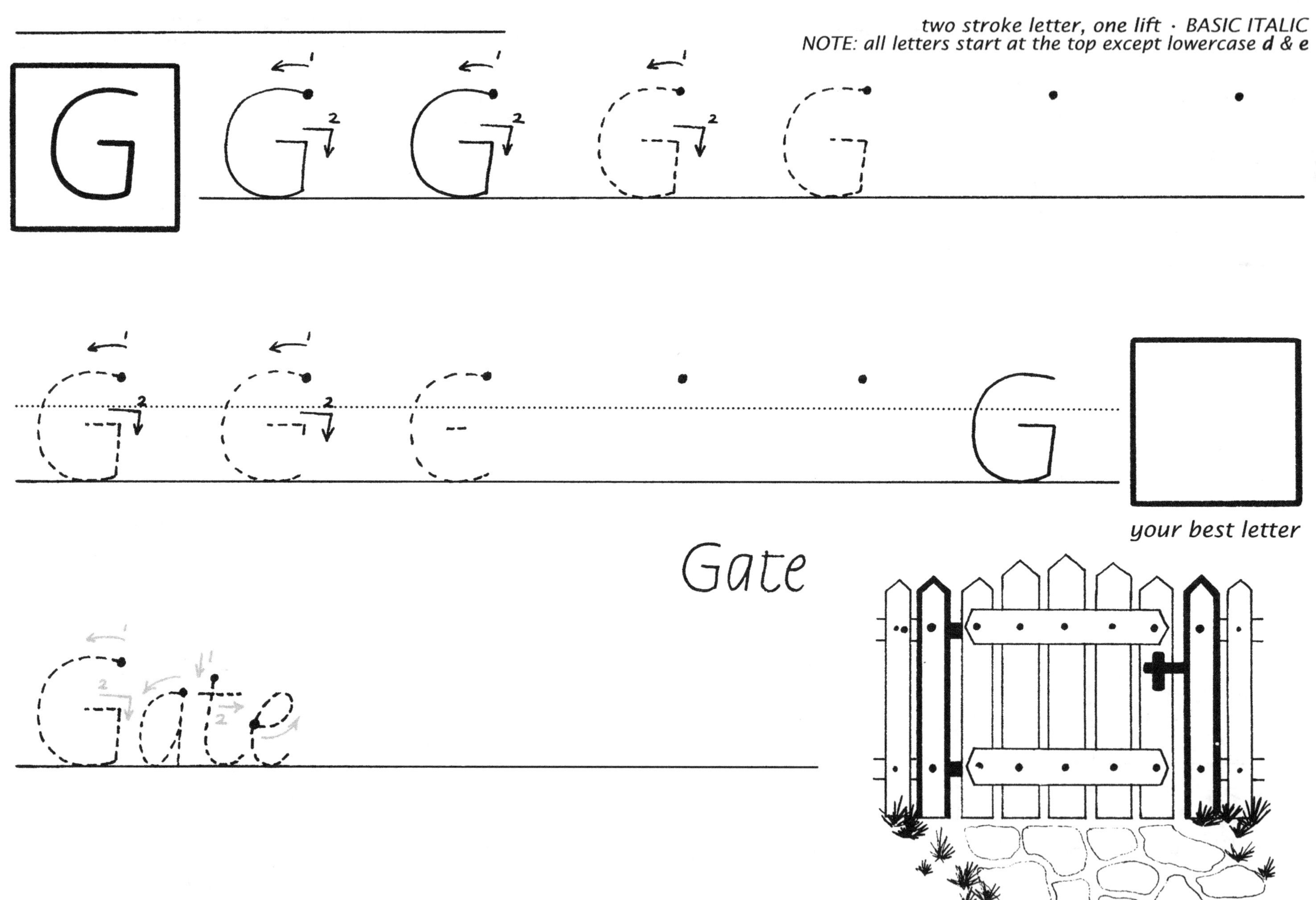

your best letter
Gate
Gate

LOOK: Did you trace each letter before writing your own? ✏ Circle: Yes   No

your best letter

Dinosaur

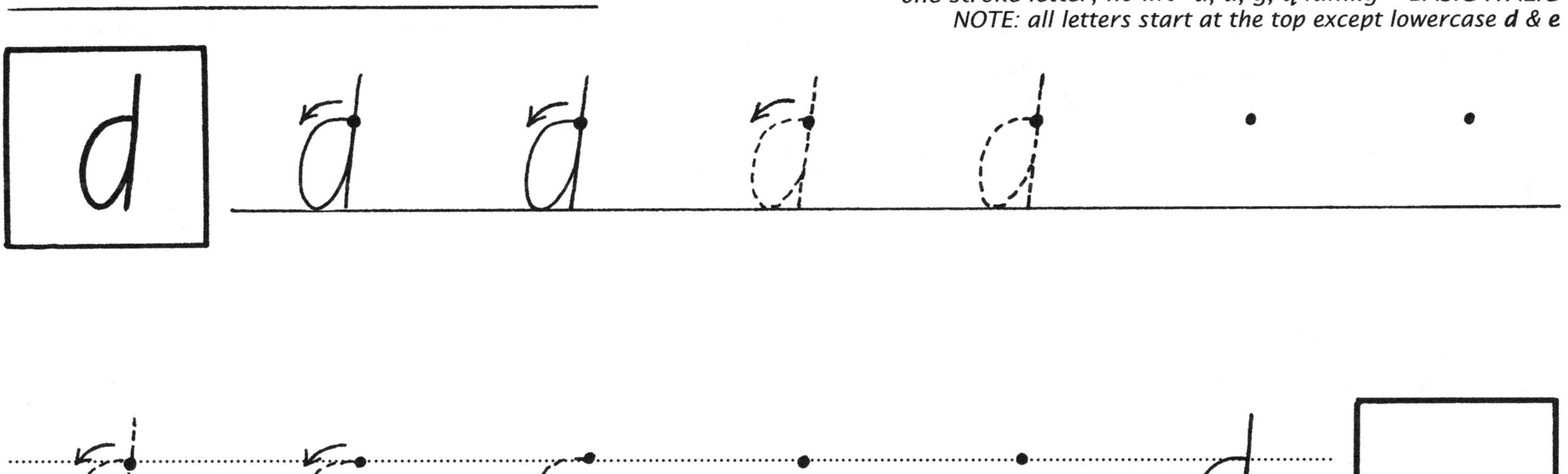

your best letter

dog

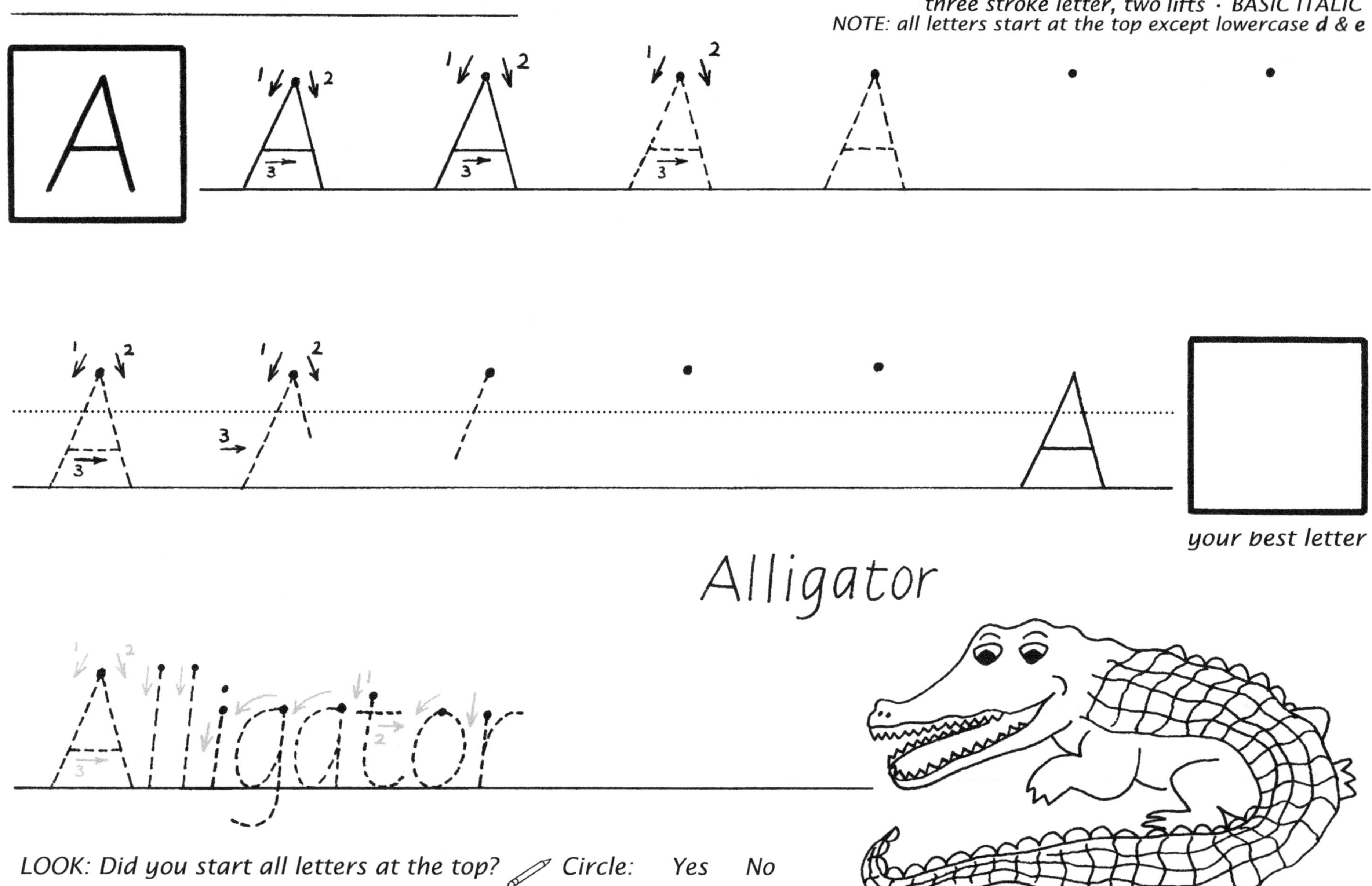

LOOK: Did you start all letters at the top? Circle: Yes   No

LOOK: Did you close each **a** at the top?   Circle: Yes   No

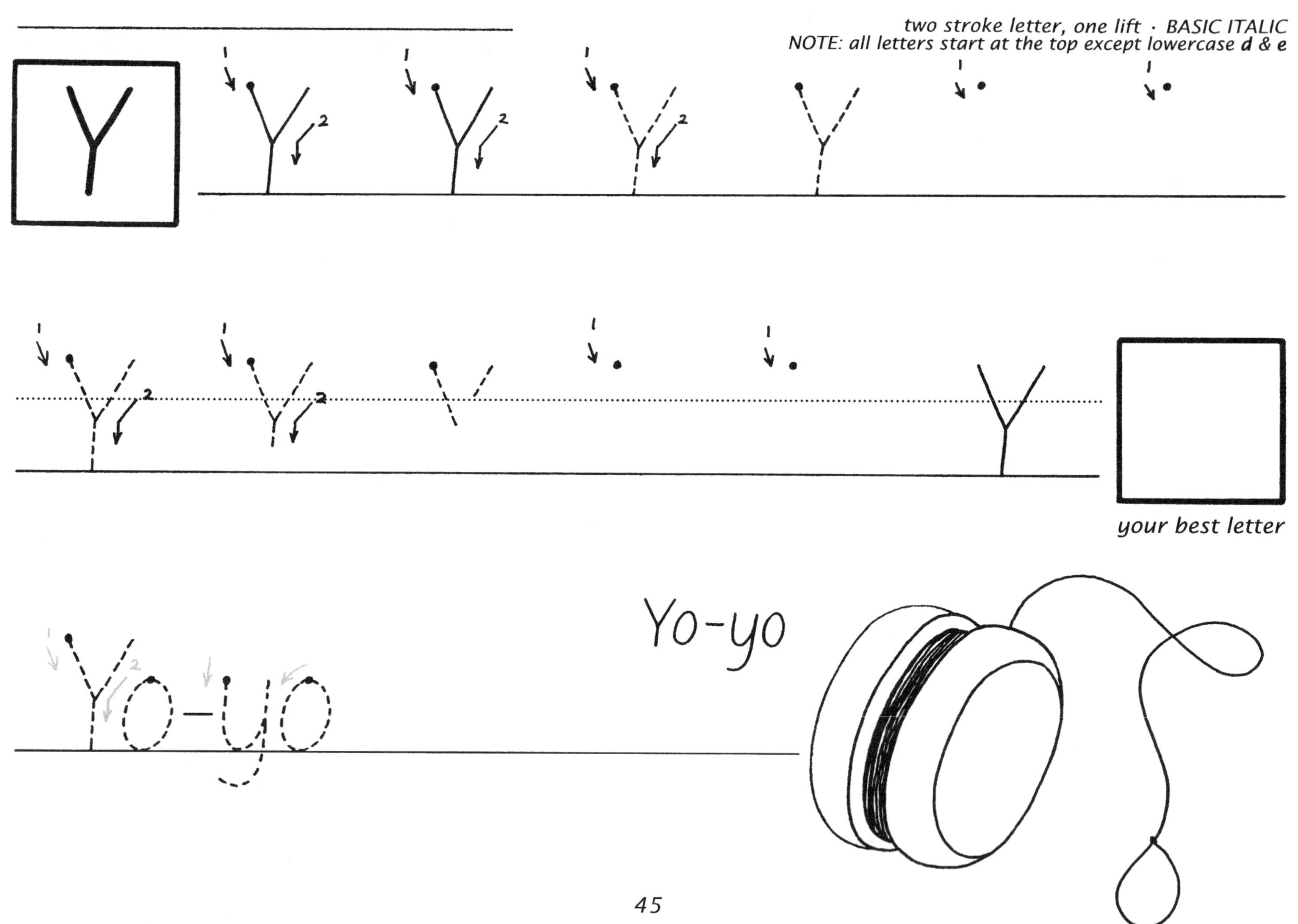

Getty-Dubay™ Italic Handwriting Series · Book A · © 2012 Getty-Dubay

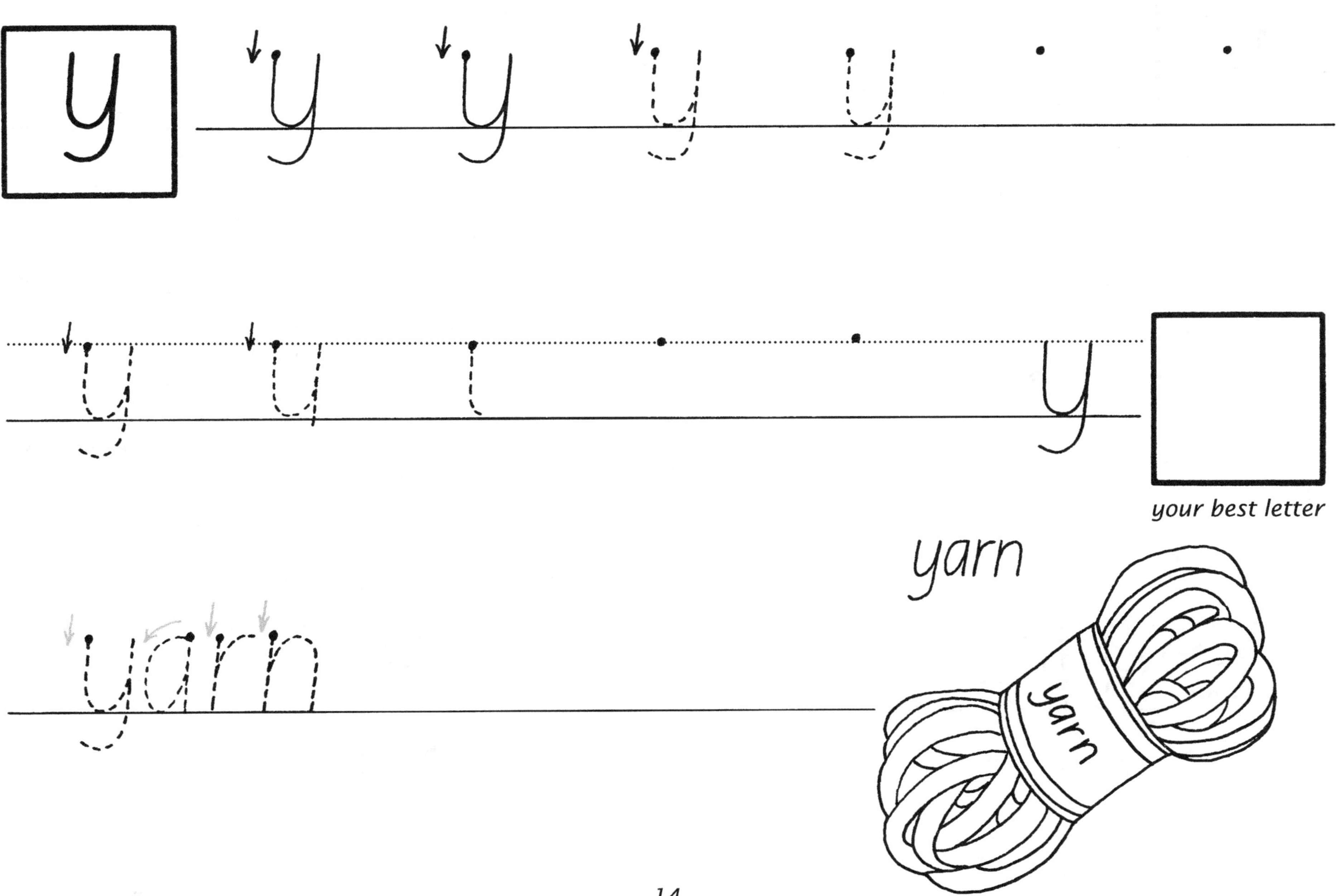

your best letter

yarn

U

your best letter

Ukulele

LOOK: Did you trace each letter before writing your own?

Circle: Yes   No

u

your best letter

umbrella

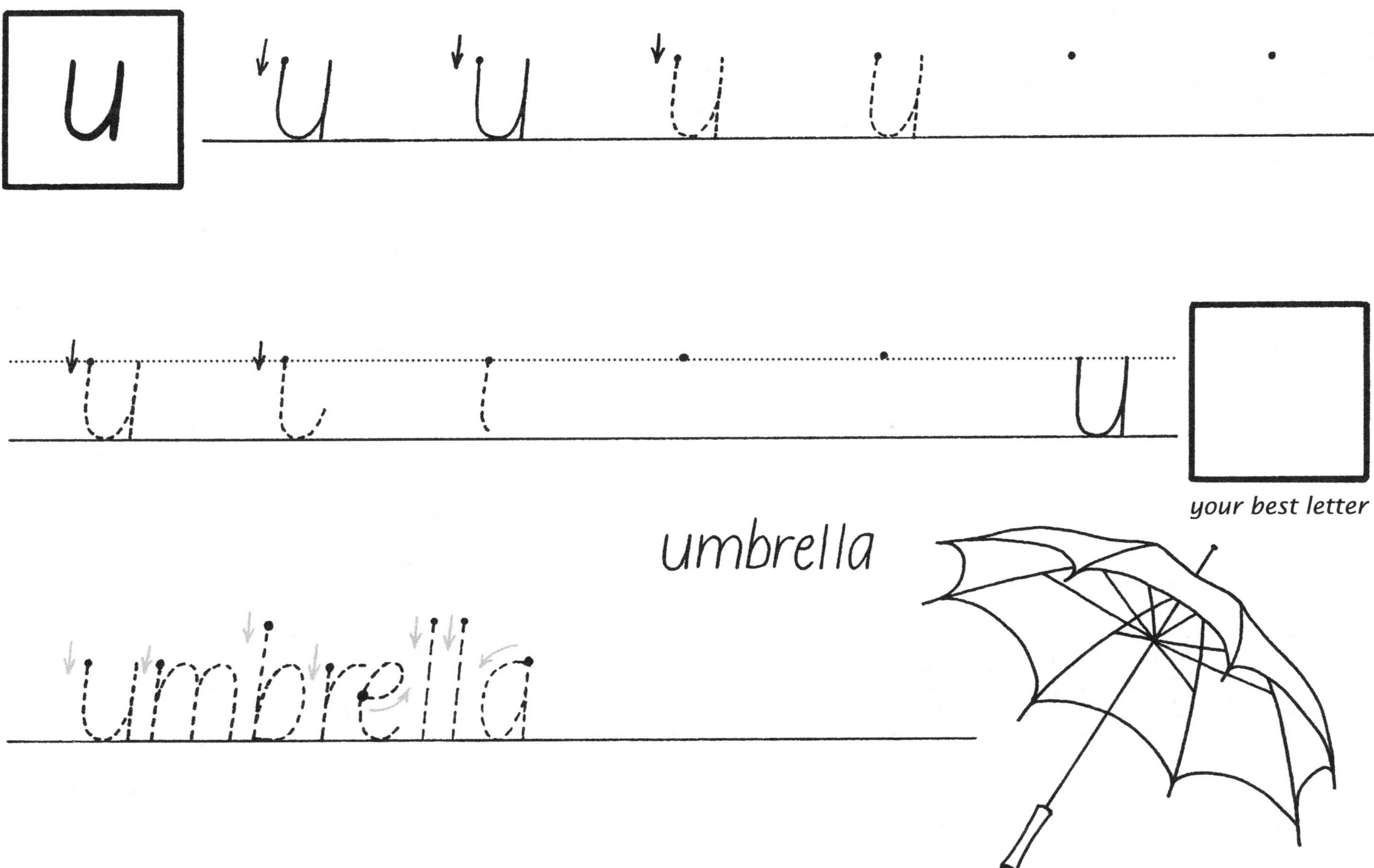

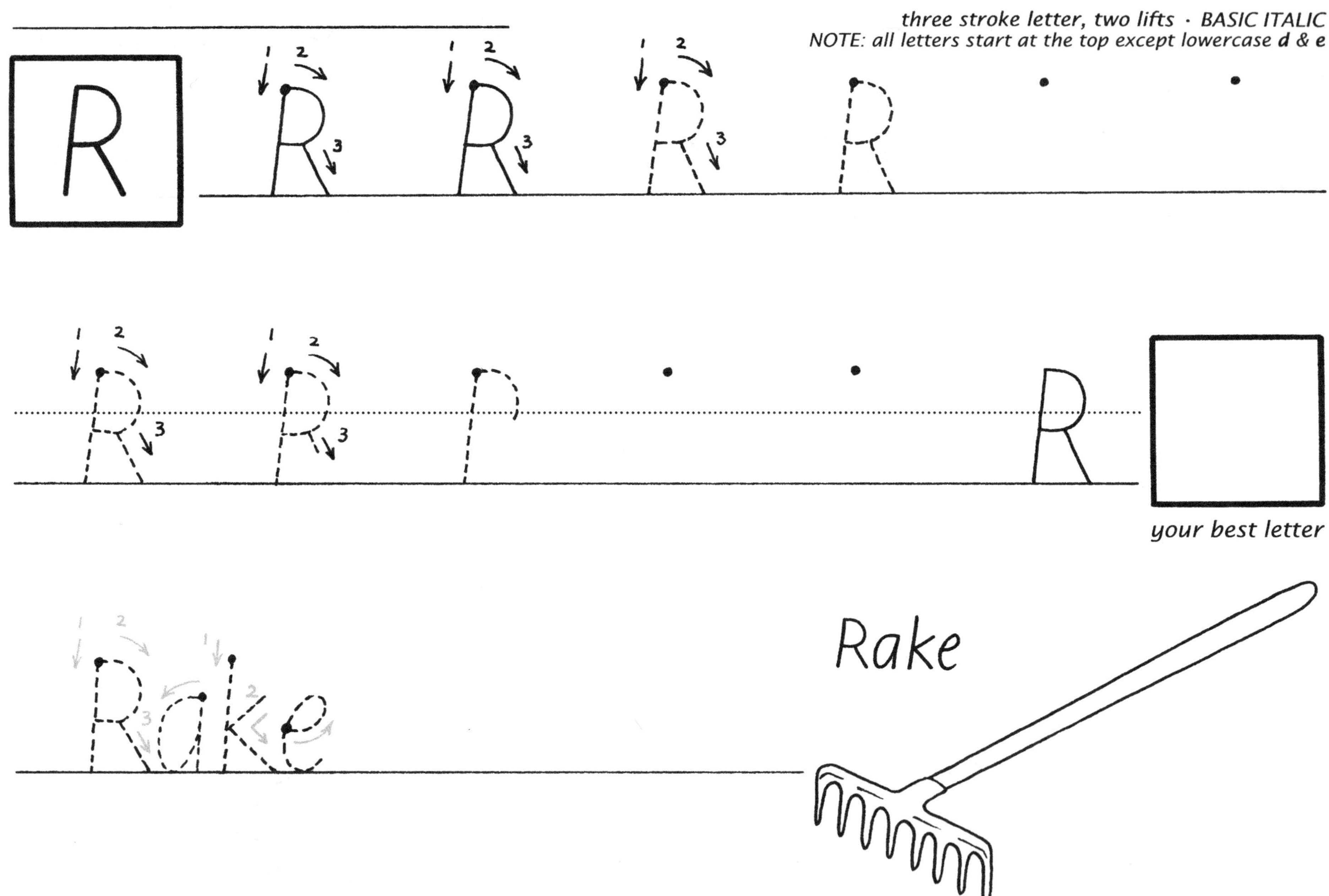

your best letter

Rake

your best letter

rabbit

LOOK: Did you start each letter at the top? Circle: Yes   No

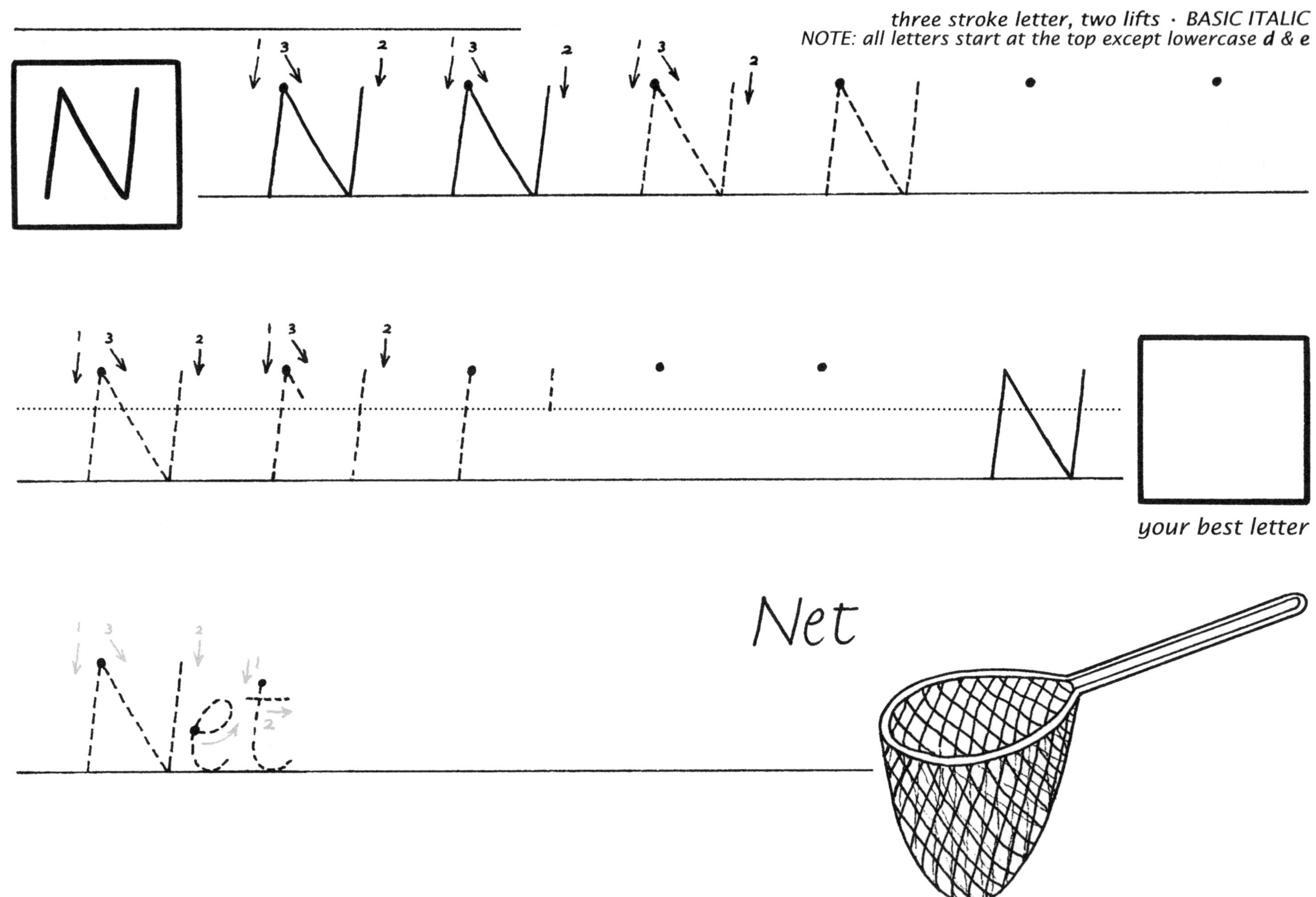

three stroke letter, two lifts · BASIC ITALIC
NOTE: all letters start at the top except lowercase d & e
your best letter
Net

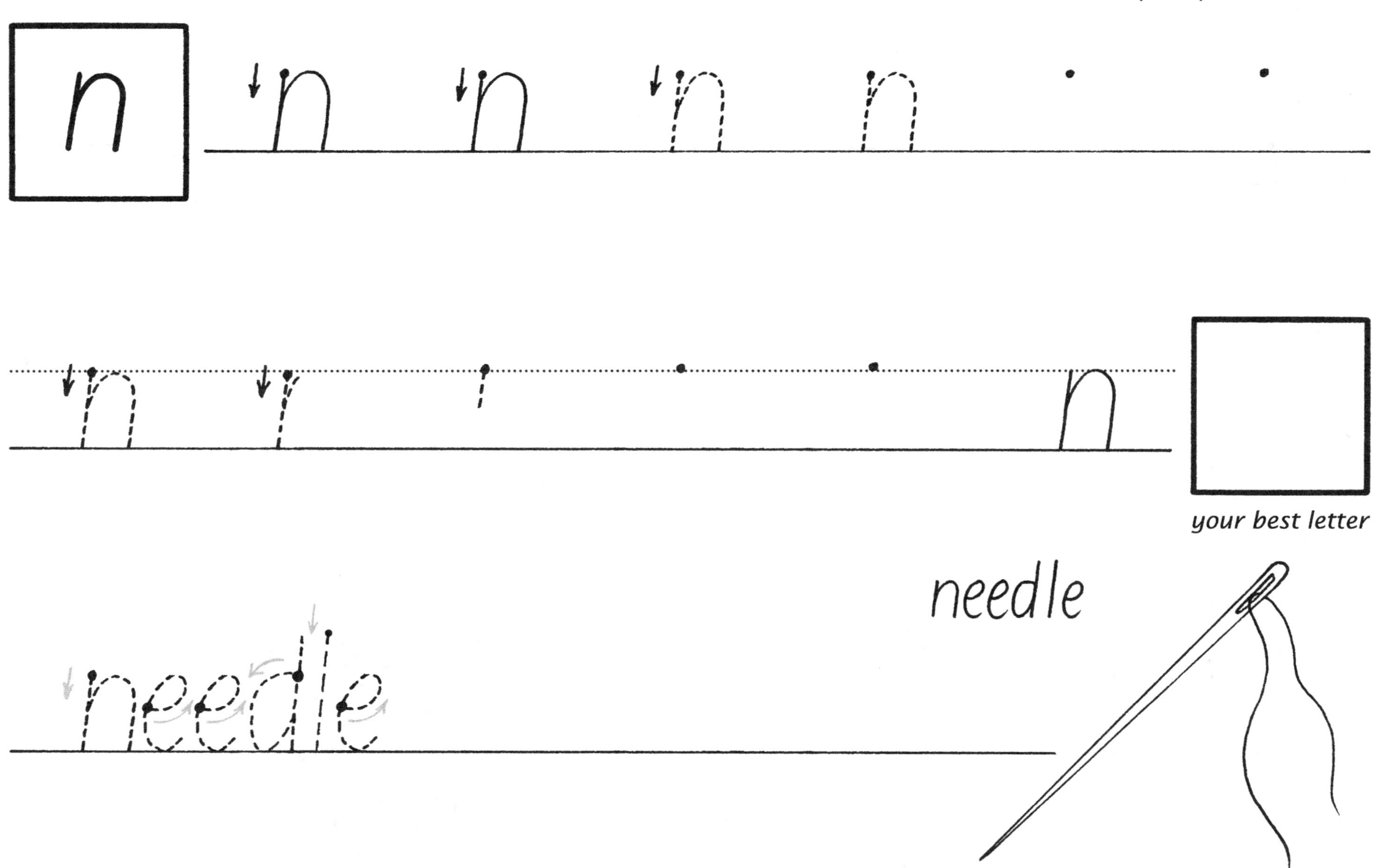

your best letter
needle

your best letter

Mittens

Mittens

your best letter

mouse

LOOK: Did you start all letters at the top? Circle: Yes   No

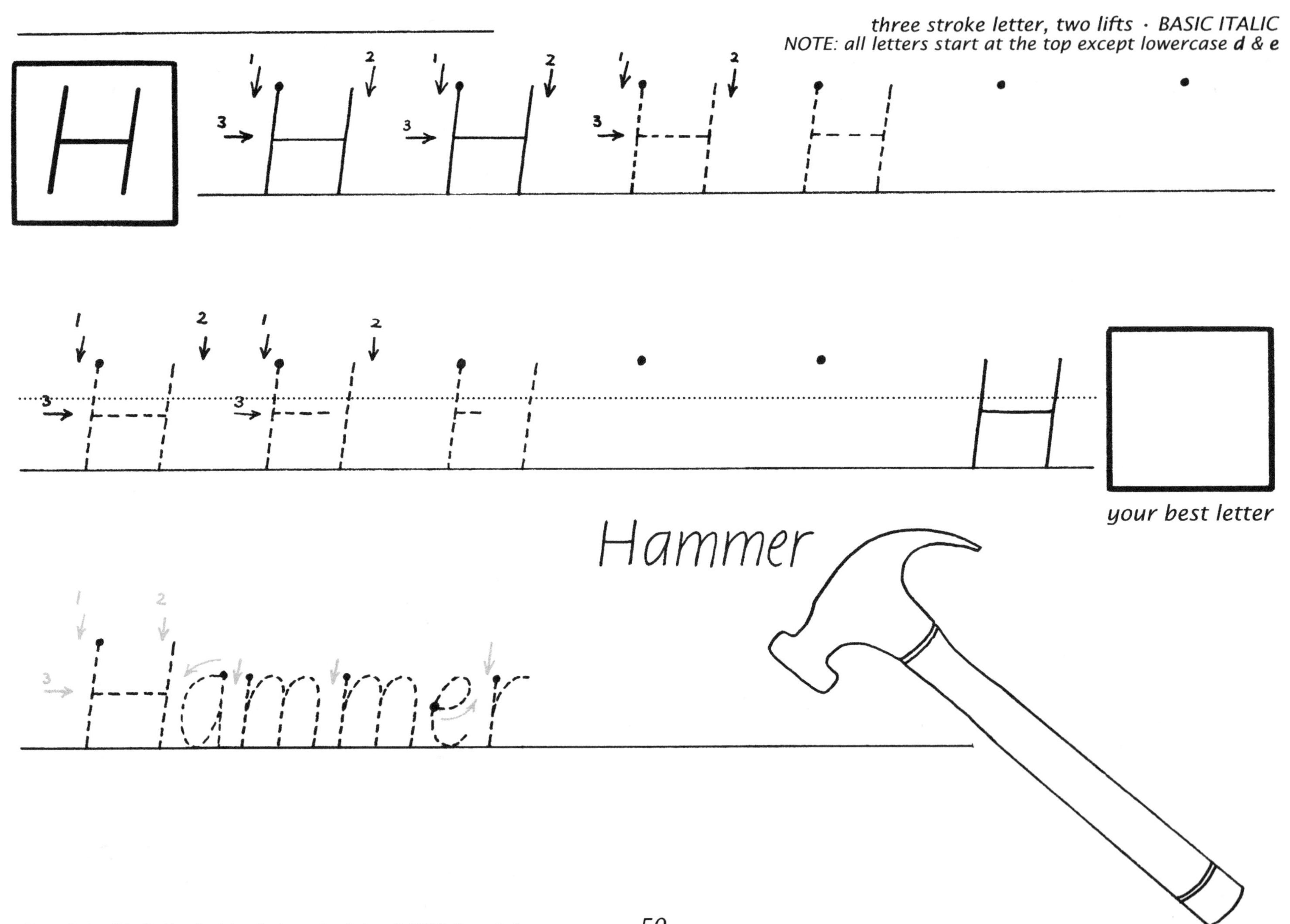

three stroke letter, two lifts · BASIC ITALIC
NOTE: all letters start at the top except lowercase d & e
your best letter
Hammer

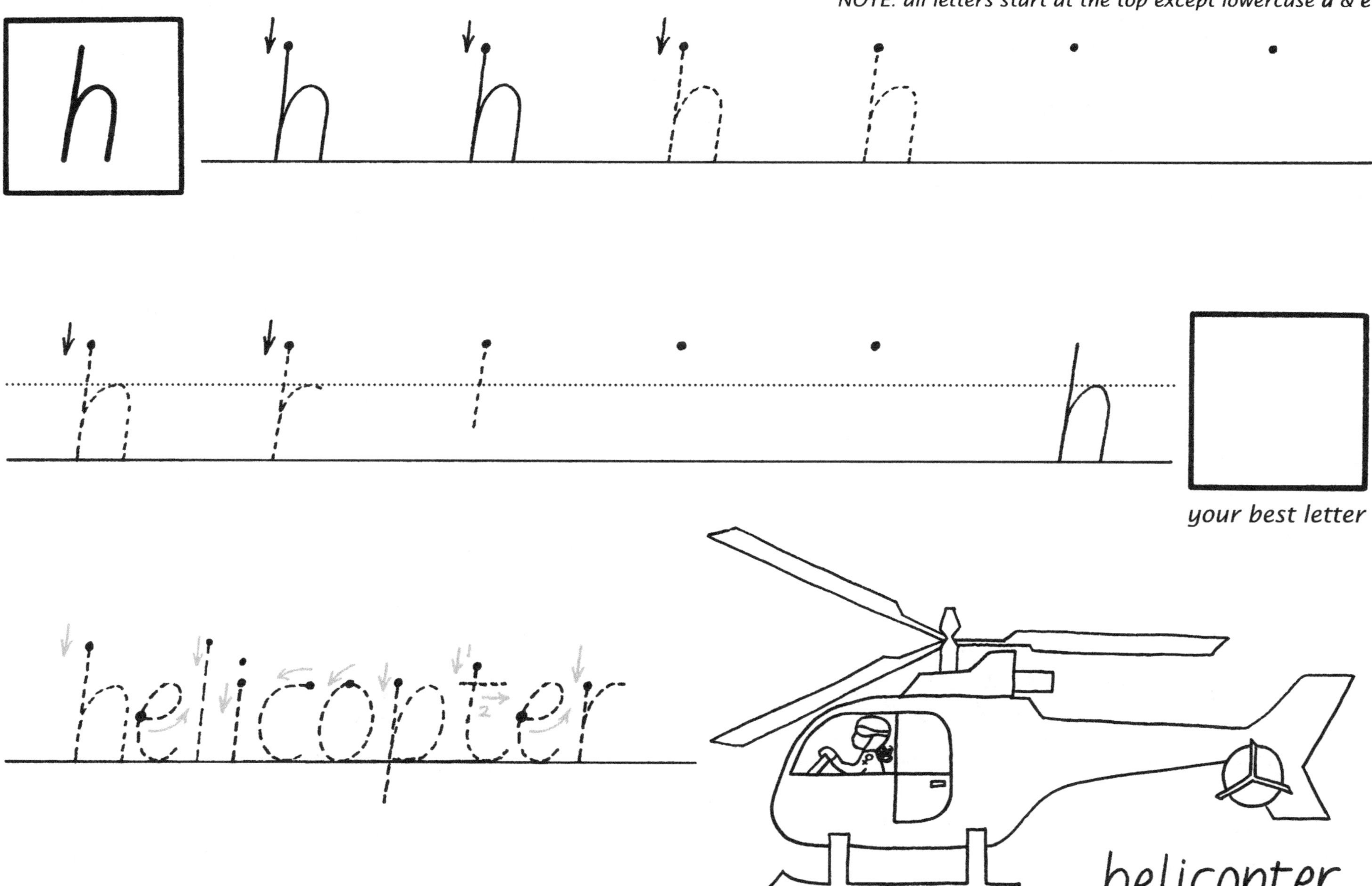

your best letter

helicopter

your best letter

Zipper

Zipper

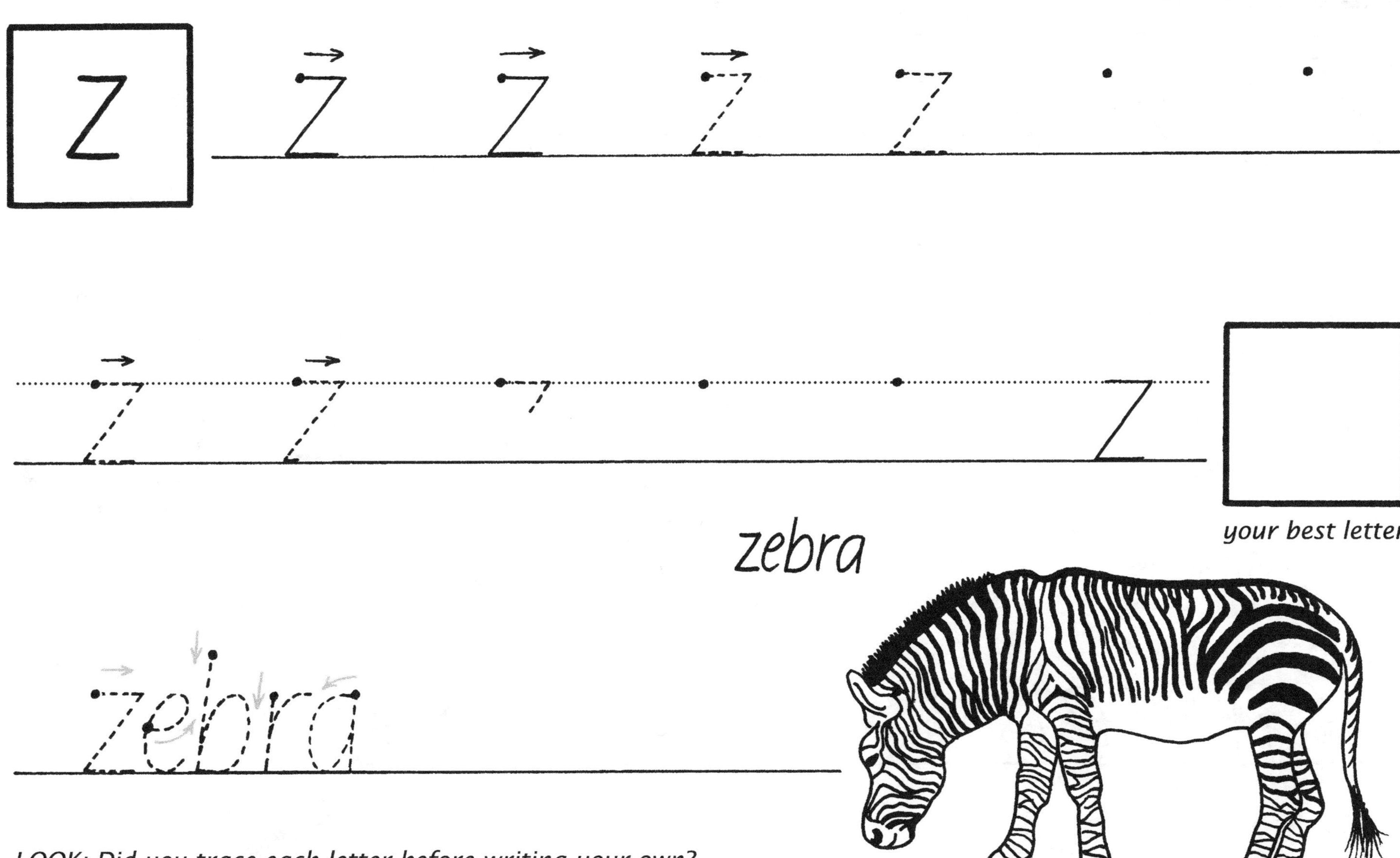

your best letter

zebra

LOOK: Did you trace each letter before writing your own?

Circle: Yes   No

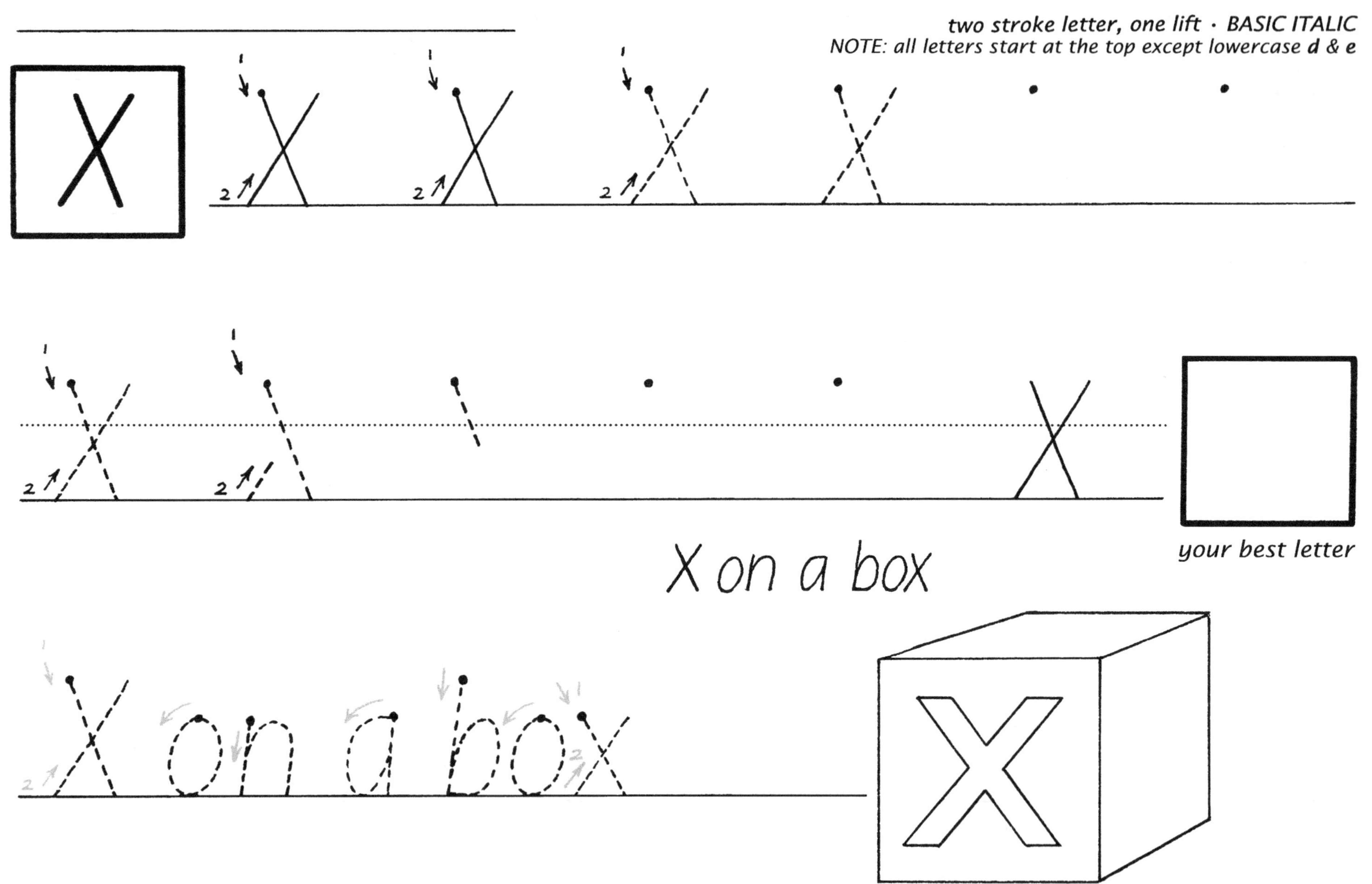
X on a box
your best letter

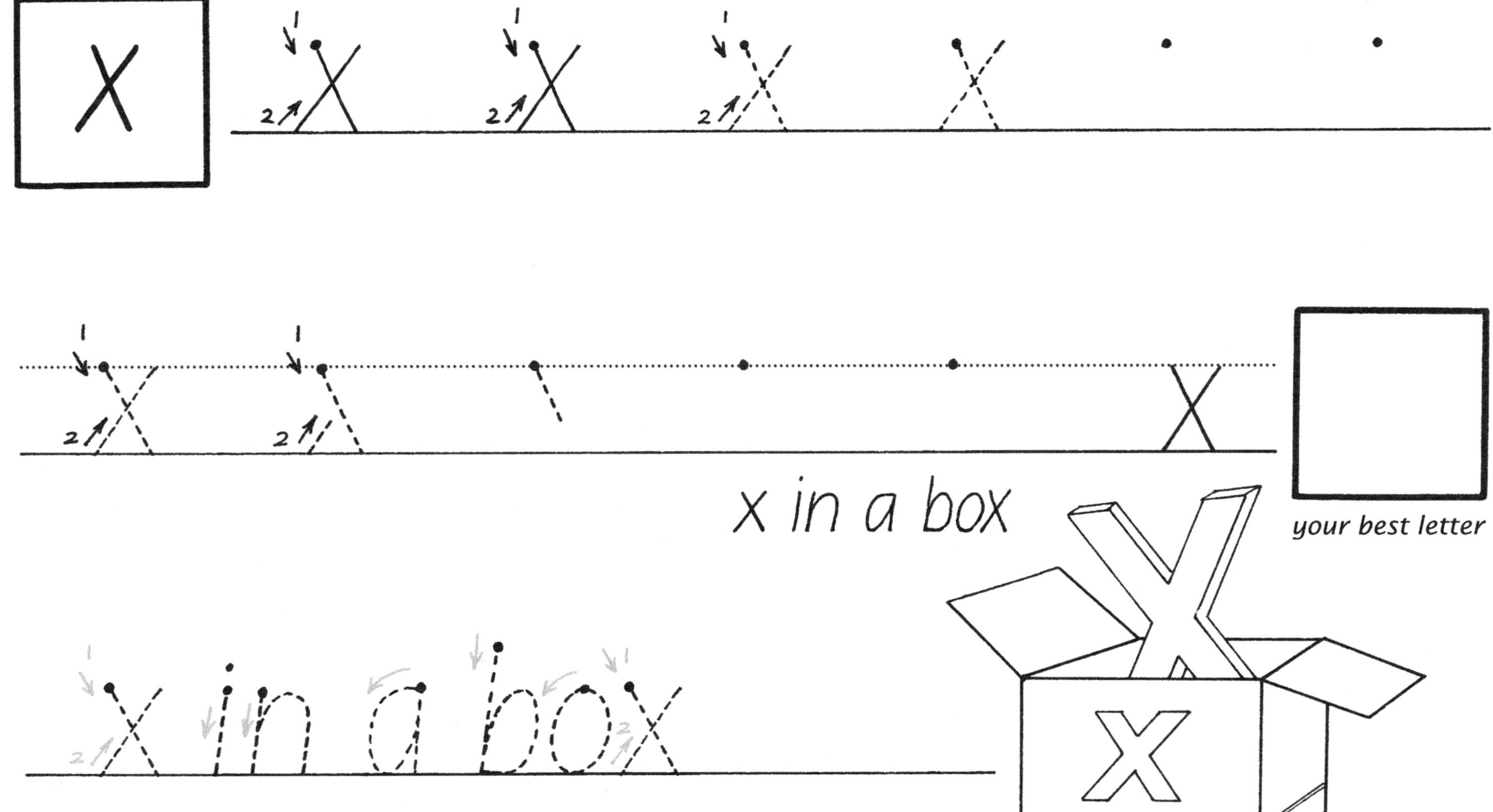

x in a box

your best letter

your best letter

Watch

W

w

your best letter

walrus

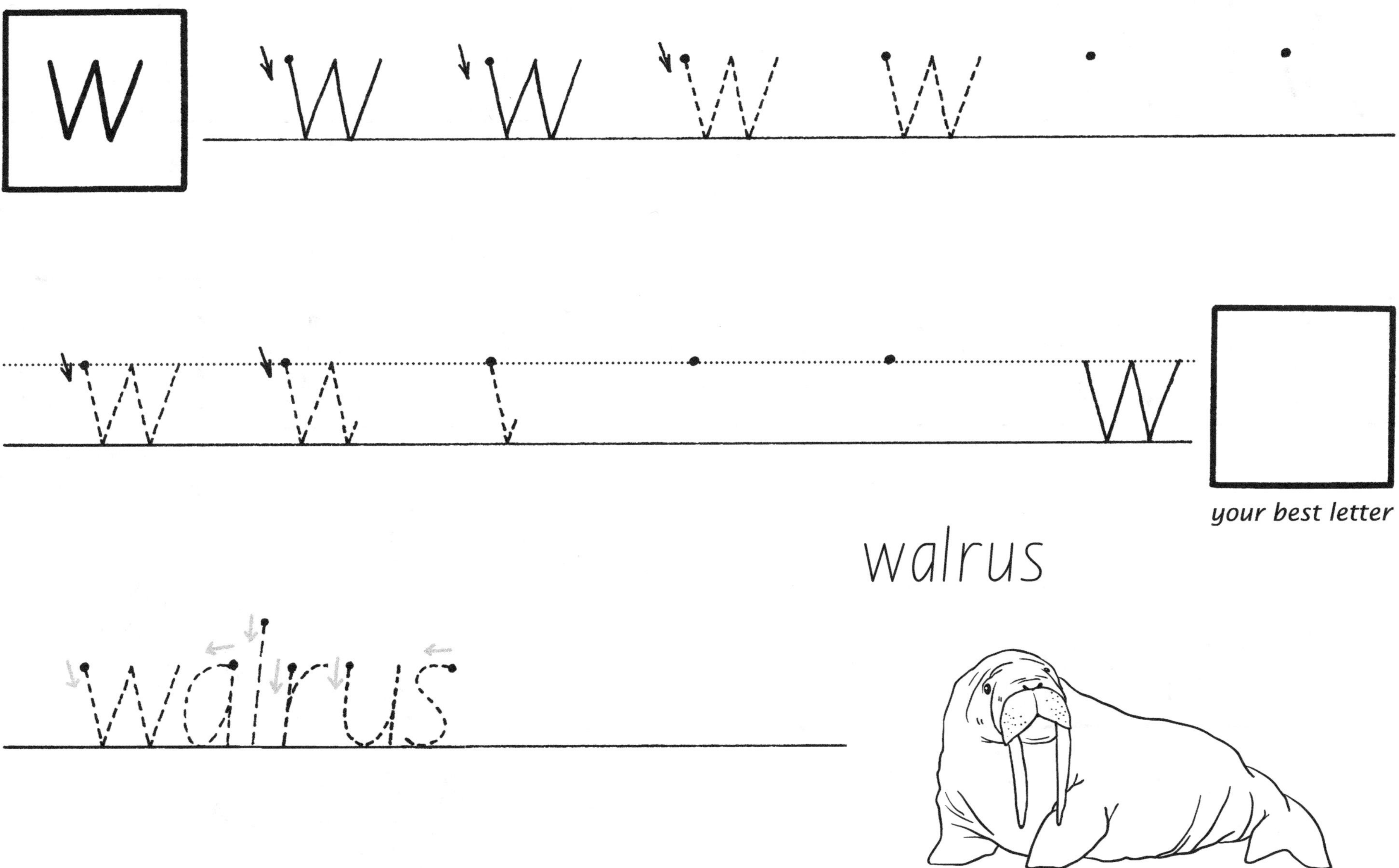

walrus

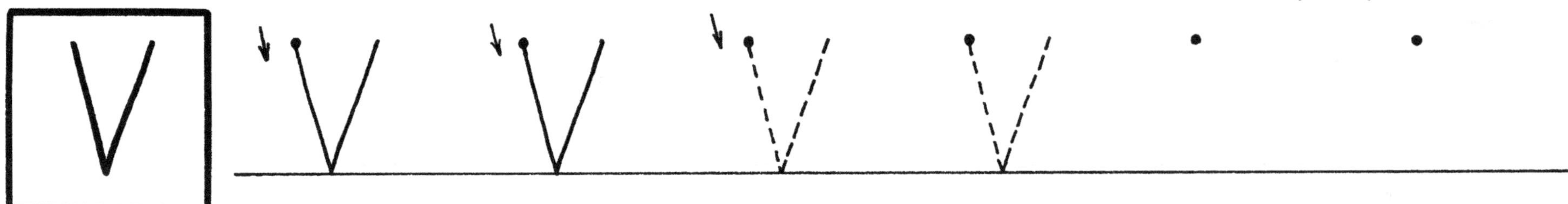

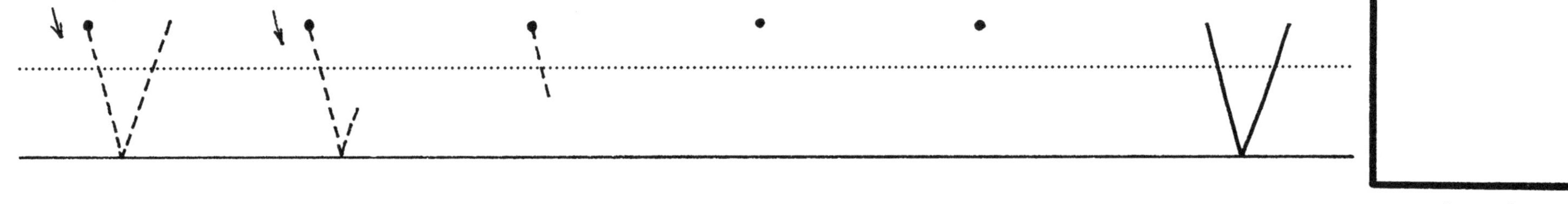

your best letter

Valentine

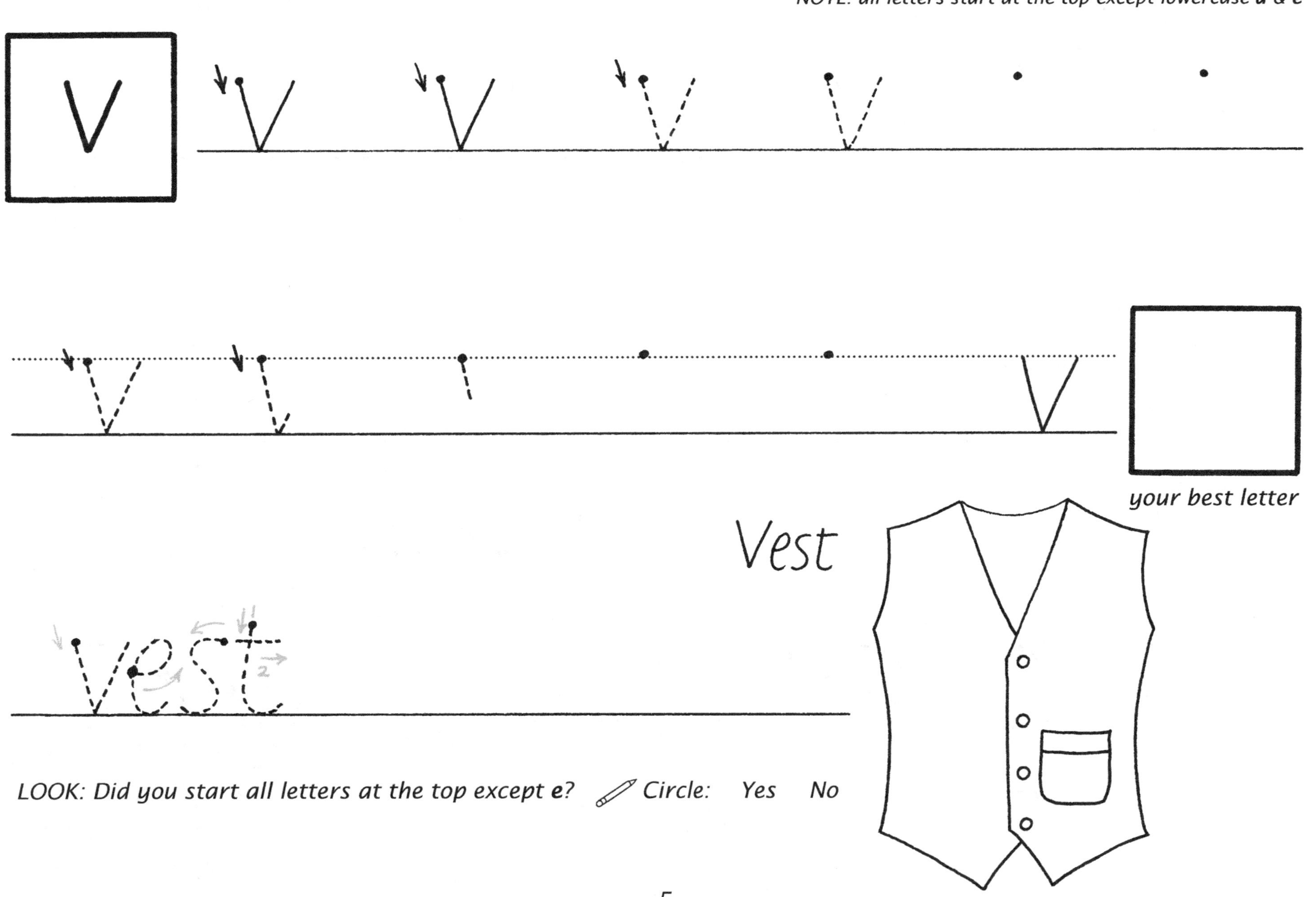

your best letter

Vest

LOOK: Did you start all letters at the top except **e**? Circle: Yes   No

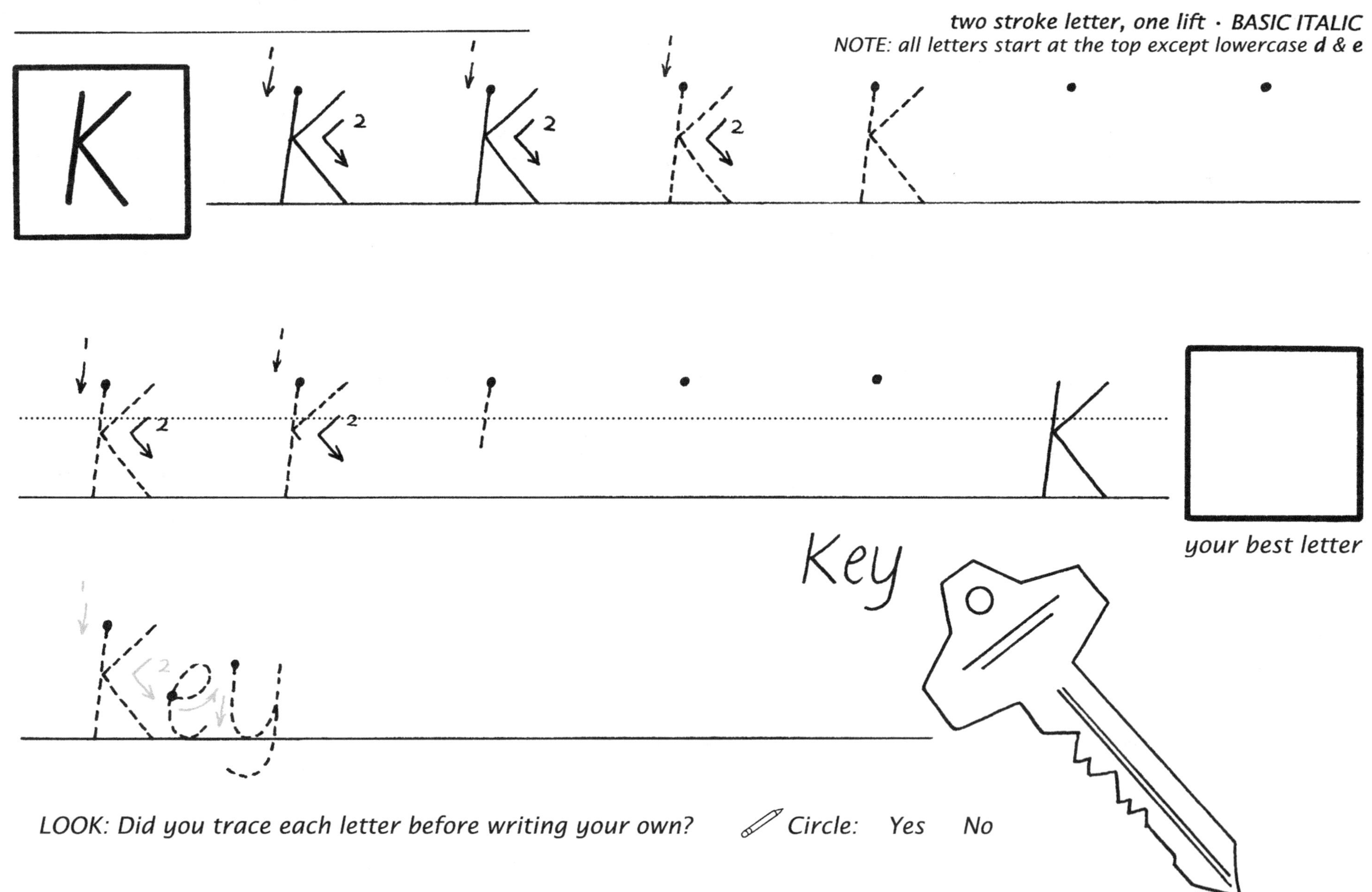

LOOK: Did you trace each letter before writing your own?   Circle: Yes   No

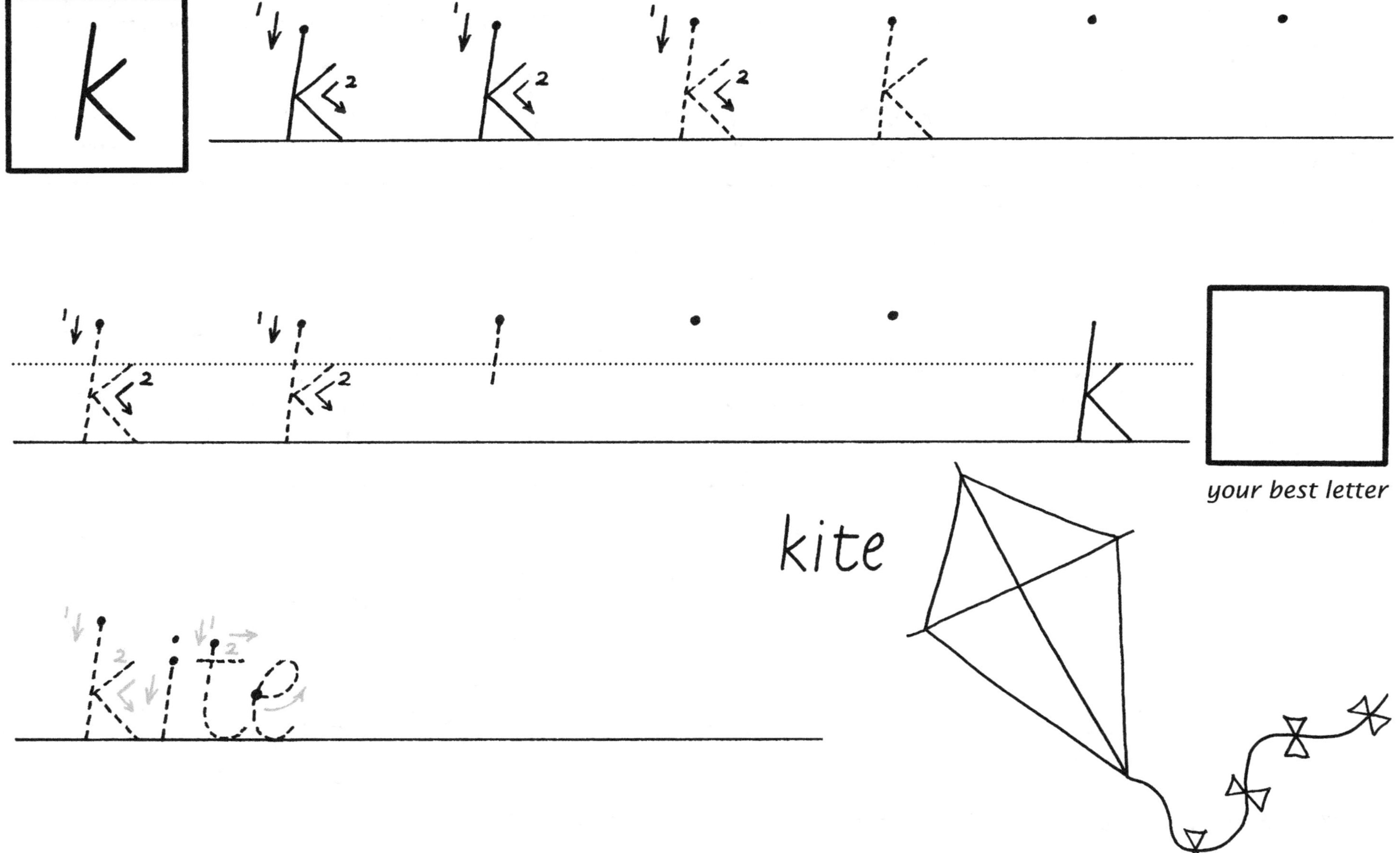

your best letter
kite

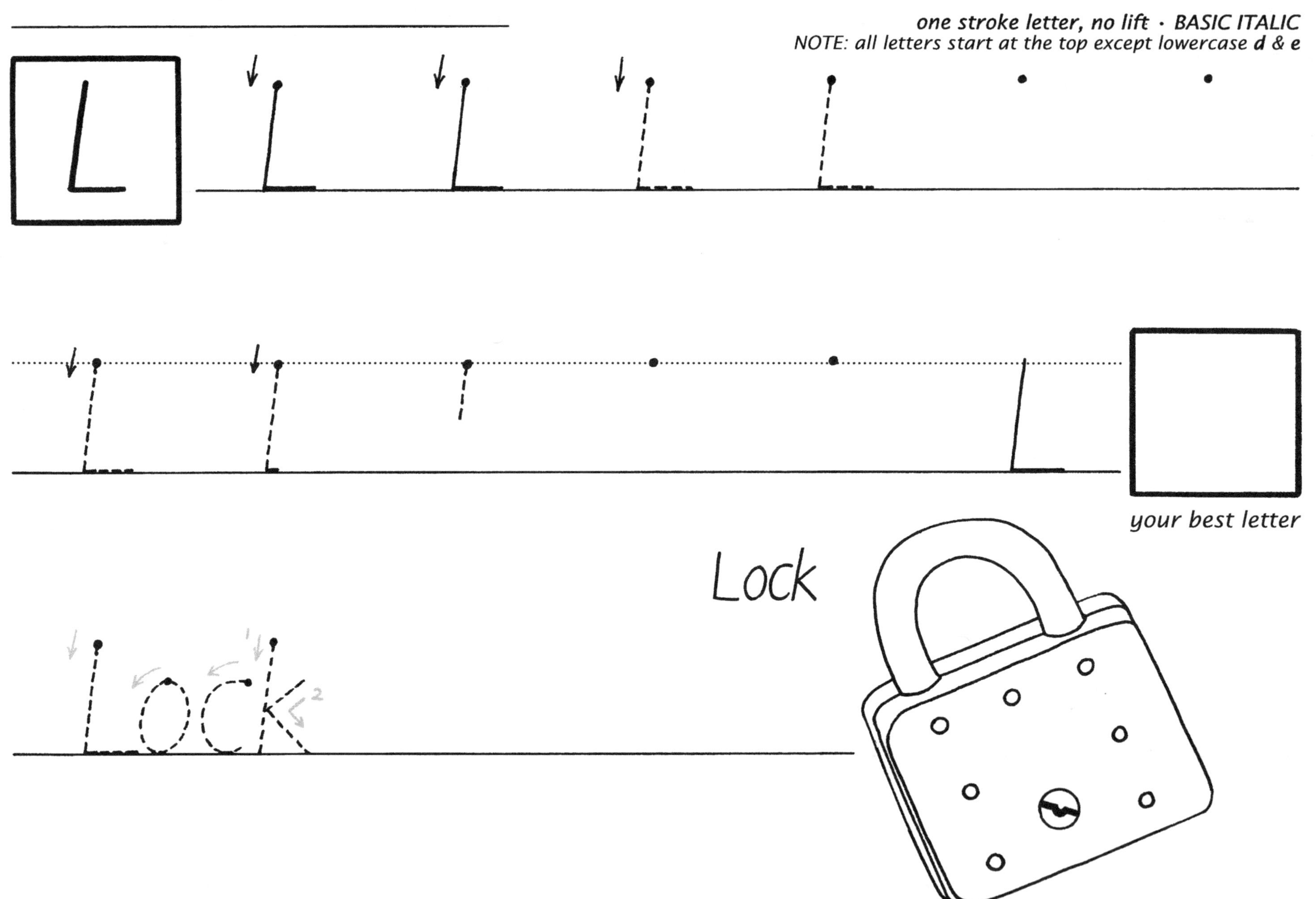

your best letter

Lock

l

your best letter

lamb

lamb

J

your best letter

Jack-in-the-box

Jack-in-the-box

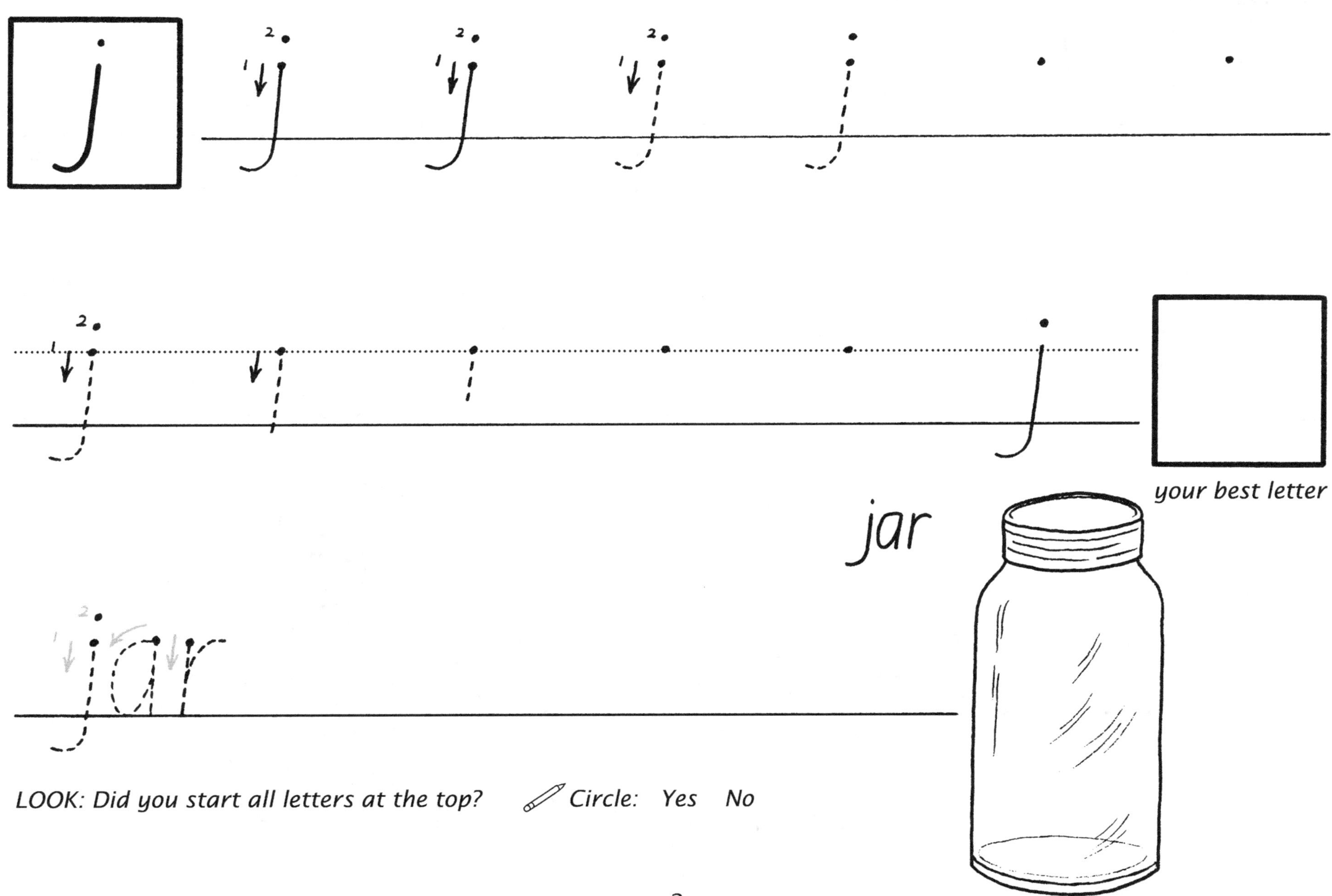

your best letter

jar

LOOK: Did you start all letters at the top?   Circle: Yes   No

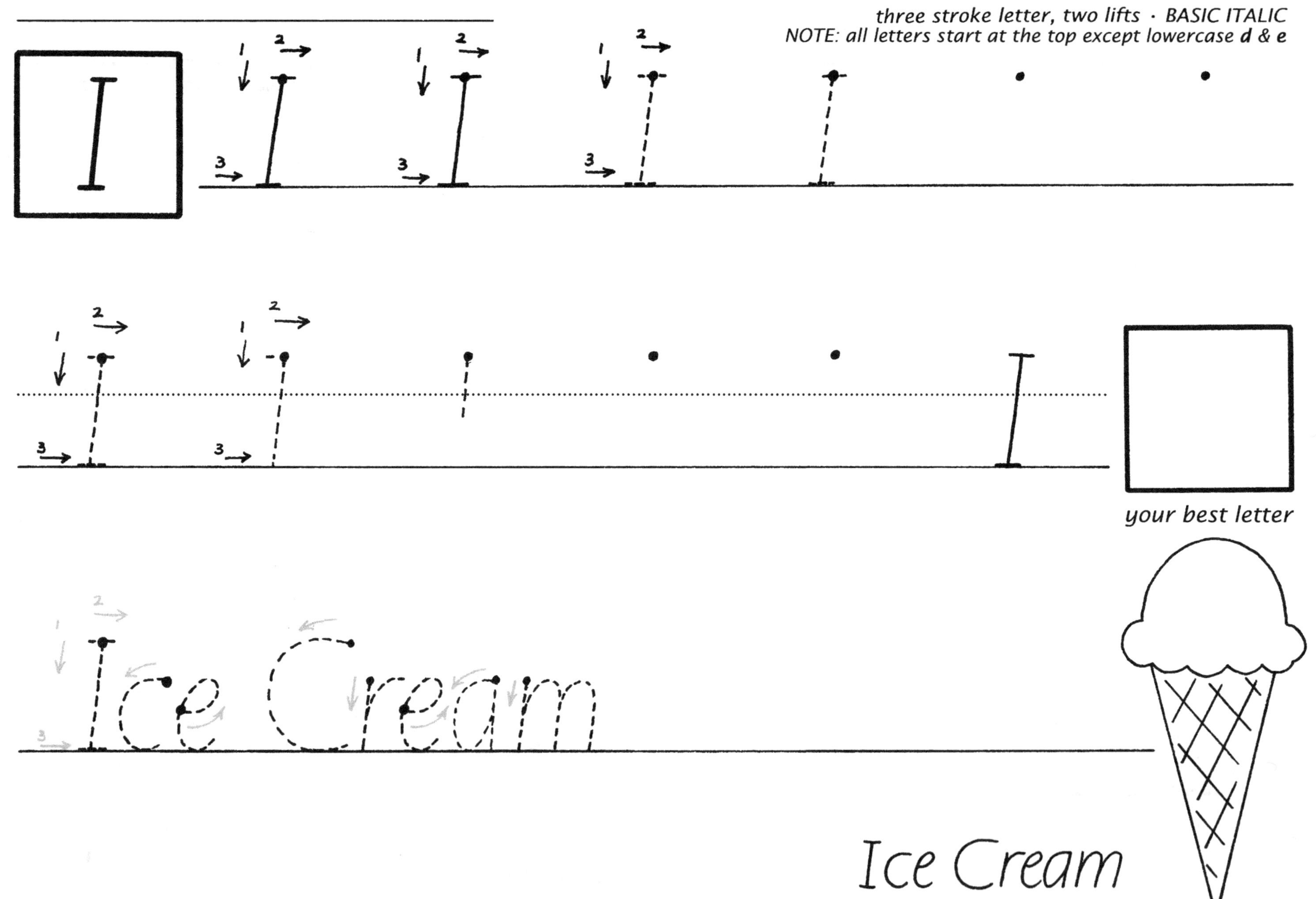

your best letter

Ice Cream

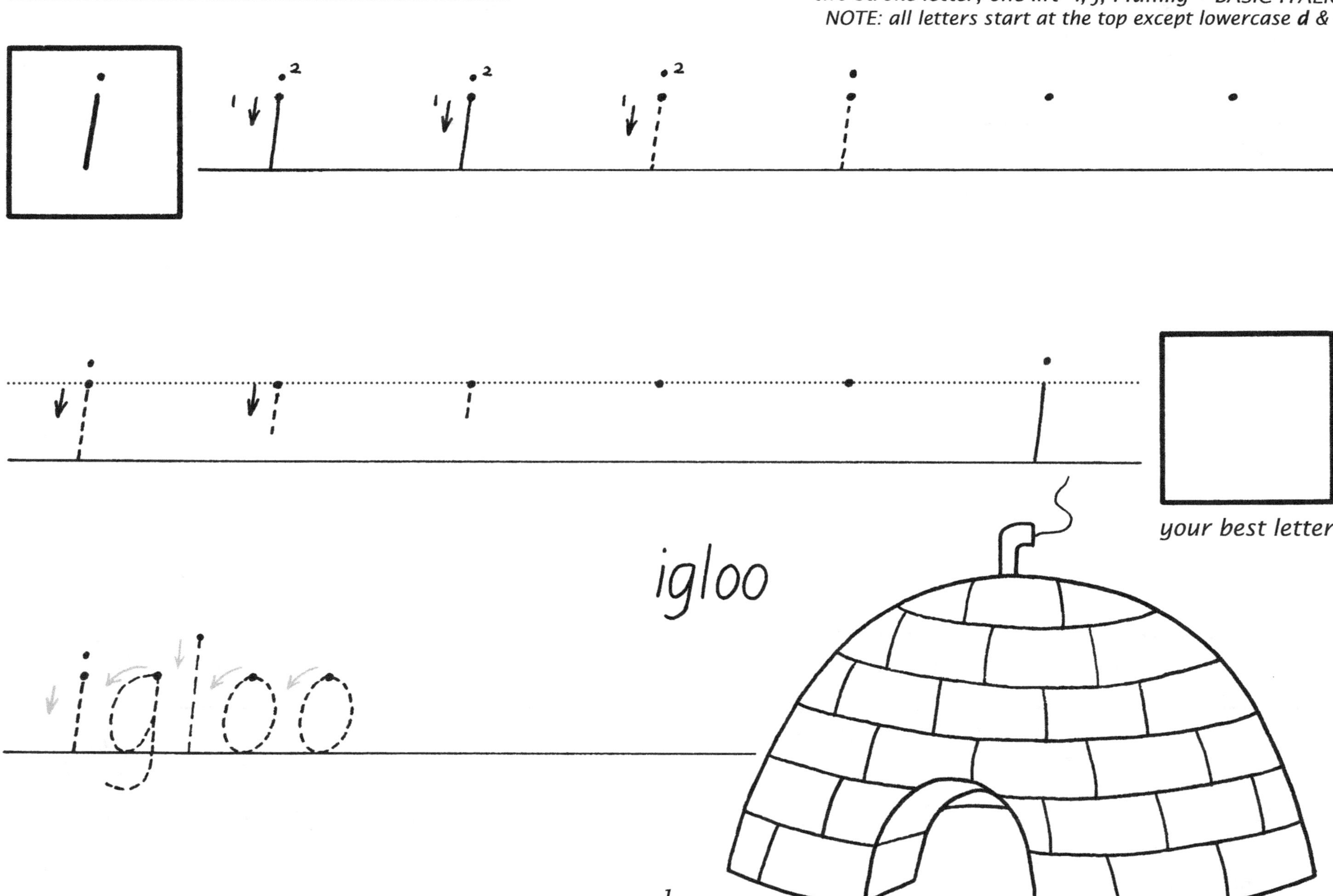

your best letter

igloo

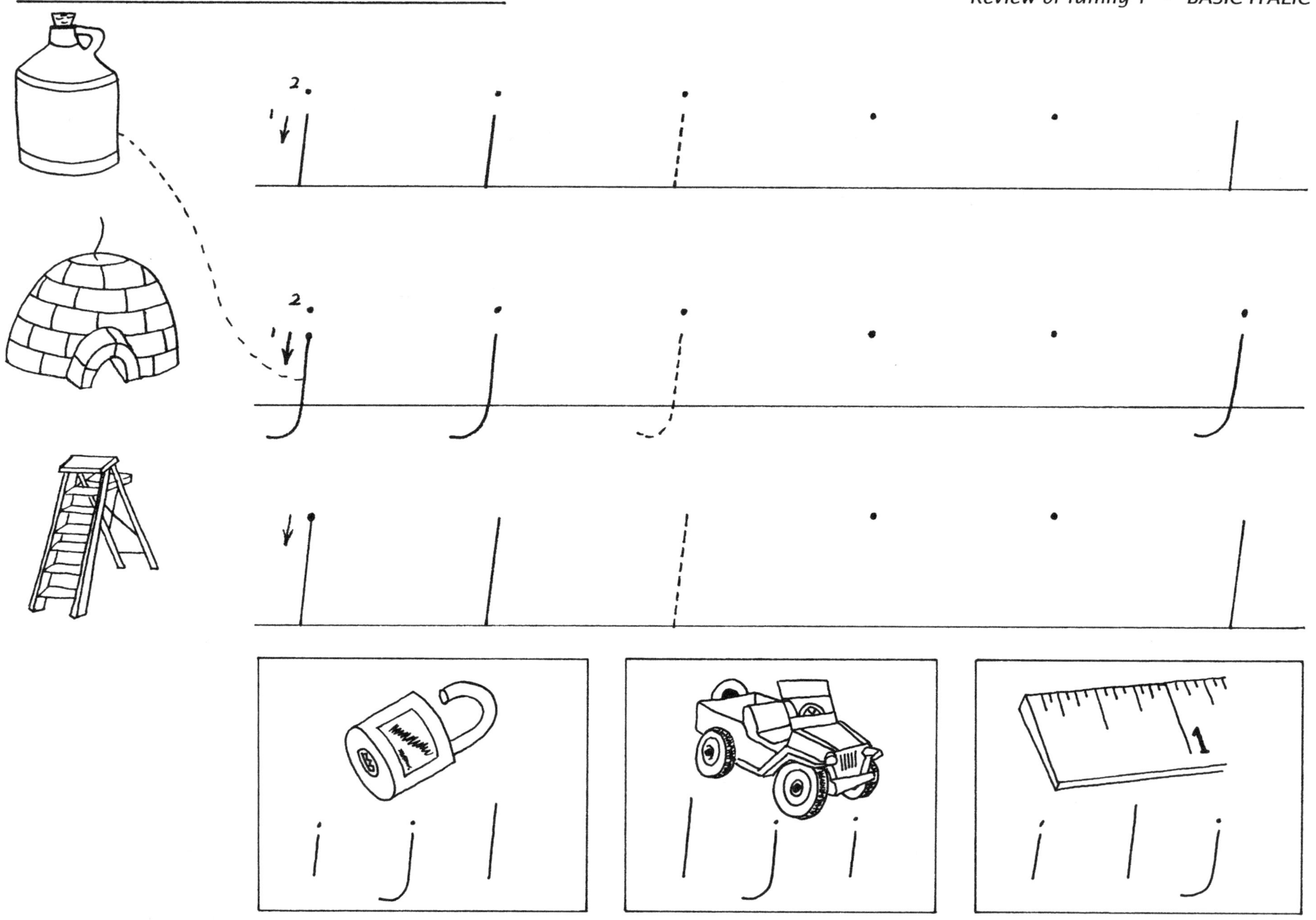

TOP THREE LINES: Ask the student to draw a line from the picture
to the letter that stands for the correct beginning sound.

BOTTOM THREE BOXES: Ask the student to circle the letter that
stands for the beginning sound of the picture.

BASIC SHAPES

Before the student begins writing in BOOK A, the authors recommend that the student practice the following shapes on unlined paper, one shape at a time. Allow the student to write each shape any size at first. Later, ask the student to write very large and very small forms of that same shape. We suggest the student also practice these shapes on a chalkboard and/or in cornmeal. (See INSTRUCTION MANUAL, "*Activity*," pp. 35 & 41.)

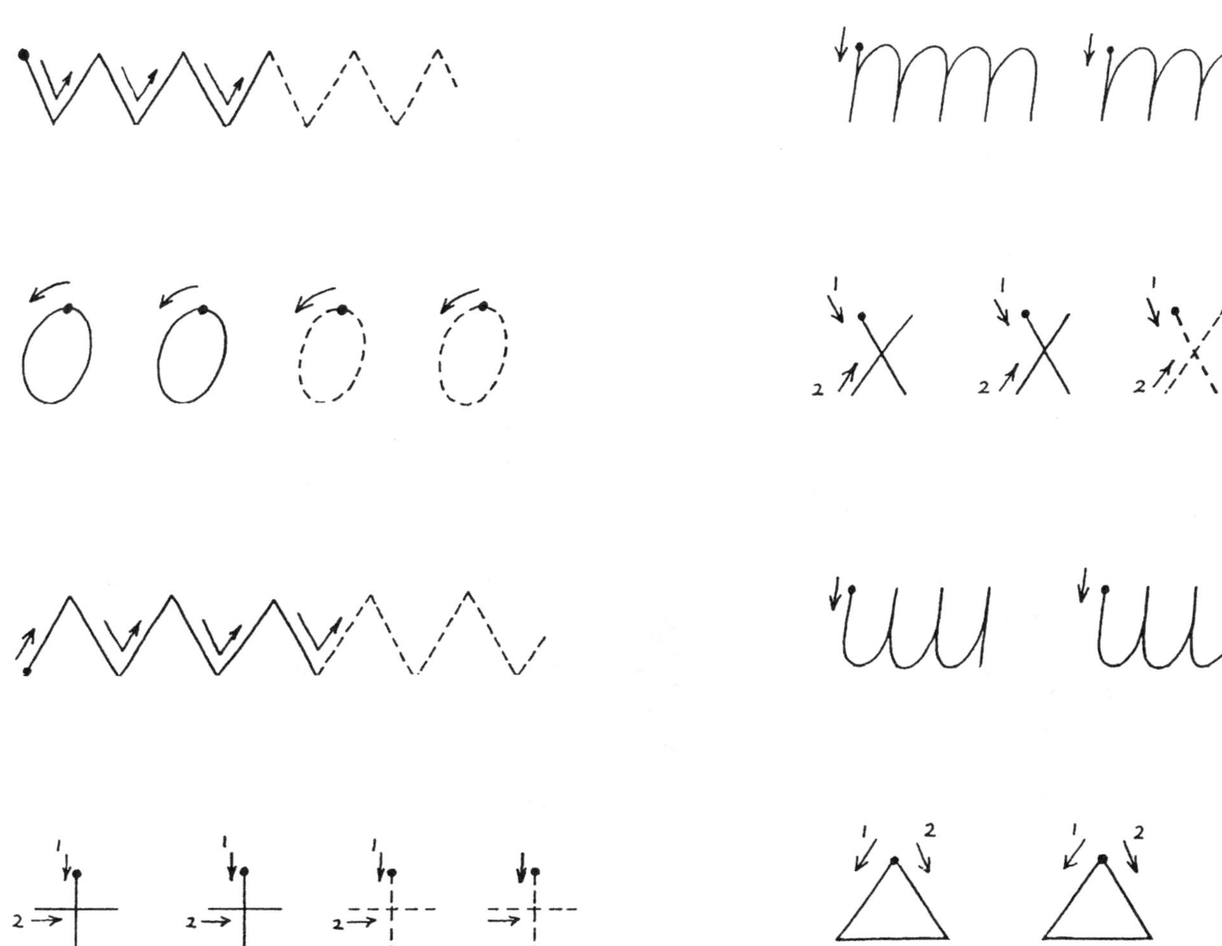

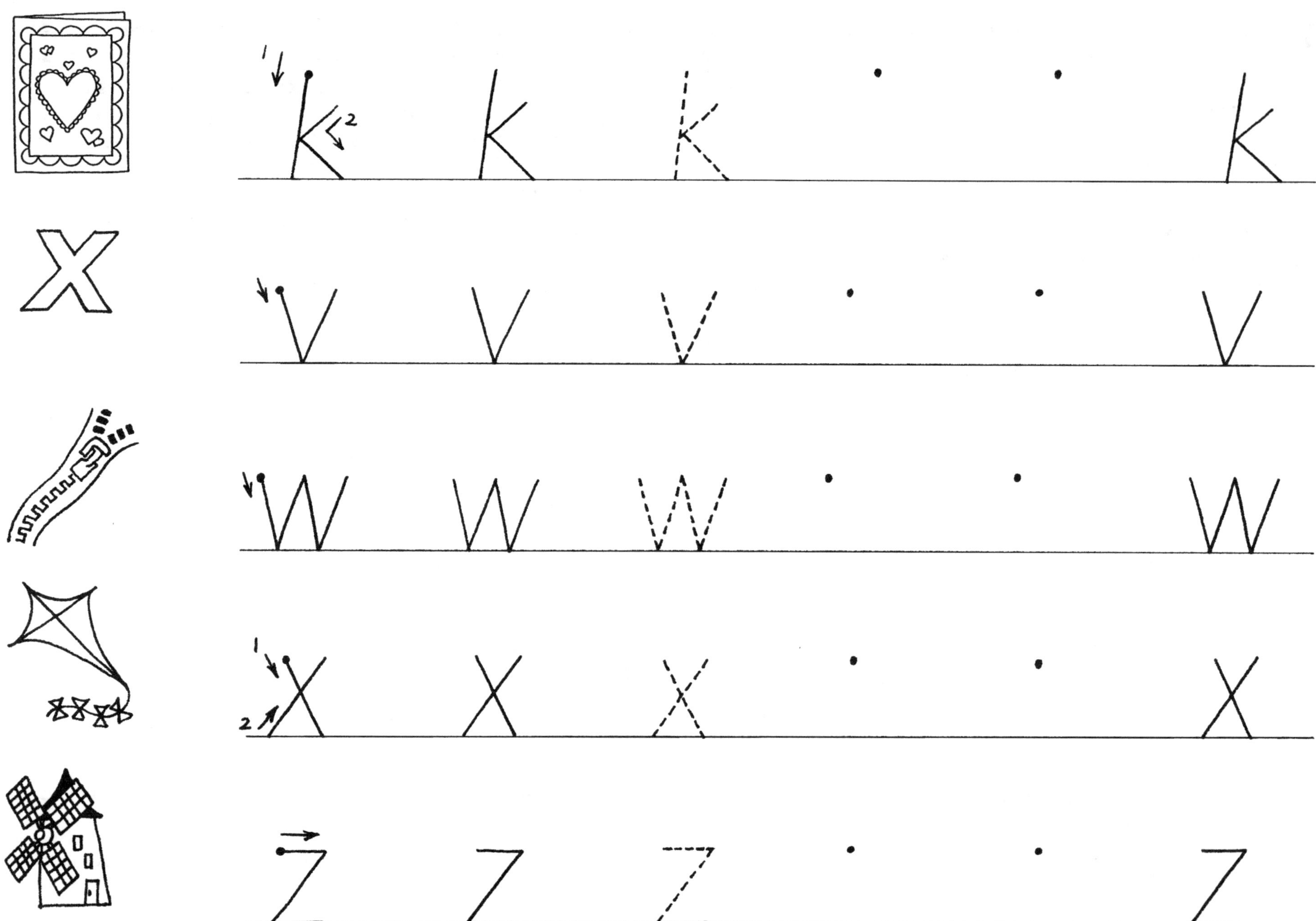

Ask the student to draw a line from the picture to the letter
that stands for the correct beginning sound.

Getty-Dubay™ Italic Handwriting Series · Book A · © 2012 Getty-Dubay

Learning how to write involves much more than learning to write letters. It is a sophisticated, complex process involving learning letterforms, learning how to space within and between words, and learning how to organize writing on a page. Research indicates that there exists an almost perfect correlation between measures evaluating the children's *awareness* of their fingers and the ability to *use* their fingers in precise manual skills.

Ways to determine manual ability

To assist young students increase awareness of their hands and fingers, and to help you, the teacher, evaluate students' manual skills, have your students perform these tasks:

1. Direct the students to touch each of their fingers to their thumb, in order, from the first to the little finger. (By the age of six years, most children should be able to complete this exercise using one or both hands at a time.)

2. Have the students connect two dots that are spaced approximately eight inches apart on a page. (Most children of five years can accomplish this. However, if the student draws beyond the second dot or draws an unusually shaky line when nearing the second dot, it may indicate potential deficiencies in handwriting skills.)

Ways to improve kinesthetic perception of the hands

1. Unstructured clay modeling facilitates a student's perception of his or her hands. Encourage the student to manipulate the clay in every possible way—squeezing, flattening, poking, making shapes, etc.

2. To heighten the student's perception of shape, use a box in which a variety of small objects are placed for the student to feel but not see.

   a. Ask the student to reach in the box and find an unseen object that matches the one he or she is looking at.

   b. Direct the student to locate in the box an object that you or another student has described.

   c. Ask the student to find two objects with similar characteristics— two fuzzy objects, two heavy objects, two small objects, etc.

3. Draw several circles on a sheet of paper. To determine the student's ability to aim the finger and hand and also to point, have the student place dots in the circles with a pencil, pen, or crayon. Vary the difficulty of this task by increasing or decreasing the size of the circles or increasing the rate at which the dots are made. (The student must be able to point at a given or imaginary point in order to begin the stroke of a letter.)

Ways to confirm hand-eye tracking skills

The ability to control continuous hand movements while drawing lines of varying difficulty is basic to handwriting. If you are able to detect problems as the student completes the following tasks and are able to obtain appropriate assistance for the student, subsequent difficulties may be avoided.

1. Demonstrate drawing parallel lines. Then direct the student to draw parallel lines of a given length, first at a relaxed pace then at a faster one.

2. Direct the student to draw two curved lines equal in distance from one another. Later require more difficult shapes that combine straight lines, angles, and/or curves.

3. Direct the student to connect numbered dots on a sheet of paper that require horizontal, vertical and lateral movements. Place the paper in front of the student, close to the dominant hand. Later, space the dots further apart and require the student to cross the midline of his or her body. This latter task may cause the neuro-logically challenged student some difficulty.

The above evaluative tasks may be of help in assisting the learning of handwriting and in discovering deficiencies.

(See INSTRUCTION MANUAL, p. 13, for more suggestions concerning the beginning writer.)

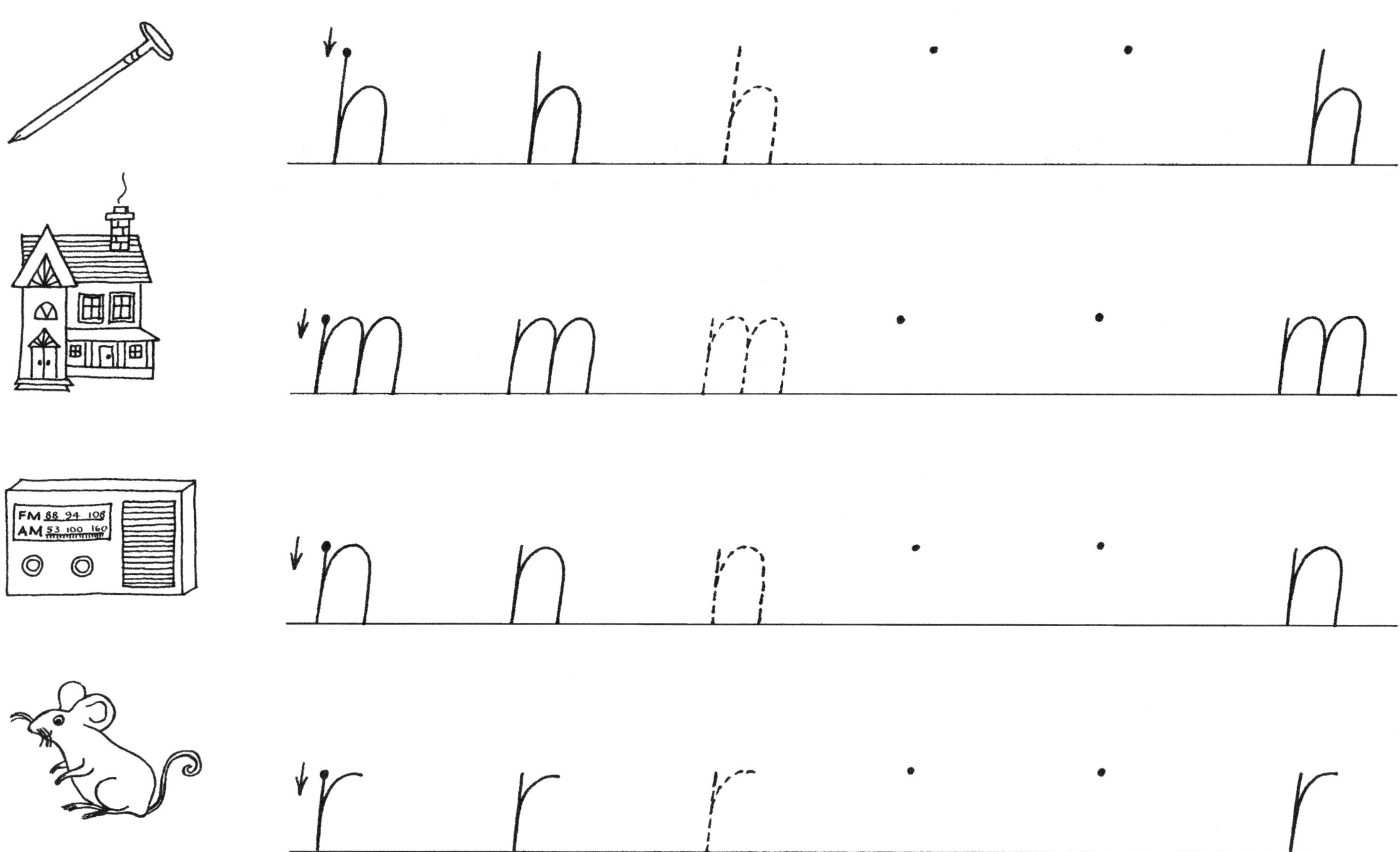

Ask the student to draw a line from the picture to the letter
that stands for the correct beginning sound.

GETTY-DUBAY™ ITALIC HANDWRITING SERIES
BASIC ITALIC ALPHABET

All letters written in one stroke unless otherwise indicated.   *All letters start at the top except lowercase **d** and **e**.*

Aa Bb Cc Dd Ee Ff Gg

alternate 2-stroke e

Hh Ii Jj Kk Ll Mm

Nn Oo Pp Qq Rr Ss Tt

Uu Vv Ww Xx Yy Zz

0 1 2 3 4 5 6 7 8 9

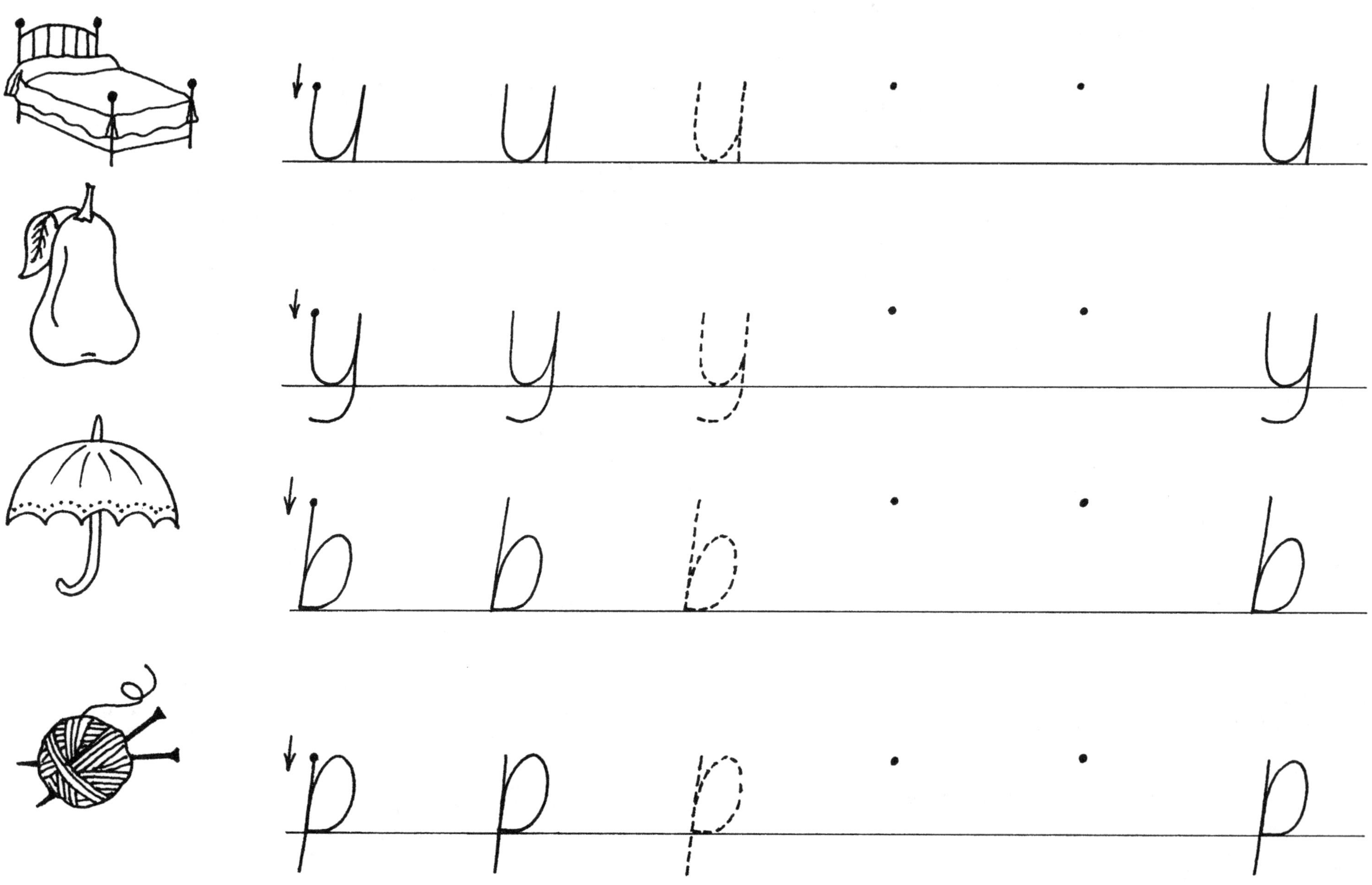

Ask the student to draw a line from the picture to the letter that stands for the correct beginning sound.

GETTY-DUBAY™ HANDWRITING REMINDERS

PENCIL HOLD

Hold the pencil with the thumb and index finger, resting it on the middle finger. Rest the shaft of the pencil near the large knuckle. Hold the tool firmly and avoid pinching. To relax the hand, tap index finger on the pencil three times. Avoid "thumb wrap" and a "death grip".

PAPER POSITION

LEFT-HANDED: If the left-handed student writes with the wrist below the writing line, turn paper clockwise so it is slanted to the right, as illustrated.

If the left-handed student writes with a hook, with the wrist above the writing line, turn the paper counter-clockwise so it is slanted to the left, as illustrated. (Similar to right-handed position)

RIGHT-HANDED: If the student is right-handed, turn paper counter-clockwise so it is slanted to the left, as illustrated.

POSTURE

Rest feet flat on the floor and keep back comfortably straight without slumping. Rest forearms on writing surface. The student holds workbook or paper with the nonwriting hand so that the writing area is centered in the front of the student.

PRACTICE PAPER

Book A—Use unlined or lined paper together with workbooks.

MATERIALS

The *Getty-Dubay™ Italic Handwriting Series* workbooks, BOOKS A-G, and the INSTRUCTION MANUAL constitute a step-by-step program. Related materials consist of:

1. BLACKLINE MASTERS/WORKSHEETS - half sheets for introduction to, or review of, workbook pages.
2. CLASSROOM WALL CHARTS - basic & cursive italic.
3. DESK STRIPS - basic & cursive italic.

VOCABULARY

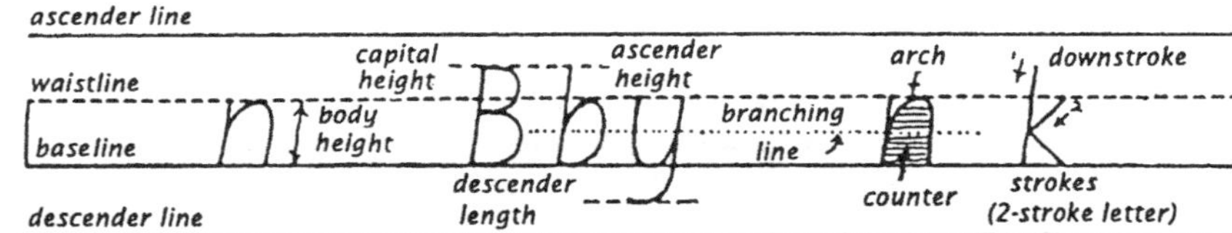

DIRECT INSTRUCTION

Several sessions of direct instruction each week are essential for a successful program. BOOK A – 5 to 10 minute sessions a day are recommended, see INSTRUCTION MANUAL, pp. 18-19

- SHAPE & STROKE SEQUENCE – teach basic italic in letter family groups, or according to the reading program in grade 1.
- SLOPE – encourage a consistent letter slope. Vertical letters (0° slope) may be the easiest to teach to beginning writers.
- SIZE – At first, allow students to write letters any size they wish on unlined paper, then introduce the workbook. A recommended progression through this book is one letter (lowercase and/or capital) per week.

SPACING

When young students are writing words, at first have them leave a space about the width of their two small fingers between words. As they become more proficient, they can leave less space.

ASSESSMENT

The *Getty-Dubay™ Italic Handwriting Series* provides a self-assessment process, LOOK, PLAN, PRACTICE, to enable the student to monitor progress. LOOK, step 1 of this process begins on some of the student pages in BOOK A. Assessment is the key to improving handwriting; in this book we introduce the first of three steps in the LOOK, PLAN, PRACTICE self-assessment process. The students look at their own writing and answer any questions on the page. The pencil indicates the student is to make a written response, generally by circling "yes" or "no". The teacher may encourage students to award themselves a star or a smiling face at the top of the page when they notice self-improvement.

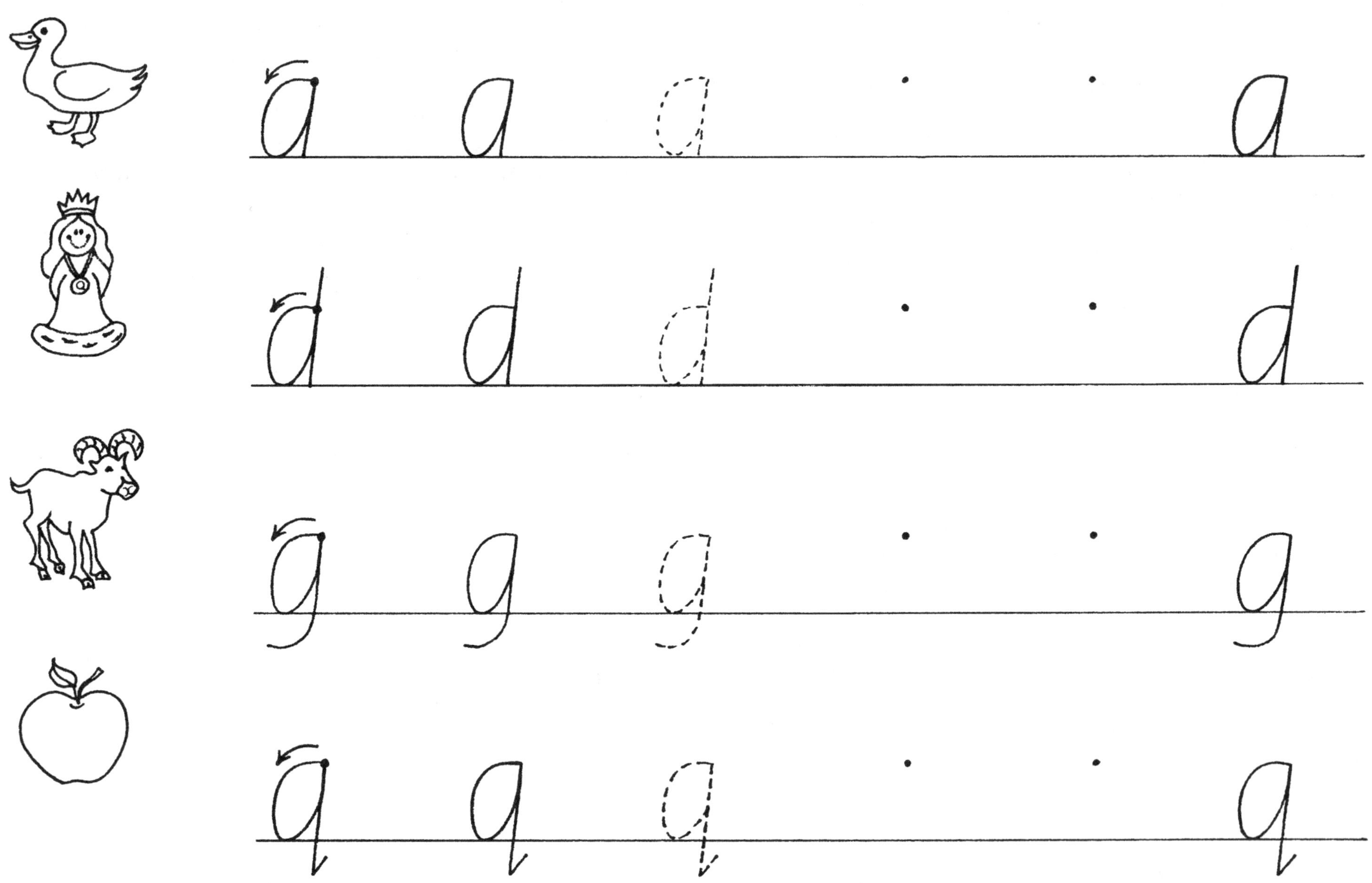

Ask the student to draw a line from the picture to the letter
that stands for the correct beginning sound.

INTRODUCTION

This is the first of seven workbooks providing instruction in basic italic handwriting. It is designed for the beginning student of handwriting and is recommended for preschool, kindergarten and/or early first grade (5 to 7 years of age).

The twenty-six lowercase letters and the twenty-six capitals are introduced one letter per page. Letters are arranged in the order of lowercase families, which group letters with similar strokes together and progress from simple to more complex forms. The matching capital letter occurs on the reverse of each lowercase page allowing introduction of both lowercase and capital together if preferred.

Each page is designed for the student to trace the models provided, write letters at the given dots, and to write a "best" letter in the empty box on each alphabet page. The standard writing tool is the pencil although other writing instruments such as the fiber tip pen may be used. When students are ready, they should trace the word describing the illustration on each letter page, following the dots and arrows.

It is essential that the instructor provide an understanding of the dot and the arrow to assist the writer in completing the pages successfully. The self-assessment method used in the *Getty-Dubay* ™ *Italic Handwriting Series* enables students to monitor their individual progress. Step 1, LOOK, of the three-step LOOK, PLAN, PRACTICE format, is incorporated on 21 of the student pages. Students are asked to "LOOK" at their writing and affirm what is best. On the 21 pages with "LOOK" questions, students should circle their chosen answers. See INSTRUCTION MANUAL, PP. 13, 18 & 19.

The *Getty-Dubay* ™ *Italic Handwriting Series* INSTRUCTION MANUAL is to be used in conjunction with this workbook. Explanations and in-depth descriptions of lowercase letters, capitals, joins, and numerals are presented in the manual, emphasizing shape, strokes, size, slope and spacing of the letters. Also included in the manual are: a rationale for italic handwriting, techniques for teaching and assessing handwriting, sequence of skills, handwriting activities, and a brief history of our alphabet.

BOOK B, basic italic, follows this workbook and is designed for the beginning reader. In the third book, BOOK C, basic italic letterforms are reinforced and cursive italic is introduced. BOOKS D, E, F, and G provide a complete basic italic and cursive italic handwriting program. BOOKS B, C, and/or D may also be suitable for the person learning English as a second language.

The format of this book was chosen to accommodate both the left- and right-handed writer. When open, the book fits easily on a small desk, and the writer is not encumbered with an additional page to the left or right. From day one, use a Getty-Dubay ™ basic italic desk strip as a reminder. Blackline masters are designed for supplementary practice and are available for each workbook in the series. See www.handwritingsuccess.com for these supplementary materials.

You can guide children toward the challenge and delight in the writing process by reading to them, modeling handwriting, providing writing materials, and especially by building enthusiasm for the letters of our alphabet and for the written word.

·abcdefghijklmnopqrstuvwxyz·

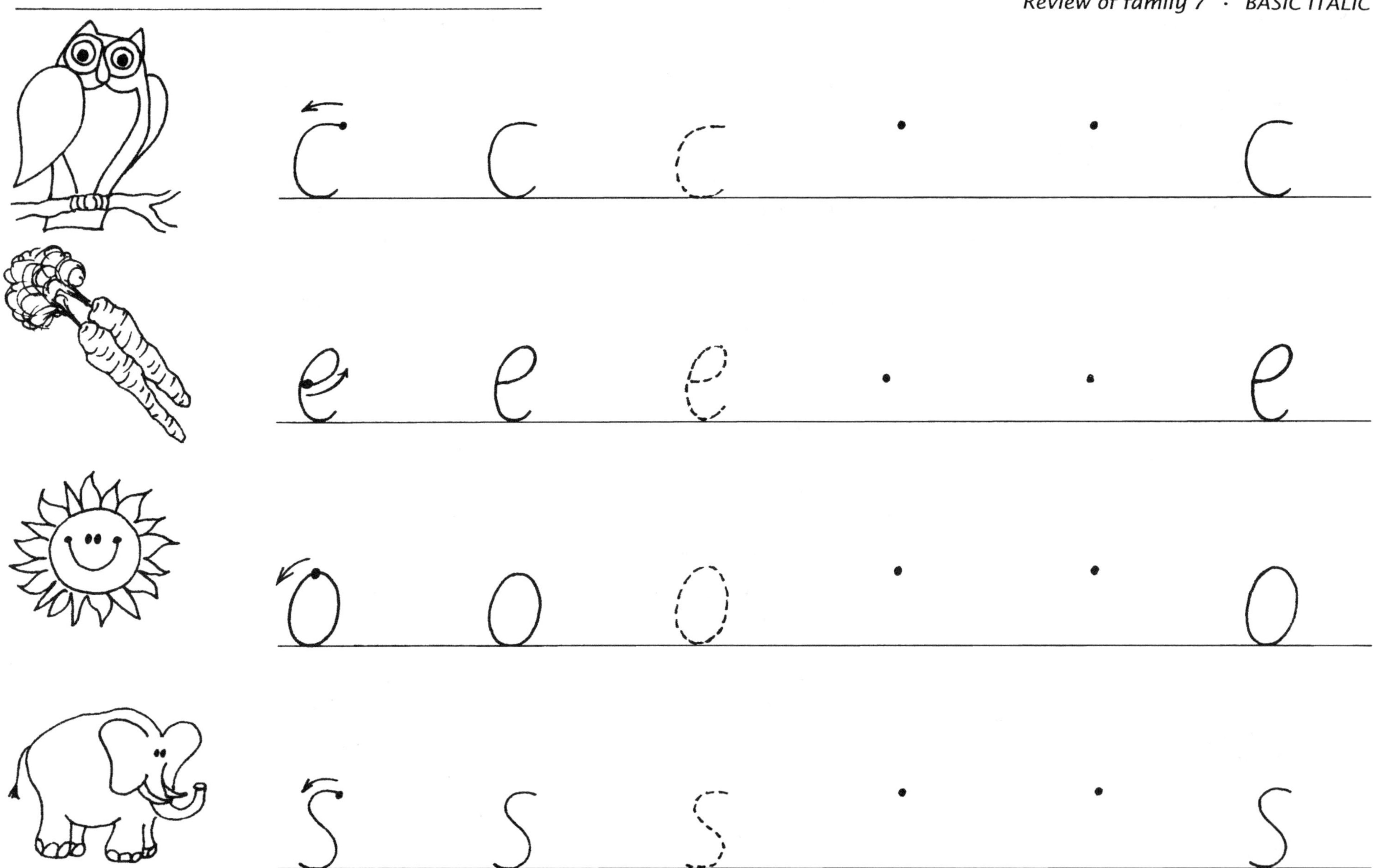

Ask the student to draw a line from the picture to the letter that stands for the correct beginning sound.

CONTENTS

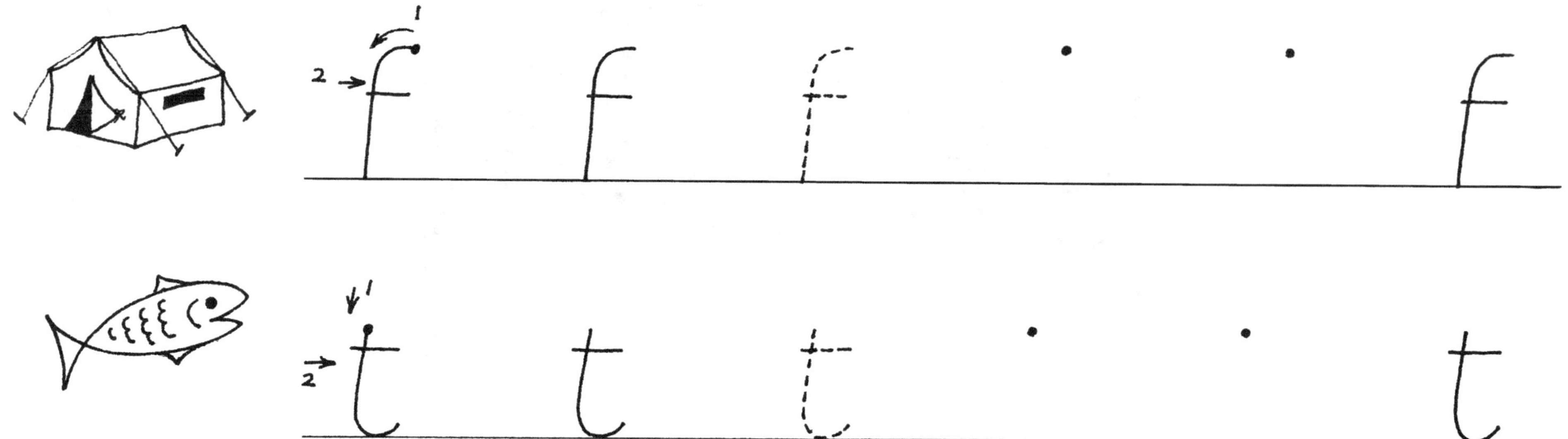

b c l

m k y

s n e

v d w

TOP TWO LINES: Ask the student to draw a line from the picture to the letter that stands for the correct beginning sound.

BOTTOM FOUR SQUARES: Ask the student to circle the letter that stands for the beginning sound of the picture.

by
Barbara Getty & Inga Dubay

GETTY-DUBAY™ ITALIC HANDWRITING SERIES

BOOK A ▪ Basic Italic
14 mm body height

BOOK B ▪ Basic Italic
11 mm body height, 9 mm

BOOK C ▪ Basic & Cursive Italic
9 mm, 6 mm body height   Introduction to Cursive Italic

BOOK D ▪ Basic & Cursive Italic
6 mm, 5 mm body height

BOOK E ▪ Basic & Cursive Italic
6 mm, 5 mm, 4 mm body height

BOOK F ▪ Basic & Cursive Italic
6 mm, 5 mm, 4 mm body height

BOOK G ▪ Basic & Cursive Italic
5 mm, 4 mm body height

INSTRUCTION MANUAL

BOOK A ▪ INTERNATIONAL EDITION
Copyright 2012 by Barbara M. Getty and Inga S. Dubay
ISBN 978-0-9827762-7-8

FOURTH EDITION
Copyright 2012 by Barbara M. Getty and Inga S. Dubay
THIRD EDITION
Copyright 1999 by Barbara M. Getty and Inga S. Dubay
SECOND EDITION
Copyright 1986 by Barbara M. Getty and Inga S. Dubay
REVISED EDITION
Copyright 1980 by Barbara M. Getty and Inga S. Dubay
FIRST EDITION
Copyright 1979 by Barbara M. Getty and Inga S. Dubay

All rights reserved. This text may not be reproduced in whole or in part without the express written permission of the copyright holder.

Published by Handwriting Success, LLC,
Portland, Oregon USA

www.handwritingsuccess.com

Printed at various locations around the world by IngramSpark.

Cover Design: Sinda Markham
Front cover picture: Flowers of the sunflower family in the Ochoco National Forest, Oregon, USA
Back cover pictures: Columbine flower, Golden-mantled squirrel

www.ingramcontent.com/pod-product-compliance
Lightning Source LLC
Chambersburg PA
CBHW081423210726
48464CB00020B/1370

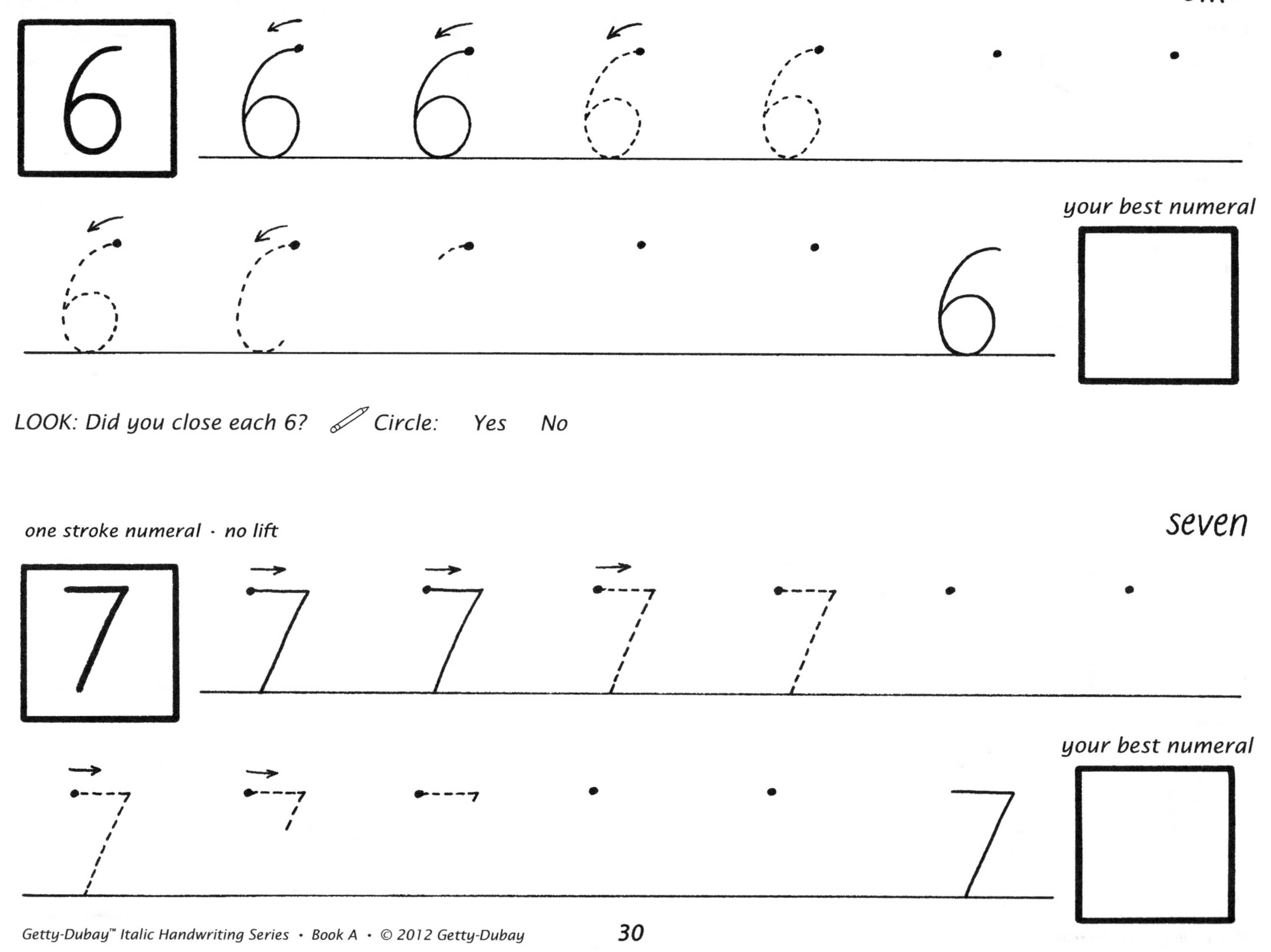
one stroke numeral · no lift
six
6 6 6 6
your best numeral
6 6 6
LOOK: Did you close each 6? Circle: Yes No
one stroke numeral · no lift
seven
7 7 7 7
your best numeral
7 7 7

four

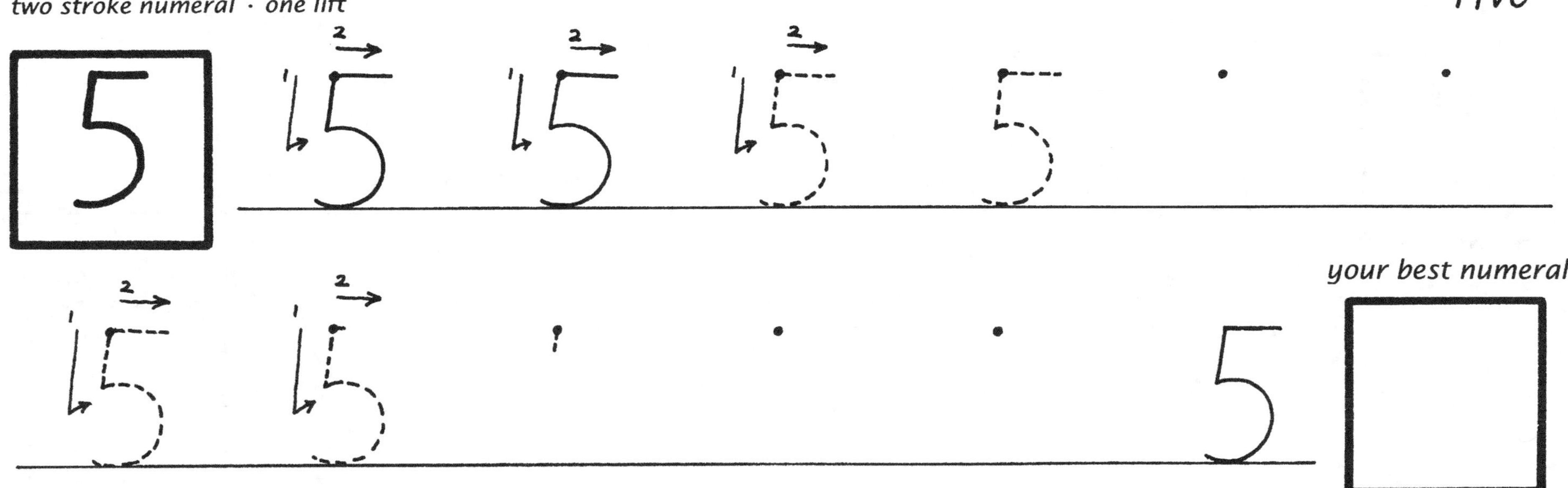

your best numeral

five

your best numeral

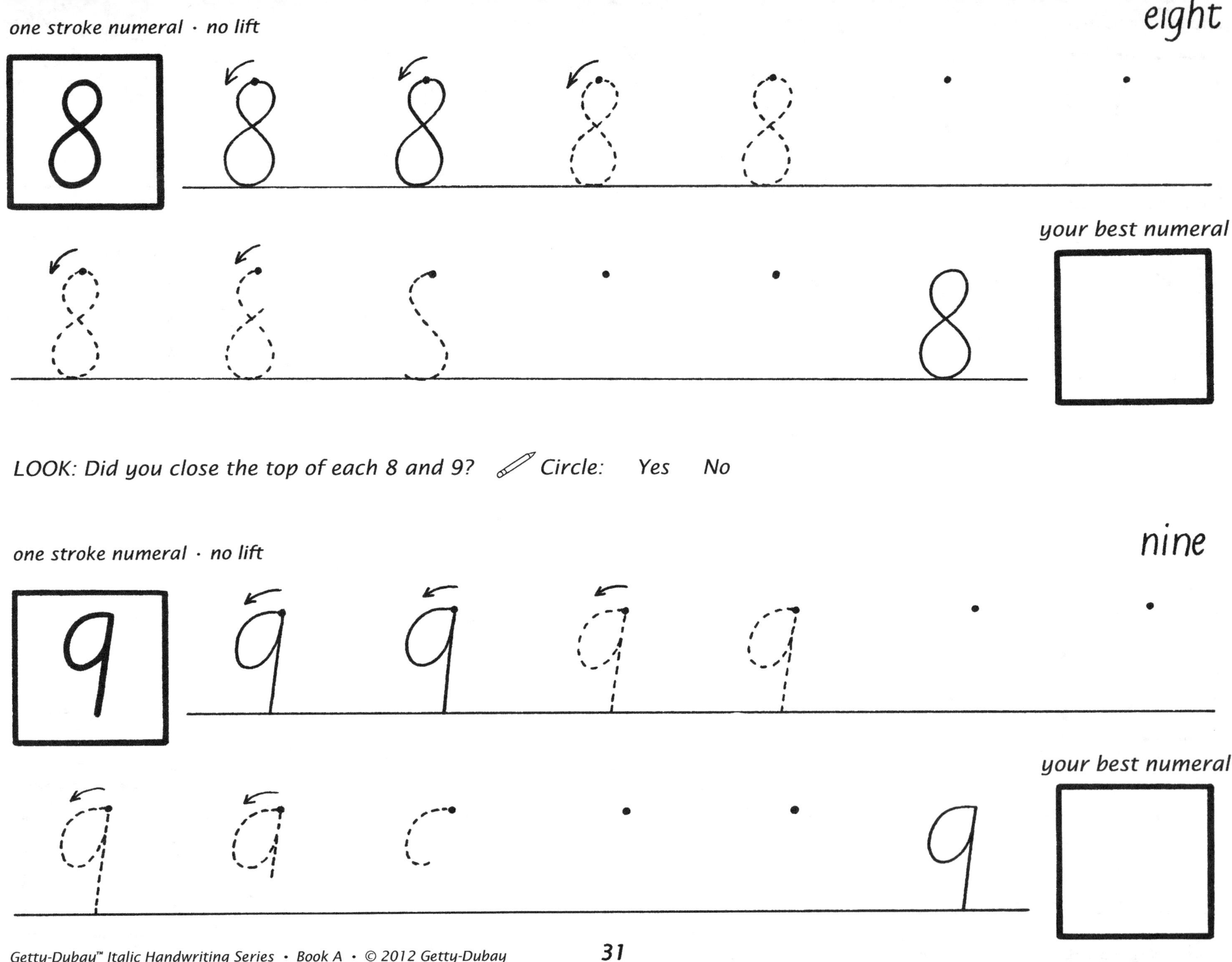

one stroke numeral · no lift
eight
8
your best numeral
LOOK: Did you close the top of each 8 and 9?   Circle: Yes   No
one stroke numeral · no lift
nine
9
your best numeral

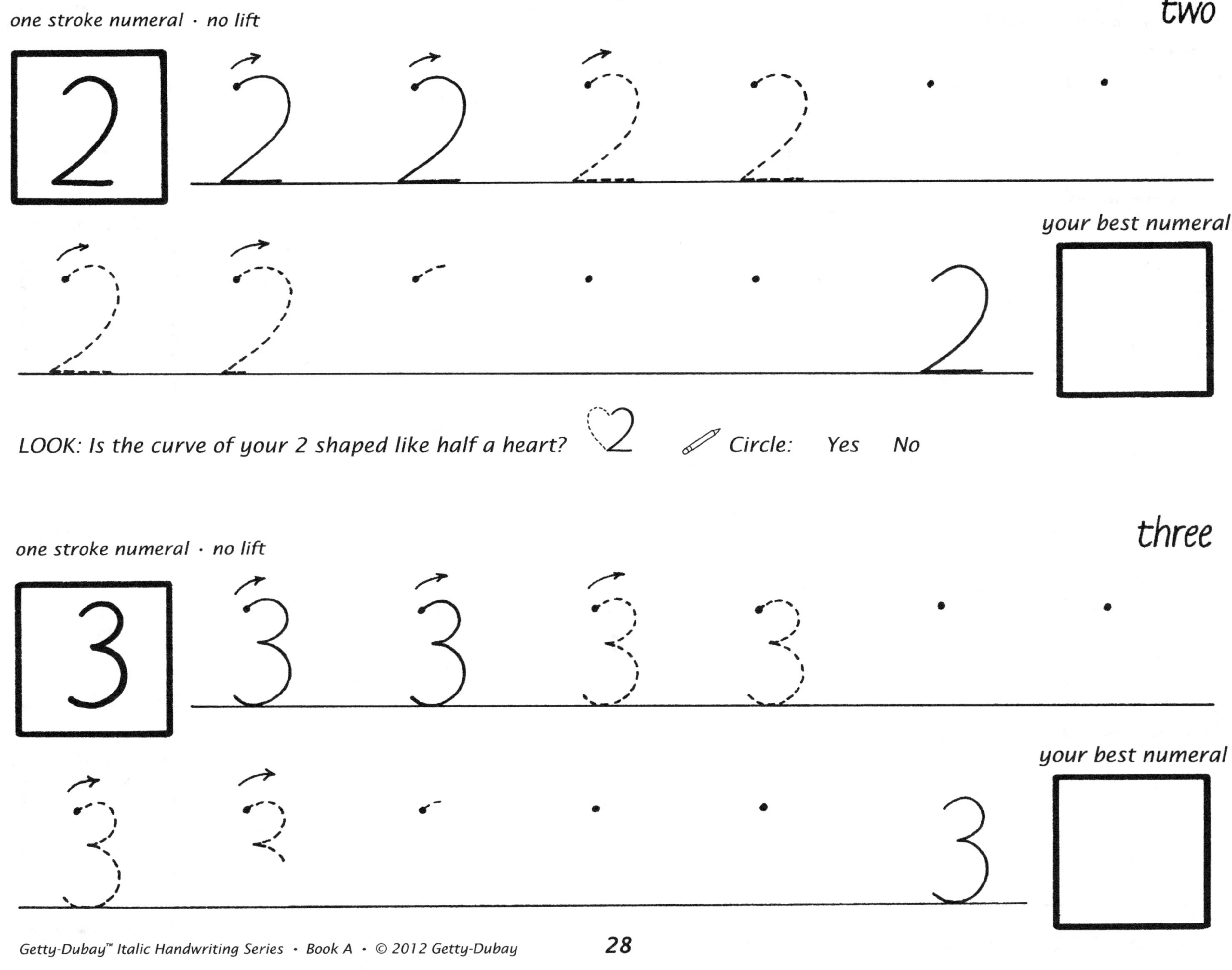

one stroke numeral · no lift

your best numeral

LOOK: Is the curve of your 2 shaped like half a heart?   Circle: Yes   No

three

one stroke numeral · no lift

your best numeral

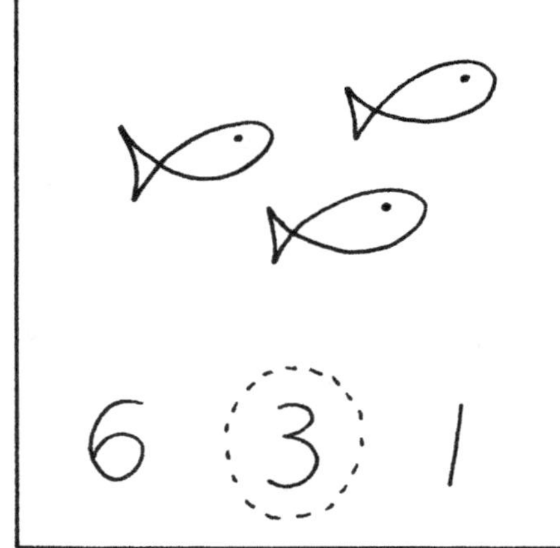

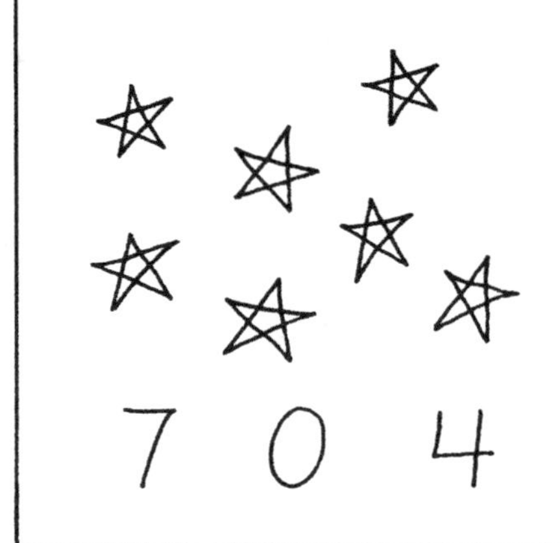

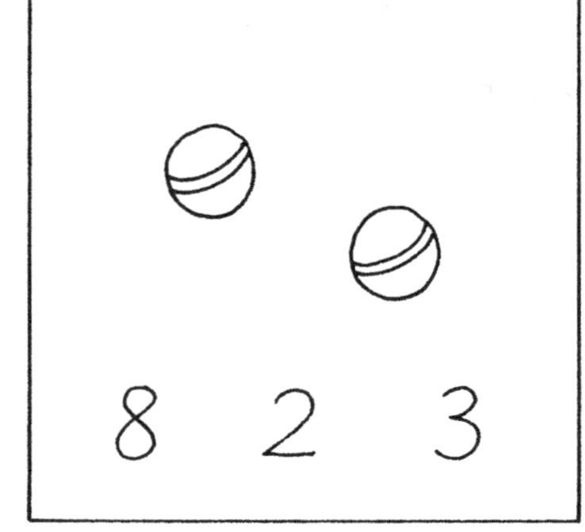

Ask the student to circle the numeral
that stands for the number of objects in the box.

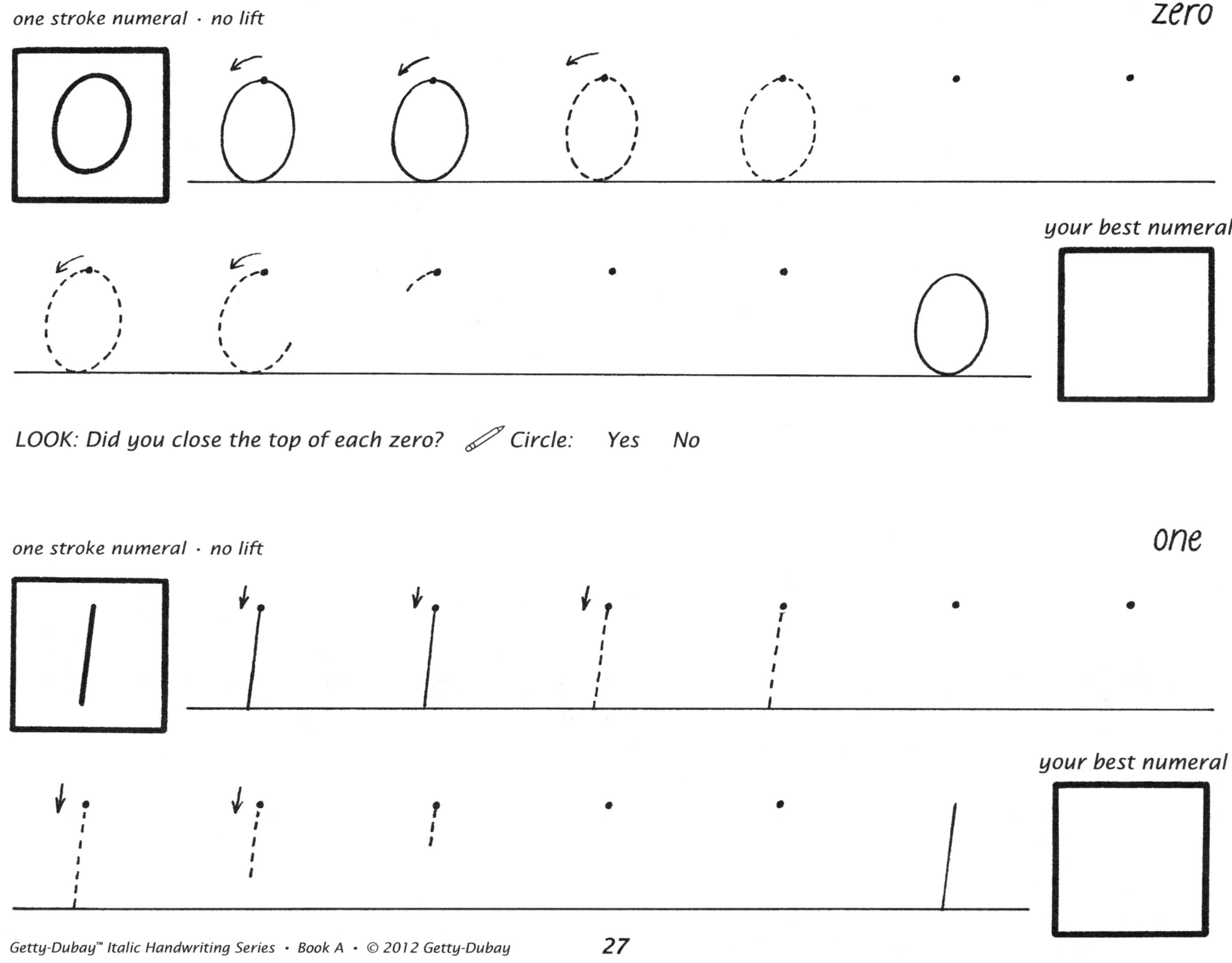

one stroke numeral · no lift
zero
your best numeral
LOOK: Did you close the top of each zero? Circle: Yes   No
one stroke numeral · no lift
one
your best numeral

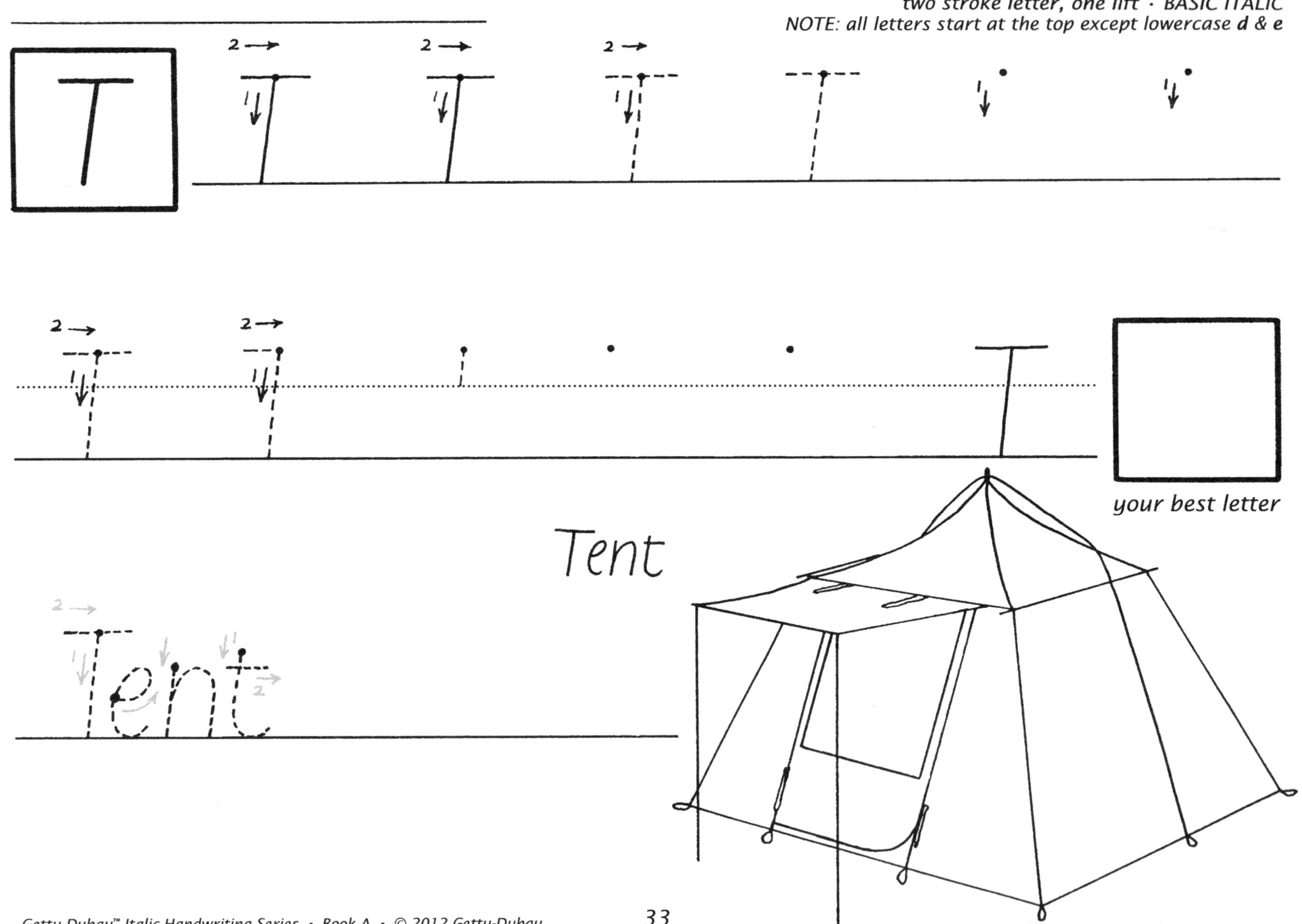

T
2
2
2
2
your best letter
Tent
Tent

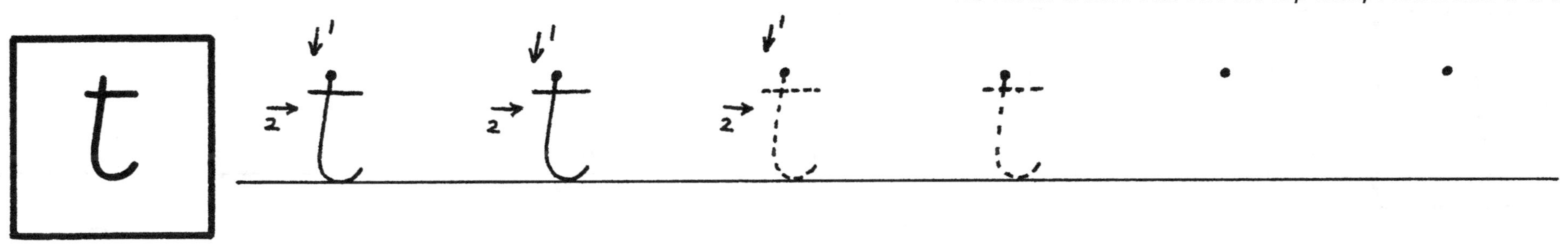

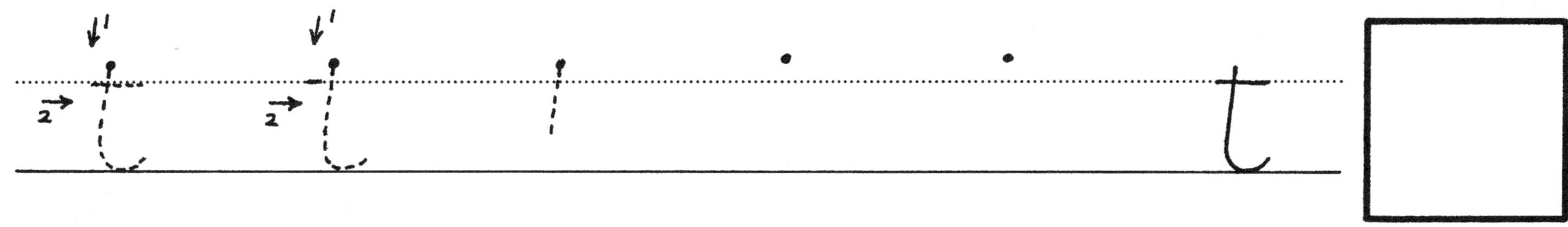

your best letter

turkey

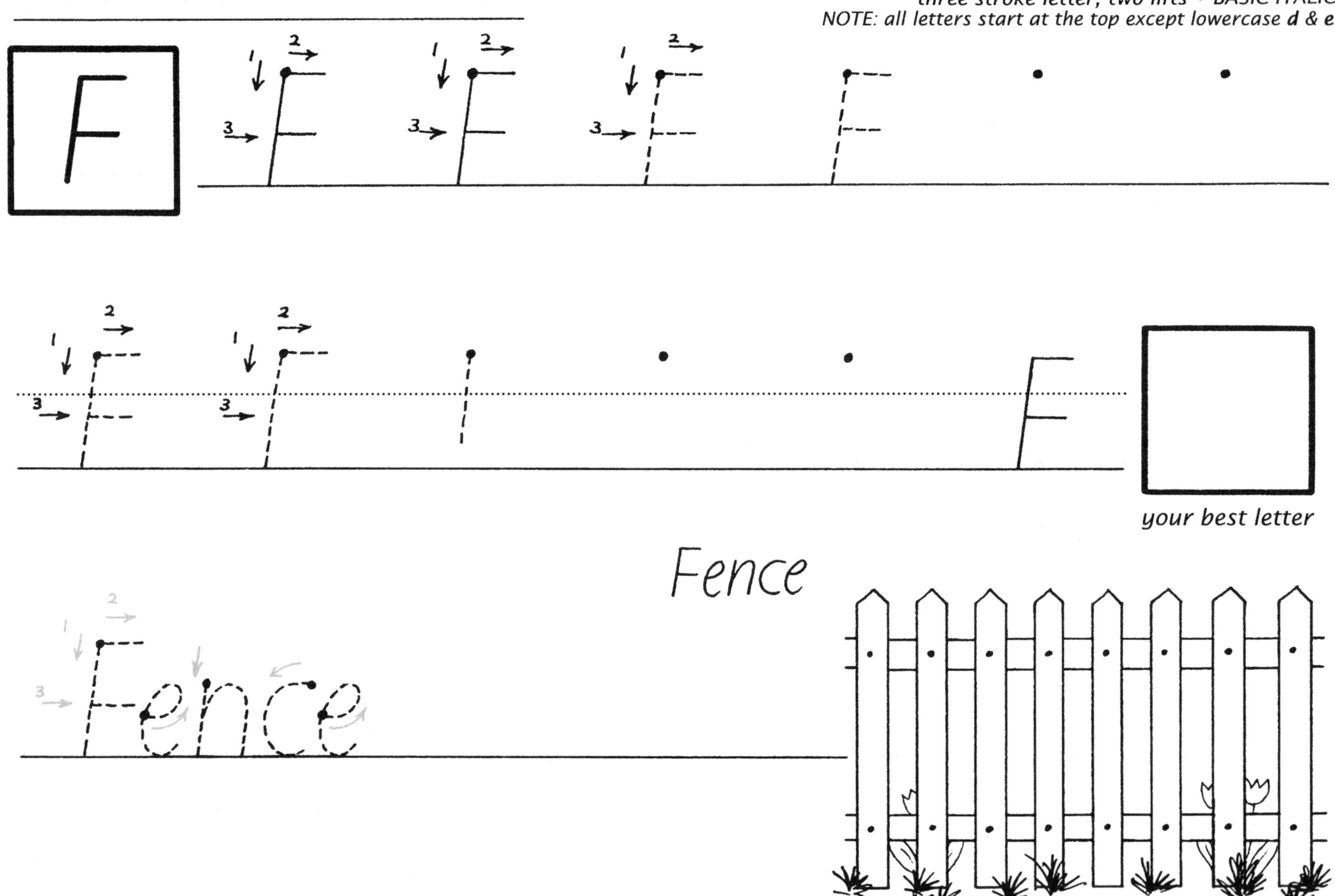

F
your best letter
Fence
Fence

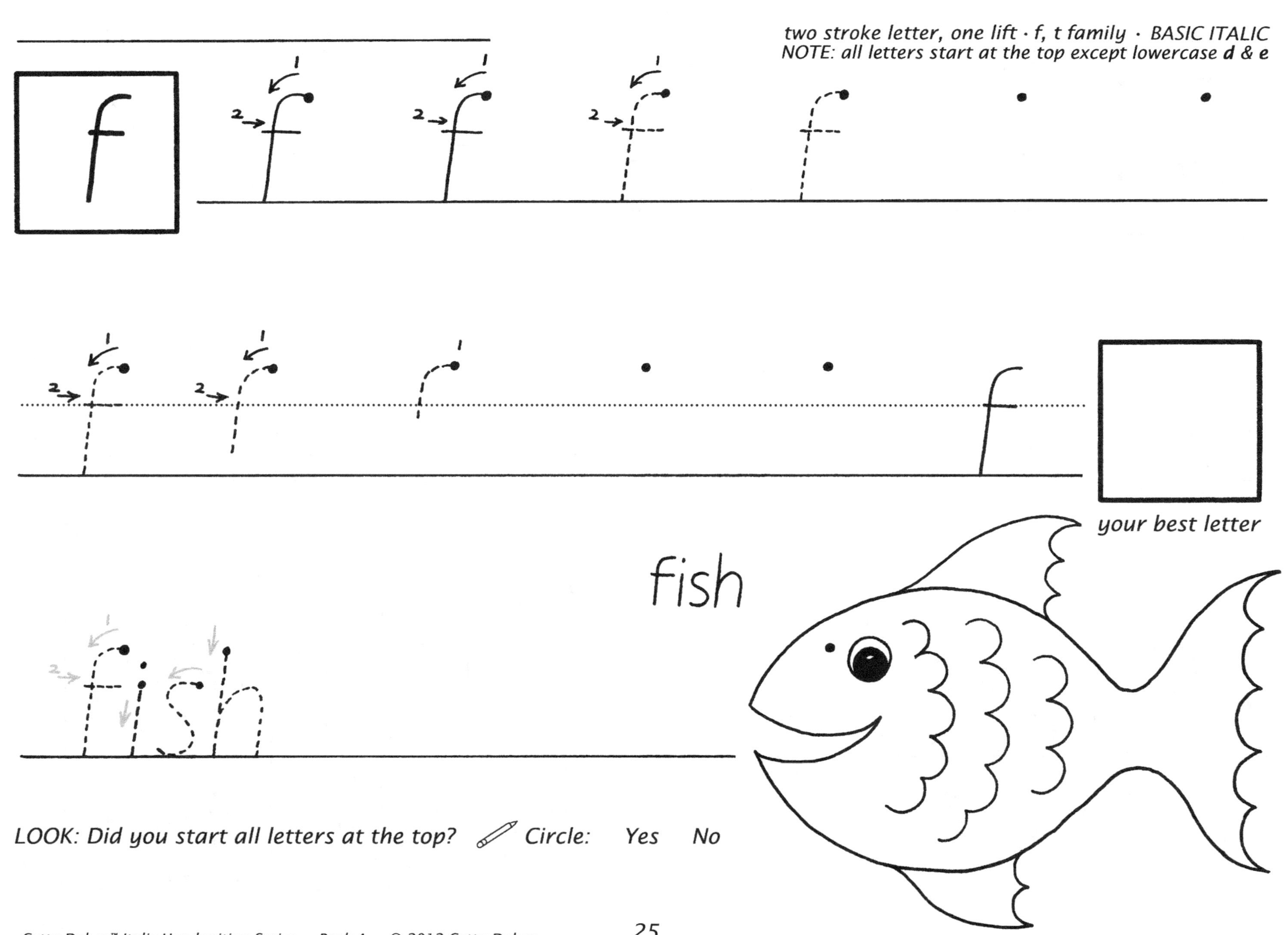

two stroke letter, one lift · f, t family · BASIC ITALIC
NOTE: all letters start at the top except lowercase d & e
f
1
2
your best letter
fish
fish
LOOK: Did you start all letters at the top? Circle: Yes No

your best letter

Sailboat

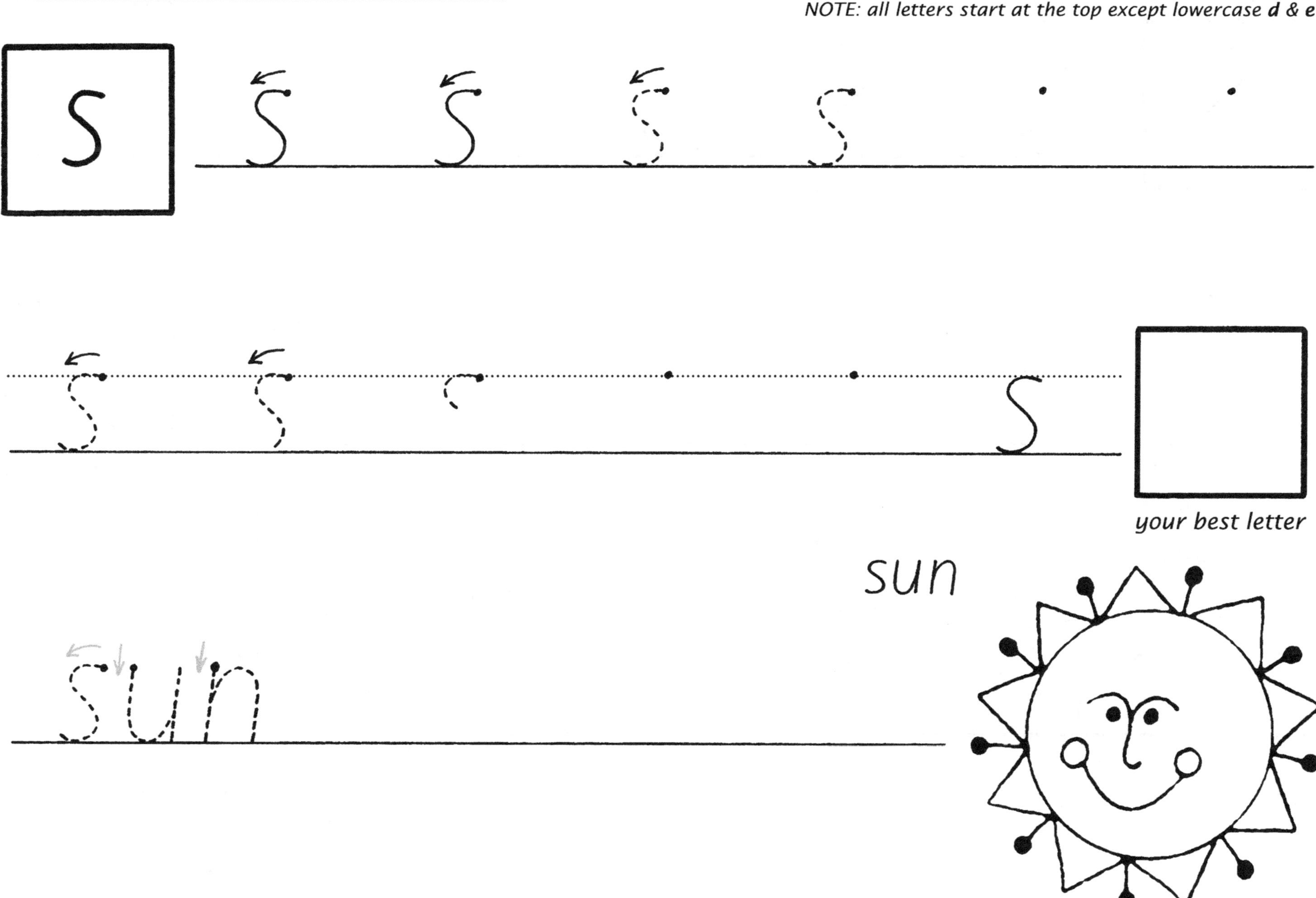

your best letter

sun

C

your best letter

Cow

LOOK: Did you trace each letter before writing your own?

Circle: Yes   No

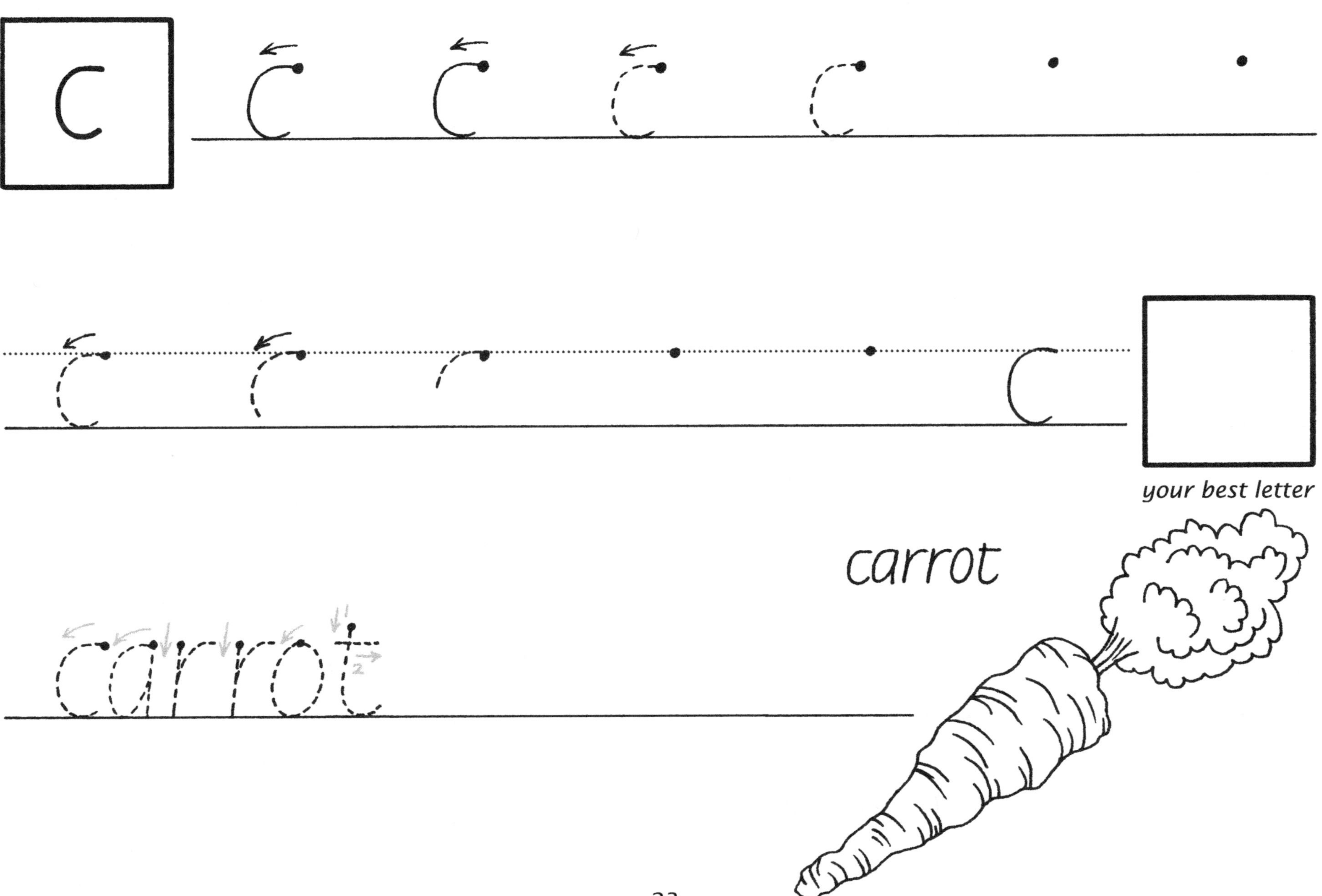

your best letter

carrot

E

your best letter

Egg

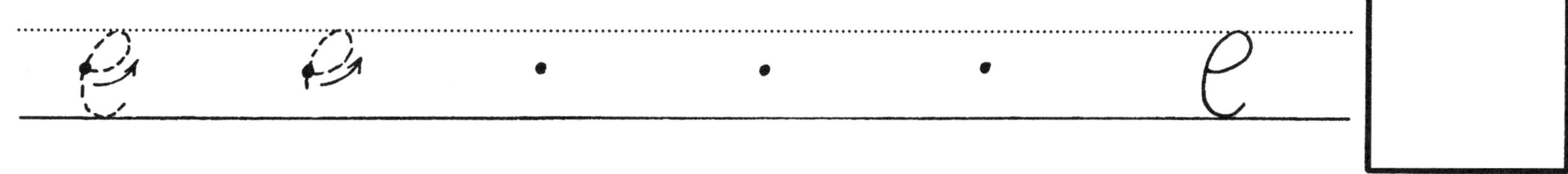

your best letter

elephant

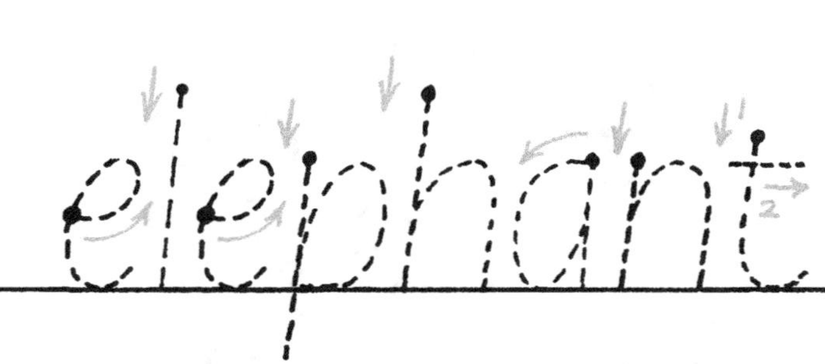

LOOK: Did you trace each **e** before writing your own?

Circle: Yes   No

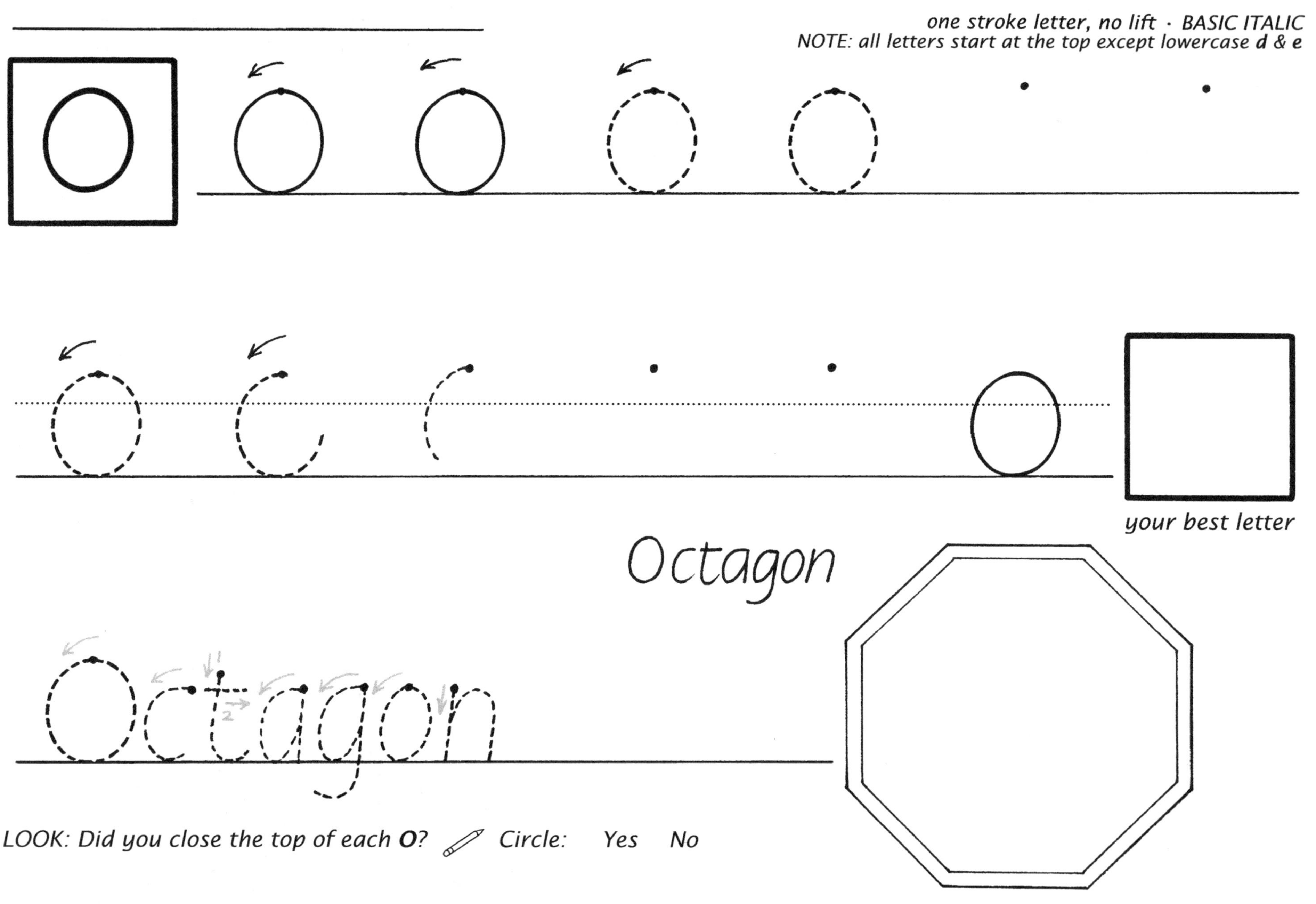

your best letter

Octagon

LOOK: Did you close the top of each **O**? Circle: Yes No

o

c r

octopus

your best letter

octopus

LOOK: Did you close the top of each **o**? Circle: Yes No

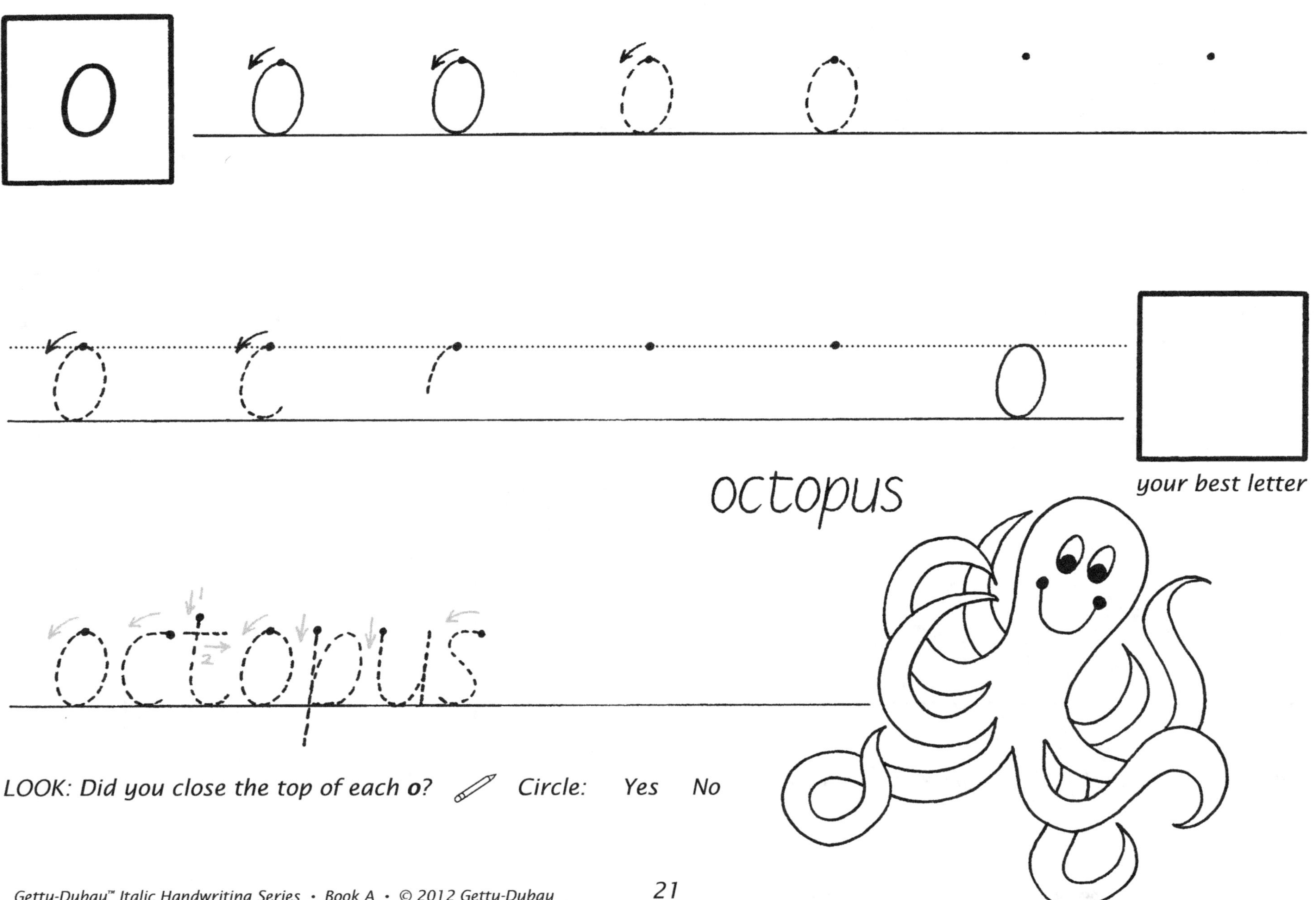

your best letter

parrot

Balloons

your best letter

Balloons

butterfly

your best letter

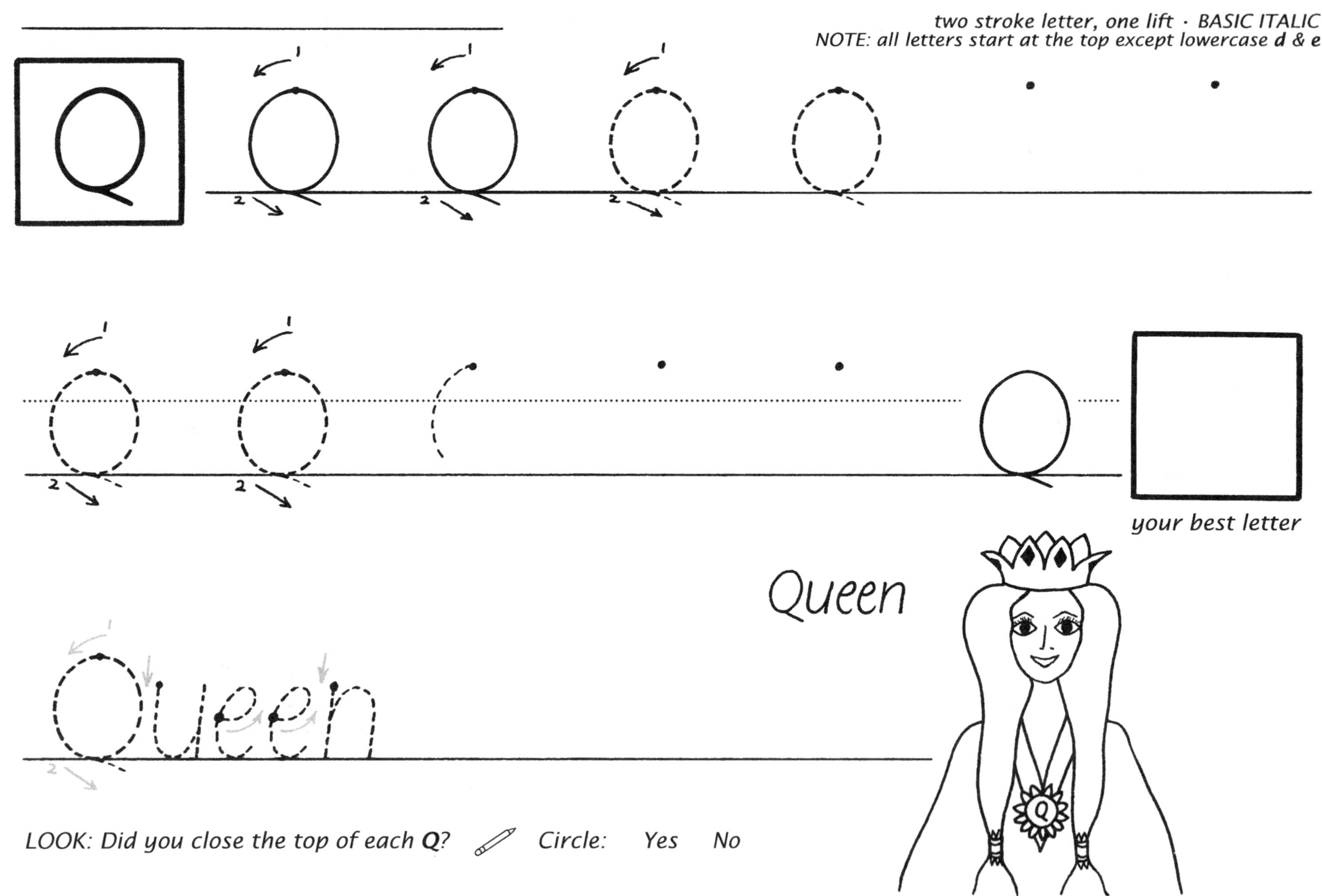

two stroke letter, one lift · BASIC ITALIC
NOTE: all letters start at the top except lowercase d & e
your best letter
Queen
Queen
LOOK: Did you close the top of each Q? Circle: Yes No

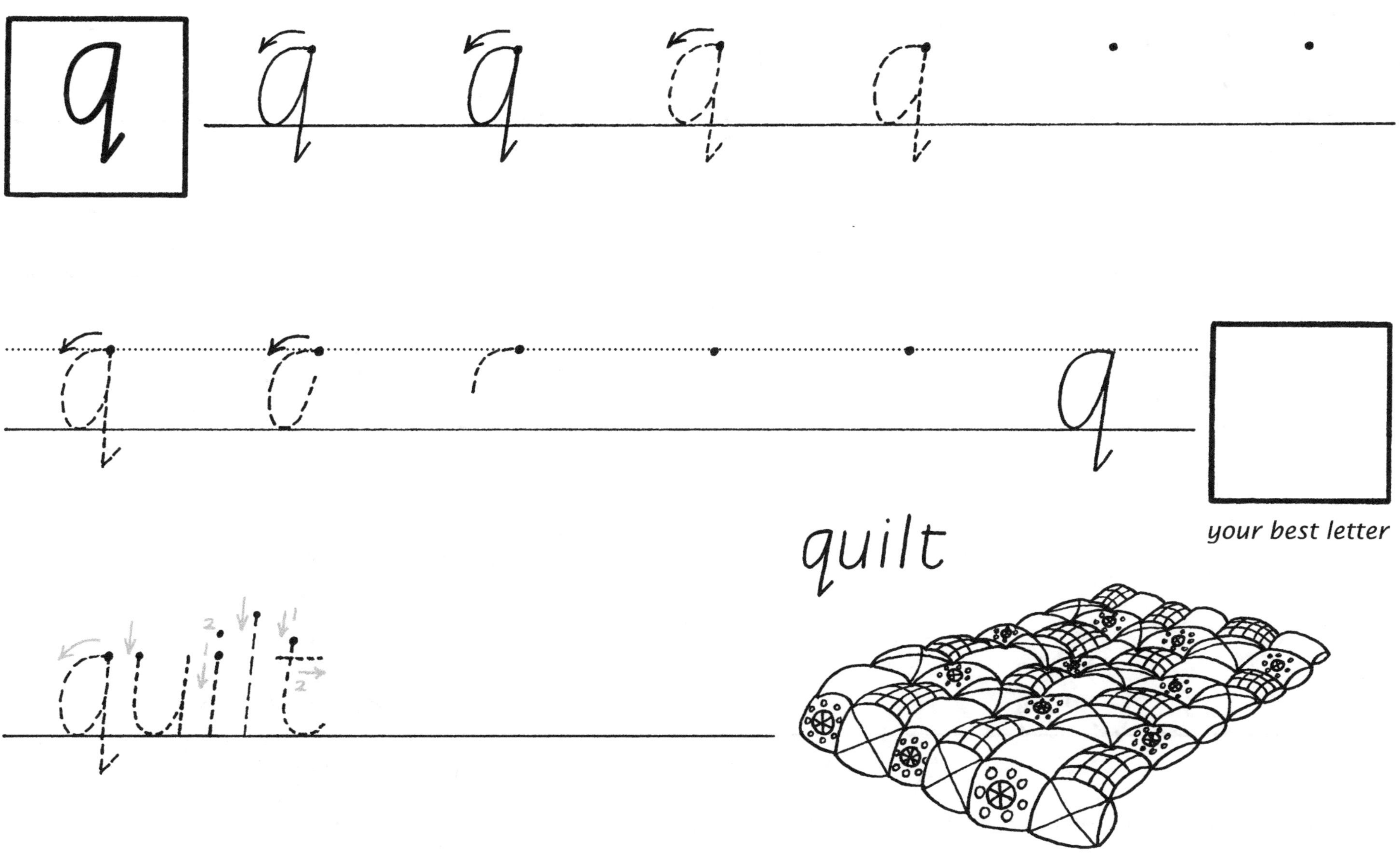

your best letter

quilt

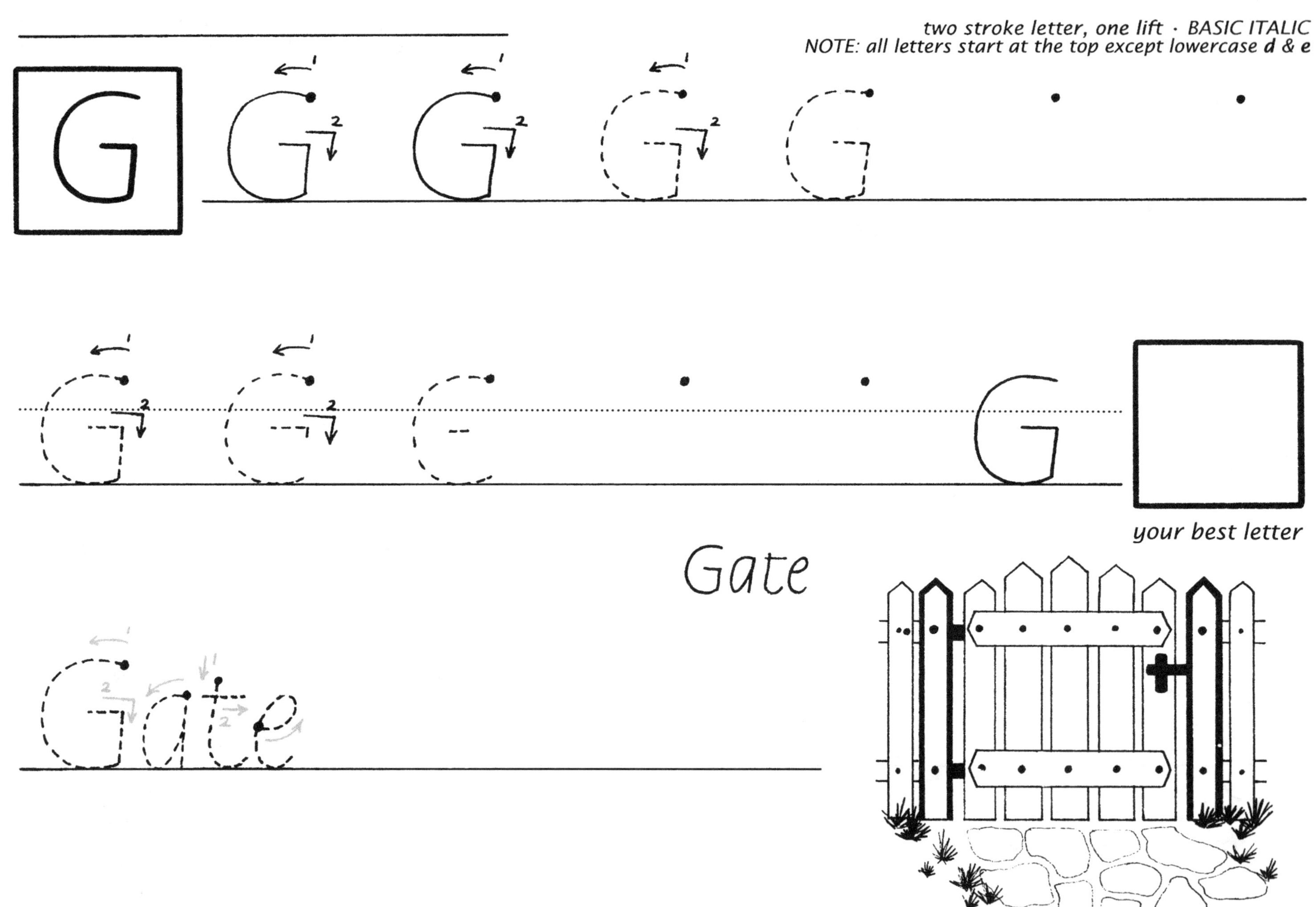
G
Gate
your best letter
Gate

LOOK: Did you trace each letter before writing your own?   Circle: Yes   No

two stroke letter, one lift · BASIC ITALIC
NOTE: all letters start at the top except lowercase d & e
your best letter
Dinosaur
Dinosaur

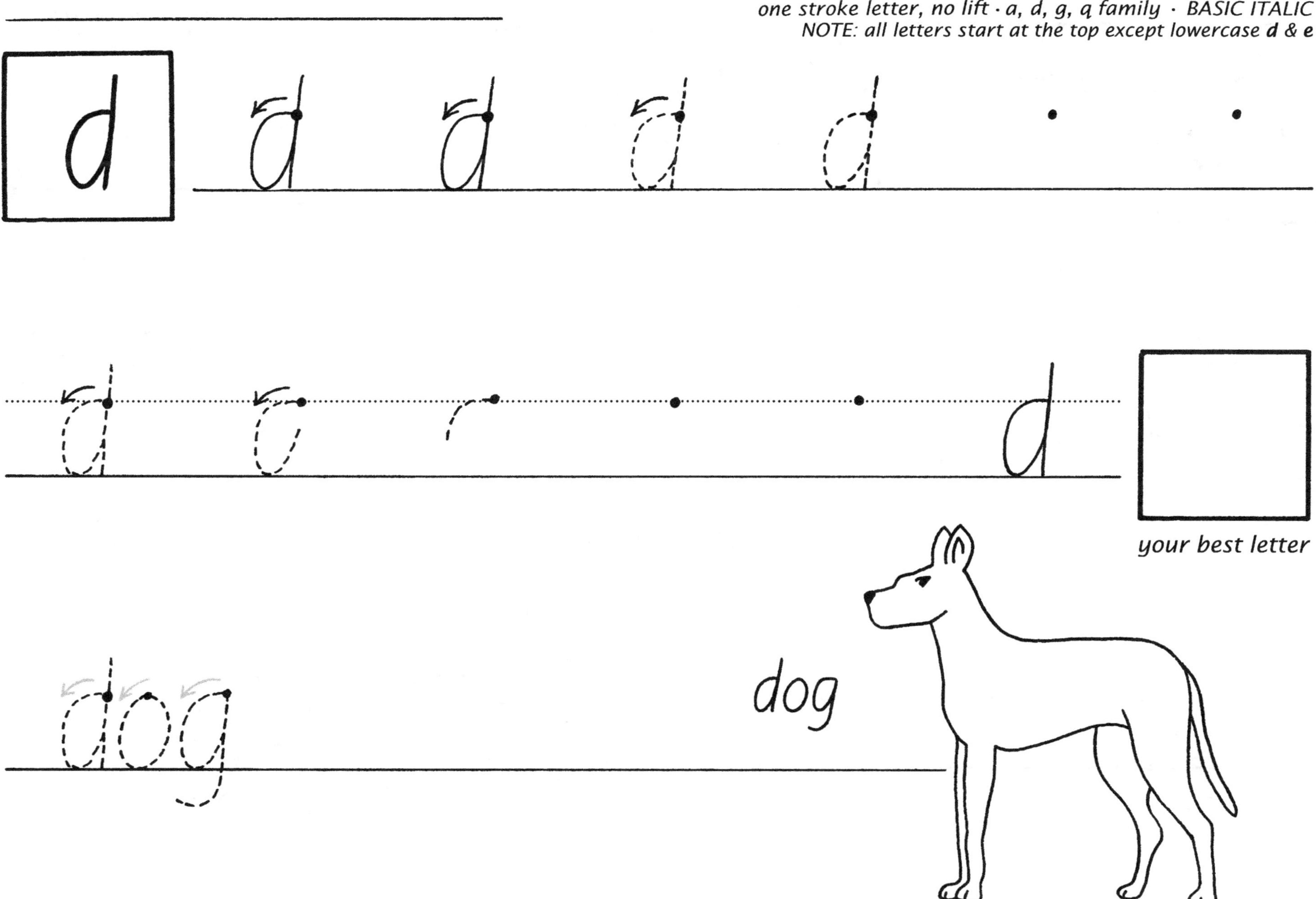

your best letter

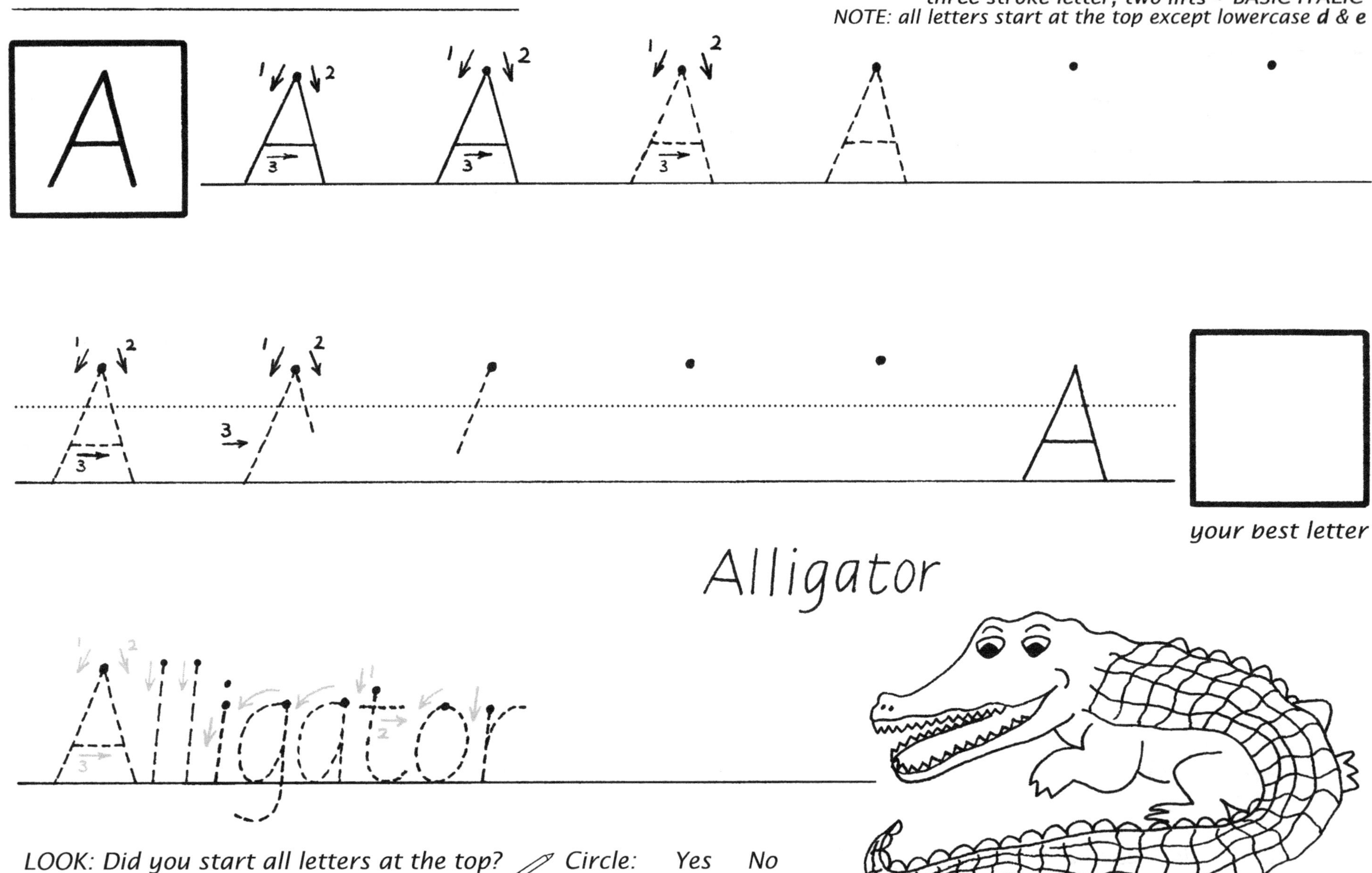

three stroke letter, two lifts · BASIC ITALIC
NOTE: all letters start at the top except lowercase d & e
your best letter
Alligator
LOOK: Did you start all letters at the top? Circle: Yes No

your best letter

apple

*LOOK: Did you close each **a** at the top?* Circle: Yes   No

Y

your best letter

Yo-yo

Getty-Dubay™ Italic Handwriting Series · Book A · © 2012 Getty-Dubay

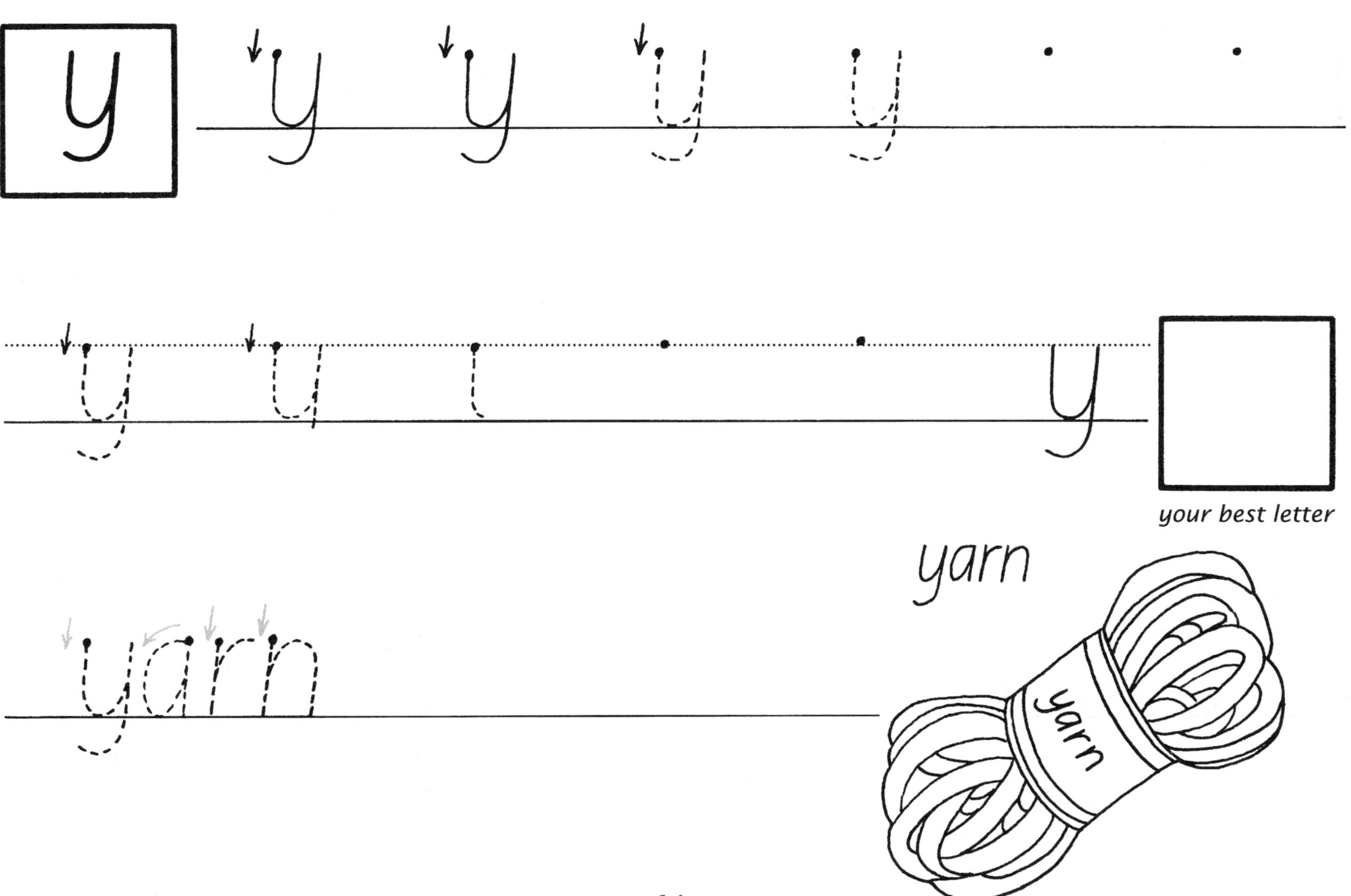

your best letter

yarn

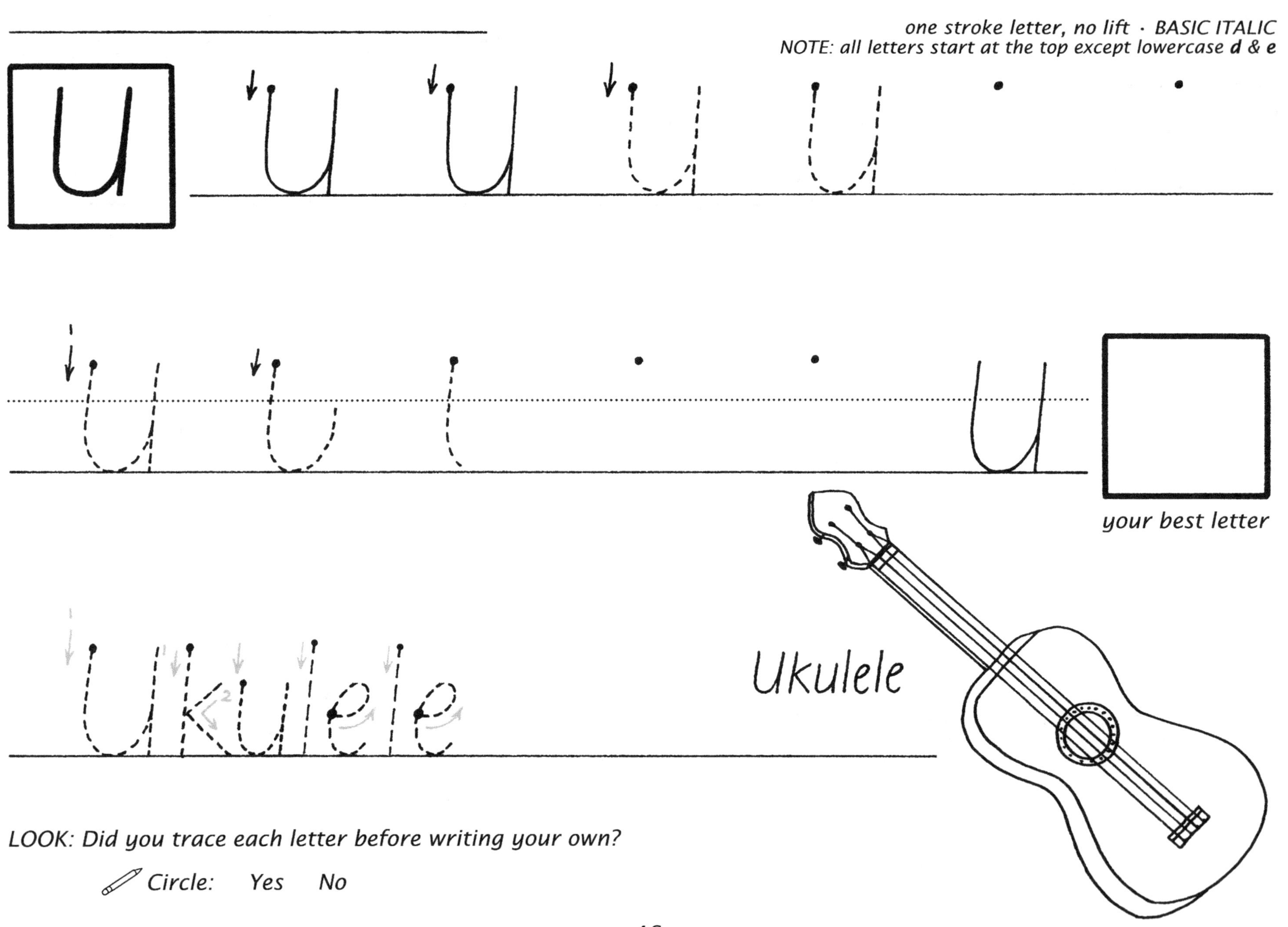

LOOK: Did you trace each letter before writing your own?

Circle: Yes   No

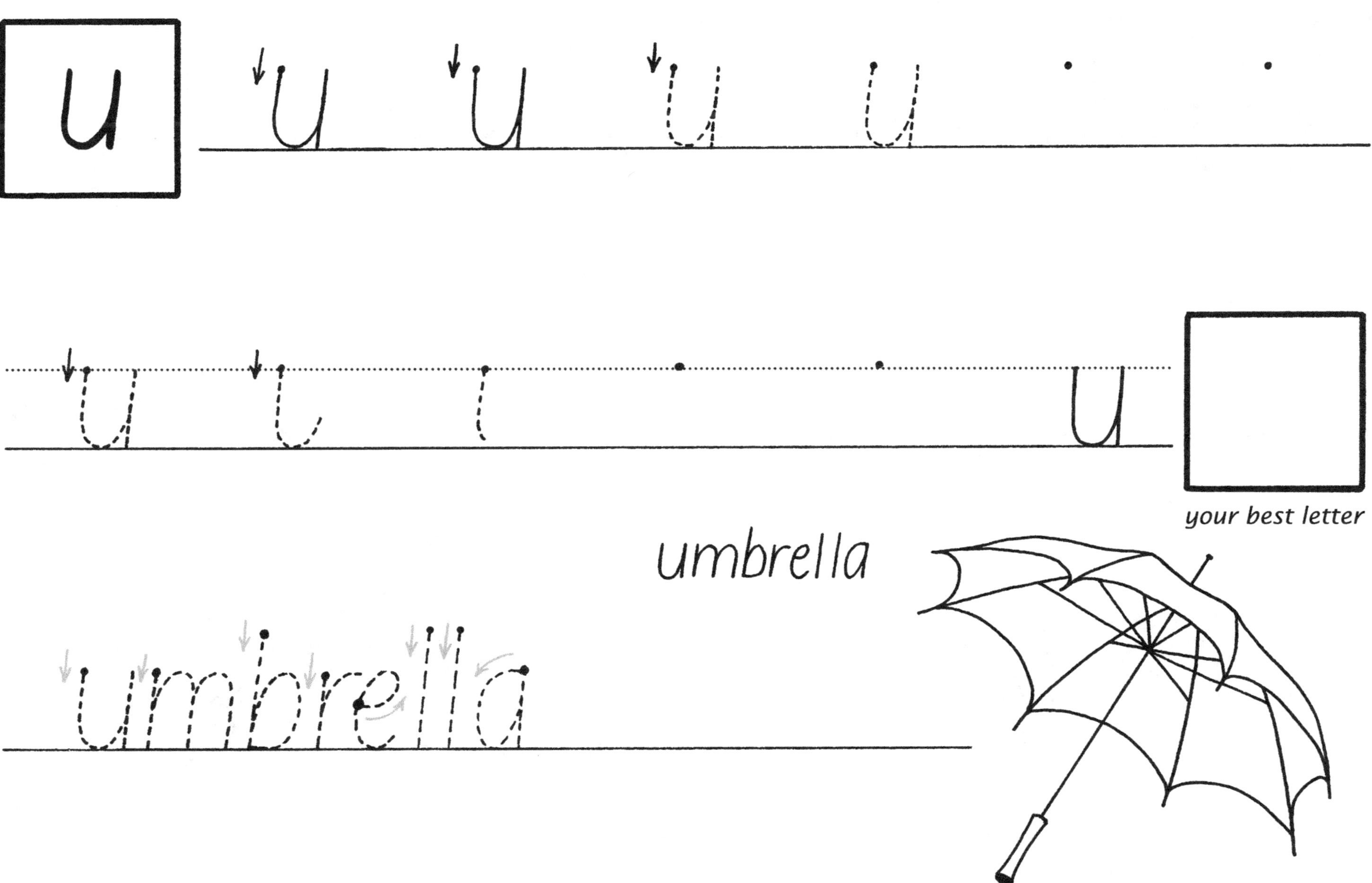

your best letter

umbrella

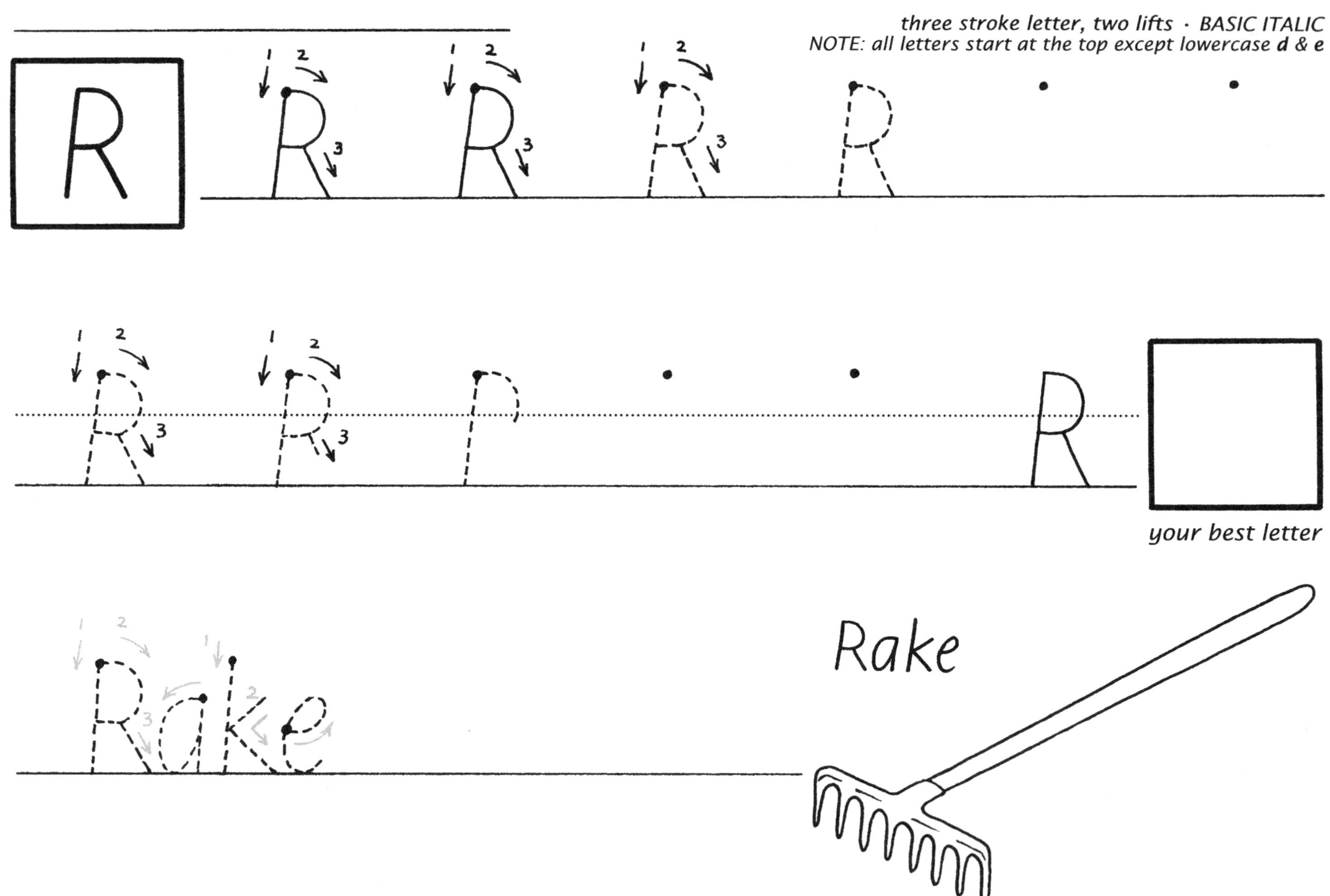

R
three stroke letter, two lifts · BASIC ITALIC
NOTE: all letters start at the top except lowercase d & e
your best letter
Rake
Rake

your best letter

rabbit

LOOK: Did you start each letter at the top? Circle: Yes   No

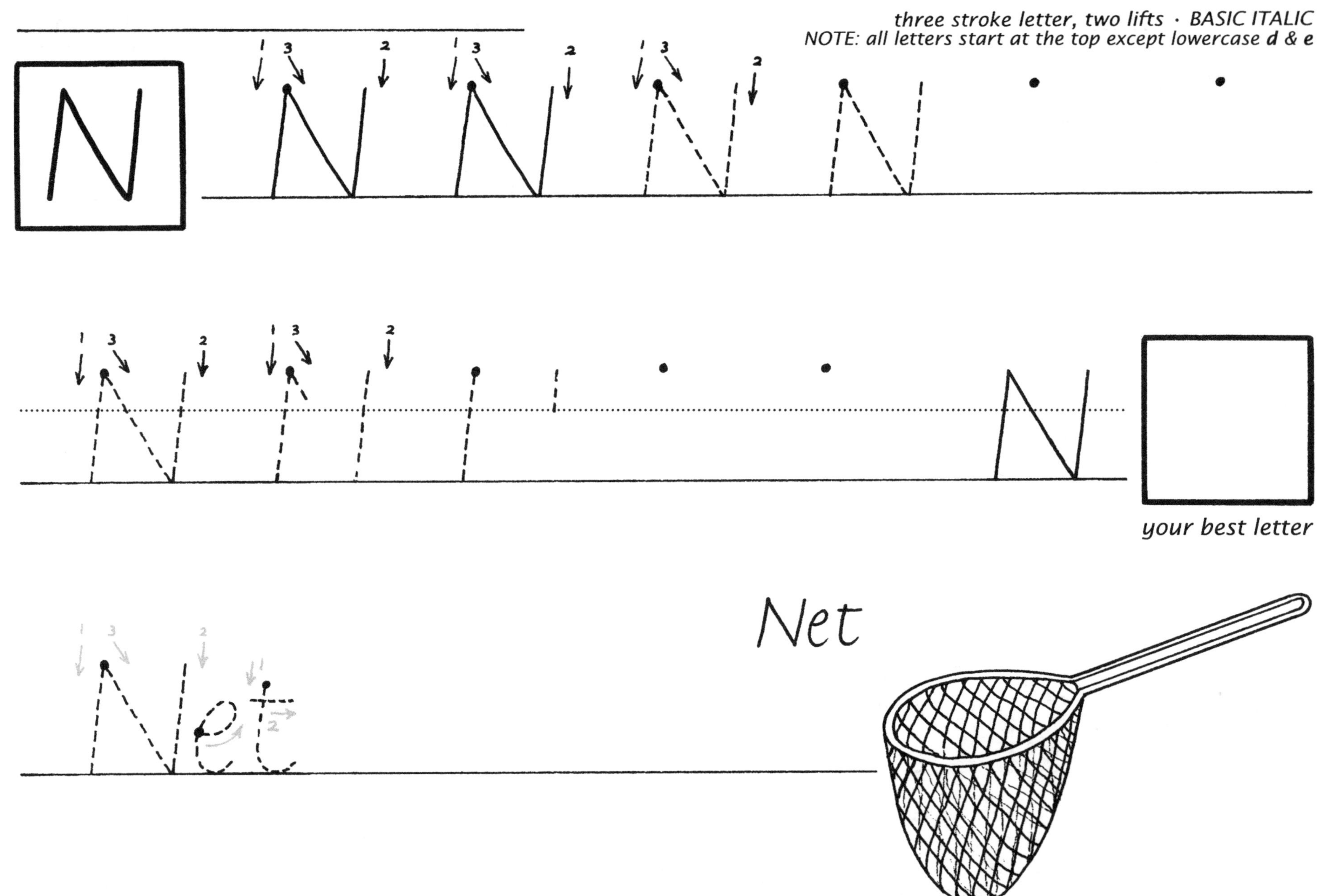

three stroke letter, two lifts · BASIC ITALIC
NOTE: all letters start at the top except lowercase d & e
1 3 2 1 3 2 1 3 2
N N N N
1 3 2 1 3 2
N N
your best letter
1 3 2 1
Net
Net

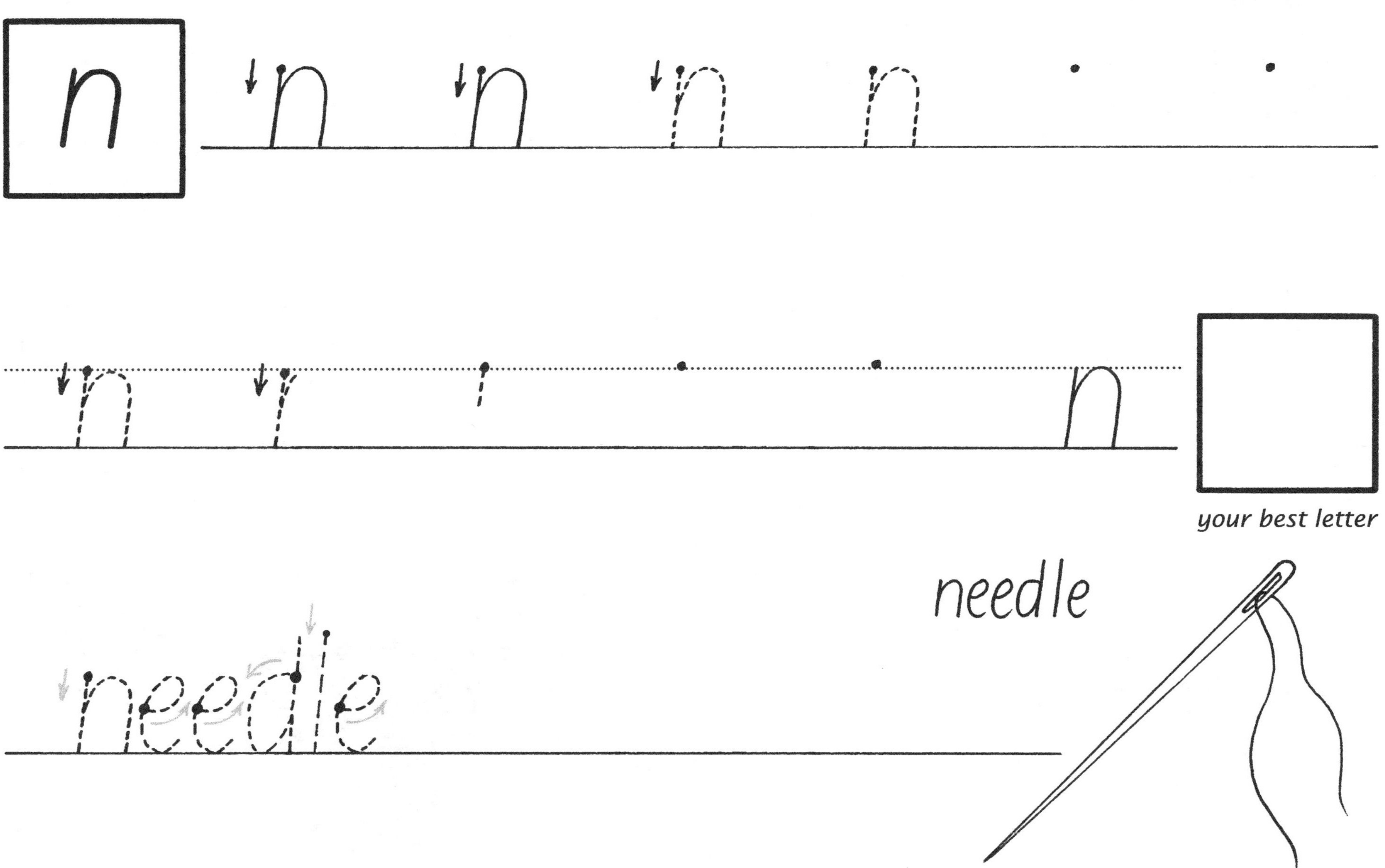

your best letter
needle

your best letter

Mittens

your best letter

mouse

mouse

LOOK: Did you start all letters at the top? ✏ Circle: Yes   No

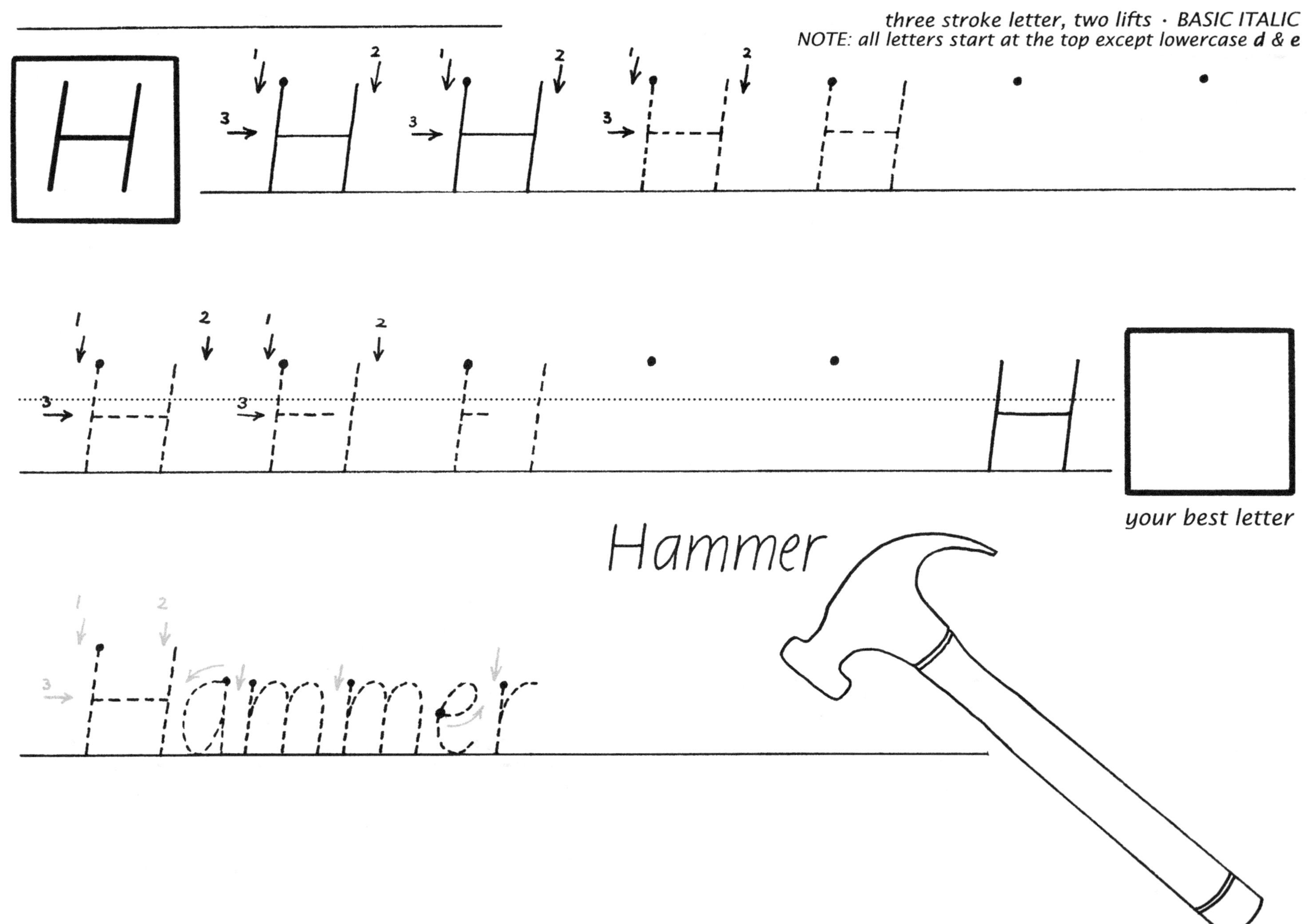

three stroke letter, two lifts · BASIC ITALIC
NOTE: all letters start at the top except lowercase d & e
your best letter
Hammer
Hammer

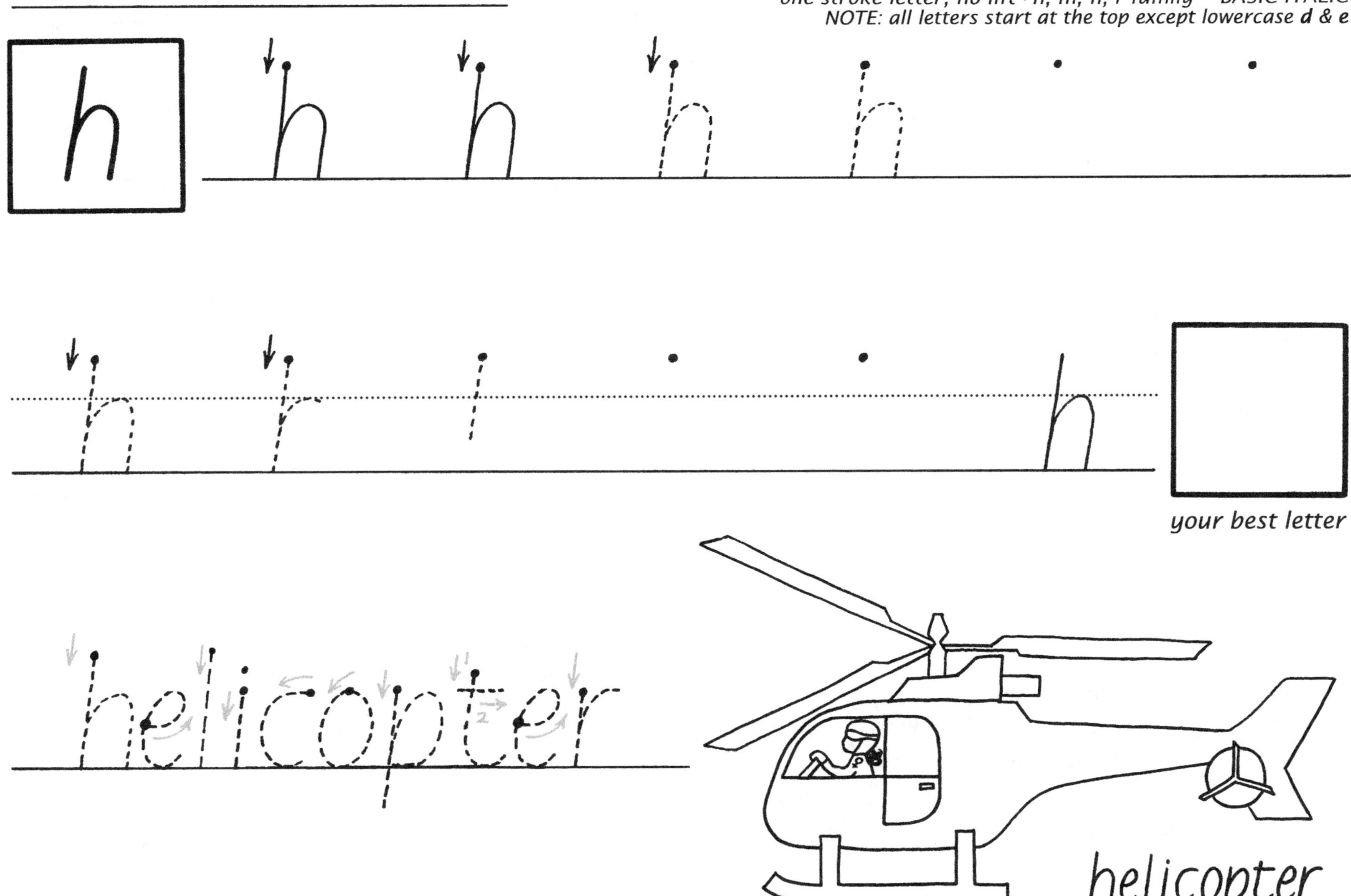

your best letter

helicopter

Zipper

your best letter

Zipper

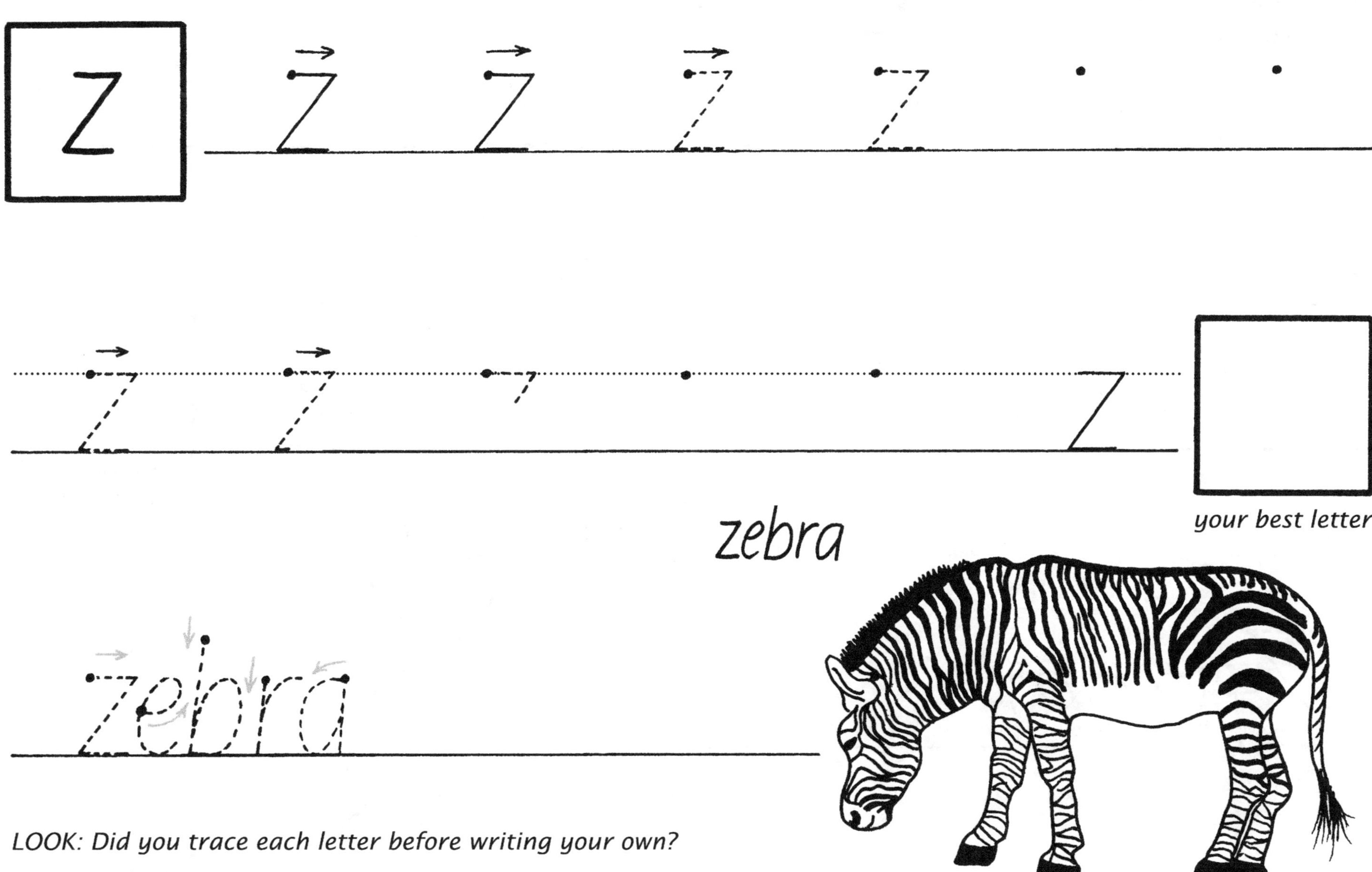

your best letter

zebra

LOOK: Did you trace each letter before writing your own?

Circle: Yes   No

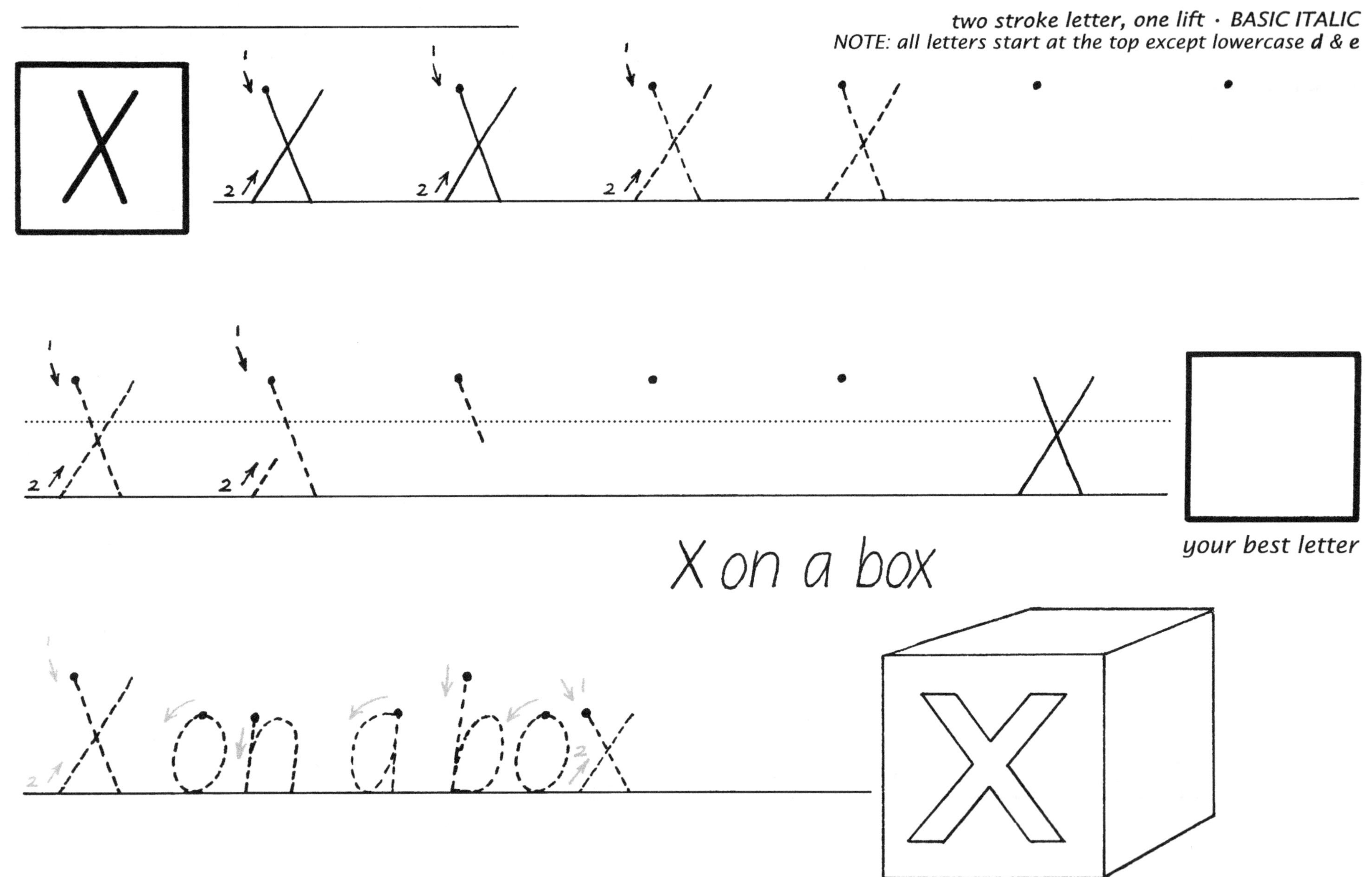
X on a box
your best letter

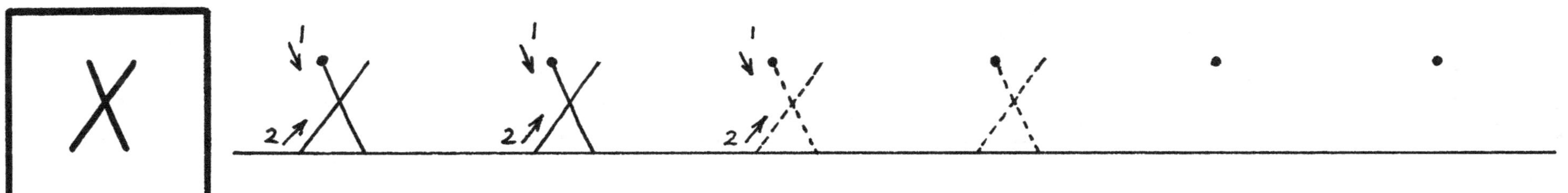

x in a box

your best letter

x in a box

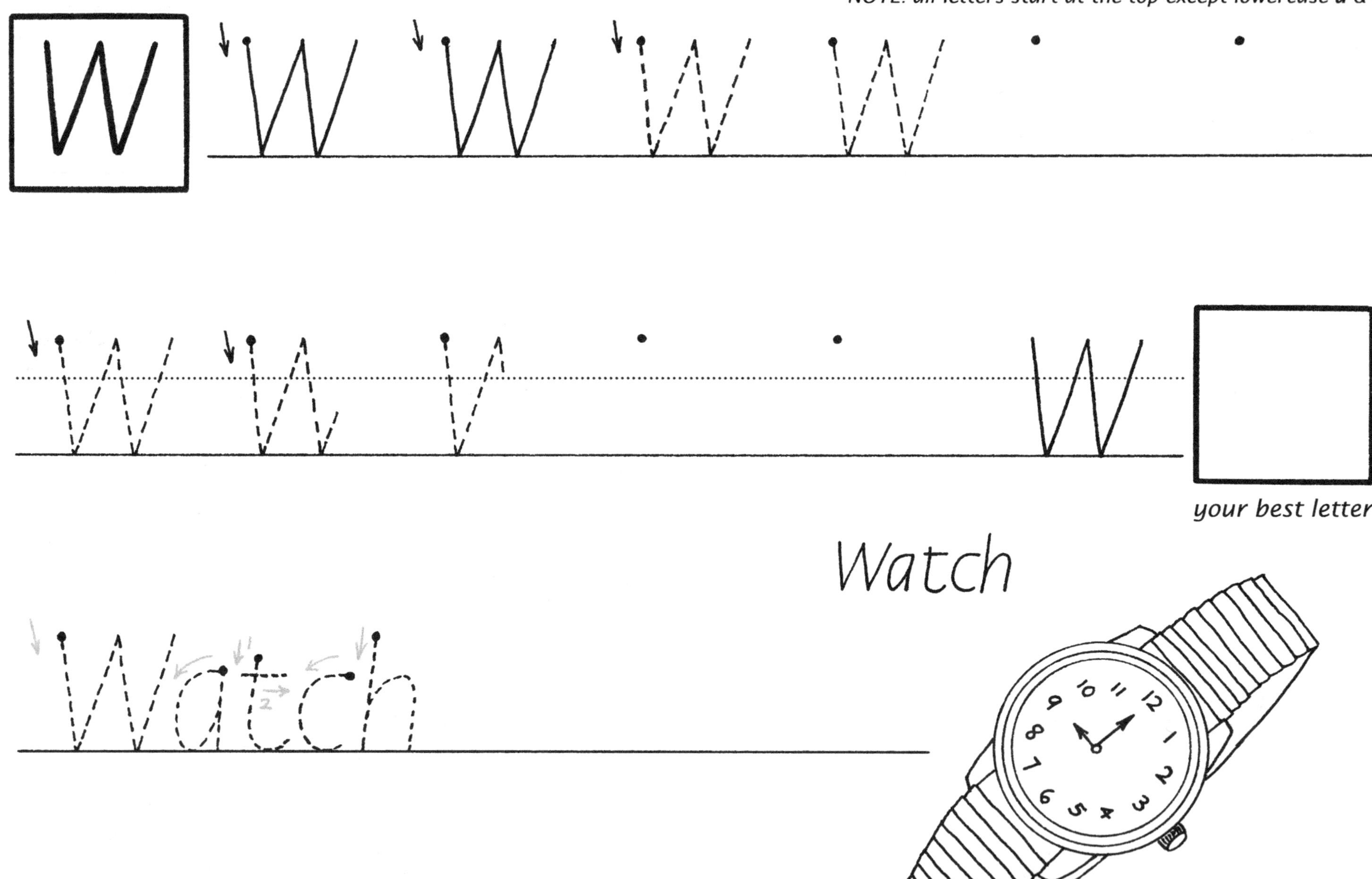

your best letter

Watch

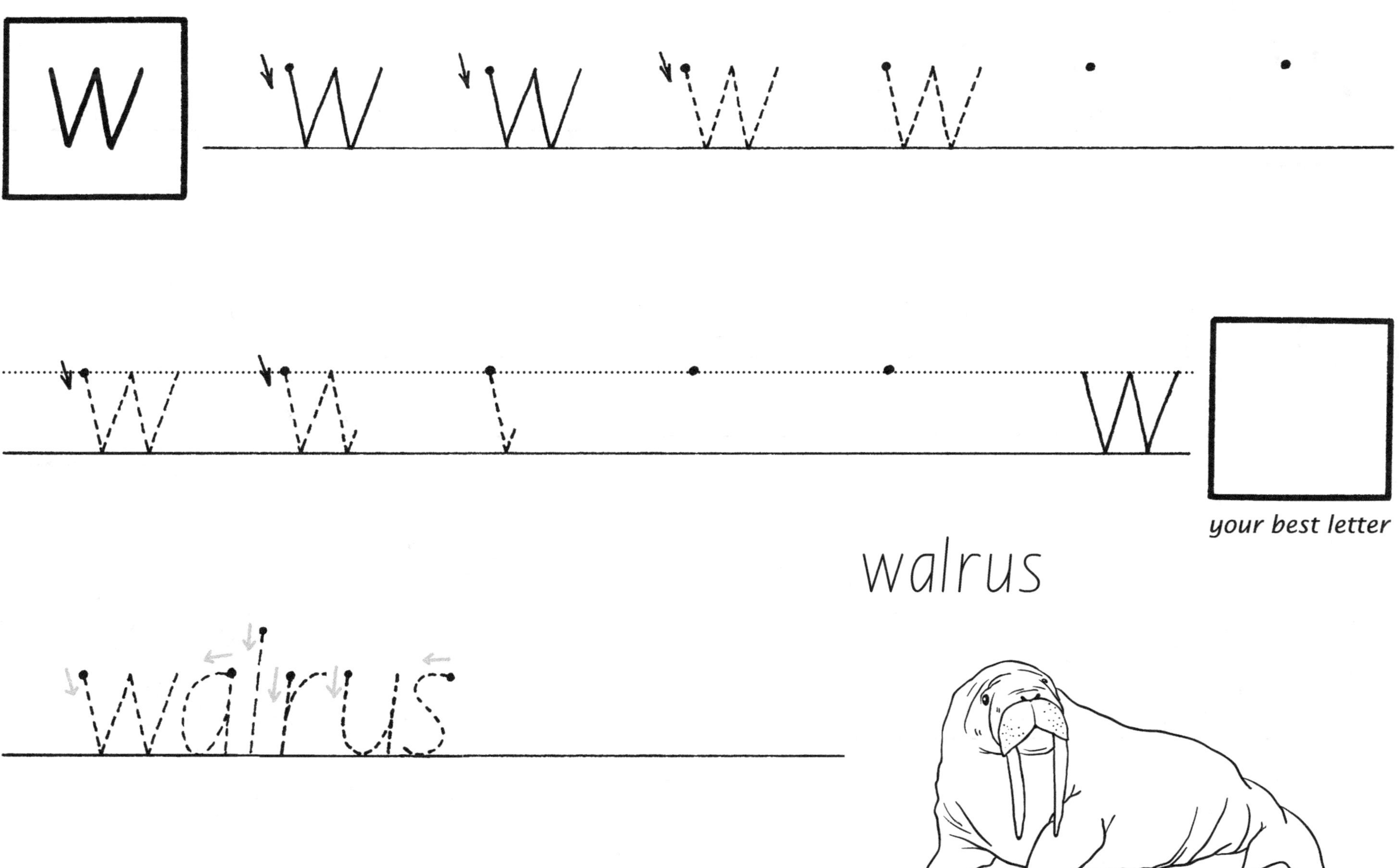

your best letter

walrus

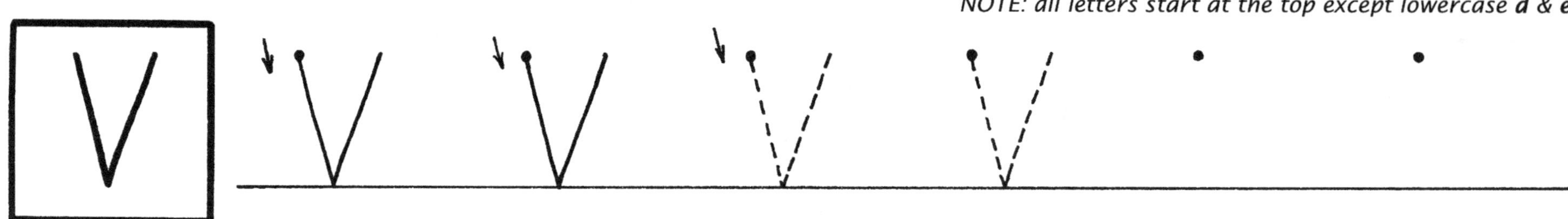

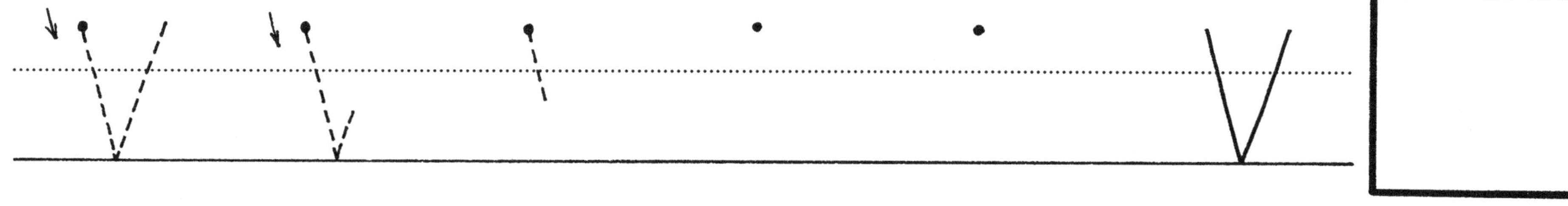

your best letter

Valentine

54

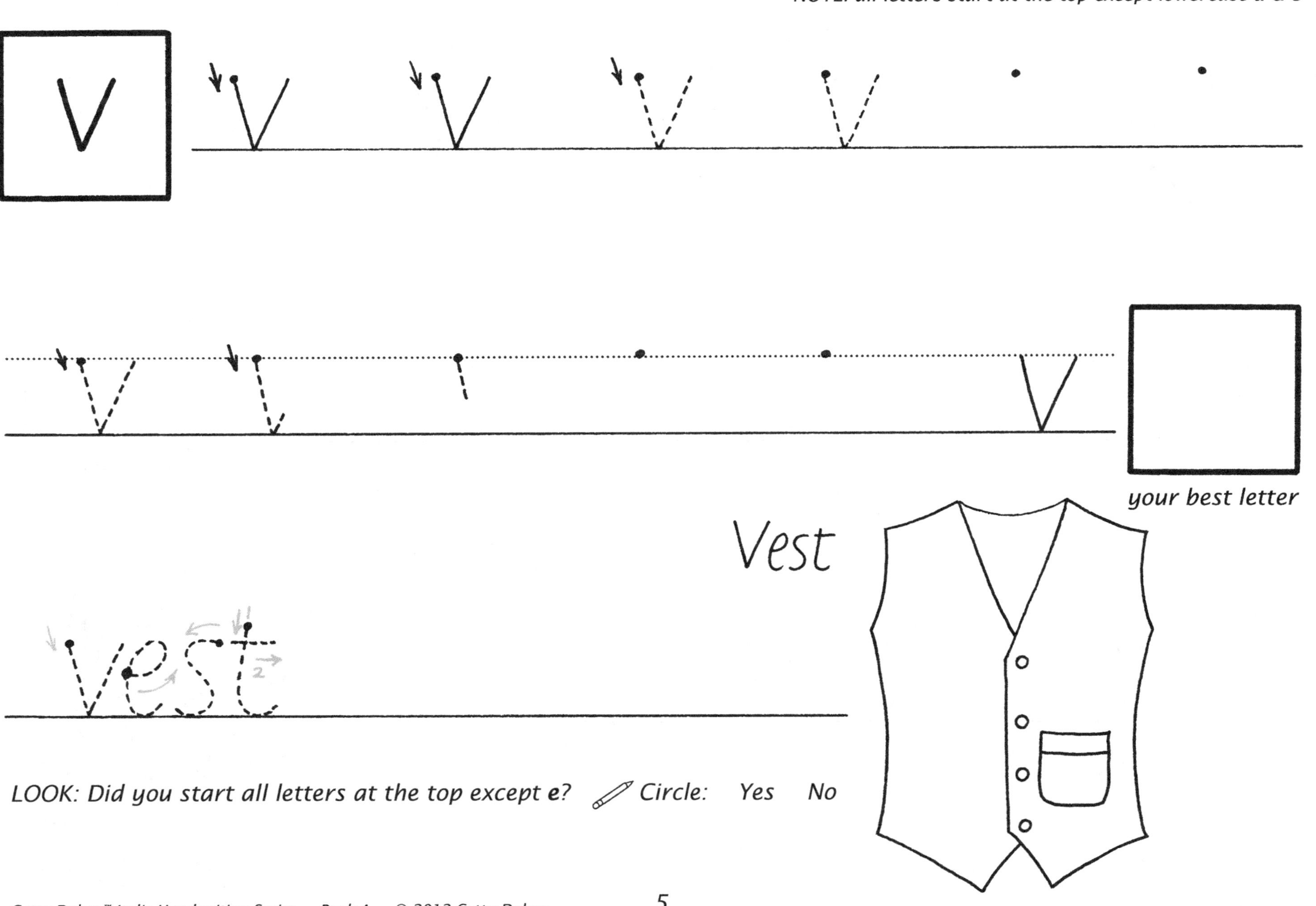

your best letter

Vest

LOOK: Did you start all letters at the top except *e*? ✎ Circle: Yes   No

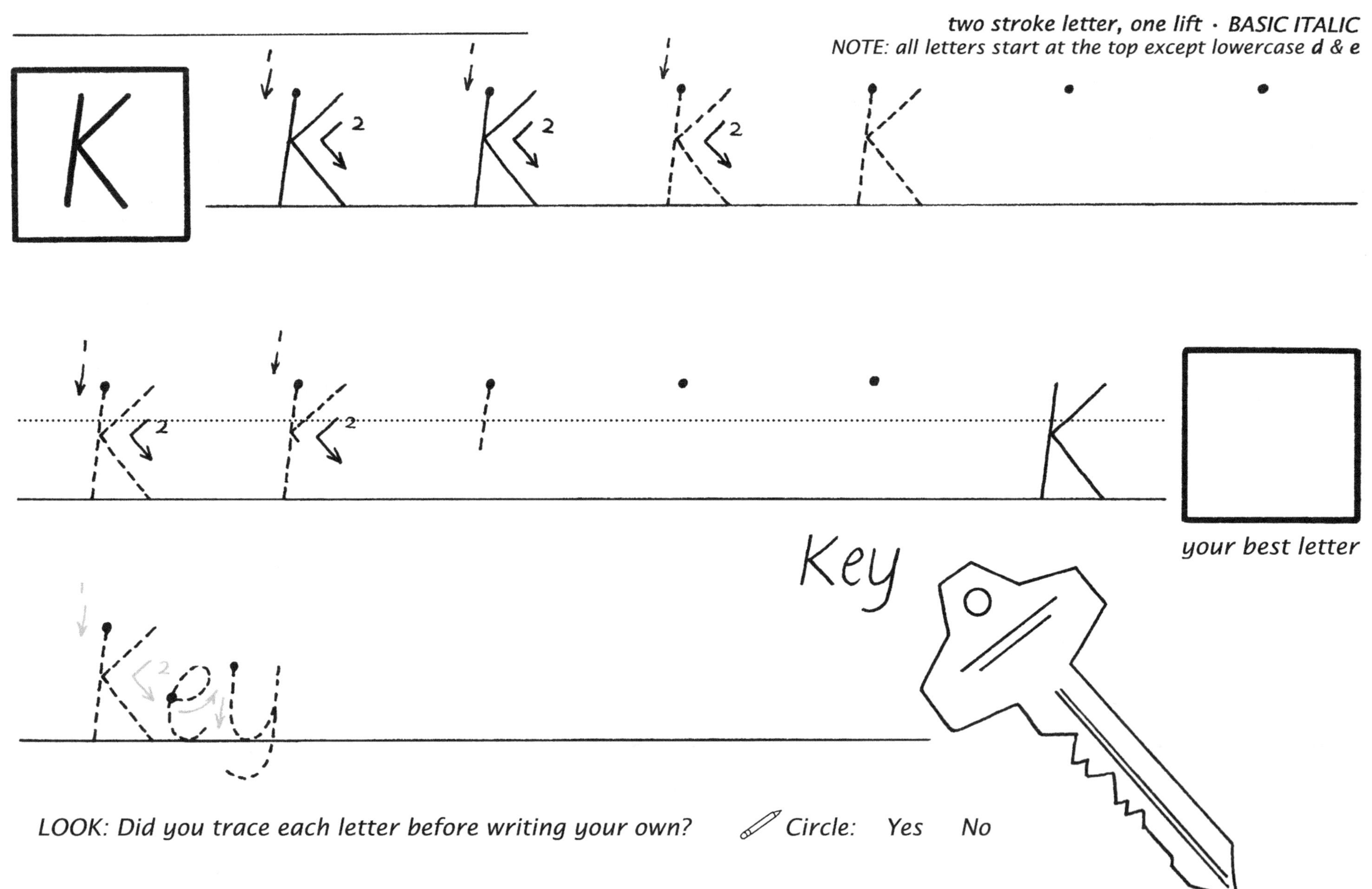

LOOK: Did you trace each letter before writing your own?   Circle: Yes   No

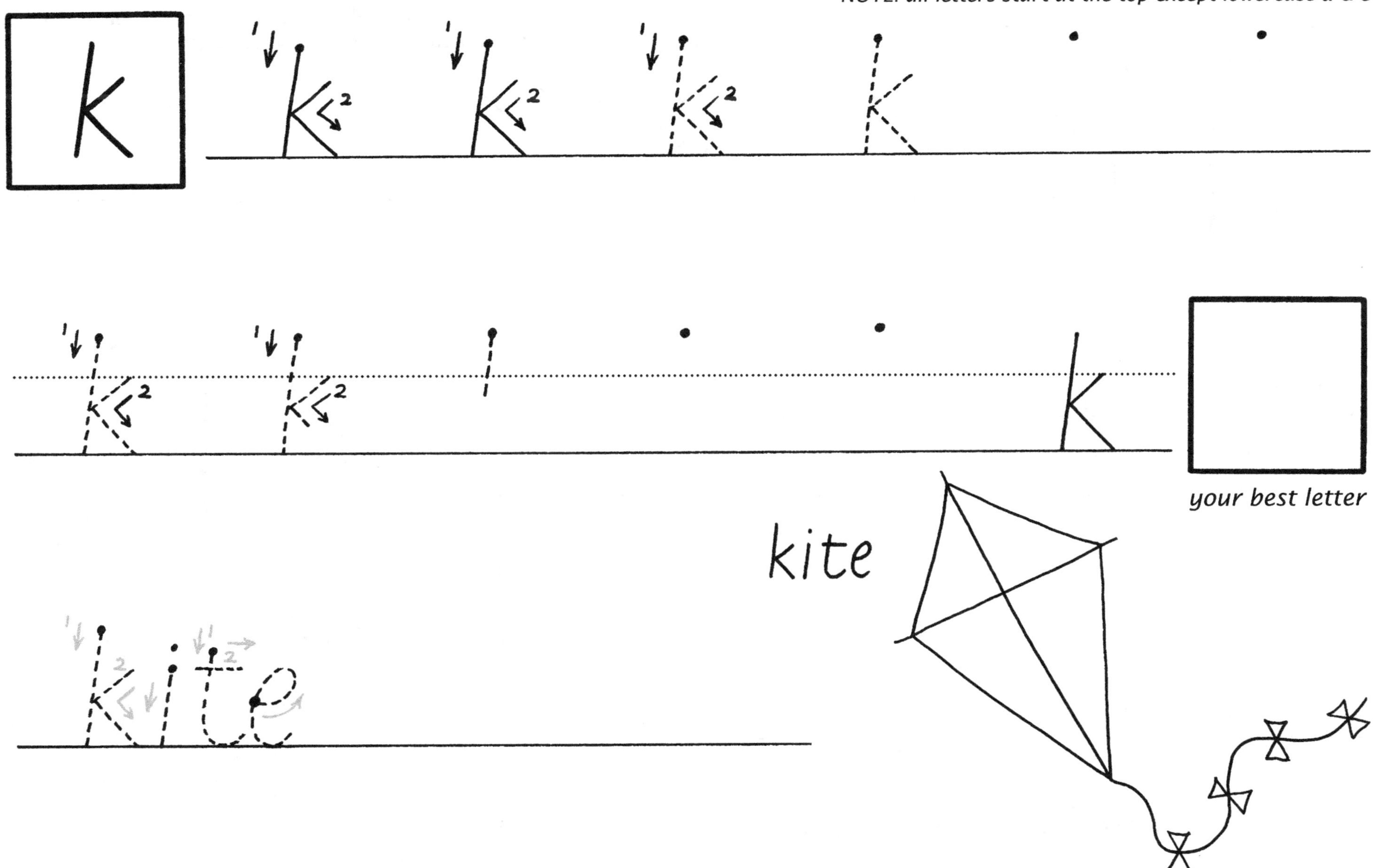
your best letter
kite

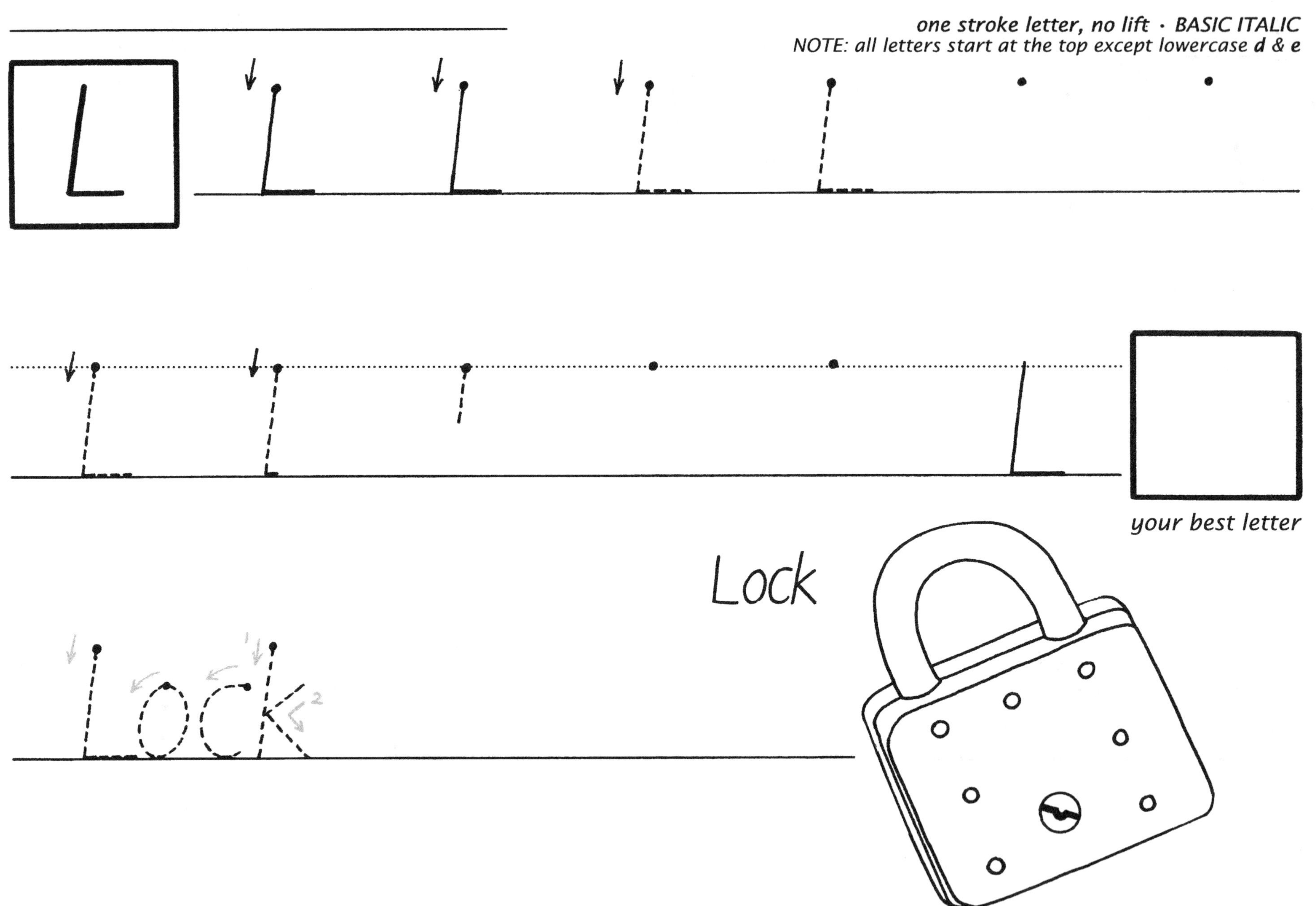

your best letter

Lock

l

your best letter

lamb

lamb

your best letter

Jack-in-the-box

LOOK: Did you start all letters at the top?   Circle: Yes   No

three stroke letter, two lifts · BASIC ITALIC
NOTE: all letters start at the top except lowercase d & e

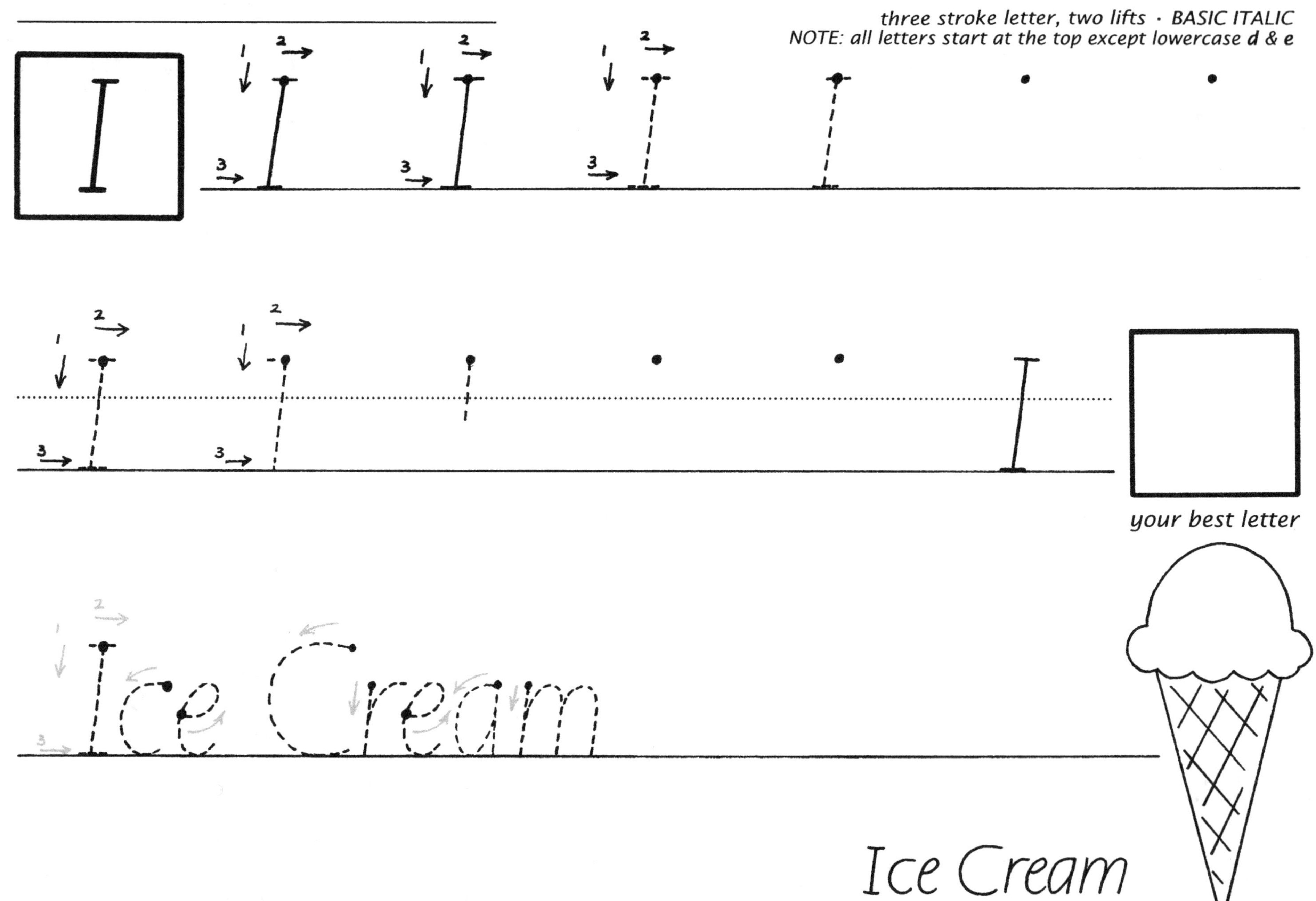

your best letter

Ice Cream

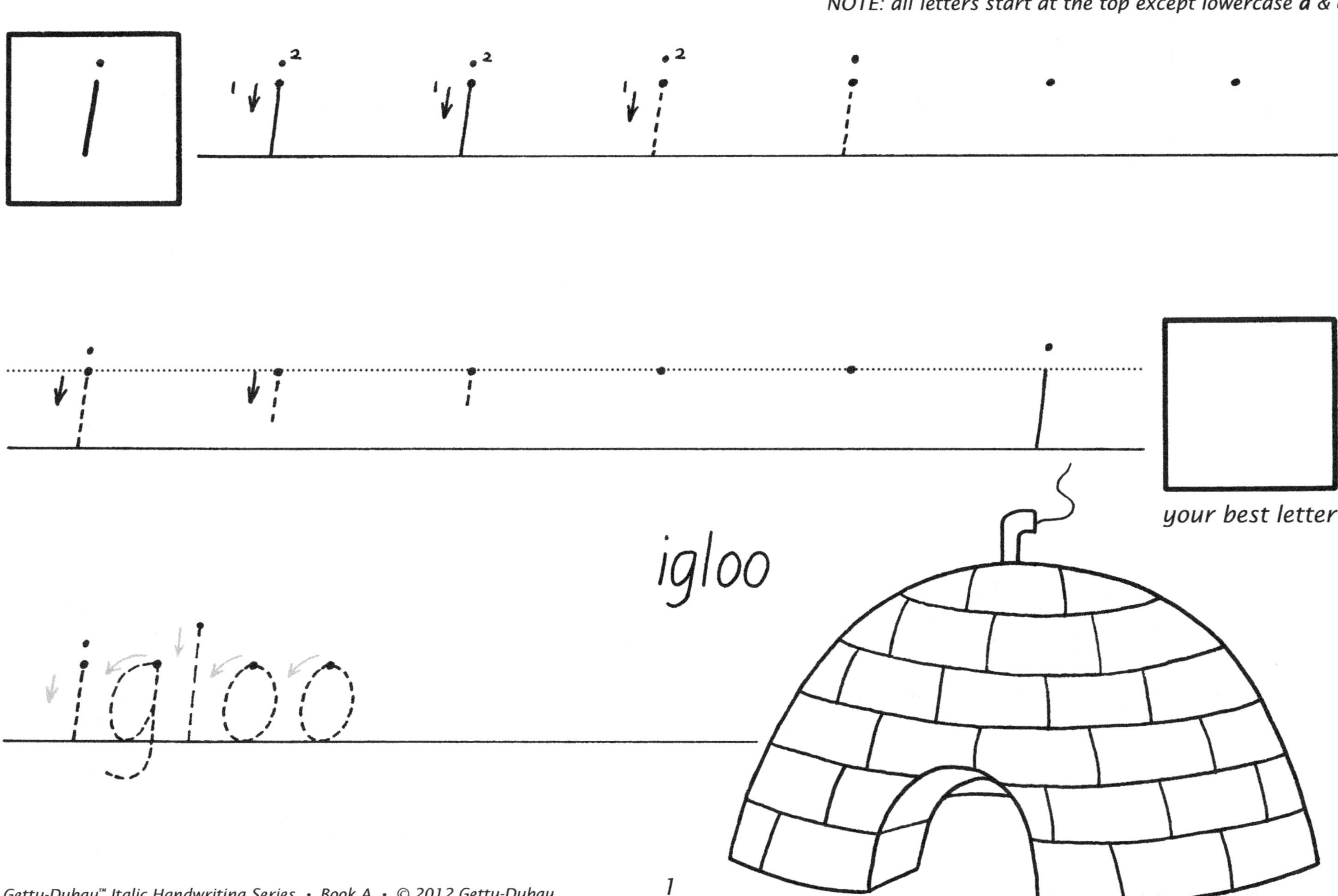

your best letter

igloo

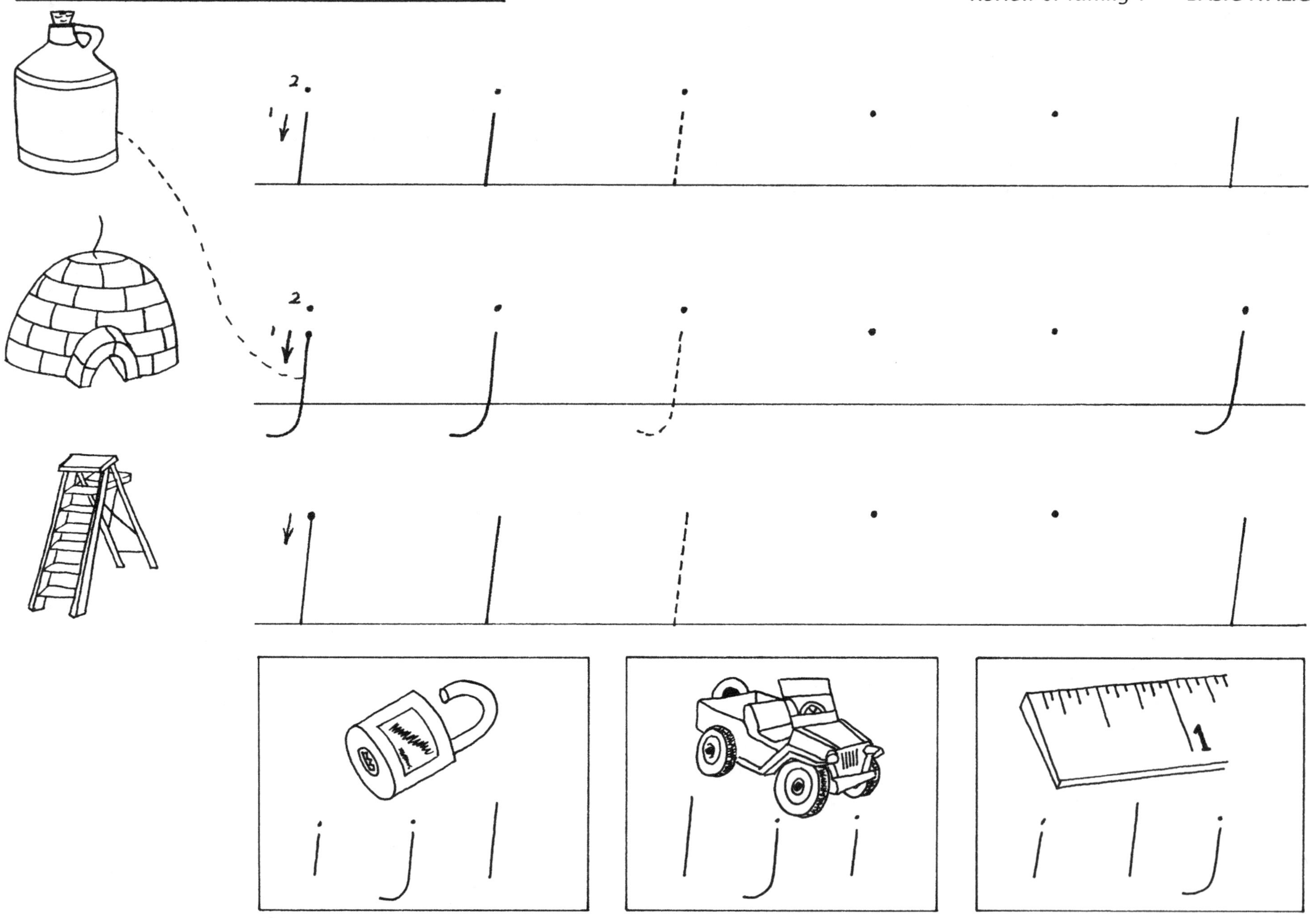

TOP THREE LINES: Ask the student to draw a line from the picture
to the letter that stands for the correct beginning sound.

BOTTOM THREE BOXES: Ask the student to circle the letter that
stands for the beginning sound of the picture.

BASIC SHAPES

Before the student begins writing in BOOK A, the authors recommend that the student practice the following shapes on unlined paper, one shape at a time. Allow the student to write each shape any size at first. Later, ask the student to write very large and very small forms of that same shape. We suggest the student also practice these shapes on a chalkboard and/or in cornmeal. (See INSTRUCTION MANUAL, "*Activity,*" pp. 35 & 41.)

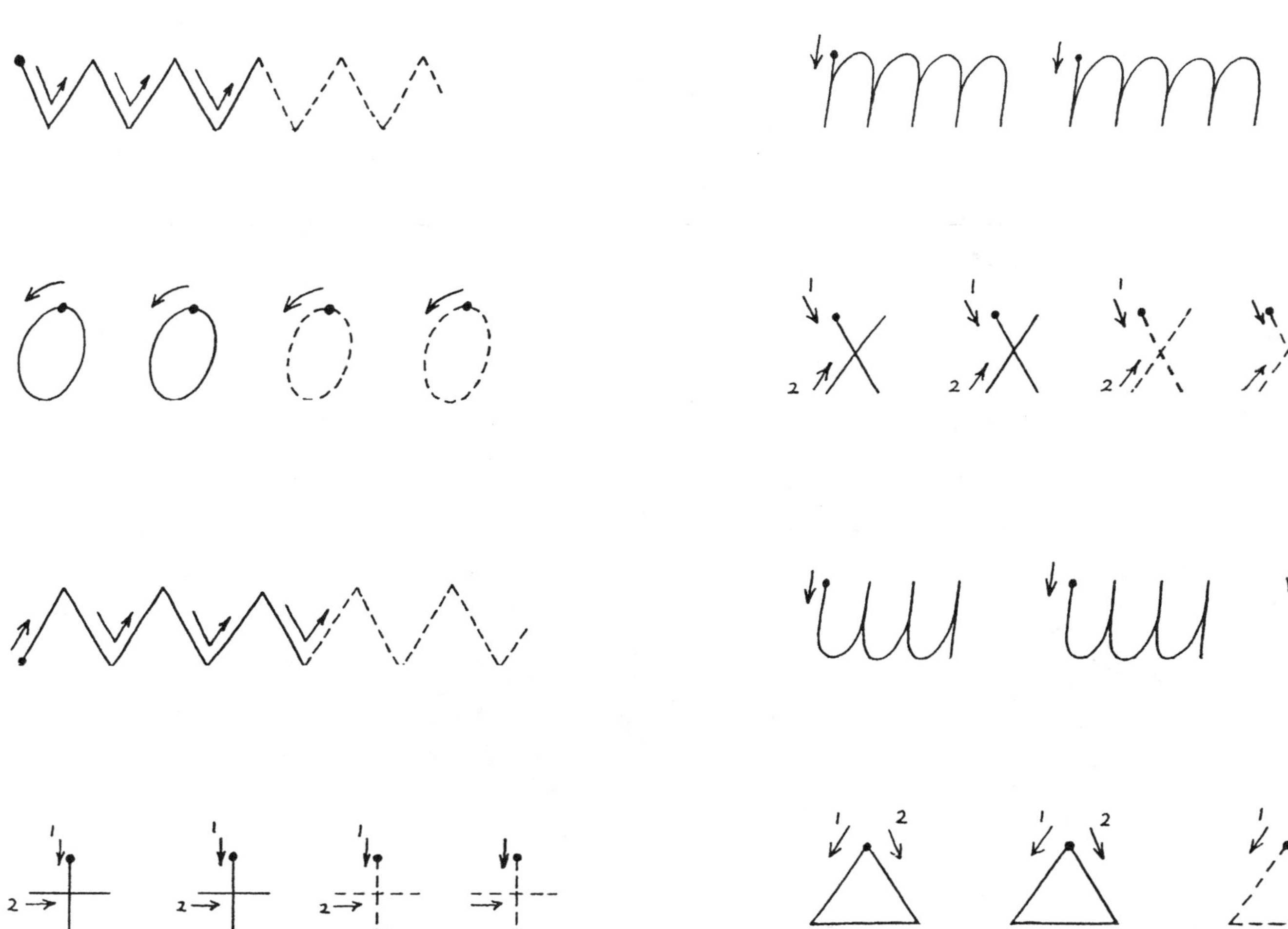

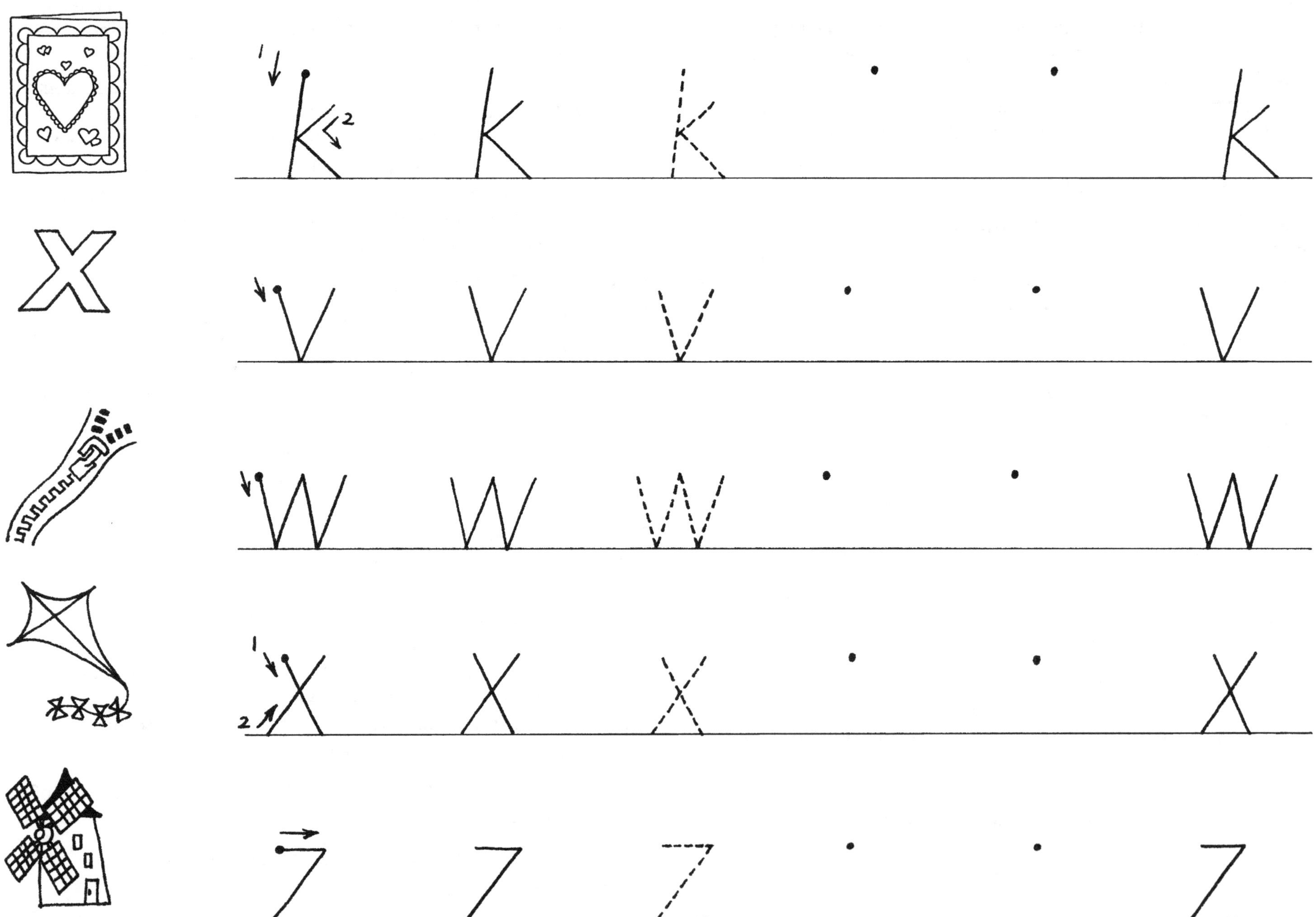

Ask the student to draw a line from the picture to the letter
that stands for the correct beginning sound.

THE BEGINNING WRITER

Learning how to write involves much more than learning to write letters. It is a sophisticated, complex process involving learning letterforms, learning how to space within and between words, and learning how to organize writing on a page. Research indicates that there exists an almost perfect correlation between measures evaluating the children's *awareness* of their fingers and the ability to *use* their fingers in precise manual skills.

Ways to determine manual ability

To assist young students increase awareness of their hands and fingers, and to help you, the teacher, evaluate students' manual skills, have your students perform these tasks:

1. Direct the students to touch each of their fingers to their thumb, in order, from the first to the little finger. (By the age of six years, most children should be able to complete this exercise using one or both hands at a time.)

2. Have the students connect two dots that are spaced approximately eight inches apart on a page. (Most children of five years can accomplish this. However, if the student draws beyond the second dot or draws an unusually shaky line when nearing the second dot, it may indicate potential deficiencies in handwriting skills.)

Ways to improve kinesthetic perception of the hands

1. Unstructured clay modeling facilitates a student's perception of his or her hands. Encourage the student to manipulate the clay in every possible way—squeezing, flattening, poking, making shapes, etc.

2. To heighten the student's perception of shape, use a box in which a variety of small objects are placed for the student to feel but not see.

   a. Ask the student to reach in the box and find an unseen object that matches the one he or she is looking at.

   b. Direct the student to locate in the box an object that you or another student has described.

   c. Ask the student to find two objects with similar characteristics—two fuzzy objects, two heavy objects, two small objects, etc.

3. Draw several circles on a sheet of paper. To determine the student's ability to aim the finger and hand and also to point, have the student place dots in the circles with a pencil, pen, or crayon. Vary the difficulty of this task by increasing or decreasing the size of the circles or increasing the rate at which the dots are made. (The student must be able to point at a given or imaginary point in order to begin the stroke of a letter.)

Ways to confirm hand-eye tracking skills

The ability to control continuous hand movements while drawing lines of varying difficulty is basic to handwriting. If you are able to detect problems as the student completes the following tasks and are able to obtain appropriate assistance for the student, subsequent difficulties may be avoided.

1. Demonstrate drawing parallel lines. Then direct the student to draw parallel lines of a given length, first at a relaxed pace then at a faster one.

2. Direct the student to draw two curved lines equal in distance from one another. Later require more difficult shapes that combine straight lines, angles, and/or curves.

3. Direct the student to connect numbered dots on a sheet of paper that require horizontal, vertical and lateral movements. Place the paper in front of the student, close to the dominant hand. Later, space the dots further apart and require the student to cross the midline of his or her body. This latter task may cause the neuro-logically challenged student some difficulty.

The above evaluative tasks may be of help in assisting the learning of handwriting and in discovering deficiencies.

(See INSTRUCTION MANUAL, p. 13, for more suggestions concerning the beginning writer.)

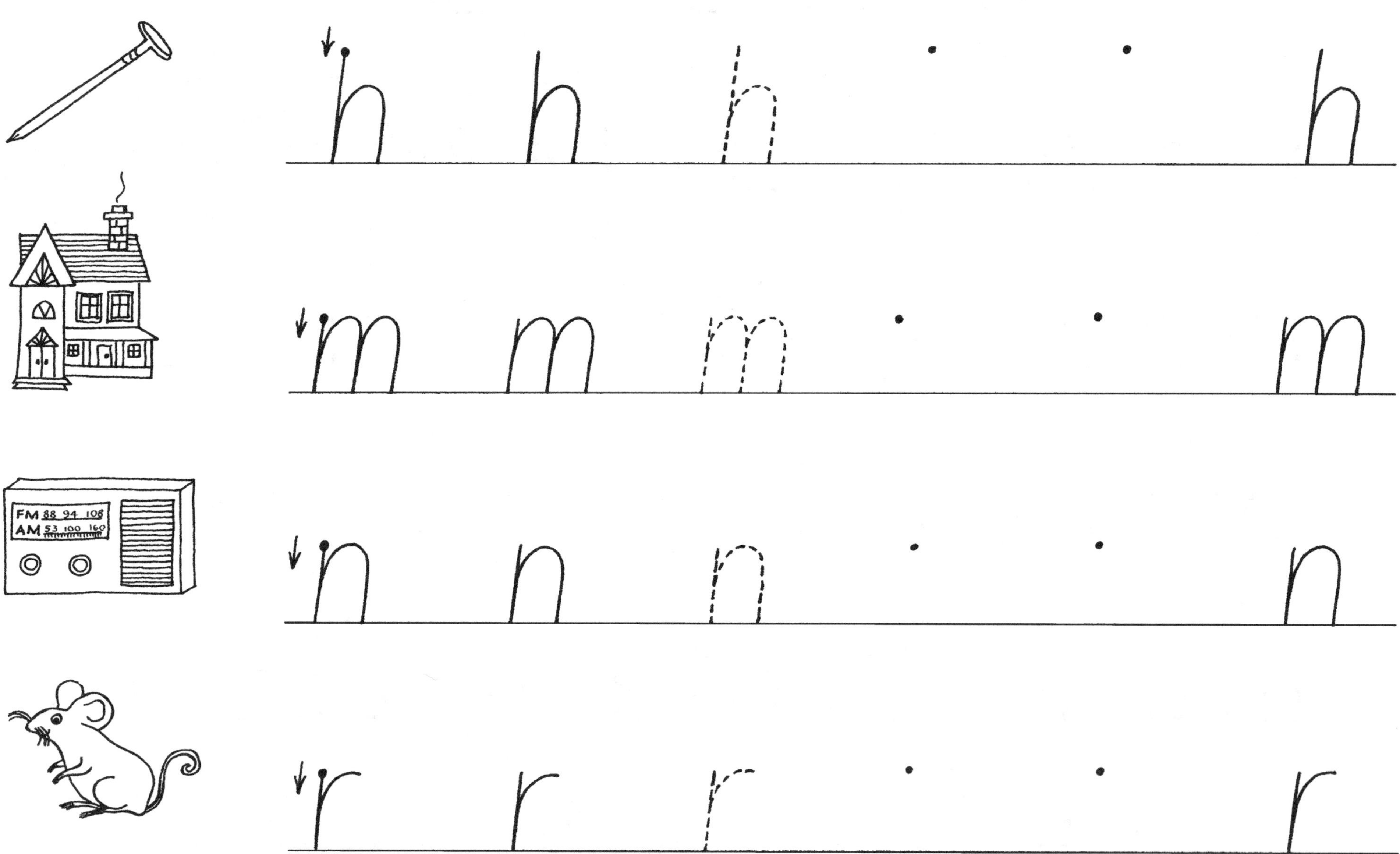

Ask the student to draw a line from the picture to the letter
that stands for the correct beginning sound.

BASIC ITALIC ALPHABET

All letters written in one stroke unless otherwise indicated.   *All letters start at the top except lowercase **d** and **e**.*

Aa Bb Cc Dd Ee Ff Gg

or

alternate
2-stroke e

Hh Ii Jj Kk Ll Mm

or

Nn Oo Pp Qq Rr Ss Tt

or

Uu Vv Ww Xx Yy Zz

0 1 2 3 4 5 6 7 8 9

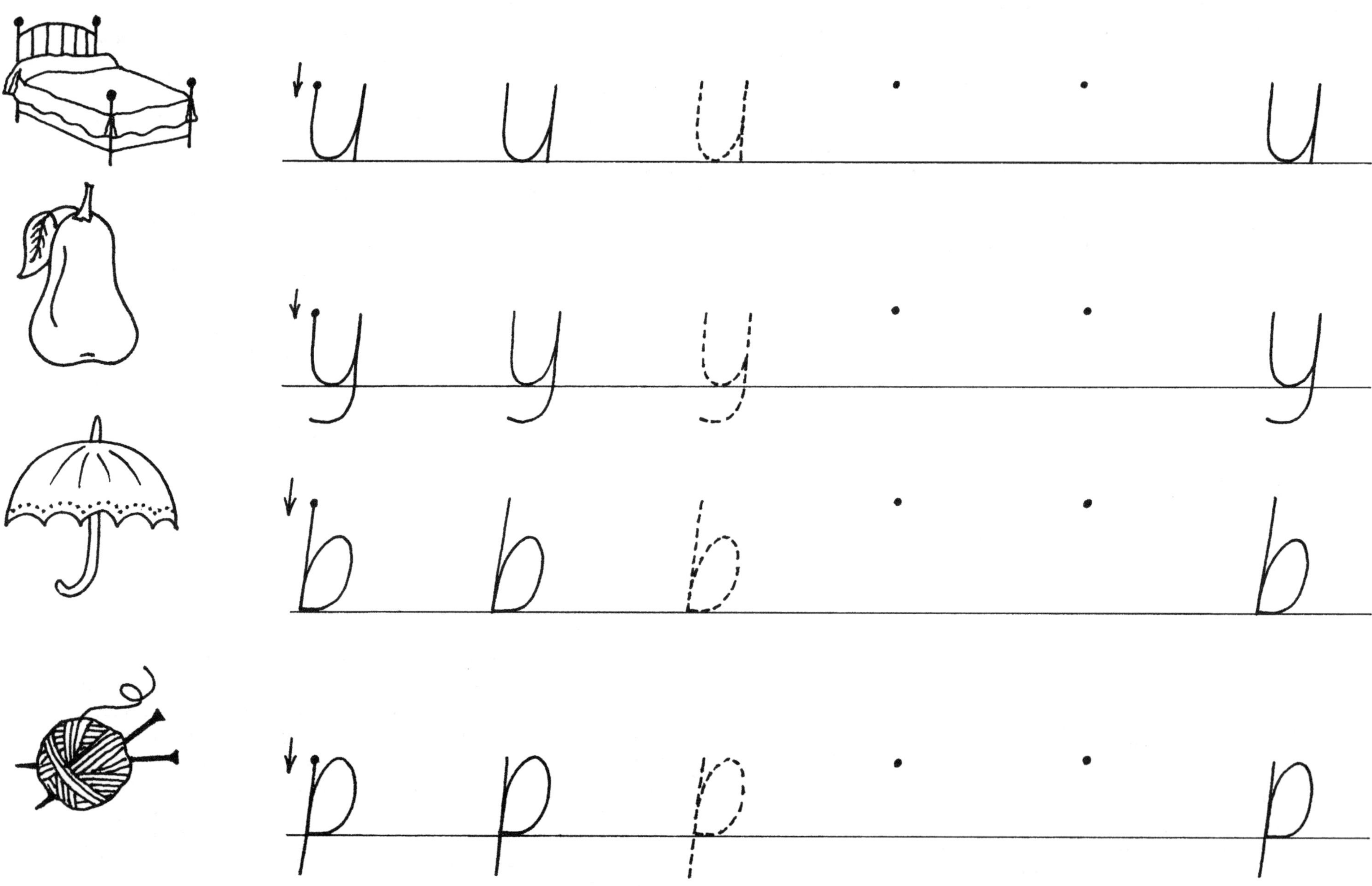

Ask the student to draw a line from the picture to the letter
that stands for the correct beginning sound.

GETTY-DUBAY™ HANDWRITING REMINDERS

PENCIL HOLD

Hold the pencil with the thumb and index finger, resting it on the middle finger. Rest the shaft of the pencil near the large knuckle. Hold the tool firmly and avoid pinching. To relax the hand, tap index finger on the pencil three times. Avoid "thumb wrap" and a "death grip".

PAPER POSITION

LEFT-HANDED: If the left-handed student writes with the wrist below the writing line, turn paper clockwise so it is slanted to the right, as illustrated.

If the left-handed student writes with a hook, with the wrist above the writing line, turn the paper counter-clockwise so it is slanted to the left, as illustrated. (Similar to right-handed position)

RIGHT-HANDED: If the student is right-handed, turn paper counter-clockwise so it is slanted to the left, as illustrated.

POSTURE

Rest feet flat on the floor and keep back comfortably straight without slumping. Rest forearms on writing surface. The student holds workbook or paper with the nonwriting hand so that the writing area is centered in the front of the student.

PRACTICE PAPER

Book A—Use unlined or lined paper together with workbooks.

MATERIALS

The *Getty-Dubay™ Italic Handwriting Series* workbooks, BOOKS A-G, and the INSTRUCTION MANUAL constitute a step-by-step program. Related materials consist of:

1. BLACKLINE MASTERS/WORKSHEETS - half sheets for introduction to, or review of, workbook pages.
2. CLASSROOM WALL CHARTS - basic & cursive italic.
3. DESK STRIPS - basic & cursive italic.

VOCABULARY

DIRECT INSTRUCTION

Several sessions of direct instruction each week are essential for a successful program. BOOK A – 5 to 10 minute sessions a day are recommended, see INSTRUCTION MANUAL, pp. 18-19

- SHAPE & STROKE SEQUENCE – teach basic italic in letter family groups, or according to the reading program in grade 1.
- SLOPE – encourage a consistent letter slope. Vertical letters (0° slope) may be the easiest to teach to beginning writers.
- SIZE – At first, allow students to write letters any size they wish on unlined paper, then introduce the workbook. A recommended progression through this book is one letter (lowercase and/or capital) per week.

SPACING

When young students are writing words, at first have them leave a space about the width of their two small fingers between words. As they become more proficient, they can leave less space.

ASSESSMENT

The *Getty-Dubay™ Italic Handwriting Series* provides a self-assessment process, LOOK, PLAN, PRACTICE, to enable the student to monitor progress. LOOK, step 1 of this process begins on some of the student pages in BOOK A. Assessment is the key to improving handwriting; in this book we introduce the first of three steps in the LOOK, PLAN, PRACTICE self-assessment process. The students look at their own writing and answer any questions on the page. The pencil indicates the student is to make a written response, generally by circling "yes" or "no". The teacher may encourage students to award themselves a star or a smiling face at the top of the page when they notice self-improvement.

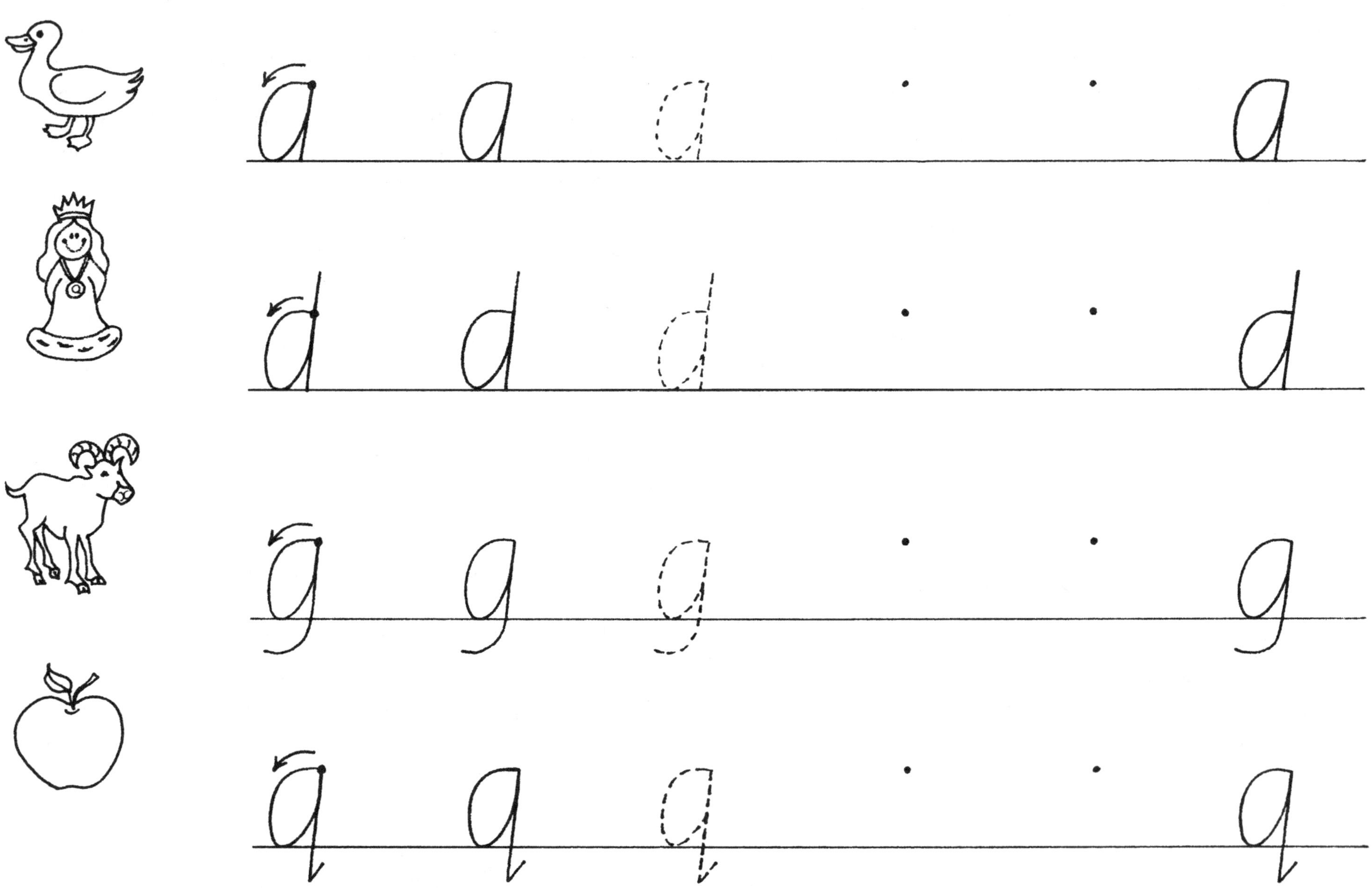

Ask the student to draw a line from the picture to the letter
that stands for the correct beginning sound.

INTRODUCTION

This is the first of seven workbooks providing instruction in basic italic handwriting. It is designed for the beginning student of handwriting and is recommended for preschool, kindergarten and/or early first grade (5 to 7 years of age).

The twenty-six lowercase letters and the twenty-six capitals are introduced one letter per page. Letters are arranged in the order of lowercase families, which group letters with similar strokes together and progress from simple to more complex forms. The matching capital letter occurs on the reverse of each lowercase page allowing introduction of both lowercase and capital together if preferred.

Each page is designed for the student to trace the models provided, write letters at the given dots, and to write a "best" letter in the empty box on each alphabet page. The standard writing tool is the pencil although other writing instruments such as the fiber tip pen may be used. When students are ready, they should trace the word describing the illustration on each letter page, following the dots and arrows.

It is essential that the instructor provide an understanding of the dot and the arrow to assist the writer in completing the pages successfully. The self-assessment method used in the *Getty-Dubay™ Italic Handwriting Series* enables students to monitor their individual progress. Step 1, LOOK, of the three-step LOOK, PLAN, PRACTICE format, is incorporated on 21 of the student pages. Students are asked to "LOOK" at their writing and affirm what is best. On the 21 pages with "LOOK" questions, students should circle their chosen answers. See INSTRUCTION MANUAL, PP. 13, 18 & 19.

The *Getty-Dubay™ Italic Handwriting Series* INSTRUCTION MANUAL is to be used in conjunction with this workbook. Explanations and in-depth descriptions of lowercase letters, capitals, joins, and numerals are presented in the manual, emphasizing shape, strokes, size, slope and spacing of the letters. Also included in the manual are: a rationale for italic handwriting, techniques for teaching and assessing handwriting, sequence of skills, handwriting activities, and a brief history of our alphabet.

BOOK B, basic italic, follows this workbook and is designed for the beginning reader. In the third book, BOOK C, basic italic letterforms are reinforced and cursive italic is introduced. BOOKS D, E, F, and G provide a complete basic italic and cursive italic handwriting program. BOOKS B, C, and/or D may also be suitable for the person learning English as a second language.

The format of this book was chosen to accommodate both the left- and right-handed writer. When open, the book fits easily on a small desk, and the writer is not encumbered with an additional page to the left or right. From day one, use a Getty-Dubay™ basic italic desk strip as a reminder. Blackline masters are designed for supplementary practice and are available for each workbook in the series. See www.handwritingsuccess.com for these supplementary materials.

You can guide children toward the challenge and delight in the writing process by reading to them, modeling handwriting, providing writing materials, and especially by building enthusiasm for the letters of our alphabet and for the written word.

·abcdefghijklmnopqrstuvwxyz·

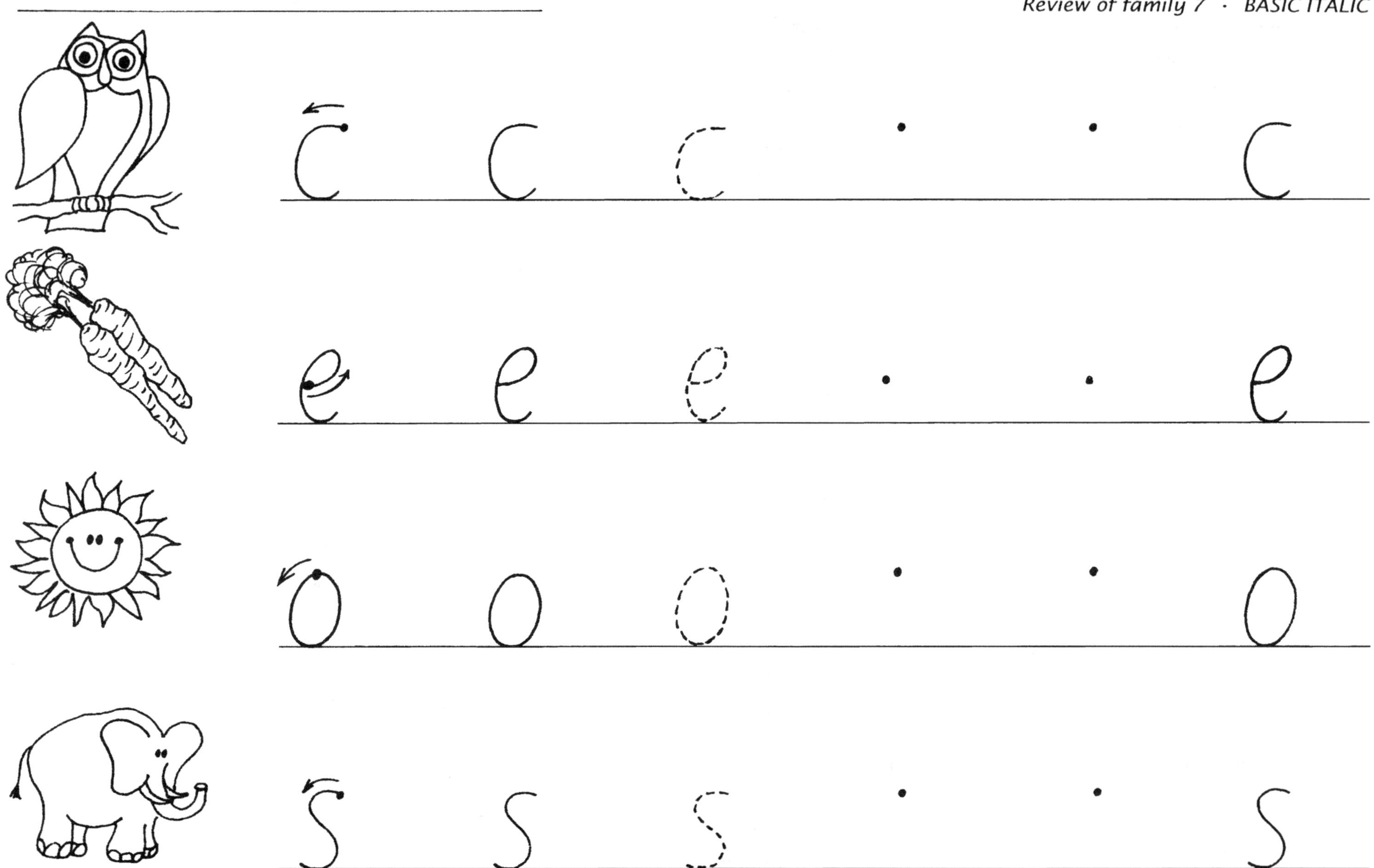

*Ask the student to draw a line from the picture to the letter
that stands for the correct beginning sound.*

Getty-Dubay™ Italic Handwriting Series · Book A · © 2012 Getty-Dubay

CONTENTS

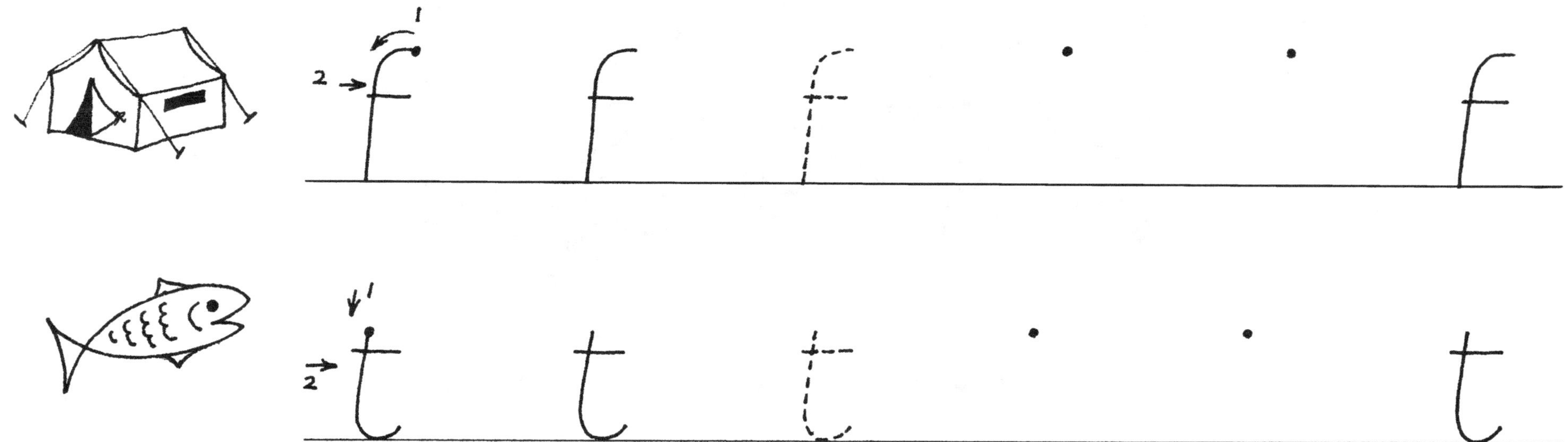

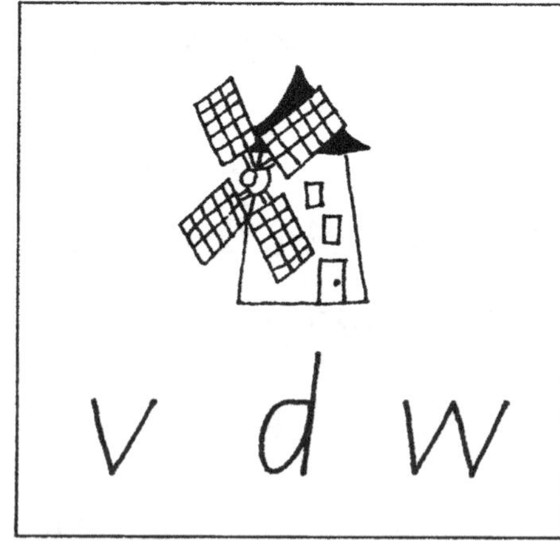

TOP TWO LINES: Ask the student to draw a line from the picture to the letter that stands for the correct beginning sound.

BOTTOM FOUR SQUARES: Ask the student to circle the letter that stands for the beginning sound of the picture.

by
Barbara Getty & Inga Dubay

GETTY-DUBAY™ ITALIC HANDWRITING SERIES

BOOK A ▪ Basic Italic
14 mm body height

BOOK B ▪ Basic Italic
11 mm body height, 9 mm

BOOK C ▪ Basic & Cursive Italic
9 mm, 6 mm body height   Introduction to Cursive Italic

BOOK D ▪ Basic & Cursive Italic
6 mm, 5 mm body height

BOOK E ▪ Basic & Cursive Italic
6 mm, 5 mm, 4 mm body height

BOOK F ▪ Basic & Cursive Italic
6 mm, 5 mm, 4 mm body height

BOOK G ▪ Basic & Cursive Italic
5 mm, 4 mm body height

INSTRUCTION MANUAL

BOOK A ▪ INTERNATIONAL EDITION

Copyright 2012 by Barbara M. Getty and Inga S. Dubay
ISBN 978-0-9827762-7-8

FOURTH EDITION
Copyright 2012 by Barbara M. Getty and Inga S. Dubay
THIRD EDITION
Copyright 1999 by Barbara M. Getty and Inga S. Dubay
SECOND EDITION
Copyright 1986 by Barbara M. Getty and Inga S. Dubay
REVISED EDITION
Copyright 1980 by Barbara M. Getty and Inga S. Dubay
FIRST EDITION
Copyright 1979 by Barbara M. Getty and Inga S. Dubay

All rights reserved. This text may not be reproduced in whole or in part without the express written permission of the copyright holder.

Published by Handwriting Success, LLC,
Portland, Oregon USA

www.handwritingsuccess.com

Printed at various locations around the world by IngramSpark.

Cover Design: Sinda Markham
Front cover picture: Flowers of the sunflower family in the Ochoco National Forest, Oregon, USA
Back cover pictures: Columbine flower, Golden-mantled squirrel

www.ingramcontent.com/pod-product-compliance
Lightning Source LLC
Chambersburg PA
CBHW081423210726
48464CB00020B/1370

9 780982 776278

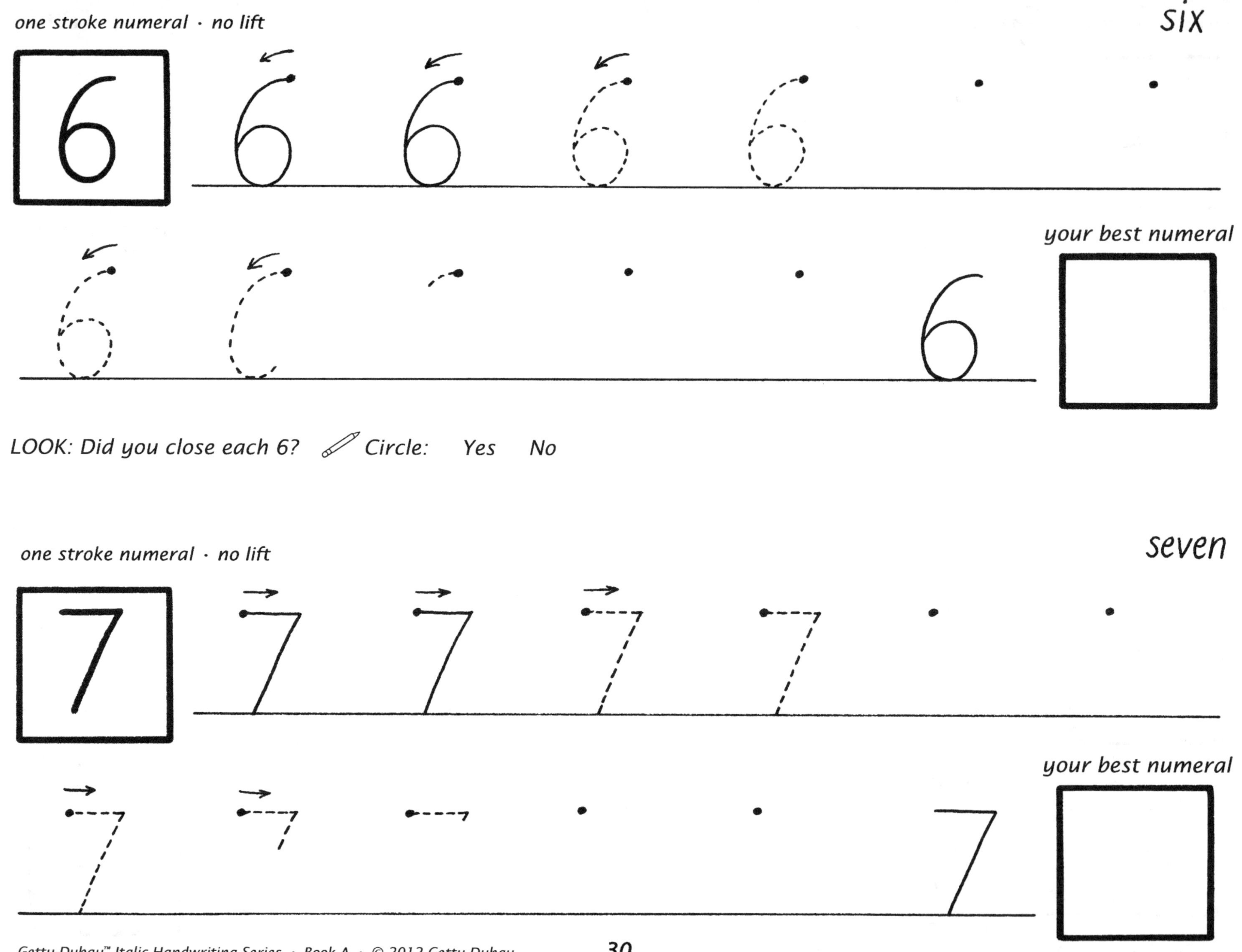
one stroke numeral · no lift
six
your best numeral
LOOK: Did you close each 6?   Circle: Yes   No
one stroke numeral · no lift
seven
your best numeral

four

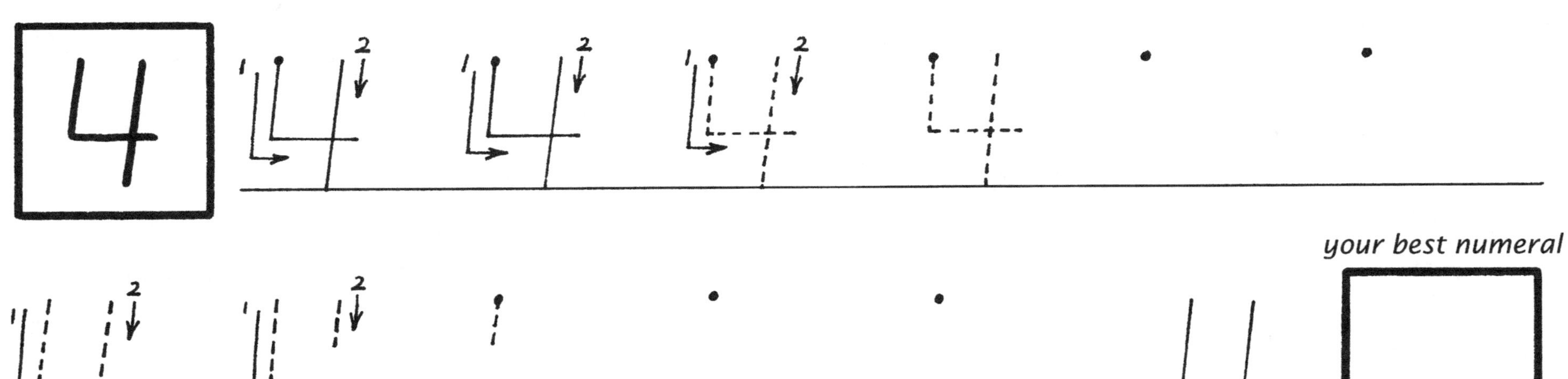

your best numeral

five

your best numeral

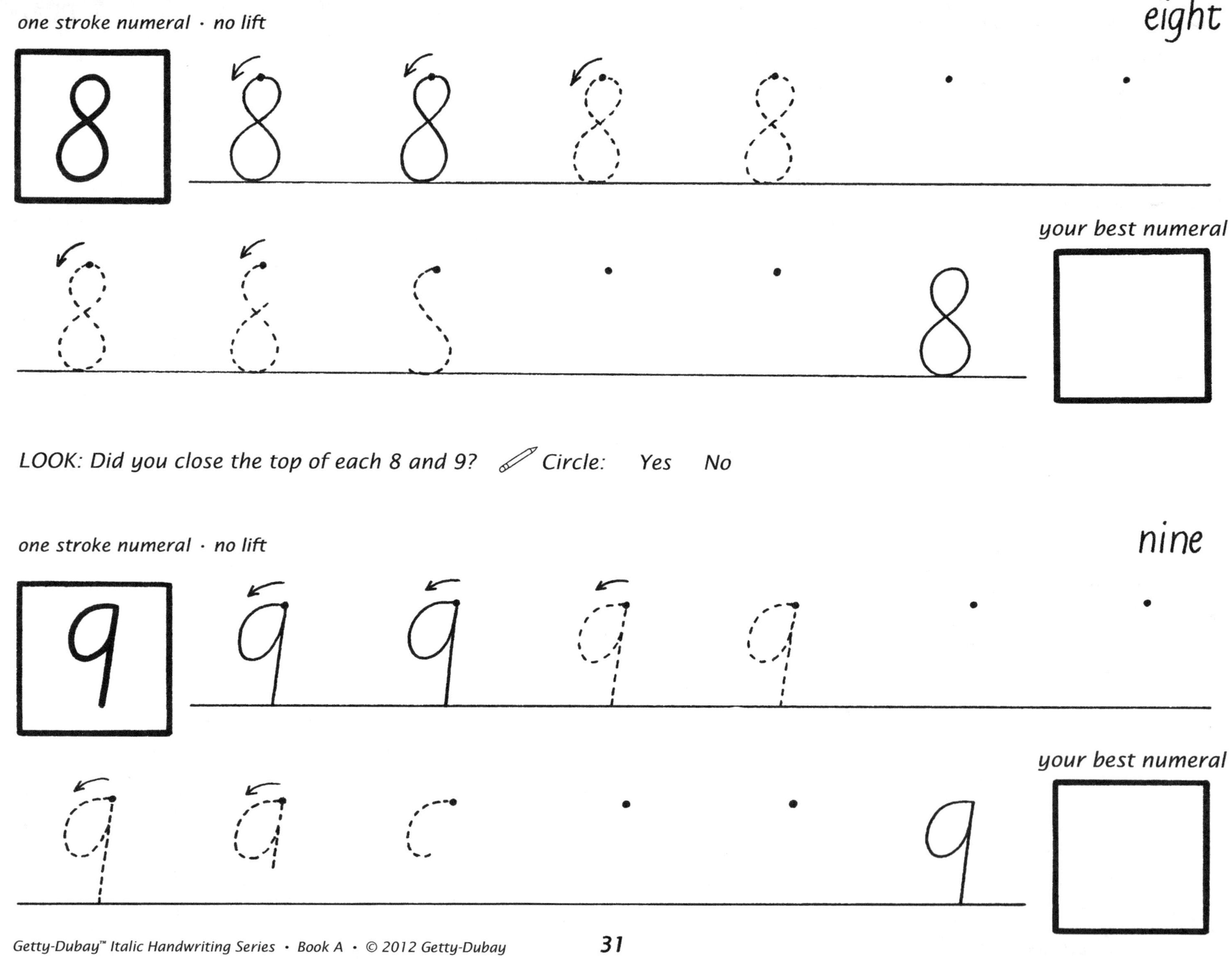

one stroke numeral · no lift
eight
8
your best numeral
LOOK: Did you close the top of each 8 and 9?   Circle: Yes   No
one stroke numeral · no lift
nine
9
your best numeral

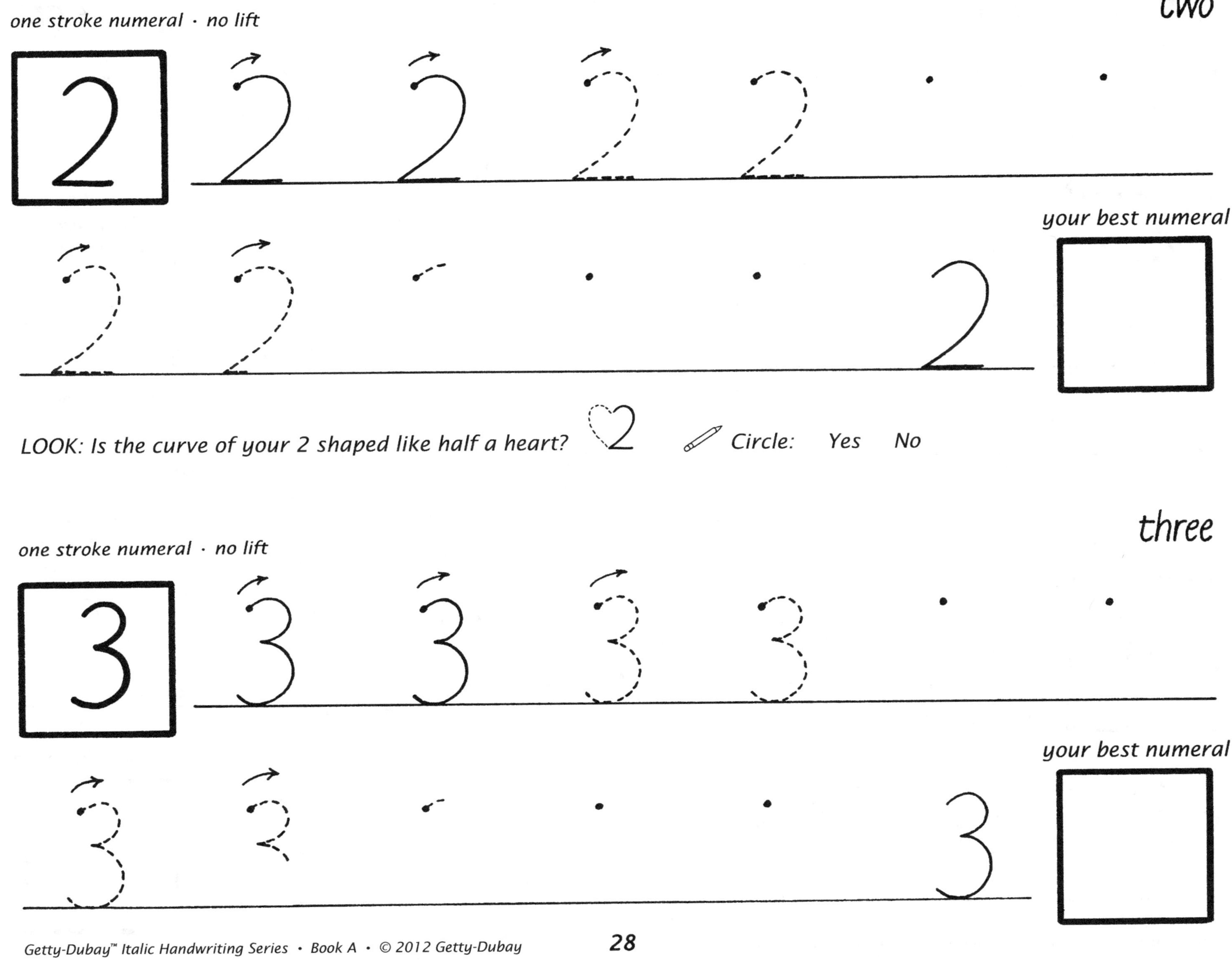

one stroke numeral · no lift
your best numeral
LOOK: Is the curve of your 2 shaped like half a heart? Circle: Yes No
three
one stroke numeral · no lift
your best numeral

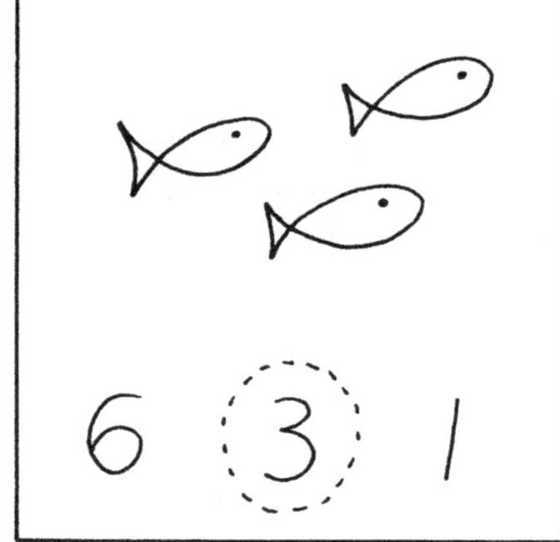

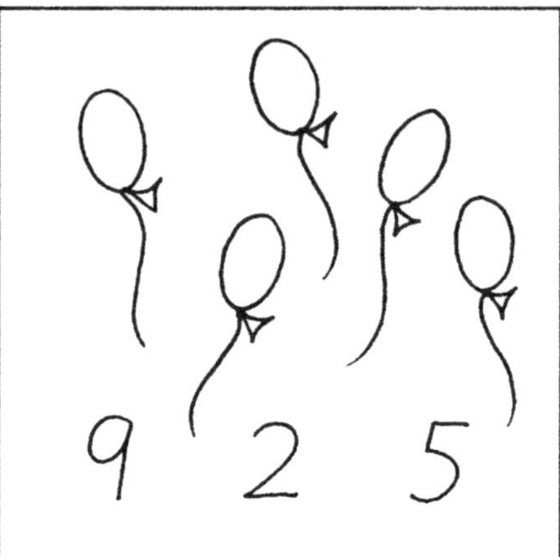

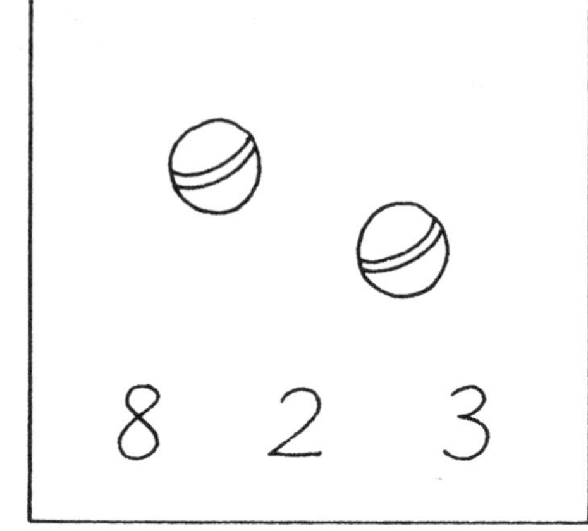

*Ask the student to circle the numeral
that stands for the number of objects in the box.*

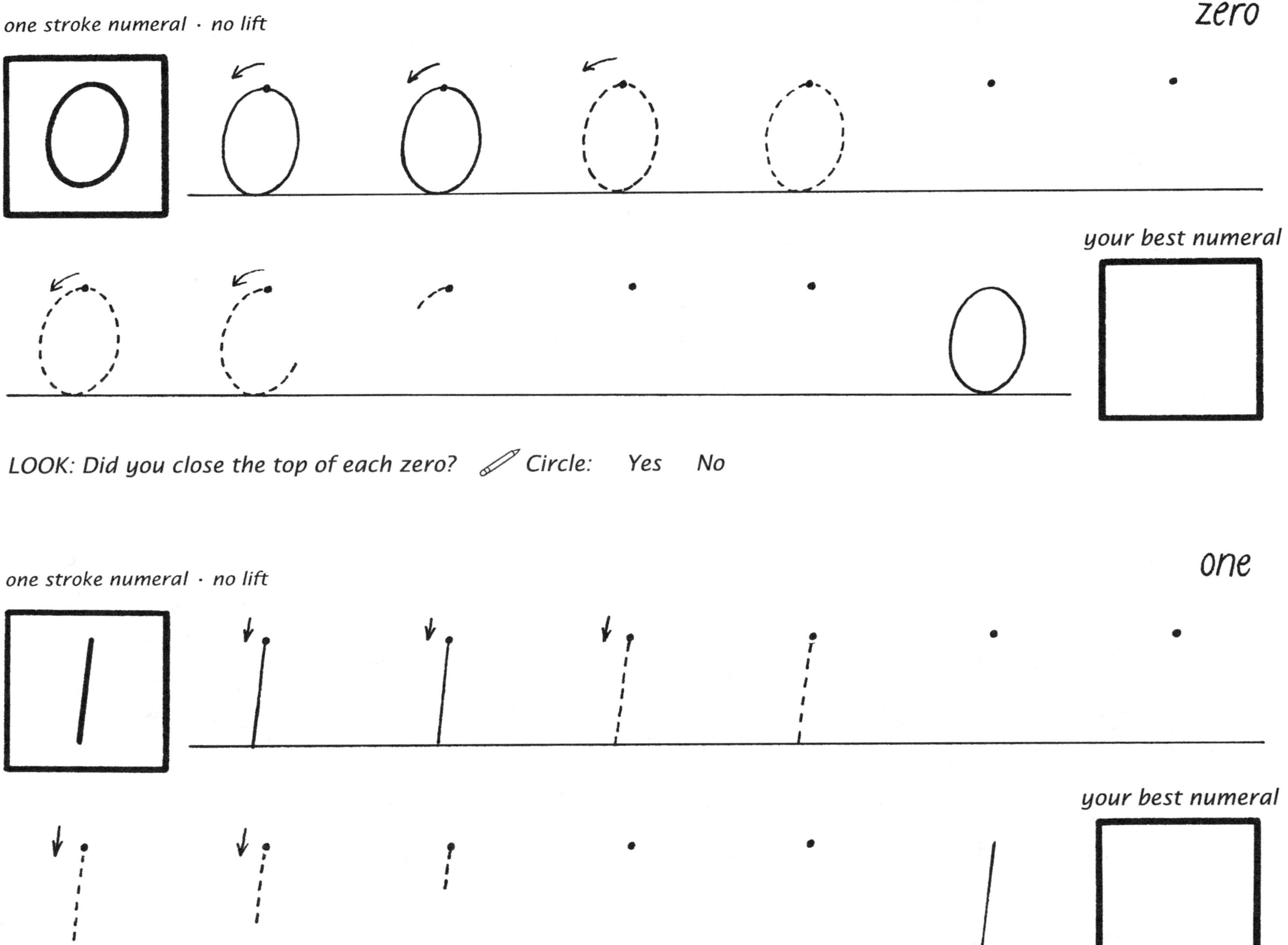

one stroke numeral · no lift
your best numeral
LOOK: Did you close the top of each zero?   Circle: Yes   No
one stroke numeral · no lift
one
your best numeral

your best letter

Tent

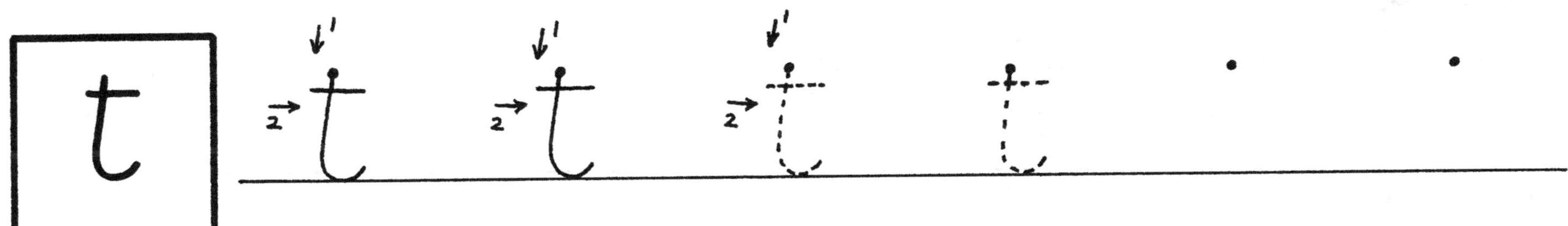

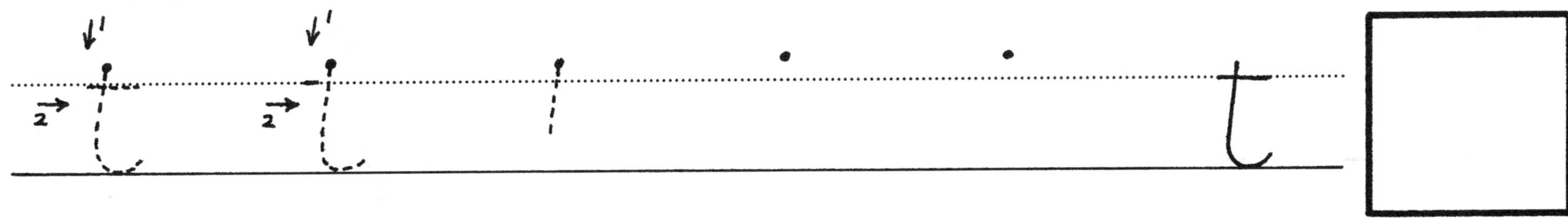

your best letter

turkey

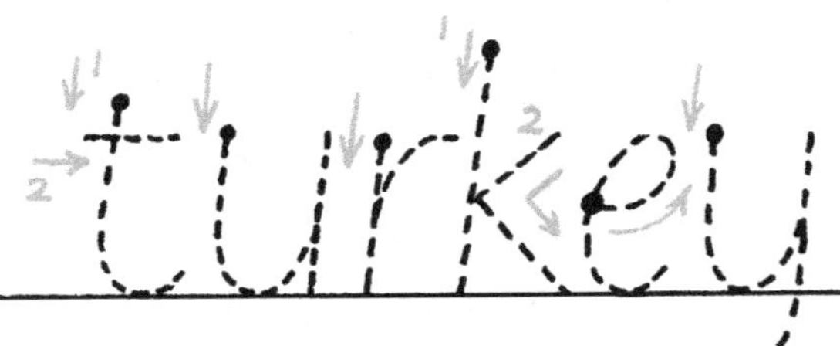

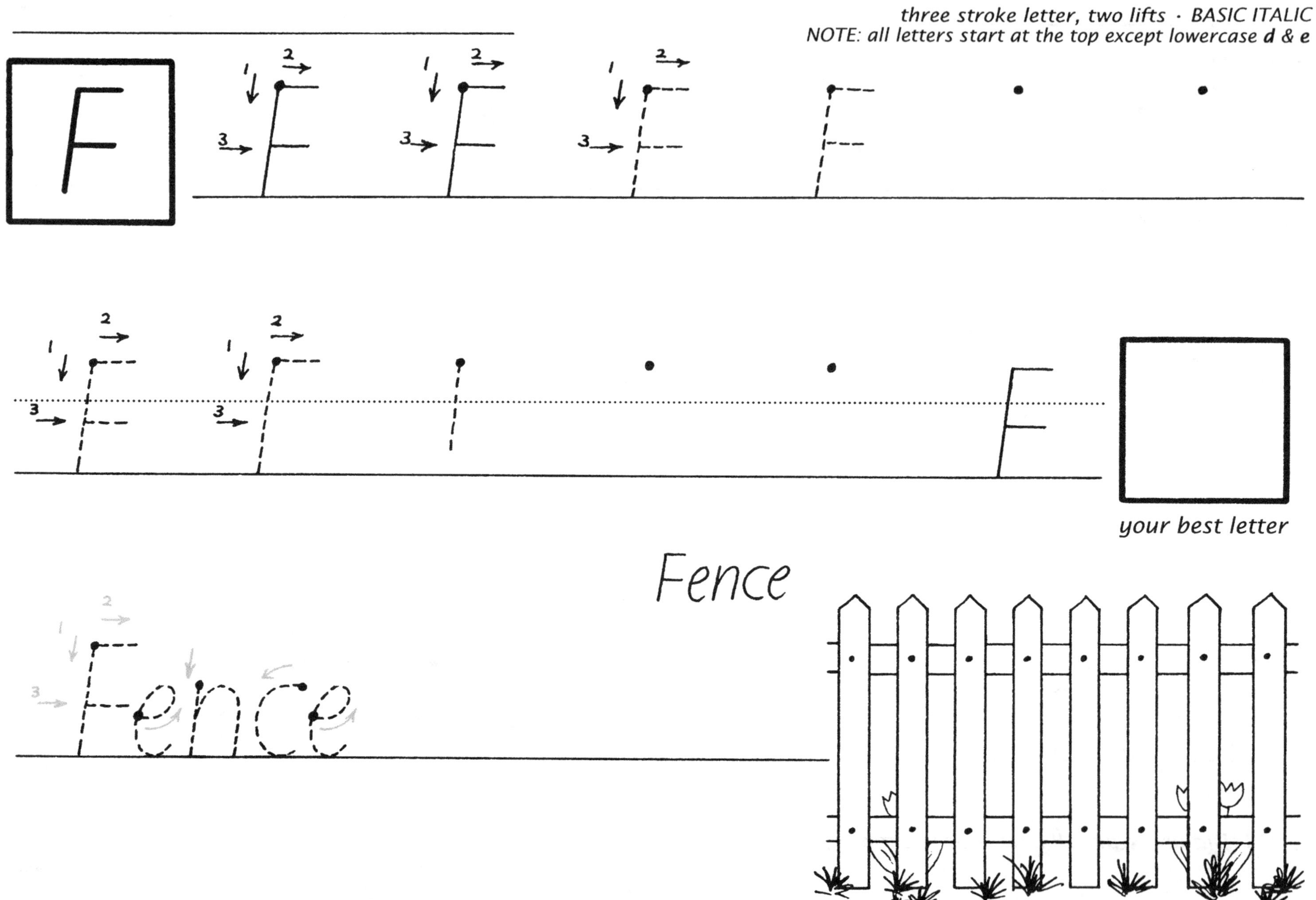

your best letter
Fence

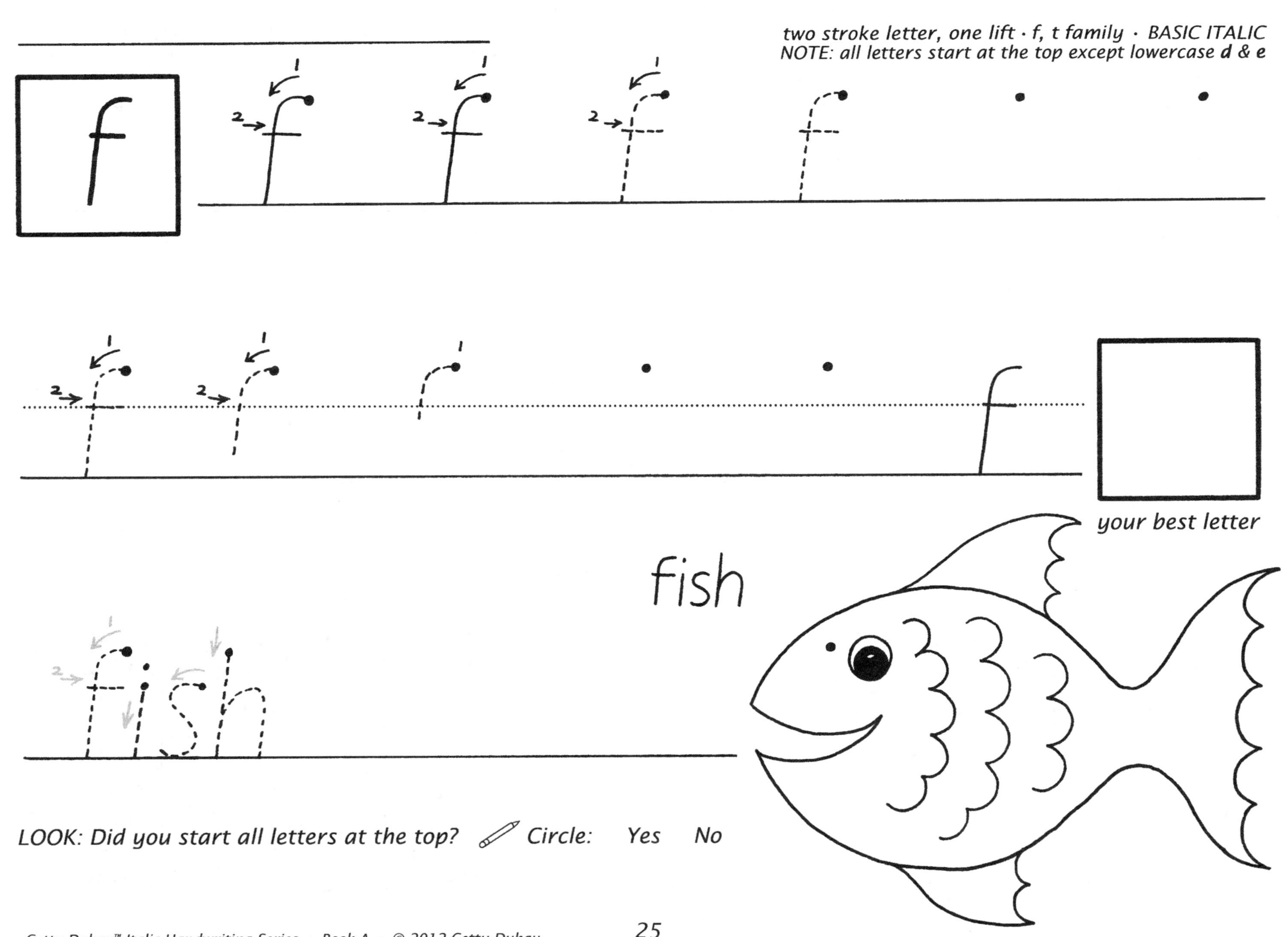

two stroke letter, one lift · f, t family · BASIC ITALIC
NOTE: all letters start at the top except lowercase d & e
your best letter
fish
LOOK: Did you start all letters at the top? Circle: Yes No

S

your best letter

Sailboat

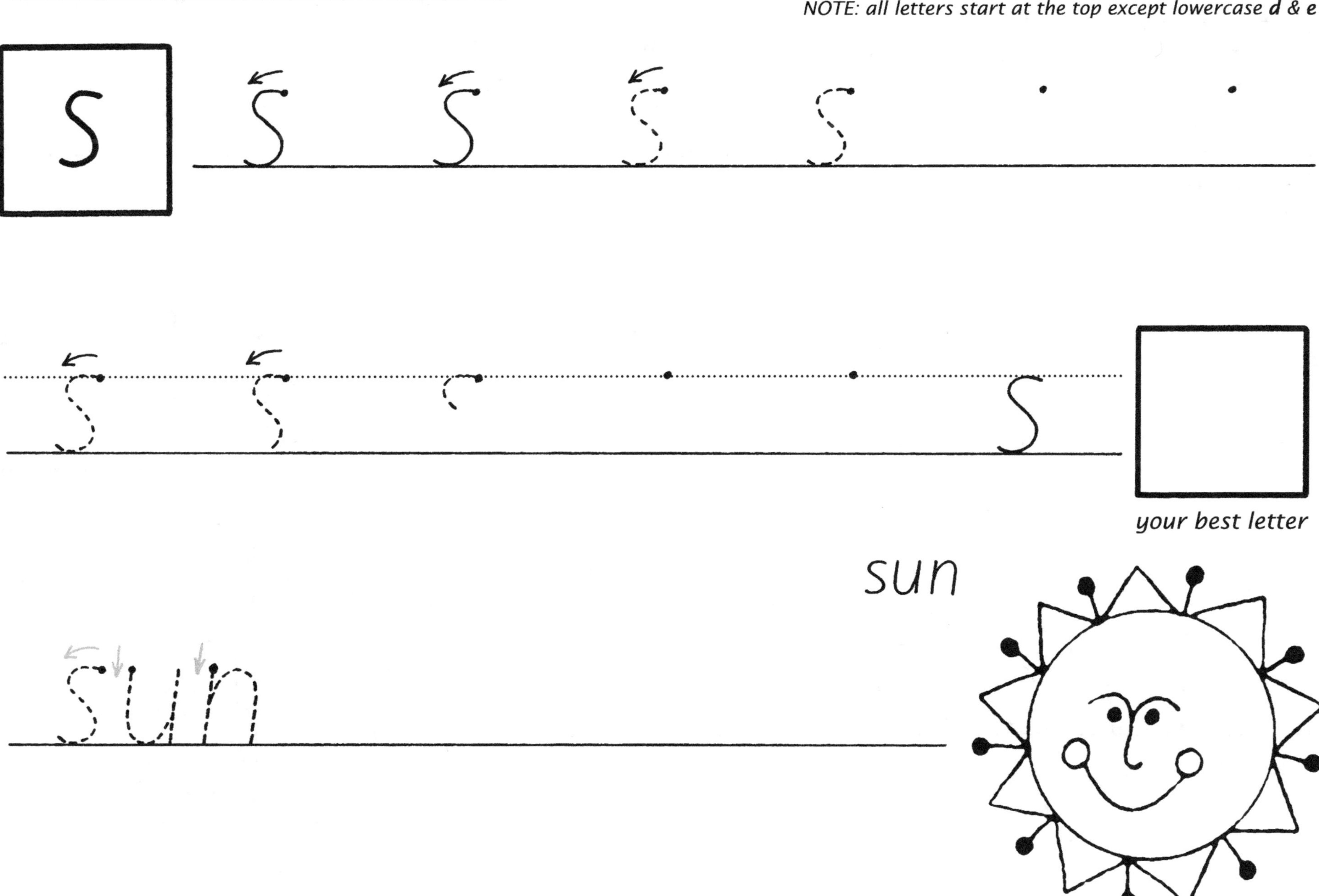

your best letter
sun

your best letter

Cow

LOOK: Did you trace each letter before writing your own?

✎ Circle: Yes   No

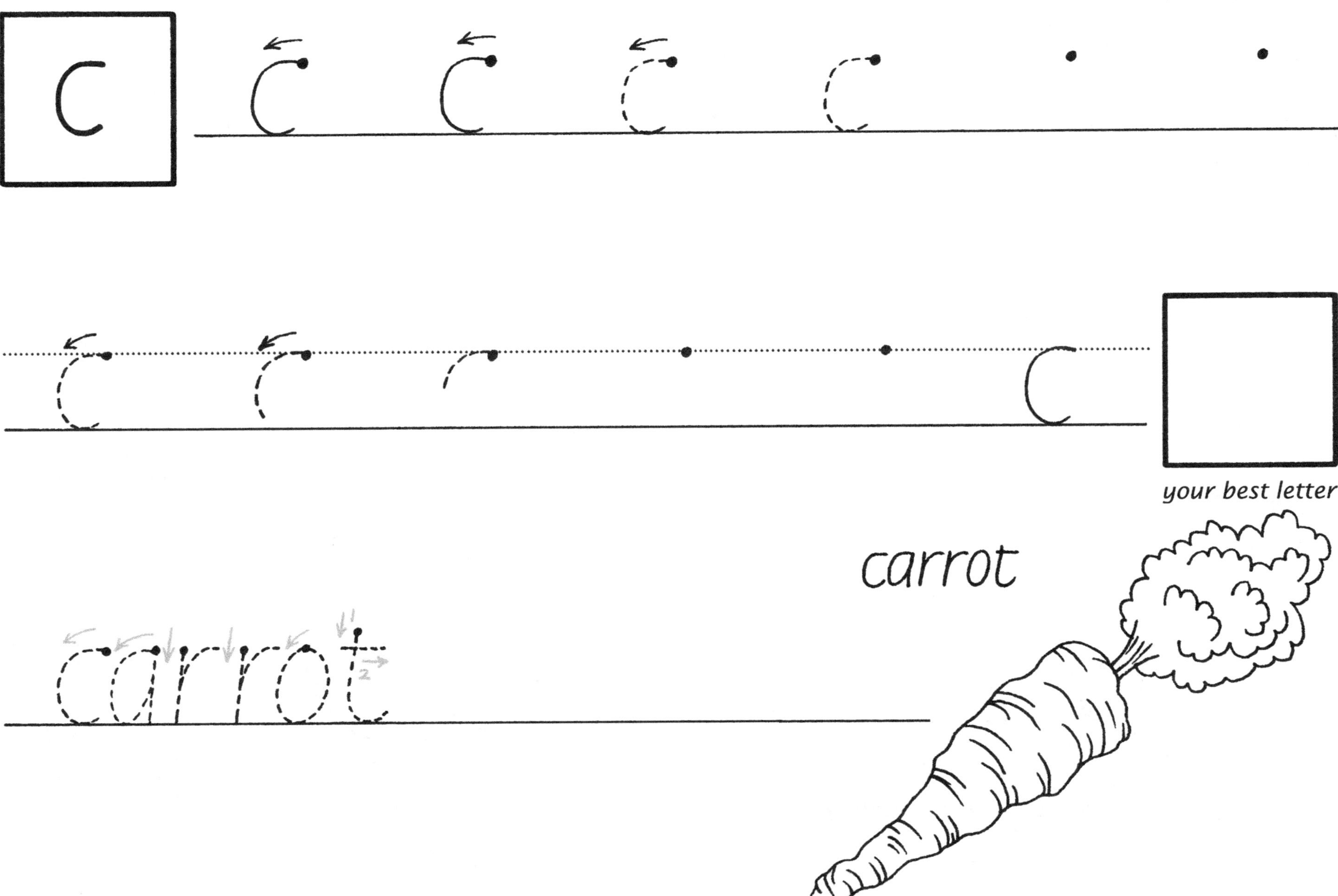

your best letter
carrot

E

your best letter

Egg

Egg

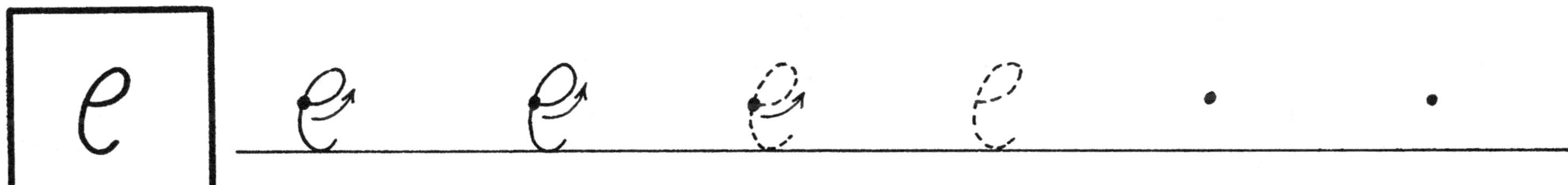

your best letter

elephant

LOOK: Did you trace each **e** before writing your own?

Circle: Yes   No

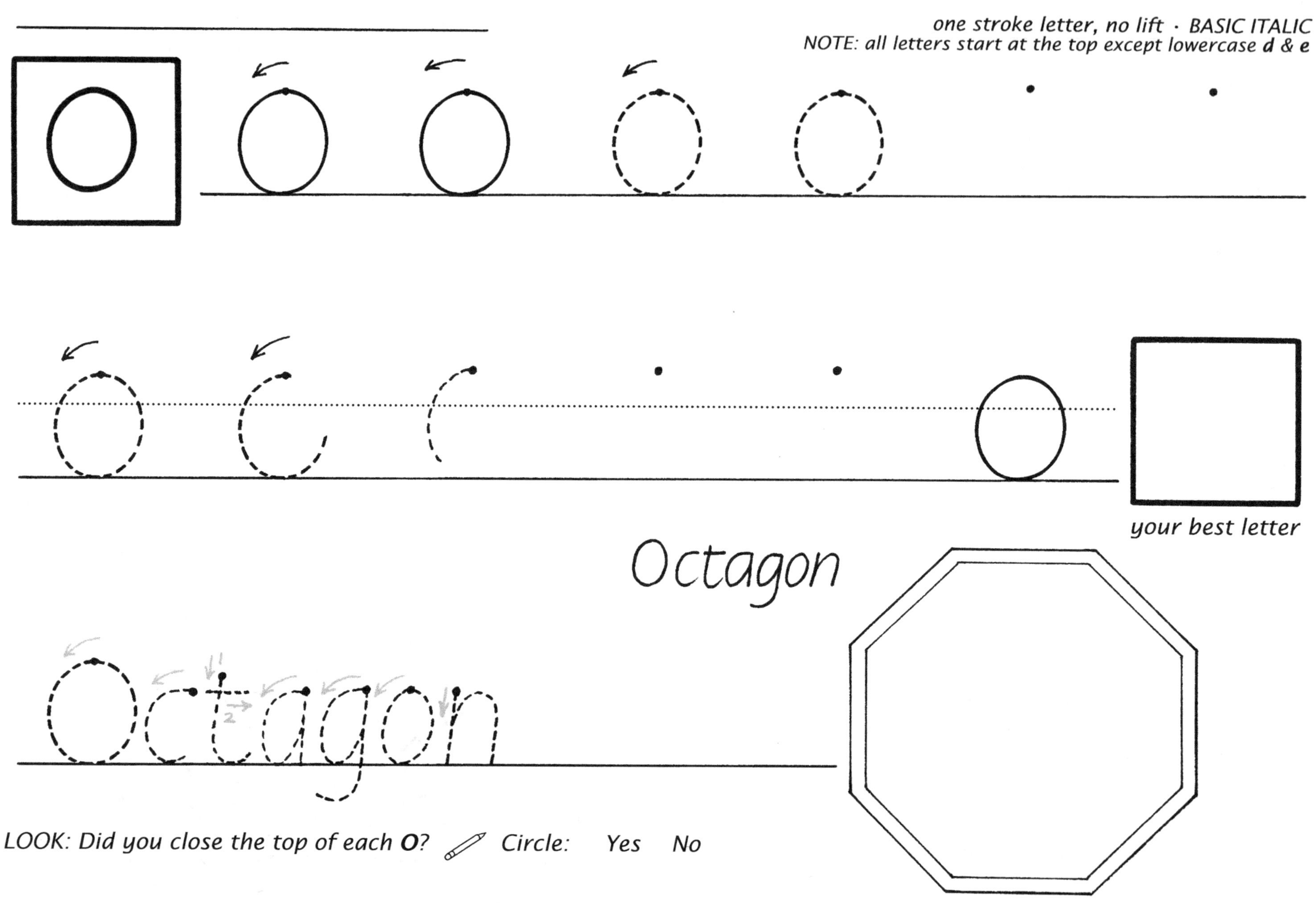

LOOK: Did you close the top of each **O**? Circle: Yes   No

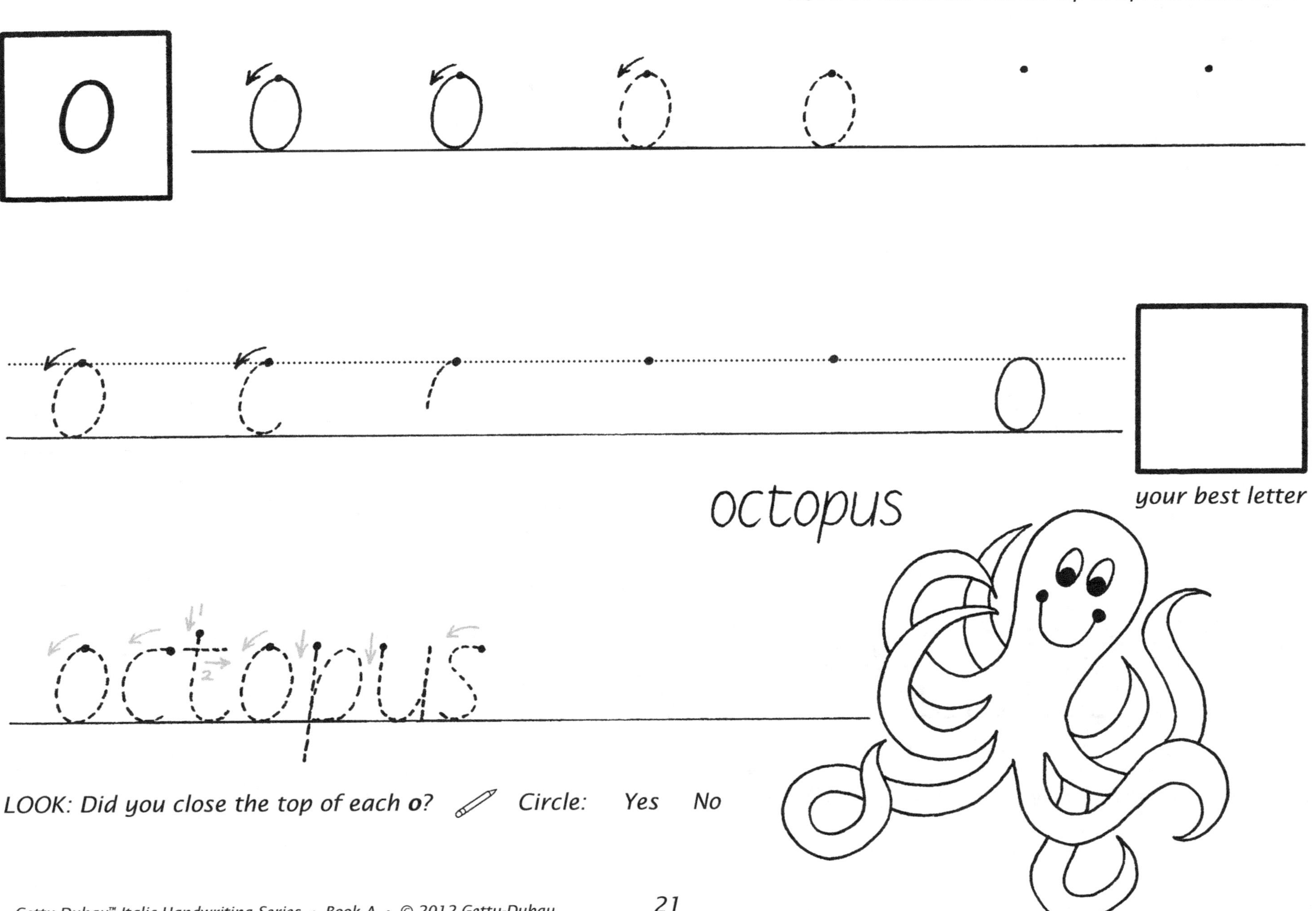

LOOK: Did you close the top of each **o**?   Circle: Yes   No

your best letter

Peacock

your best letter

parrot

B

your best letter

Balloons

Balloons

your best letter
butterfly

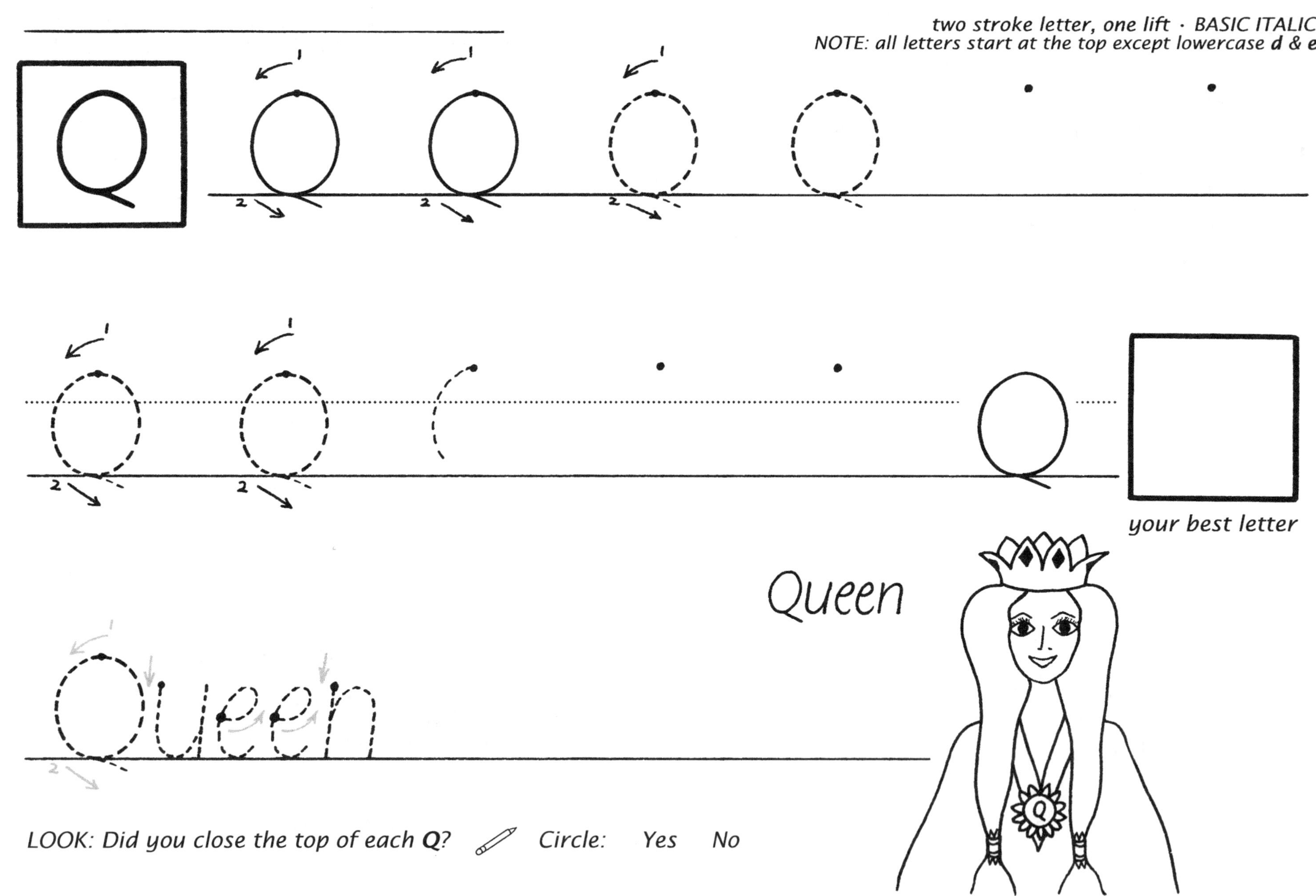

your best letter

Queen

LOOK: Did you close the top of each **Q**? Circle: Yes No

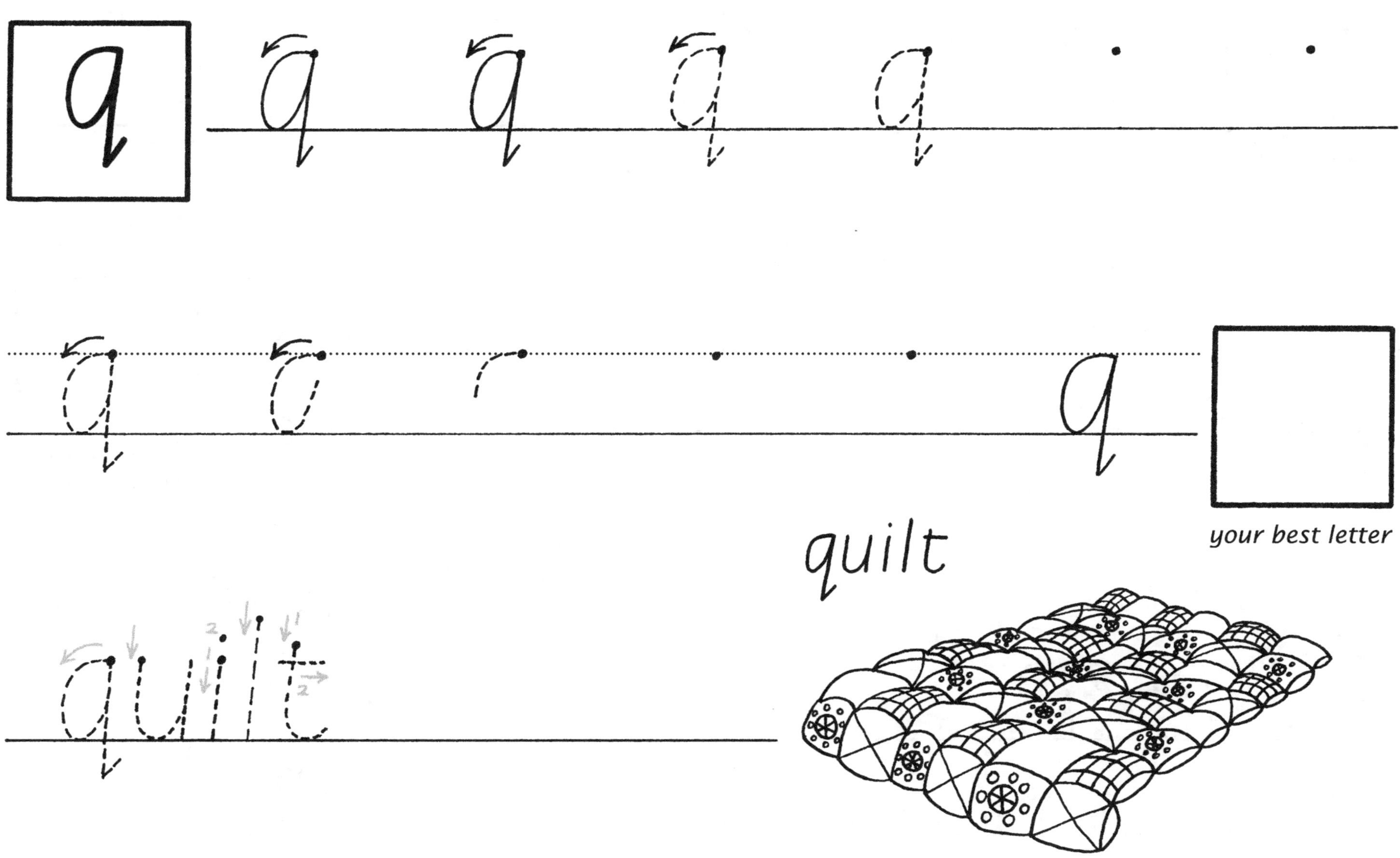

your best letter

quilt

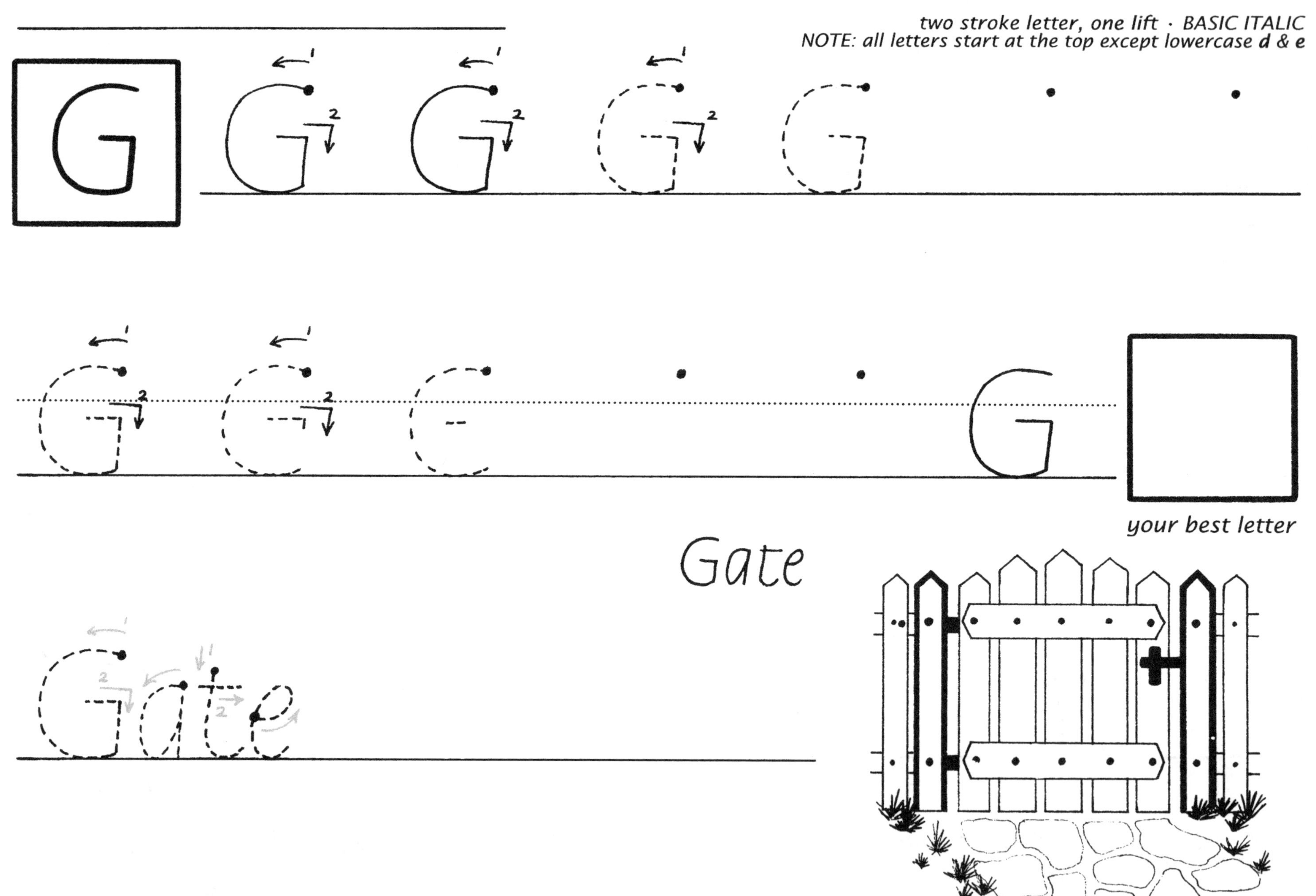
G
your best letter
Gate

your best letter

goat

LOOK: Did you trace each letter before writing your own?   Circle: Yes   No

Dinosaur
your best letter
Dinosaur

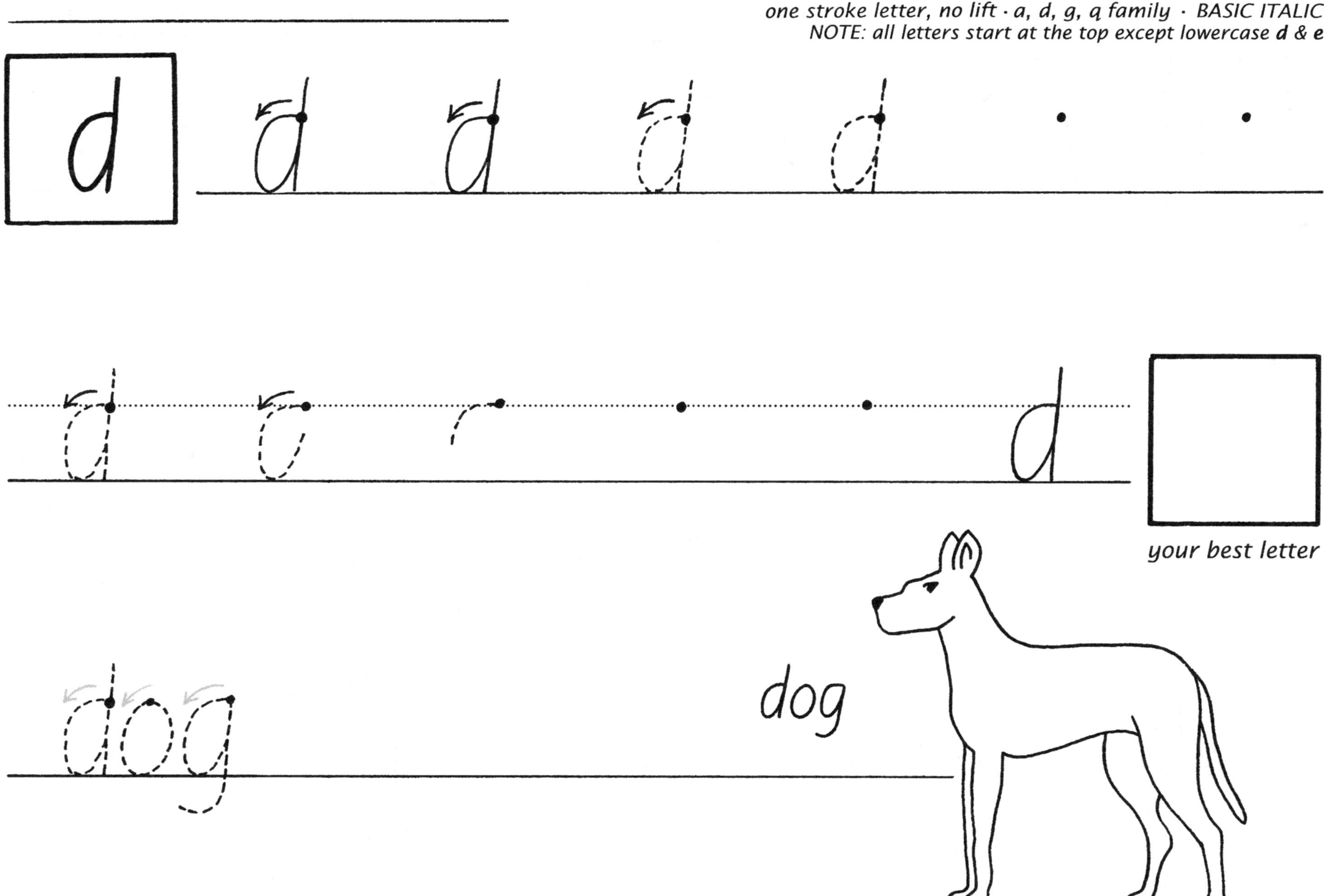

your best letter
dog

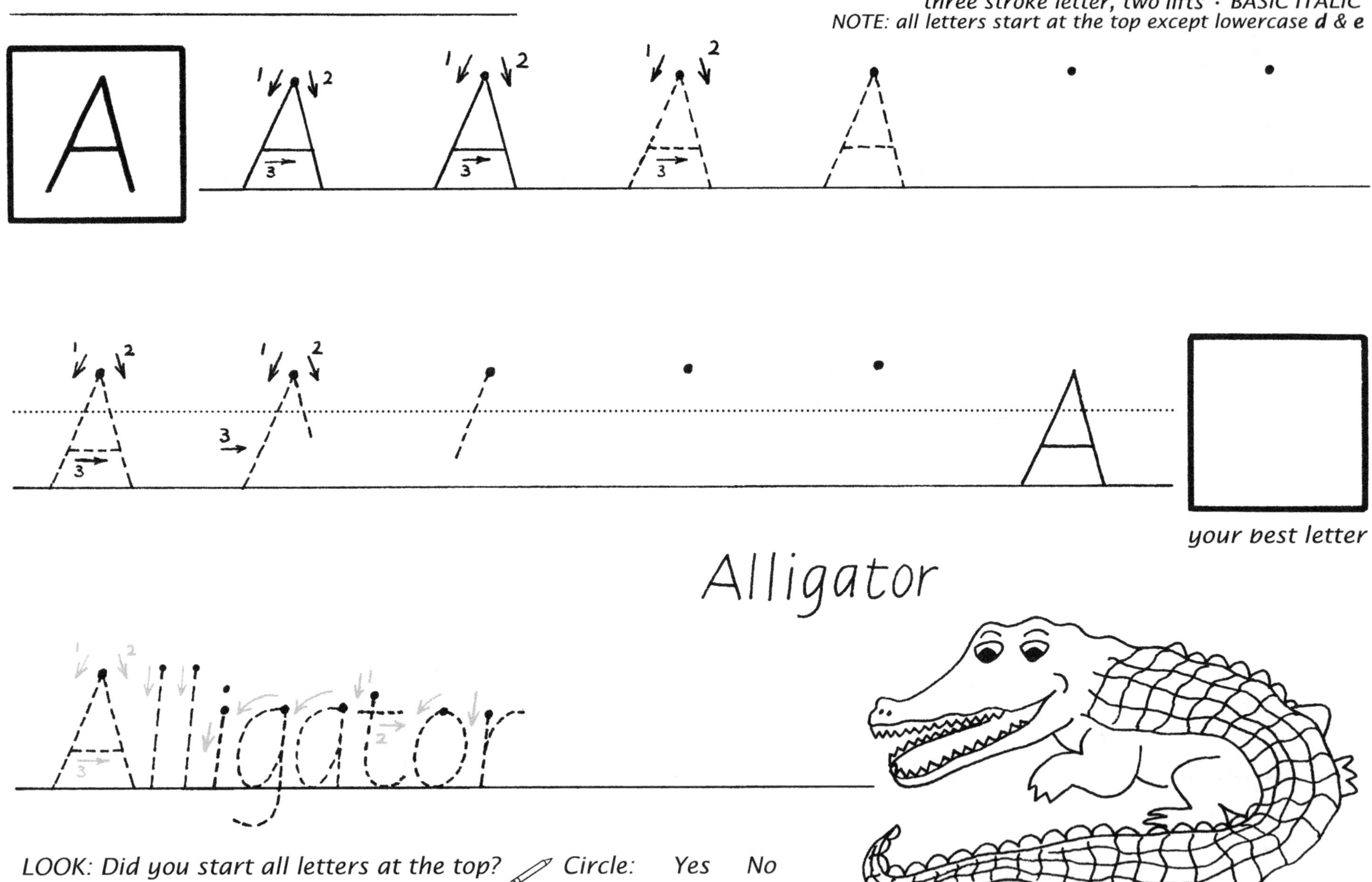

your best letter

Alligator

LOOK: Did you start all letters at the top? Circle: Yes   No

your best letter

apple

LOOK: Did you close each **a** at the top?   Circle: Yes   No

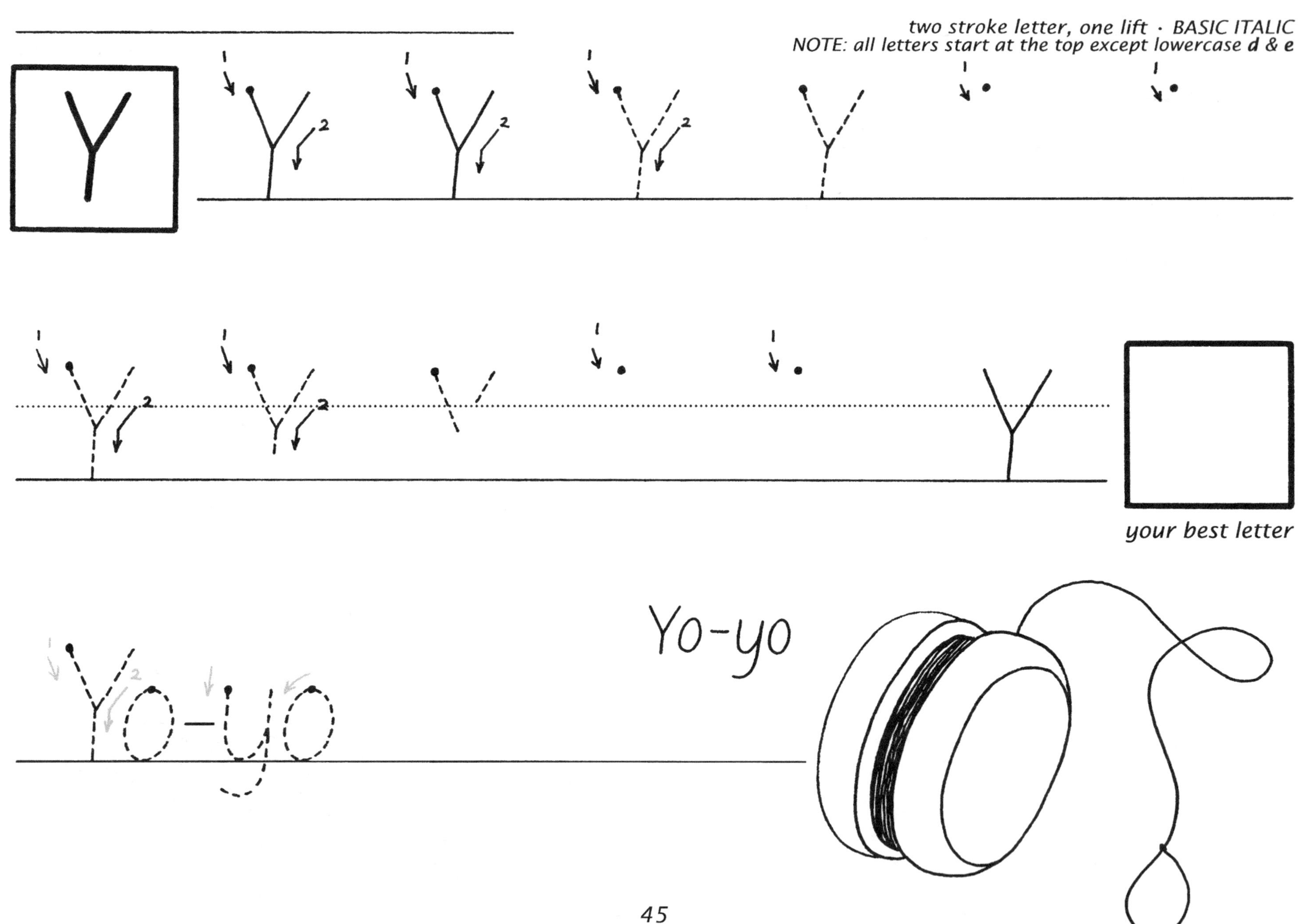

45

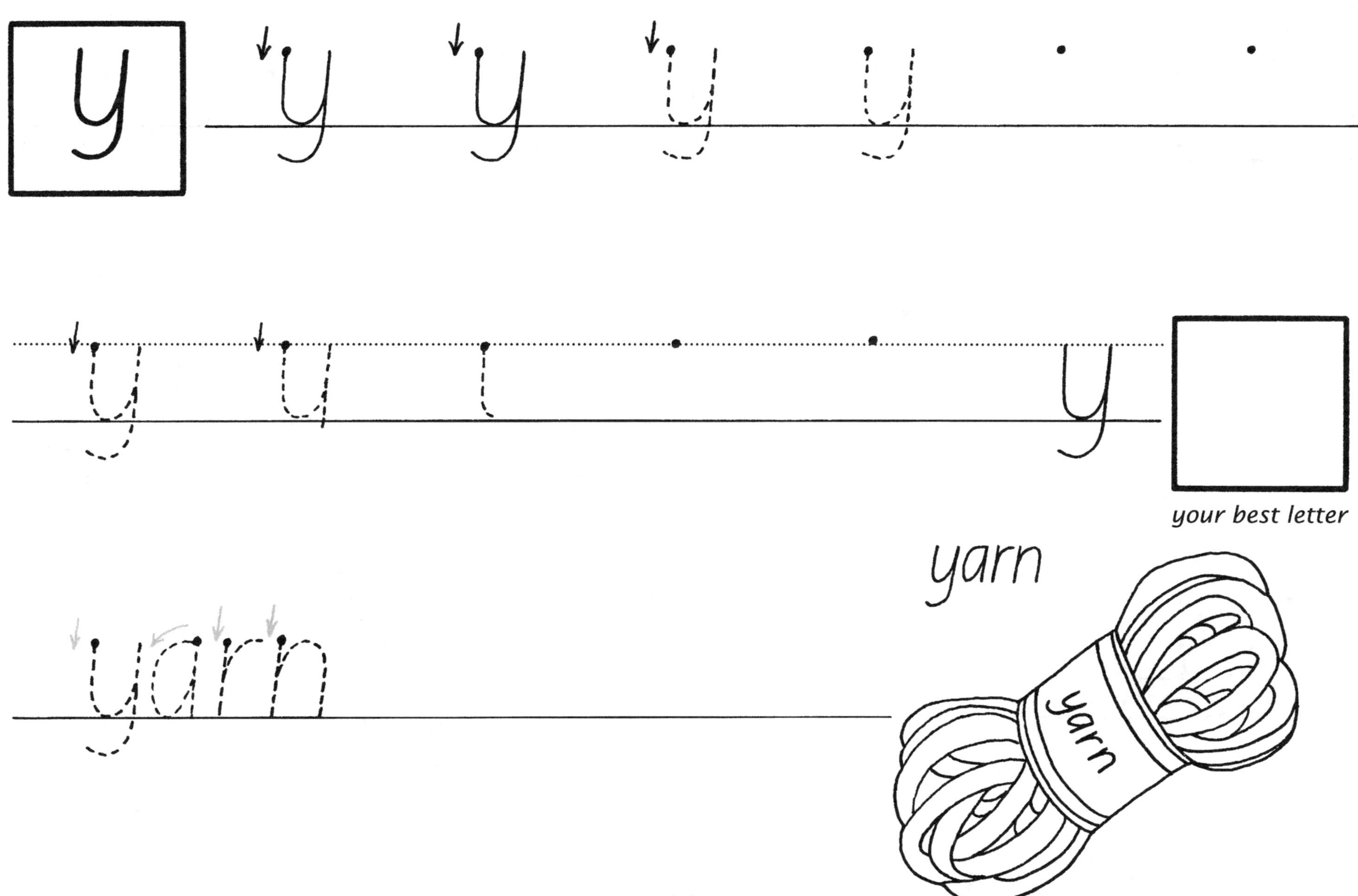

your best letter

yarn

U

your best letter

Ukulele

LOOK: Did you trace each letter before writing your own?

Circle: Yes   No

your best letter

umbrella

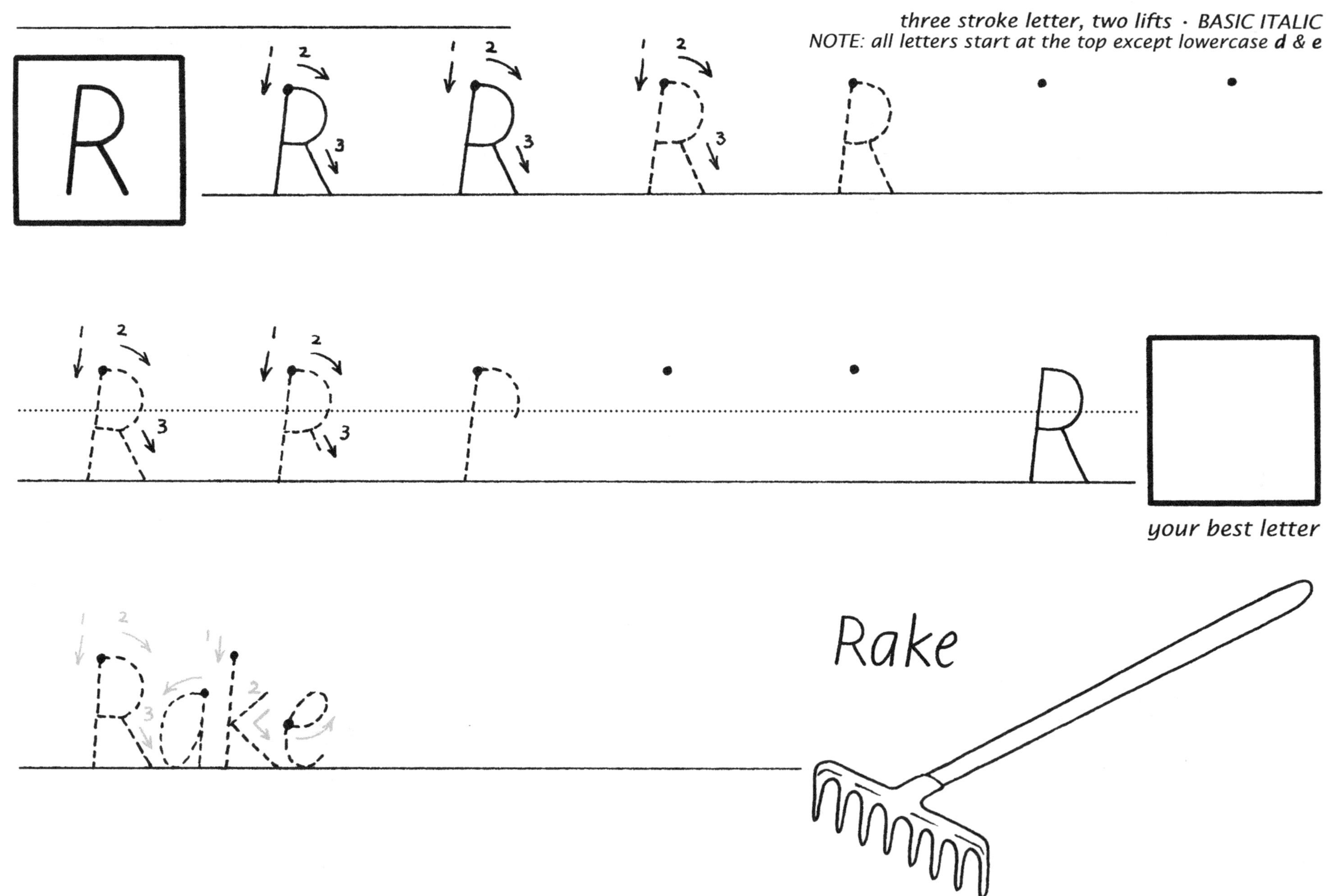
your best letter
Rake

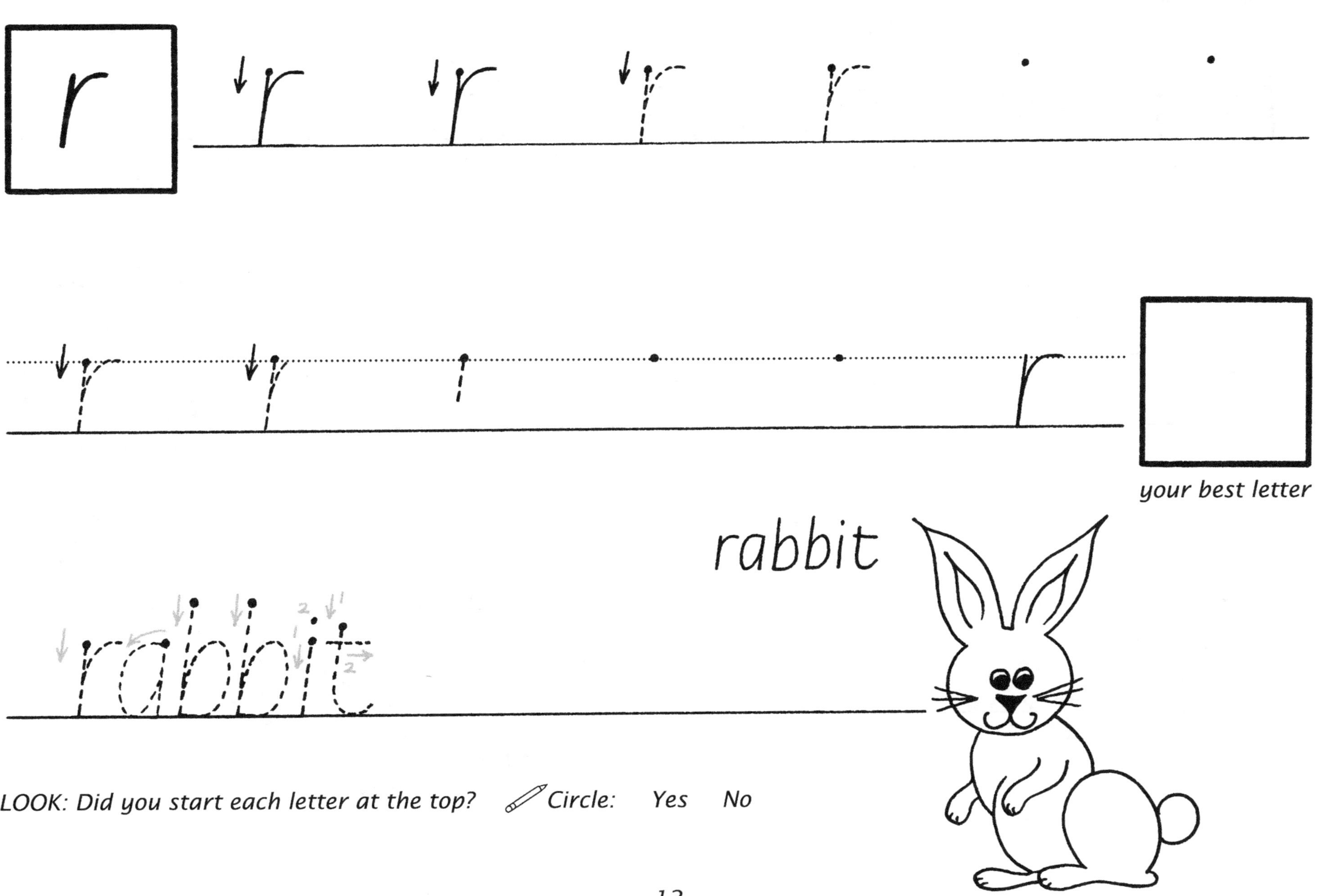

your best letter

rabbit

LOOK: Did you start each letter at the top?　Circle:　Yes　No

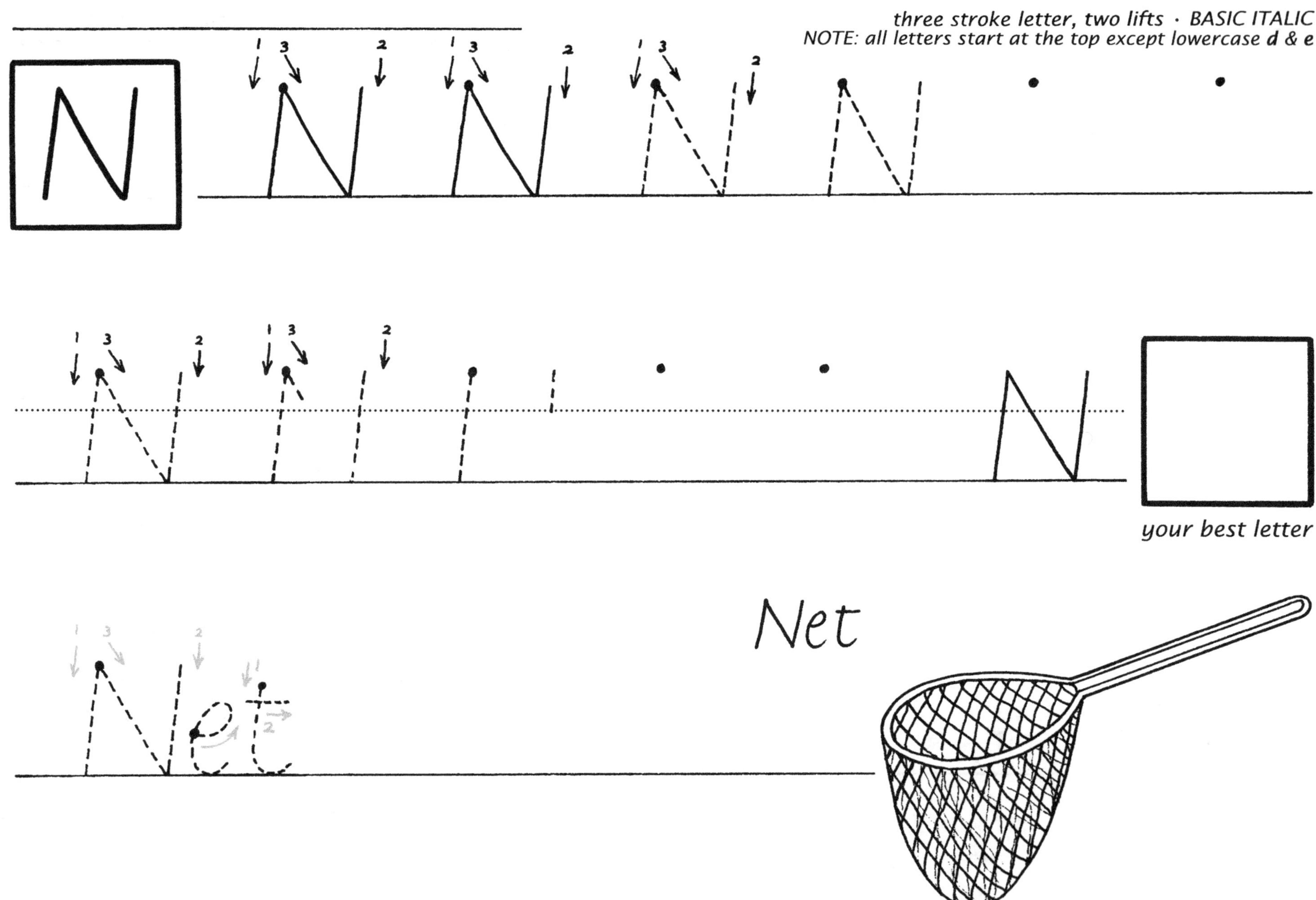

your best letter

Net

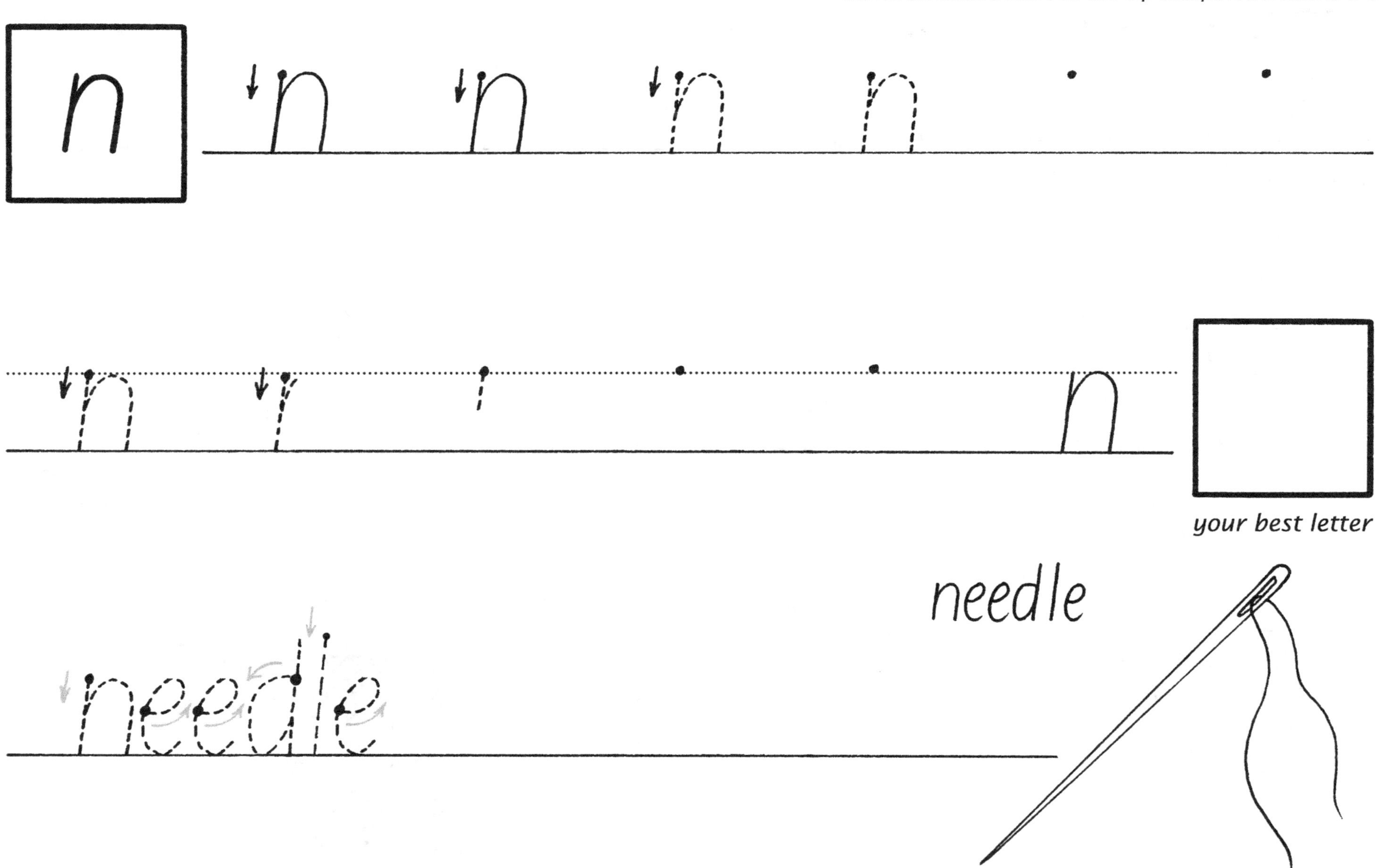

n
n   n   n   n   .   .
n   r   i   .   .   n
your best letter
needle
needle

M

your best letter

Mittens

LOOK: Did you start all letters at the top?   Circle: Yes   No

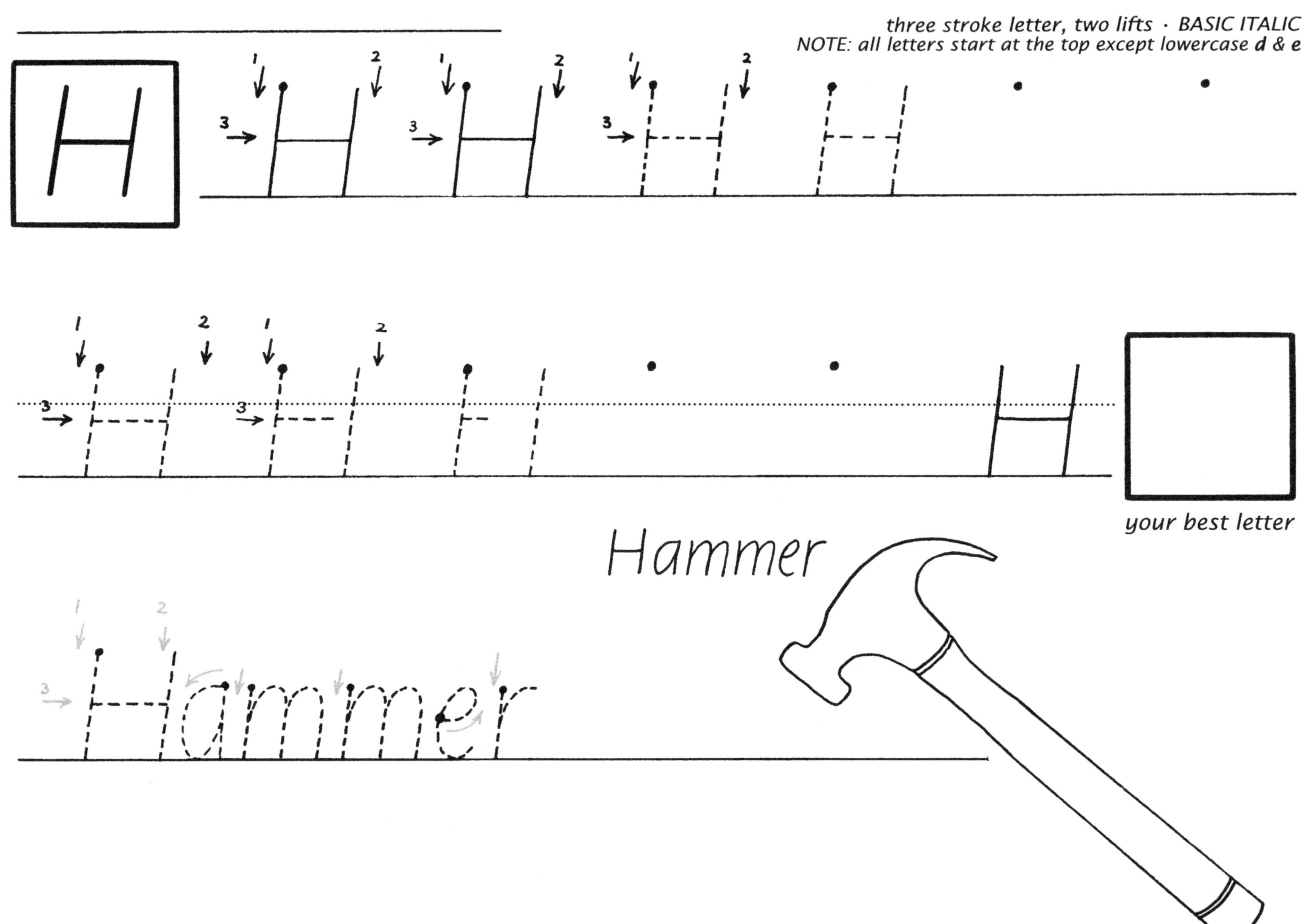
Hammer
your best letter
Hammer

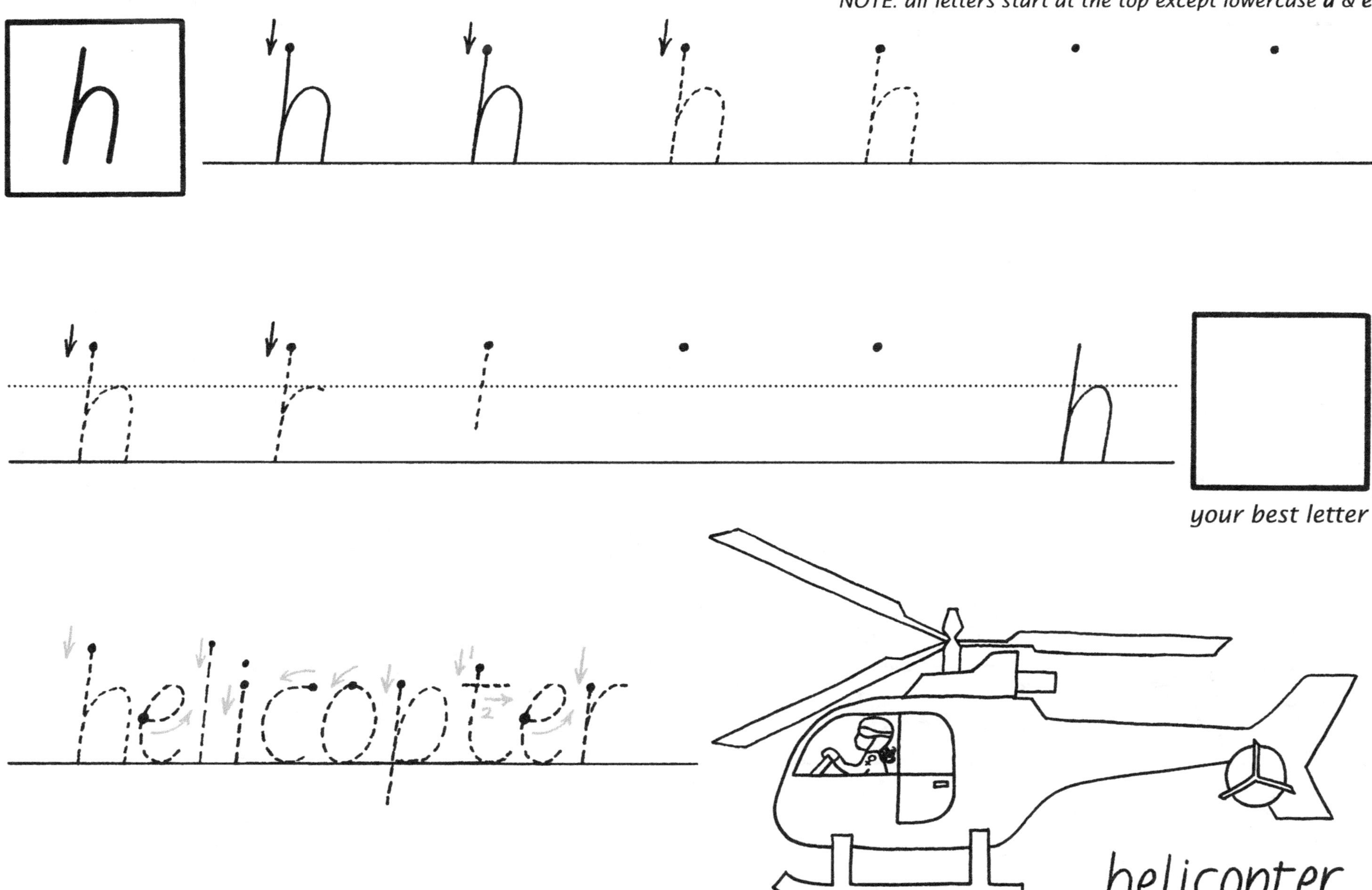

your best letter
helicopter

Z

your best letter

Zipper

Zipper

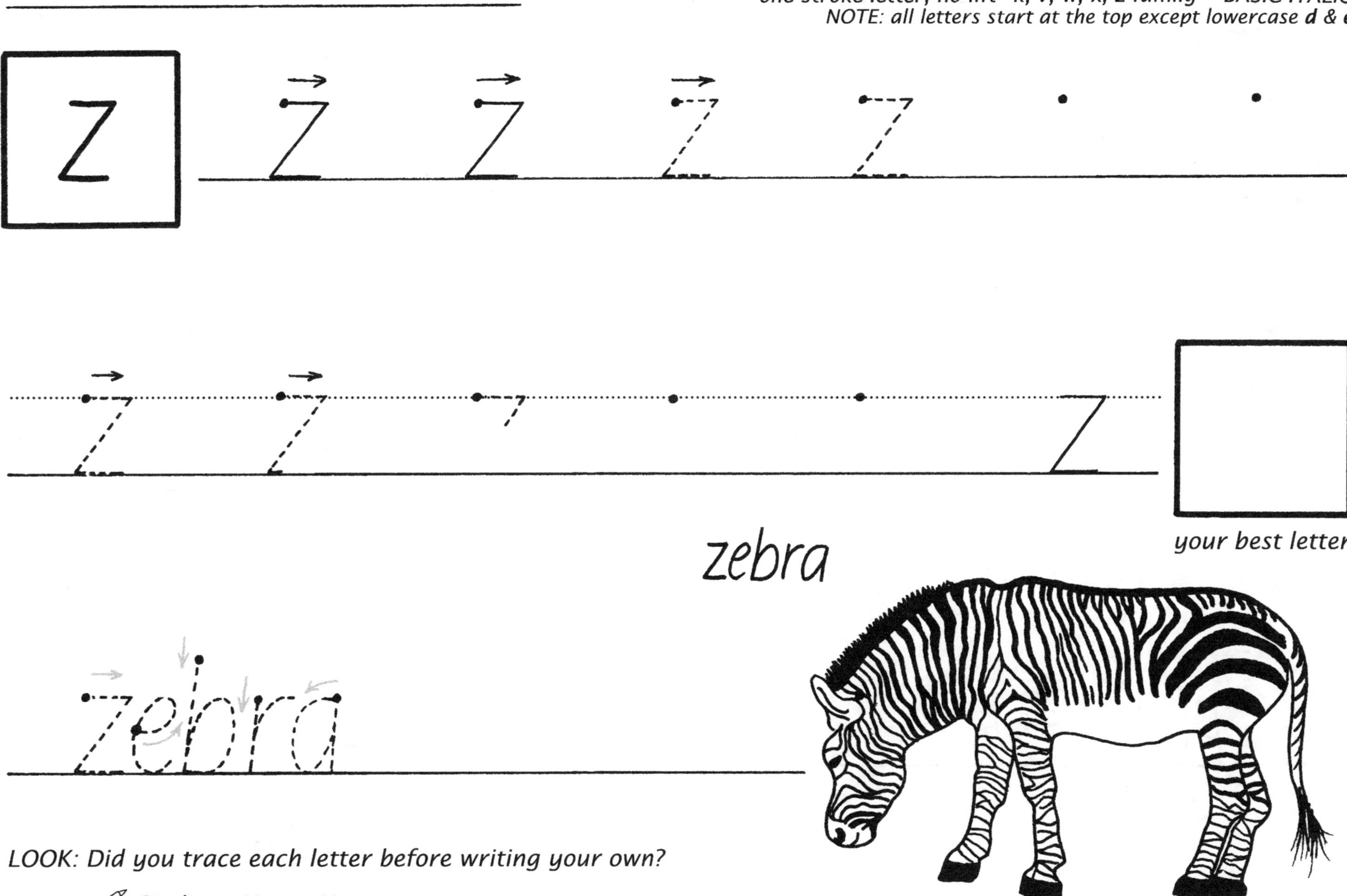

your best letter

zebra

LOOK: Did you trace each letter before writing your own?

Circle: Yes   No

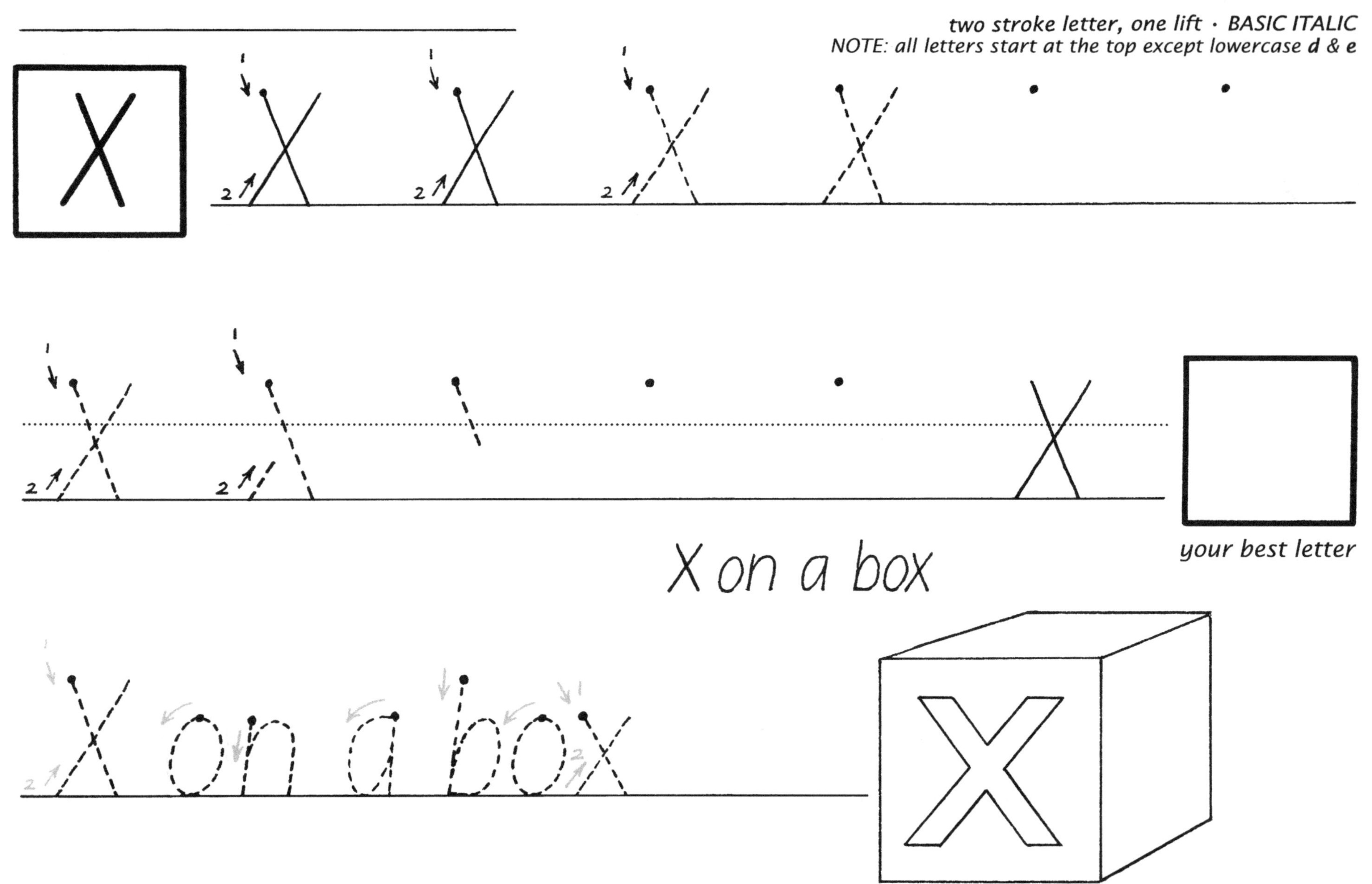

X on a box
your best letter
X on a box

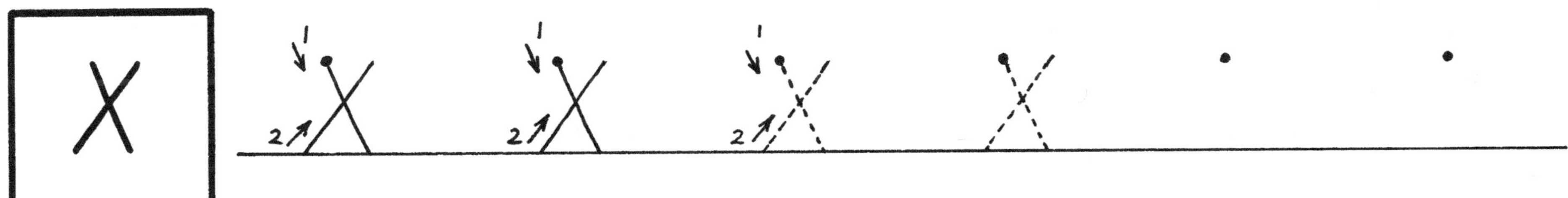

x in a box

your best letter

x in a box

one stroke letter, no lift · BASIC ITALIC
NOTE: all letters start at the top except lowercase d & e
your best letter
Watch

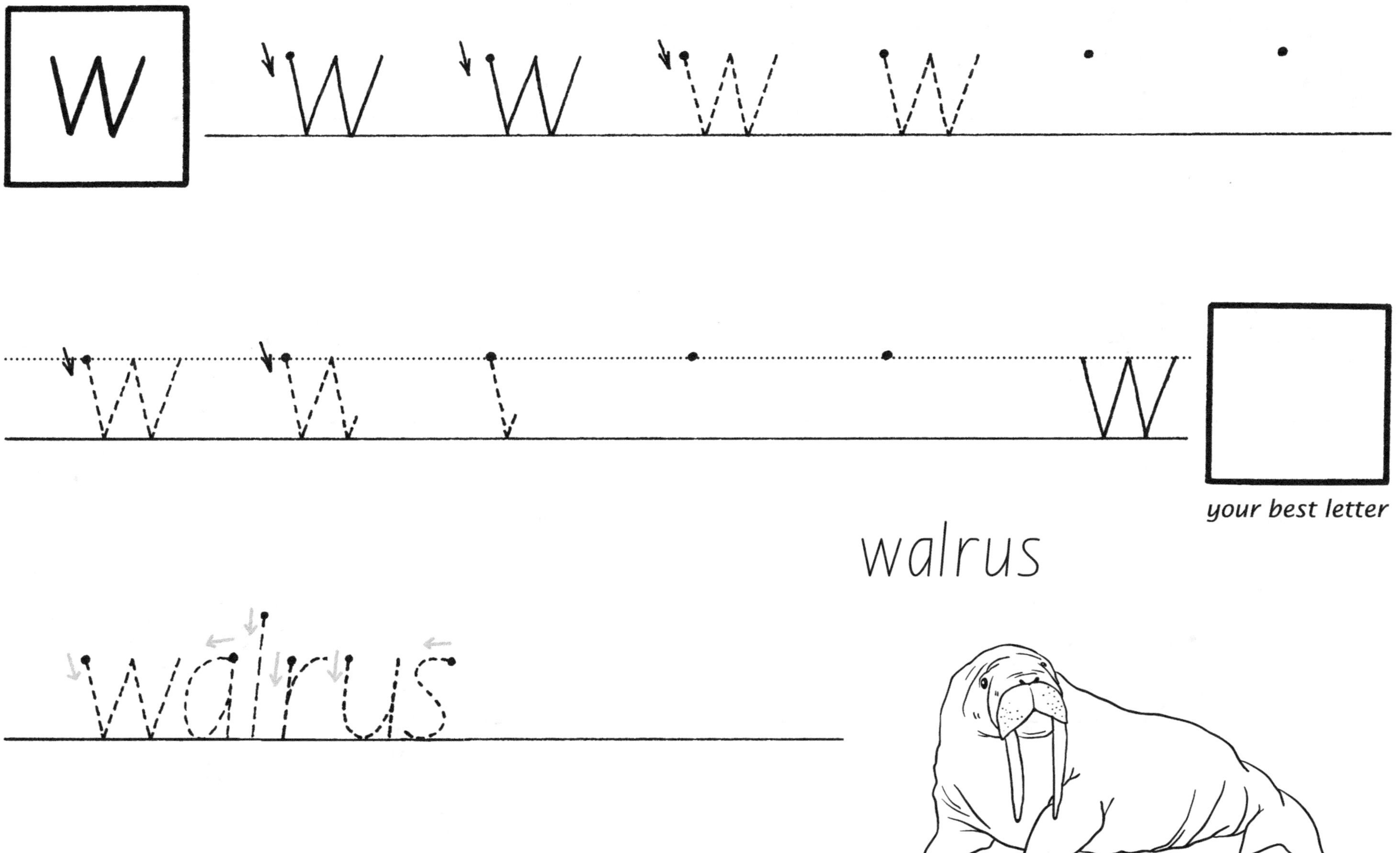

your best letter

walrus

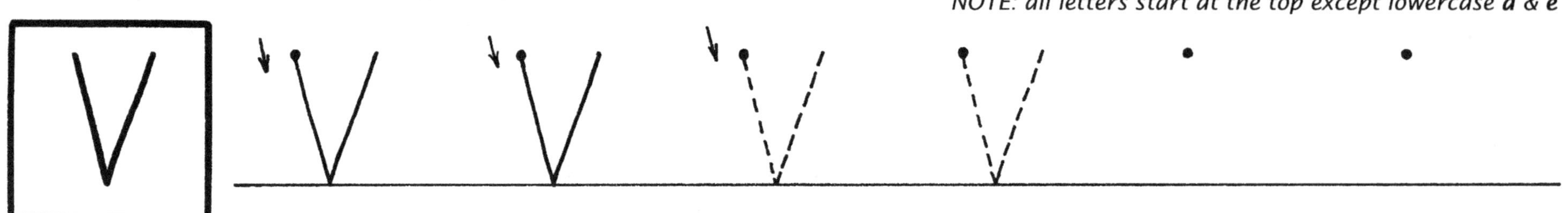

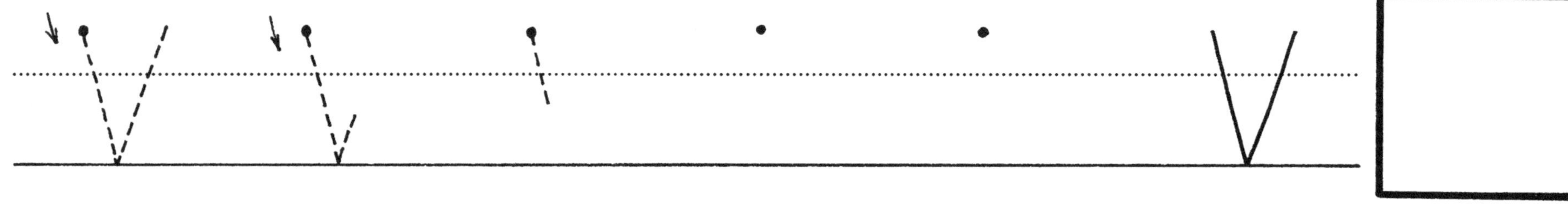

your best letter

Valentine

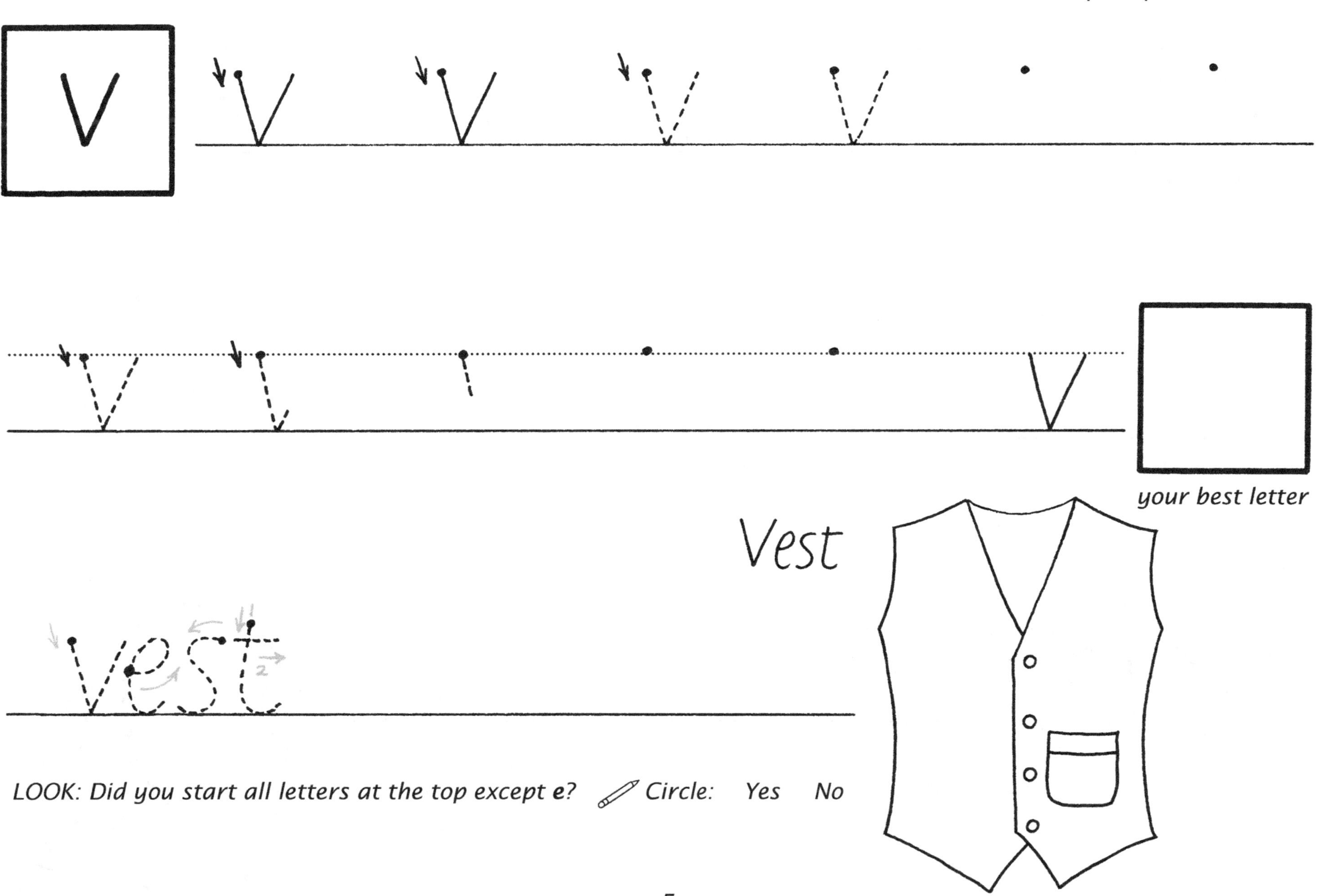

your best letter

Vest

LOOK: Did you start all letters at the top except *e*? Circle: Yes   No

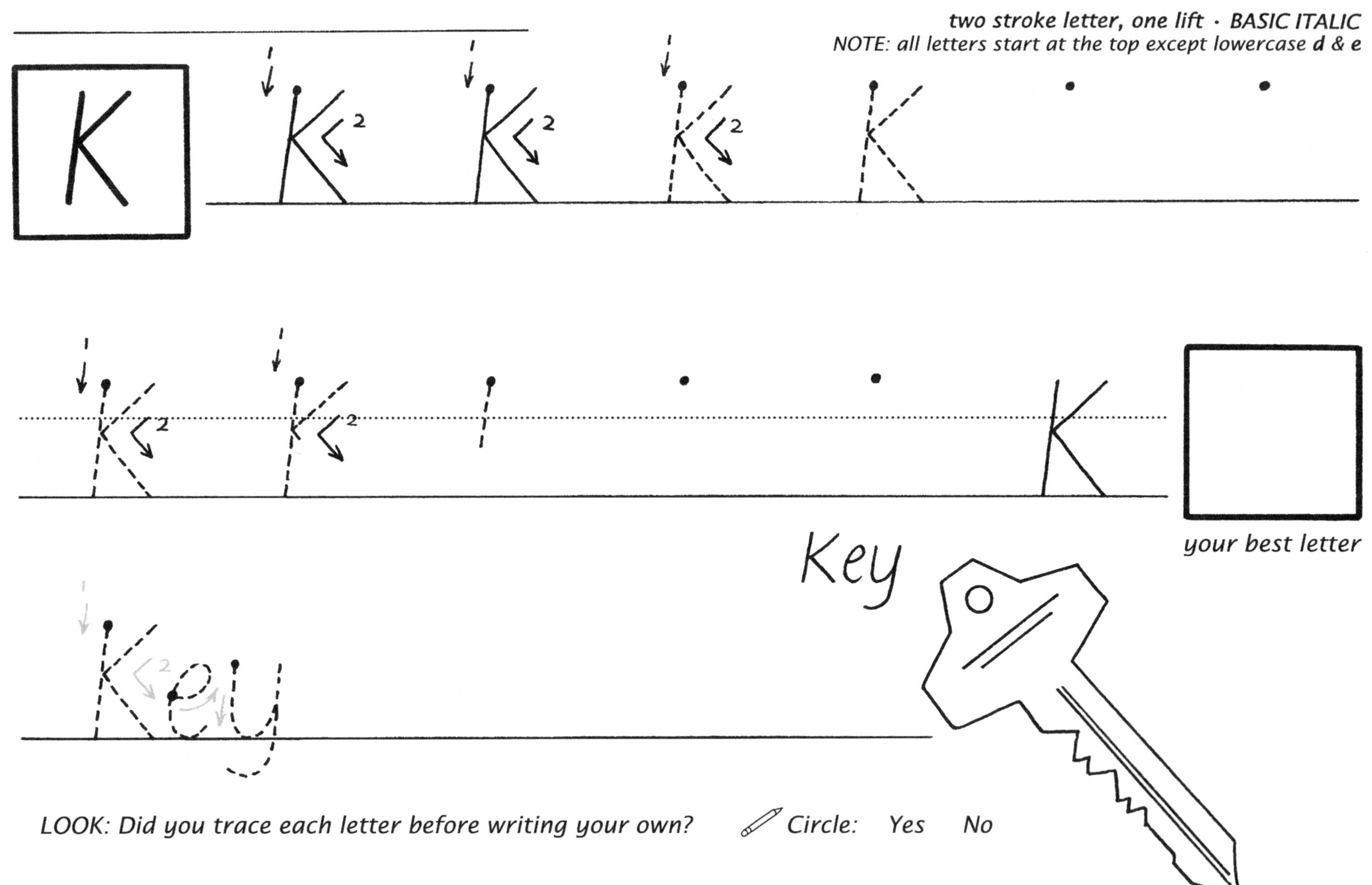

LOOK: Did you trace each letter before writing your own?   Circle: Yes   No

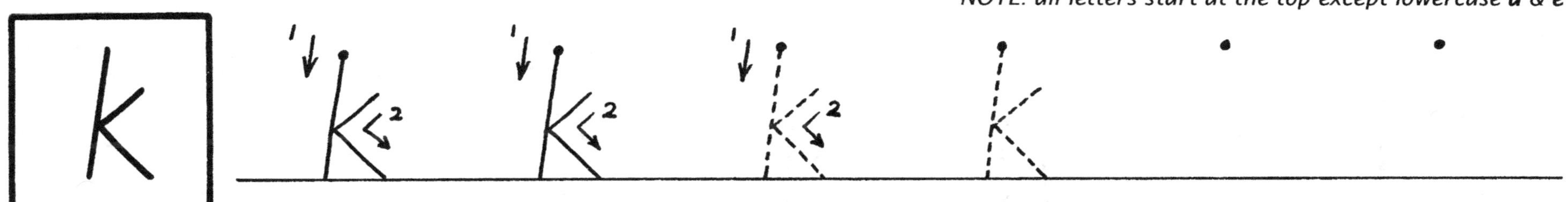

your best letter

kite

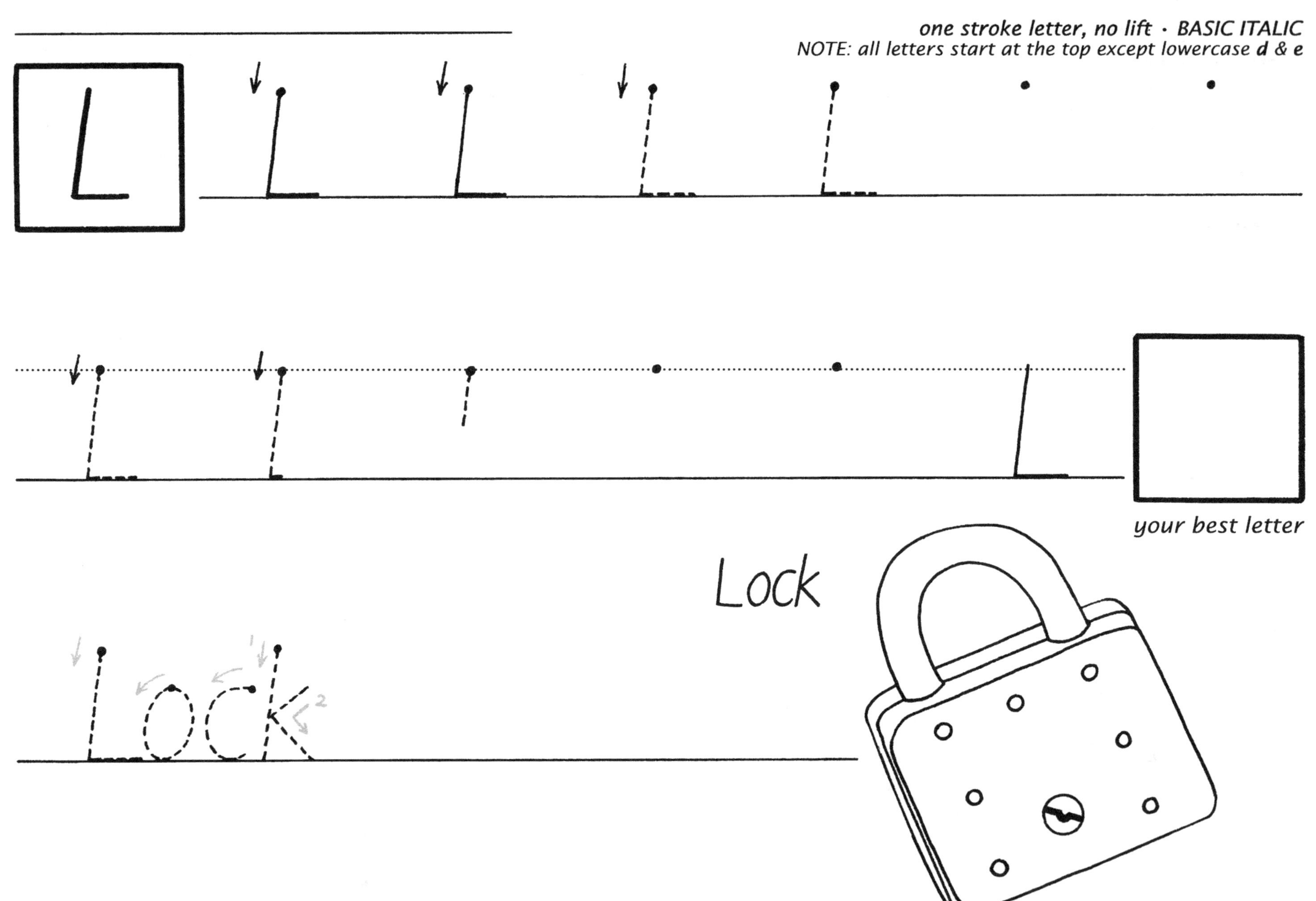
L
your best letter
Lock

l

your best letter

lamb

J

your best letter

Jack-in-the-box

Jack-in-the-box

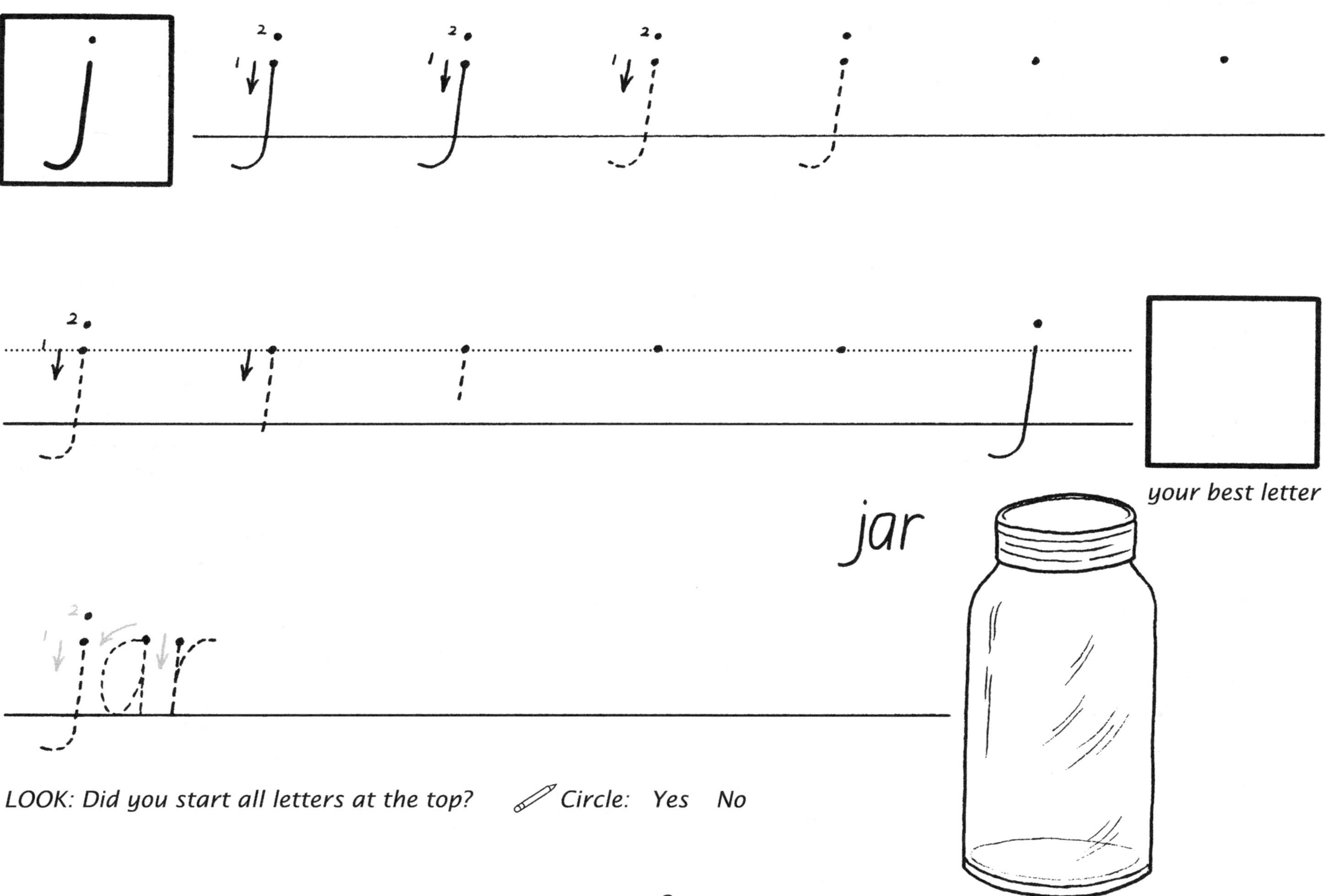

LOOK: Did you start all letters at the top?   Circle: Yes   No

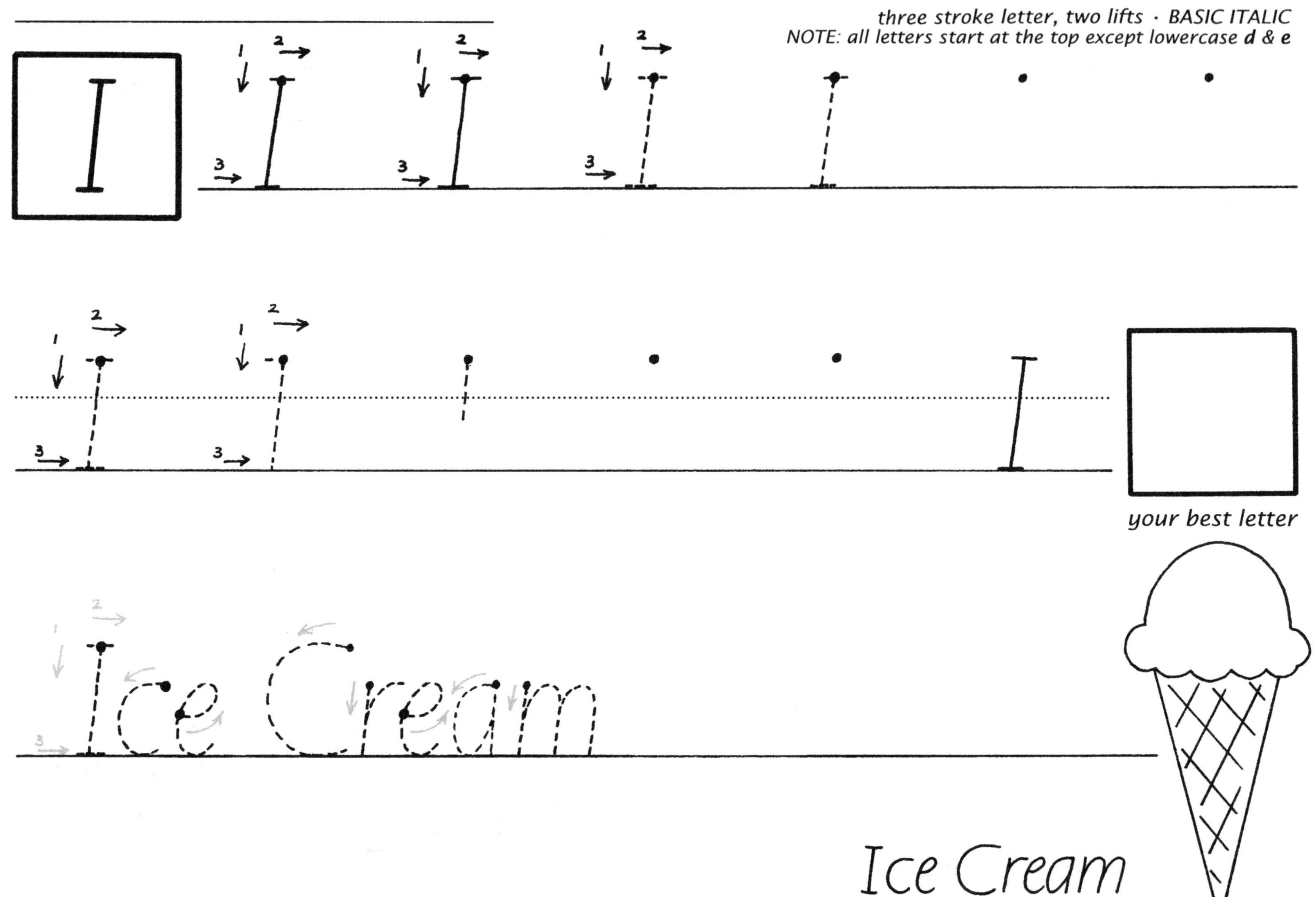
your best letter
Ice Cream

two stroke letter, one lift i, j, l family · BASIC ITALIC
NOTE: all letters start at the top except lowercase d & e

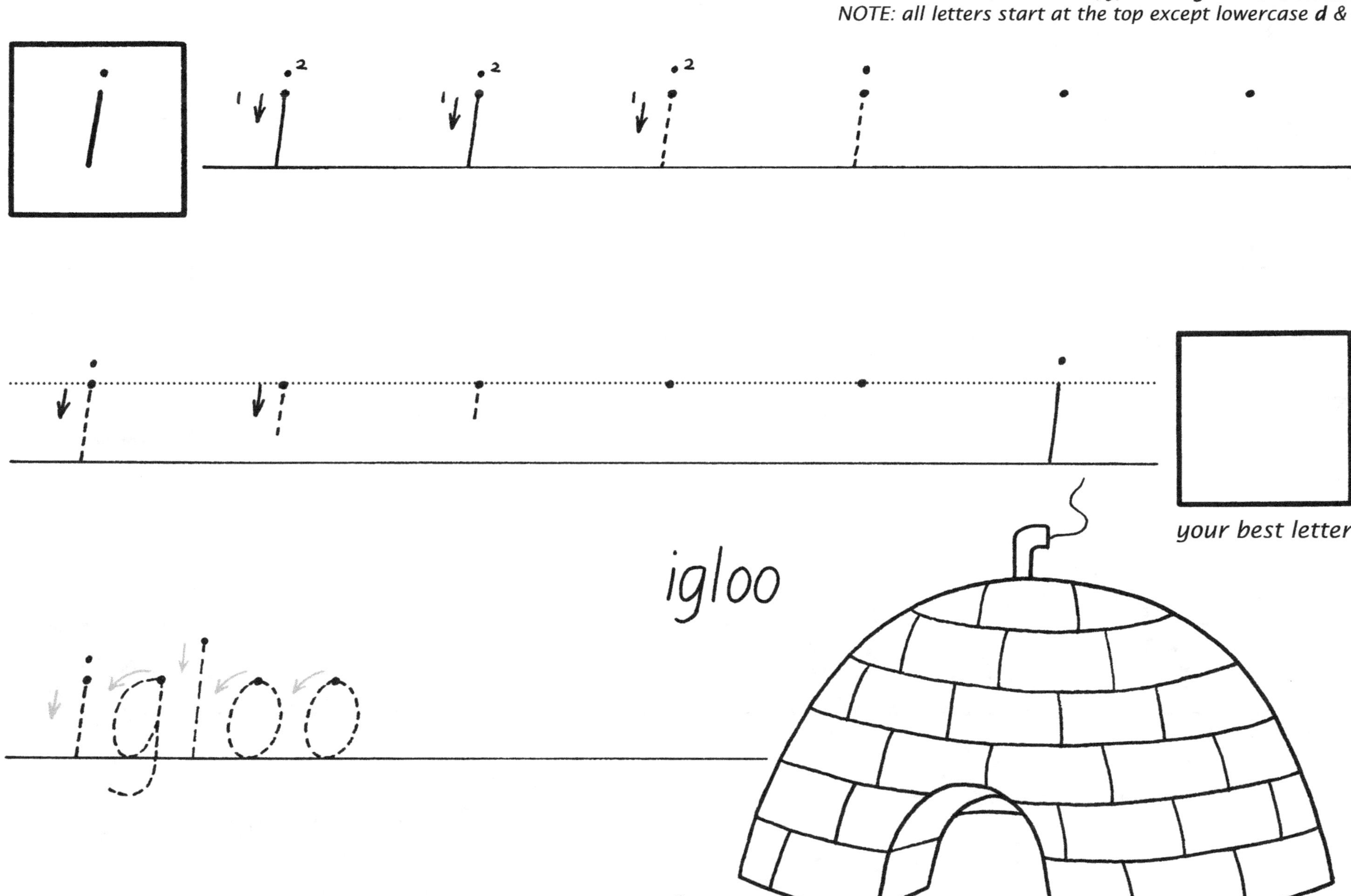

your best letter
igloo

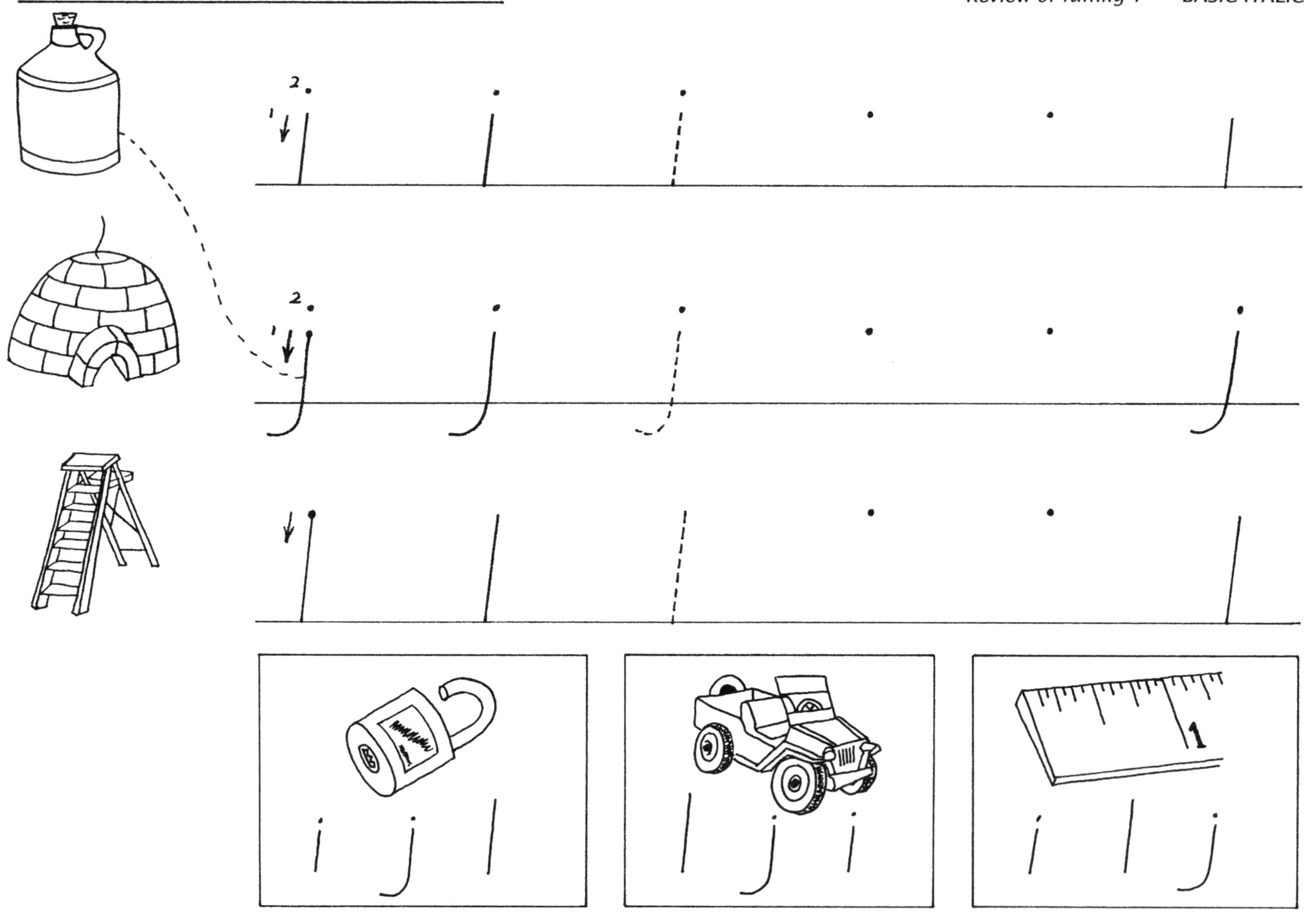

TOP THREE LINES: *Ask the student to draw a line from the picture to the letter that stands for the correct beginning sound.*

BOTTOM THREE BOXES: *Ask the student to circle the letter that stands for the beginning sound of the picture.*

BASIC SHAPES

Before the student begins writing in BOOK A, the authors recommend that the student practice the following shapes on unlined paper, one shape at a time. Allow the student to write each shape any size at first. Later, ask the student to write very large and very small forms of that same shape. We suggest the student also practice these shapes on a chalkboard and/or in cornmeal. (See INSTRUCTION MANUAL, "*Activity*," pp. 35 & 41.)

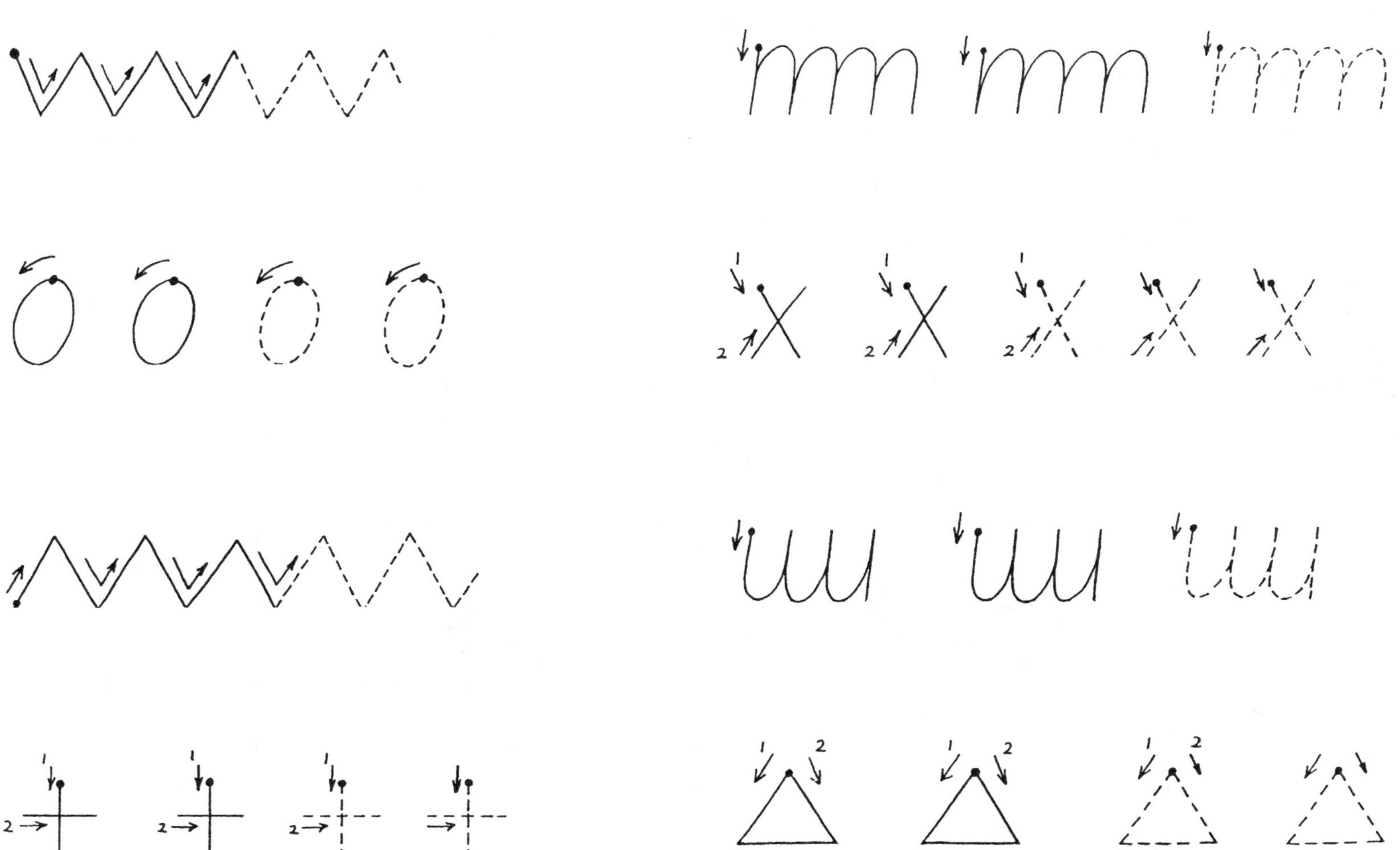

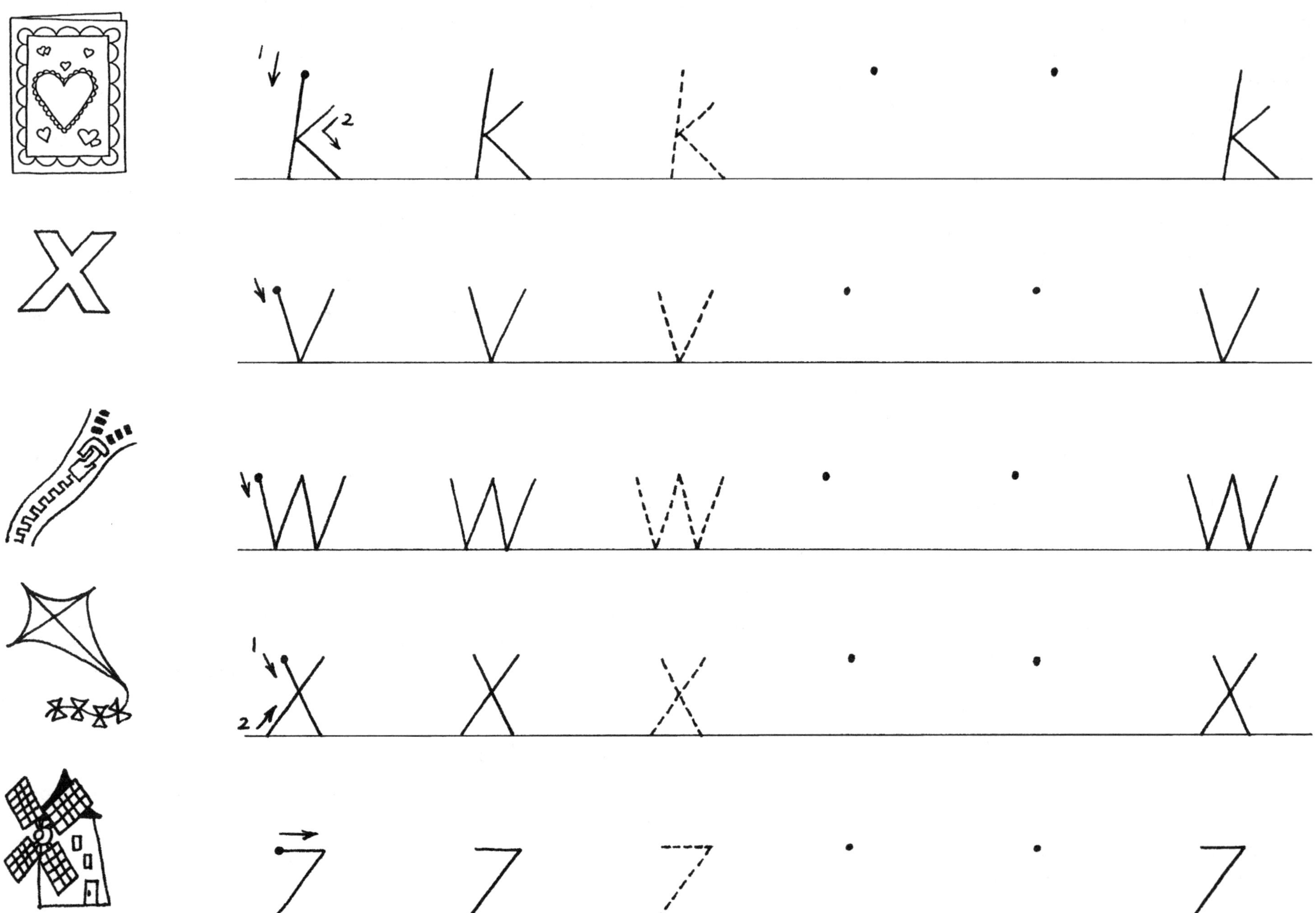

Ask the student to draw a line from the picture to the letter
that stands for the correct beginning sound.

Learning how to write involves much more than learning to write letters. It is a sophisticated, complex process involving learning letterforms, learning how to space within and between words, and learning how to organize writing on a page. Research indicates that there exists an almost perfect correlation between measures evaluating the children's *awareness* of their fingers and the ability to *use* their fingers in precise manual skills.

Ways to determine manual ability

To assist young students increase awareness of their hands and fingers, and to help you, the teacher, evaluate students' manual skills, have your students perform these tasks:

1. Direct the students to touch each of their fingers to their thumb, in order, from the first to the little finger. (By the age of six years, most children should be able to complete this exercise using one or both hands at a time.)

2. Have the students connect two dots that are spaced approximately eight inches apart on a page. (Most children of five years can accomplish this. However, if the student draws beyond the second dot or draws an unusually shaky line when nearing the second dot, it may indicate potential deficiencies in handwriting skills.)

Ways to improve kinesthetic perception of the hands

1. Unstructured clay modeling facilitates a student's perception of his or her hands. Encourage the student to manipulate the clay in every possible way—squeezing, flattening, poking, making shapes, etc.

2. To heighten the student's perception of shape, use a box in which a variety of small objects are placed for the student to feel but not see.

   a. Ask the student to reach in the box and find an unseen object that matches the one he or she is looking at.

   b. Direct the student to locate in the box an object that you or another student has described.

   c. Ask the student to find two objects with similar characteristics—two fuzzy objects, two heavy objects, two small objects, etc.

3. Draw several circles on a sheet of paper. To determine the student's ability to aim the finger and hand and also to point, have the student place dots in the circles with a pencil, pen, or crayon. Vary the difficulty of this task by increasing or decreasing the size of the circles or increasing the rate at which the dots are made. (The student must be able to point at a given or imaginary point in order to begin the stroke of a letter.)

Ways to confirm hand-eye tracking skills

The ability to control continuous hand movements while drawing lines of varying difficulty is basic to handwriting. If you are able to detect problems as the student completes the following tasks and are able to obtain appropriate assistance for the student, subsequent difficulties may be avoided.

1. Demonstrate drawing parallel lines. Then direct the student to draw parallel lines of a given length, first at a relaxed pace then at a faster one.

2. Direct the student to draw two curved lines equal in distance from one another. Later require more difficult shapes that combine straight lines, angles, and/or curves.

3. Direct the student to connect numbered dots on a sheet of paper that require horizontal, vertical and lateral movements. Place the paper in front of the student, close to the dominant hand. Later, space the dots further apart and require the student to cross the midline of his or her body. This latter task may cause the neuro-logically challenged student some difficulty.

The above evaluative tasks may be of help in assisting the learning of handwriting and in discovering deficiencies.

(See INSTRUCTION MANUAL, p. 13, for more suggestions concerning the beginning writer.)

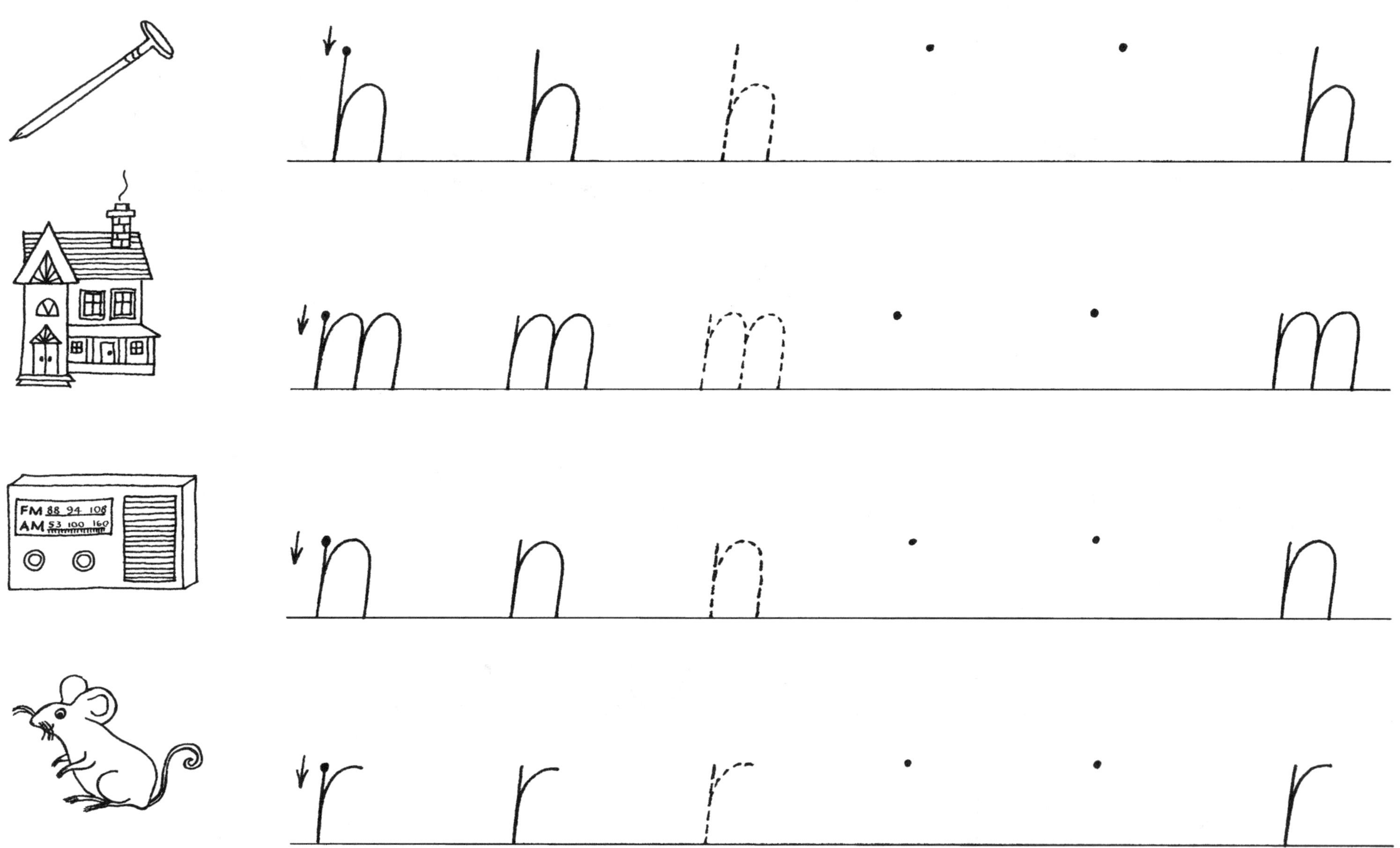

*Ask the student to draw a line from the picture to the letter
that stands for the correct beginning sound.*

BASIC ITALIC ALPHABET

All letters written in one stroke unless otherwise indicated.   *All letters start at the top except lowercase **d** and **e**.*

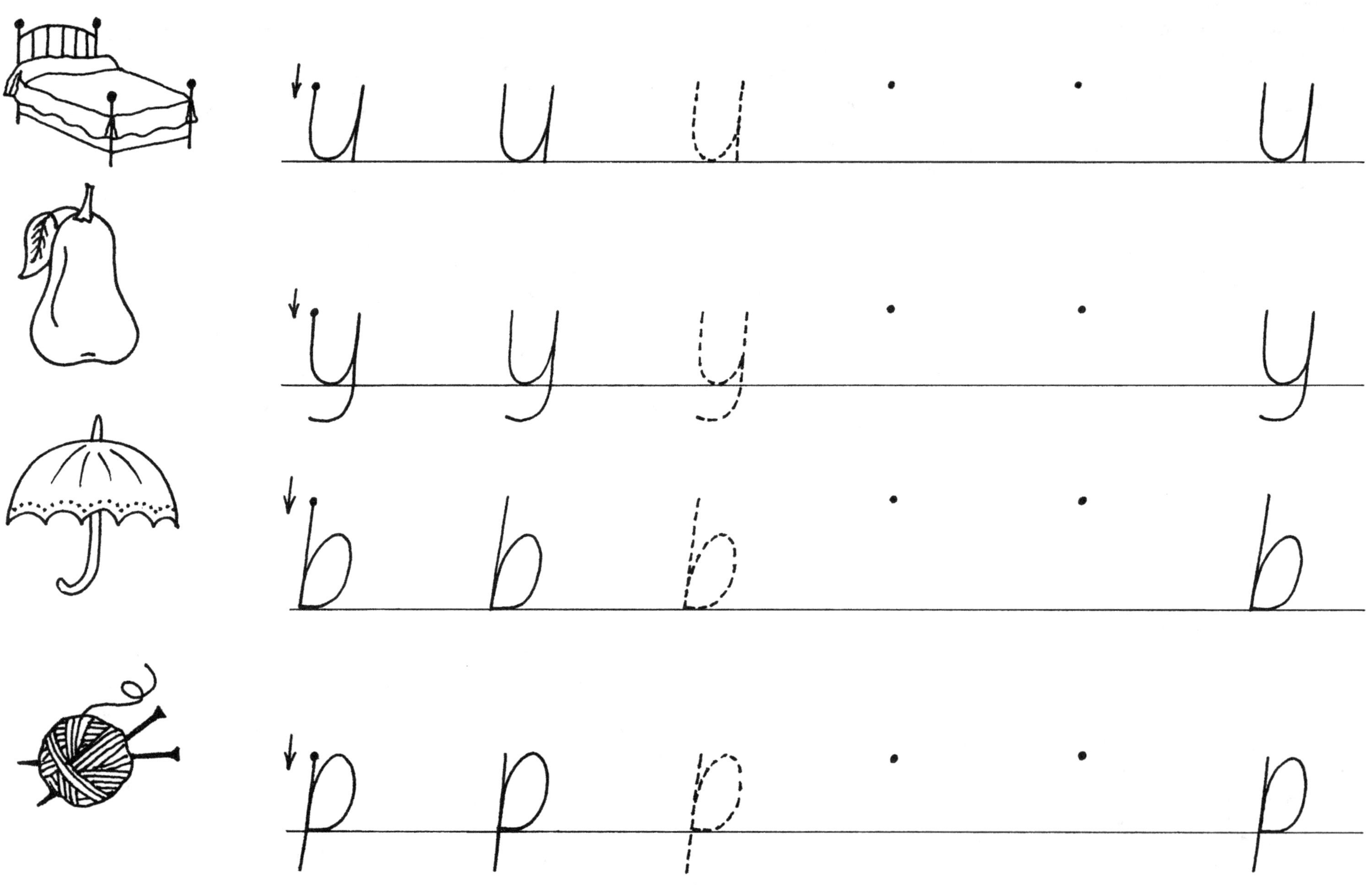

Ask the student to draw a line from the picture to the letter
that stands for the correct beginning sound.

Getty-Dubay™ Italic Handwriting Series · Book A · © 2012 Getty-Dubay

GETTY-DUBAY™ HANDWRITING REMINDERS

PENCIL HOLD

Hold the pencil with the thumb and index finger, resting it on the middle finger. Rest the shaft of the pencil near the large knuckle. Hold the tool firmly and avoid pinching. To relax the hand, tap index finger on the pencil three times. Avoid "thumb wrap" and a "death grip". 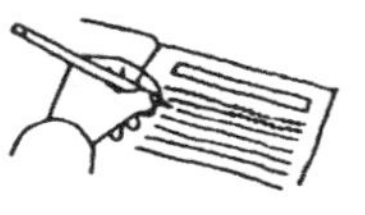

PAPER POSITION

LEFT-HANDED: If the left-handed student writes with the wrist below the writing line, turn paper clockwise so it is slanted to the right, as illustrated.

If the left-handed student writes with a hook, with the wrist above the writing line, turn the paper counter-clockwise so it is slanted to the left, as illustrated. (Similar to right-handed position)

RIGHT-HANDED: If the student is right-handed, turn paper counter-clockwise so it is slanted to the left, as illustrated. 

POSTURE

Rest feet flat on the floor and keep back comfortably straight without slumping. Rest forearms on writing surface. The student  holds workbook or paper with the nonwriting hand so that the writing area is centered in the front of the student.

PRACTICE PAPER

Book A—Use unlined or lined paper together with workbooks.

MATERIALS

The *Getty-Dubay™ Italic Handwriting Series* workbooks, BOOKS A-G, and the INSTRUCTION MANUAL constitute a step-by-step program. Related materials consist of:

1. BLACKLINE MASTERS/WORKSHEETS - half sheets for introduction to, or review of, workbook pages.
2. CLASSROOM WALL CHARTS - basic & cursive italic.
3. DESK STRIPS - basic & cursive italic.

VOCABULARY

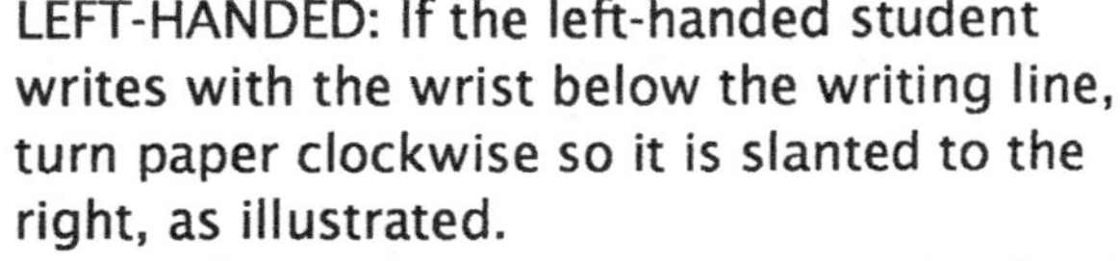

DIRECT INSTRUCTION

Several sessions of direct instruction each week are essential for a successful program. BOOK A – 5 to 10 minute sessions a day are recommended, see INSTRUCTION MANUAL, pp. 18-19

- SHAPE & STROKE SEQUENCE – teach basic italic in letter family groups, or according to the reading program in grade 1.
- SLOPE – encourage a consistent letter slope. Vertical letters (0° slope) may be the easiest to teach to beginning writers.
- SIZE – At first, allow students to write letters any size they wish on unlined paper, then introduce the workbook. A recommended progression through this book is one letter (lowercase and/or capital) per week.

SPACING

When young students are writing words, at first have them leave a space about the width of their two small fingers between words. As they become more proficient, they can leave less space.

ASSESSMENT

The *Getty-Dubay™ Italic Handwriting Series* provides a self-assessment process, LOOK, PLAN, PRACTICE, to enable the student to monitor progress. LOOK, step 1 of this process begins on some of the student pages in BOOK A. Assessment is the key to improving handwriting; in this book we introduce the first of three steps in the LOOK, PLAN, PRACTICE self-assessment process. The students look at their own writing and answer any questions on the page. The pencil indicates the student is to make a written response, generally by circling "yes" or "no". The teacher may encourage students to award themselves a star or a smiling face at the top of the page when they notice self-improvement.

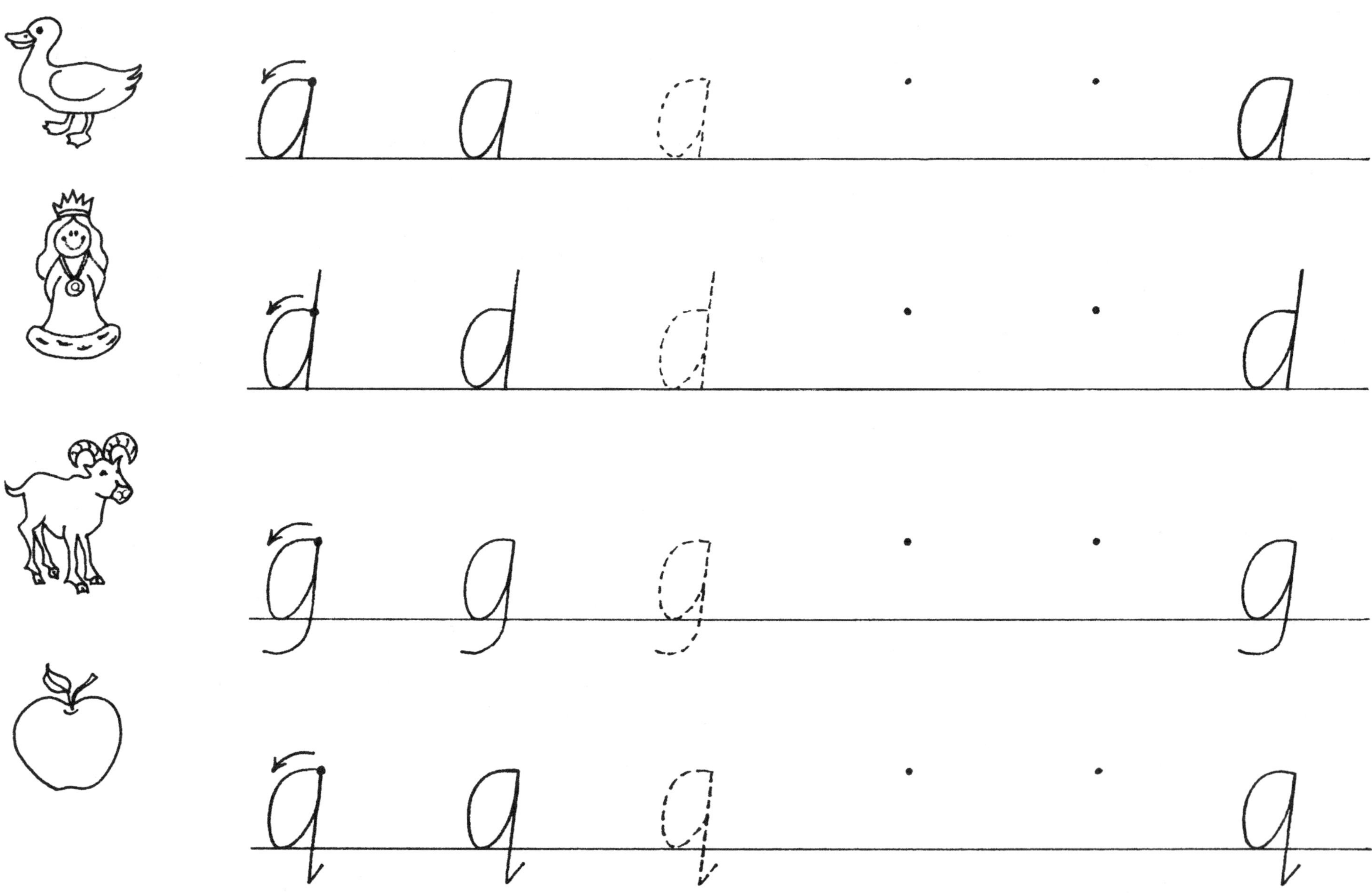

Ask the student to draw a line from the picture to the letter
that stands for the correct beginning sound.

Getty-Dubay™ Italic Handwriting Series · Book A · © 2012 Getty-Dubay

INTRODUCTION

This is the first of seven workbooks providing instruction in basic italic handwriting. It is designed for the beginning student of handwriting and is recommended for preschool, kindergarten and/or early first grade (5 to 7 years of age).

The twenty-six lowercase letters and the twenty-six capitals are introduced one letter per page. Letters are arranged in the order of lowercase families, which group letters with similar strokes together and progress from simple to more complex forms. The matching capital letter occurs on the reverse of each lowercase page allowing introduction of both lowercase and capital together if preferred.

Each page is designed for the student to trace the models provided, write letters at the given dots, and to write a "best" letter in the empty box on each alphabet page. The standard writing tool is the pencil although other writing instruments such as the fiber tip pen may be used. When students are ready, they should trace the word describing the illustration on each letter page, following the dots and arrows.

It is essential that the instructor provide an understanding of the dot and the arrow to assist the writer in completing the pages successfully. The self-assessment method used in the *Getty-Dubay™ Italic Handwriting Series* enables students to monitor their individual progress. Step 1, LOOK, of the three-step LOOK, PLAN, PRACTICE format, is incorporated on 21 of the student pages. Students are asked to "LOOK" at their writing and affirm what is best. On the 21 pages with "LOOK" questions, students should circle their chosen answers. See INSTRUCTION MANUAL, PP. 13, 18 & 19.

The *Getty-Dubay™ Italic Handwriting Series* INSTRUCTION MANUAL is to be used in conjunction with this workbook. Explanations and in-depth descriptions of lowercase letters, capitals, joins, and numerals are presented in the manual, emphasizing shape, strokes, size, slope and spacing of the letters. Also included in the manual are: a rationale for italic handwriting, techniques for teaching and assessing handwriting, sequence of skills, handwriting activities, and a brief history of our alphabet.

BOOK B, basic italic, follows this workbook and is designed for the beginning reader. In the third book, BOOK C, basic italic letterforms are reinforced and cursive italic is introduced. BOOKS D, E, F, and G provide a complete basic italic and cursive italic handwriting program. BOOKS B, C, and/or D may also be suitable for the person learning English as a second language.

The format of this book was chosen to accommodate both the left- and right-handed writer. When open, the book fits easily on a small desk, and the writer is not encumbered with an additional page to the left or right. From day one, use a Getty-Dubay™ basic italic desk strip as a reminder. Blackline masters are designed for supplementary practice and are available for each workbook in the series. See www.handwritingsuccess.com for these supplementary materials.

You can guide children toward the challenge and delight in the writing process by reading to them, modeling handwriting, providing writing materials, and especially by building enthusiasm for the letters of our alphabet and for the written word.

·abcdefghijklmnopqrstuvwxyz·

iii

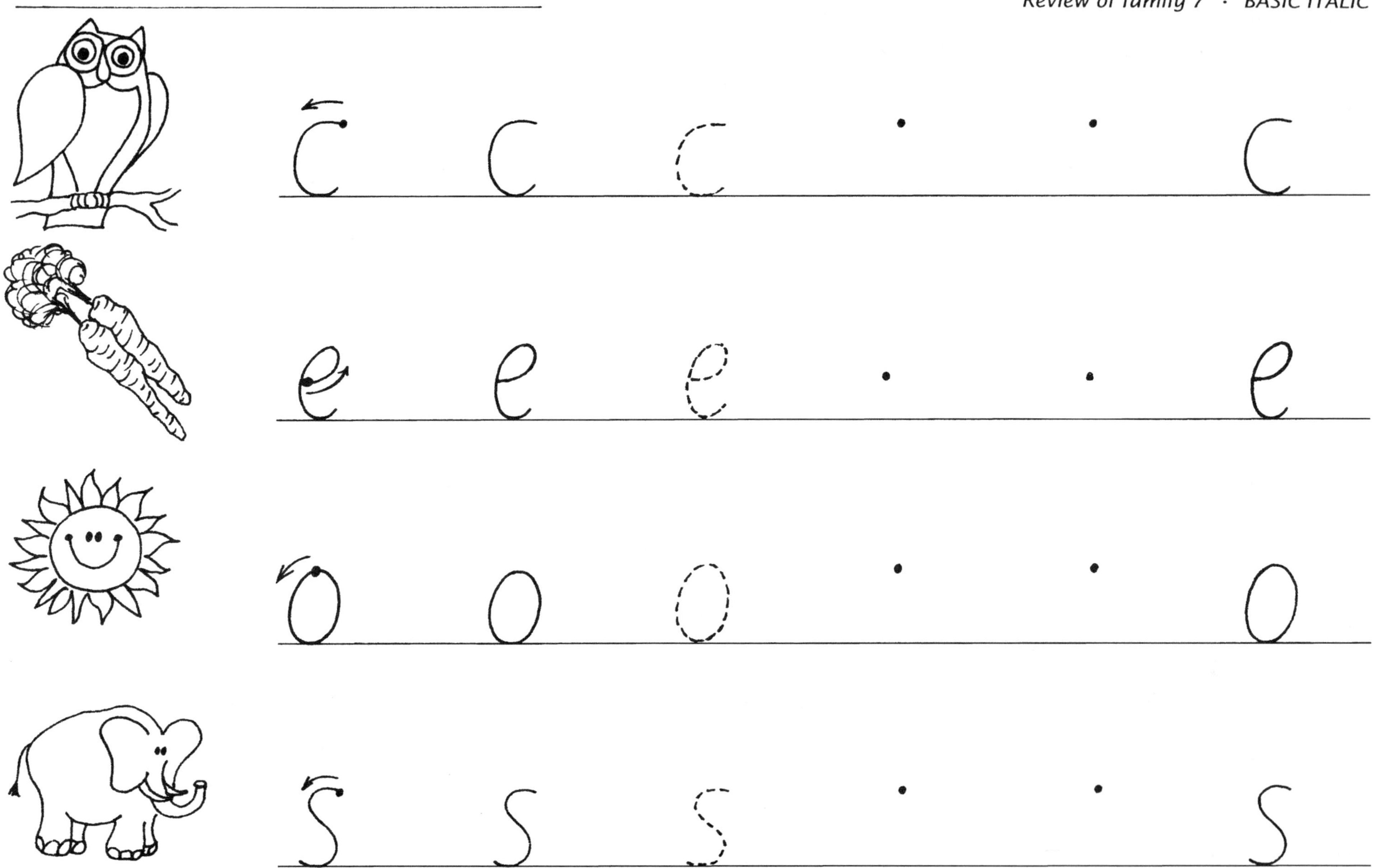

Ask the student to draw a line from the picture to the letter
that stands for the correct beginning sound.

CONTENTS

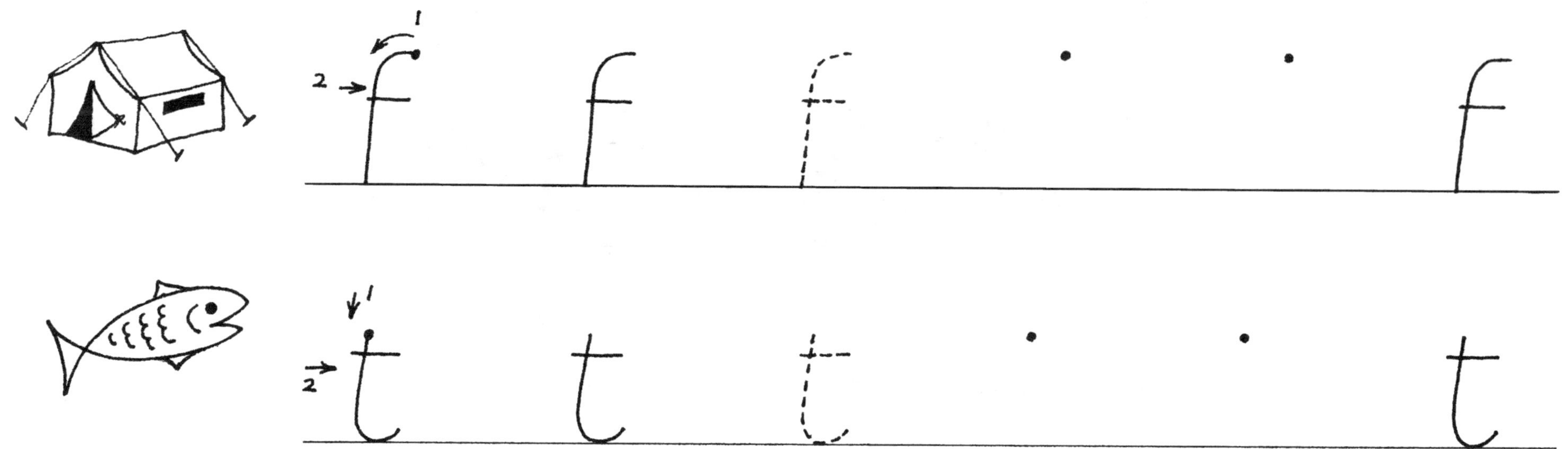

TOP TWO LINES: Ask the student to draw a line from the picture to the letter that stands for the correct beginning sound.

BOTTOM FOUR SQUARES: Ask the student to circle the letter that stands for the beginning sound of the picture.

by
Barbara Getty & Inga Dubay

GETTY-DUBAY™ ITALIC HANDWRITING SERIES

BOOK A ▪ Basic Italic
14 mm body height

BOOK B ▪ Basic Italic
11 mm body height, 9 mm

BOOK C ▪ Basic & Cursive Italic
9 mm, 6 mm body height   Introduction to Cursive Italic

BOOK D ▪ Basic & Cursive Italic
6 mm, 5 mm body height

BOOK E ▪ Basic & Cursive Italic
6 mm, 5 mm, 4 mm body height

BOOK F ▪ Basic & Cursive Italic
6 mm, 5 mm, 4 mm body height

BOOK G ▪ Basic & Cursive Italic
5 mm, 4 mm body height

INSTRUCTION MANUAL

BOOK A ▪ INTERNATIONAL EDITION

Copyright 2012 by Barbara M. Getty and Inga S. Dubay
ISBN 978-0-9827762-7-8

FOURTH EDITION
Copyright 2012 by Barbara M. Getty and Inga S. Dubay
THIRD EDITION
Copyright 1999 by Barbara M. Getty and Inga S. Dubay
SECOND EDITION
Copyright 1986 by Barbara M. Getty and Inga S. Dubay
REVISED EDITION
Copyright 1980 by Barbara M. Getty and Inga S. Dubay
FIRST EDITION
Copyright 1979 by Barbara M. Getty and Inga S. Dubay

All rights reserved. This text may not be reproduced in whole or in part without the express written permission of the copyright holder.

Published by Handwriting Success, LLC,
Portland, Oregon USA

www.handwritingsuccess.com

Printed at various locations around the world by IngramSpark.

Cover Design: Sinda Markham
Front cover picture: Flowers of the sunflower family in the Ochoco National Forest, Oregon, USA
Back cover pictures: Columbine flower, Golden-mantled squirrel

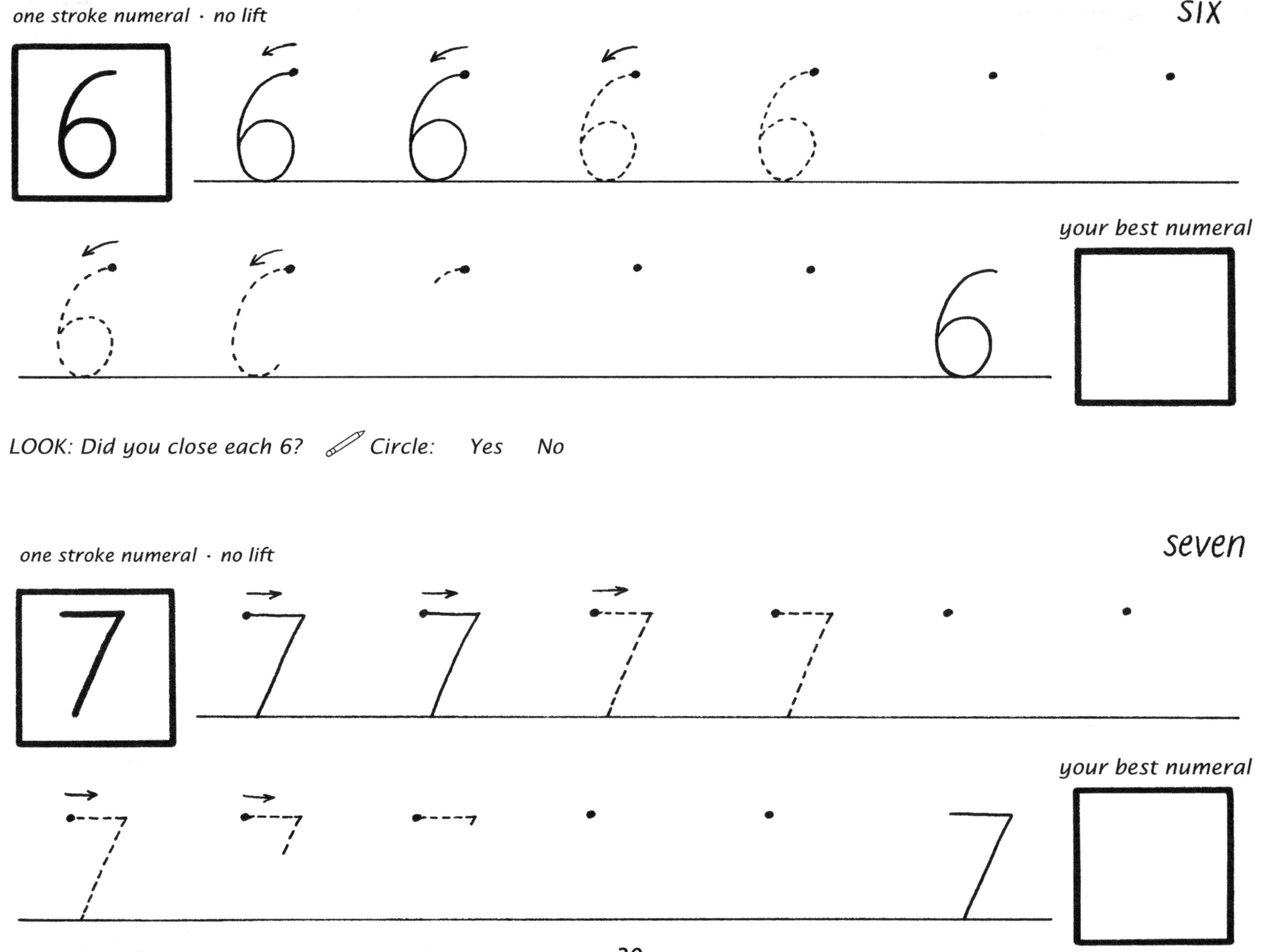
one stroke numeral · no lift
6
your best numeral
LOOK: Did you close each 6?   Circle: Yes   No
one stroke numeral · no lift
seven
7
your best numeral

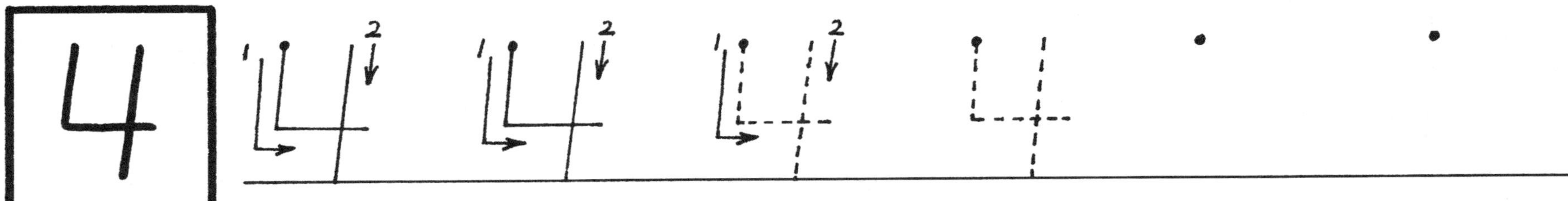

your best numeral

five

your best numeral

eight

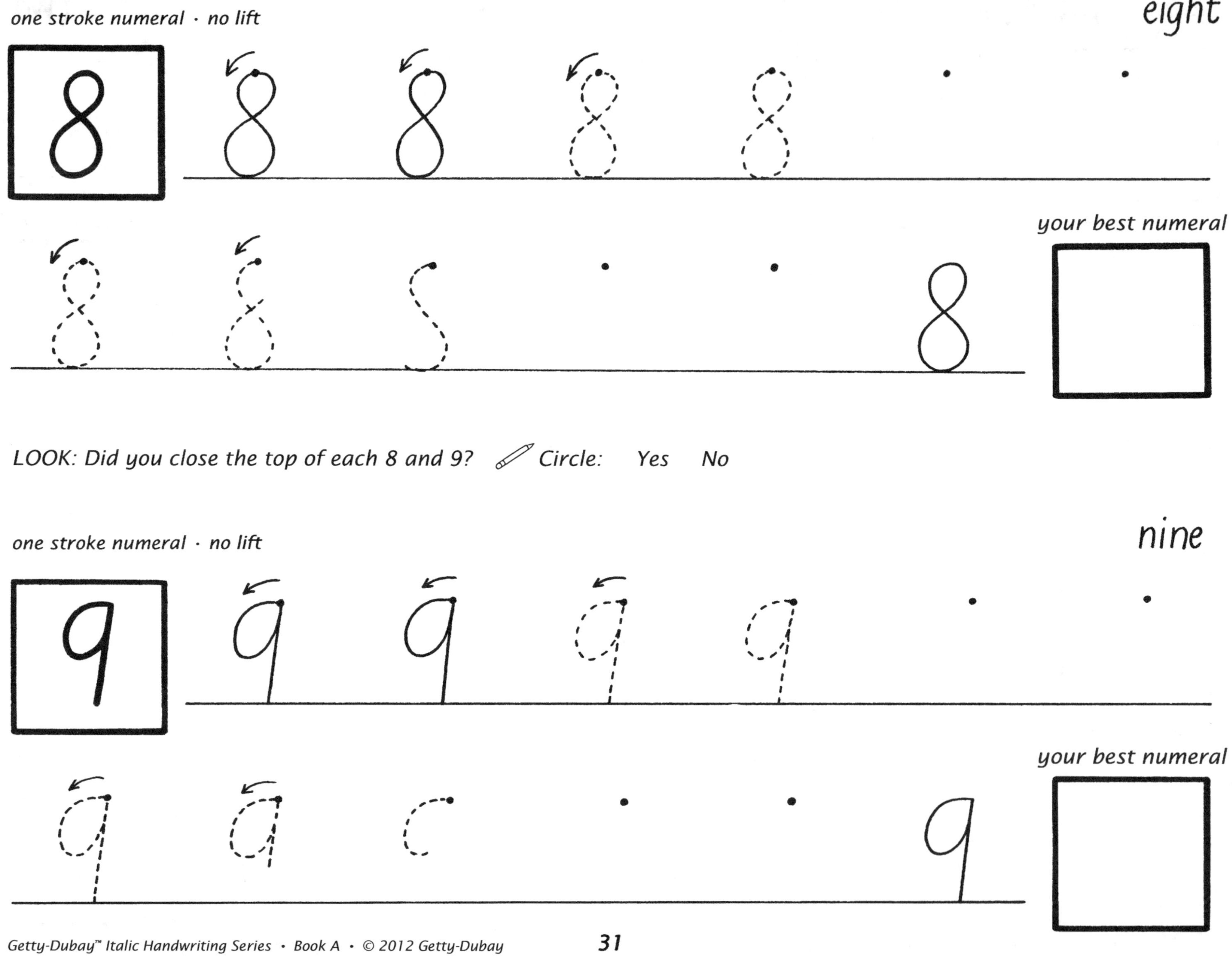

your best numeral

LOOK: Did you close the top of each 8 and 9?   Circle: Yes   No

one stroke numeral · no lift

nine

your best numeral

one stroke numeral · no lift

your best numeral

LOOK: Is the curve of your 2 shaped like half a heart?   Circle: Yes   No

one stroke numeral · no lift

your best numeral

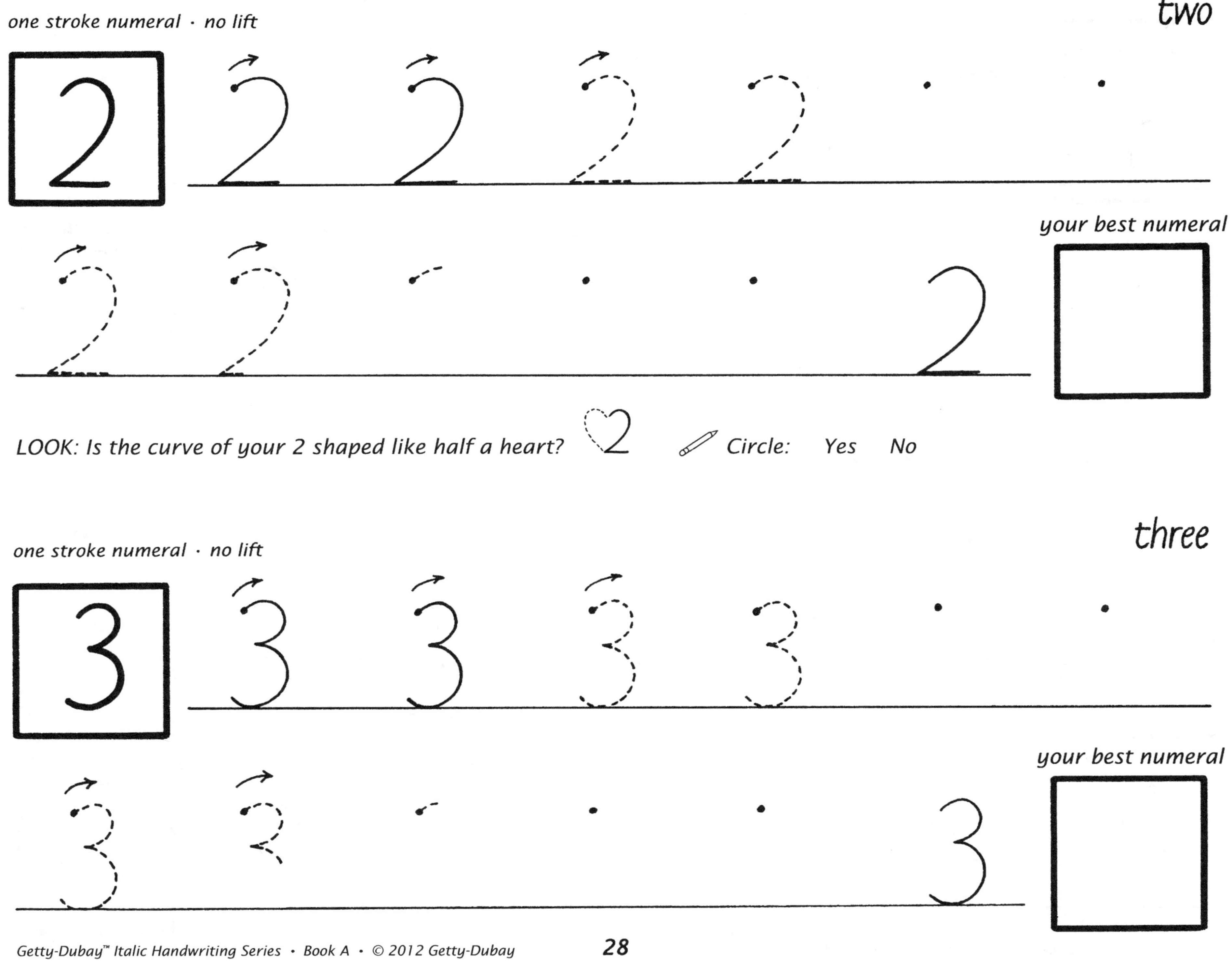

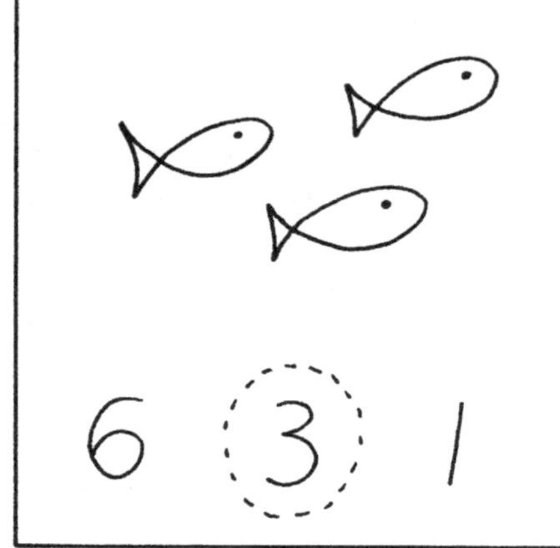

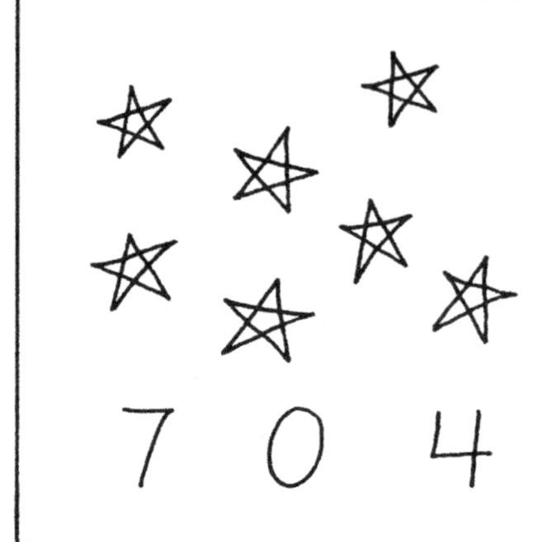

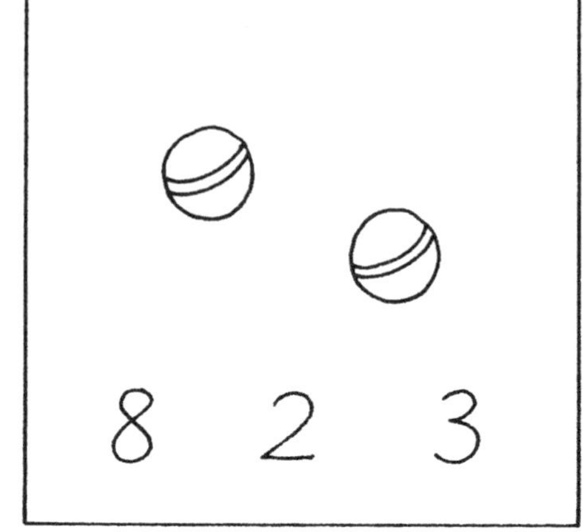

*Ask the student to circle the numeral
that stands for the number of objects in the box.*

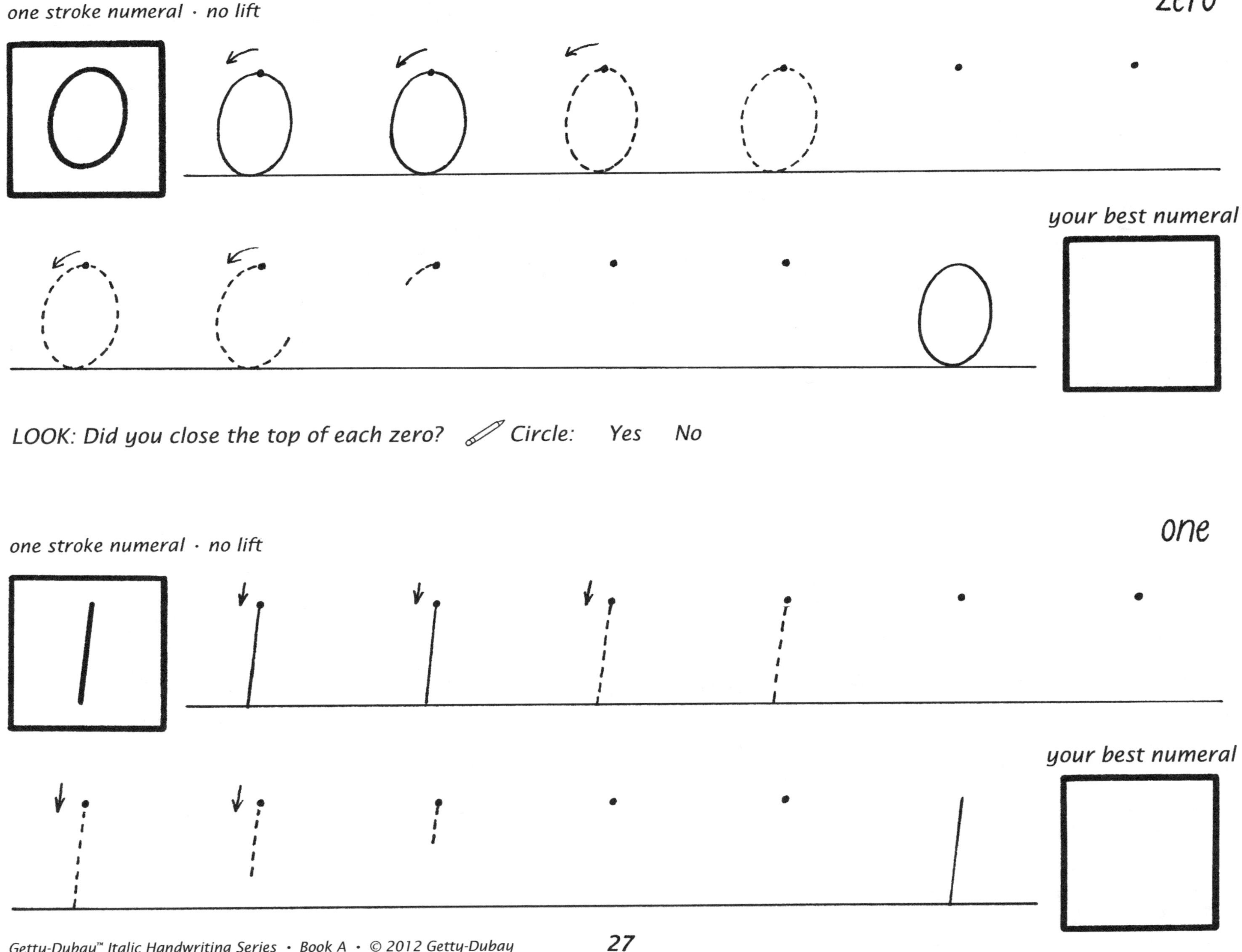

zero
one stroke numeral · no lift
your best numeral
LOOK: Did you close the top of each zero? Circle: Yes   No
one
one stroke numeral · no lift
your best numeral

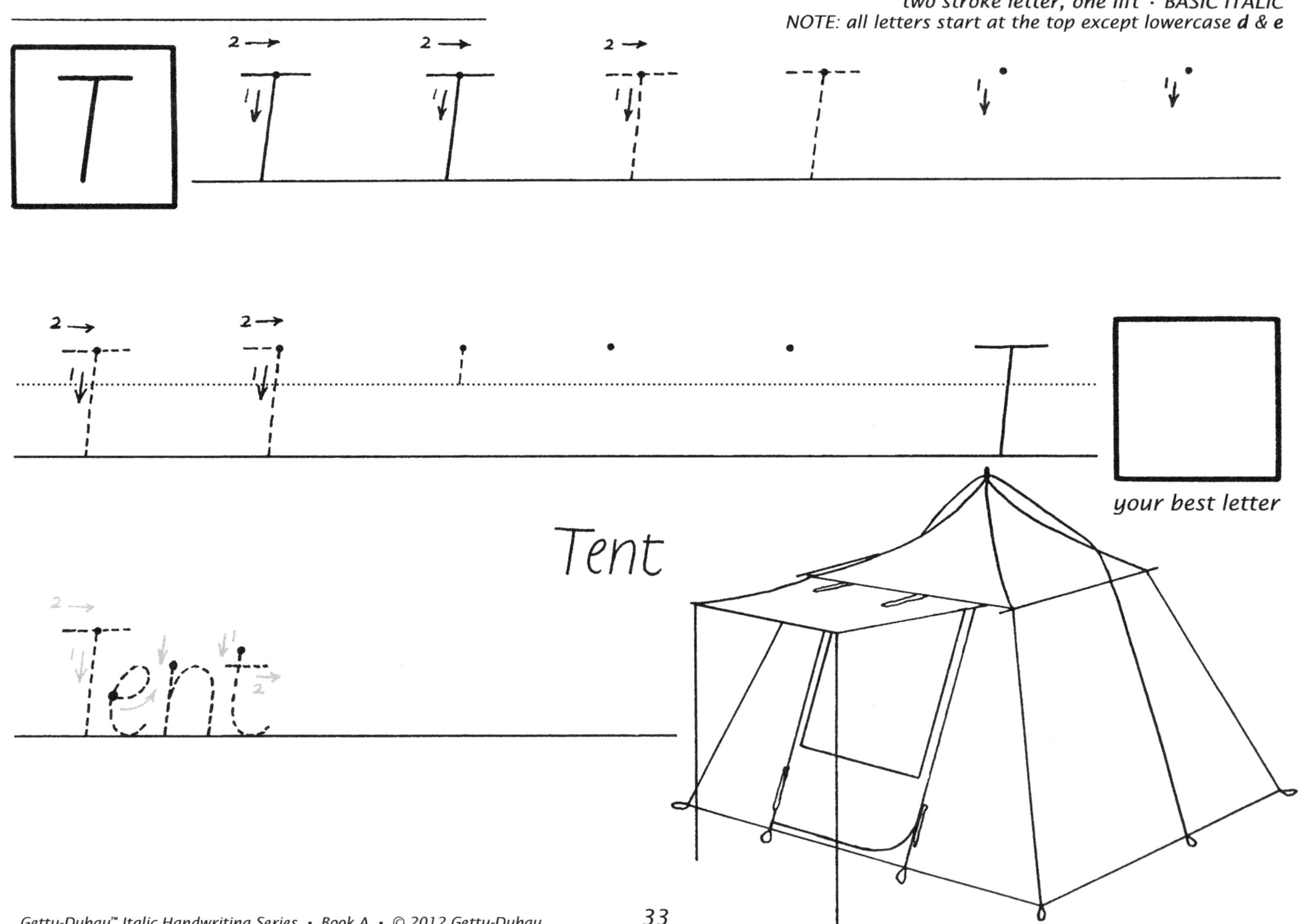

T
2
1
your best letter
Tent
Tent

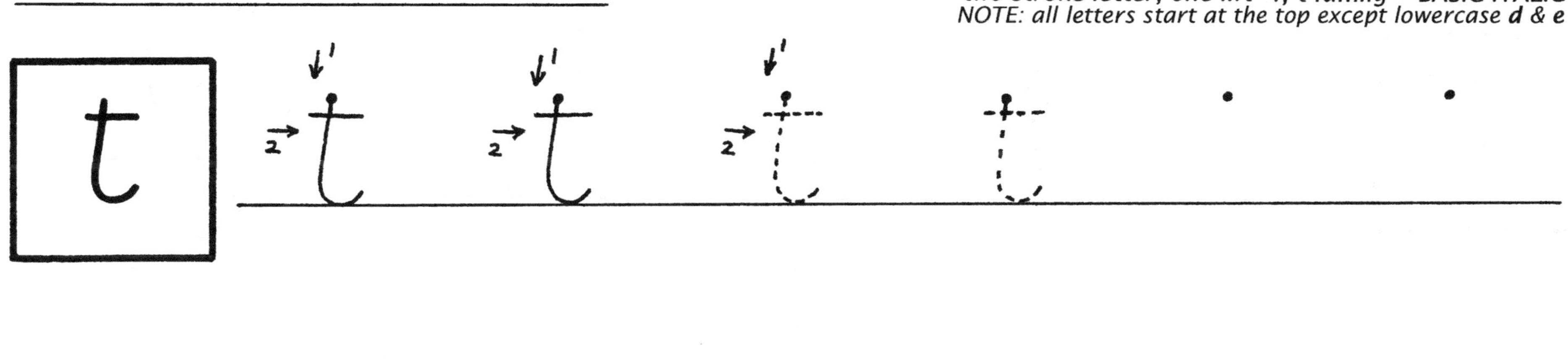

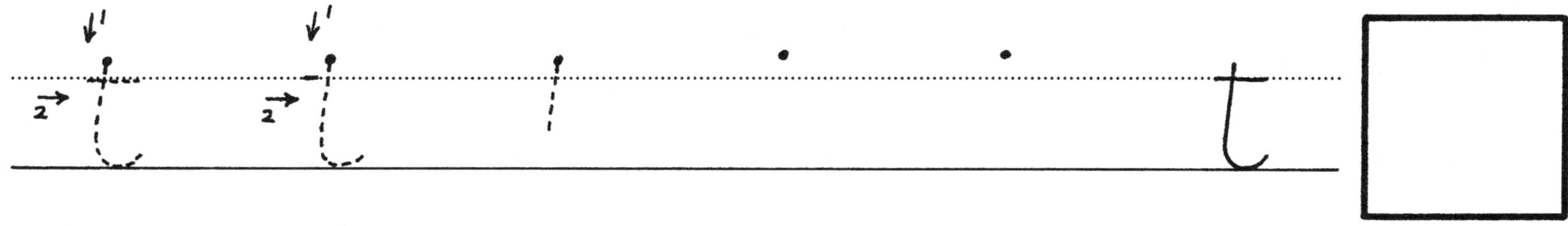

your best letter

turkey

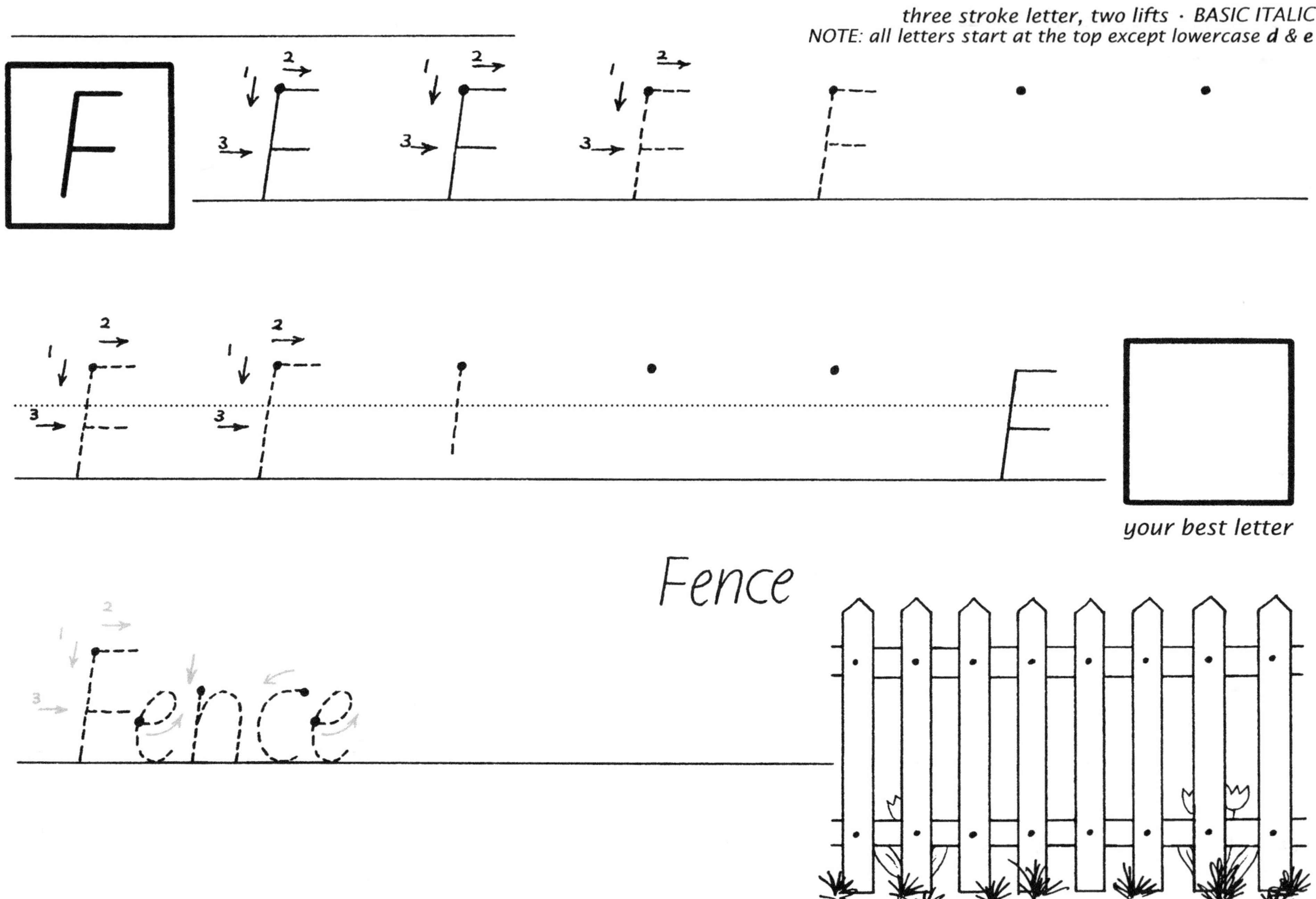

your best letter
Fence

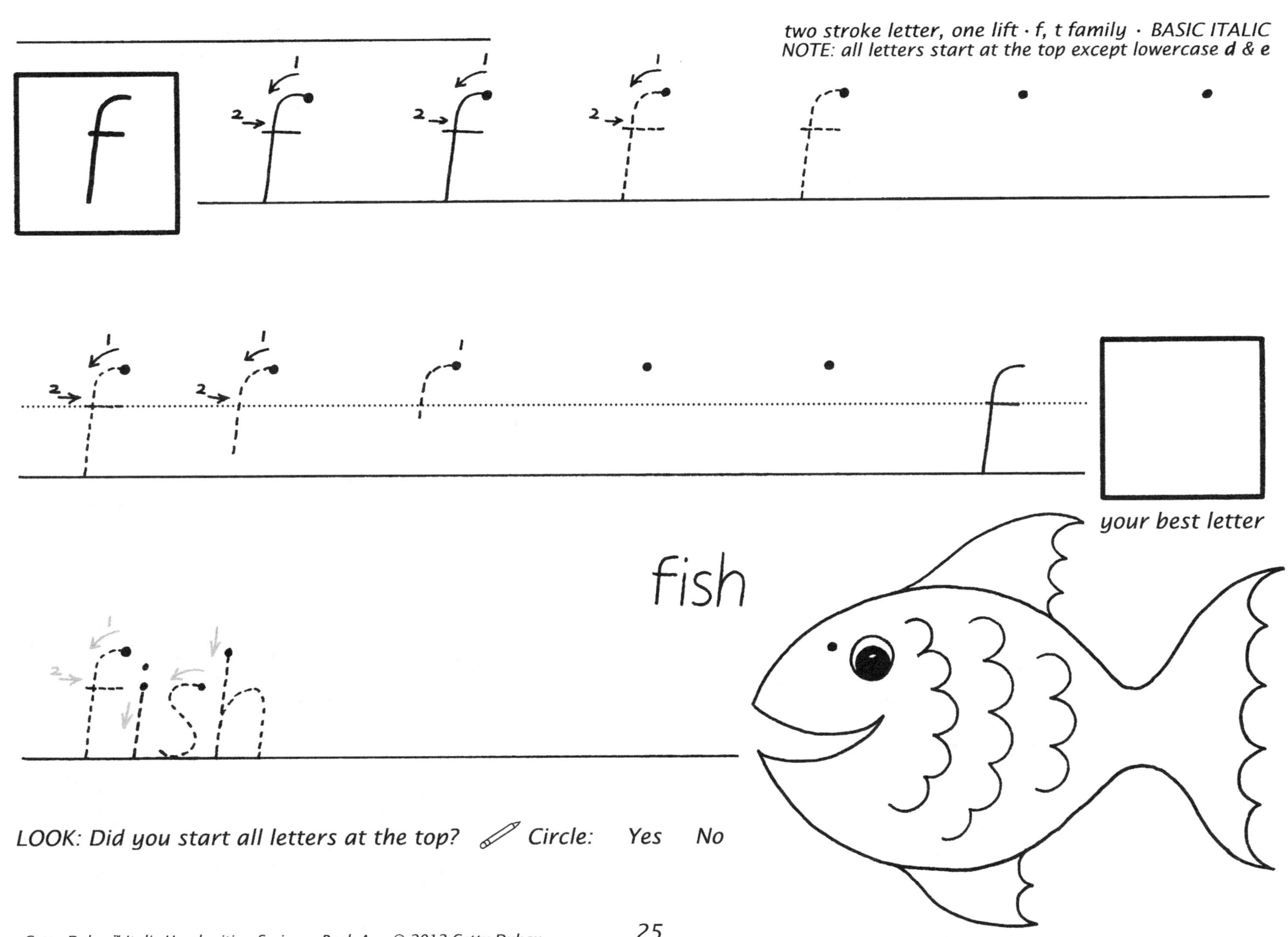

two stroke letter, one lift · f, t family · BASIC ITALIC
NOTE: all letters start at the top except lowercase d & e
f
your best letter
fish
fish
LOOK: Did you start all letters at the top?   Circle: Yes   No

S

your best letter

Sailboat

S

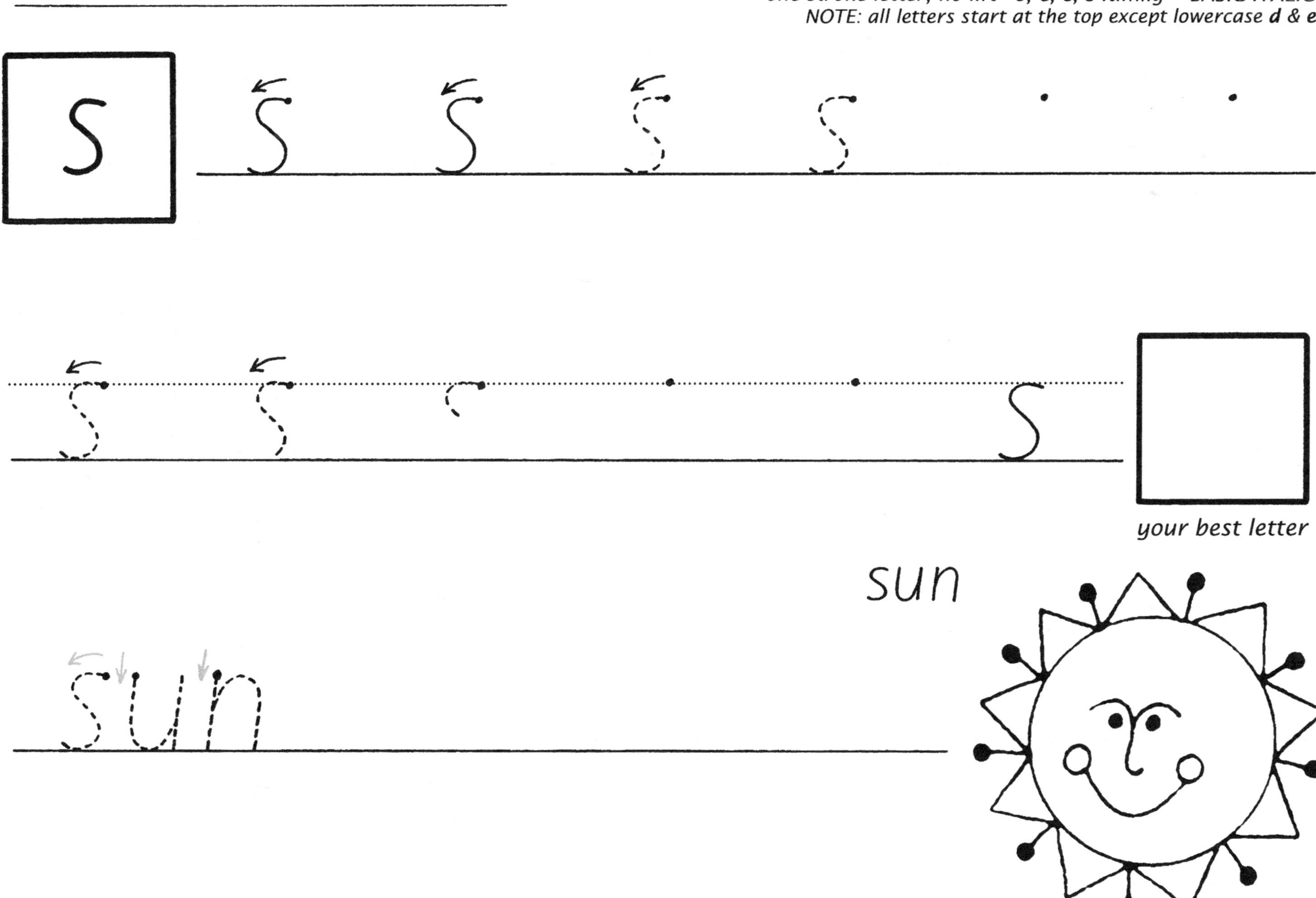

your best letter

sun

your best letter

Cow

LOOK: Did you trace each letter before writing your own?

Circle: Yes   No

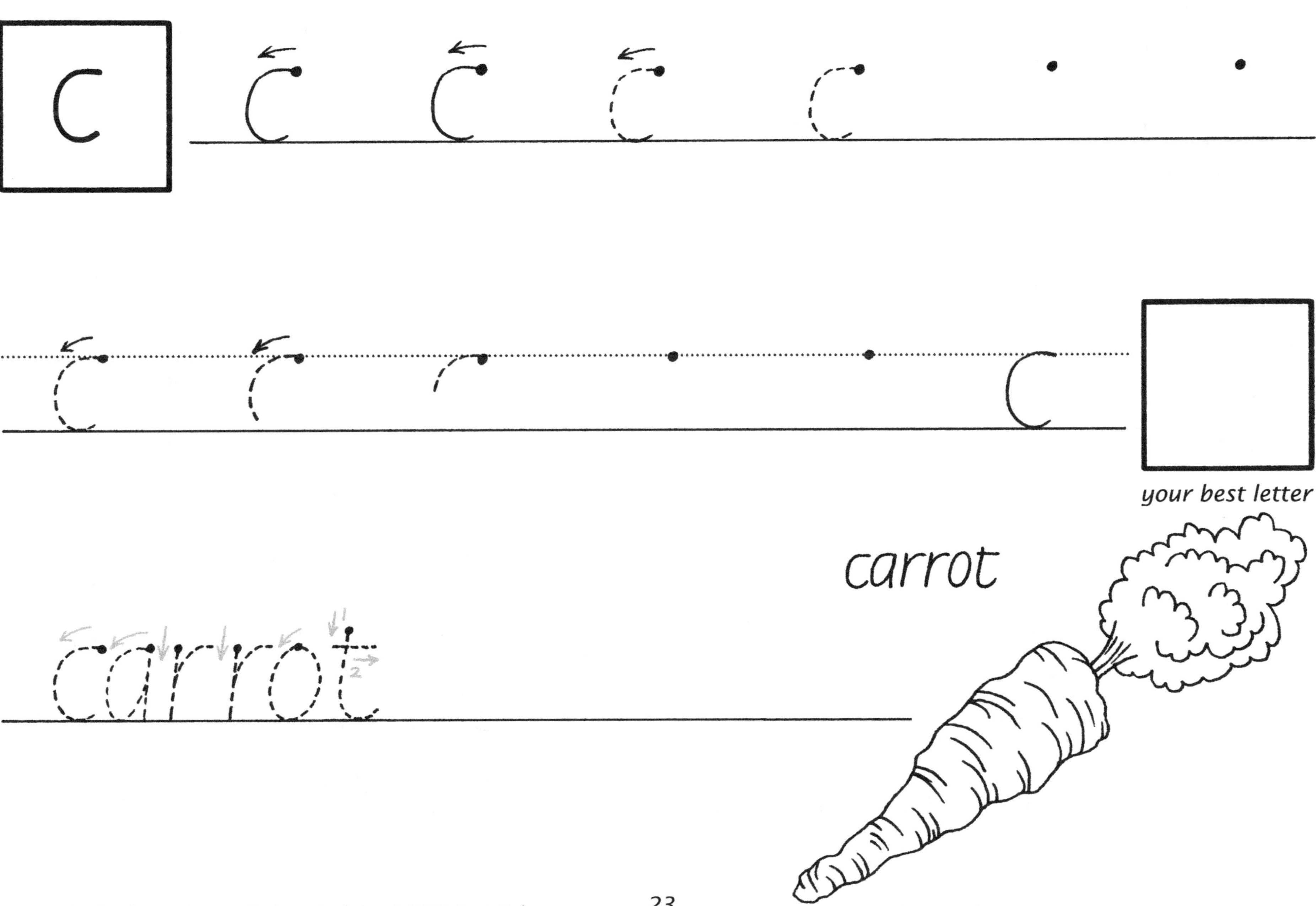

your best letter

carrot

carrot

23

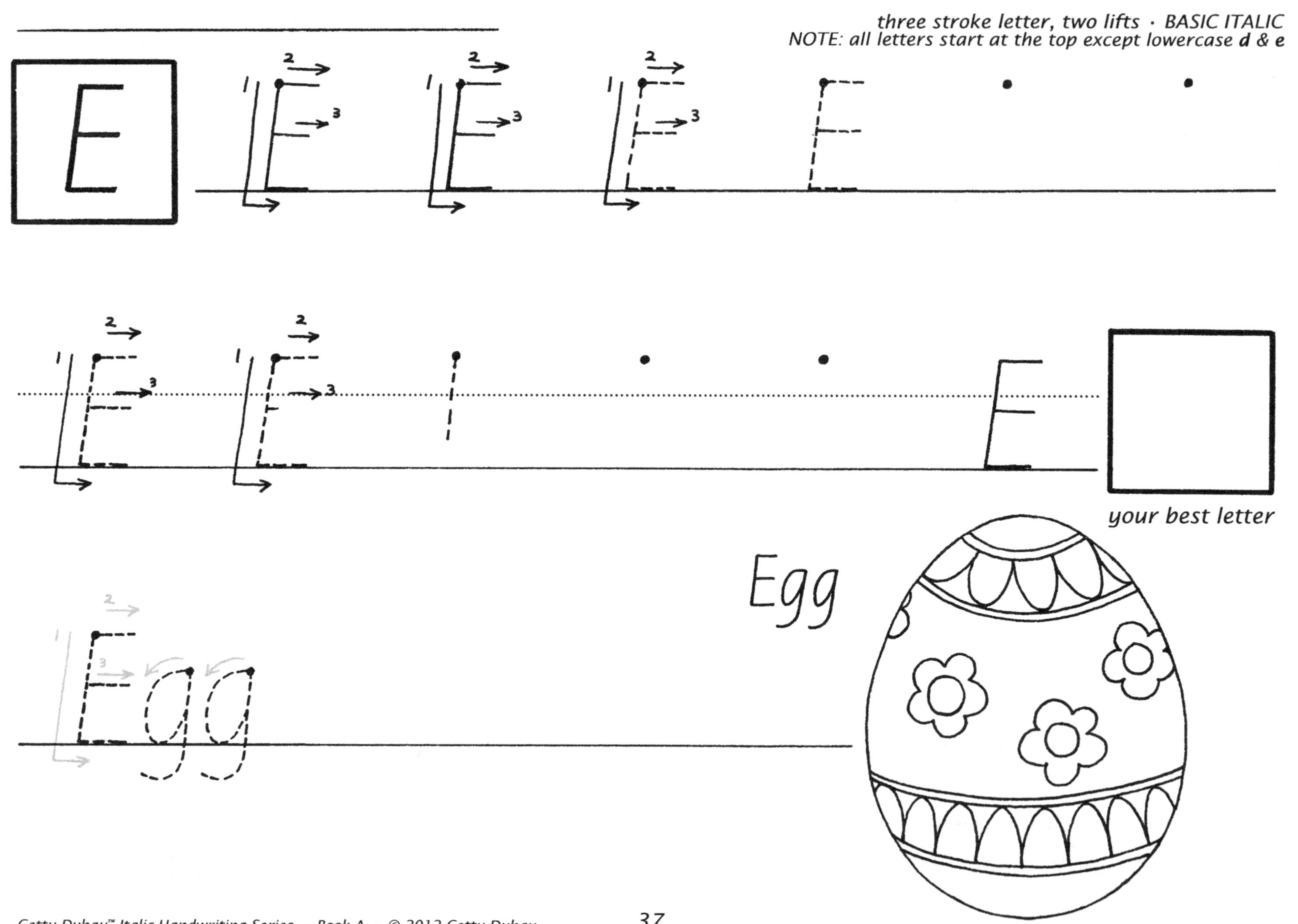
your best letter
Egg

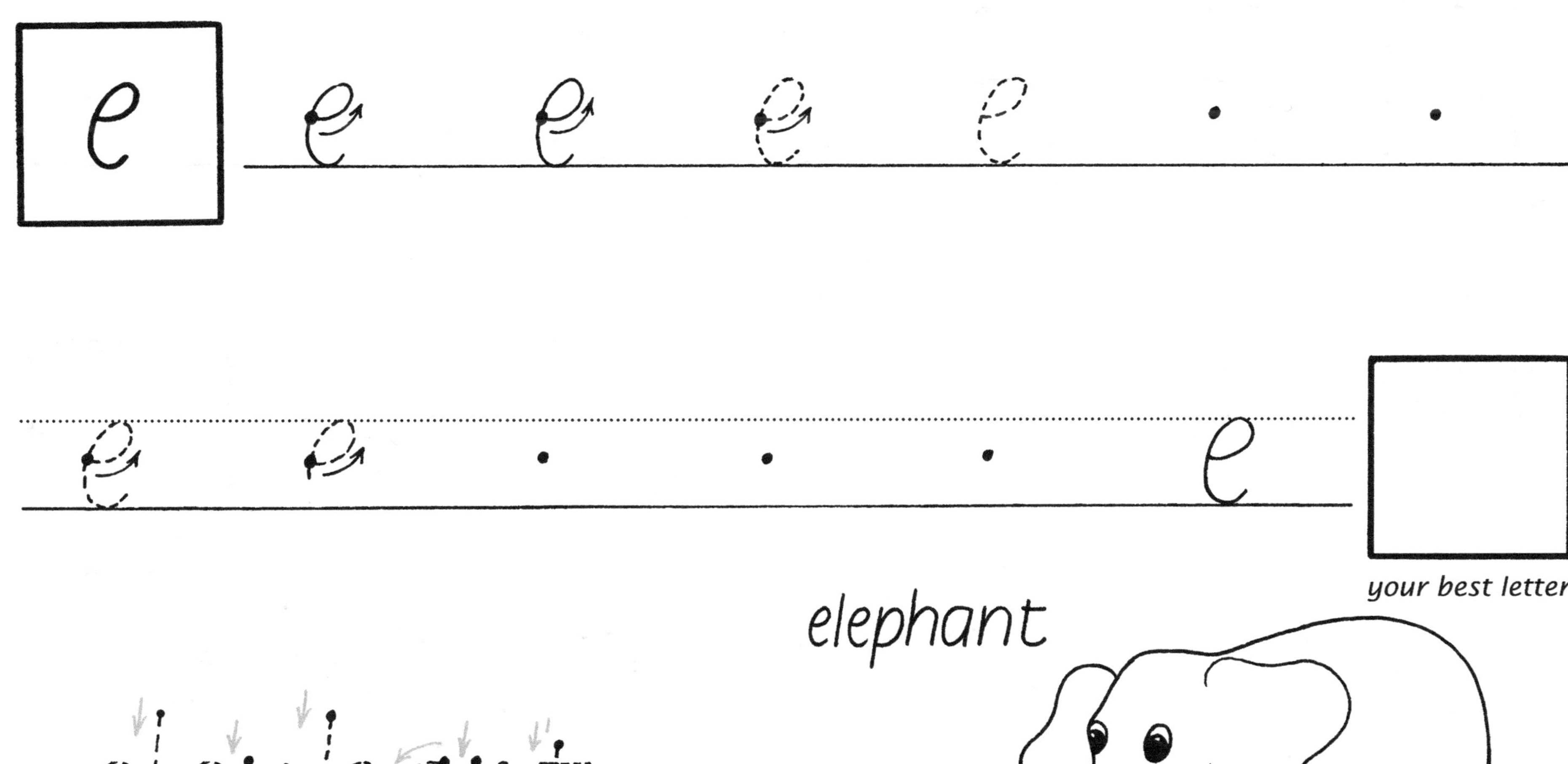

your best letter

elephant

LOOK: Did you trace each **e** before writing your own?

Circle: Yes   No

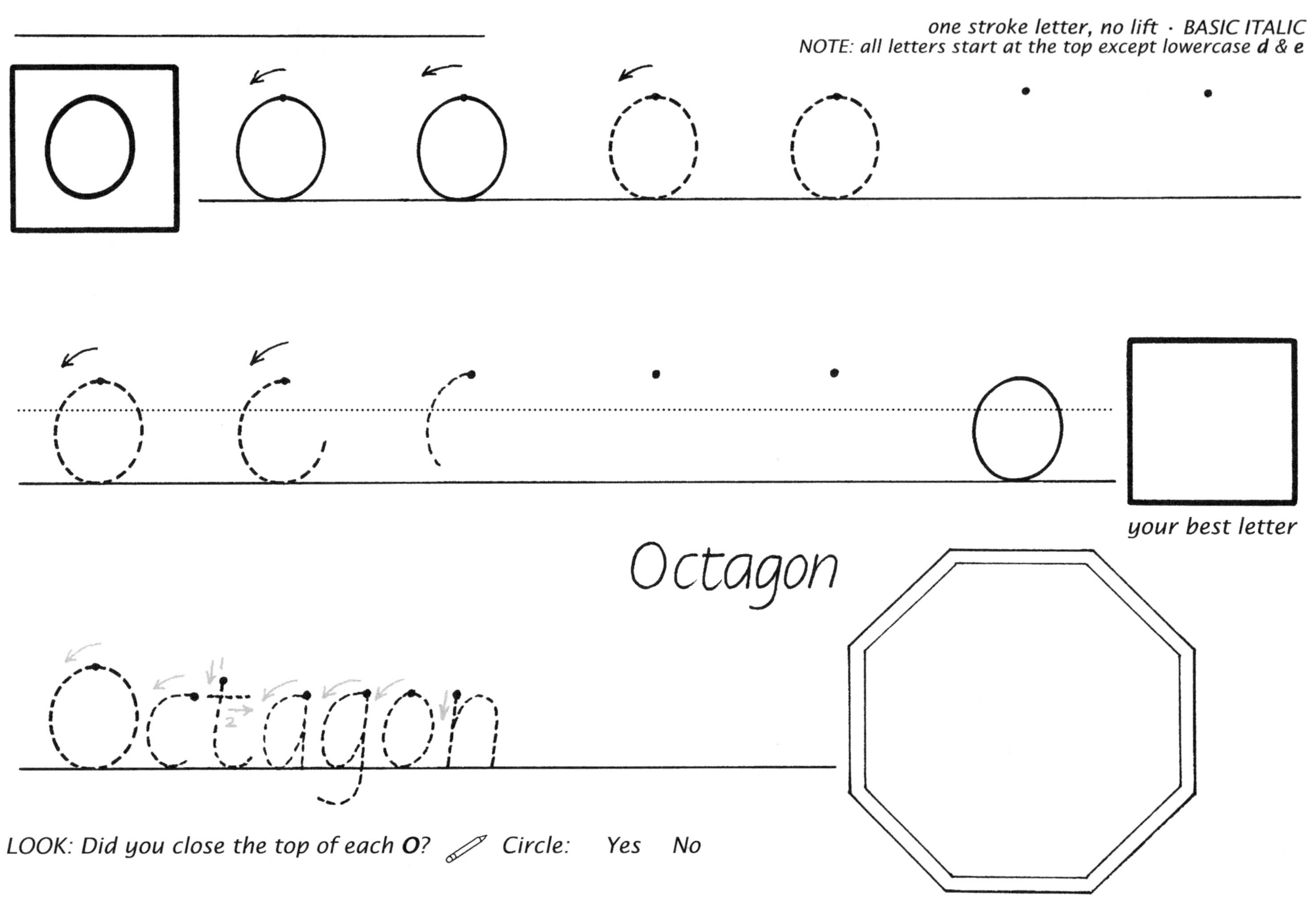

one stroke letter, no lift · BASIC ITALIC
NOTE: all letters start at the top except lowercase d & e
your best letter
Octagon
LOOK: Did you close the top of each O? Circle: Yes   No

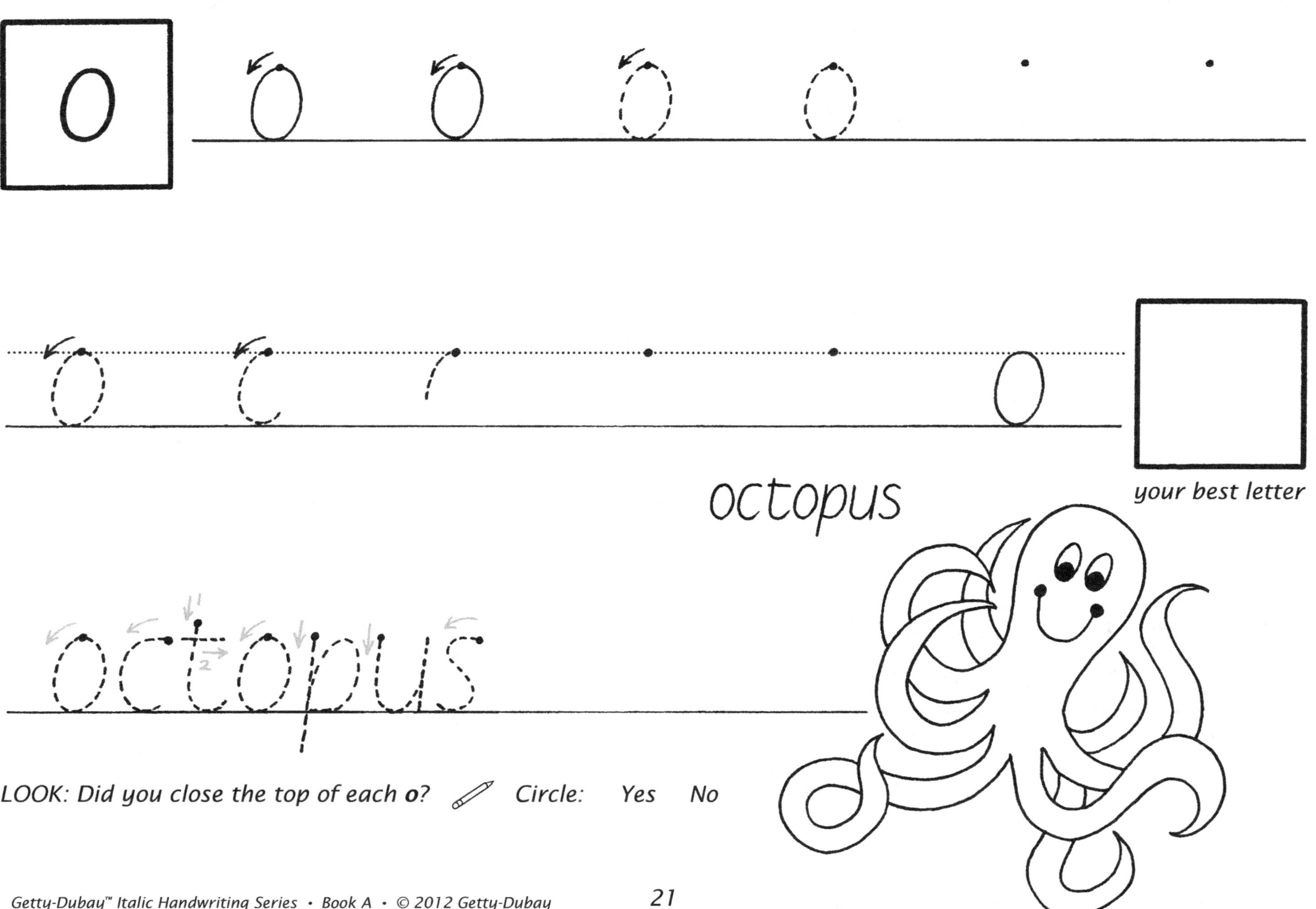

octopus

your best letter

LOOK: Did you close the top of each **o**?   Circle: Yes   No

two stroke letter, one lift · BASIC ITALIC
NOTE: all letters start at the top except lowercase d & e
P
your best letter
Peacock

your best letter

parrot

Balloons

your best letter

your best letter

butterfly

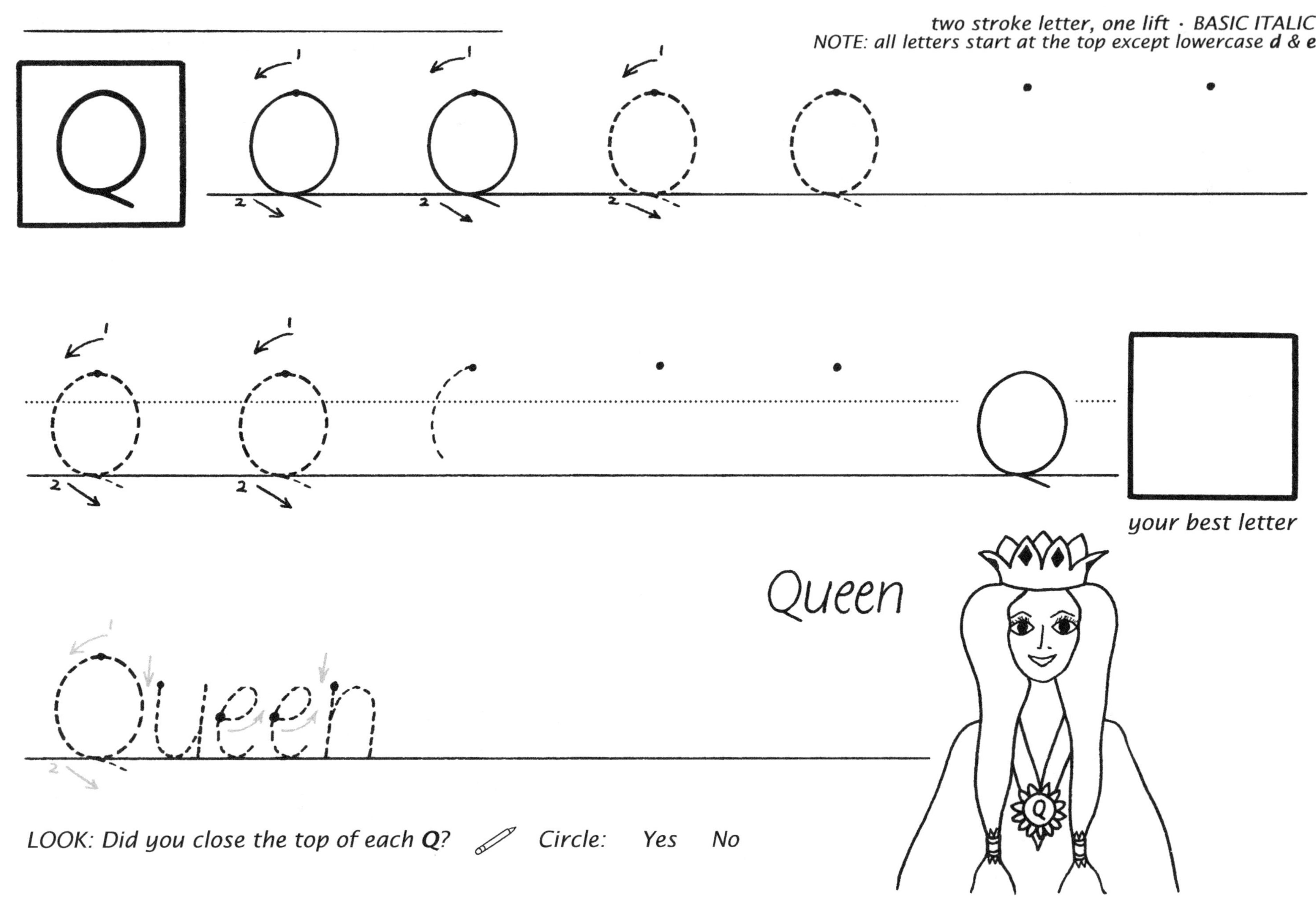
your best letter
Queen
LOOK: Did you close the top of each Q? Circle: Yes No

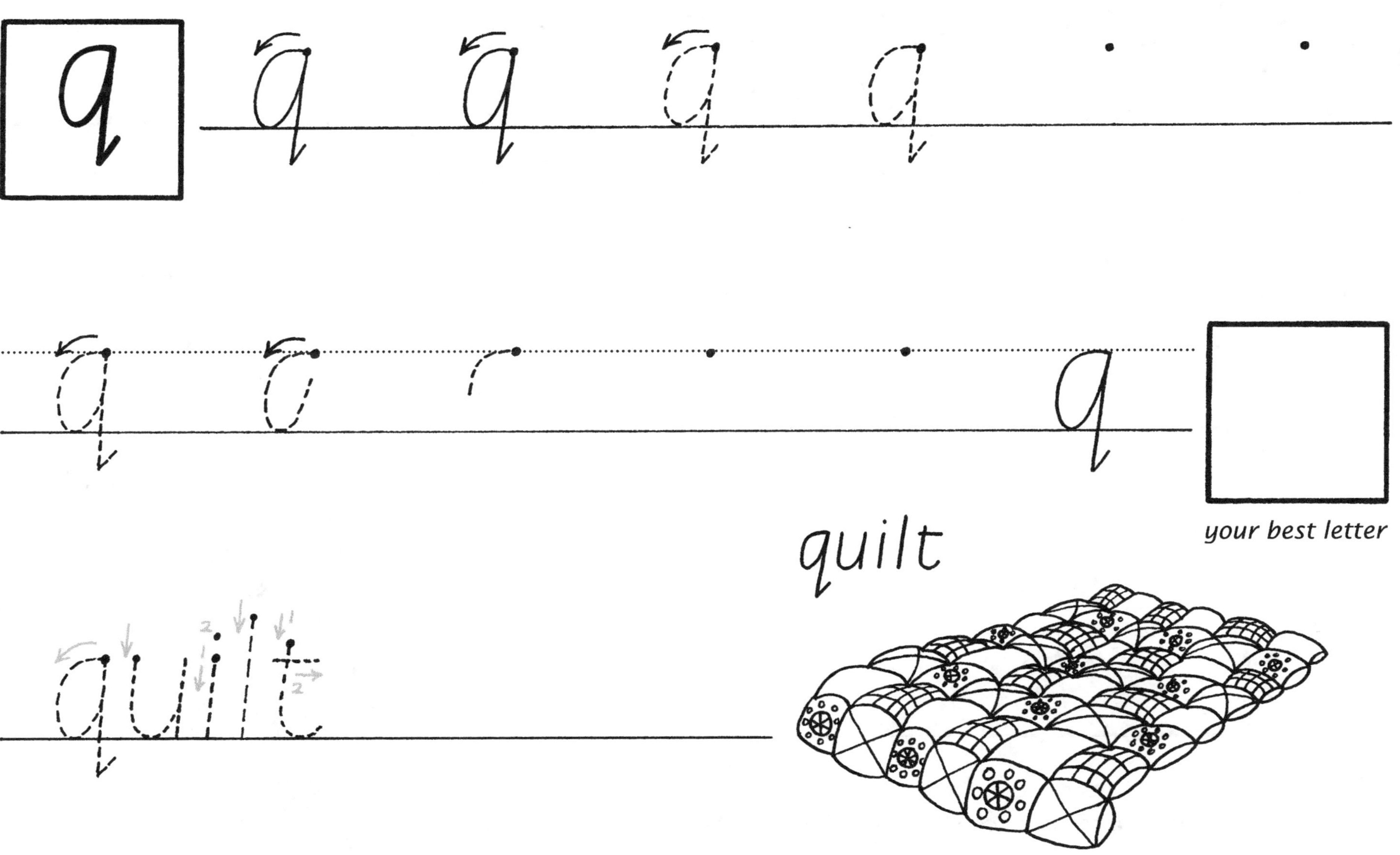

your best letter

quilt

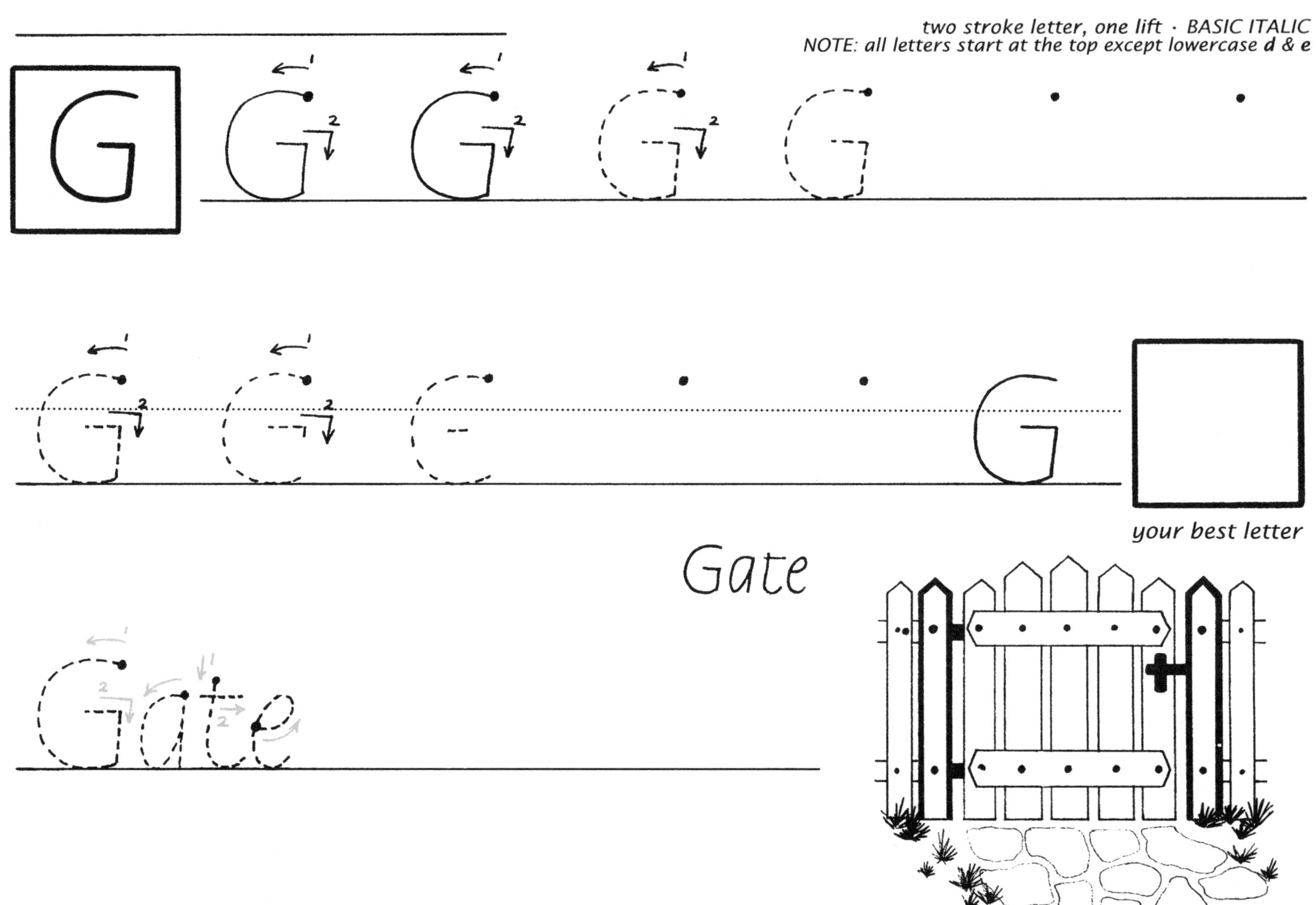

your best letter

Gate

42

your best letter

goat

LOOK: Did you trace each letter before writing your own?   Circle: Yes   No

two stroke letter, one lift · BASIC ITALIC
NOTE: all letters start at the top except lowercase d & e
2
2
2
1
1
1
2
2
1
1
your best letter
Dinosaur
Dinosaur

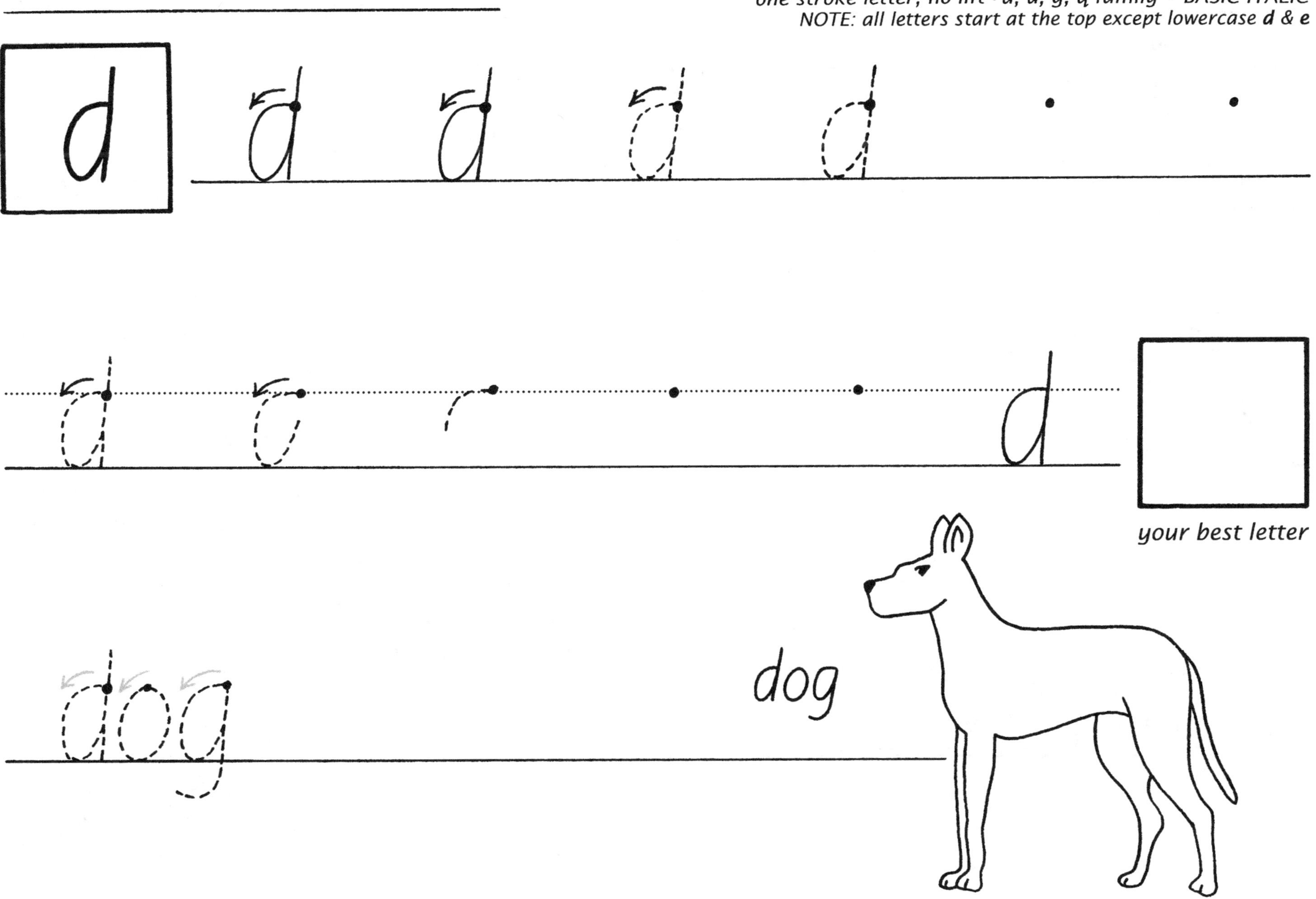

your best letter

dog

your best letter

Alligator

LOOK: Did you start all letters at the top? Circle: Yes   No

your best letter

apple

LOOK: Did you close each **a** at the top?   Circle: Yes   No

Y

your best letter

Yo-yo

45

your best letter

yarn

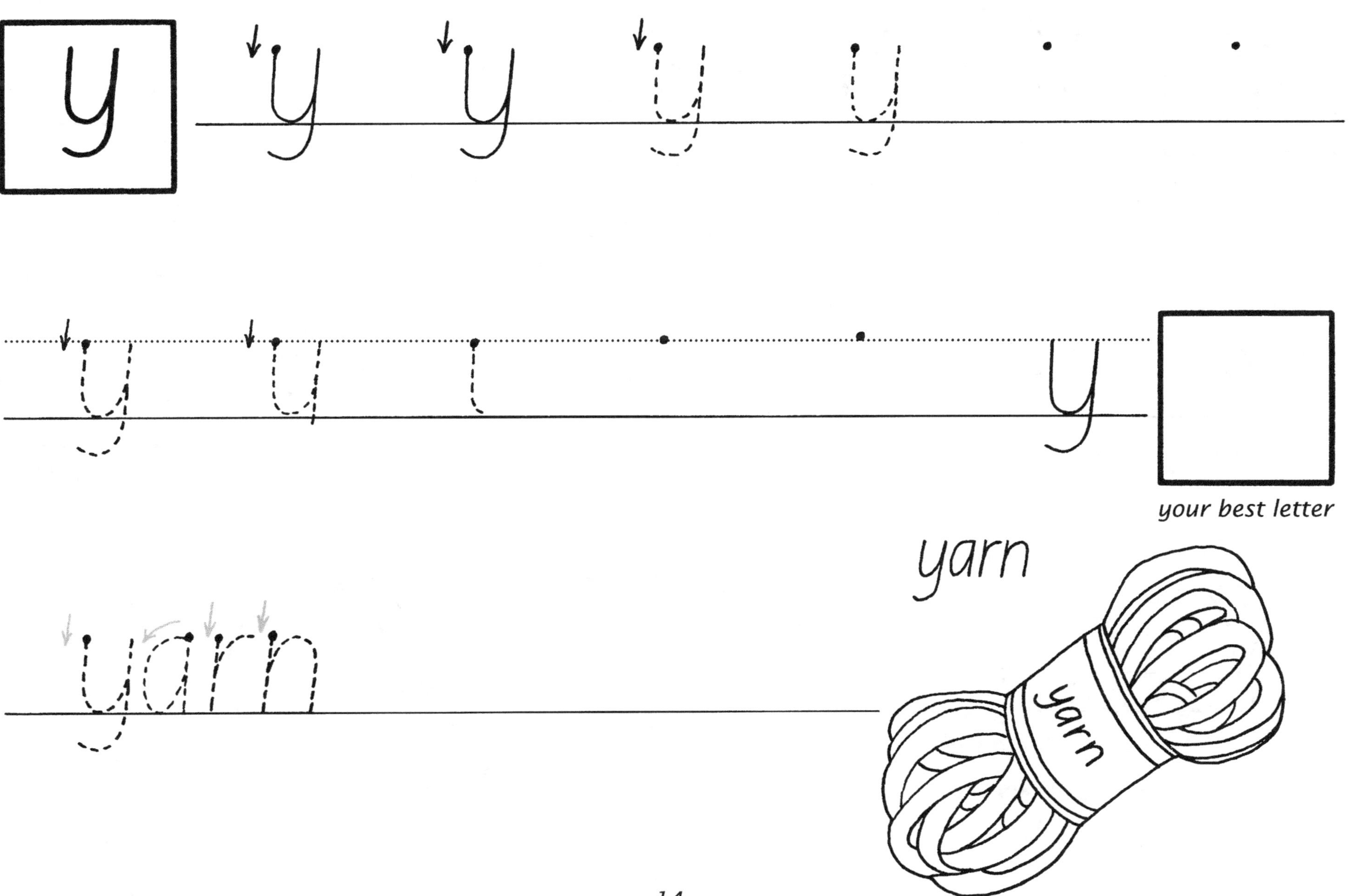

14

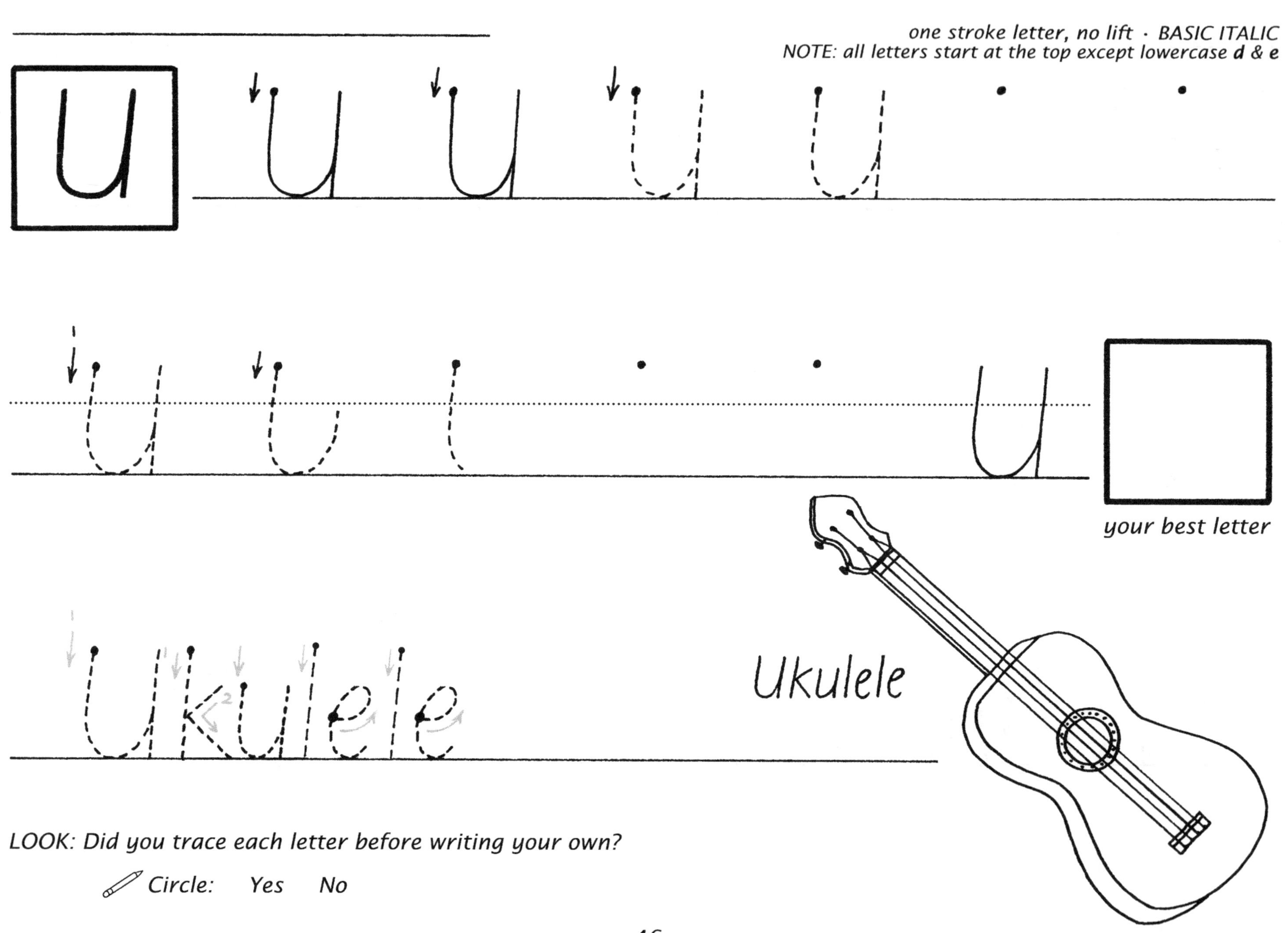

LOOK: Did you trace each letter before writing your own?

Circle: Yes   No

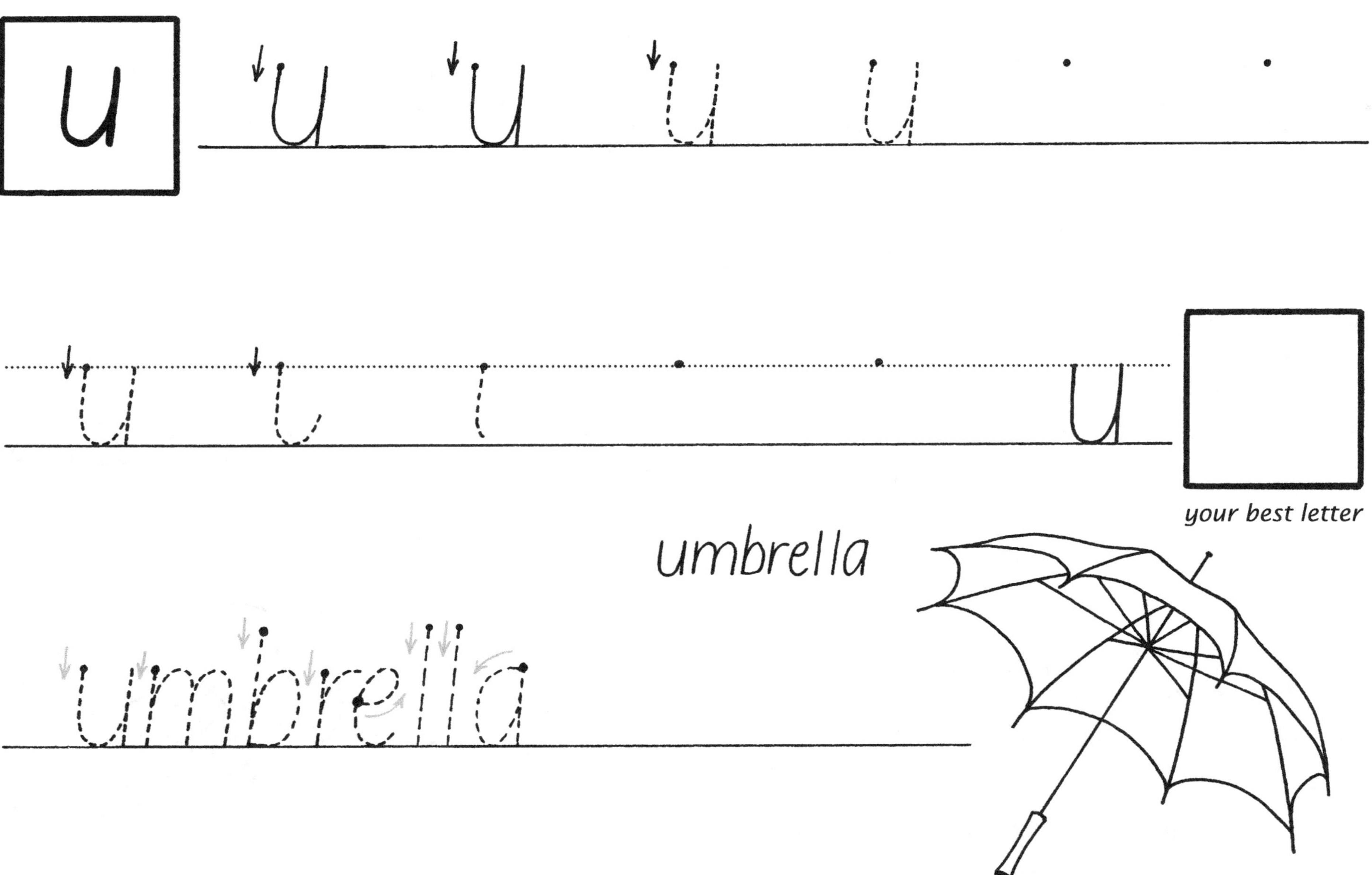

your best letter

umbrella

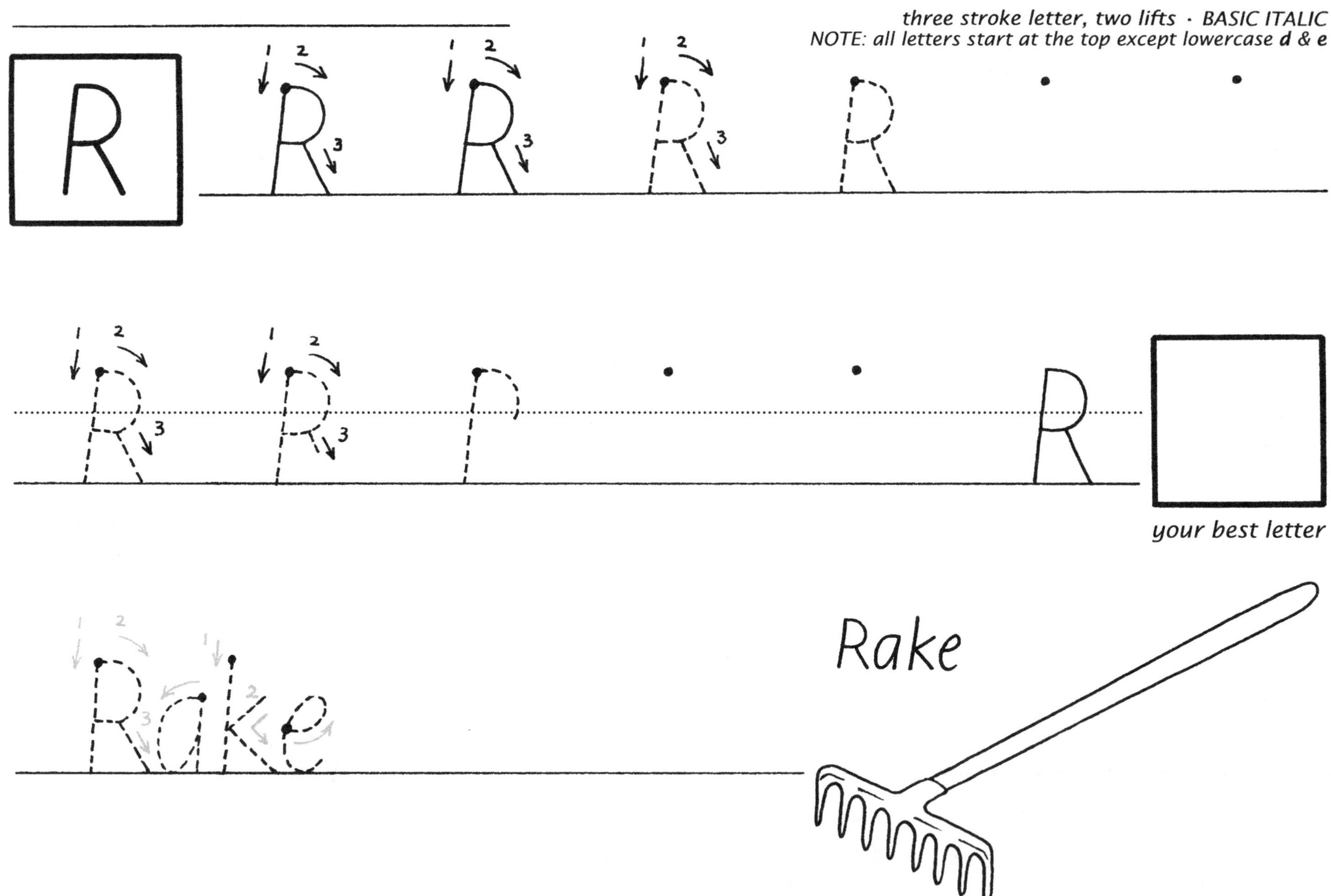

three stroke letter, two lifts · BASIC ITALIC
NOTE: all letters start at the top except lowercase d & e
your best letter
Rake

your best letter

rabbit

LOOK: Did you start each letter at the top? ✎ Circle: Yes No

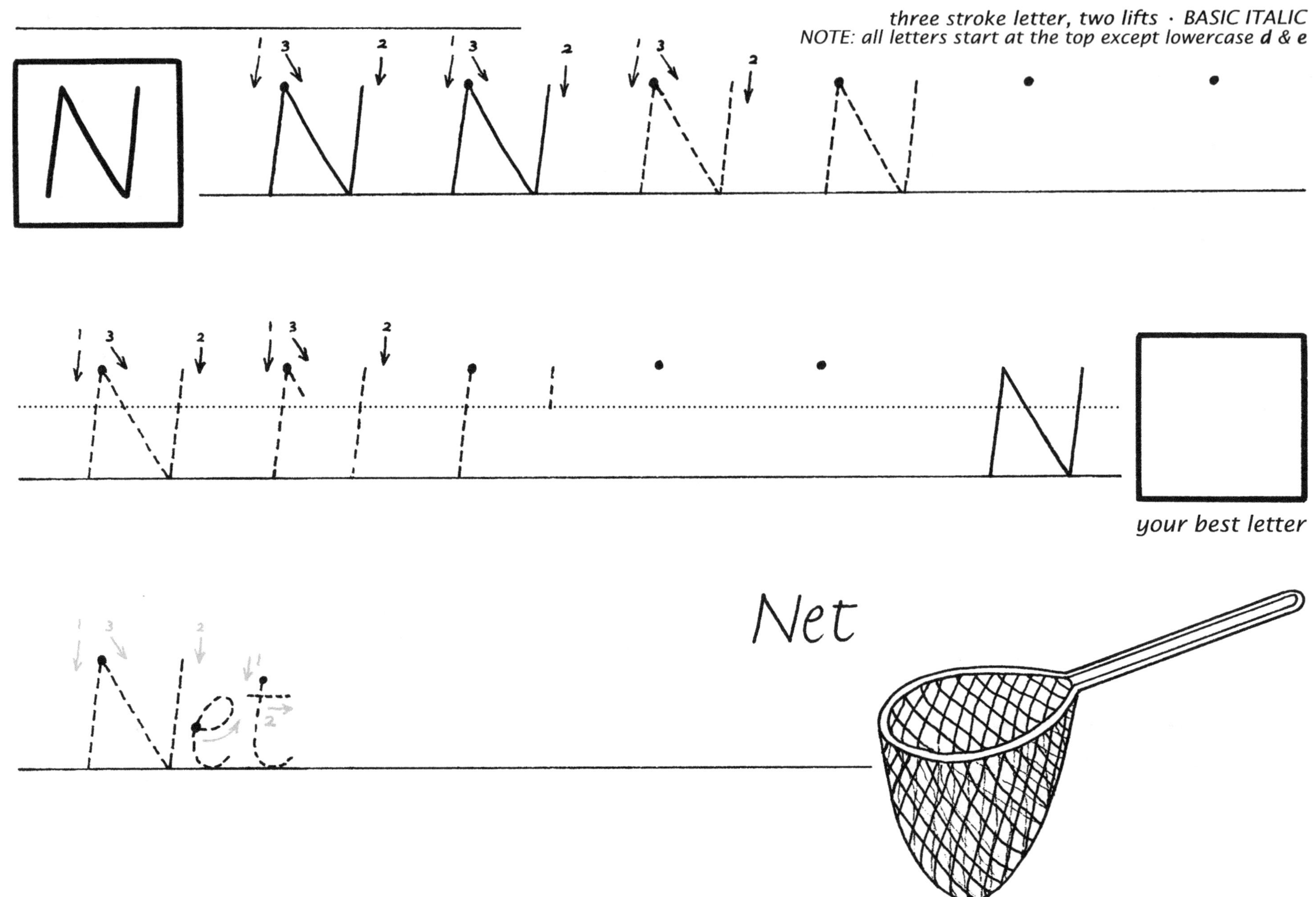

three stroke letter, two lifts · BASIC ITALIC
NOTE: all letters start at the top except lowercase d & e
your best letter
Net

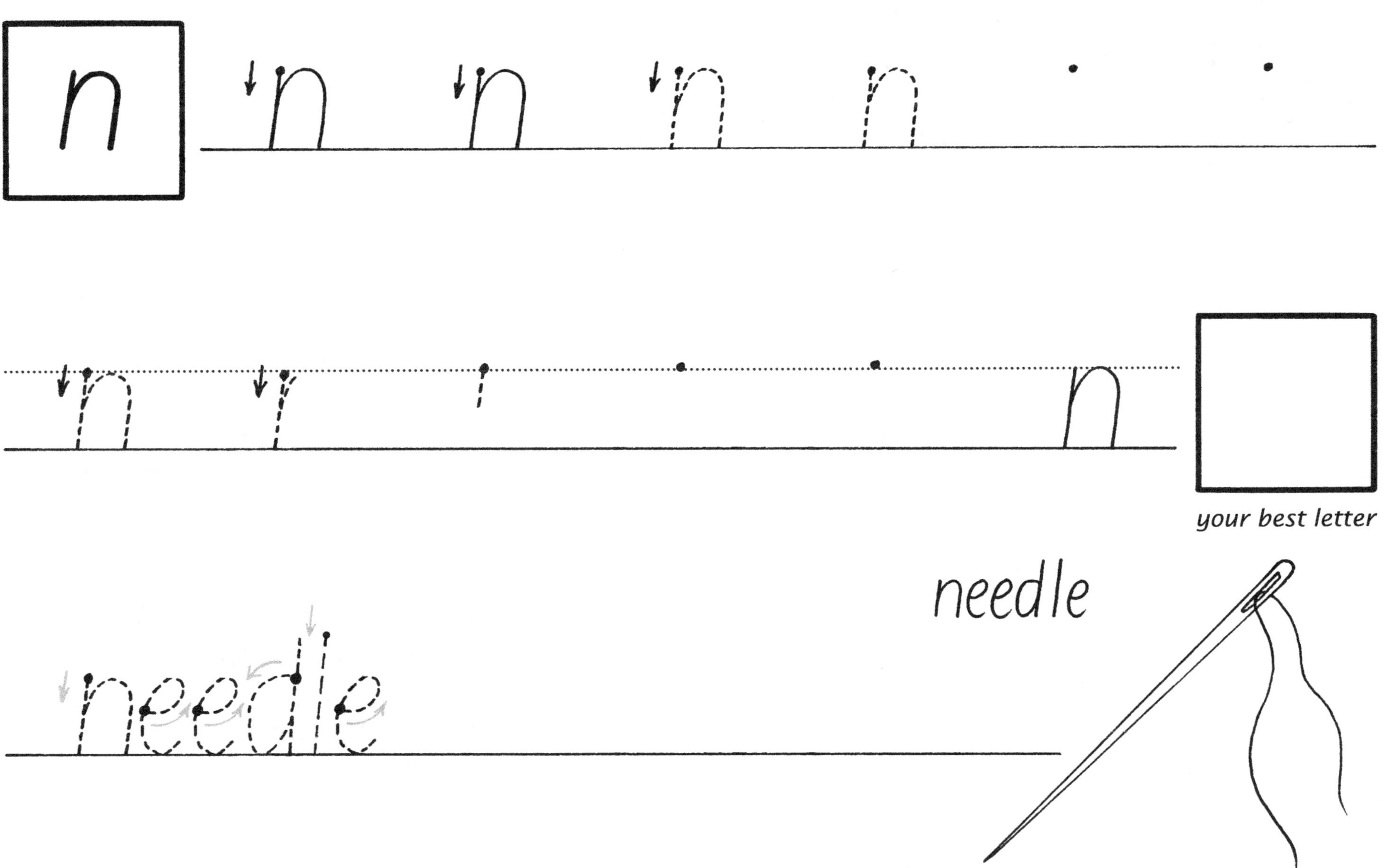

your best letter
needle
needle

M

M M M M M

M M M I

your best letter

Mittens

Mittens

m   'm   'm   'm   m

'm   'r   r   m

your best letter

mouse

mouse

LOOK: Did you start all letters at the top?   Circle: Yes   No

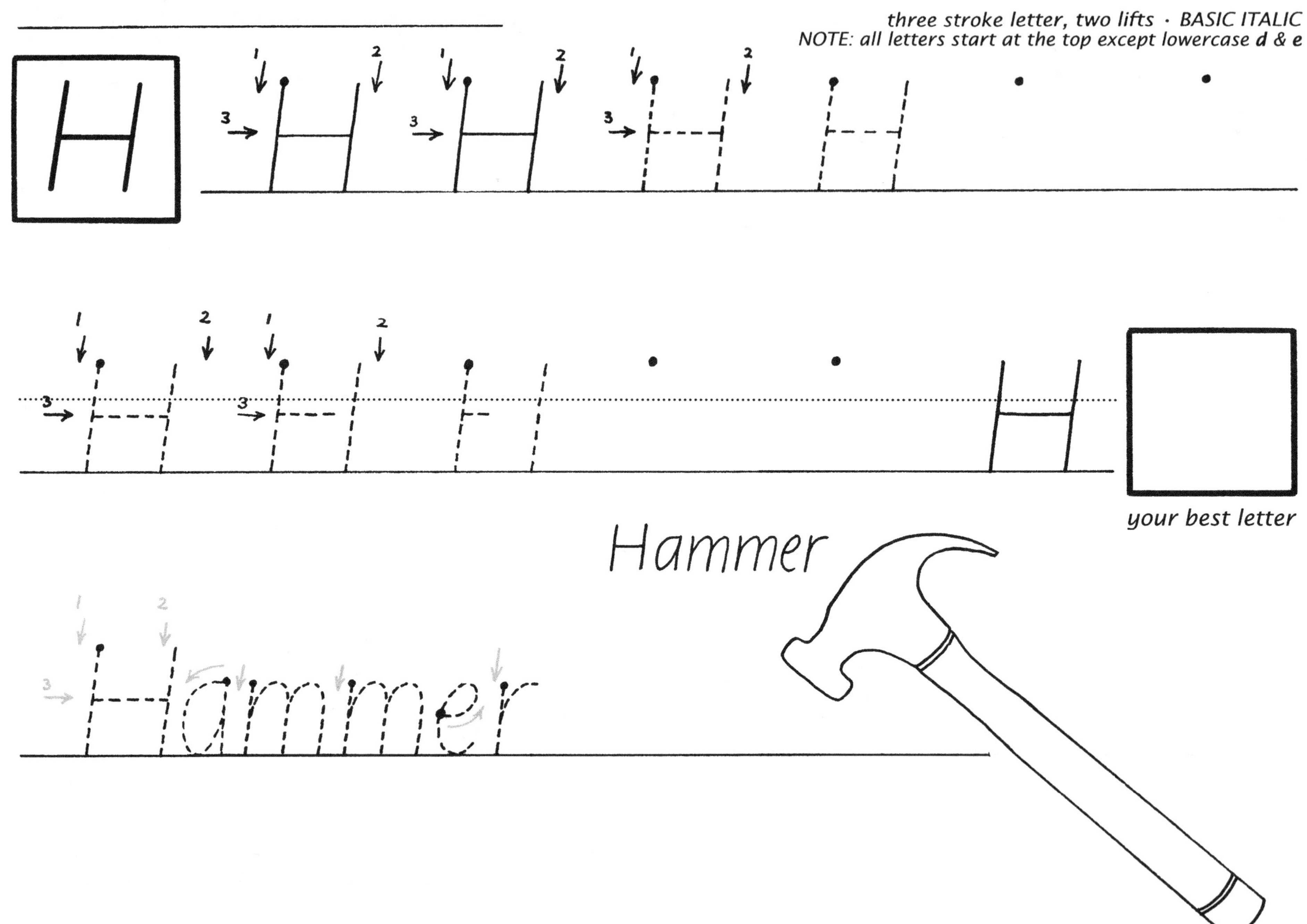
your best letter
Hammer
Hammer

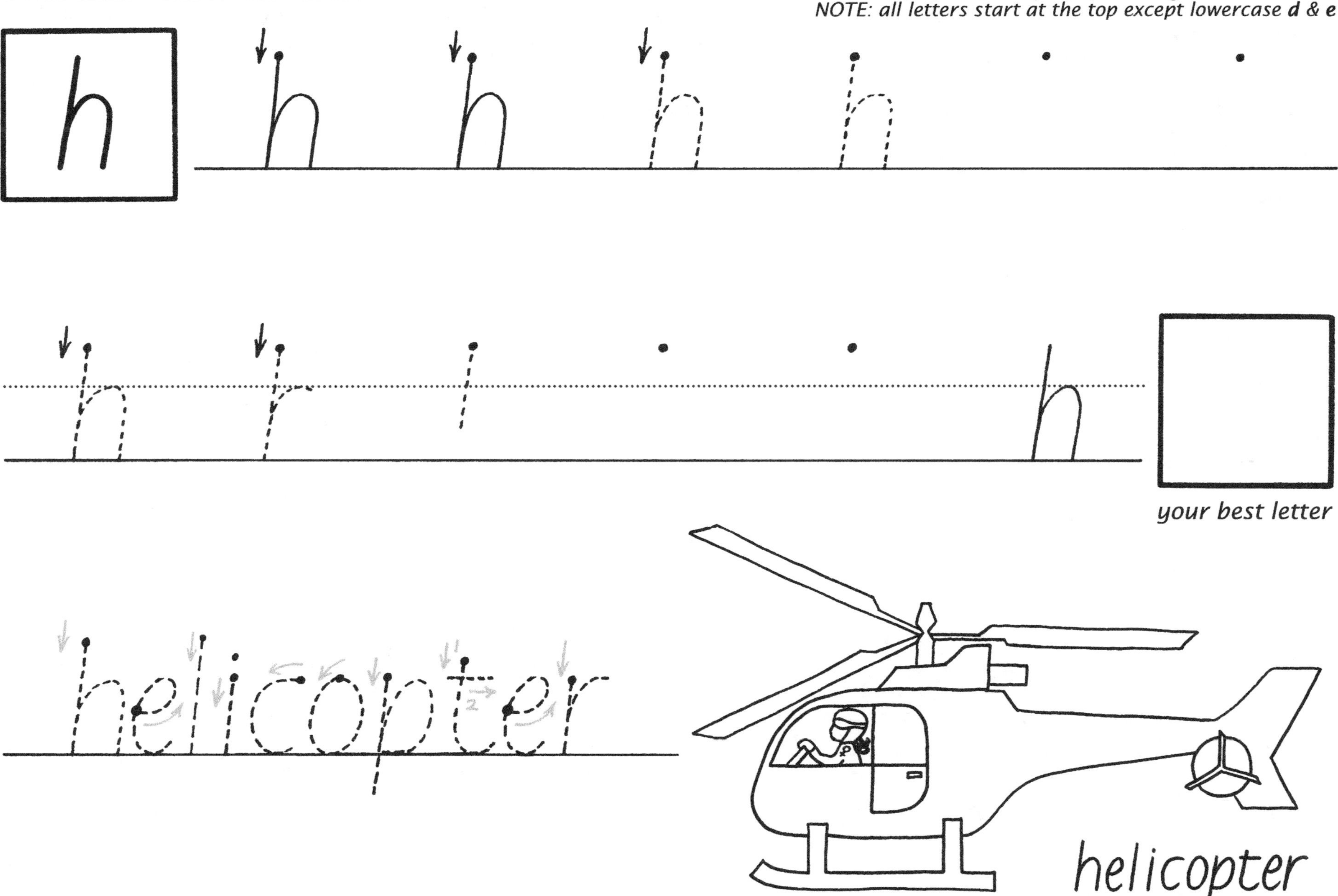

your best letter

Zipper

your best letter

Zipper

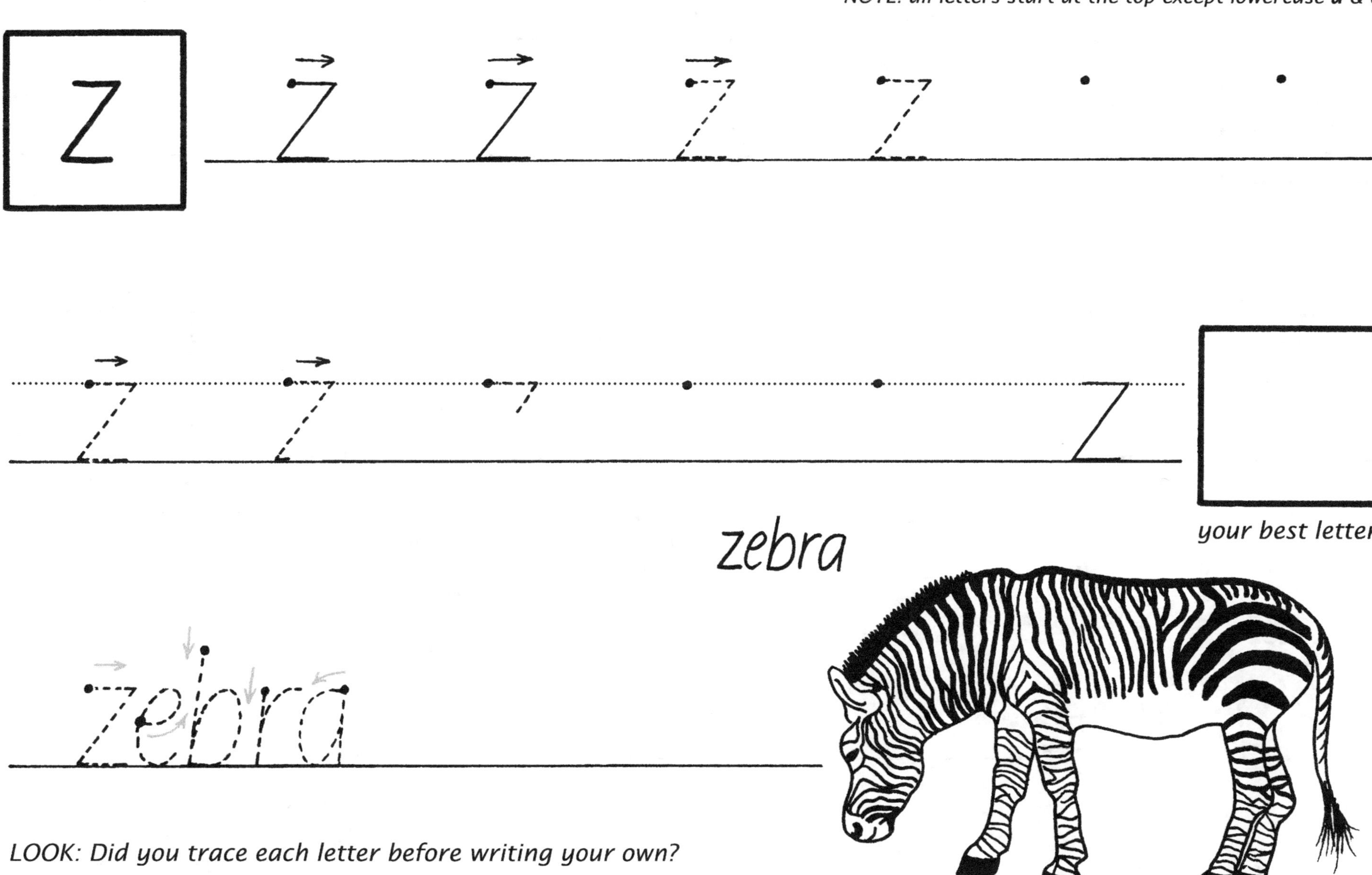

your best letter

zebra

LOOK: Did you trace each letter before writing your own?

Circle: Yes   No

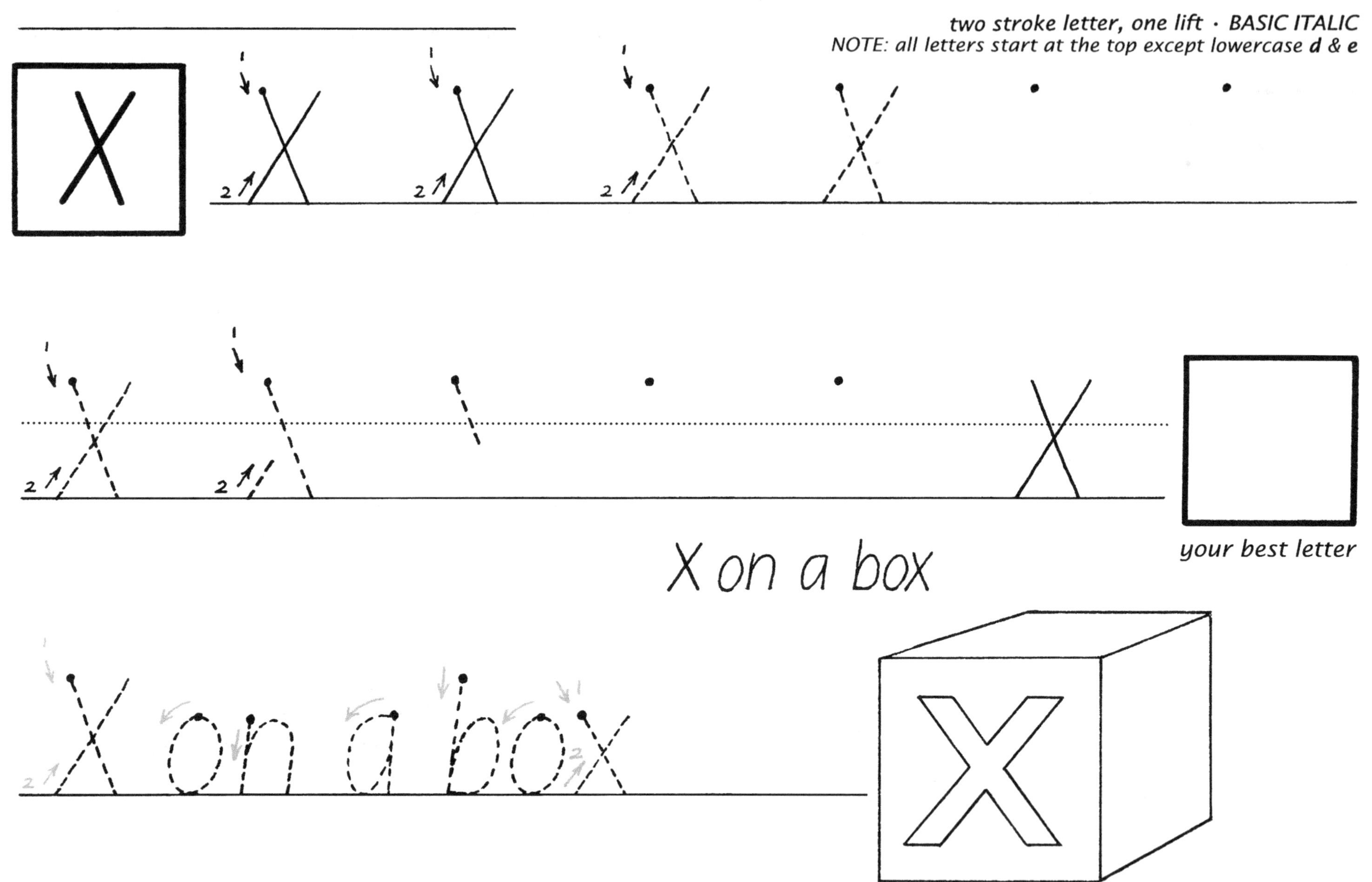

X on a box
your best letter

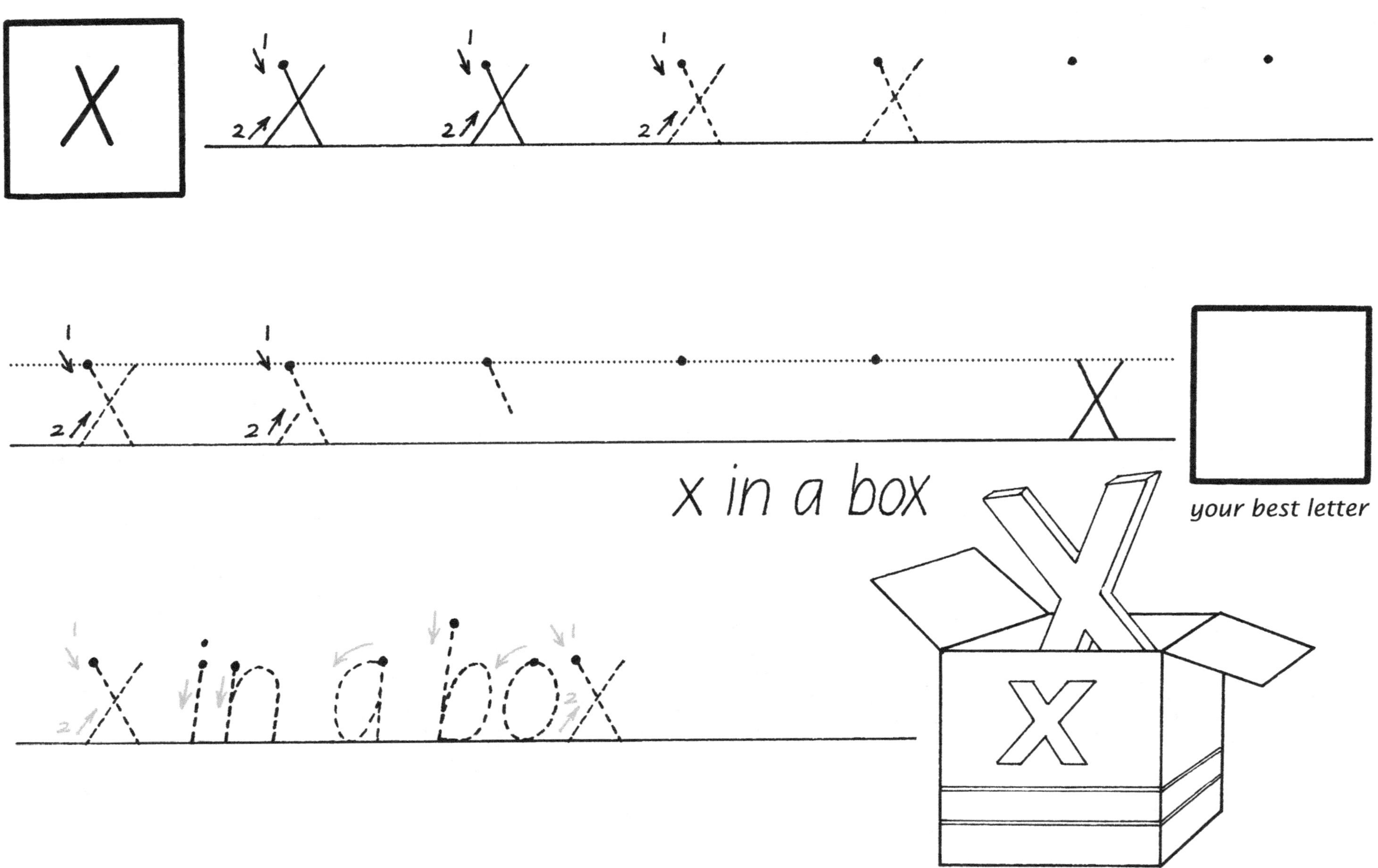
x in a box
your best letter
x in a box

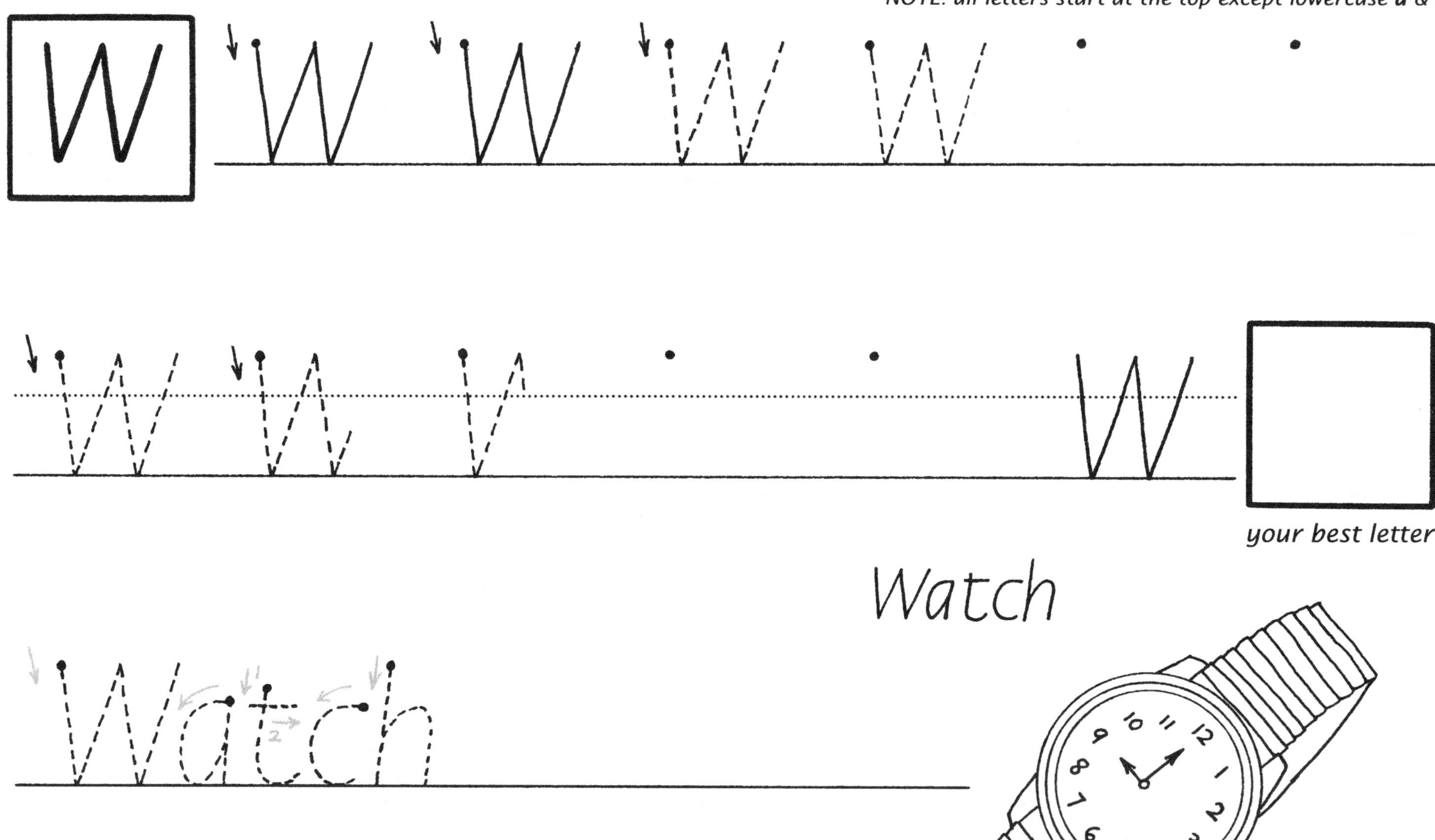

one stroke letter, no lift · BASIC ITALIC
NOTE: all letters start at the top except lowercase d & e

your best letter

Watch

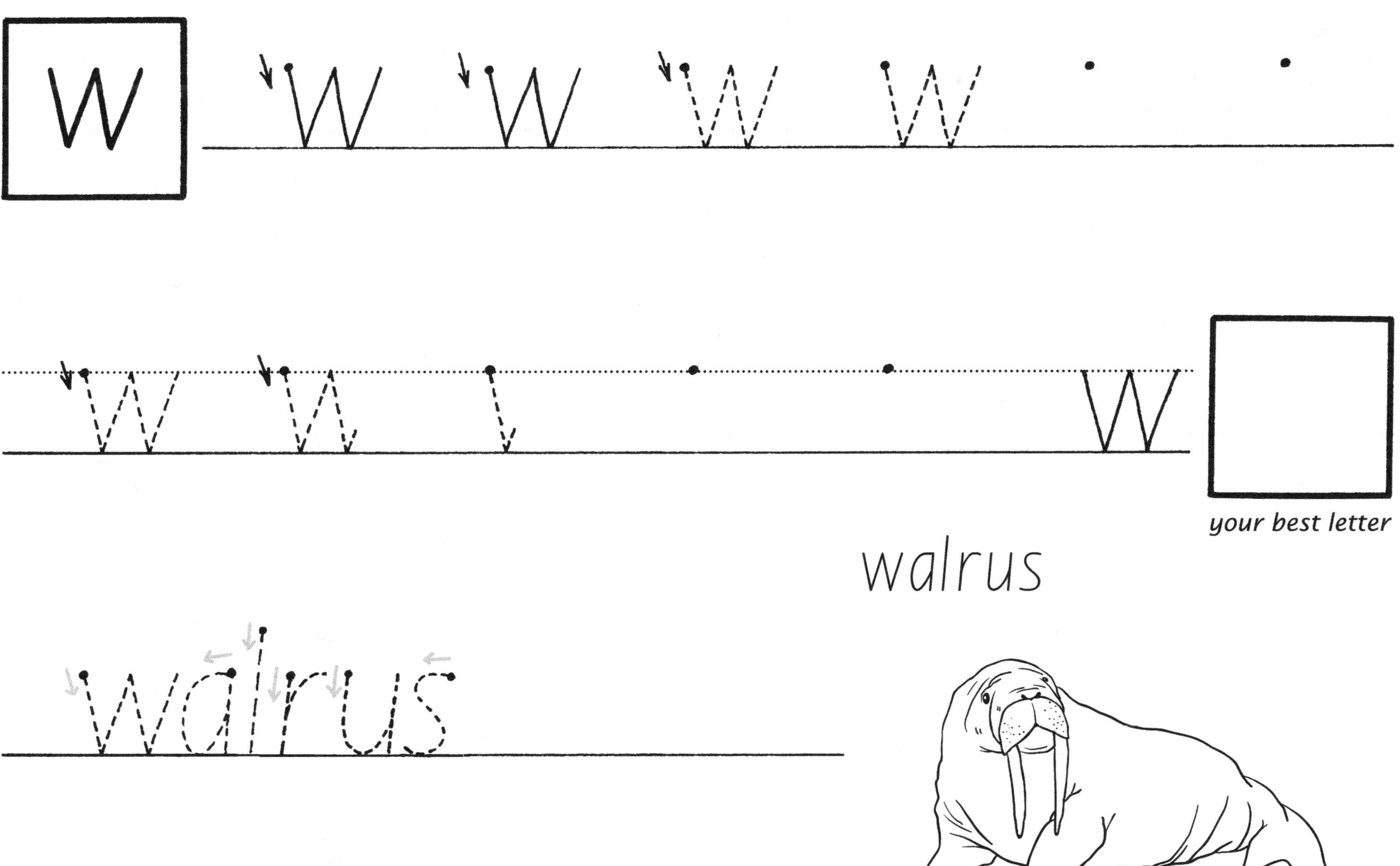

your best letter

walrus

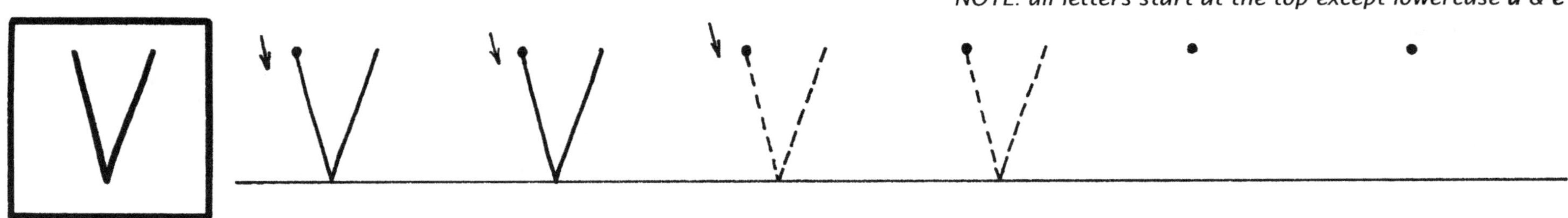

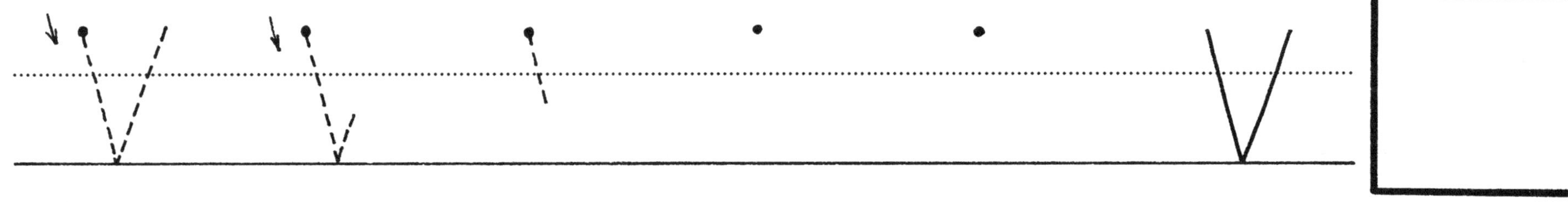

your best letter

Valentine

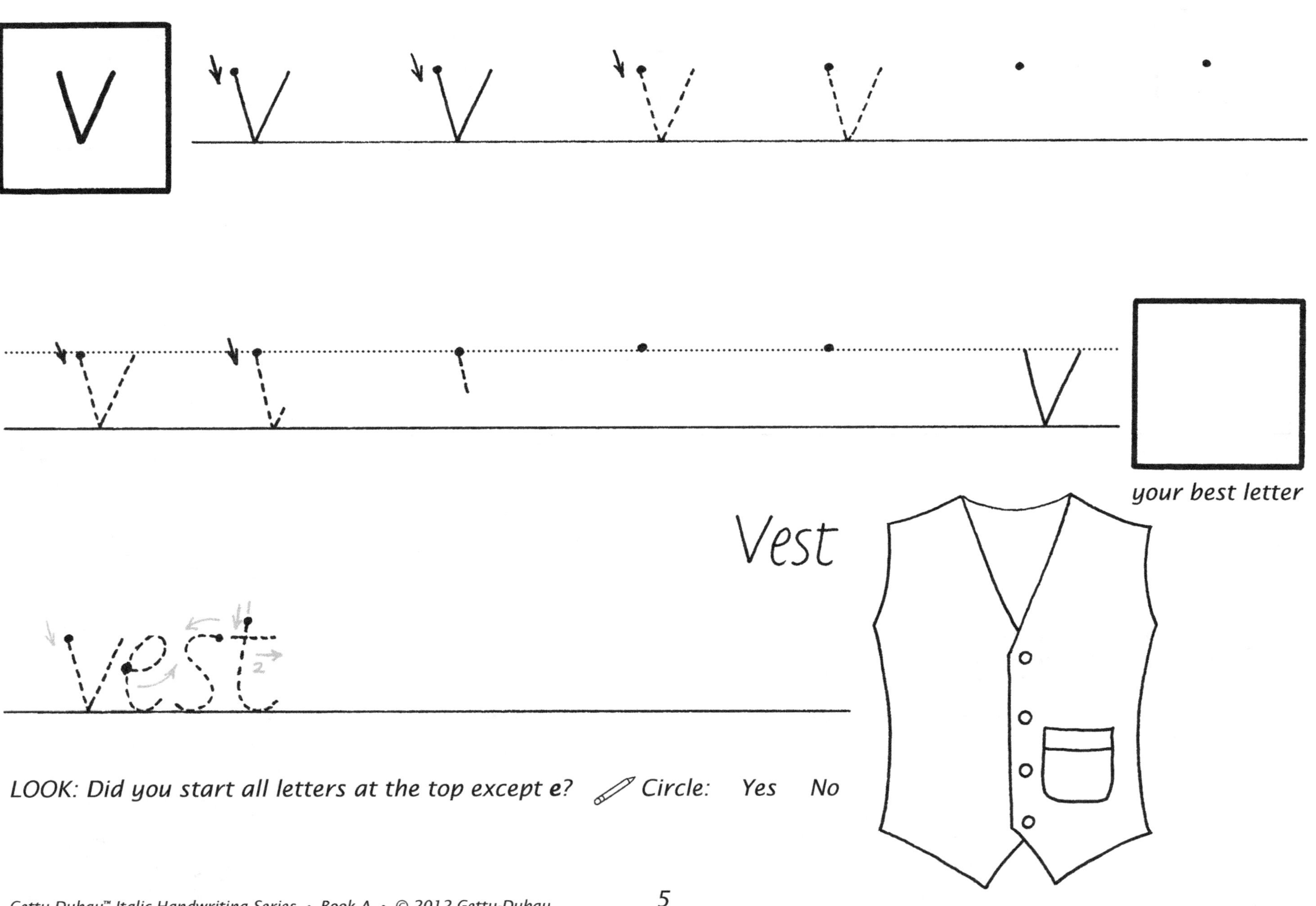

your best letter

Vest

LOOK: Did you start all letters at the top except *e*? ✎ Circle: Yes   No

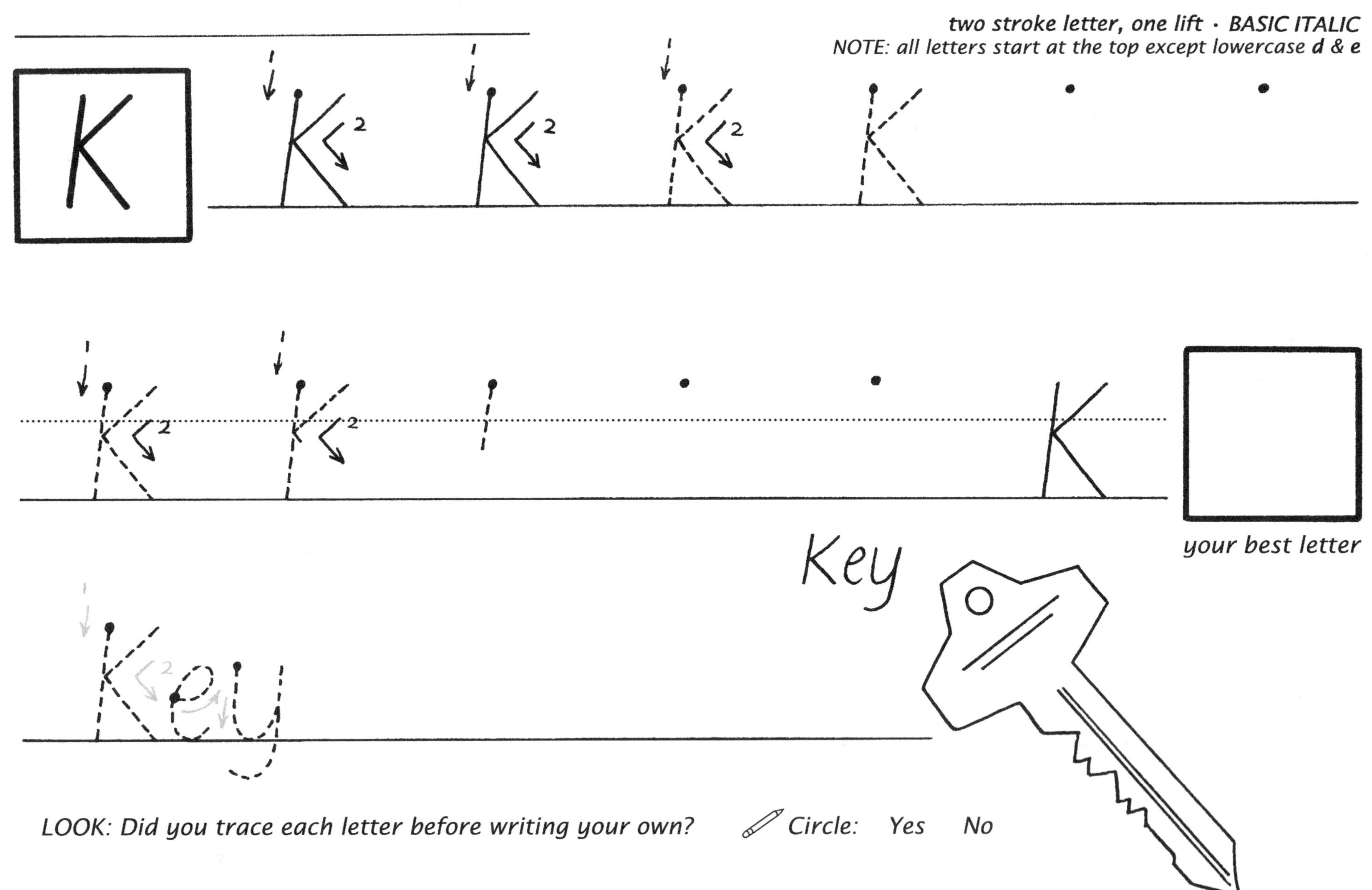

LOOK: Did you trace each letter before writing your own?   Circle: Yes   No

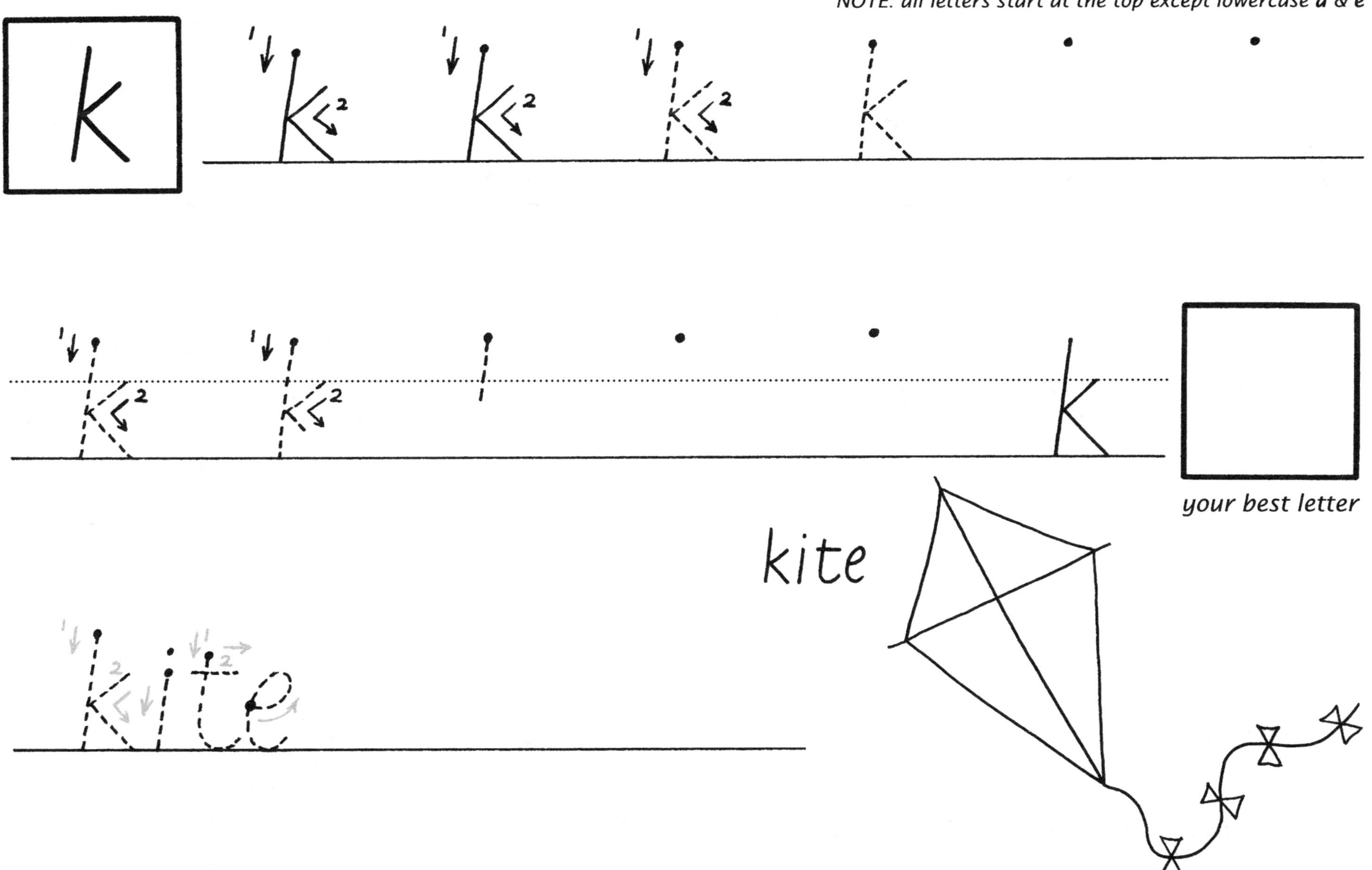

kite
your best letter

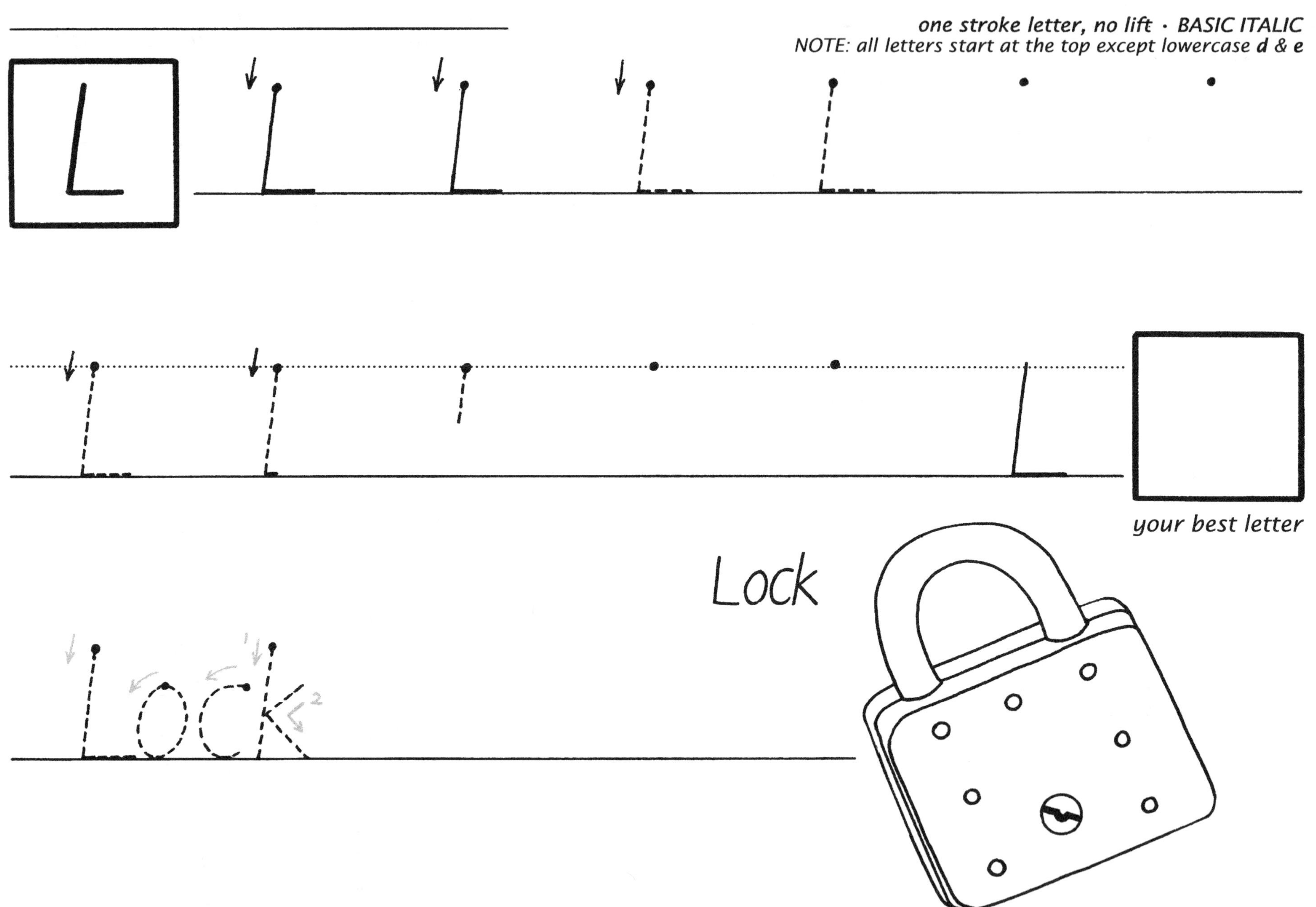
your best letter
Lock

your best letter

lamb

your best letter

Jack-in-the-box

Jack-in-the-box

your best letter

jar

LOOK: Did you start all letters at the top?   Circle: Yes   No

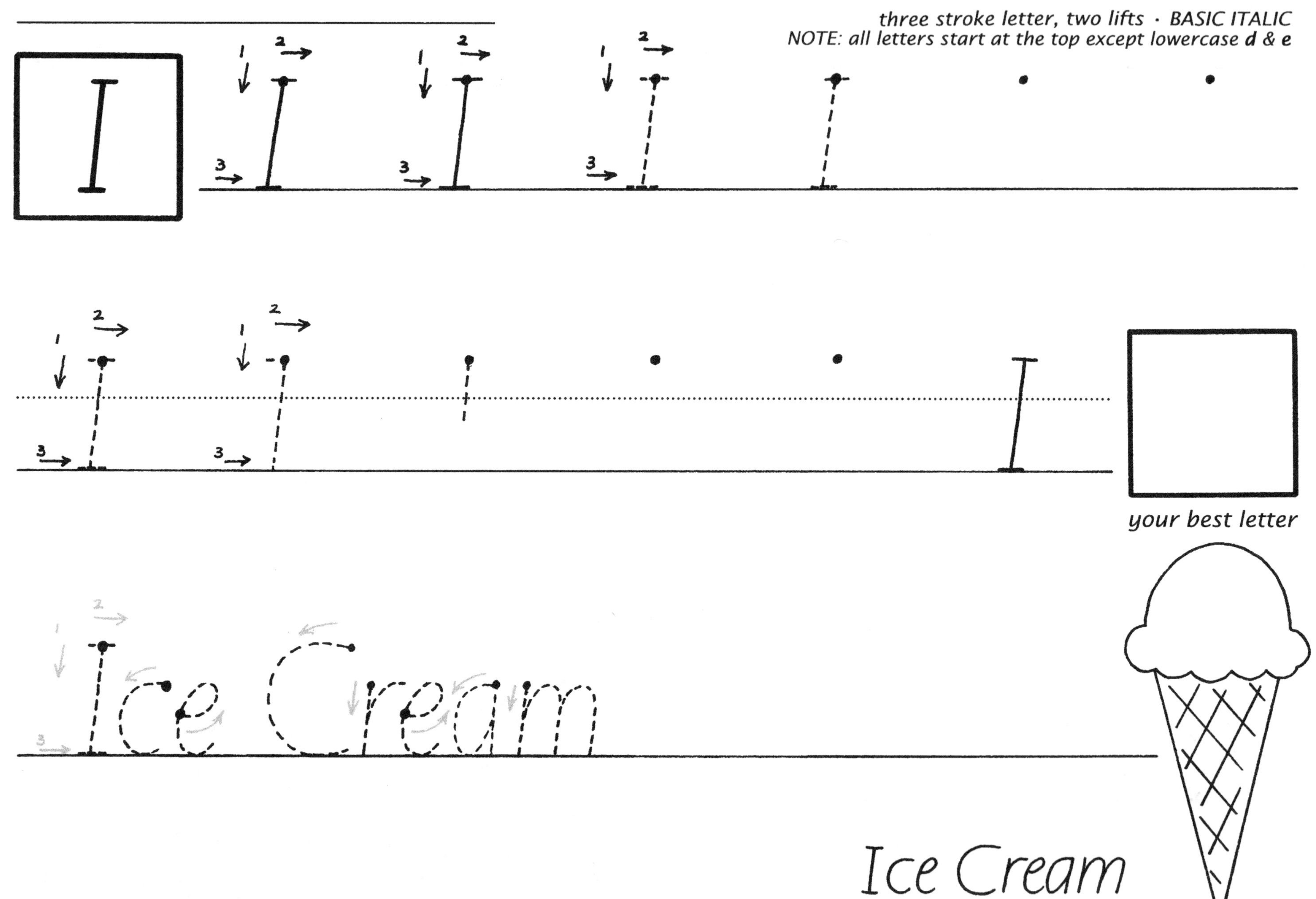

three stroke letter, two lifts · BASIC ITALIC
NOTE: all letters start at the top except lowercase d & e
your best letter
Ice Cream

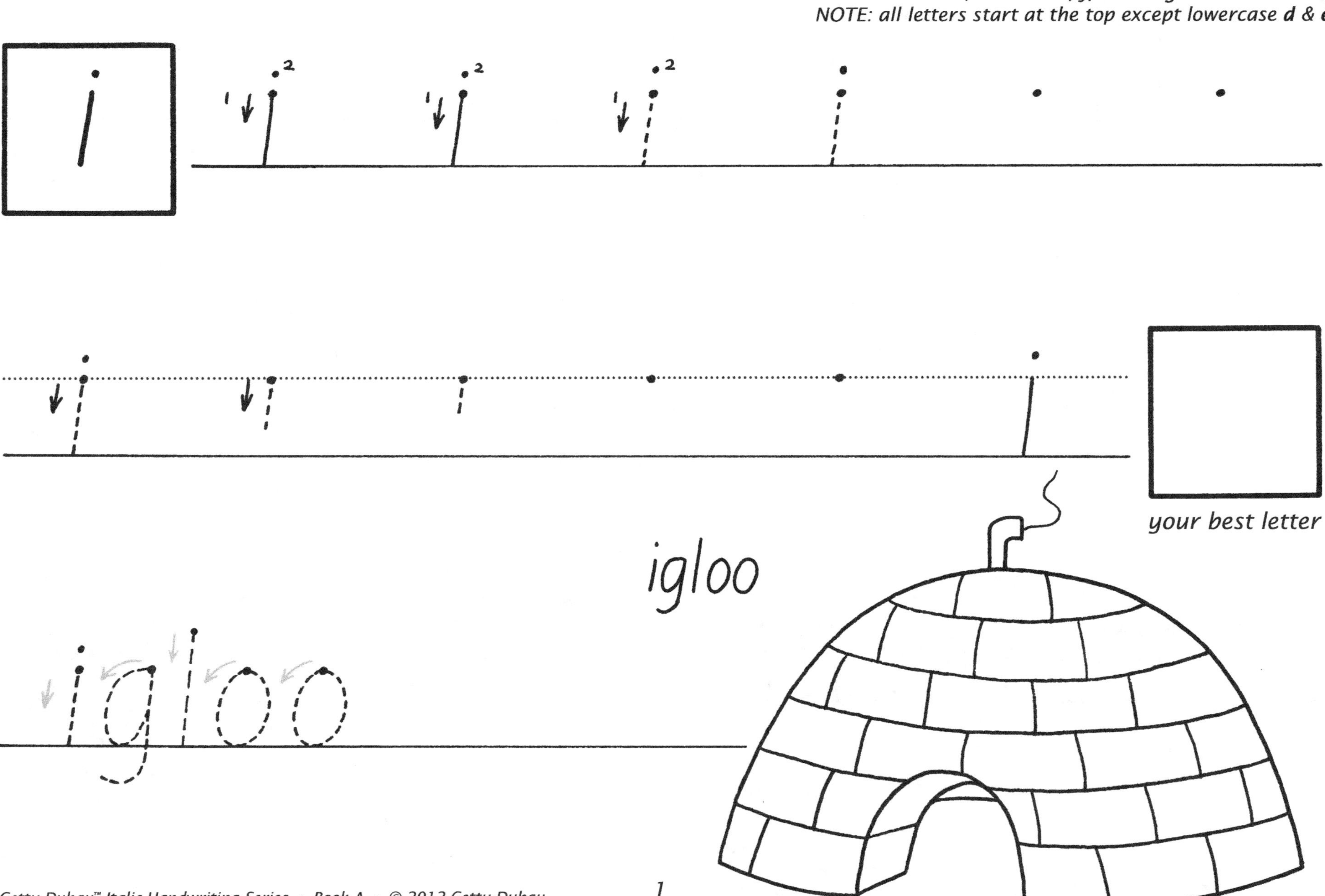

igloo
your best letter

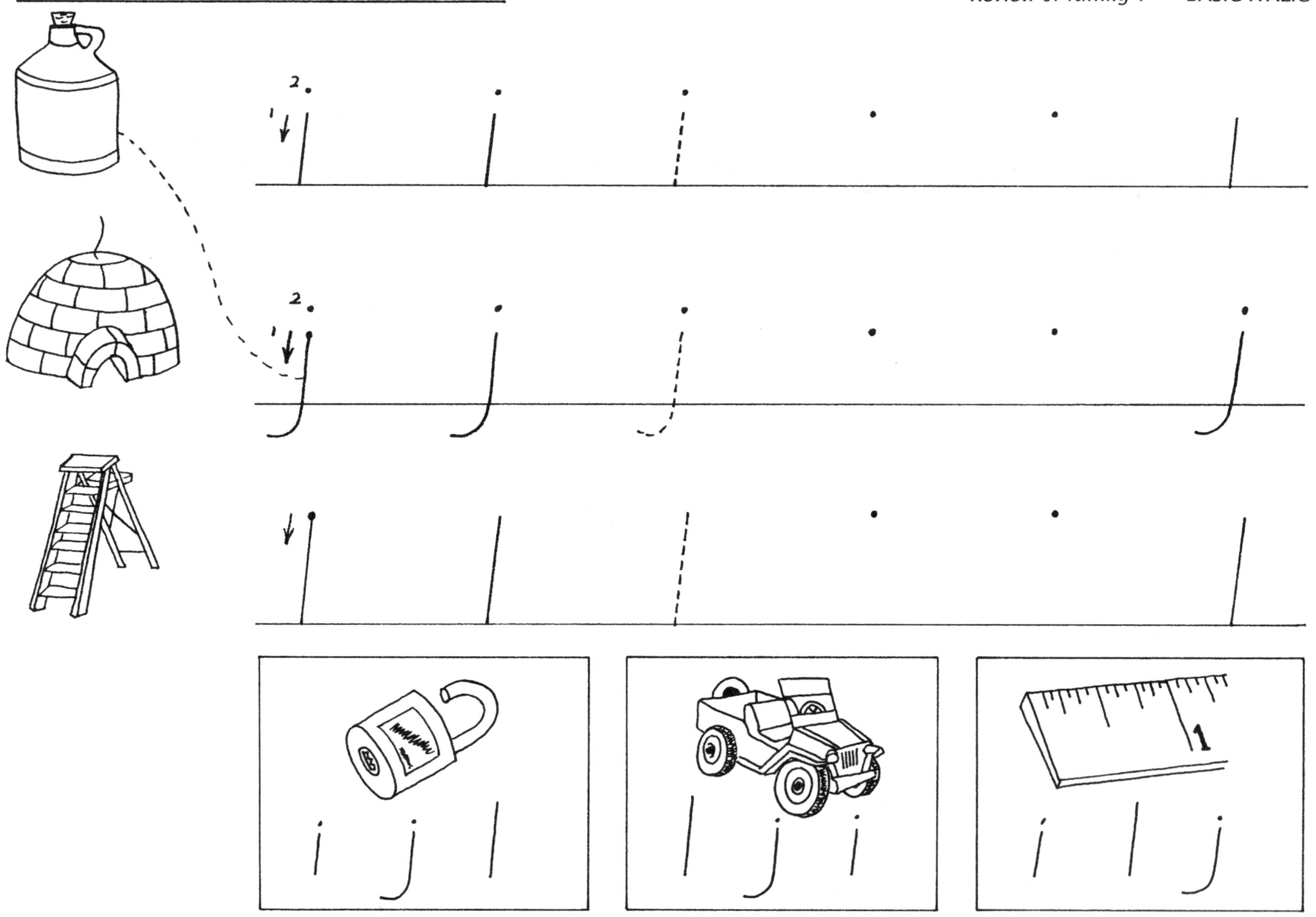

TOP THREE LINES: Ask the student to draw a line from the picture
to the letter that stands for the correct beginning sound.

BOTTOM THREE BOXES: Ask the student to circle the letter that
stands for the beginning sound of the picture.

BASIC SHAPES

Before the student begins writing in BOOK A, the authors recommend that the student practice the following shapes on unlined paper, one shape at a time. Allow the student to write each shape any size at first. Later, ask the student to write very large and very small forms of that same shape. We suggest the student also practice these shapes on a chalkboard and/or in cornmeal. (See INSTRUCTION MANUAL, "*Activity,*" pp. 35 & 41.)

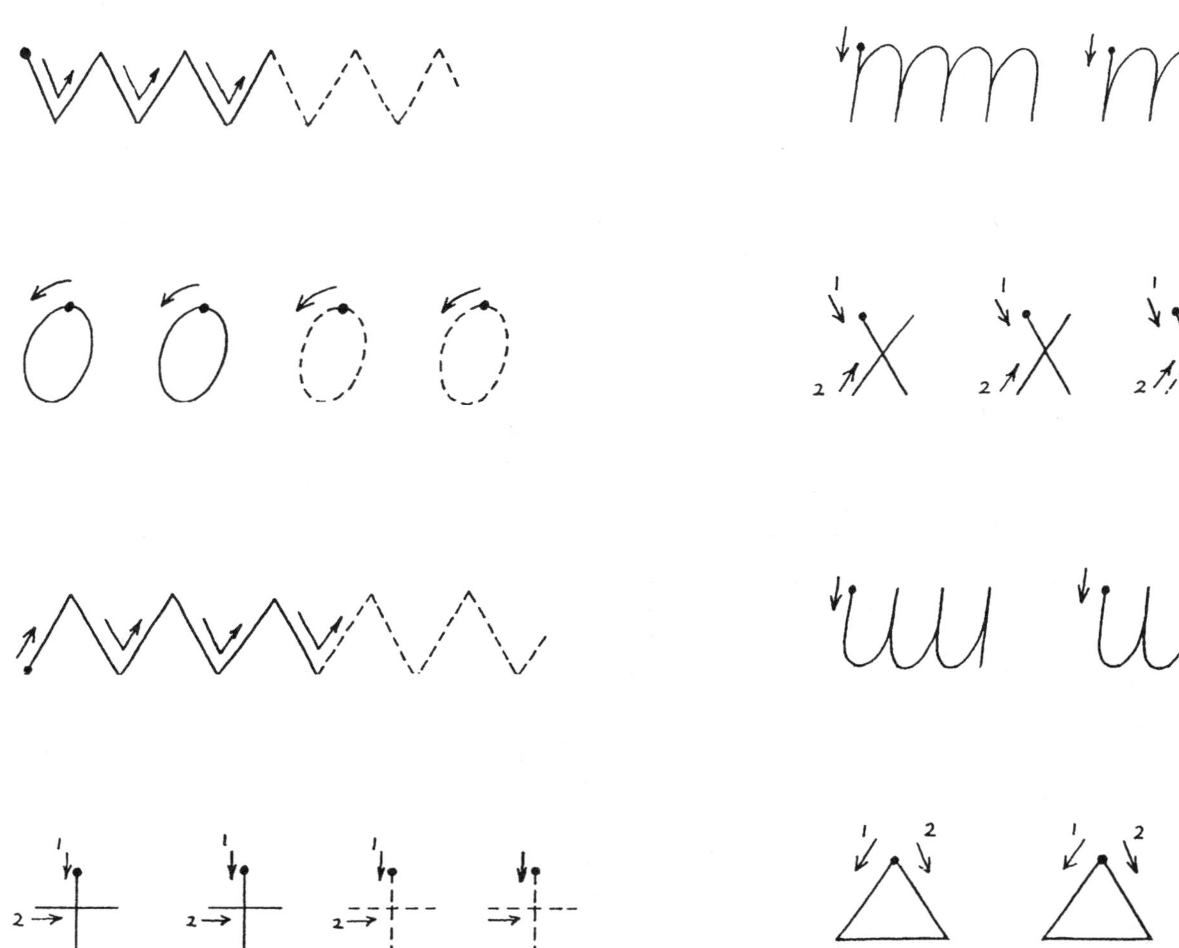

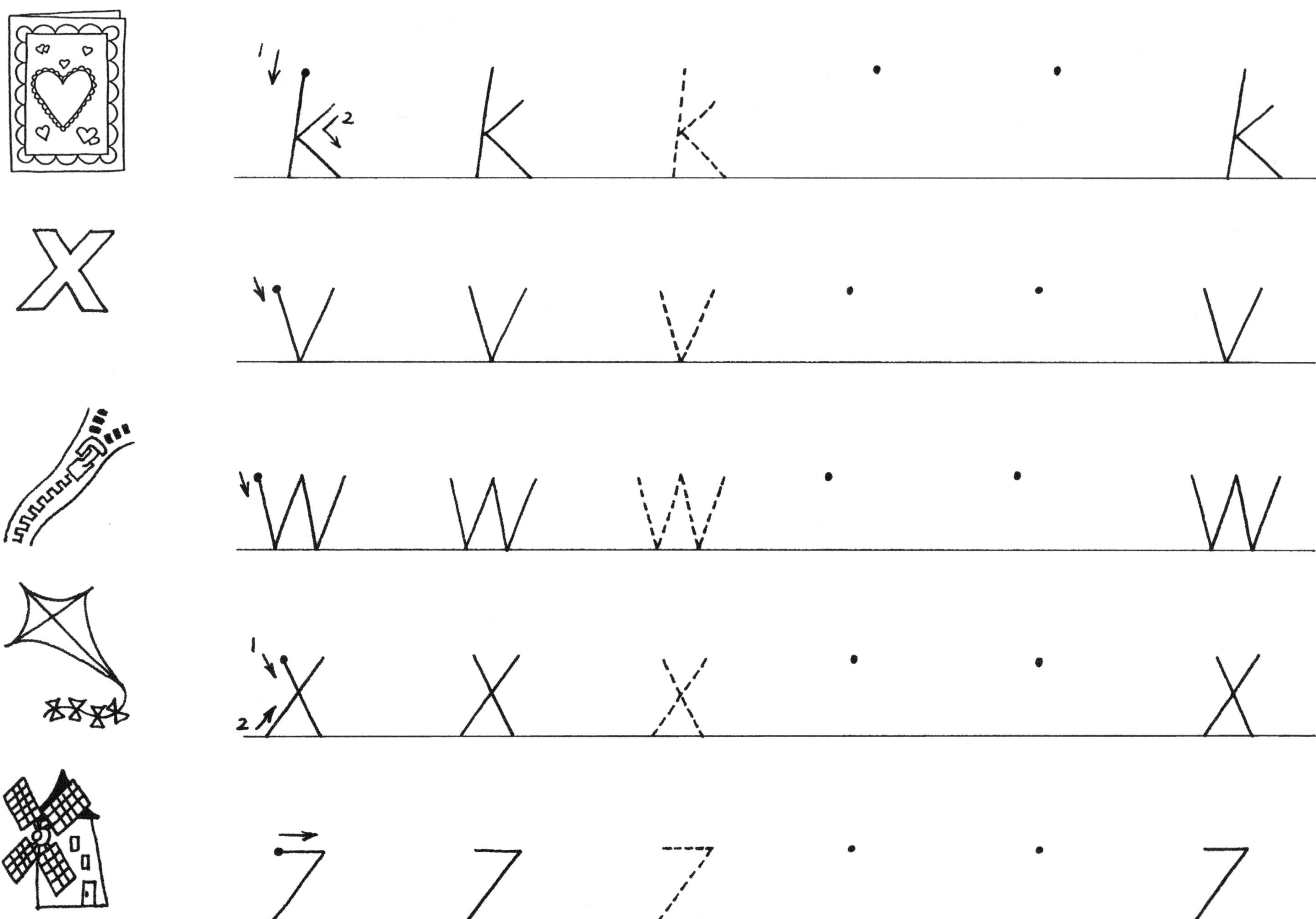

Ask the student to draw a line from the picture to the letter
that stands for the correct beginning sound.

THE BEGINNING WRITER

Learning how to write involves much more than learning to write letters. It is a sophisticated, complex process involving learning letterforms, learning how to space within and between words, and learning how to organize writing on a page. Research indicates that there exists an almost perfect correlation between measures evaluating the children's *awareness* of their fingers and the ability to *use* their fingers in precise manual skills.

Ways to determine manual ability

To assist young students increase awareness of their hands and fingers, and to help you, the teacher, evaluate students' manual skills, have your students perform these tasks:

1. Direct the students to touch each of their fingers to their thumb, in order, from the first to the little finger. (By the age of six years, most children should be able to complete this exercise using one or both hands at a time.)

2. Have the students connect two dots that are spaced approximately eight inches apart on a page. (Most children of five years can accomplish this. However, if the student draws beyond the second dot or draws an unusually shaky line when nearing the second dot, it may indicate potential deficiencies in handwriting skills.)

Ways to improve kinesthetic perception of the hands

1. Unstructured clay modeling facilitates a student's perception of his or her hands. Encourage the student to manipulate the clay in every possible way—squeezing, flattening, poking, making shapes, etc.

2. To heighten the student's perception of shape, use a box in which a variety of small objects are placed for the student to feel but not see.

   a. Ask the student to reach in the box and find an unseen object that matches the one he or she is looking at.

   b. Direct the student to locate in the box an object that you or another student has described.

   c. Ask the student to find two objects with similar characteristics—two fuzzy objects, two heavy objects, two small objects, etc.

3. Draw several circles on a sheet of paper. To determine the student's ability to aim the finger and hand and also to point, have the student place dots in the circles with a pencil, pen, or crayon. Vary the difficulty of this task by increasing or decreasing the size of the circles or increasing the rate at which the dots are made. (The student must be able to point at a given or imaginary point in order to begin the stroke of a letter.)

Ways to confirm hand-eye tracking skills

The ability to control continuous hand movements while drawing lines of varying difficulty is basic to handwriting. If you are able to detect problems as the student completes the following tasks and are able to obtain appropriate assistance for the student, subsequent difficulties may be avoided.

1. Demonstrate drawing parallel lines. Then direct the student to draw parallel lines of a given length, first at a relaxed pace then at a faster one.

2. Direct the student to draw two curved lines equal in distance from one another. Later require more difficult shapes that combine straight lines, angles, and/or curves.

3. Direct the student to connect numbered dots on a sheet of paper that require horizontal, vertical and lateral movements. Place the paper in front of the student, close to the dominant hand. Later, space the dots further apart and require the student to cross the midline of his or her body. This latter task may cause the neurologically challenged student some difficulty.

The above evaluative tasks may be of help in assisting the learning of handwriting and in discovering deficiencies.

(See INSTRUCTION MANUAL, p. 13, for more suggestions concerning the beginning writer.)

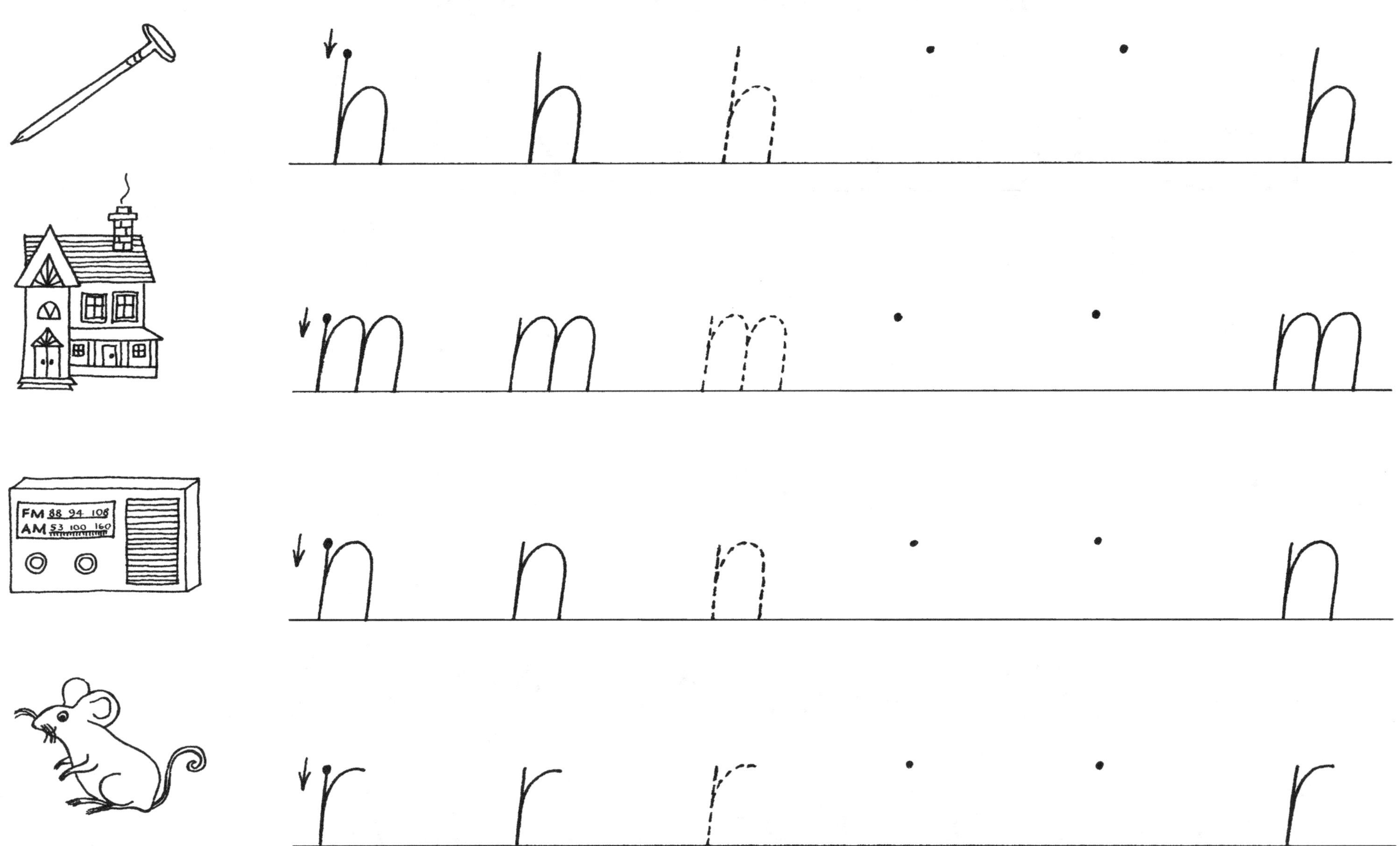

*Ask the student to draw a line from the picture to the letter
that stands for the correct beginning sound.*

BASIC ITALIC ALPHABET

All letters written in one stroke unless otherwise indicated.   *All letters start at the top except lowercase **d** and **e**.*

Aa Bb Cc Dd Ee Ff Gg

or

alternate
2-stroke e

Hh Ii Jj Kk Ll Mm

or

or

Nn Oo Pp Qq Rr Ss Tt

or

or

Uu Vv Ww Xx Yy Zz

0 1 2 3 4 5 6 7 8 9

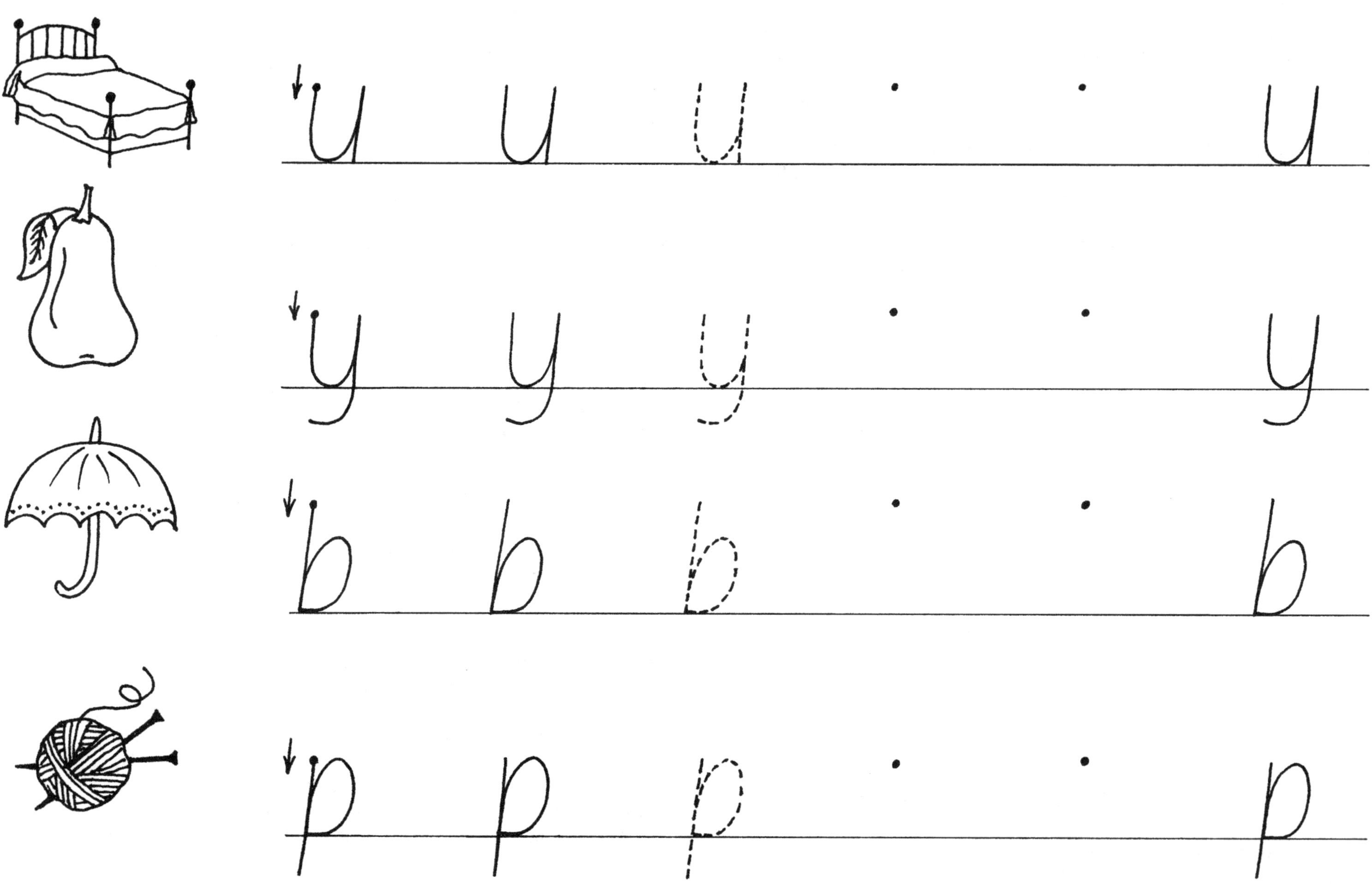

*Ask the student to draw a line from the picture to the letter
that stands for the correct beginning sound.*

GETTY-DUBAY™ HANDWRITING REMINDERS

PENCIL HOLD

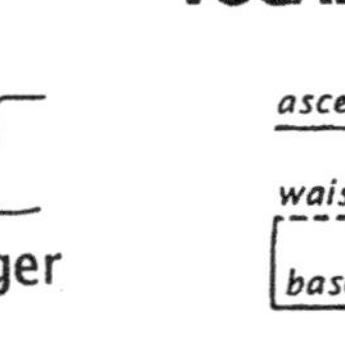

Hold the pencil with the thumb and index finger, resting it on the middle finger. Rest the shaft of the pencil near the large knuckle. Hold the tool firmly and avoid pinching. To relax the hand, tap index finger on the pencil three times. Avoid "thumb wrap" and a "death grip".

PAPER POSITION

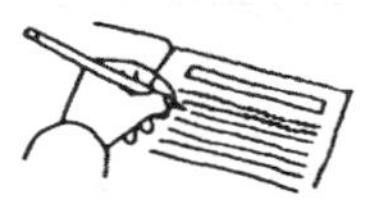

LEFT-HANDED: If the left-handed student writes with the wrist below the writing line, turn paper clockwise so it is slanted to the right, as illustrated.

If the left-handed student writes with a hook, with the wrist above the writing line, turn the paper counter-clockwise so it is slanted to the left, as illustrated. (Similar to right-handed position)

RIGHT-HANDED: If the student is right-handed, turn paper counter-clockwise so it is slanted to the left, as illustrated.

POSTURE

Rest feet flat on the floor and keep back comfortably straight without slumping. Rest forearms on writing surface. The student holds workbook or paper with the nonwriting hand so that the writing area is centered in the front of the student.

PRACTICE PAPER

Book A—Use unlined or lined paper together with workbooks.

MATERIALS

The *Getty-Dubay™ Italic Handwriting Series* workbooks, BOOKS A-G, and the INSTRUCTION MANUAL constitute a step-by-step program. Related materials consist of:

1. BLACKLINE MASTERS/WORKSHEETS - half sheets for introduction to, or review of, workbook pages.
2. CLASSROOM WALL CHARTS - basic & cursive italic.
3. DESK STRIPS - basic & cursive italic.

VOCABULARY

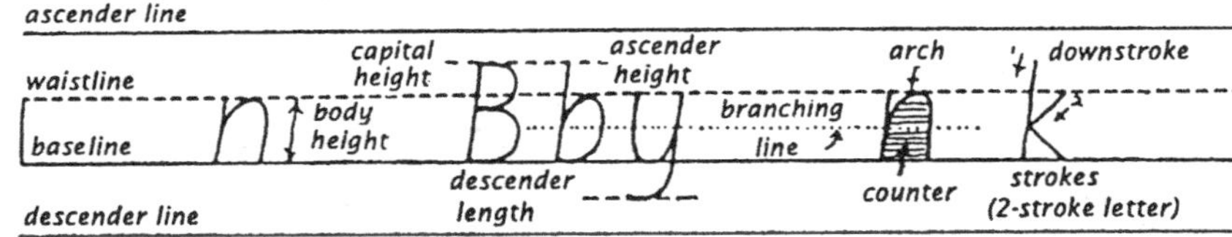

DIRECT INSTRUCTION

Several sessions of direct instruction each week are essential for a successful program. BOOK A – 5 to 10 minute sessions a day are recommended, see INSTRUCTION MANUAL, pp. 18-19

- SHAPE & STROKE SEQUENCE – teach basic italic in letter family groups, or according to the reading program in grade 1.

- SLOPE – encourage a consistent letter slope. Vertical letters (0° slope) may be the easiest to teach to beginning writers.

- SIZE – At first, allow students to write letters any size they wish on unlined paper, then introduce the workbook. A recommended progression through this book is one letter (lowercase and/or capital) per week.

SPACING

When young students are writing words, at first have them leave a space about the width of their two small fingers between words. As they become more proficient, they can leave less space.

ASSESSMENT

The *Getty-Dubay™ Italic Handwriting Series* provides a self-assessment process, LOOK, PLAN, PRACTICE, to enable the student to monitor progress. LOOK, step 1 of this process begins on some of the student pages in BOOK A. Assessment is the key to improving handwriting; in this book we introduce the first of three steps in the LOOK, PLAN, PRACTICE self-assessment process. The students look at their own writing and answer any questions on the page. The pencil indicates the student is to make a written response, generally by circling "yes" or "no". The teacher may encourage students to award themselves a star or a smiling face at the top of the page when they notice self-improvement.

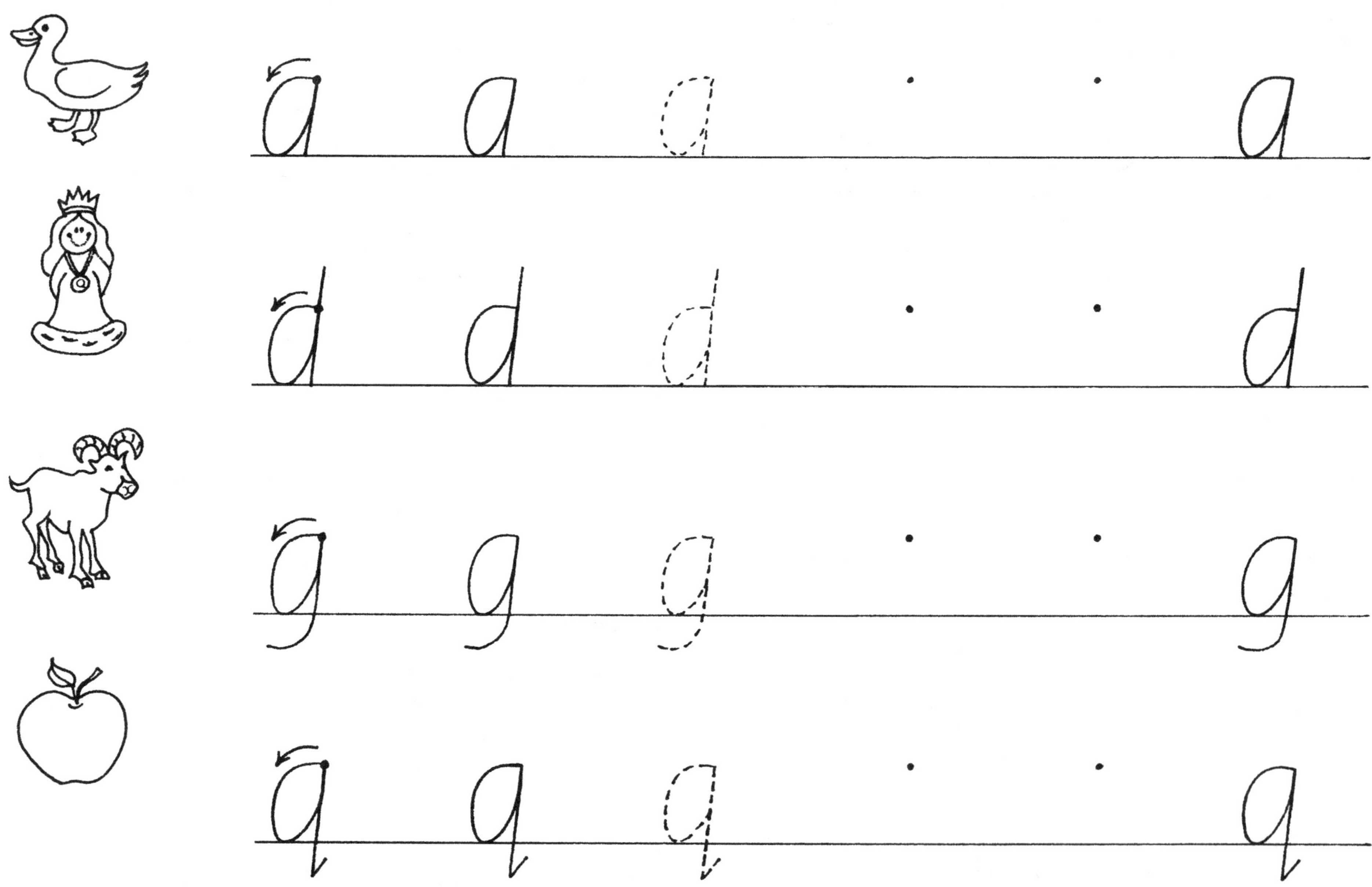

Ask the student to draw a line from the picture to the letter
that stands for the correct beginning sound.

INTRODUCTION

This is the first of seven workbooks providing instruction in basic italic handwriting. It is designed for the beginning student of handwriting and is recommended for preschool, kindergarten and/or early first grade (5 to 7 years of age).

The twenty-six lowercase letters and the twenty-six capitals are introduced one letter per page. Letters are arranged in the order of lowercase families, which group letters with similar strokes together and progress from simple to more complex forms. The matching capital letter occurs on the reverse of each lowercase page allowing introduction of both lowercase and capital together if preferred.

Each page is designed for the student to trace the models provided, write letters at the given dots, and to write a "best" letter in the empty box on each alphabet page. The standard writing tool is the pencil although other writing instruments such as the fiber tip pen may be used. When students are ready, they should trace the word describing the illustration on each letter page, following the dots and arrows.

It is essential that the instructor provide an understanding of the dot and the arrow to assist the writer in completing the pages successfully. The self-assessment method used in the *Getty-Dubay™ Italic Handwriting Series* enables students to monitor their individual progress. Step 1, LOOK, of the three-step LOOK, PLAN, PRACTICE format, is incorporated on 21 of the student pages. Students are asked to "LOOK" at their writing and affirm what is best. On the 21 pages with "LOOK" questions, students should circle their chosen answers. See INSTRUCTION MANUAL, PP. 13, 18 & 19.

The *Getty-Dubay™ Italic Handwriting Series* INSTRUCTION MANUAL is to be used in conjunction with this workbook. Explanations and in-depth descriptions of lowercase letters, capitals, joins, and numerals are presented in the manual, emphasizing shape, strokes, size, slope and spacing of the letters. Also included in the manual are: a rationale for italic handwriting, techniques for teaching and assessing handwriting, sequence of skills, handwriting activities, and a brief history of our alphabet.

BOOK B, basic italic, follows this workbook and is designed for the beginning reader. In the third book, BOOK C, basic italic letterforms are reinforced and cursive italic is introduced. BOOKS D, E, F, and G provide a complete basic italic and cursive italic handwriting program. BOOKS B, C, and/or D may also be suitable for the person learning English as a second language.

The format of this book was chosen to accommodate both the left- and right-handed writer. When open, the book fits easily on a small desk, and the writer is not encumbered with an additional page to the left or right. From day one, use a Getty-Dubay™ basic italic desk strip as a reminder. Blackline masters are designed for supplementary practice and are available for each workbook in the series. See www.handwritingsuccess.com for these supplementary materials.

You can guide children toward the challenge and delight in the writing process by reading to them, modeling handwriting, providing writing materials, and especially by building enthusiasm for the letters of our alphabet and for the written word.

·abcdefghijklmnopqrstuvwxyz·

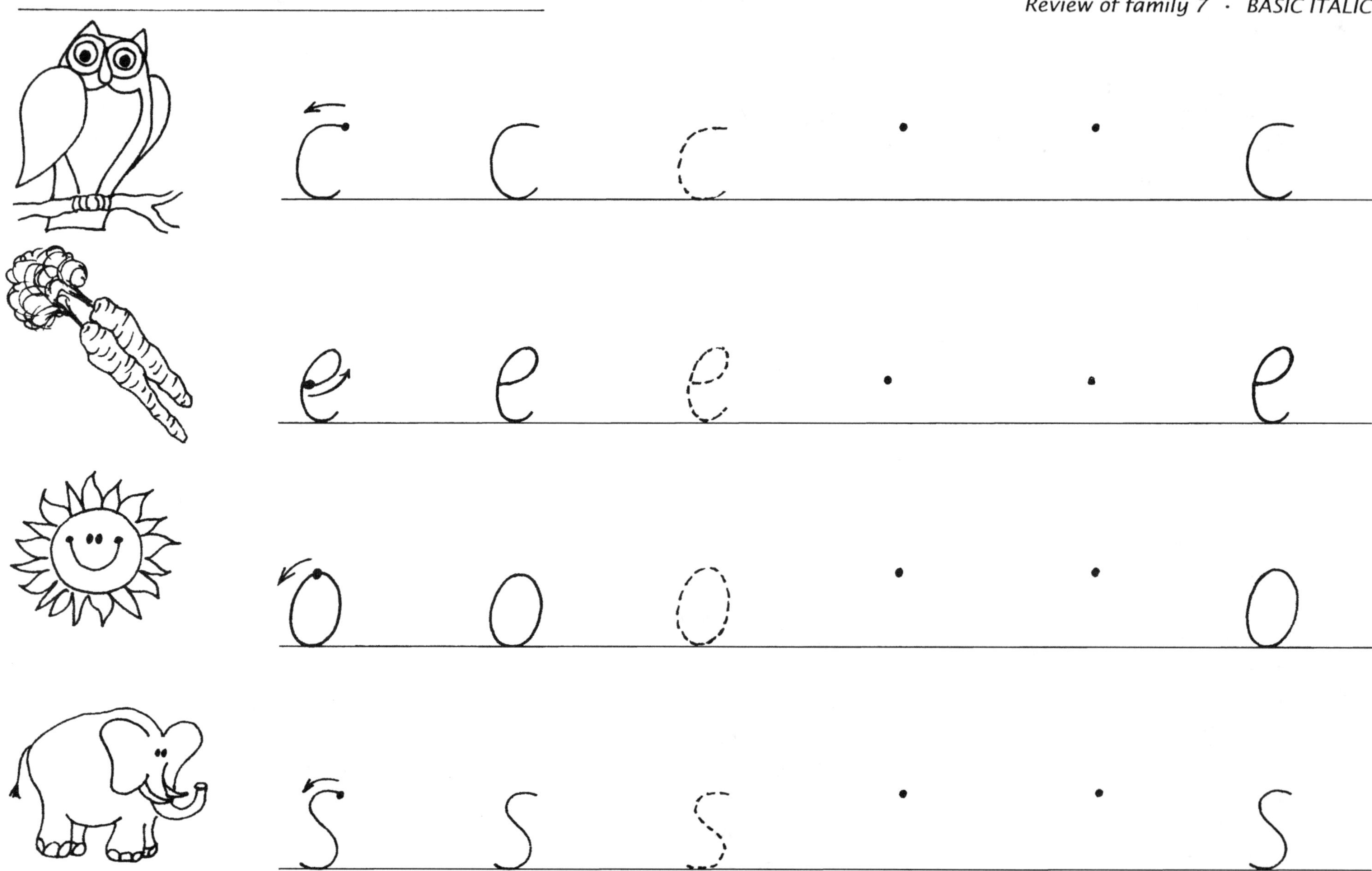

Ask the student to draw a line from the picture to the letter
that stands for the correct beginning sound.

CONTENTS

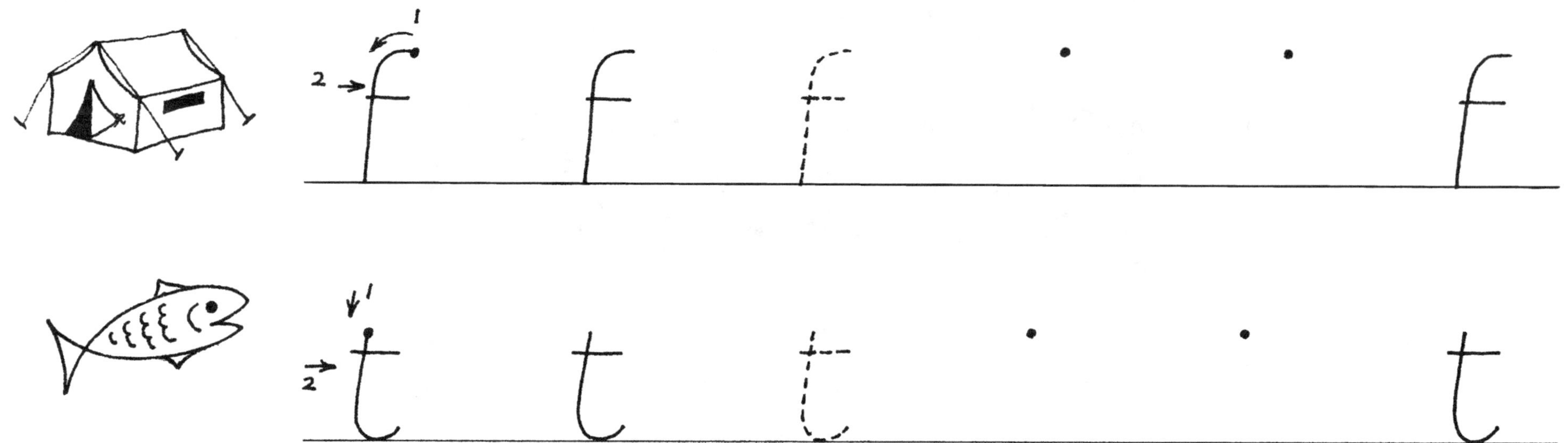

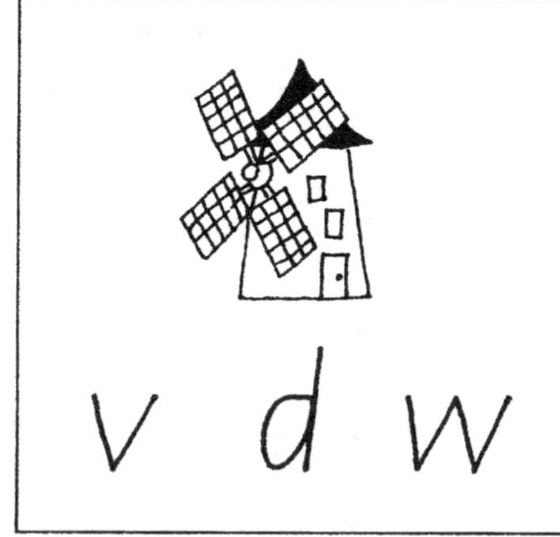

TOP TWO LINES: Ask the student to draw a line from the picture
to the letter that stands for the correct beginning sound.

BOTTOM FOUR SQUARES: Ask the student to circle the letter that
stands for the beginning sound of the picture.

by

Barbara Getty & Inga Dubay

GETTY-DUBAY™ ITALIC HANDWRITING SERIES

BOOK A ▪ Basic Italic
14 mm body height

BOOK B ▪ Basic Italic
11 mm body height, 9 mm

BOOK C ▪ Basic & Cursive Italic
9 mm, 6 mm body height   Introduction to Cursive Italic

BOOK D ▪ Basic & Cursive Italic
6 mm, 5 mm body height

BOOK E ▪ Basic & Cursive Italic
6 mm, 5 mm, 4 mm body height

BOOK F ▪ Basic & Cursive Italic
6 mm, 5 mm, 4 mm body height

BOOK G ▪ Basic & Cursive Italic
5 mm, 4 mm body height

INSTRUCTION MANUAL

BOOK A ▪ INTERNATIONAL EDITION
Copyright 2012 by Barbara M. Getty and Inga S. Dubay
ISBN 978-0-9827762-7-8

FOURTH EDITION
Copyright 2012 by Barbara M. Getty and Inga S. Dubay
THIRD EDITION
Copyright 1999 by Barbara M. Getty and Inga S. Dubay
SECOND EDITION
Copyright 1986 by Barbara M. Getty and Inga S. Dubay
REVISED EDITION
Copyright 1980 by Barbara M. Getty and Inga S. Dubay
FIRST EDITION
Copyright 1979 by Barbara M. Getty and Inga S. Dubay

All rights reserved. This text may not be reproduced in whole or in part without the express written permission of the copyright holder.

Published by Handwriting Success, LLC,
Portland, Oregon USA

www.handwritingsuccess.com

Printed at various locations around the world by IngramSpark.

Cover Design: Sinda Markham
Front cover picture: Flowers of the sunflower family in the Ochoco National Forest, Oregon, USA
Back cover pictures: Columbine flower, Golden-mantled squirrel

www.ingramcontent.com/pod-product-compliance
Lightning Source LLC
Chambersburg PA
CBHW081423210726
48464CB00020B/1370

one stroke numeral · no lift

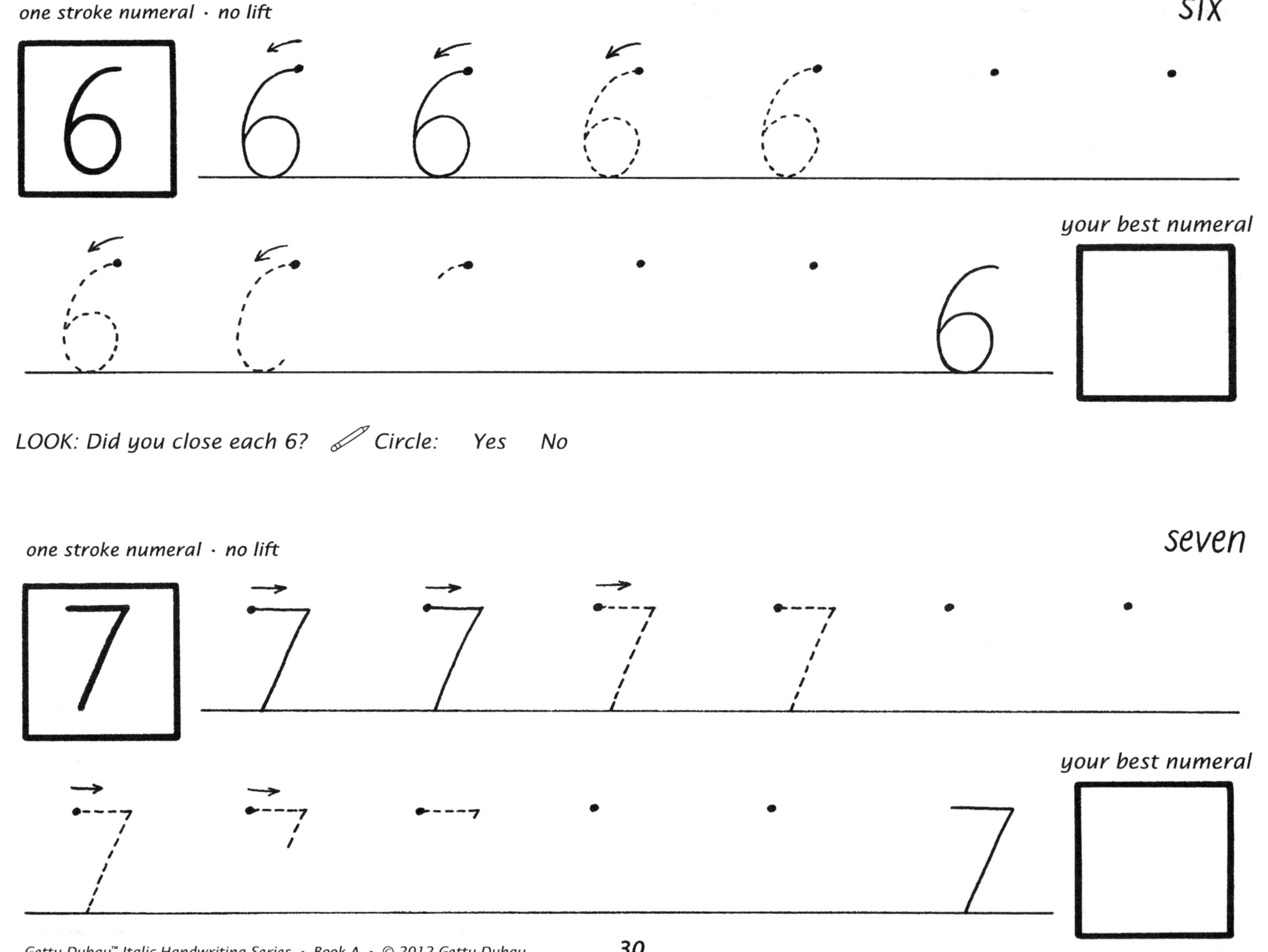

your best numeral

LOOK: Did you close each 6? Circle: Yes   No

seven

one stroke numeral · no lift

your best numeral

four

4

your best numeral

five

5

your best numeral

eight

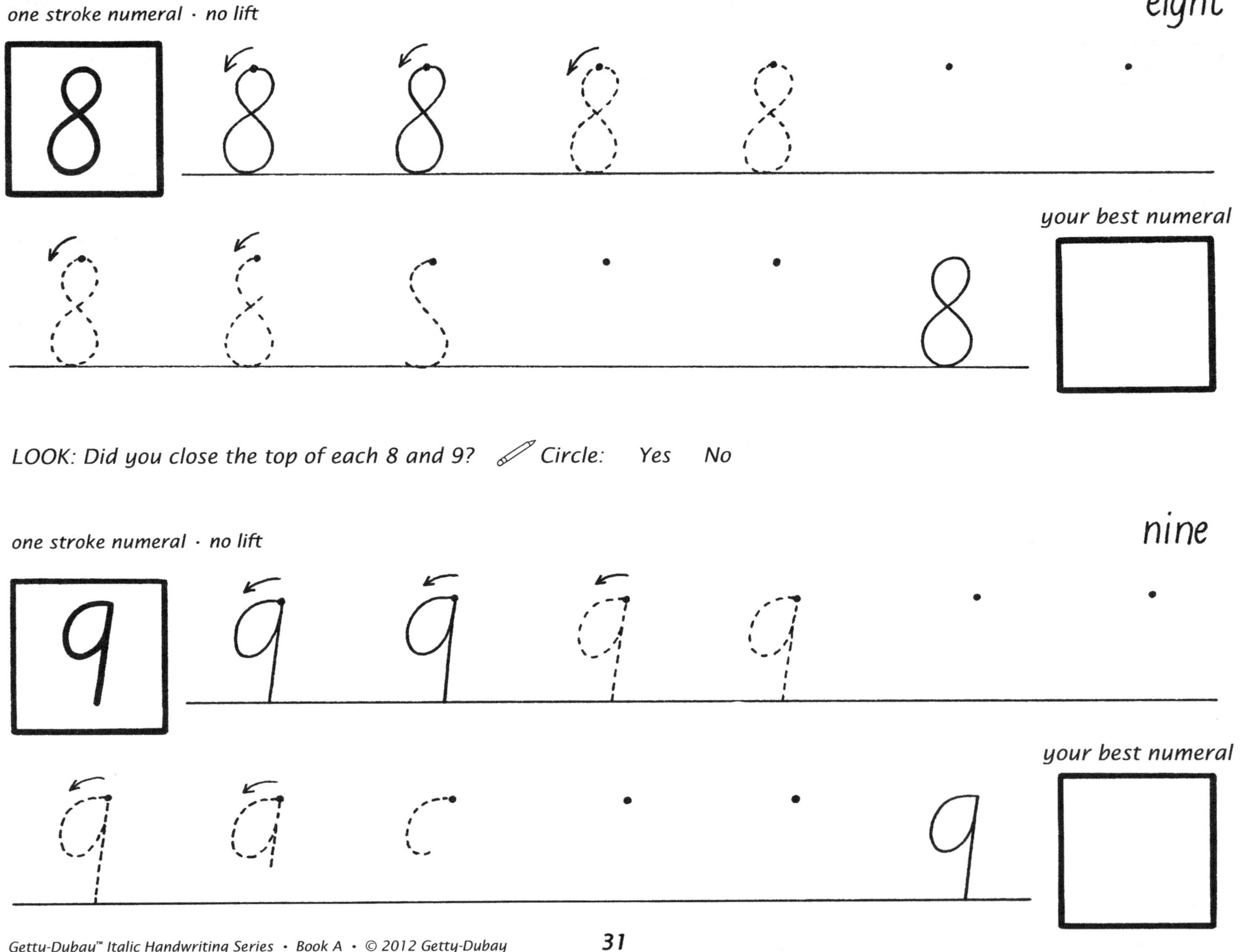

your best numeral

LOOK: Did you close the top of each 8 and 9? Circle: Yes   No

one stroke numeral · no lift

nine

your best numeral

one stroke numeral · no lift

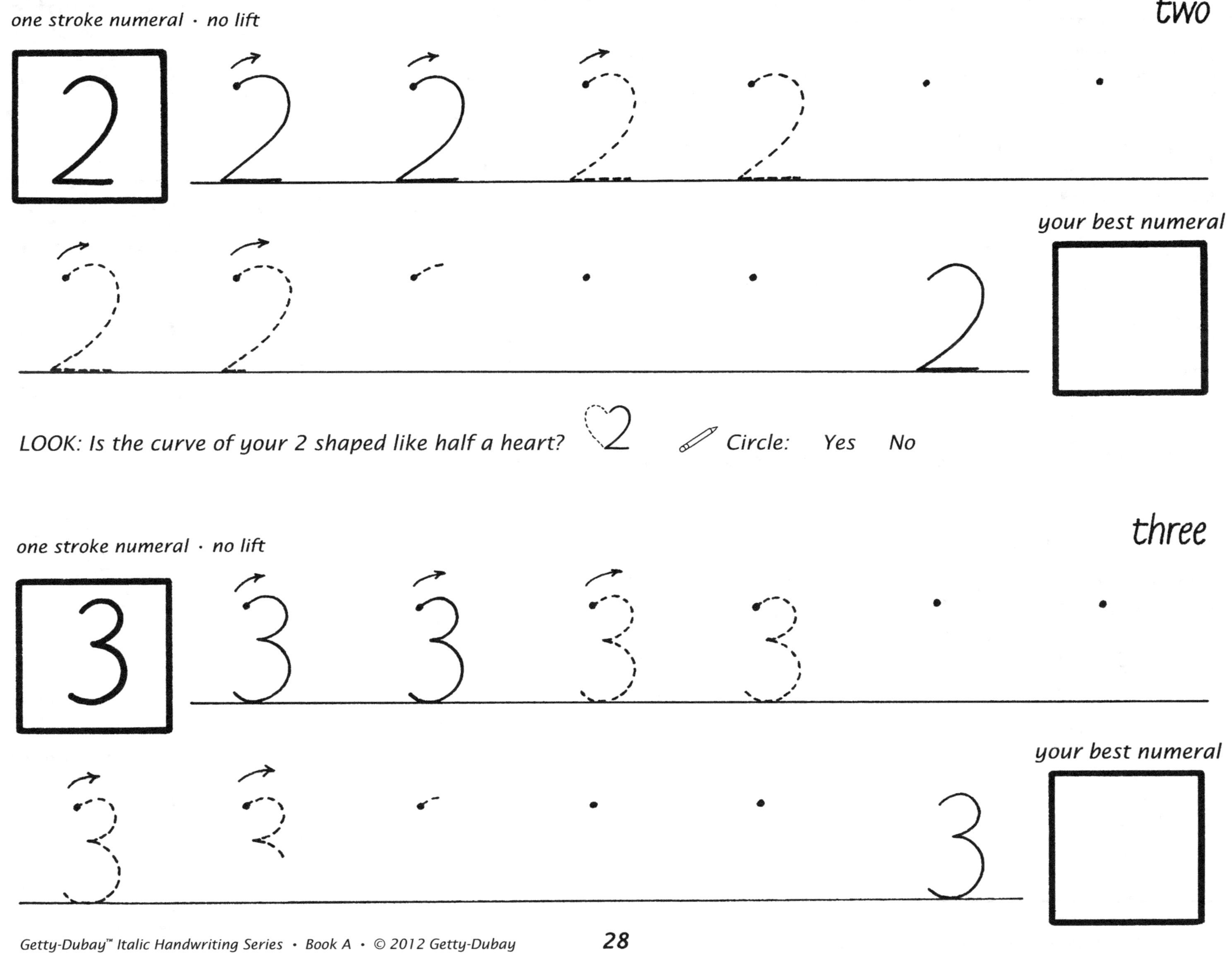

your best numeral

LOOK: Is the curve of your 2 shaped like half a heart?   ✎ Circle: Yes   No

one stroke numeral · no lift

your best numeral

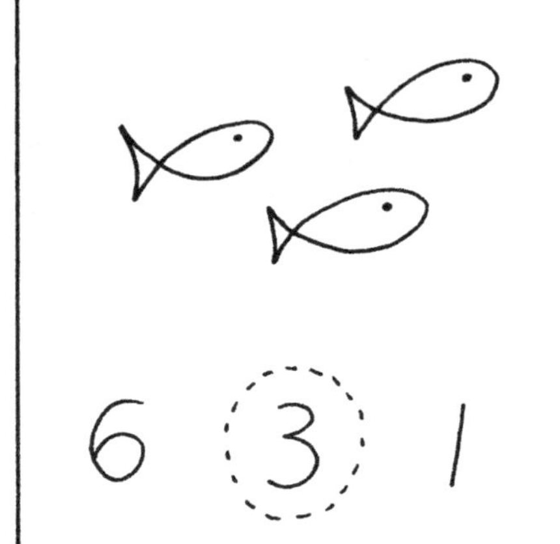

6 (3) 1

9 2 5

7 0 4

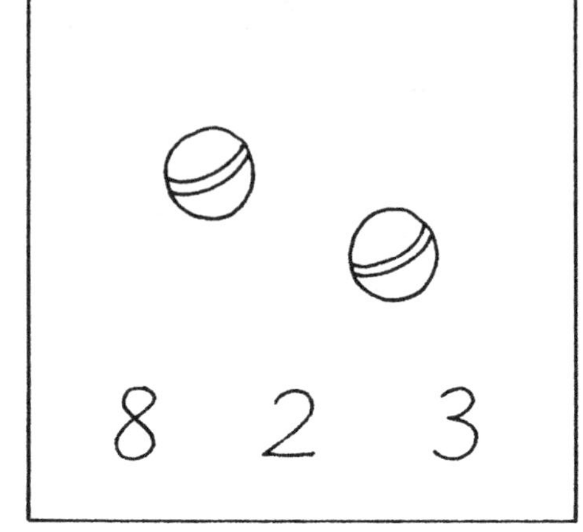

8 2 3

3 4 2

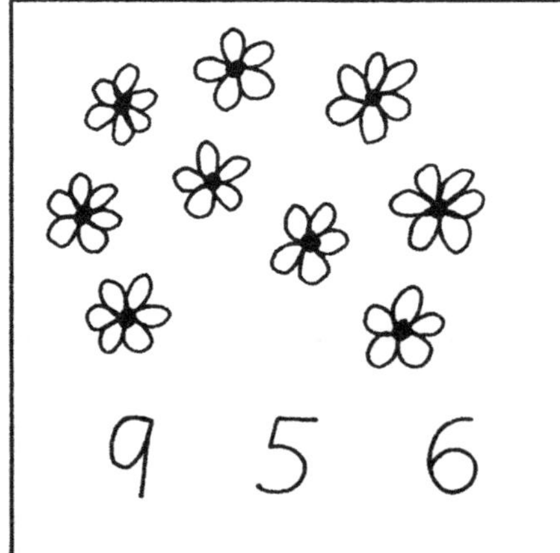

9 5 6

7 1 6

2 8 6

Ask the student to circle the numeral
that stands for the number of objects in the box.

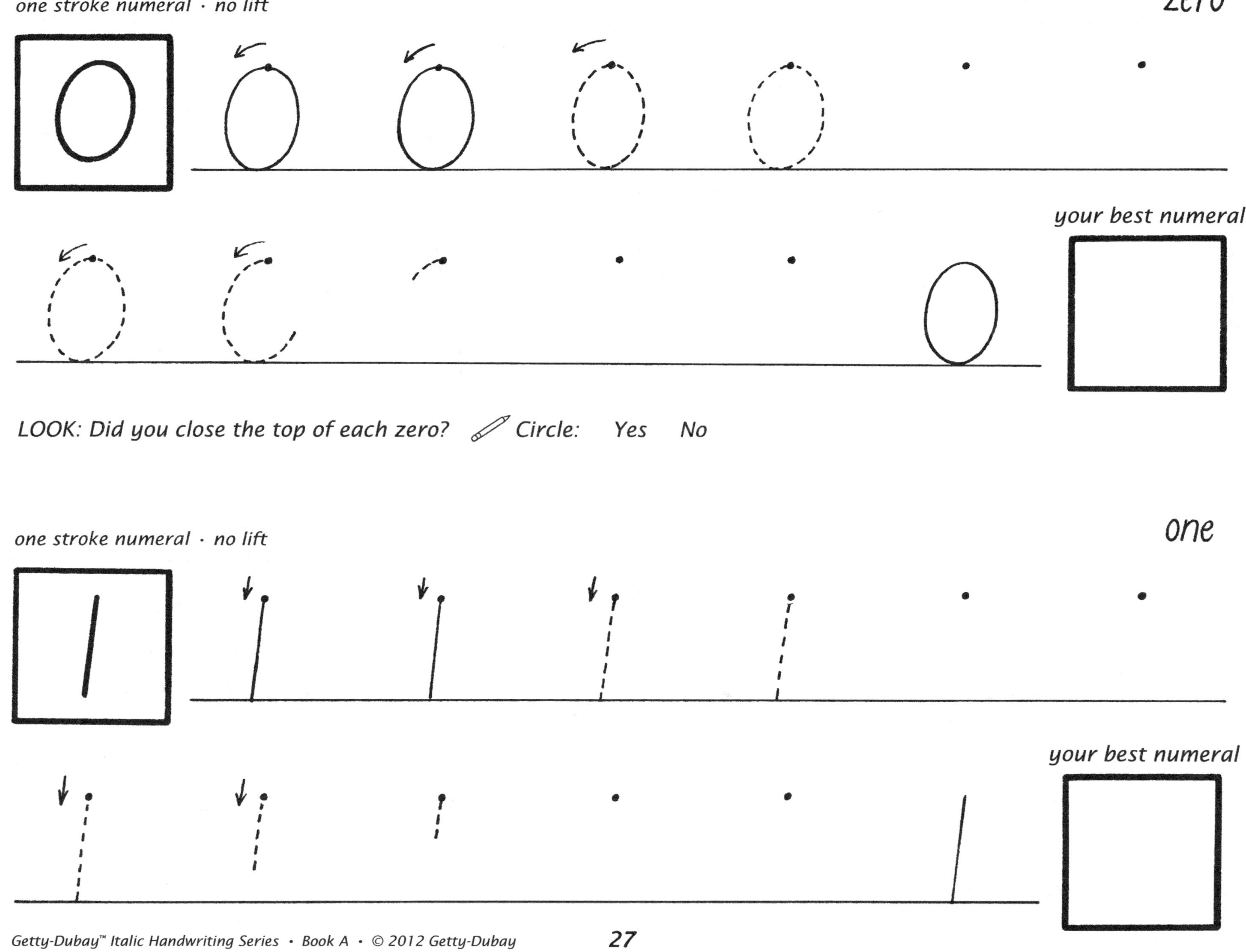

one stroke numeral · no lift
zero
your best numeral
LOOK: Did you close the top of each zero? Circle: Yes   No
one stroke numeral · no lift
one
your best numeral

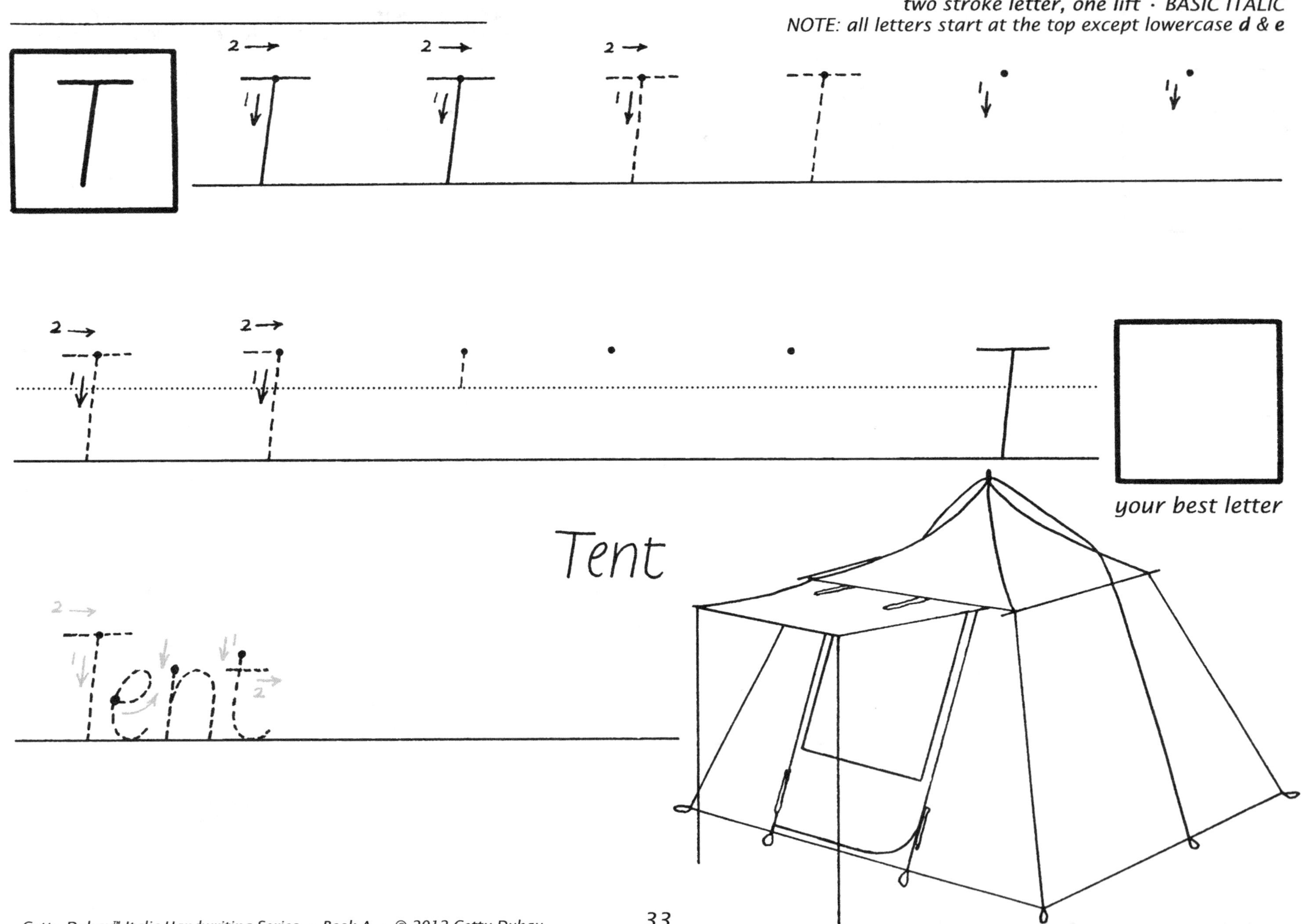

T
2 →
2 →
2 →
2 →
2 →
2 →
your best letter
Tent
Tent

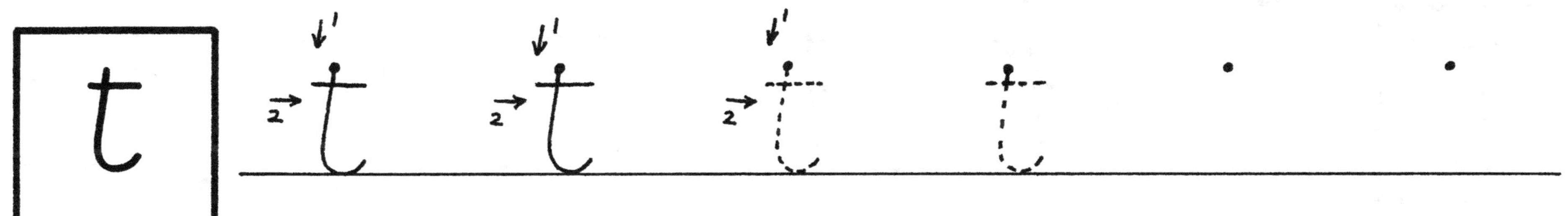

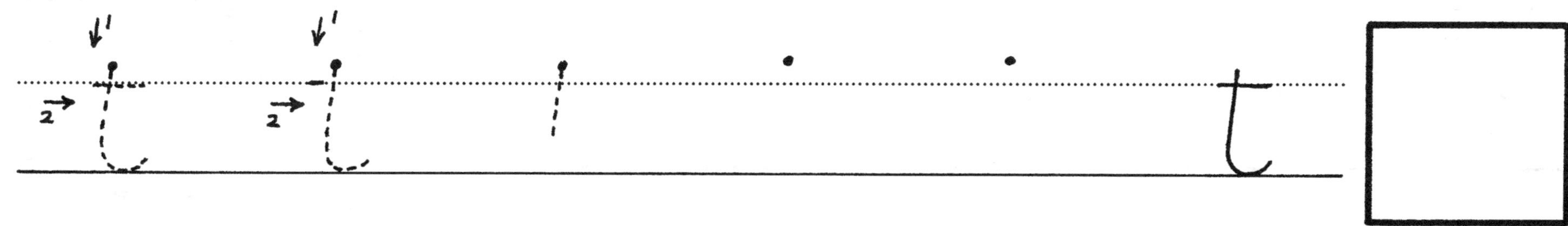

your best letter

turkey

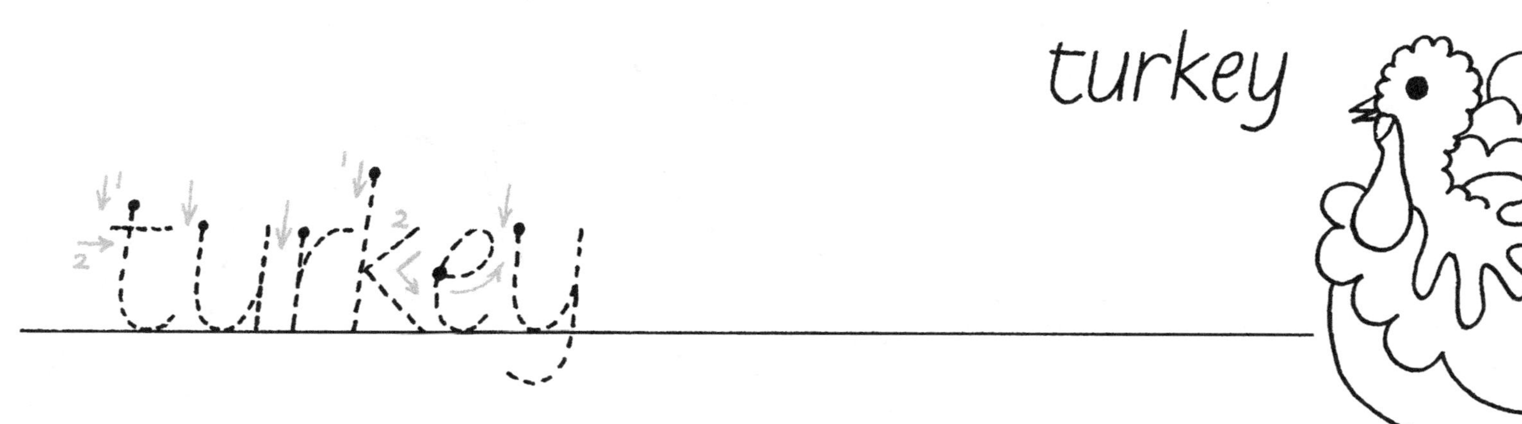

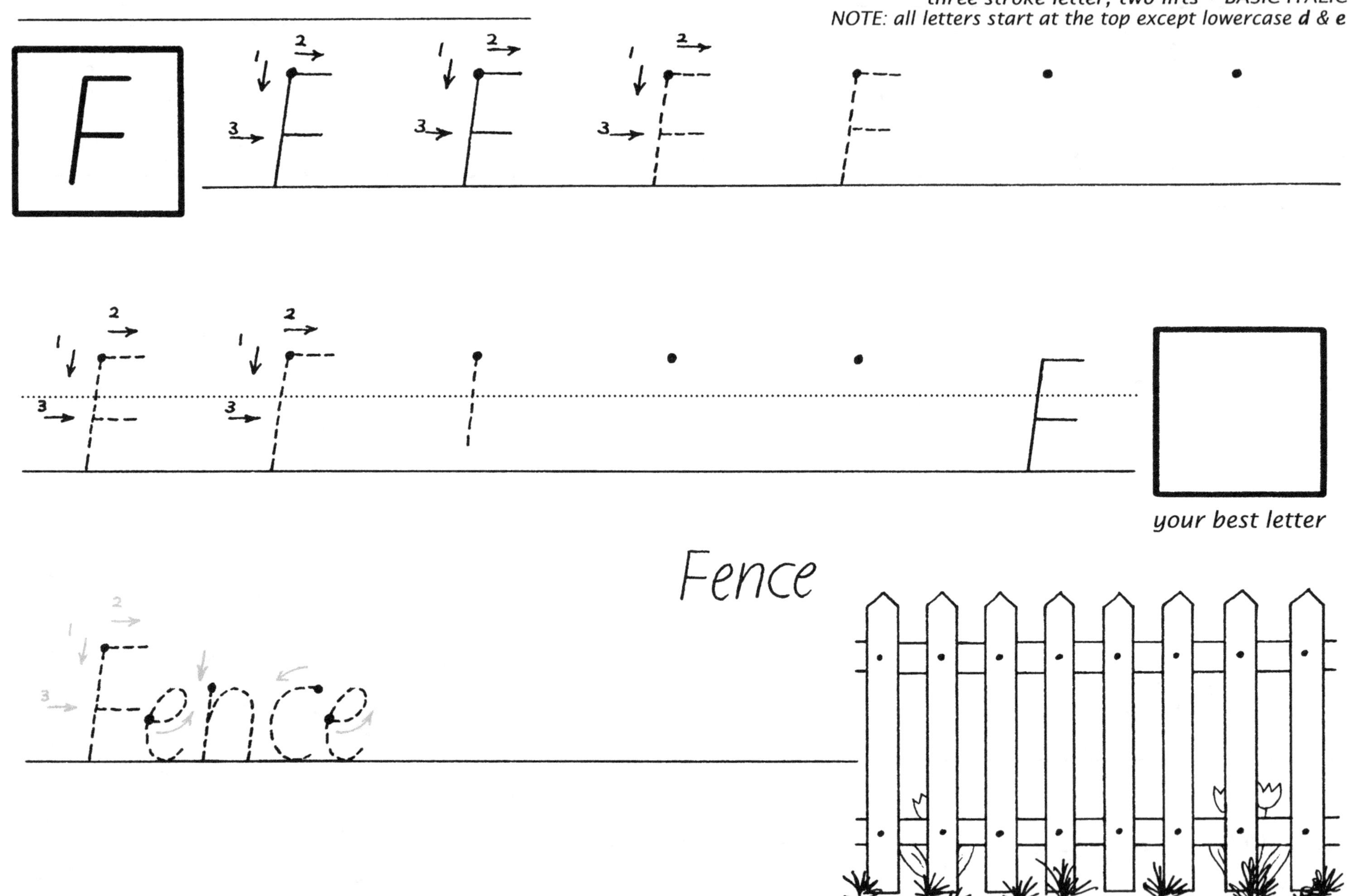

your best letter
Fence

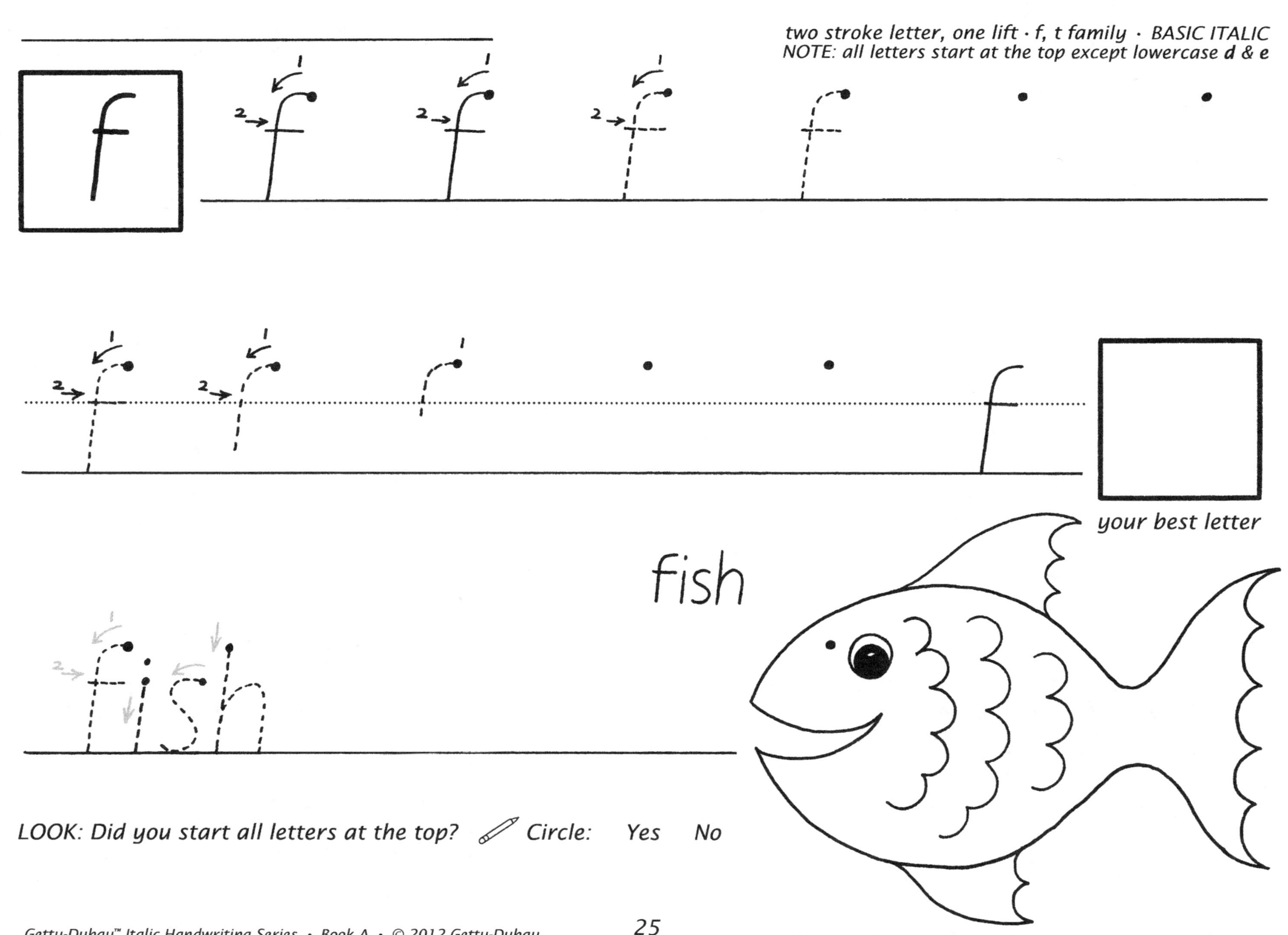

two stroke letter, one lift · f, t family · BASIC ITALIC
NOTE: all letters start at the top except lowercase d & e
f
your best letter
fish
fish
LOOK: Did you start all letters at the top?   Circle: Yes   No

your best letter

Sailboat

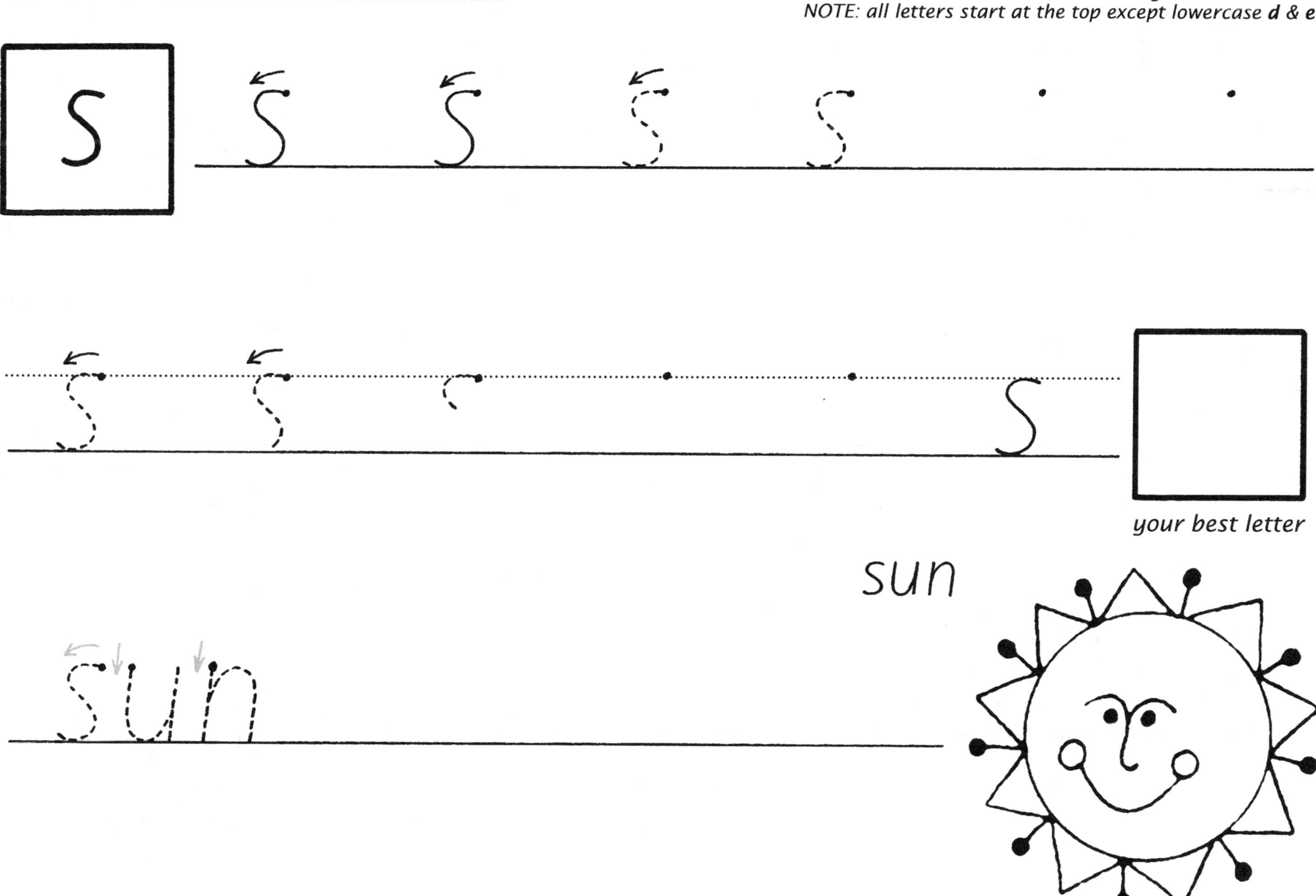

S
your best letter
sun
sun

one stroke letter, no lift · BASIC ITALIC
NOTE: all letters start at the top except lowercase d & e
your best letter
Cow
LOOK: Did you trace each letter before writing your own?
Circle: Yes   No

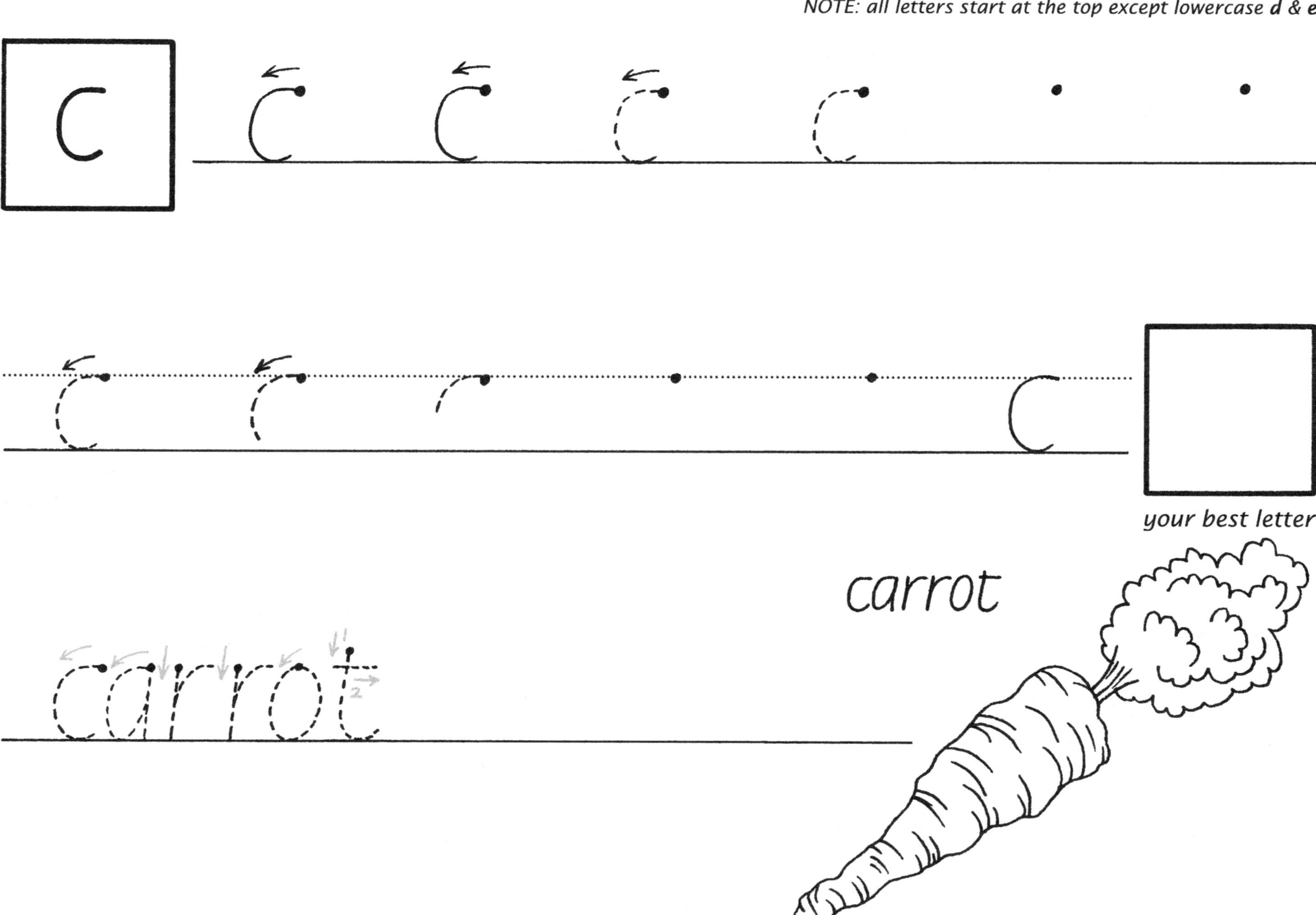

your best letter

carrot

E

your best letter

Egg

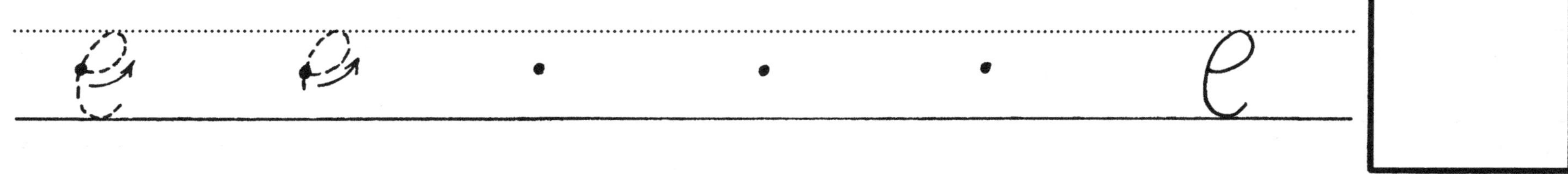

your best letter

elephant

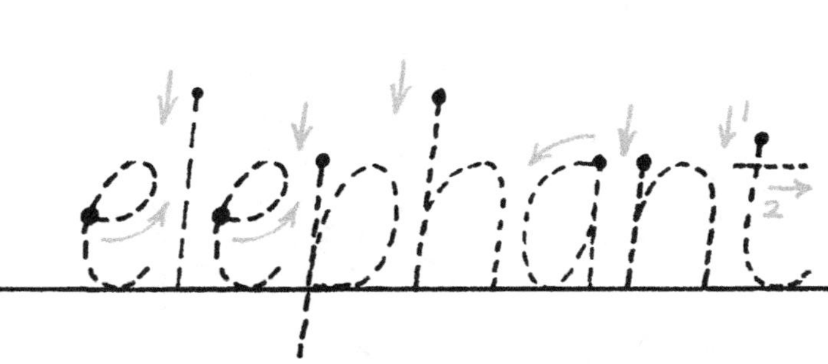

LOOK: Did you trace each **e** before writing your own?

Circle: Yes   No

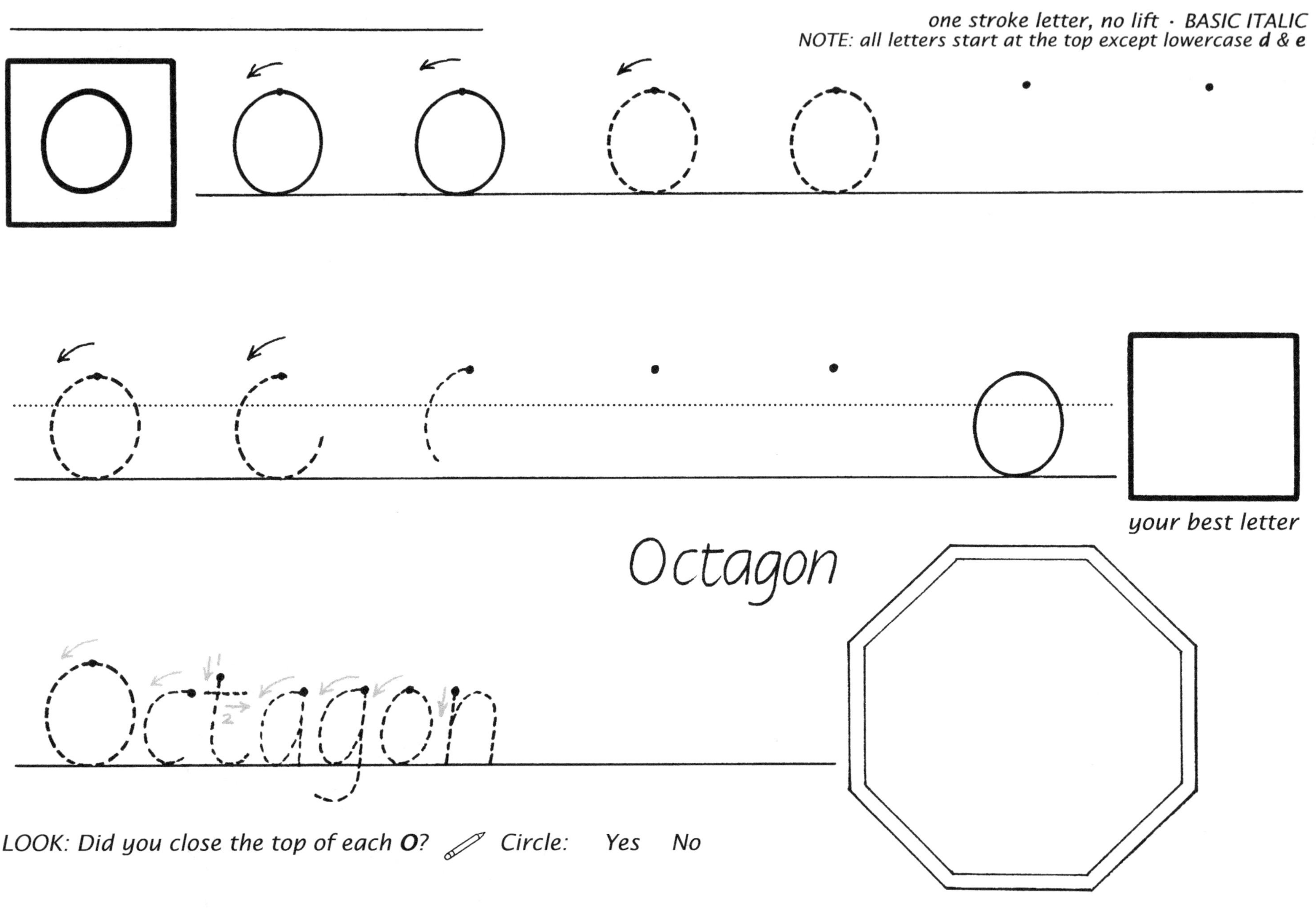

one stroke letter, no lift · BASIC ITALIC
NOTE: all letters start at the top except lowercase d & e
your best letter
Octagon
Octagon
LOOK: Did you close the top of each O? Circle: Yes No

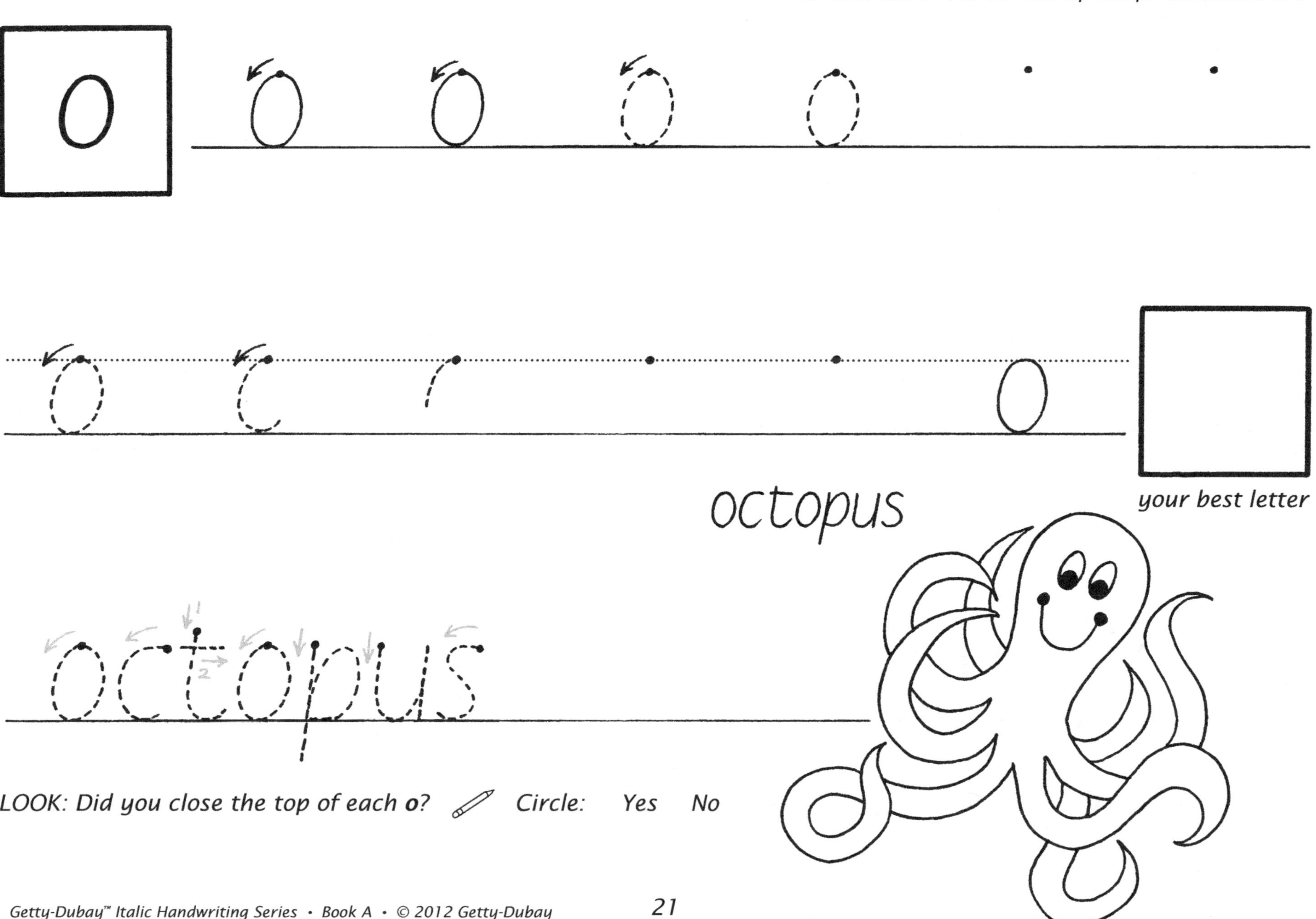

octopus

your best letter

LOOK: Did you close the top of each **o**? ✎ Circle: Yes   No

your best letter

Peacock

parrot

B

Balloons

your best letter

Balloons

your best letter
butterfly

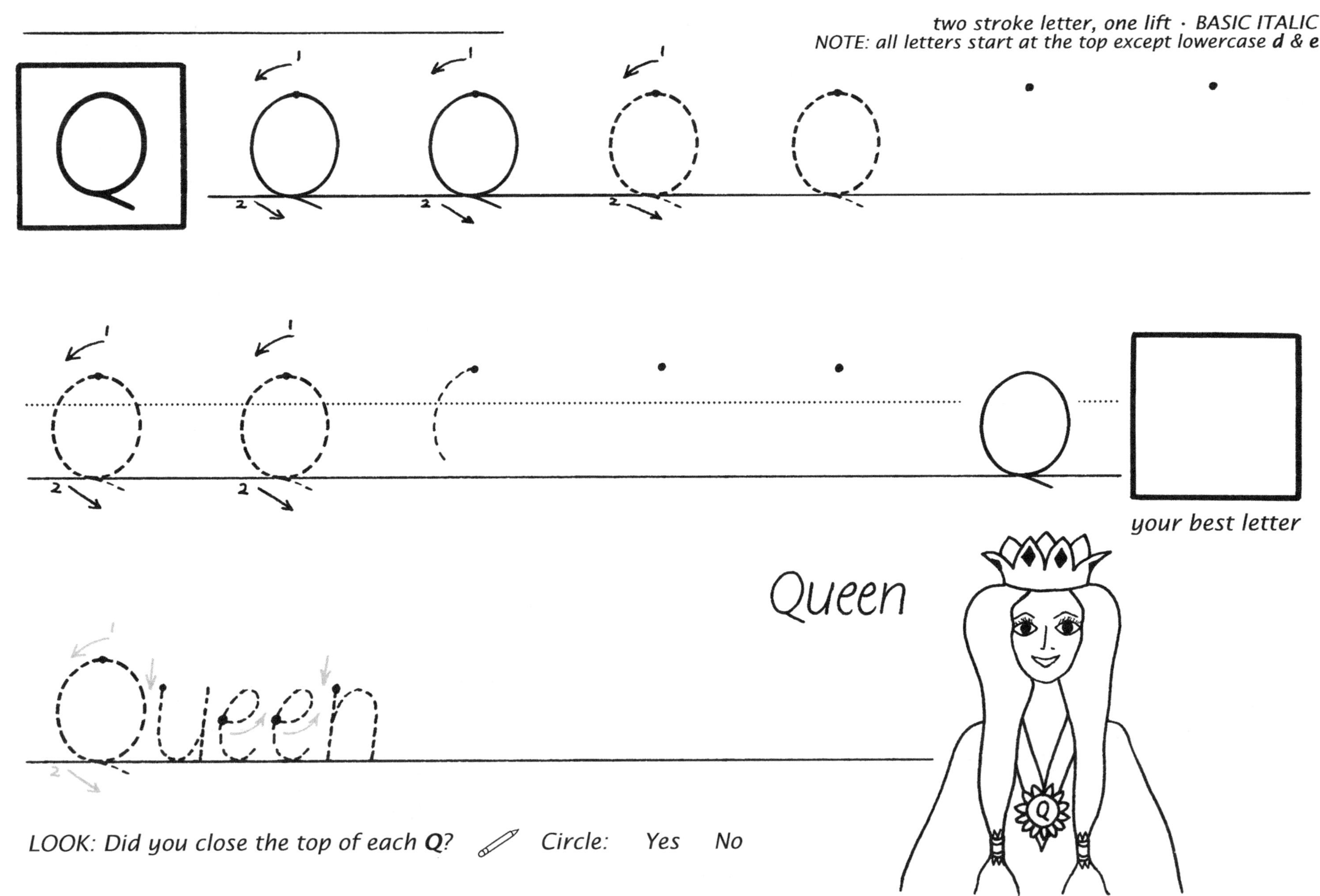

your best letter

Queen

LOOK: Did you close the top of each **Q**?   Circle: Yes   No

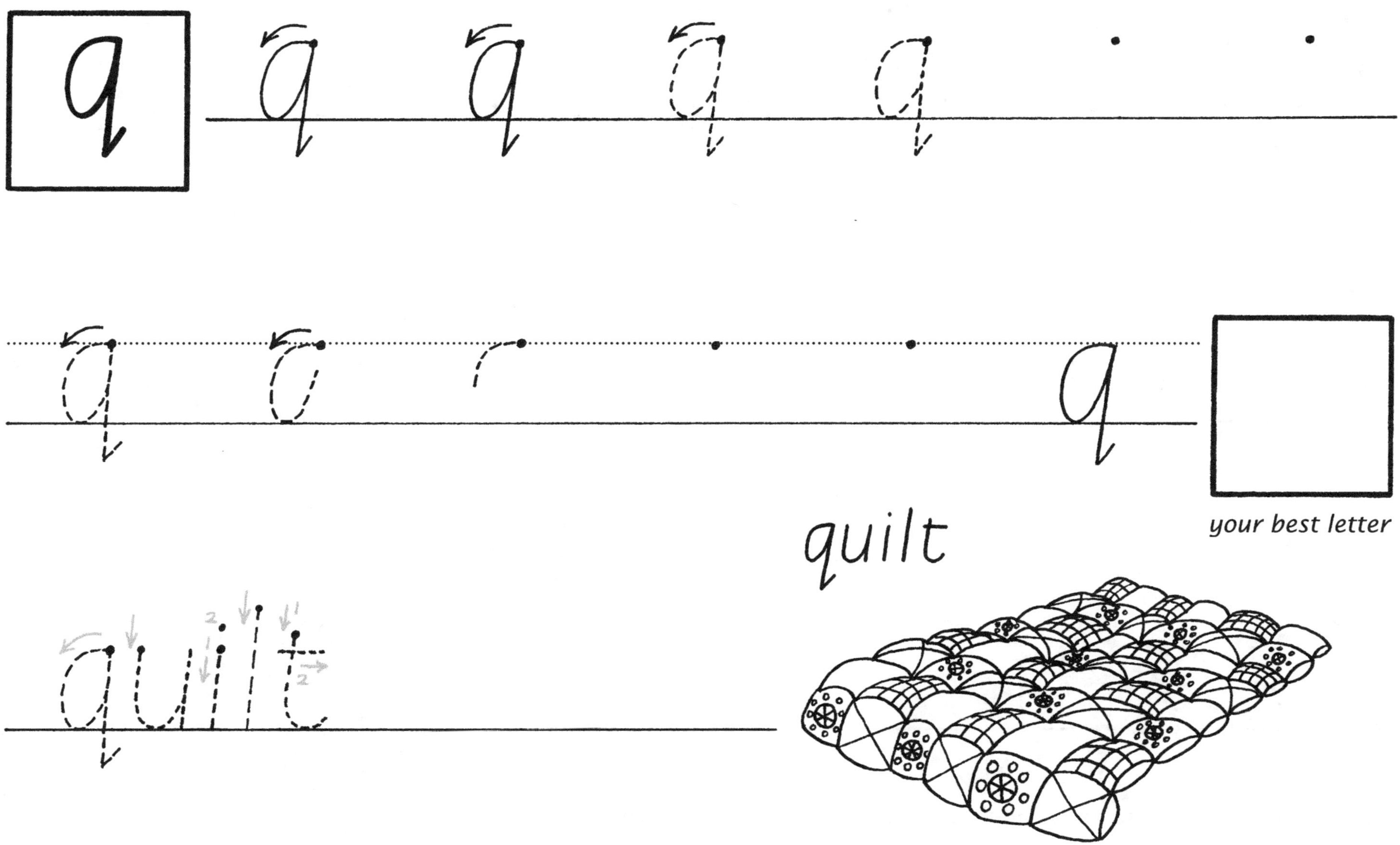

your best letter

quilt

18

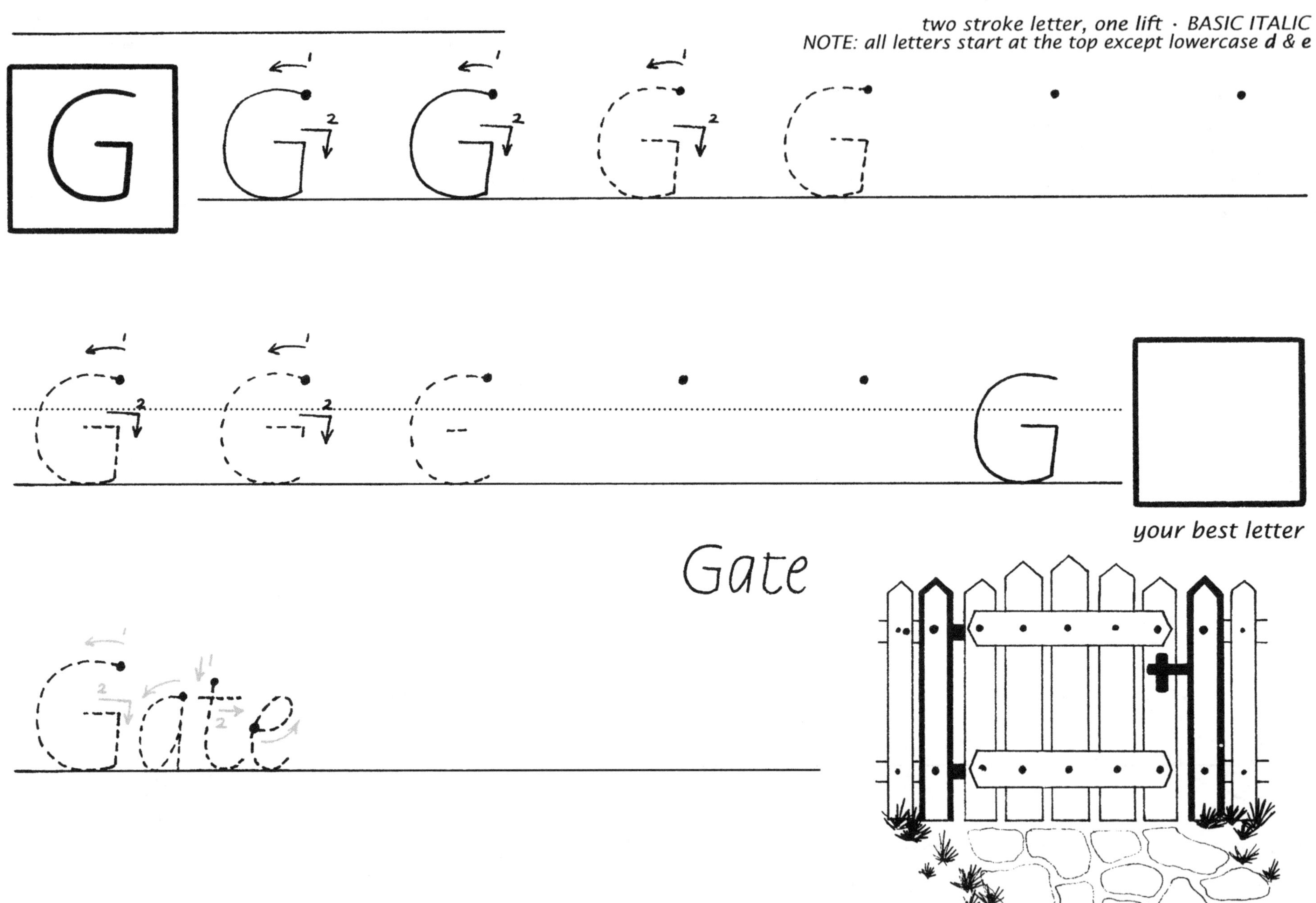

G
G
Gate
your best letter
Gate

LOOK: Did you trace each letter before writing your own?   Circle: Yes   No

D
your best letter
Dinosaur
Dinosaur

your best letter

dog

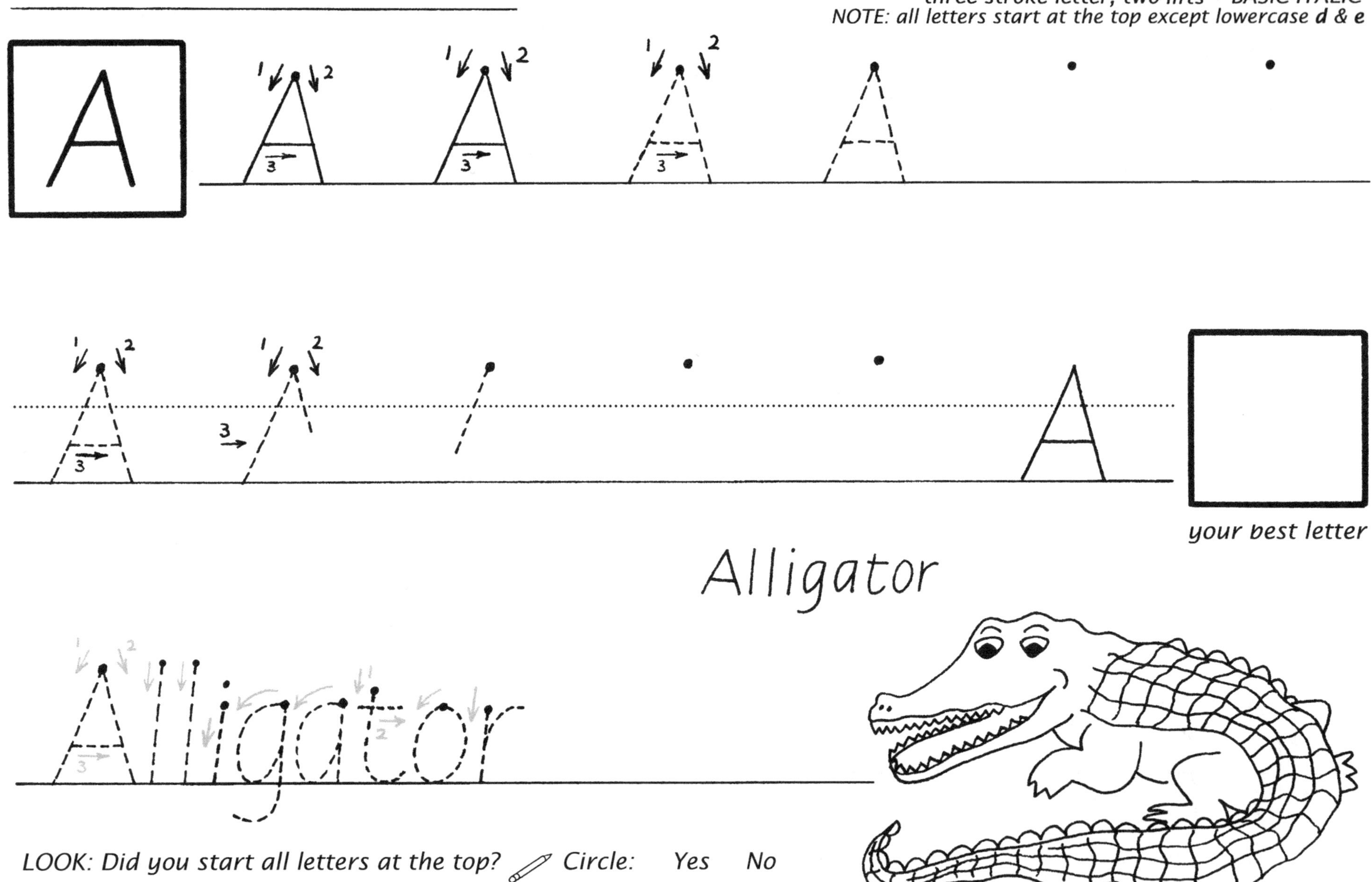

your best letter

Alligator

LOOK: Did you start all letters at the top? Circle: Yes   No

your best letter

apple

LOOK: Did you close each **a** at the top?   Circle: Yes   No

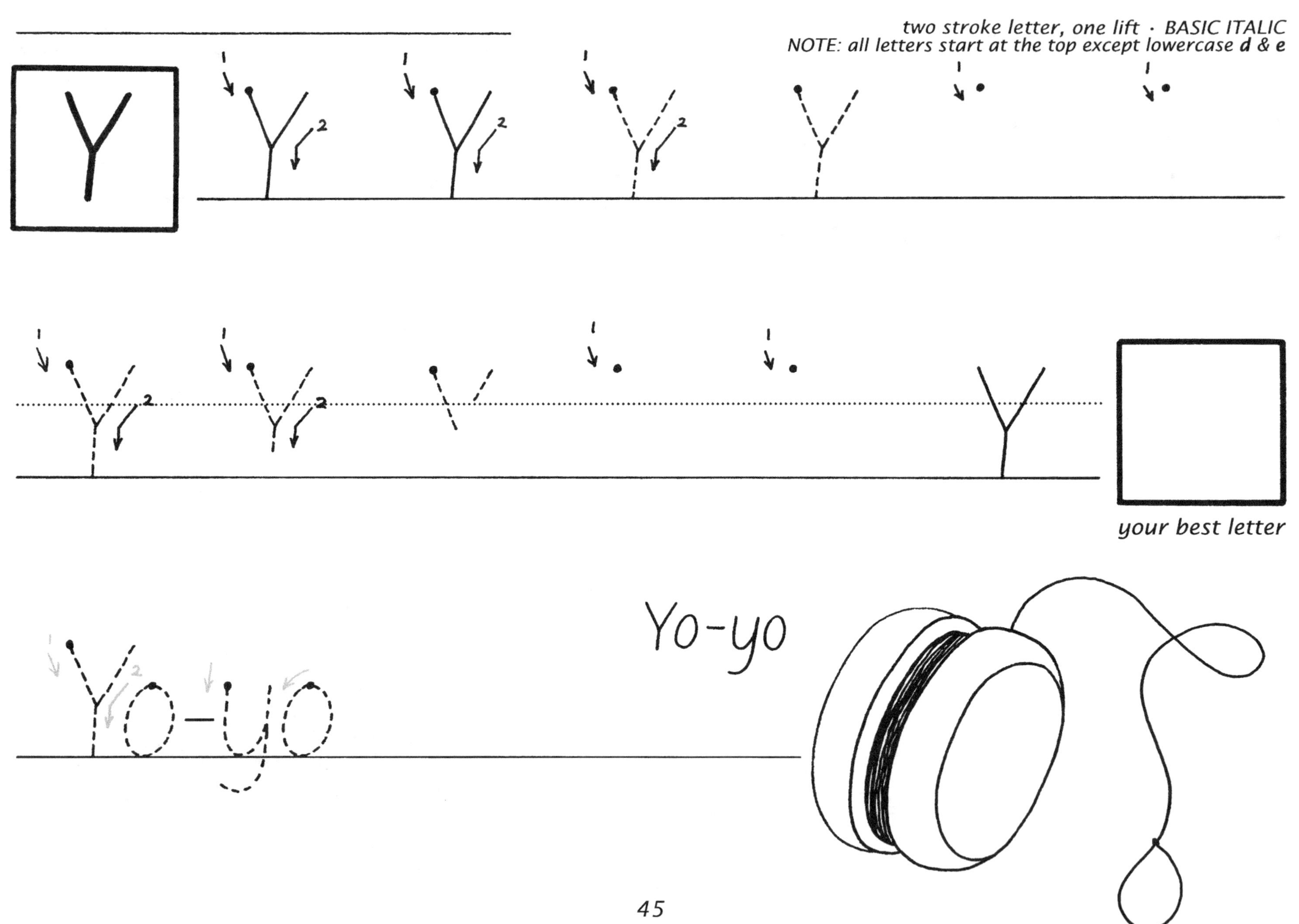

45

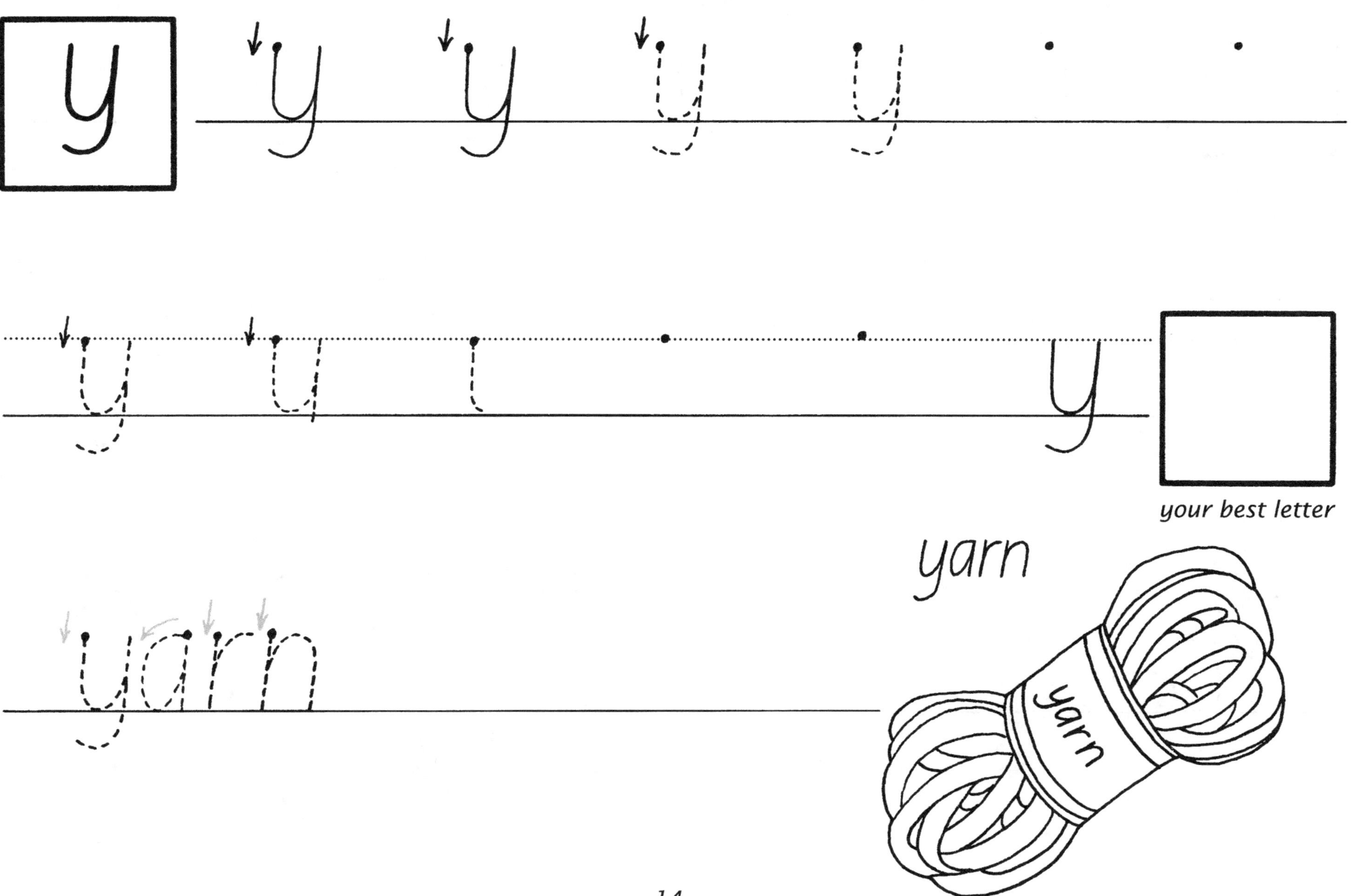

your best letter

yarn

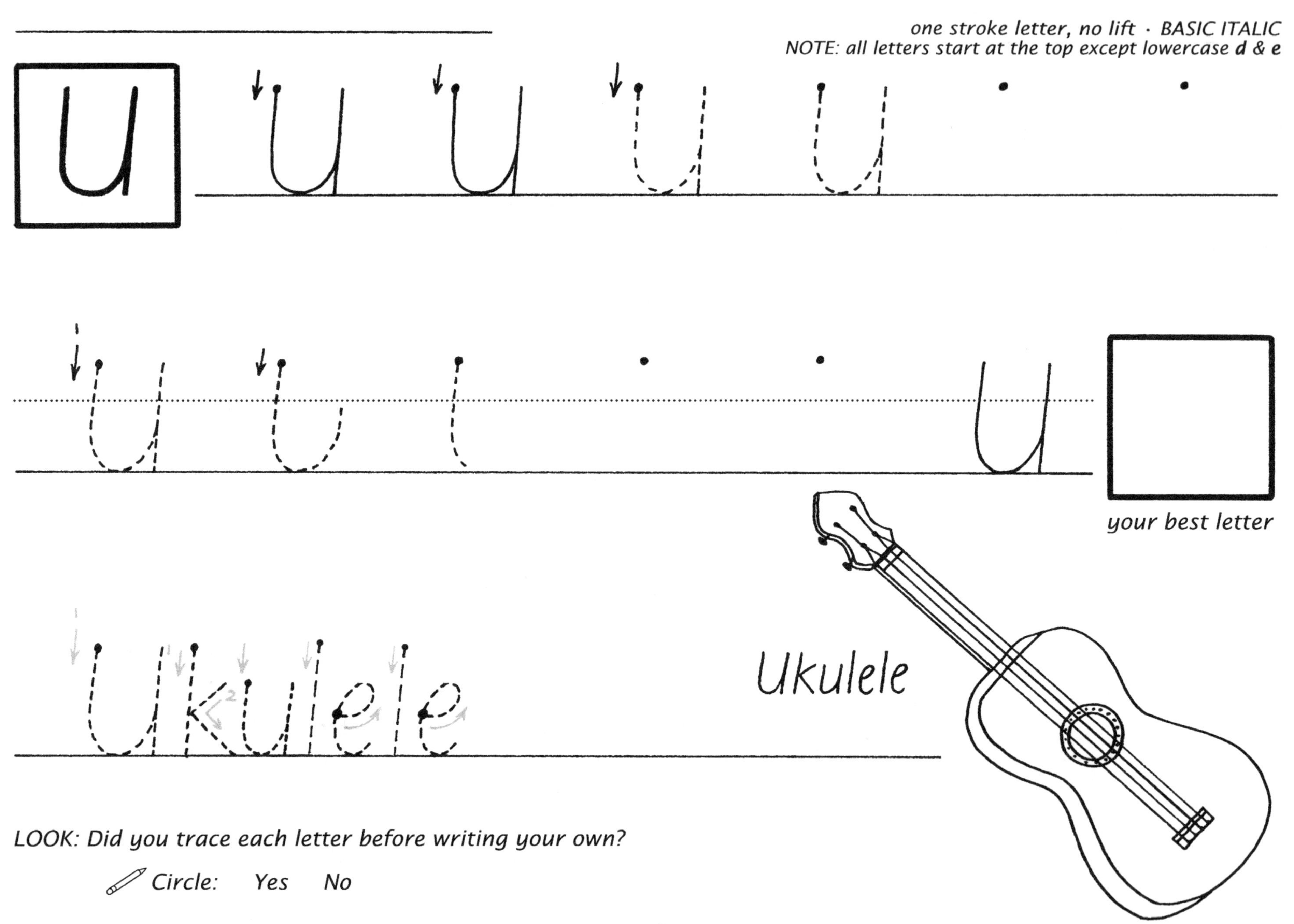

one stroke letter, no lift · BASIC ITALIC
NOTE: all letters start at the top except lowercase d & e
your best letter
Ukulele
LOOK: Did you trace each letter before writing your own?
Circle: Yes   No

u
your best letter
umbrella
umbrella

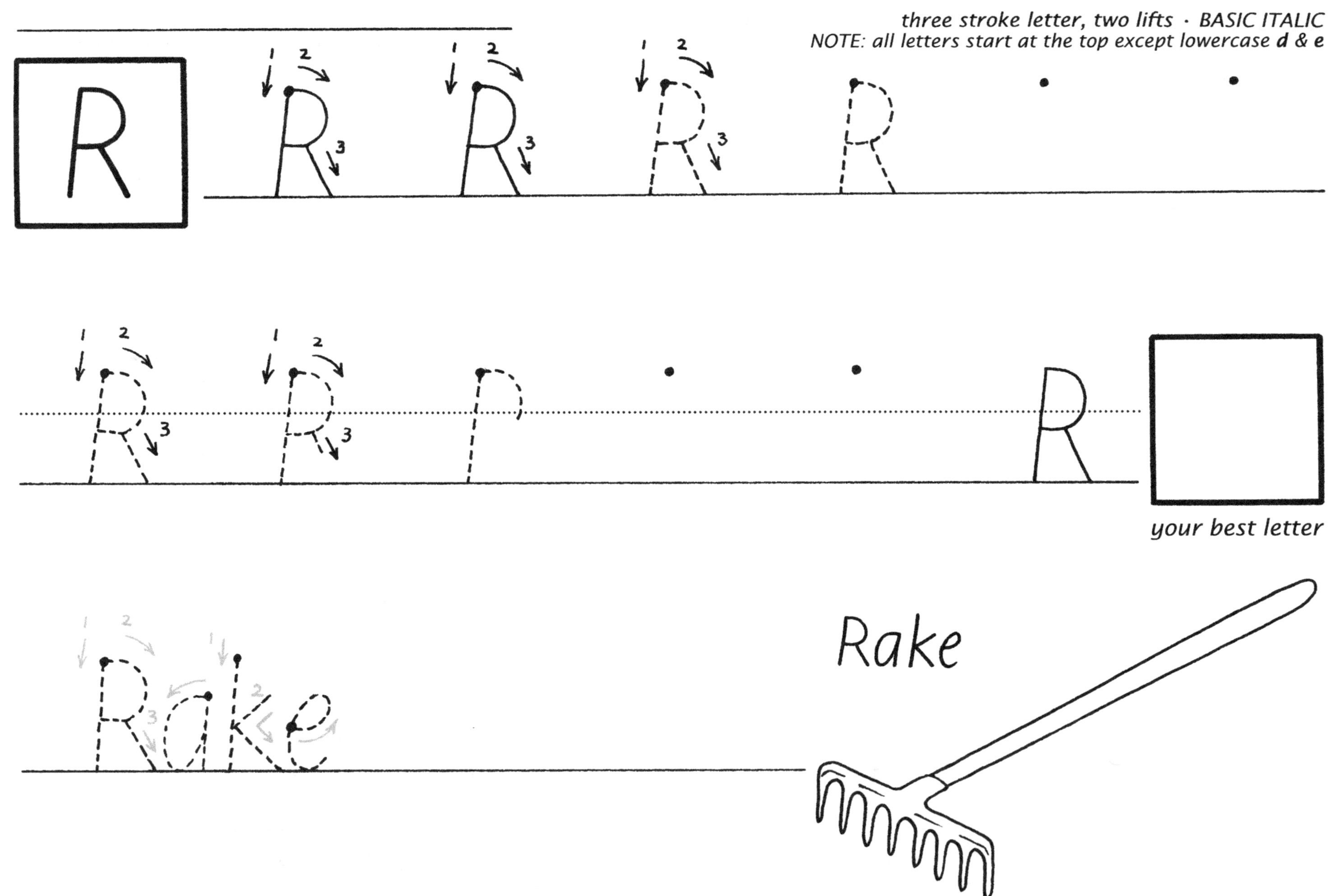

your best letter

Rake

your best letter

rabbit

LOOK: Did you start each letter at the top?   ✎ Circle: Yes   No

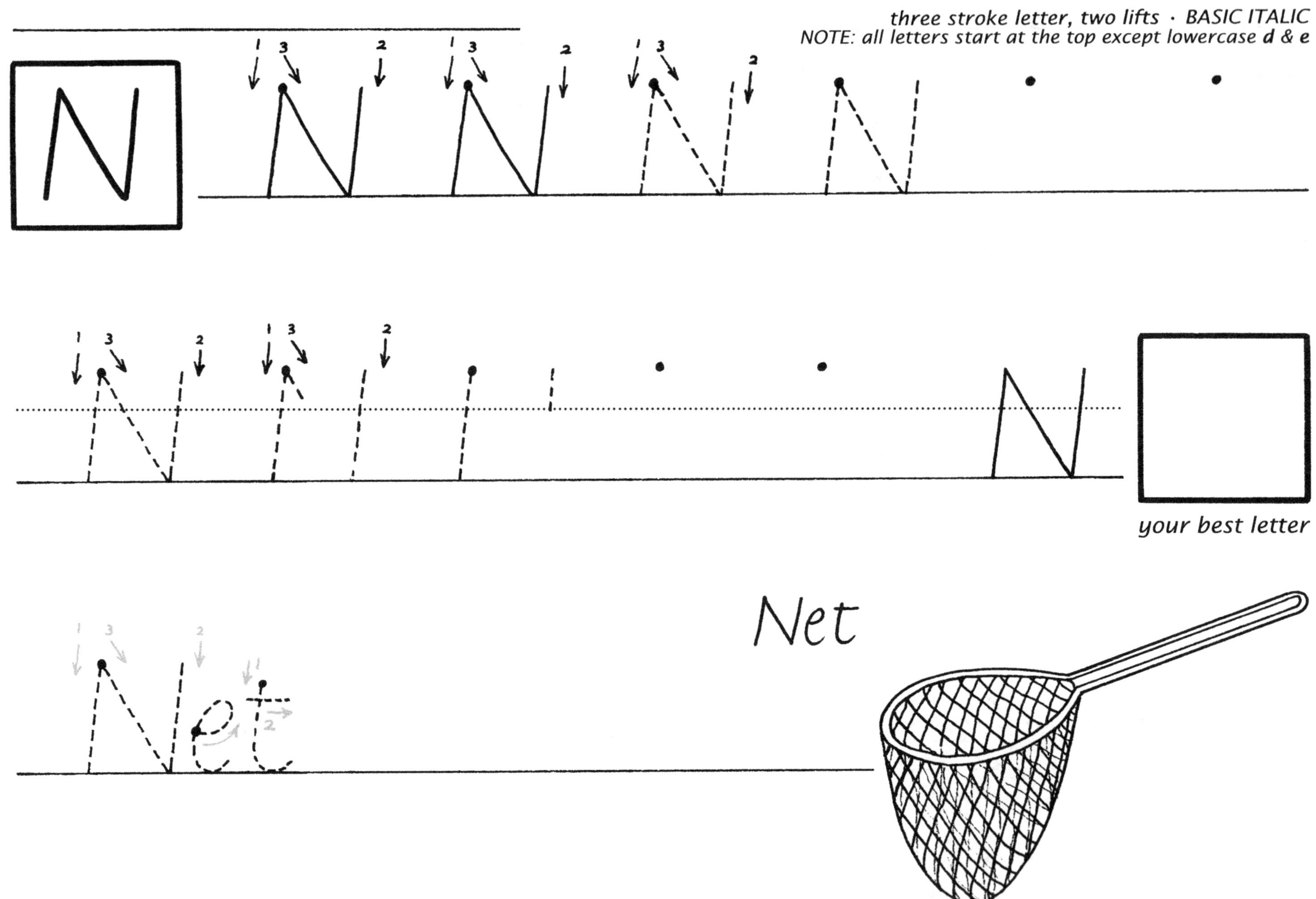

three stroke letter, two lifts · BASIC ITALIC
NOTE: all letters start at the top except lowercase d & e
your best letter
Net

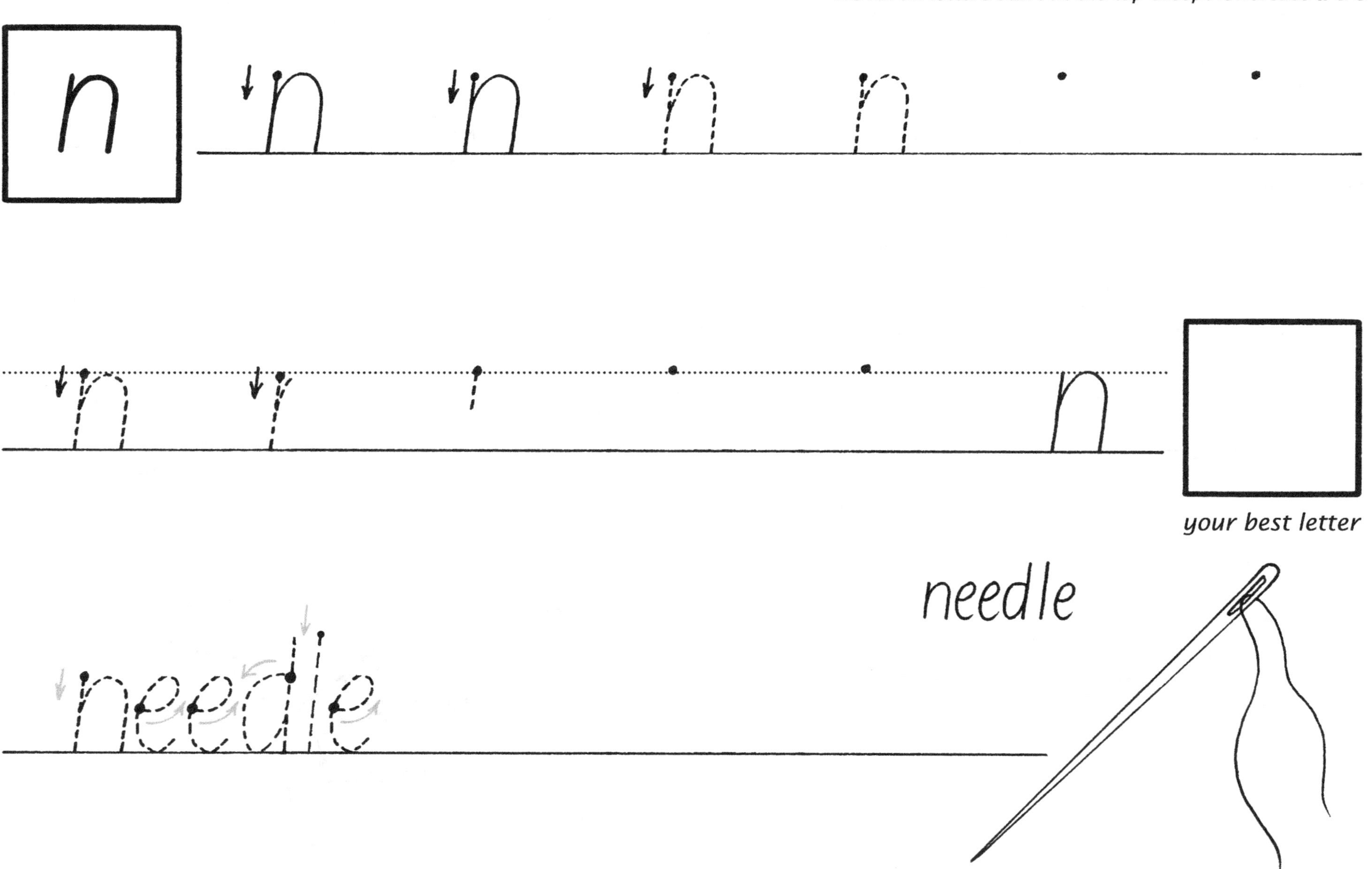

your best letter
needle
needle

M

your best letter

Mittens

Mittens

LOOK: Did you start all letters at the top? Circle: Yes   No

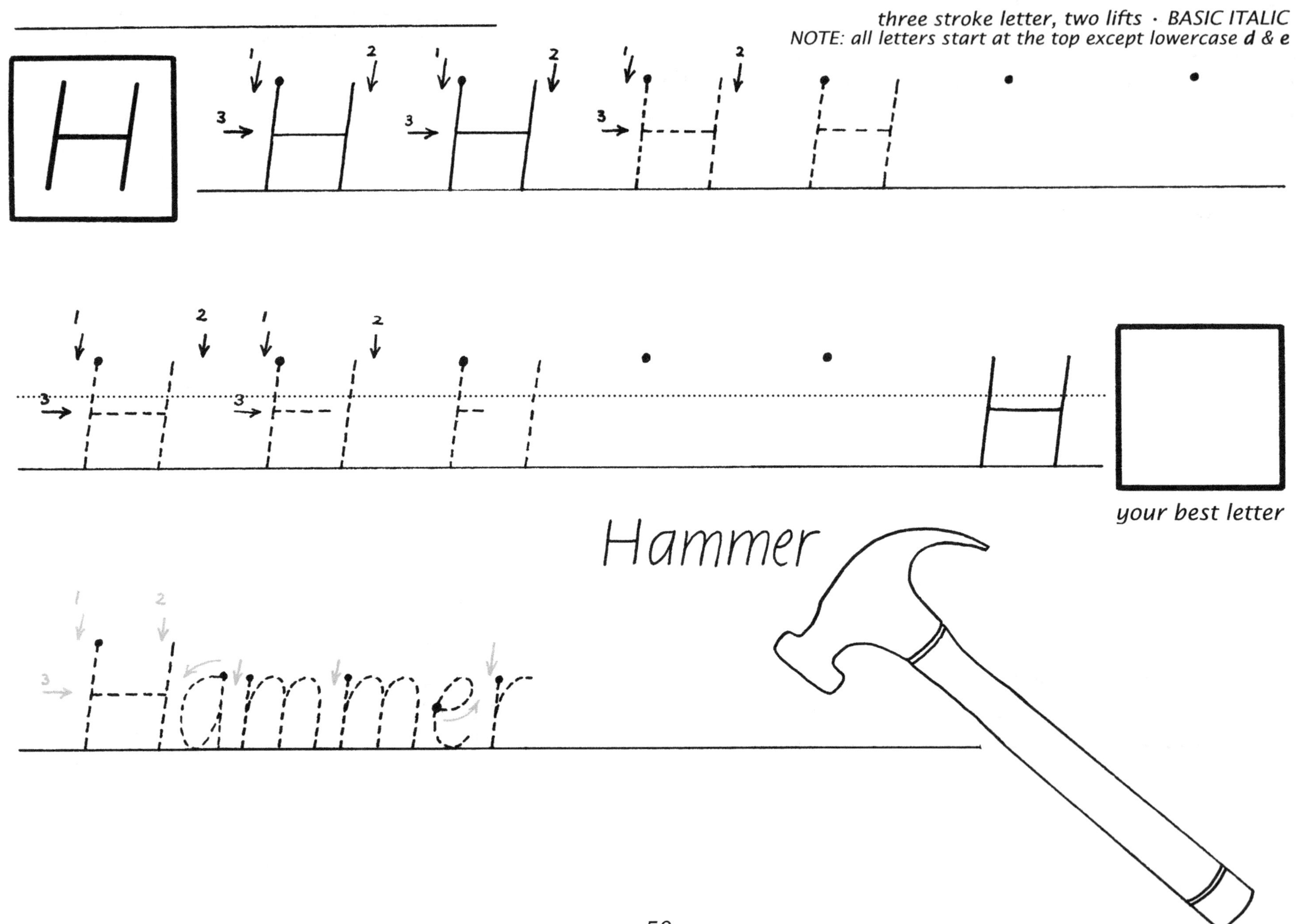

your best letter

Hammer

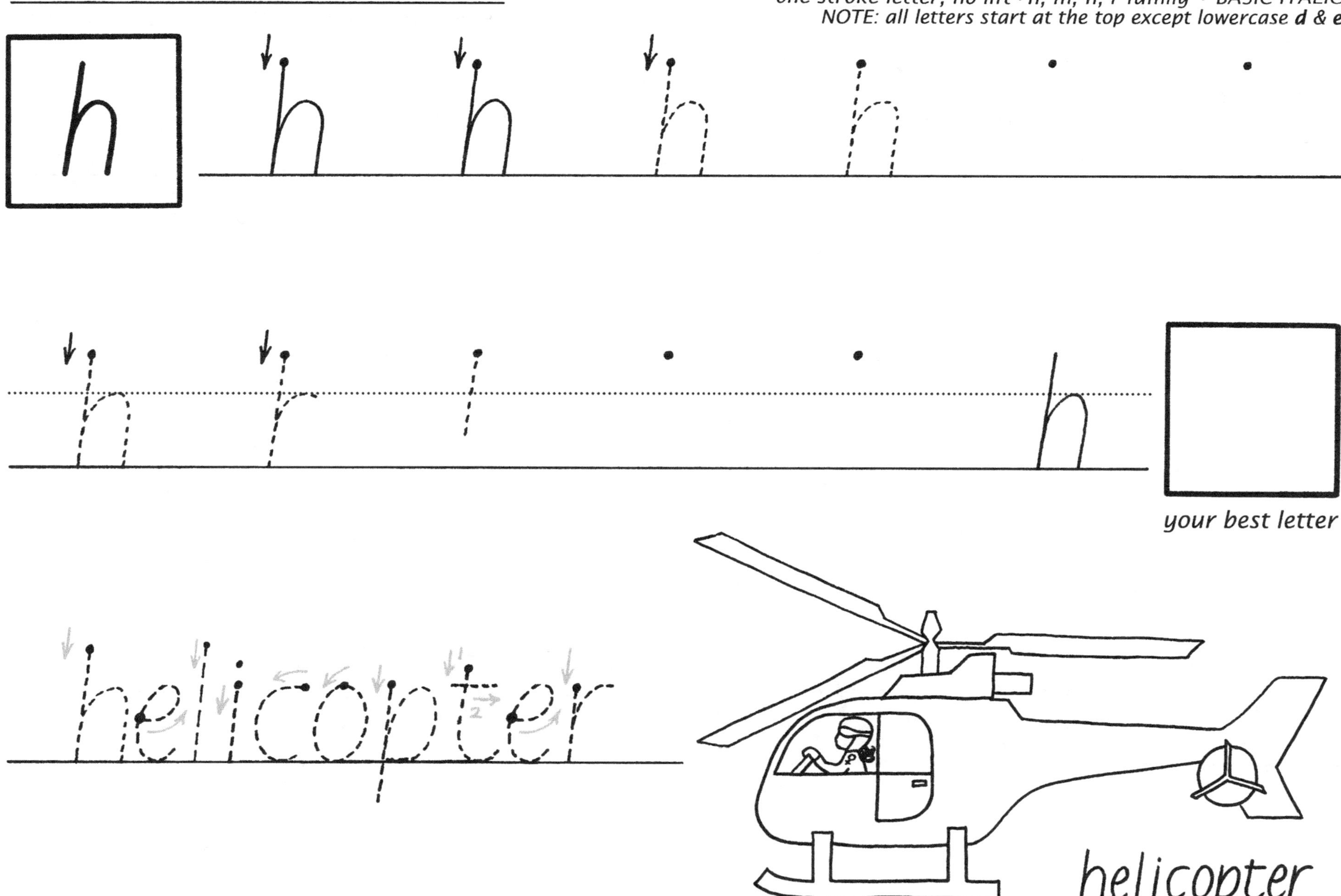

your best letter

helicopter

your best letter

Zipper

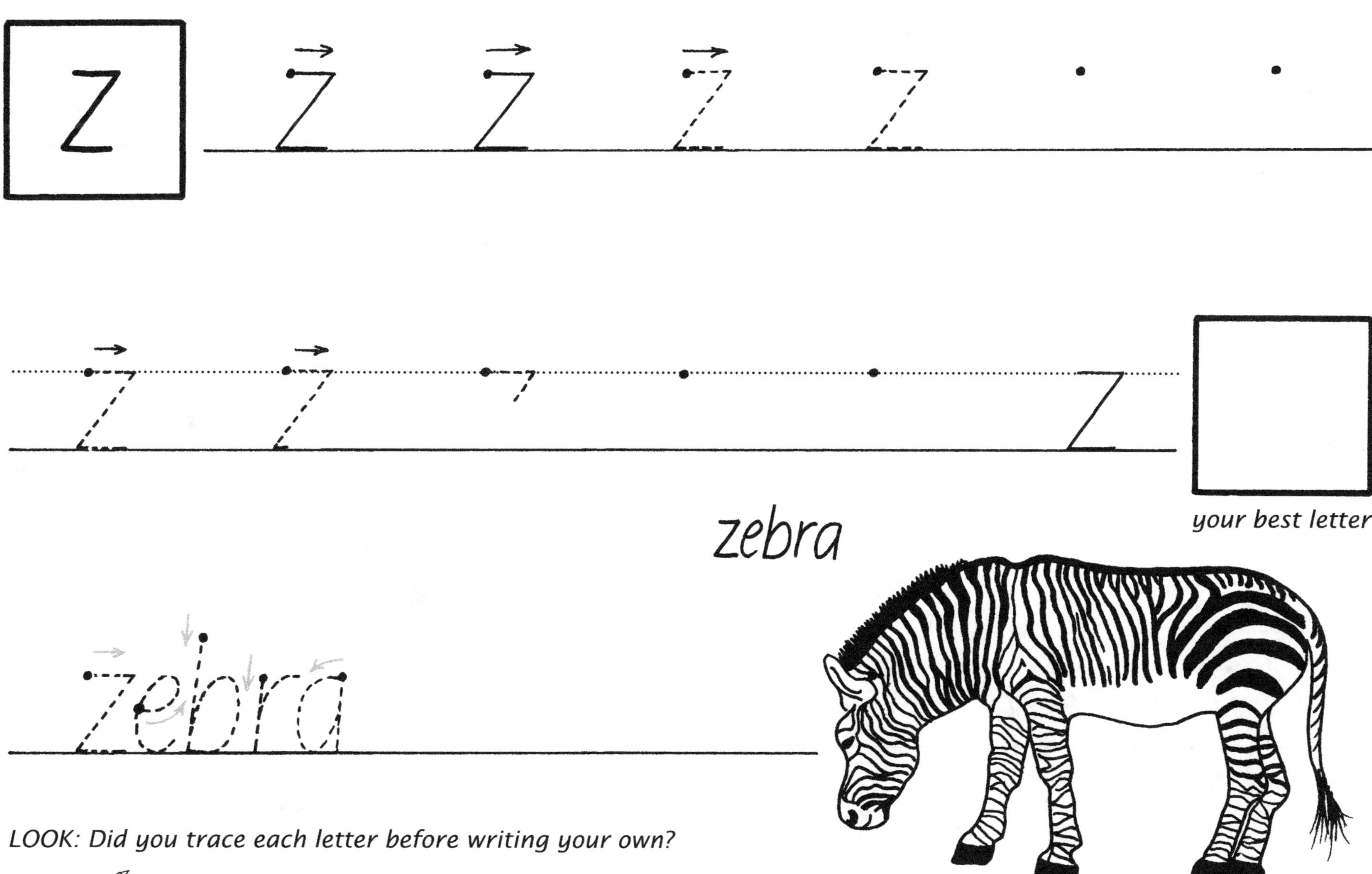

your best letter

zebra

LOOK: Did you trace each letter before writing your own?

✐ Circle: Yes   No

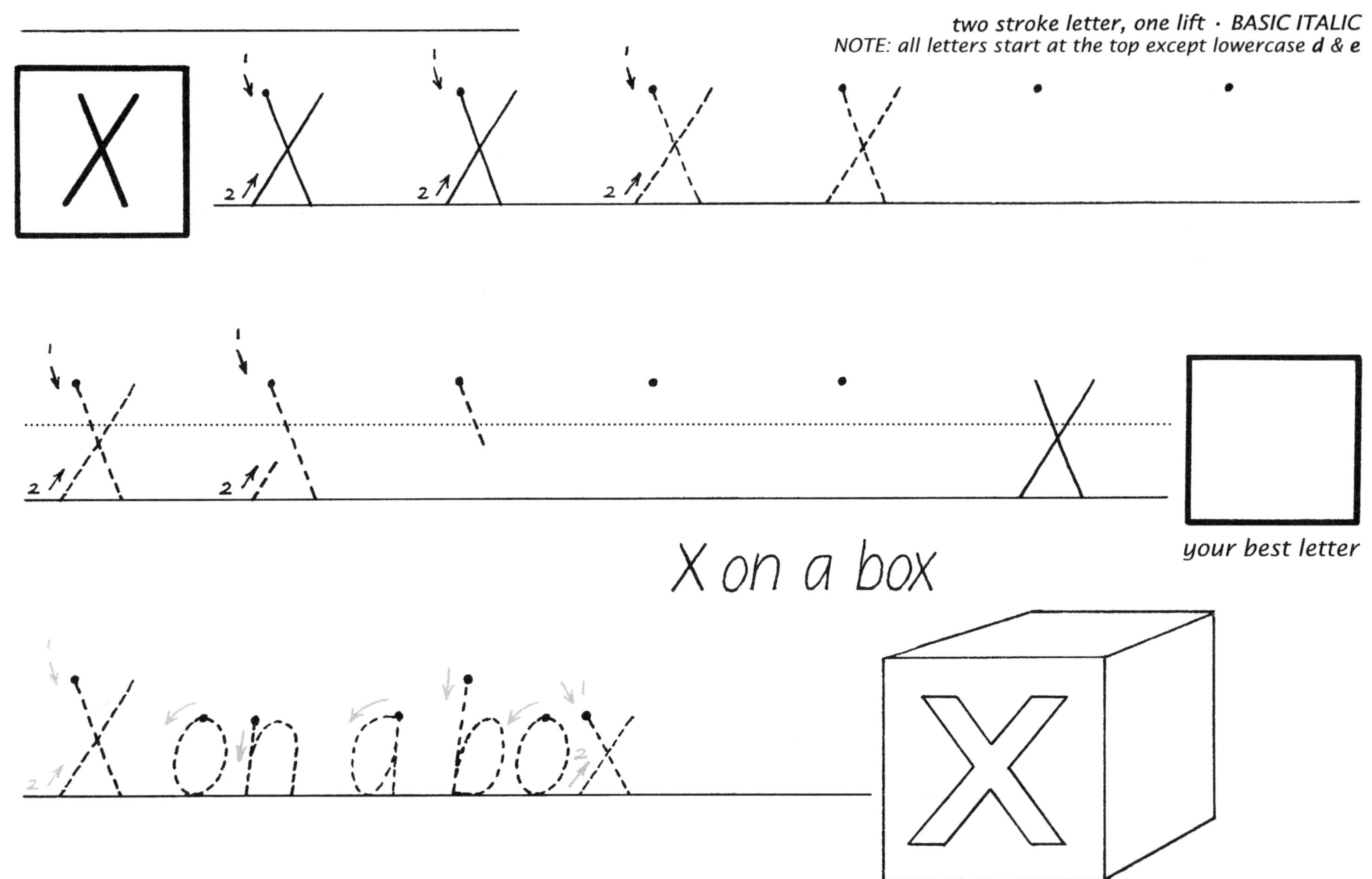

52

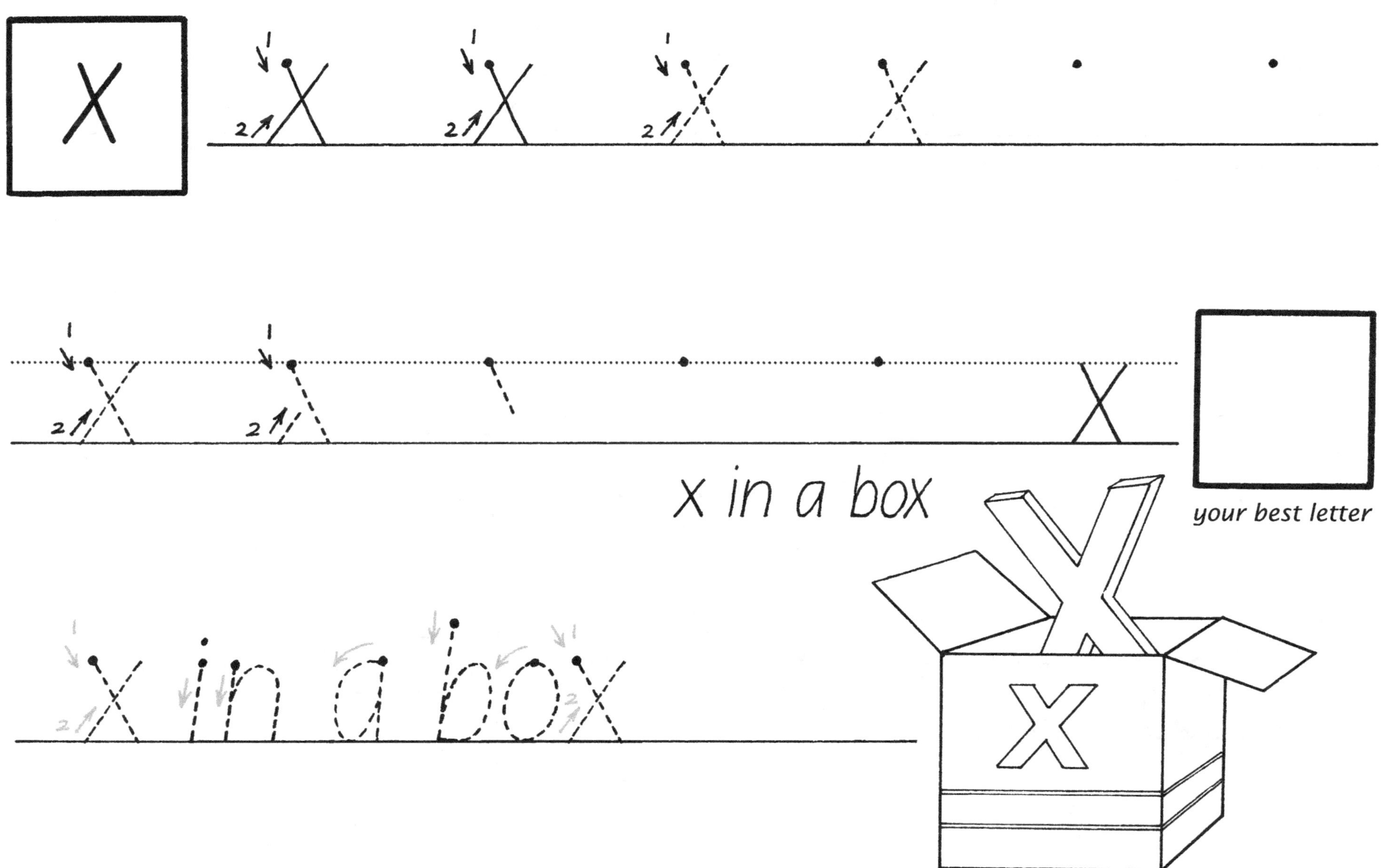

x in a box
your best letter
x in a box

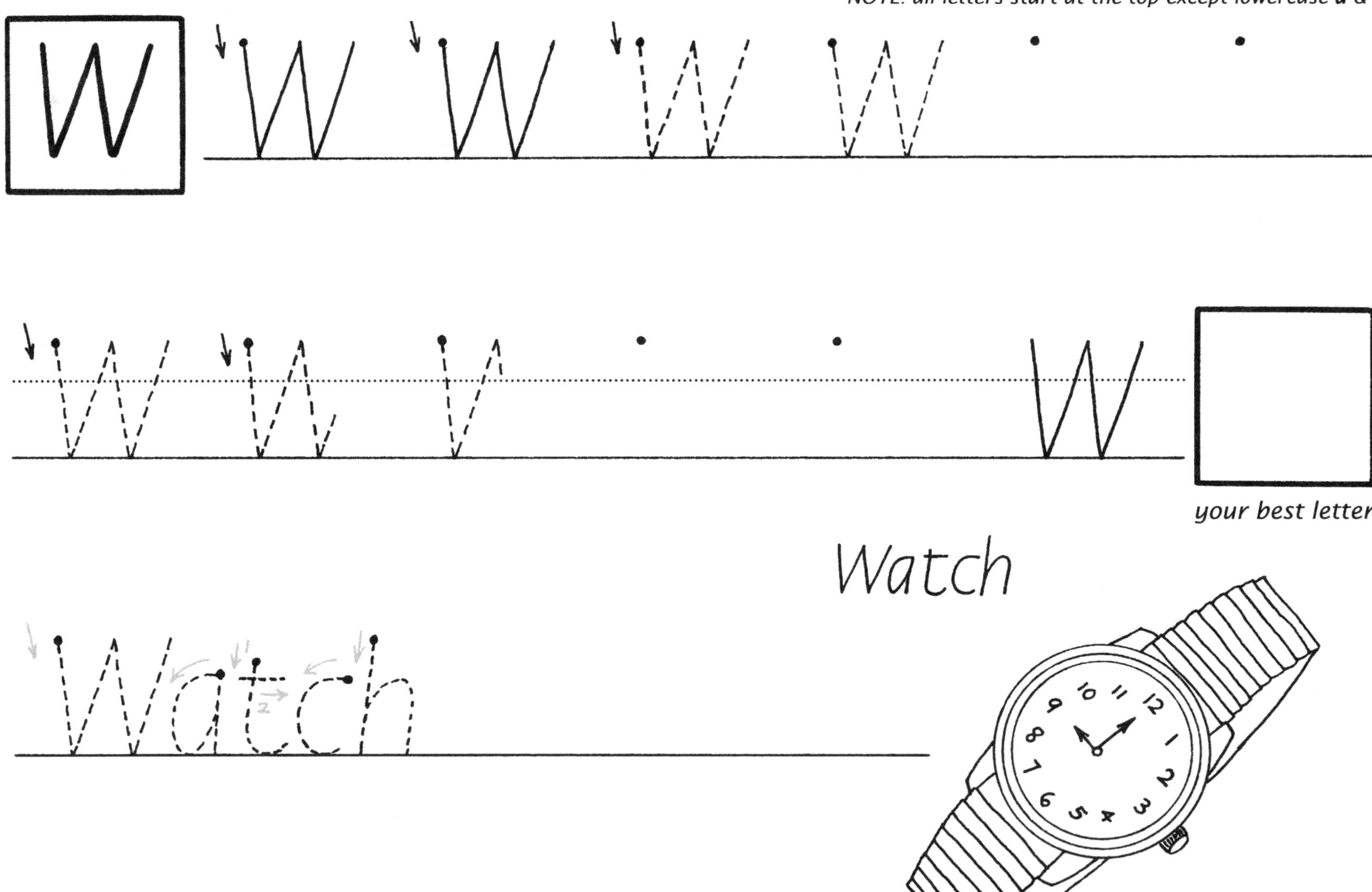

your best letter

Watch

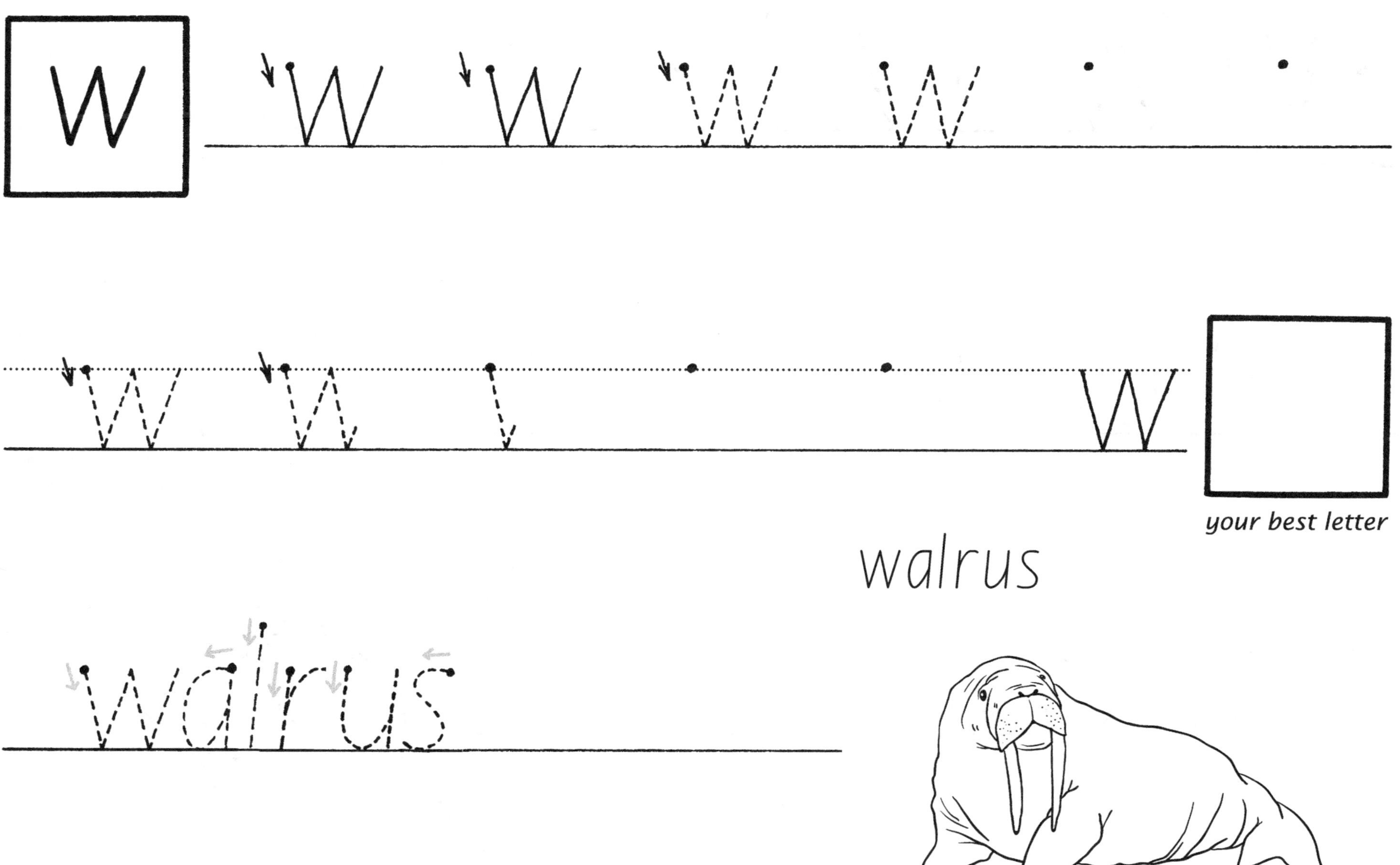

your best letter

walrus

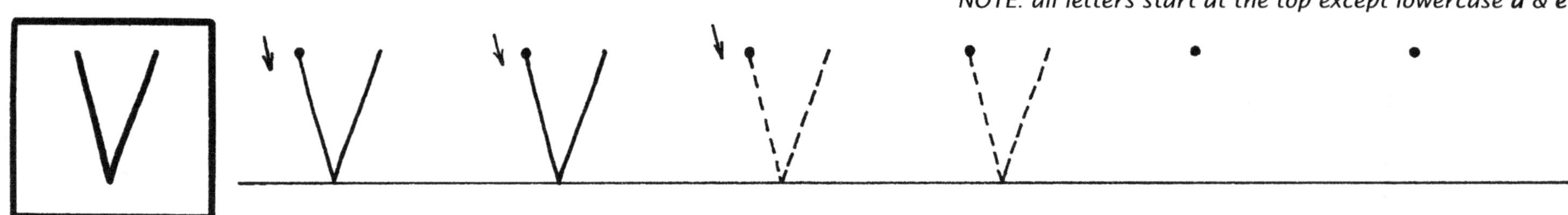

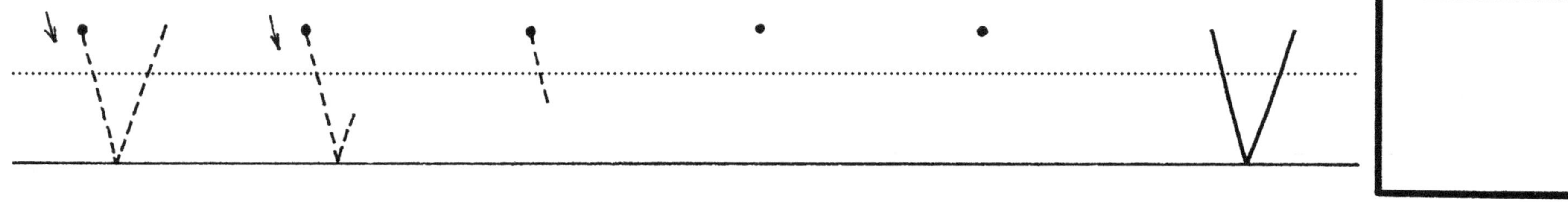

your best letter

Valentine

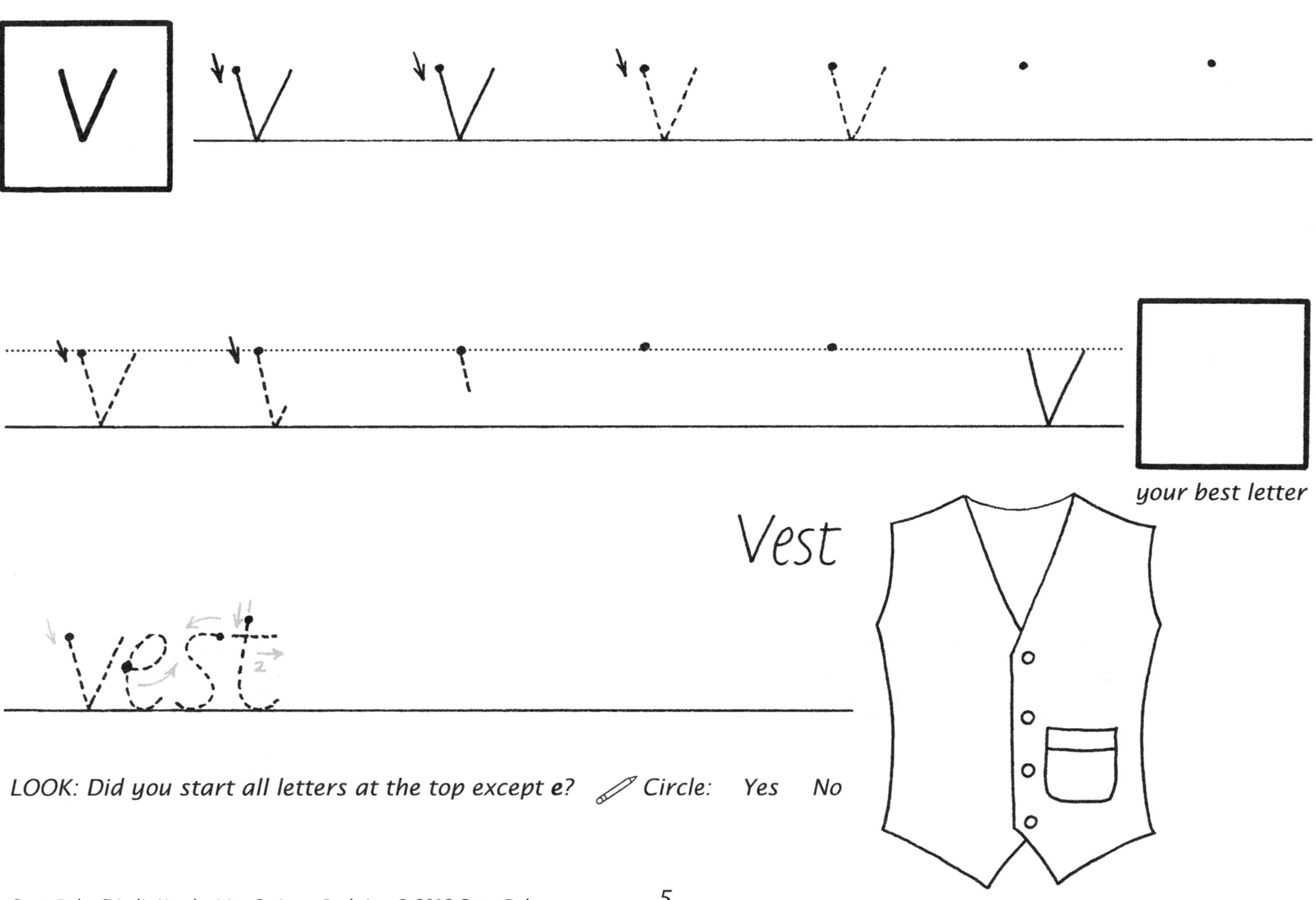

your best letter

Vest

LOOK: Did you start all letters at the top except *e*? ✏ Circle: Yes No

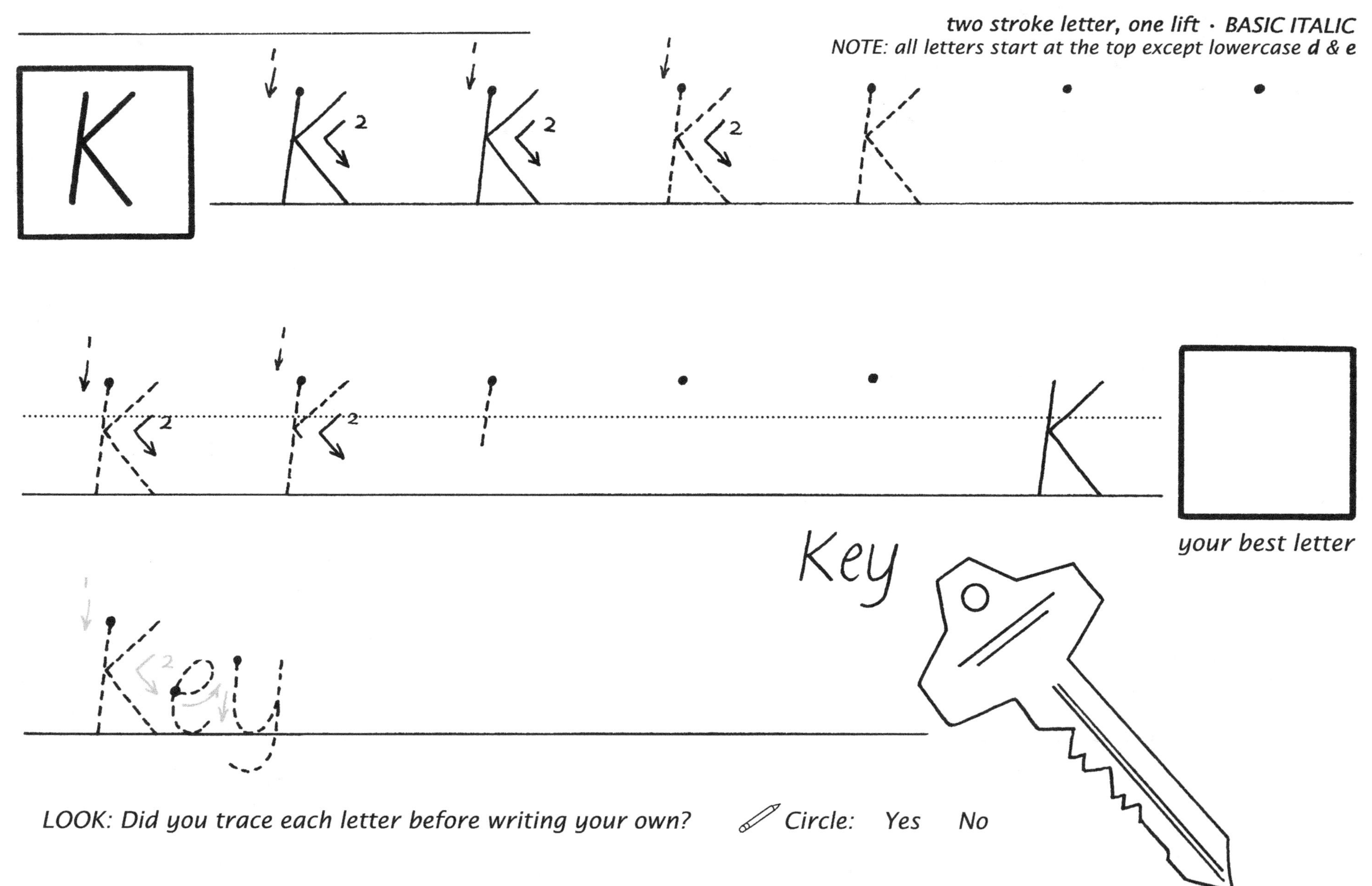

LOOK: Did you trace each letter before writing your own? Circle: Yes   No

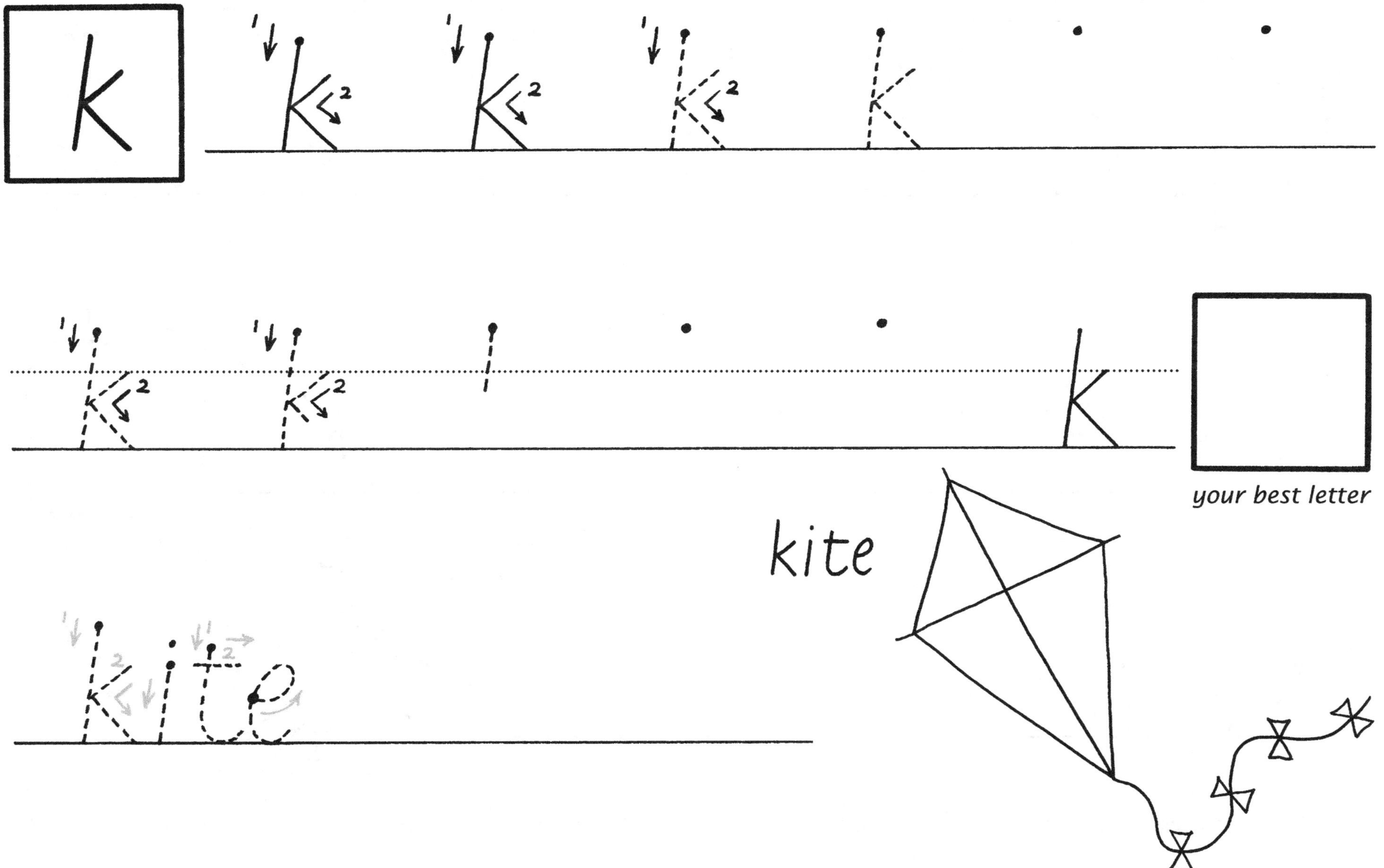

your best letter
kite

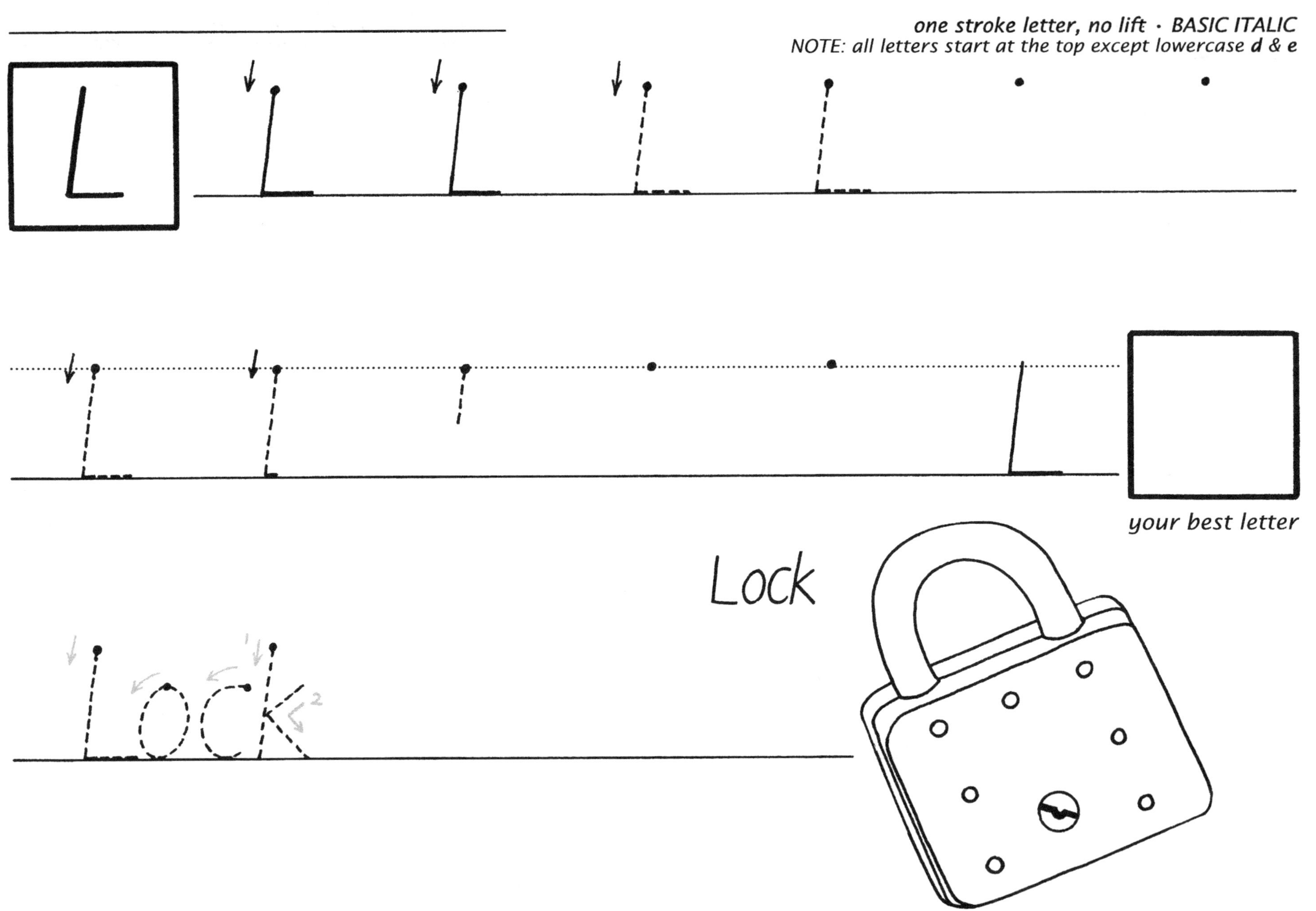

your best letter
Lock

your best letter

lamb

J

your best letter

Jack-in-the-box

Jack-in-the-box

LOOK: Did you start all letters at the top?   Circle: Yes   No

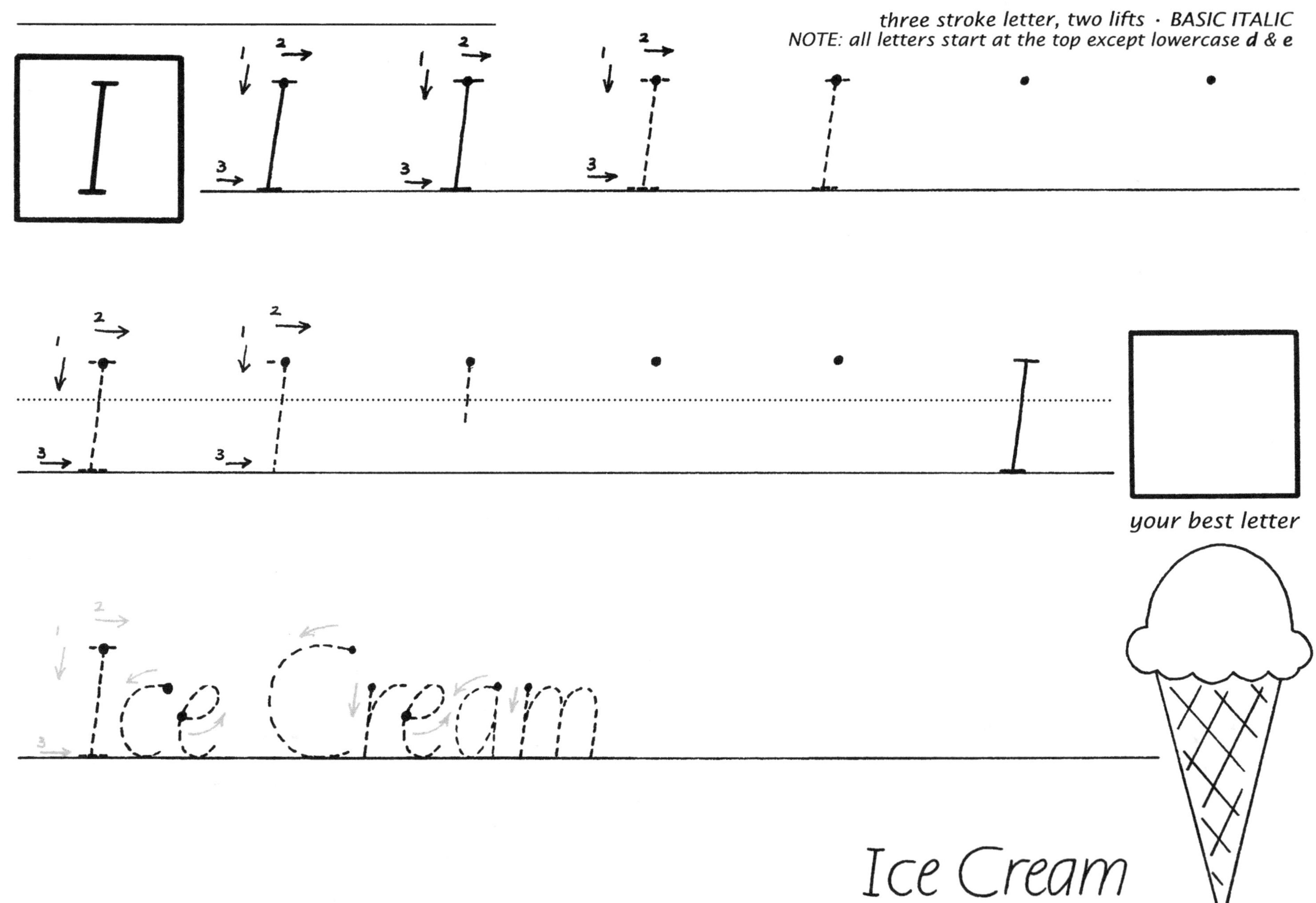

your best letter

Ice Cream

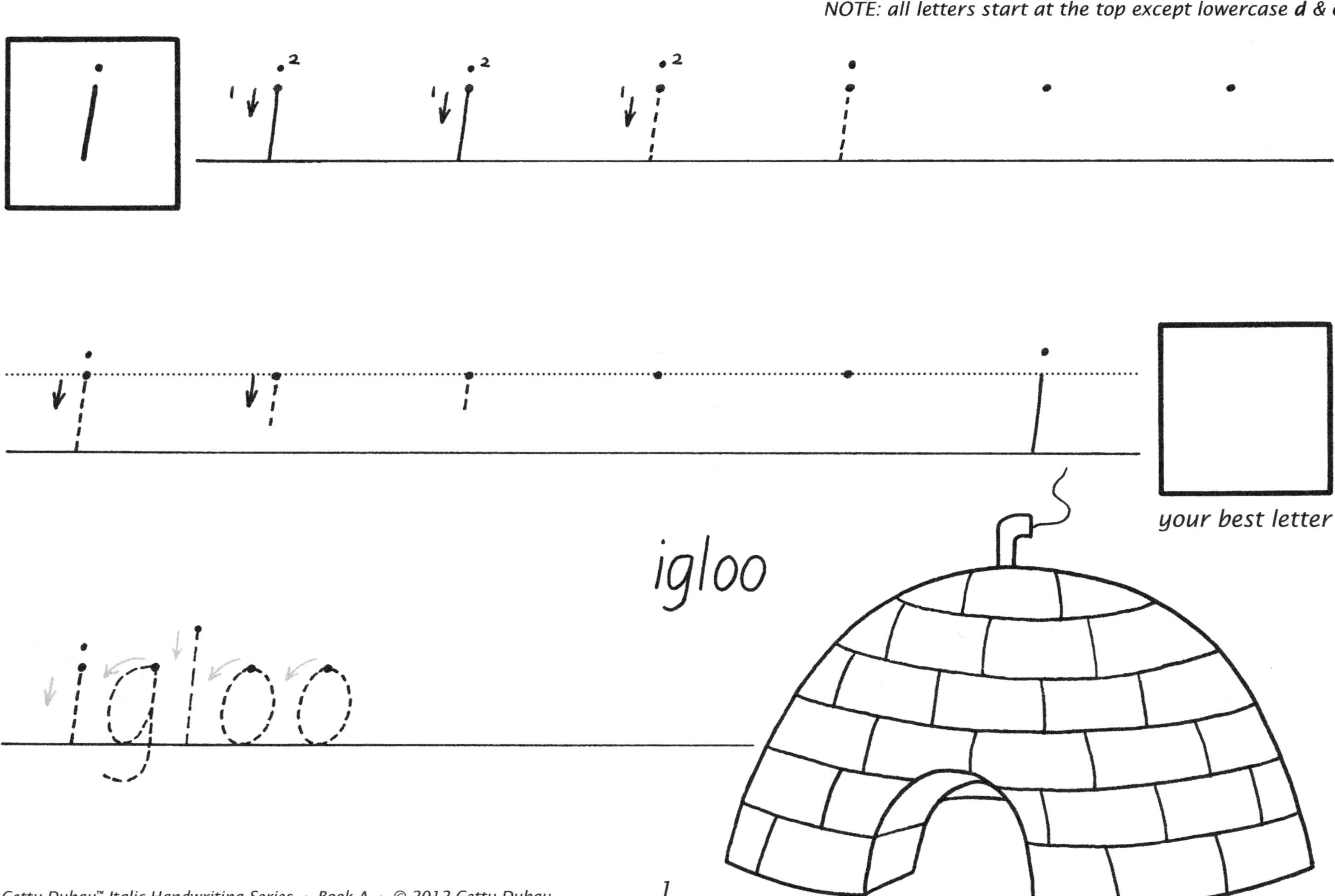

igloo
your best letter

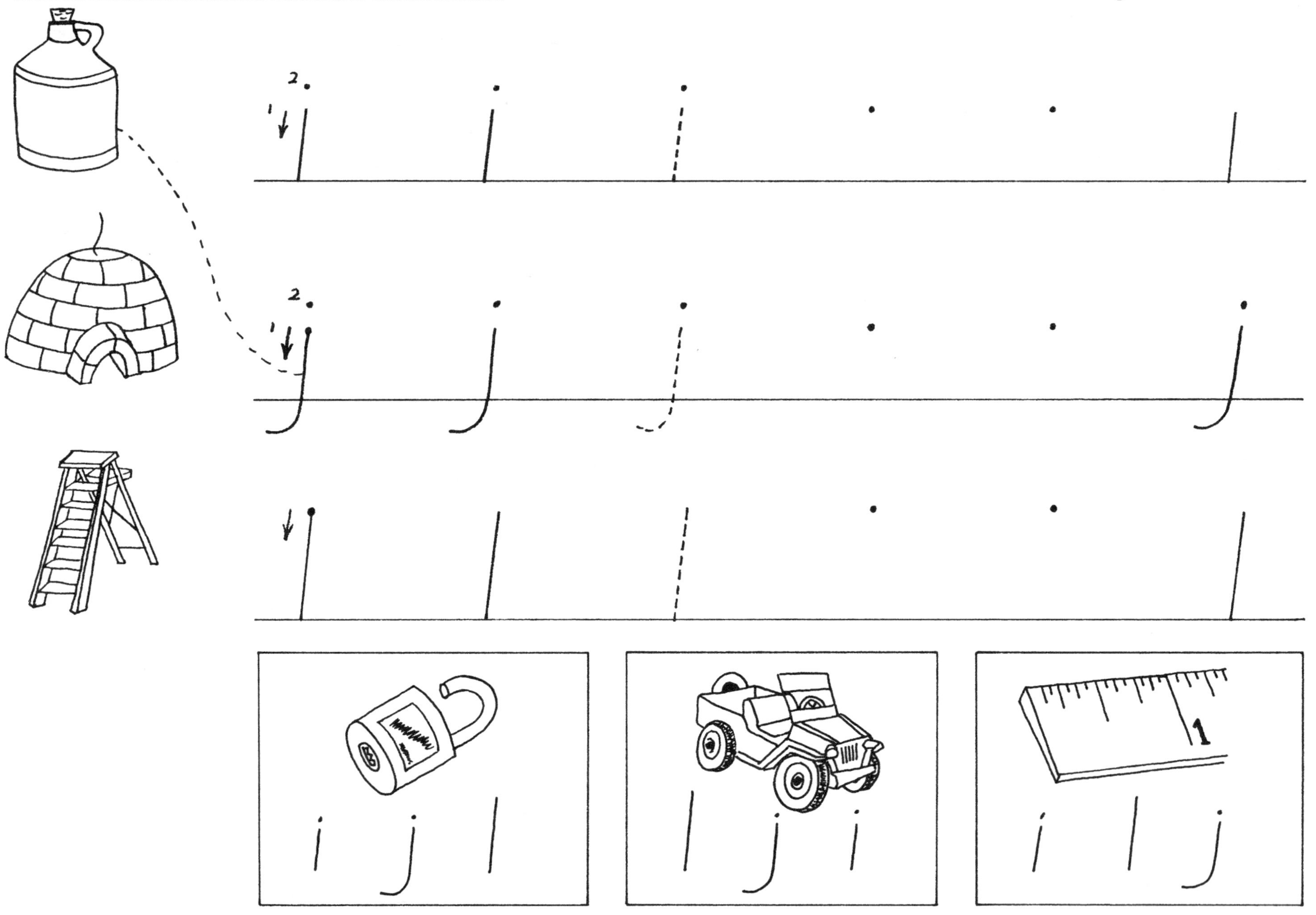

TOP THREE LINES: Ask the student to draw a line from the picture
to the letter that stands for the correct beginning sound.

BOTTOM THREE BOXES: Ask the student to circle the letter that
stands for the beginning sound of the picture.

Getty-Dubay™ Italic Handwriting Series · Book A · © 2012 Getty-Dubay

59

BASIC SHAPES

Before the student begins writing in BOOK A, the authors recommend that the student practice the following shapes on unlined paper, one shape at a time. Allow the student to write each shape any size at first. Later, ask the student to write very large and very small forms of that same shape. We suggest the student also practice these shapes on a chalkboard and/or in cornmeal. (See INSTRUCTION MANUAL, "*Activity,*" pp. 35 & 41.)

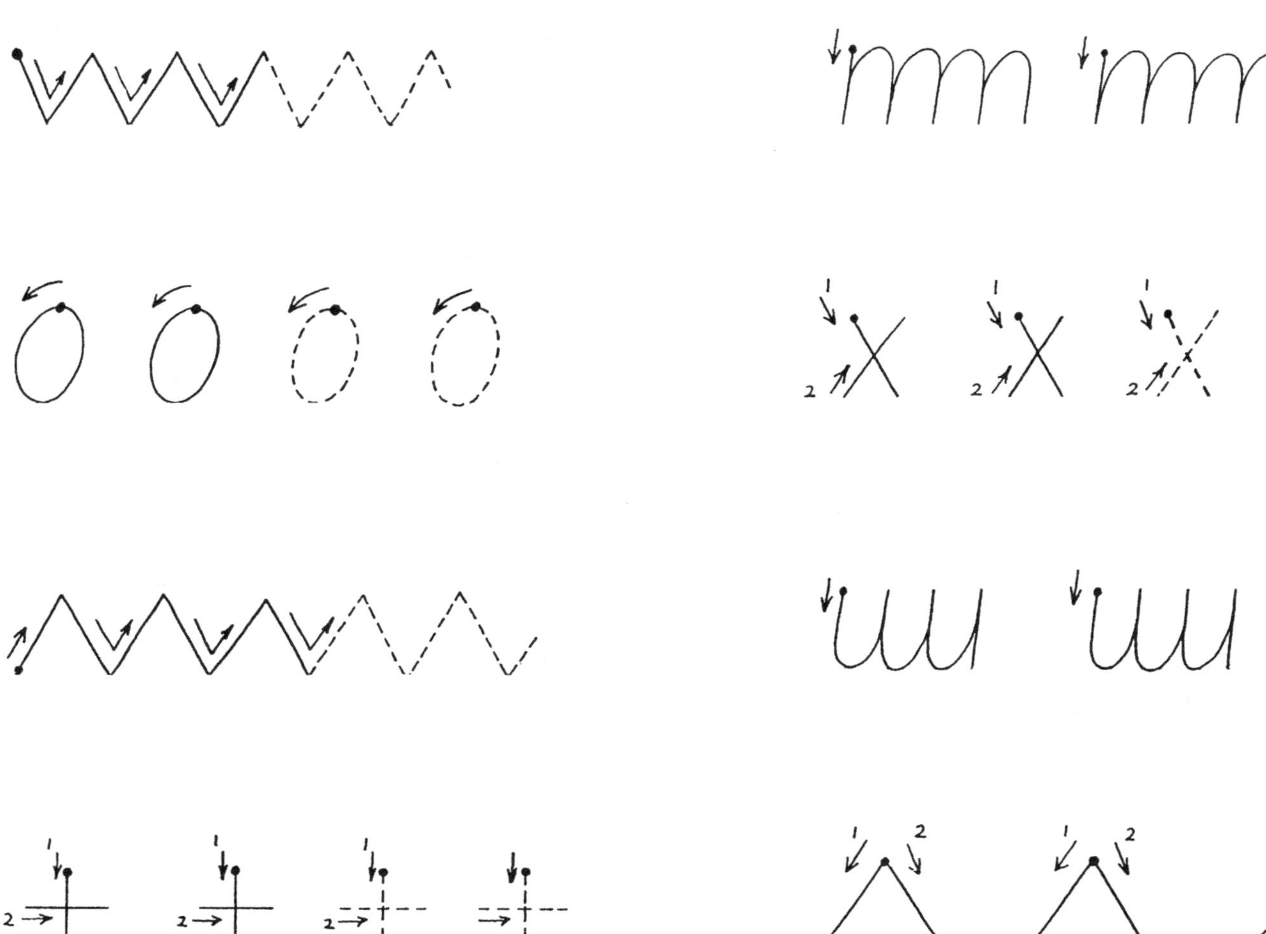

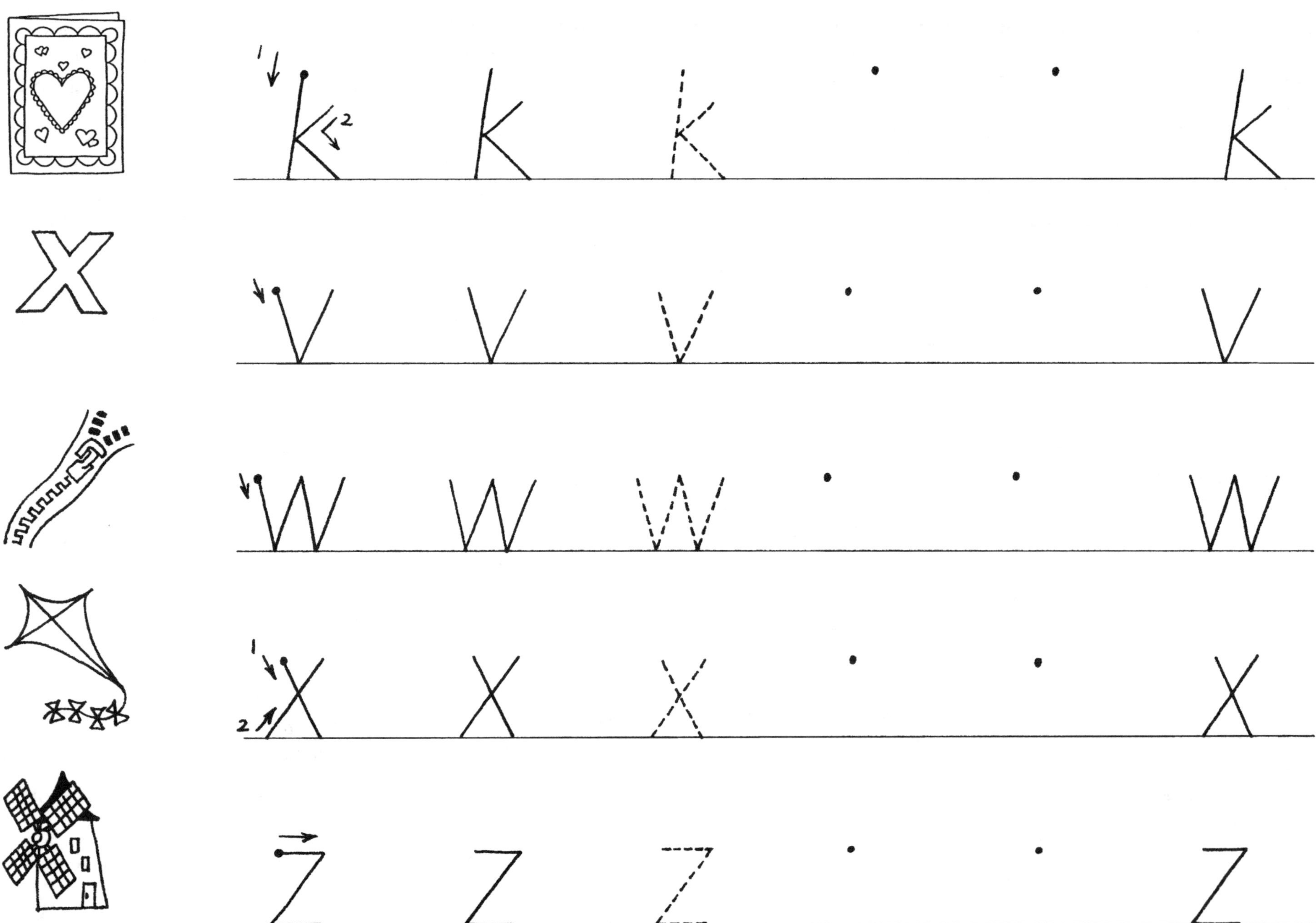

Ask the student to draw a line from the picture to the letter
that stands for the correct beginning sound.

THE BEGINNING WRITER

Learning how to write involves much more than learning to write letters. It is a sophisticated, complex process involving learning letterforms, learning how to space within and between words, and learning how to organize writing on a page. Research indicates that there exists an almost perfect correlation between measures evaluating the children's *awareness* of their fingers and the ability to *use* their fingers in precise manual skills.

Ways to determine manual ability

To assist young students increase awareness of their hands and fingers, and to help you, the teacher, evaluate students' manual skills, have your students perform these tasks:

1. Direct the students to touch each of their fingers to their thumb, in order, from the first to the little finger. (By the age of six years, most children should be able to complete this exercise using one or both hands at a time.)

2. Have the students connect two dots that are spaced approximately eight inches apart on a page. (Most children of five years can accomplish this. However, if the student draws beyond the second dot or draws an unusually shaky line when nearing the second dot, it may indicate potential deficiencies in handwriting skills.)

Ways to improve kinesthetic perception of the hands

1. Unstructured clay modeling facilitates a student's perception of his or her hands. Encourage the student to manipulate the clay in every possible way—squeezing, flattening, poking, making shapes, etc.

2. To heighten the student's perception of shape, use a box in which a variety of small objects are placed for the student to feel but not see.

   a. Ask the student to reach in the box and find an unseen object that matches the one he or she is looking at.

   b. Direct the student to locate in the box an object that you or another student has described.

   c. Ask the student to find two objects with similar characteristics—two fuzzy objects, two heavy objects, two small objects, etc.

3. Draw several circles on a sheet of paper. To determine the student's ability to aim the finger and hand and also to point, have the student place dots in the circles with a pencil, pen, or crayon. Vary the difficulty of this task by increasing or decreasing the size of the circles or increasing the rate at which the dots are made. (The student must be able to point at a given or imaginary point in order to begin the stroke of a letter.)

Ways to confirm hand-eye tracking skills

The ability to control continuous hand movements while drawing lines of varying difficulty is basic to handwriting. If you are able to detect problems as the student completes the following tasks and are able to obtain appropriate assistance for the student, subsequent difficulties may be avoided.

1. Demonstrate drawing parallel lines. Then direct the student to draw parallel lines of a given length, first at a relaxed pace then at a faster one.

2. Direct the student to draw two curved lines equal in distance from one another. Later require more difficult shapes that combine straight lines, angles, and/or curves.

3. Direct the student to connect numbered dots on a sheet of paper that require horizontal, vertical and lateral movements. Place the paper in front of the student, close to the dominant hand. Later, space the dots further apart and require the student to cross the midline of his or her body. This latter task may cause the neurologically challenged student some difficulty.

The above evaluative tasks may be of help in assisting the learning of handwriting and in discovering deficiencies.

(See INSTRUCTION MANUAL, p. 13, for more suggestions concerning the beginning writer.)

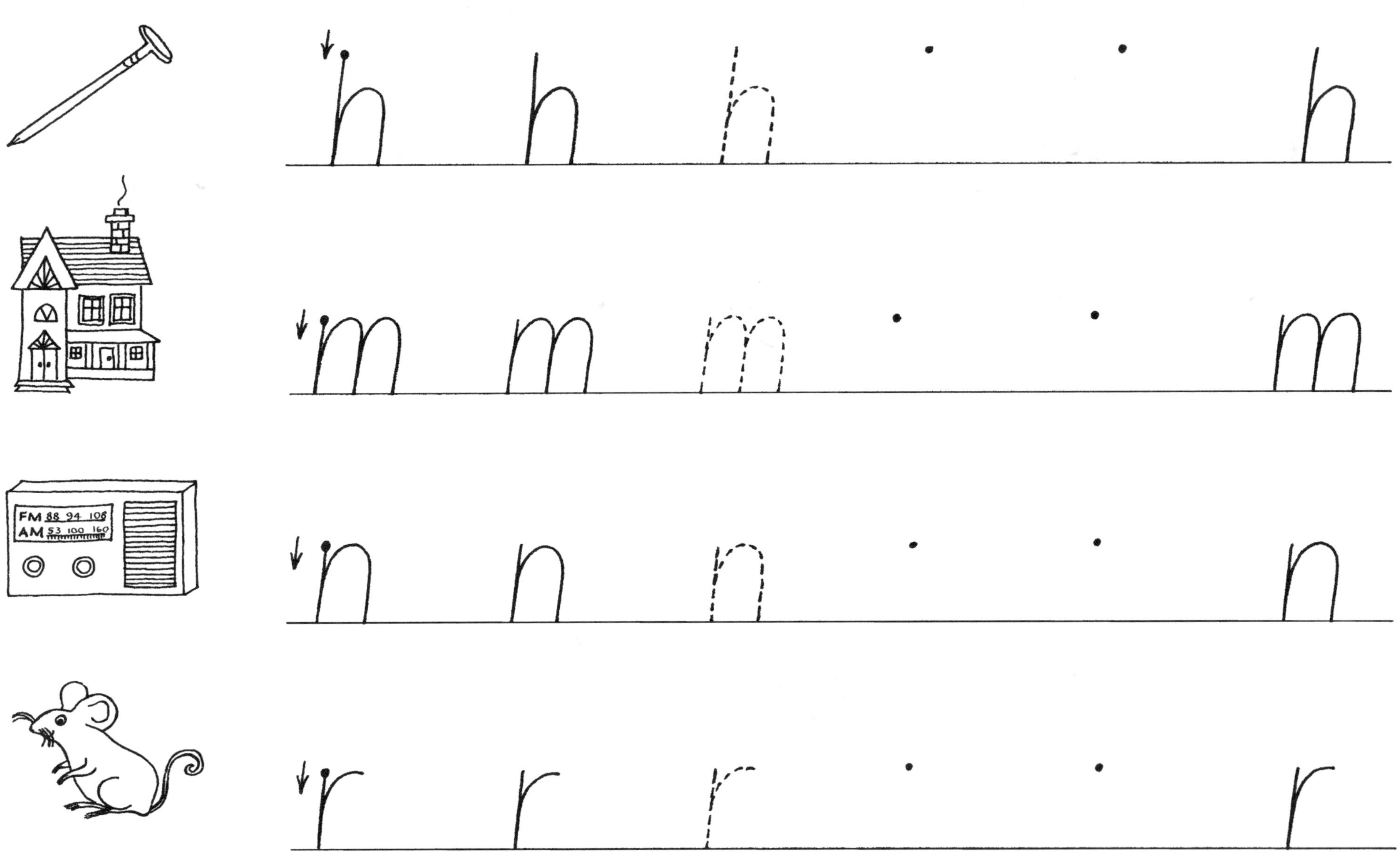

Ask the student to draw a line from the picture to the letter
that stands for the correct beginning sound.

BASIC ITALIC ALPHABET

All letters written in one stroke unless otherwise indicated.   *All letters start at the top except lowercase **d** and **e**.*

Aa Bb Cc Dd Ee Ff Gg

or

alternate
2-stroke e

Hh Ii Jj Kk Ll Mm

or

or

Nn Oo Pp Qq Rr Ss Tt

or

or

Uu Vv Ww Xx Yy Zz

0 1 2 3 4 5 6 7 8 9

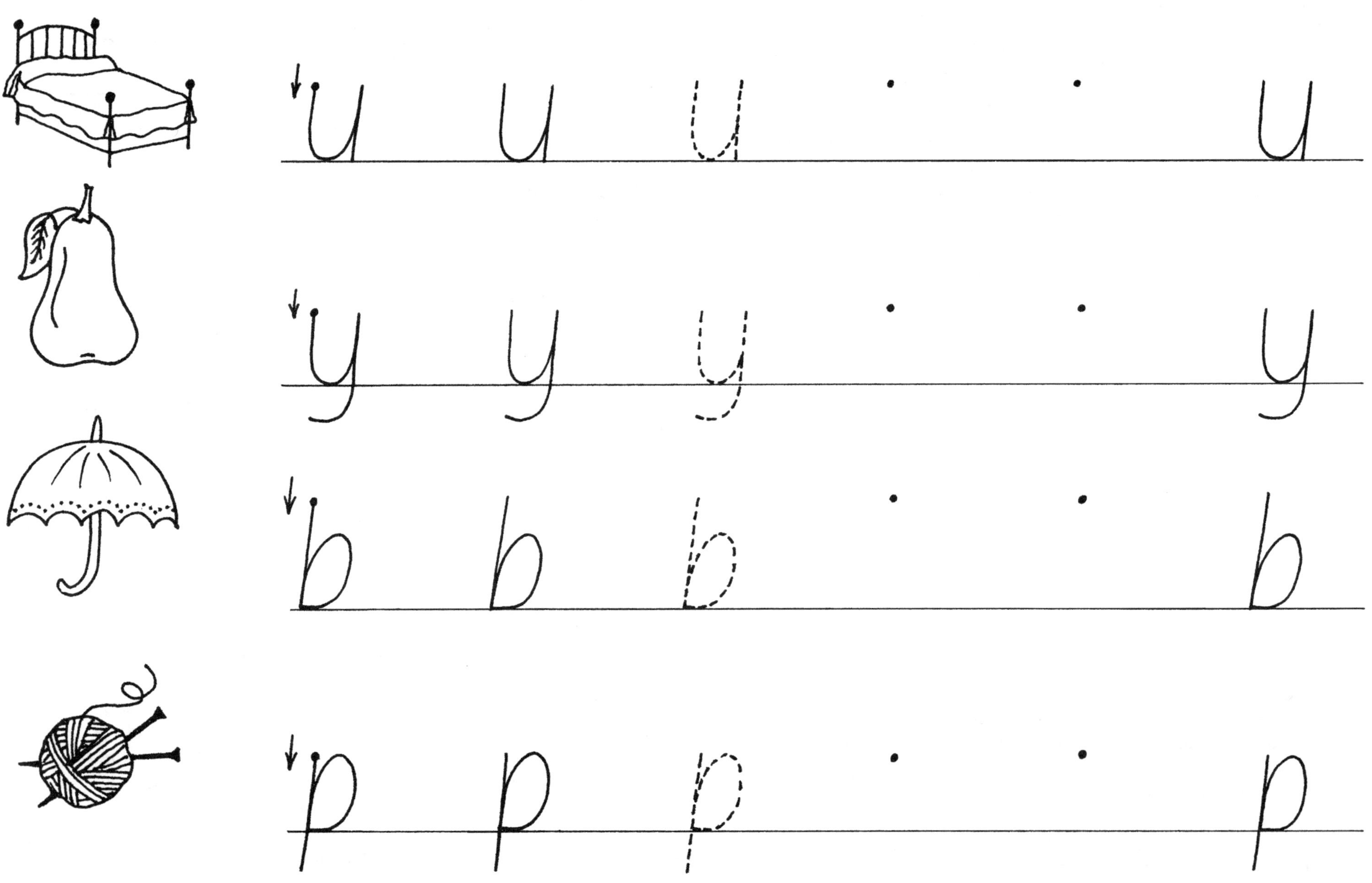

*Ask the student to draw a line from the picture to the letter
that stands for the correct beginning sound.*

GETTY-DUBAY™ HANDWRITING REMINDERS

PENCIL HOLD

Hold the pencil with the thumb and index finger, resting it on the middle finger. Rest the shaft of the pencil near the large knuckle. Hold the tool firmly and avoid pinching. To relax the hand, tap index finger on the pencil three times. Avoid "thumb wrap" and a "death grip".

PAPER POSITION

LEFT-HANDED: If the left-handed student writes with the wrist below the writing line, turn paper clockwise so it is slanted to the right, as illustrated.
If the left-handed student writes with a hook, with the wrist above the writing line, turn the paper counter-clockwise so it is slanted to the left, as illustrated. (Similar to right-handed position)

RIGHT-HANDED: If the student is right-handed, turn paper counter-clockwise so it is slanted to the left, as illustrated.

POSTURE

Rest feet flat on the floor and keep back comfortably straight without slumping. Rest forearms on writing surface. The student

holds workbook or paper with the nonwriting hand so that the writing area is centered in the front of the student.

PRACTICE PAPER

Book A—Use unlined or lined paper together with workbooks.

MATERIALS

The *Getty-Dubay™ Italic Handwriting Series* workbooks, BOOKS A-G, and the INSTRUCTION MANUAL constitute a step-by-step program. Related materials consist of:

1. BLACKLINE MASTERS/WORKSHEETS - half sheets for introduction to, or review of, workbook pages.
2. CLASSROOM WALL CHARTS - basic & cursive italic.
3. DESK STRIPS - basic & cursive italic.

VOCABULARY

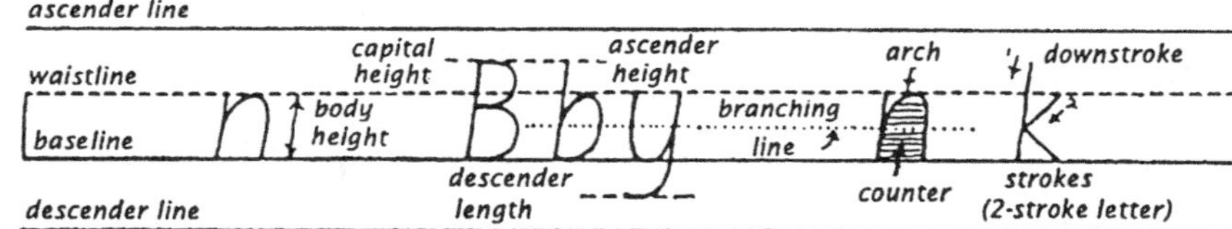

DIRECT INSTRUCTION

Several sessions of direct instruction each week are essential for a successful program. BOOK A – 5 to 10 minute sessions a day are recommended, see INSTRUCTION MANUAL, pp. 18-19

- SHAPE & STROKE SEQUENCE – teach basic italic in letter family groups, or according to the reading program in grade 1.
- SLOPE – encourage a consistent letter slope. Vertical letters (0° slope) may be the easiest to teach to beginning writers.
- SIZE – At first, allow students to write letters any size they wish on unlined paper, then introduce the workbook. A recommended progression through this book is one letter (lowercase and/or capital) per week.

SPACING

When young students are writing words, at first have them leave a space about the width of their two small fingers between words. As they become more proficient, they can leave less space.

ASSESSMENT

The *Getty-Dubay™ Italic Handwriting Series* provides a self-assessment process, LOOK, PLAN, PRACTICE, to enable the student to monitor progress. LOOK, step 1 of this process begins on some of the student pages in BOOK A. Assessment is the key to improving handwriting; in this book we introduce the first of three steps in the LOOK, PLAN, PRACTICE self-assessment process. The students look at their own writing and answer any questions on the page. The pencil indicates the student is to make a written response, generally by circling "yes" or "no". The teacher may encourage students to award themselves a star or a smiling face at the top of the page when they notice self-improvement.

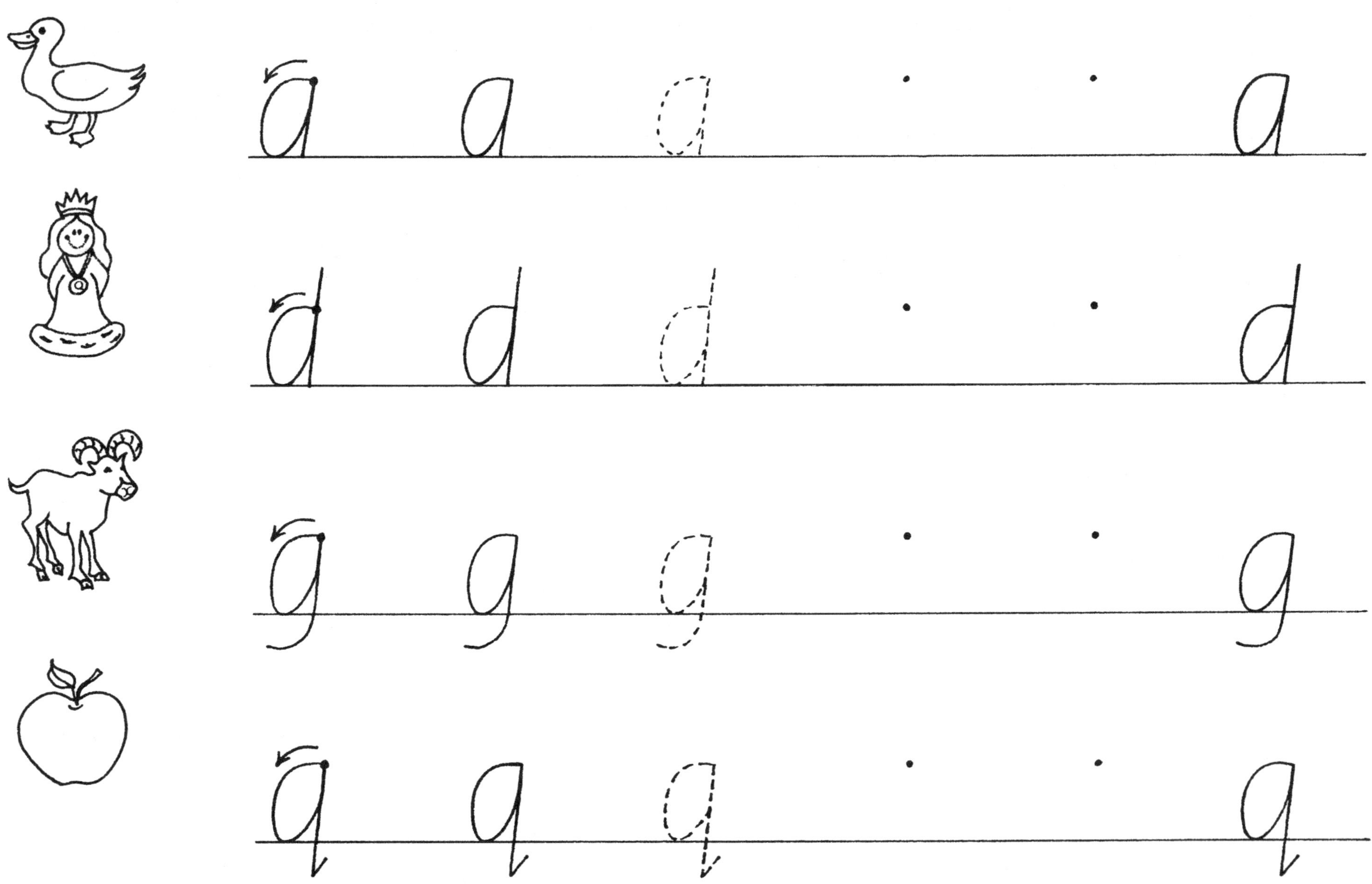

Ask the student to draw a line from the picture to the letter
that stands for the correct beginning sound.

INTRODUCTION

This is the first of seven workbooks providing instruction in basic italic handwriting. It is designed for the beginning student of handwriting and is recommended for preschool, kindergarten and/or early first grade (5 to 7 years of age).

The twenty-six lowercase letters and the twenty-six capitals are introduced one letter per page. Letters are arranged in the order of lowercase families, which group letters with similar strokes together and progress from simple to more complex forms. The matching capital letter occurs on the reverse of each lowercase page allowing introduction of both lowercase and capital together if preferred.

Each page is designed for the student to trace the models provided, write letters at the given dots, and to write a "best" letter in the empty box on each alphabet page. The standard writing tool is the pencil although other writing instruments such as the fiber tip pen may be used. When students are ready, they should trace the word describing the illustration on each letter page, following the dots and arrows.

It is essential that the instructor provide an understanding of the dot and the arrow to assist the writer in completing the pages successfully. The self-assessment method used in the *Getty-Dubay™ Italic Handwriting Series* enables students to monitor their individual progress. Step 1, LOOK, of the three-step LOOK, PLAN, PRACTICE format, is incorporated on 21 of the student pages. Students are asked to "LOOK" at their writing and affirm what is best. On the 21 pages with "LOOK" questions, students should circle their chosen answers. See INSTRUCTION MANUAL, PP. 13, 18 & 19.

The *Getty-Dubay™ Italic Handwriting Series* INSTRUCTION MANUAL is to be used in conjunction with this workbook. Explanations and in-depth descriptions of lowercase letters, capitals, joins, and numerals are presented in the manual, emphasizing shape, strokes, size, slope and spacing of the letters. Also included in the manual are: a rationale for italic handwriting, techniques for teaching and assessing handwriting, sequence of skills, handwriting activities, and a brief history of our alphabet.

BOOK B, basic italic, follows this workbook and is designed for the beginning reader. In the third book, BOOK C, basic italic letterforms are reinforced and cursive italic is introduced. BOOKS D, E, F, and G provide a complete basic italic and cursive italic handwriting program. BOOKS B, C, and/or D may also be suitable for the person learning English as a second language.

The format of this book was chosen to accommodate both the left- and right-handed writer. When open, the book fits easily on a small desk, and the writer is not encumbered with an additional page to the left or right. From day one, use a Getty-Dubay™ basic italic desk strip as a reminder. Blackline masters are designed for supplementary practice and are available for each workbook in the series. See www.handwritingsuccess.com for these supplementary materials.

You can guide children toward the challenge and delight in the writing process by reading to them, modeling handwriting, providing writing materials, and especially by building enthusiasm for the letters of our alphabet and for the written word.

·abcdefghijklmnopqrstuvwxyz·

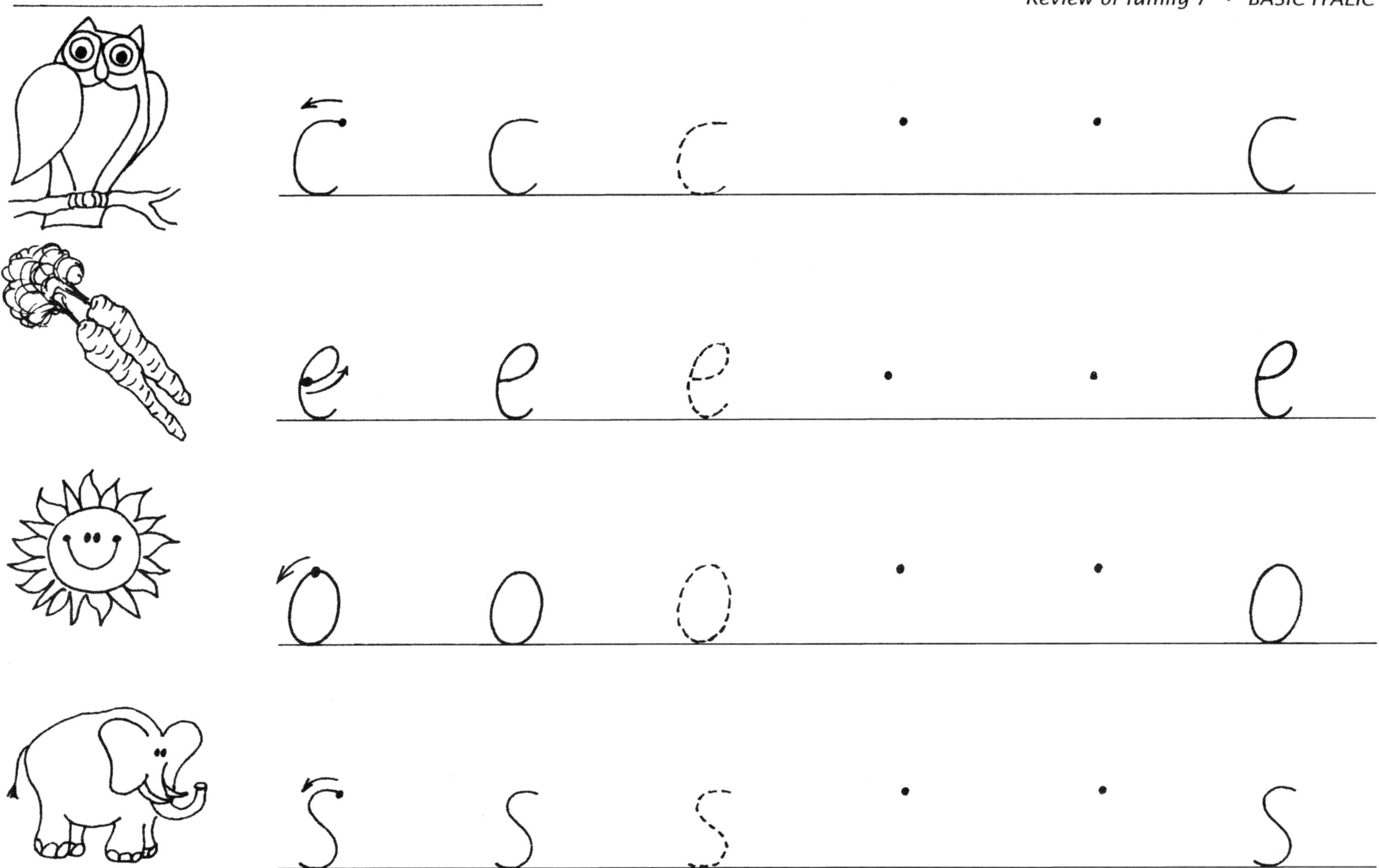

Ask the student to draw a line from the picture to the letter
that stands for the correct beginning sound.

CONTENTS

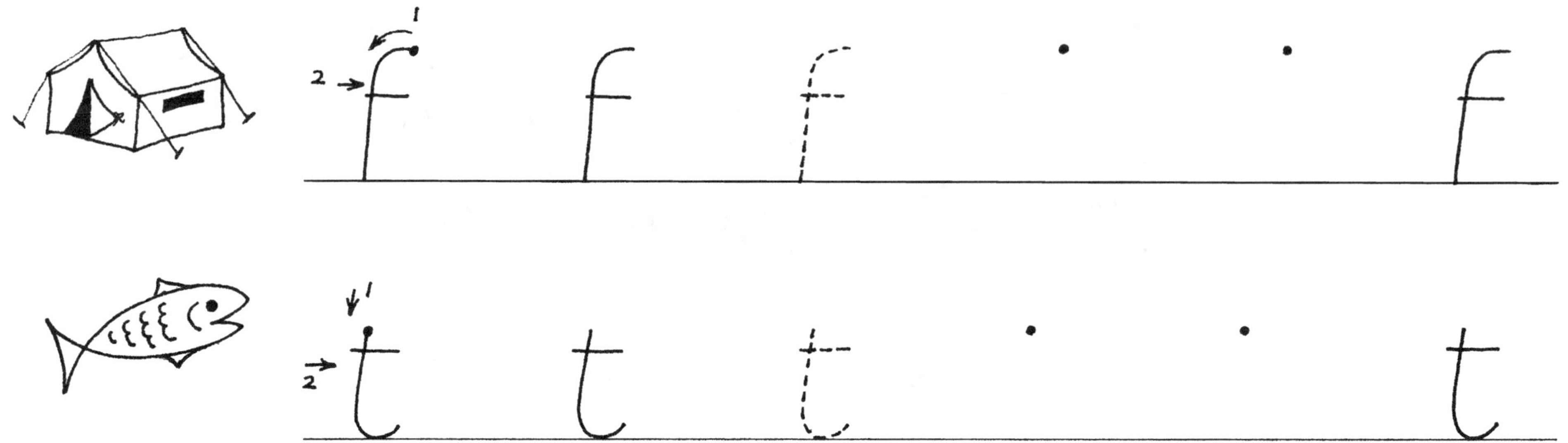

TOP TWO LINES: Ask the student to draw a line from the picture
to the letter that stands for the correct beginning sound.

BOTTOM FOUR SQUARES: Ask the student to circle the letter that
stands for the beginning sound of the picture.

by
Barbara Getty & Inga Dubay

GETTY-DUBAY™ ITALIC HANDWRITING SERIES

BOOK A ▪ Basic Italic
14 mm body height

BOOK B ▪ Basic Italic
11 mm body height, 9 mm

BOOK C ▪ Basic & Cursive Italic
9 mm, 6 mm body height   Introduction to Cursive Italic

BOOK D ▪ Basic & Cursive Italic
6 mm, 5 mm body height

BOOK E ▪ Basic & Cursive Italic
6 mm, 5 mm, 4 mm body height

BOOK F ▪ Basic & Cursive Italic
6 mm, 5 mm, 4 mm body height

BOOK G ▪ Basic & Cursive Italic
5 mm, 4 mm body height

INSTRUCTION MANUAL

BOOK A ▪ INTERNATIONAL EDITION
Copyright 2012 by Barbara M. Getty and Inga S. Dubay
ISBN 978-0-9827762-7-8

FOURTH EDITION
Copyright 2012 by Barbara M. Getty and Inga S. Dubay
THIRD EDITION
Copyright 1999 by Barbara M. Getty and Inga S. Dubay
SECOND EDITION
Copyright 1986 by Barbara M. Getty and Inga S. Dubay
REVISED EDITION
Copyright 1980 by Barbara M. Getty and Inga S. Dubay
FIRST EDITION
Copyright 1979 by Barbara M. Getty and Inga S. Dubay

All rights reserved. This text may not be reproduced in whole or in part without the express written permission of the copyright holder.

Published by Handwriting Success, LLC,
Portland, Oregon USA

www.handwritingsuccess.com

Printed at various locations around the world by IngramSpark.

Cover Design: Sinda Markham
Front cover picture: Flowers of the sunflower family in the Ochoco National Forest, Oregon, USA
Back cover pictures: Columbine flower, Golden-mantled squirrel

www.ingramcontent.com/pod-product-compliance
Lightning Source LLC
Chambersburg PA
CBHW081423210726
48464CB00020B/1370

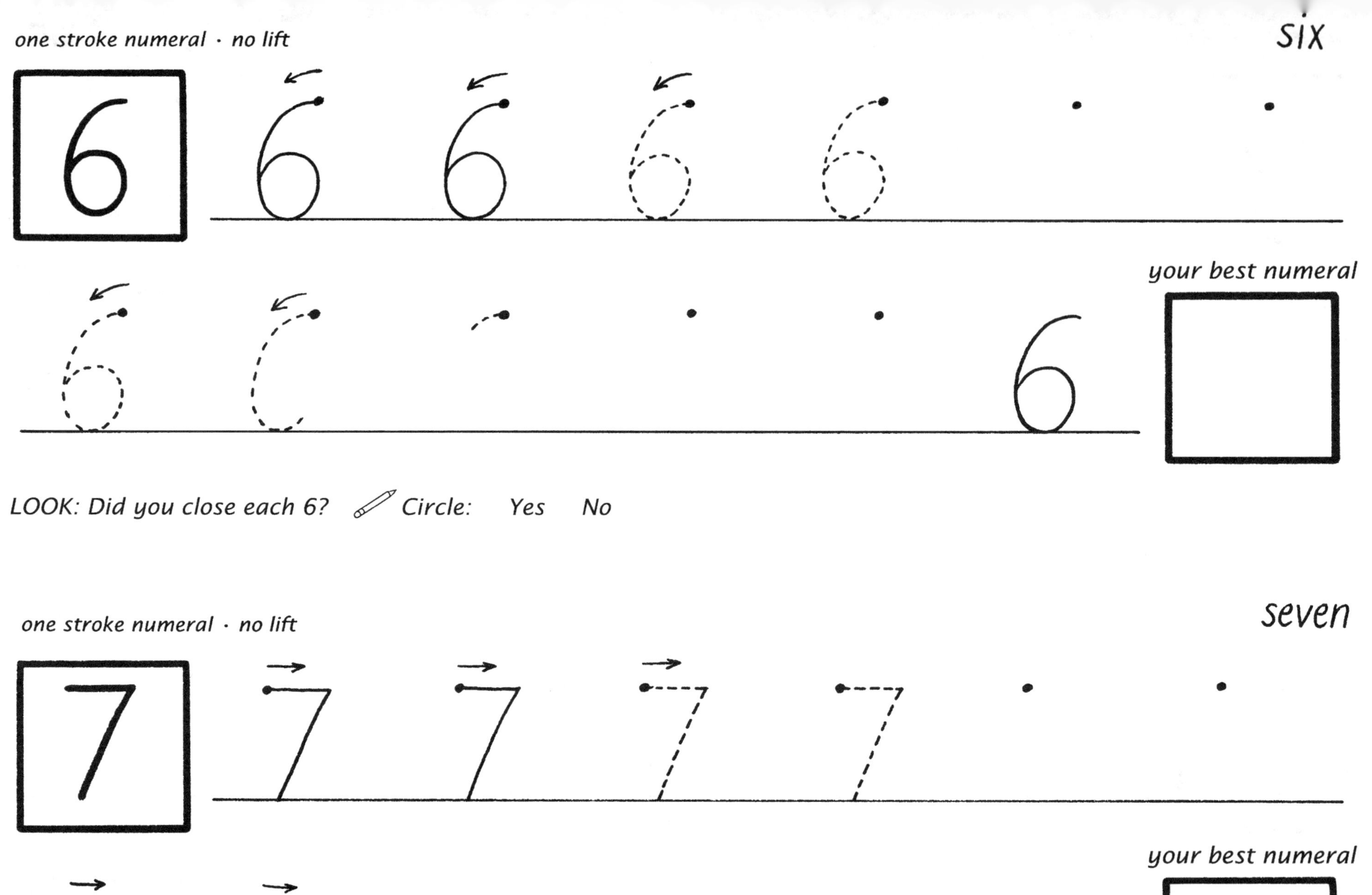

your best numeral

LOOK: Did you close each 6?   Circle: Yes   No

one stroke numeral · no lift   seven

your best numeral

two stroke numeral · one lift

your best numeral

two stroke numeral · one lift

five

your best numeral

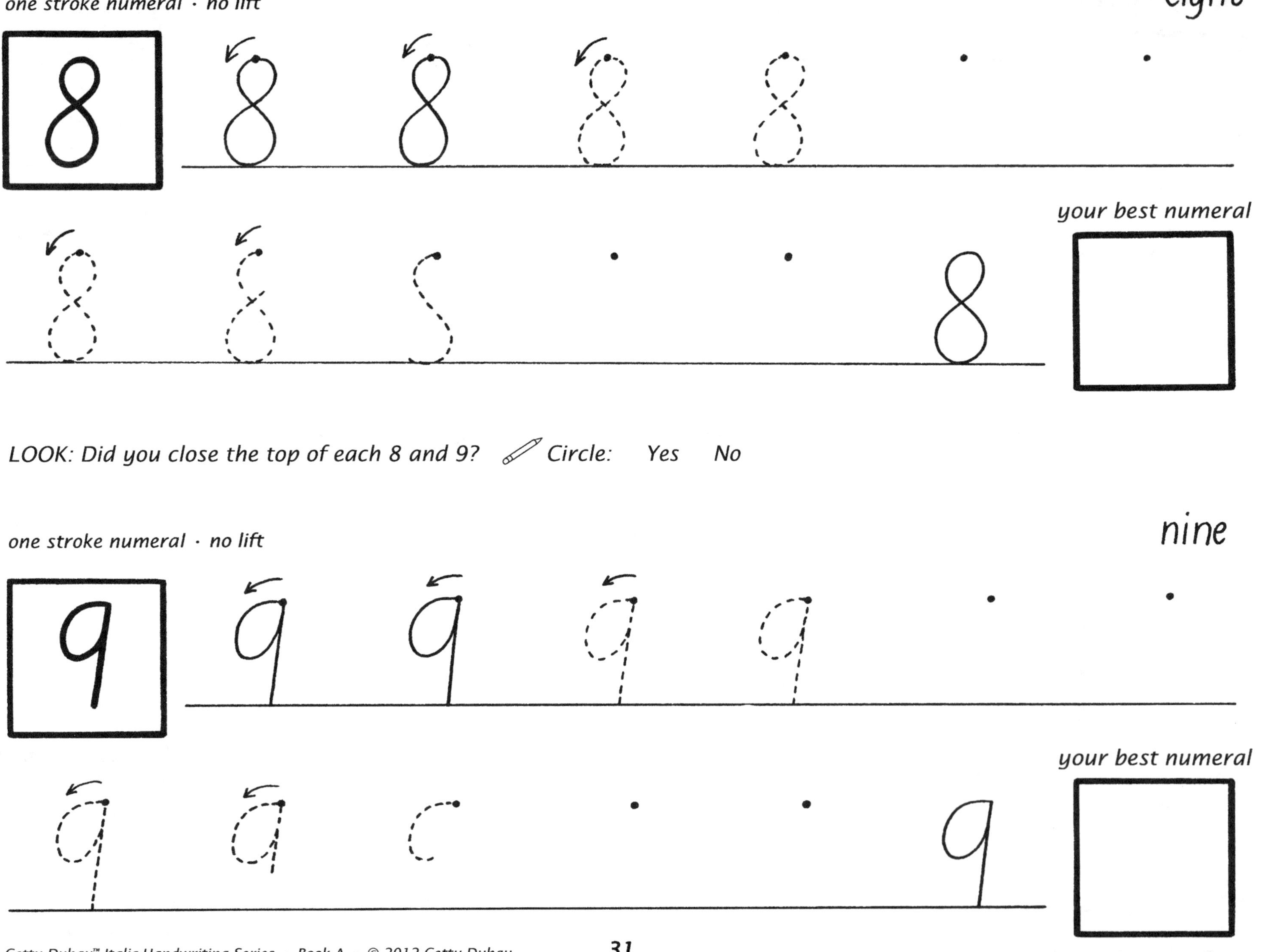

one stroke numeral · no lift
eight
your best numeral
LOOK: Did you close the top of each 8 and 9?   Circle: Yes   No
one stroke numeral · no lift
nine
your best numeral

one stroke numeral · no lift

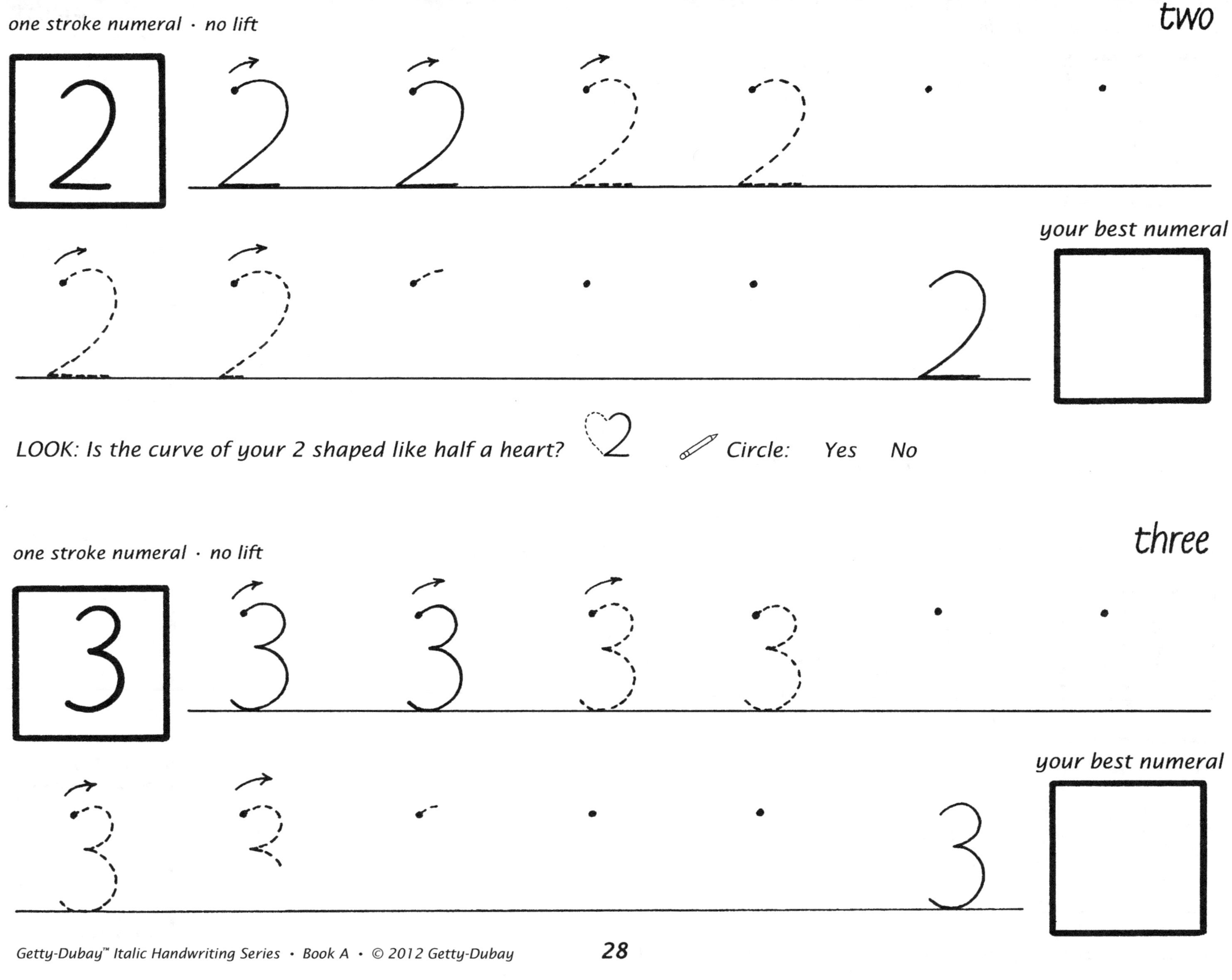

your best numeral

LOOK: Is the curve of your 2 shaped like half a heart?   Circle: Yes   No

three

one stroke numeral · no lift

your best numeral

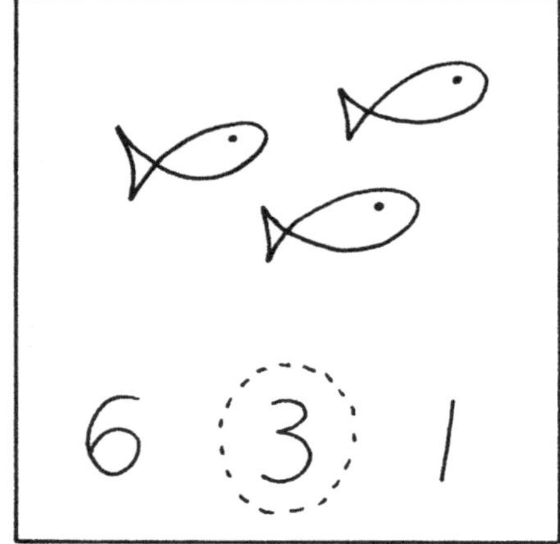

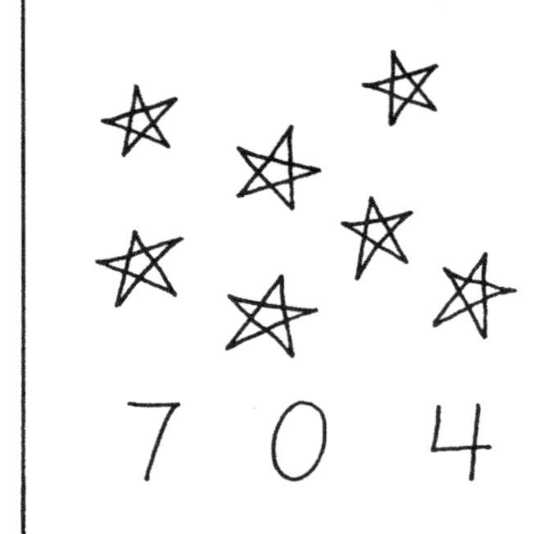
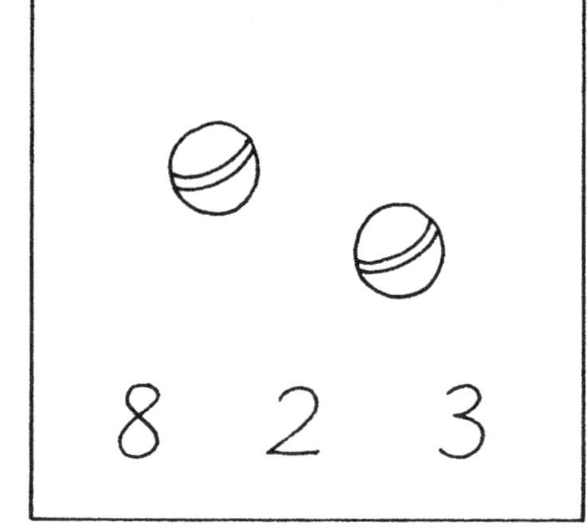

*Ask the student to circle the numeral
that stands for the number of objects in the box.*

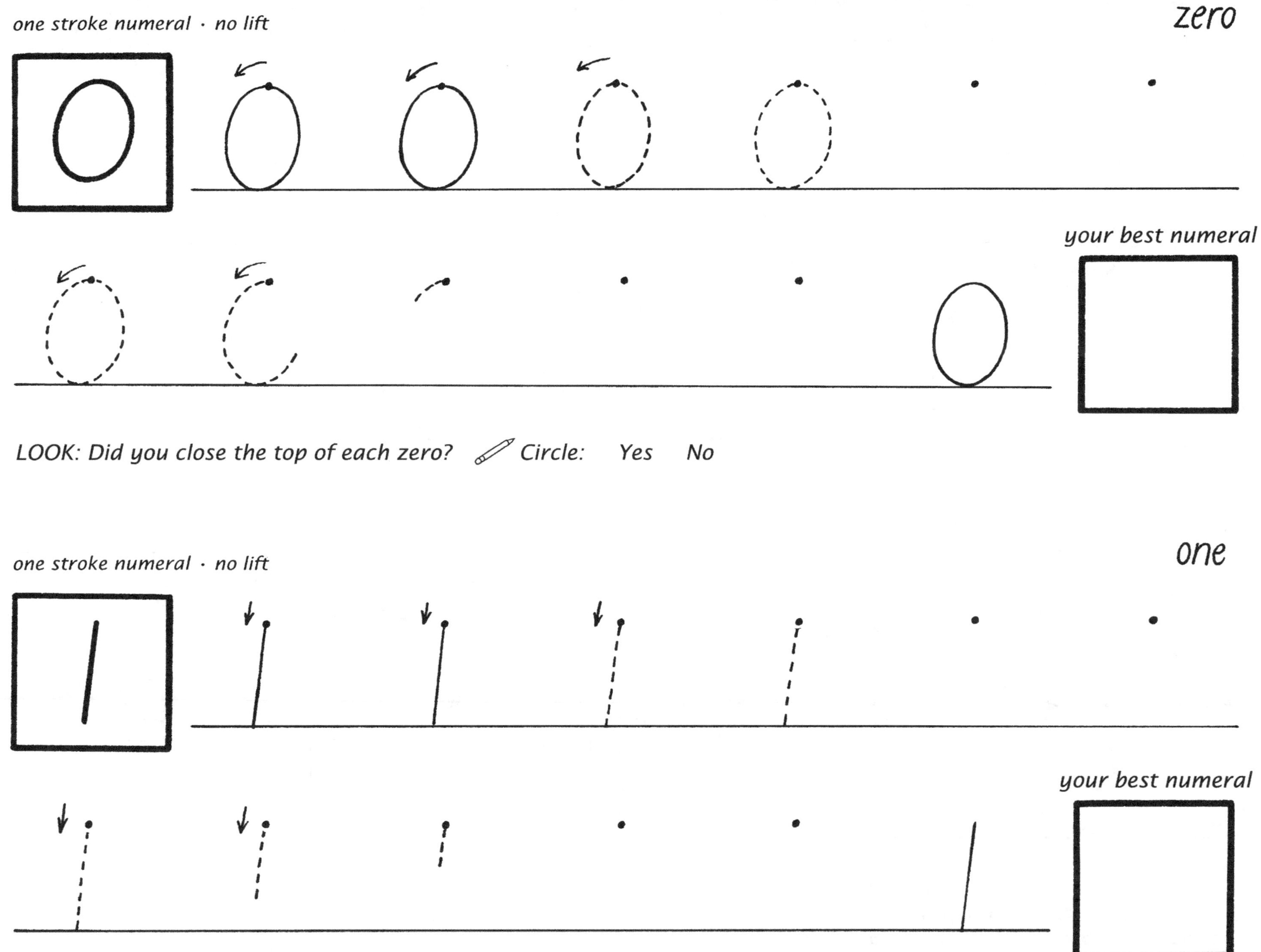

LOOK: Did you close the top of each zero? Circle: Yes No

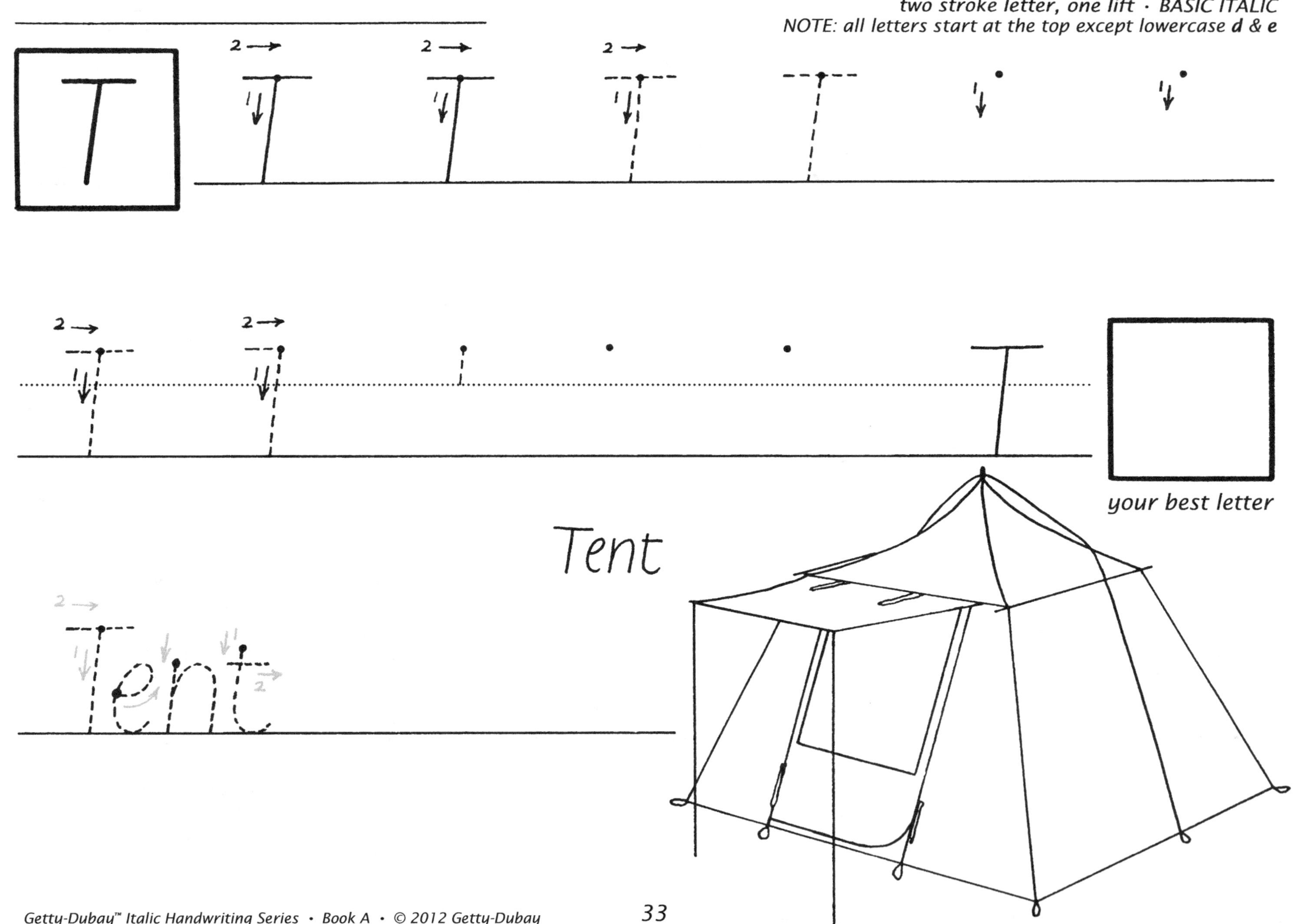

Tent

your best letter

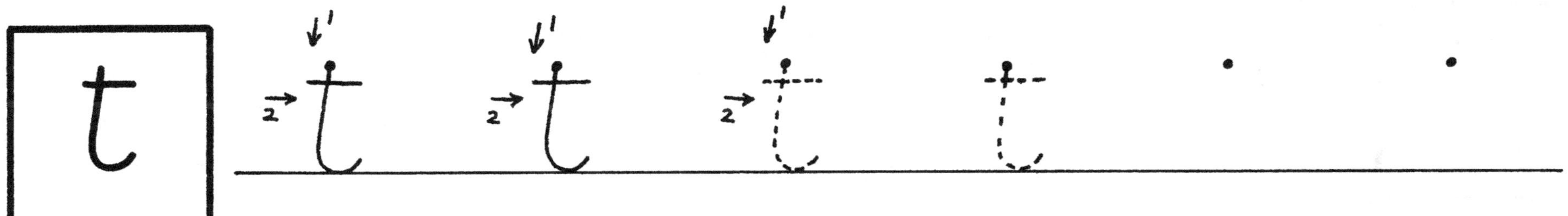

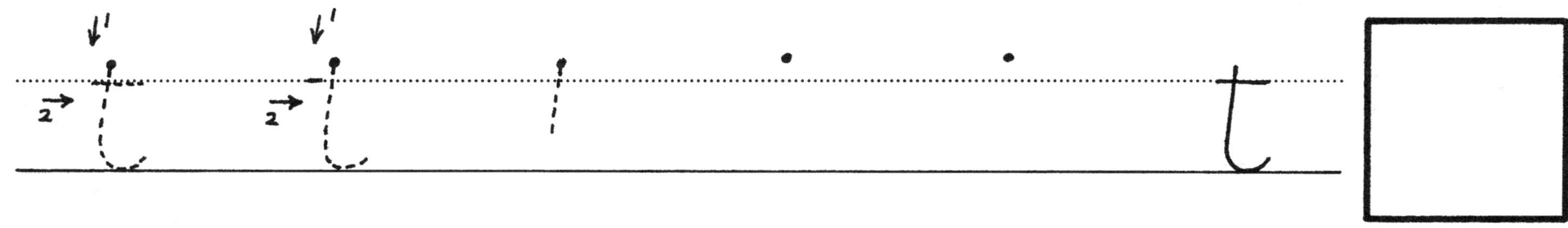

your best letter

turkey

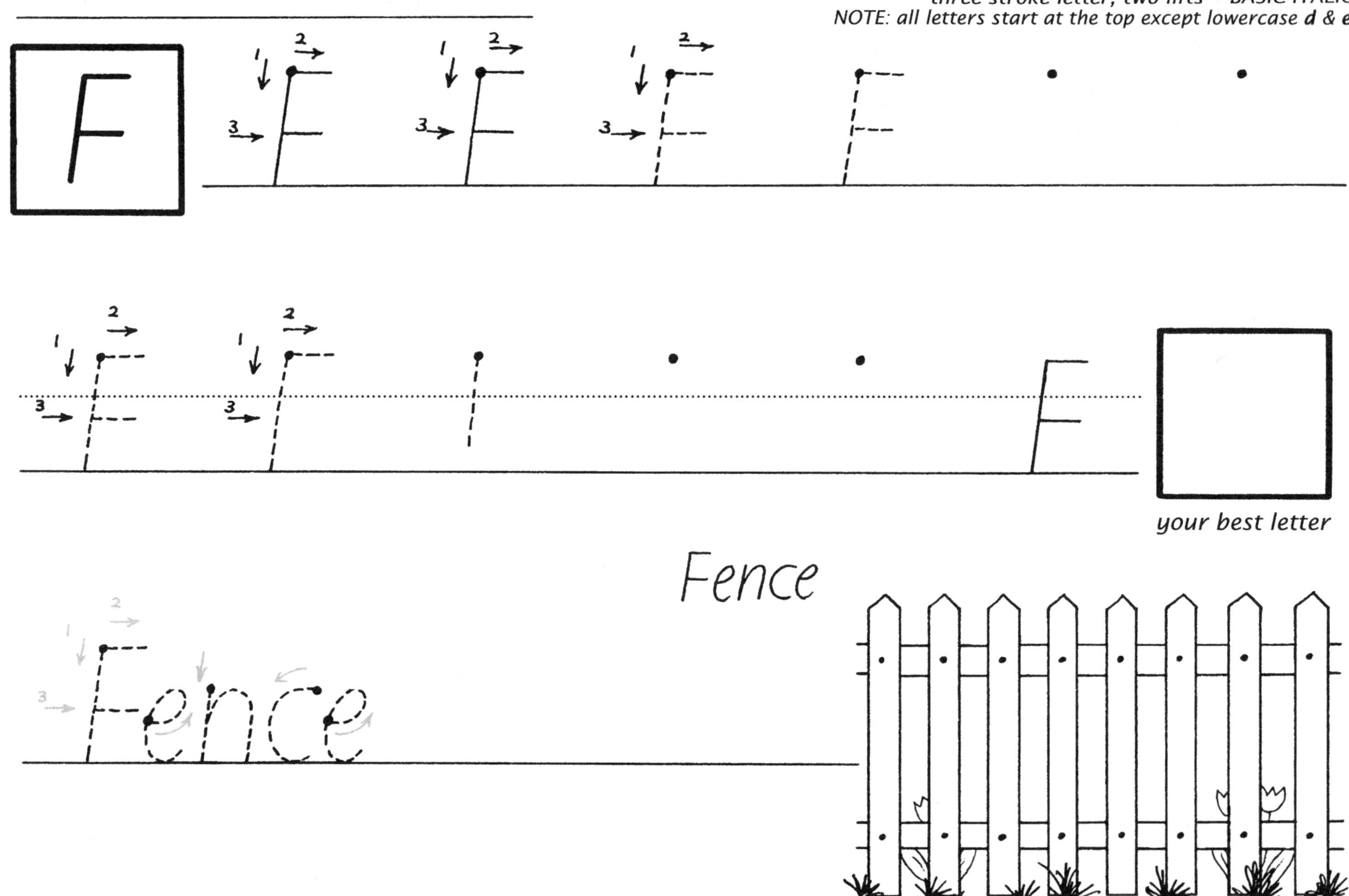

your best letter

Fence

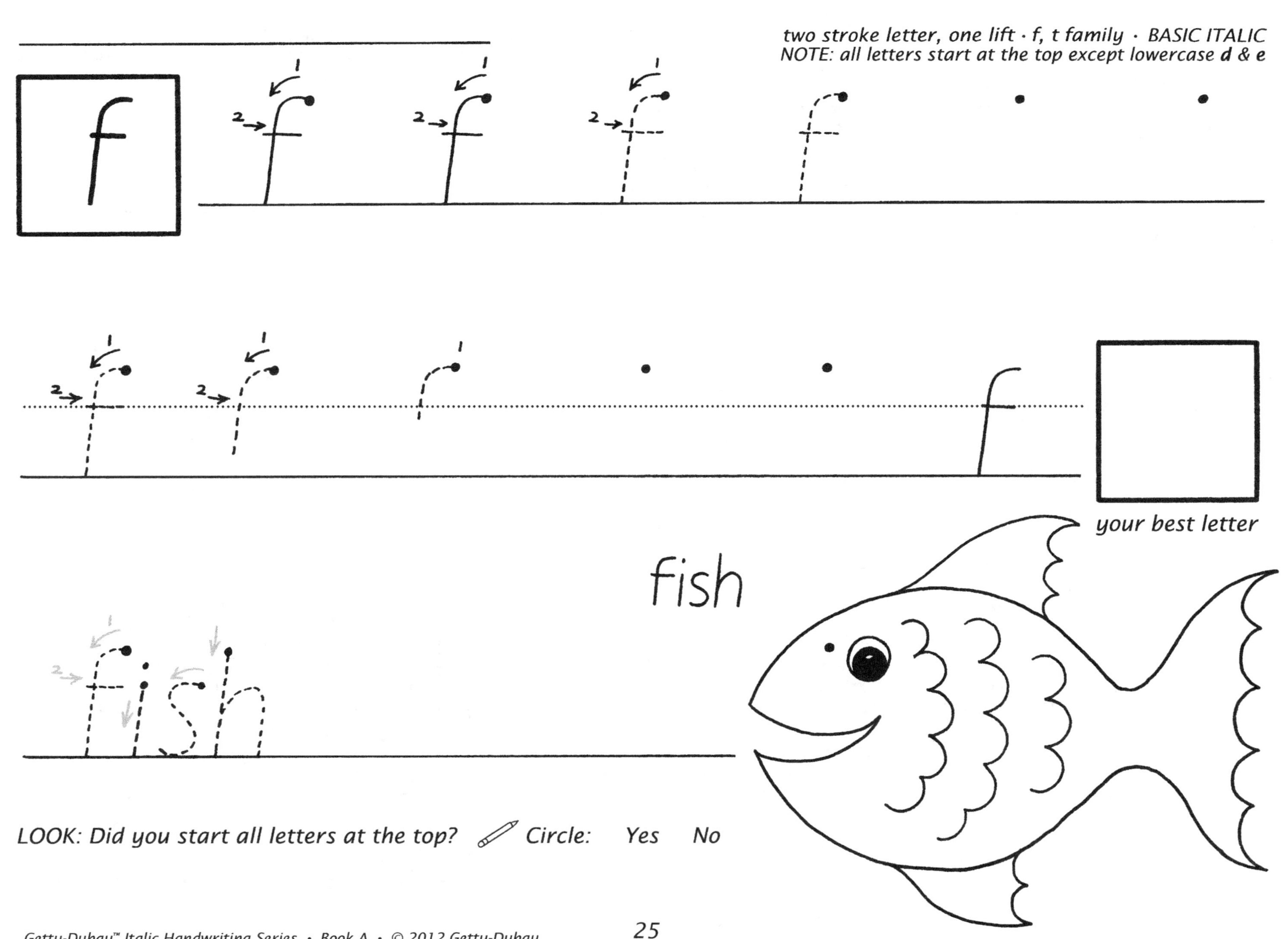

LOOK: Did you start all letters at the top? Circle: Yes   No

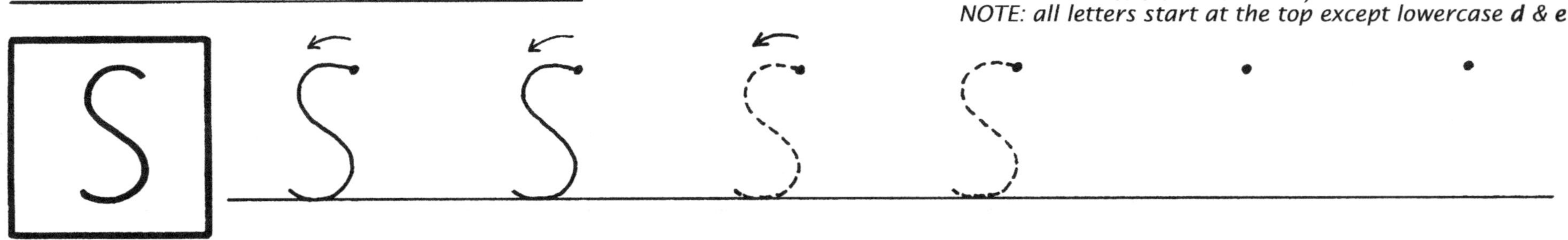

your best letter

Sailboat

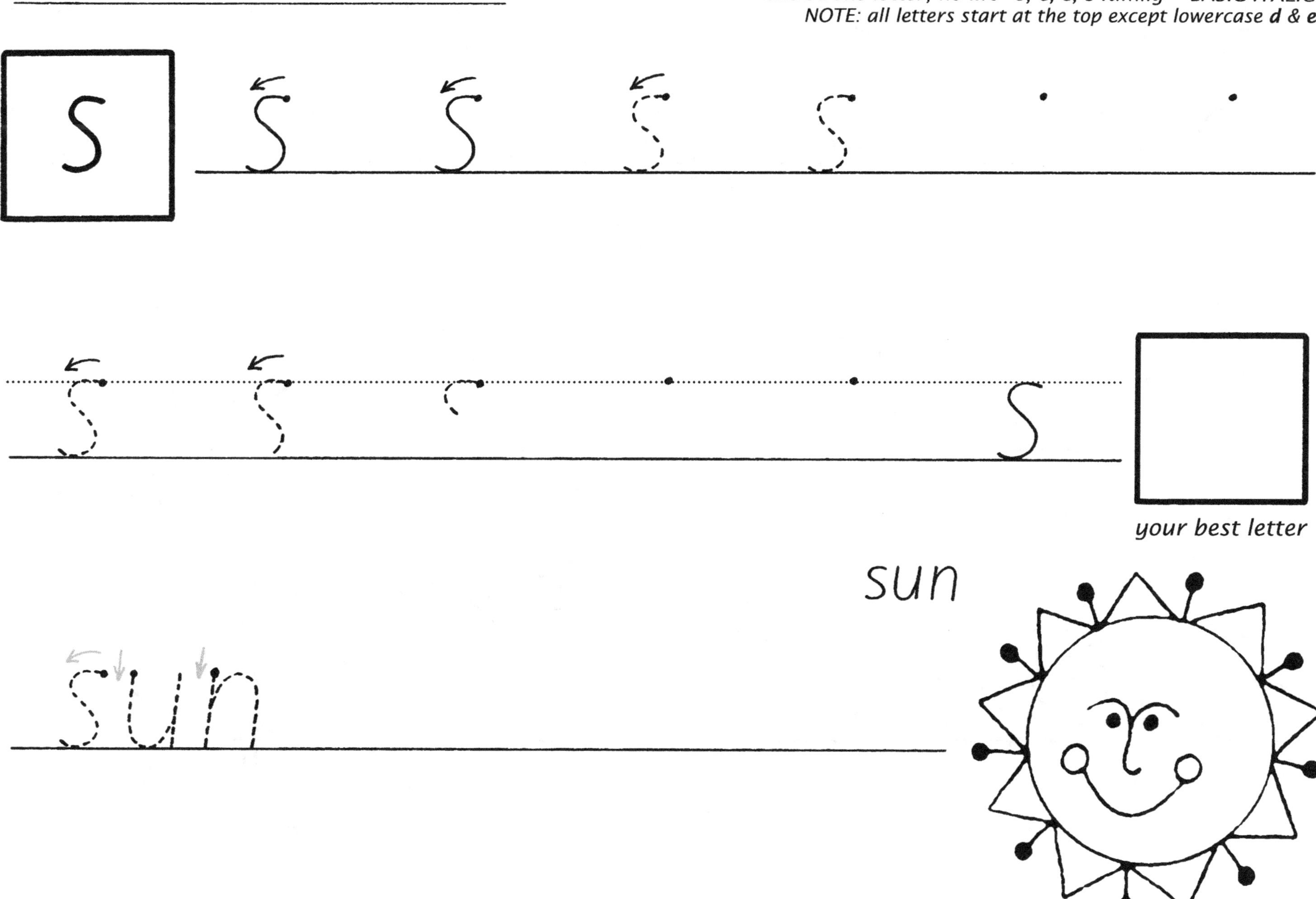

S
your best letter
sun
sun

LOOK: Did you trace each letter before writing your own?

Circle: Yes   No

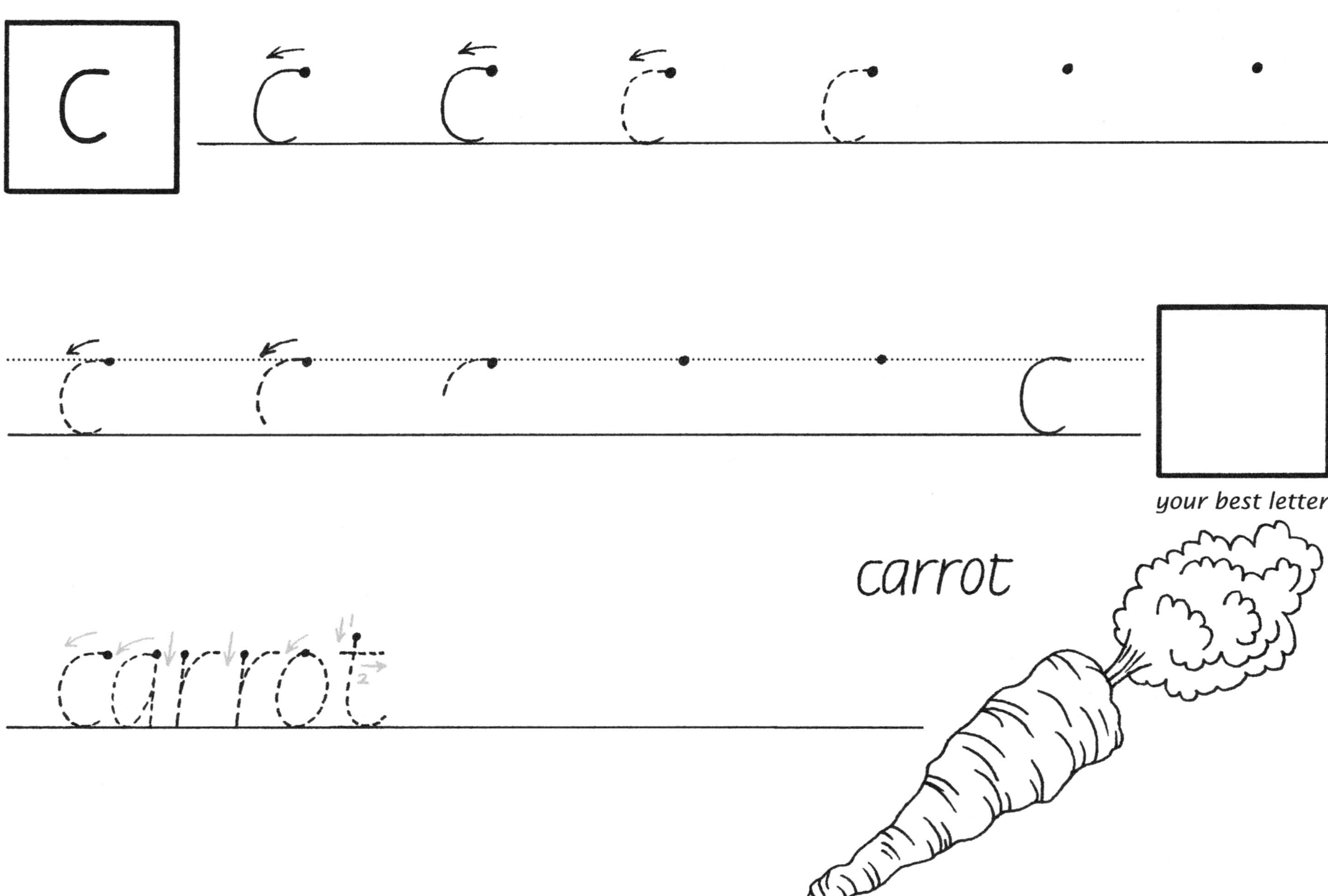

C
your best letter
carrot
carrot

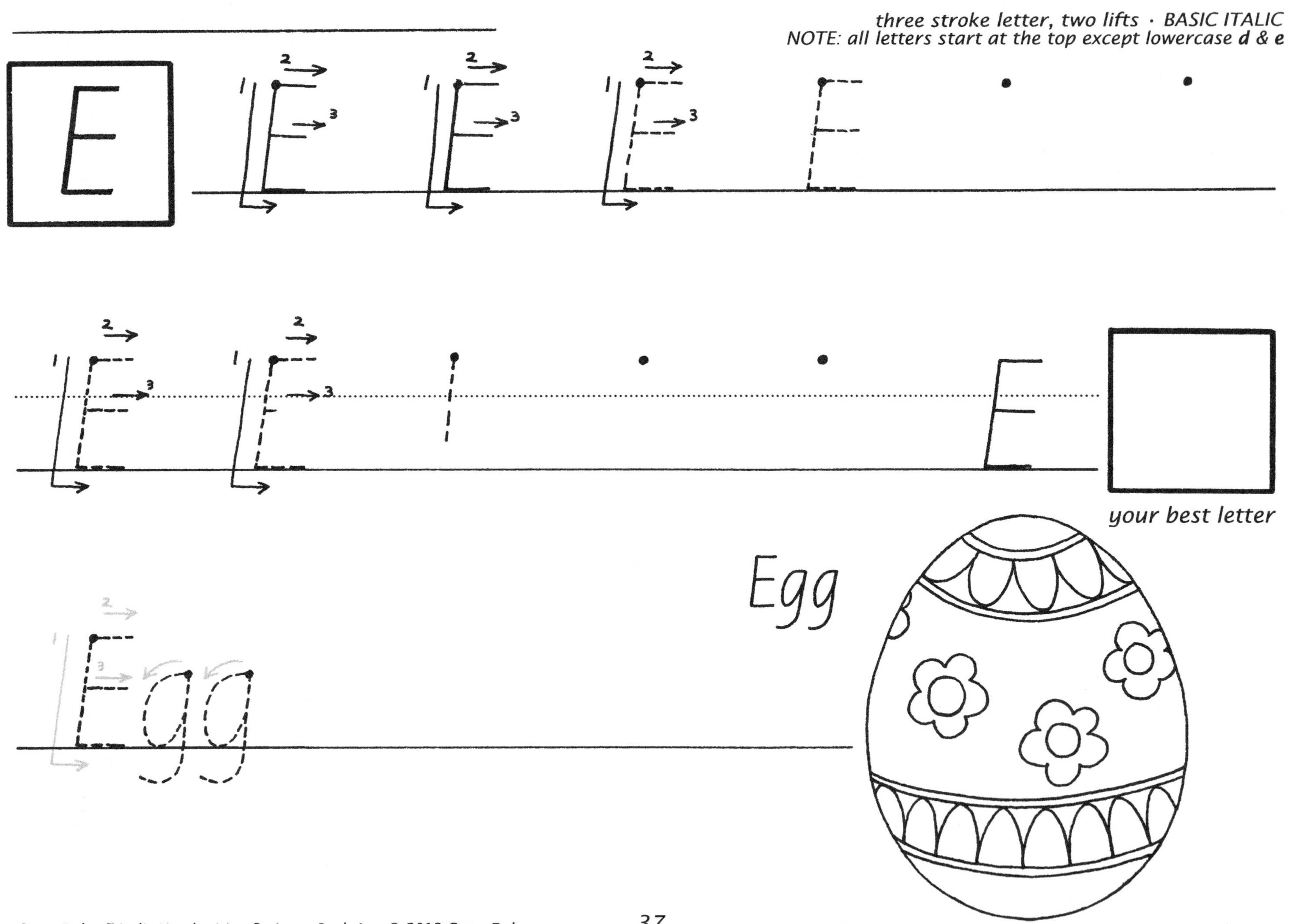

your best letter

Egg

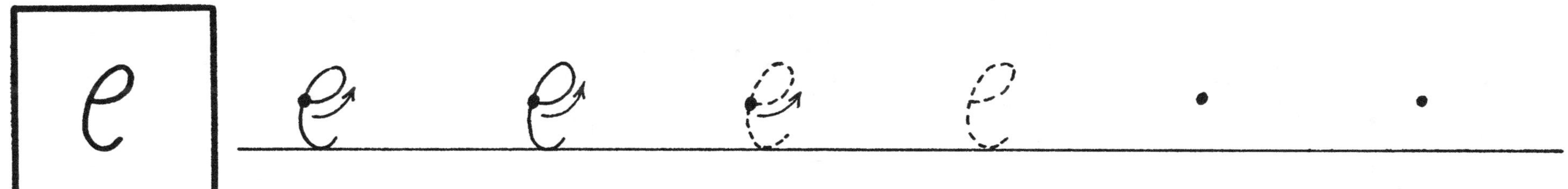

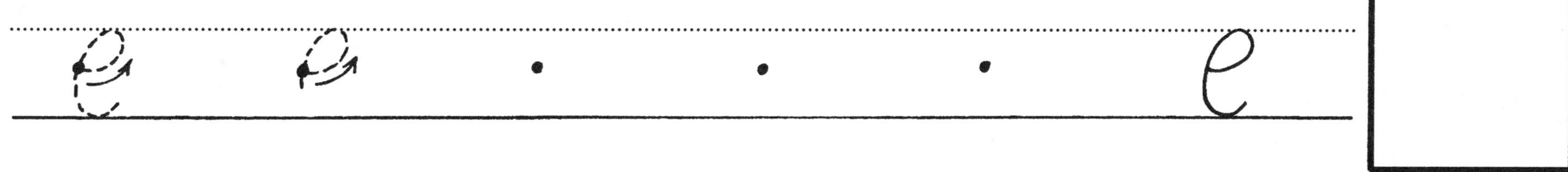

your best letter

elephant

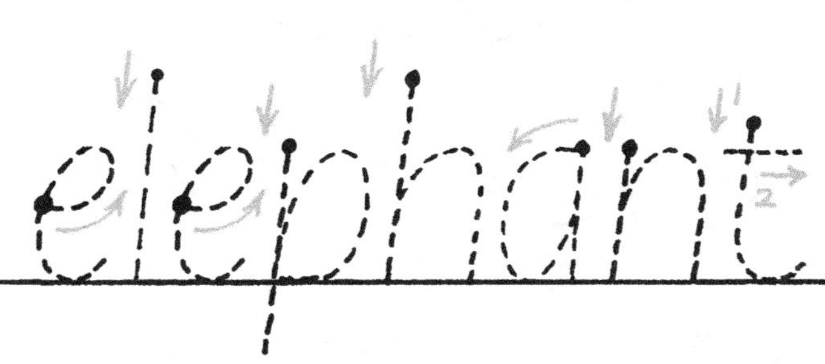

LOOK: Did you trace each **e** before writing your own?

Circle: Yes   No

your best letter

Octagon

LOOK: Did you close the top of each **O**? ✏ Circle: Yes   No

o

octopus

your best letter

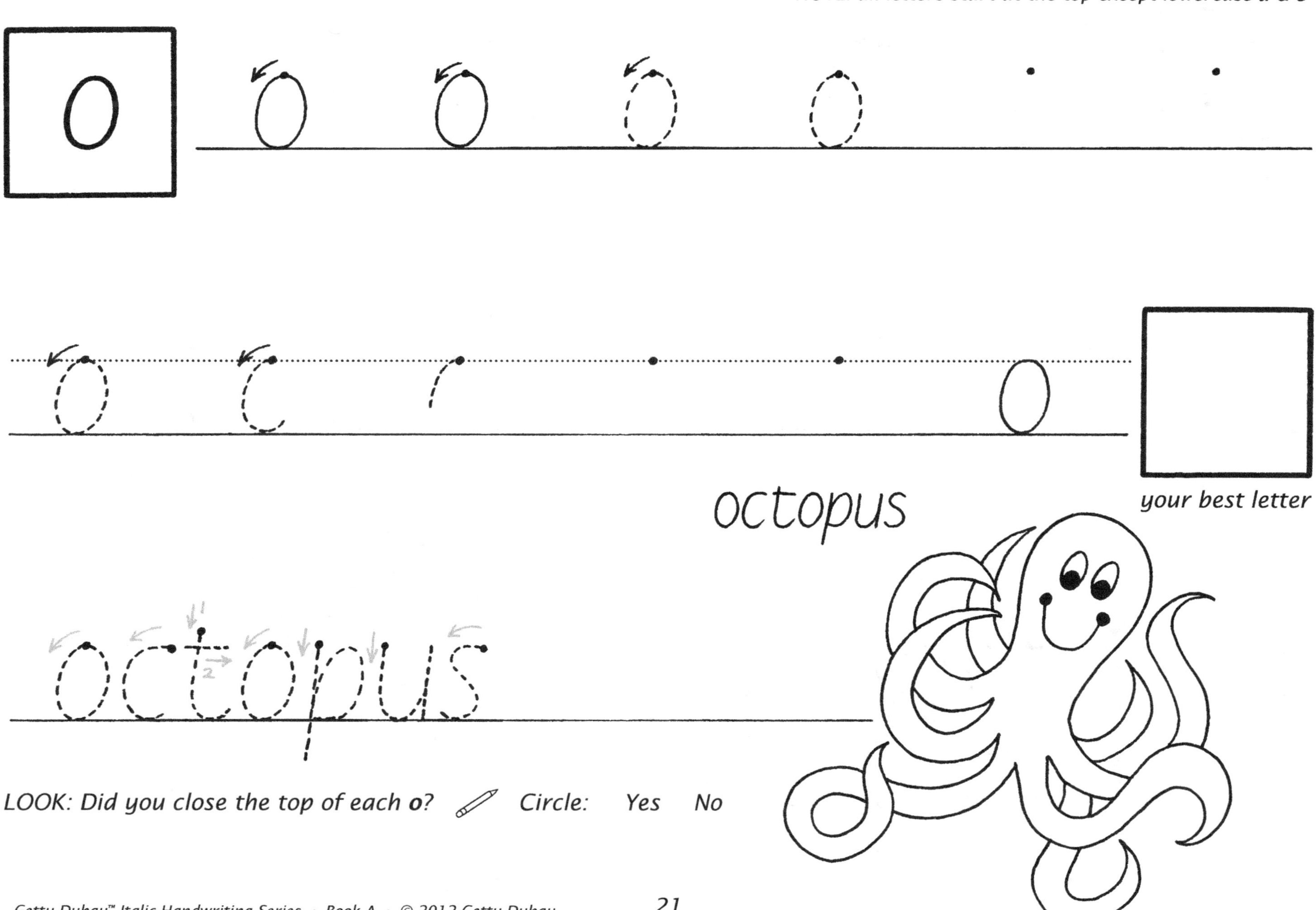

octopus

LOOK: Did you close the top of each **o**?   Circle: Yes   No

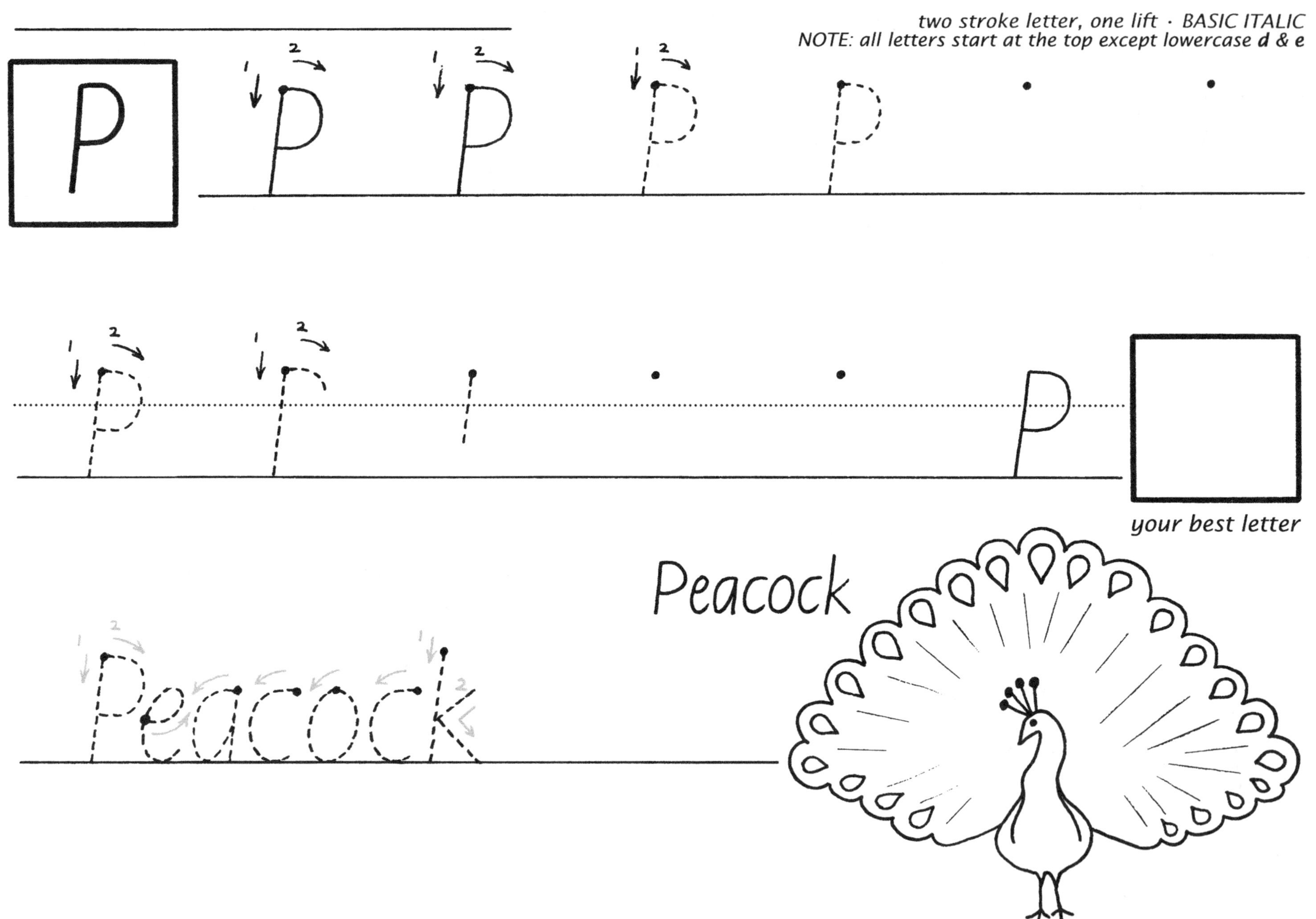

your best letter

Peacock

your best letter

parrot

your best letter

Balloons

Balloons

your best letter

butterfly

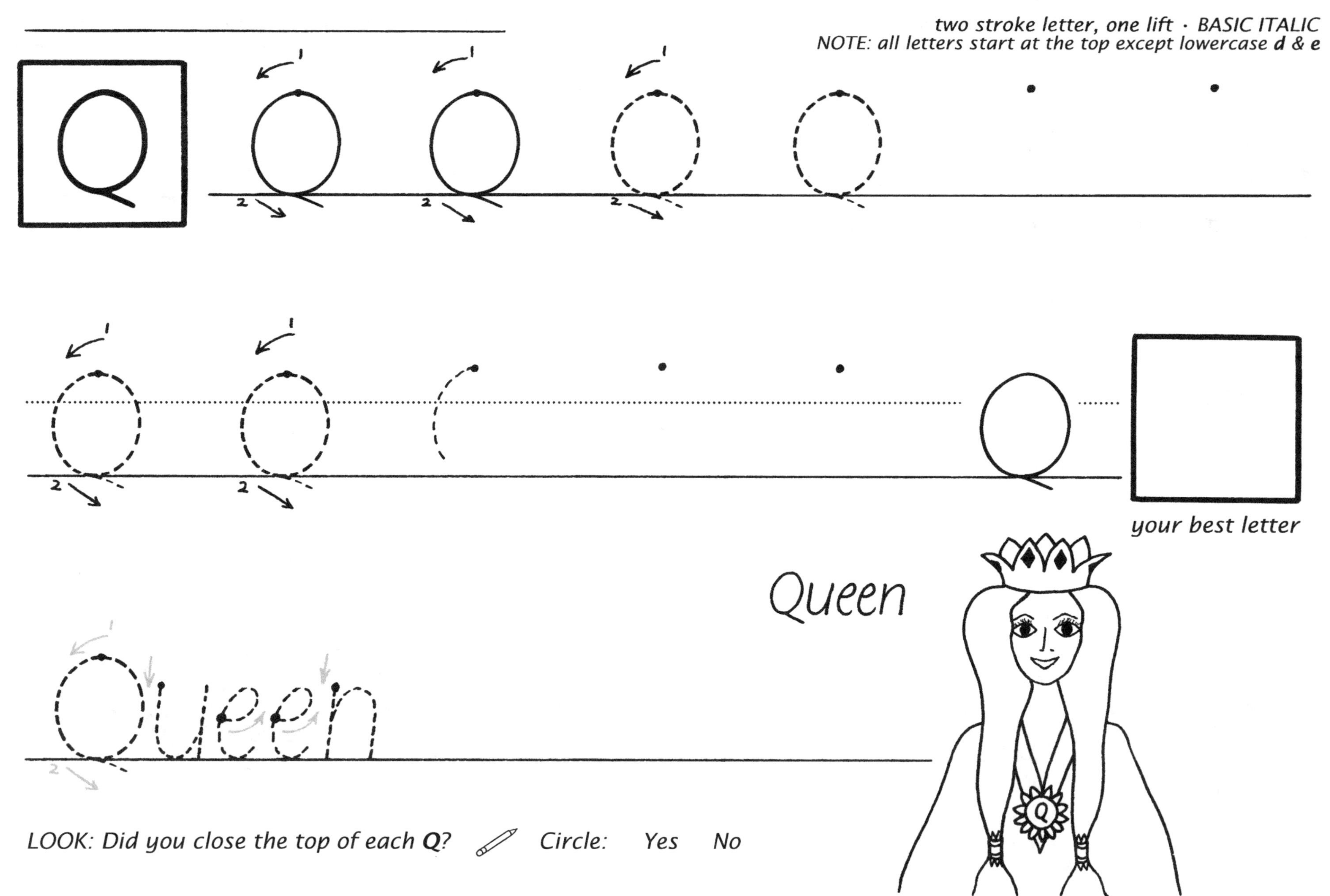

your best letter

Queen

LOOK: Did you close the top of each **Q**? ✎ Circle: Yes   No

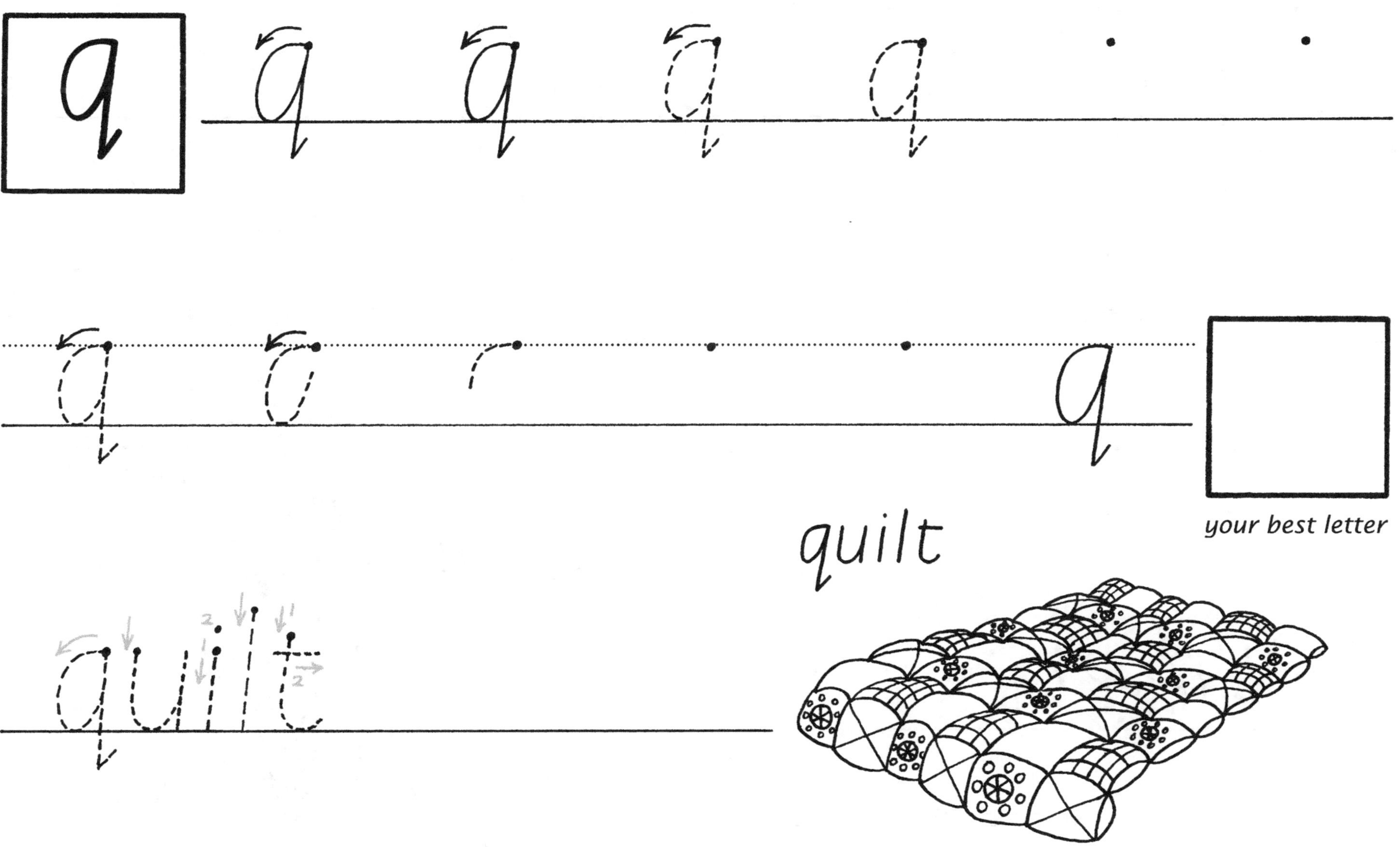

quilt

your best letter

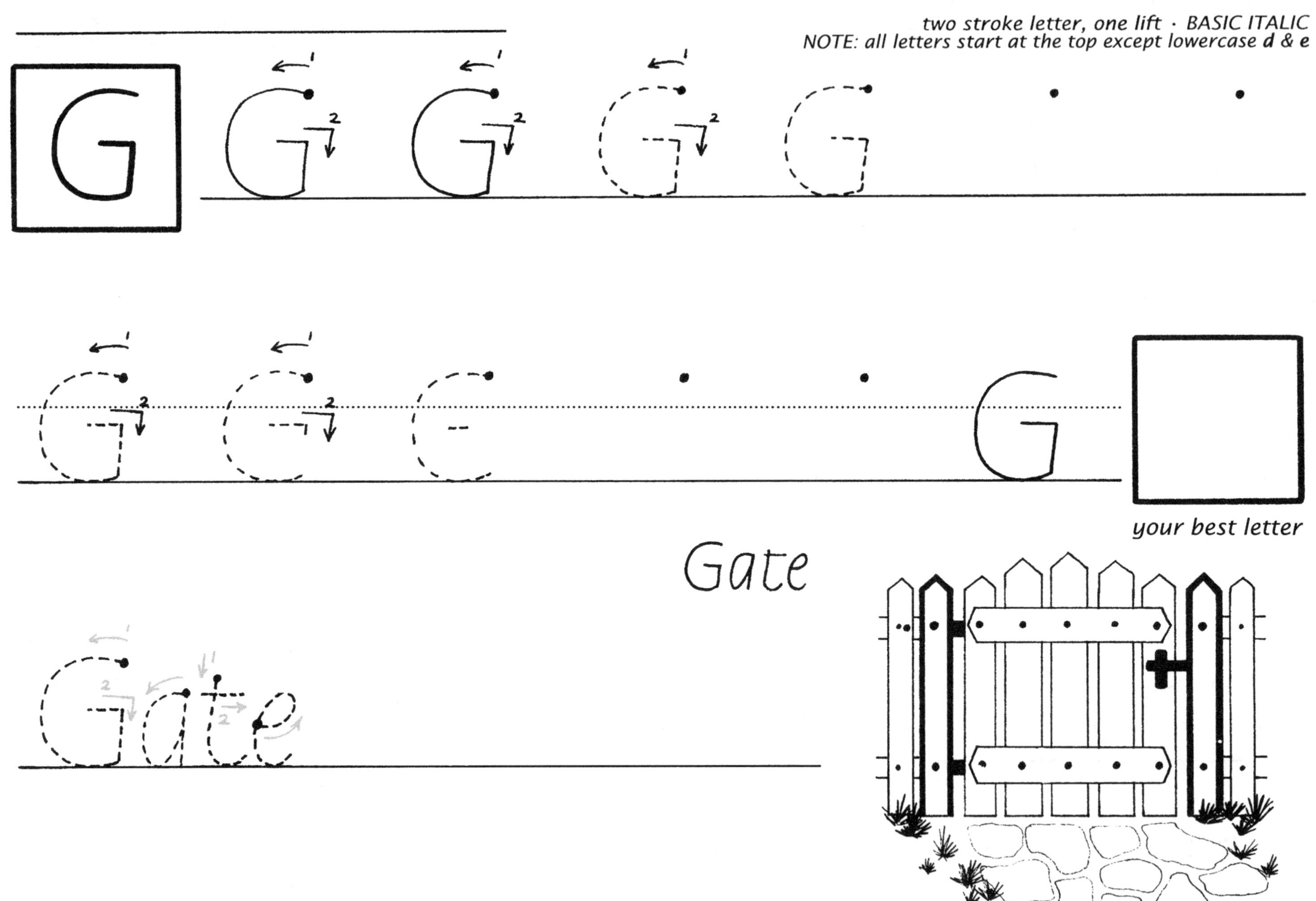

your best letter

Gate

LOOK: Did you trace each letter before writing your own?　✐ Circle:　Yes　No

your best letter

Dinosaur

Dinosaur

your best letter

dog

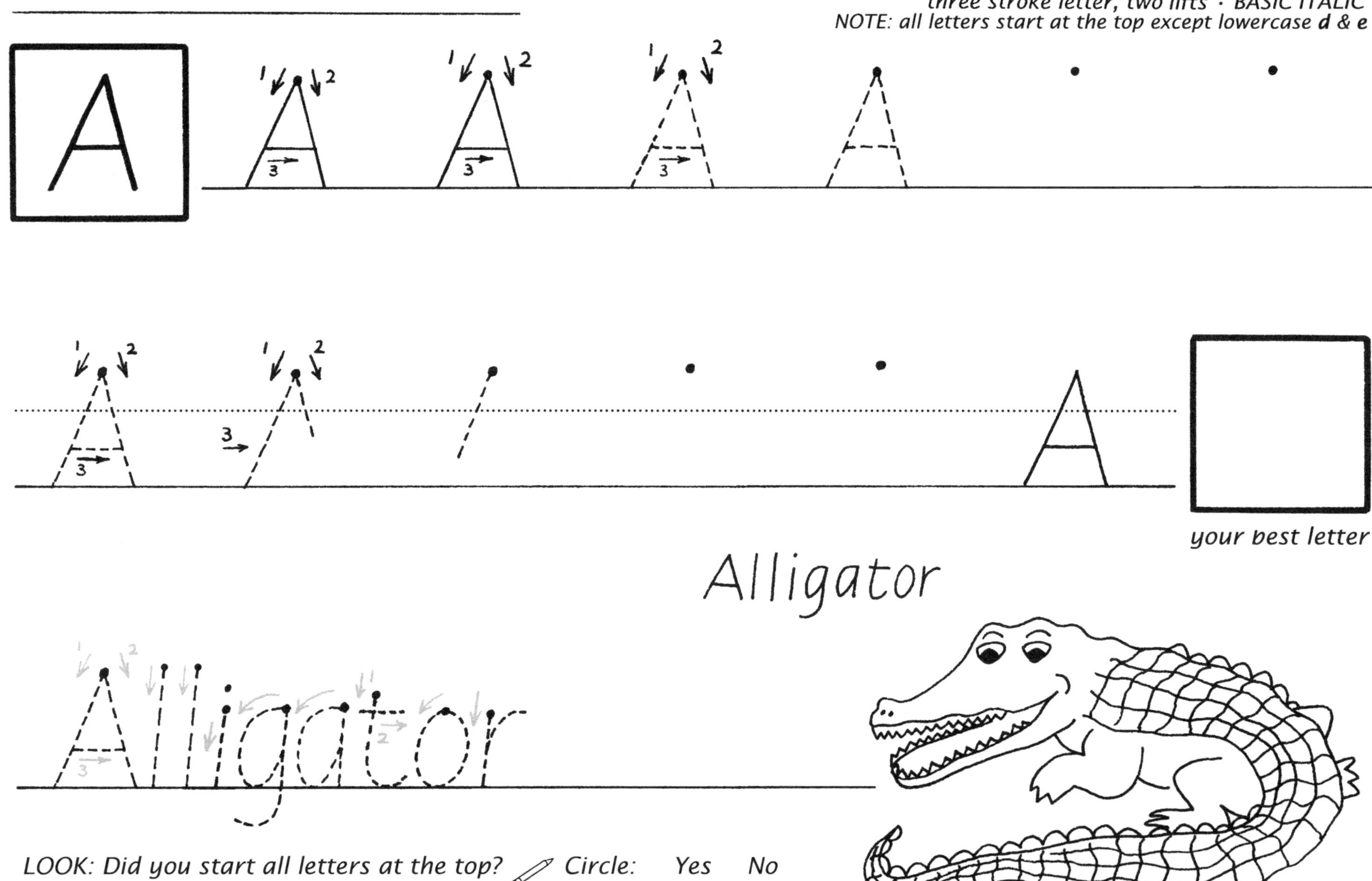

LOOK: Did you start all letters at the top? Circle: Yes   No

your best letter

apple

LOOK: Did you close each **a** at the top? Circle: Yes No

Y

your best letter

Yo-yo

45

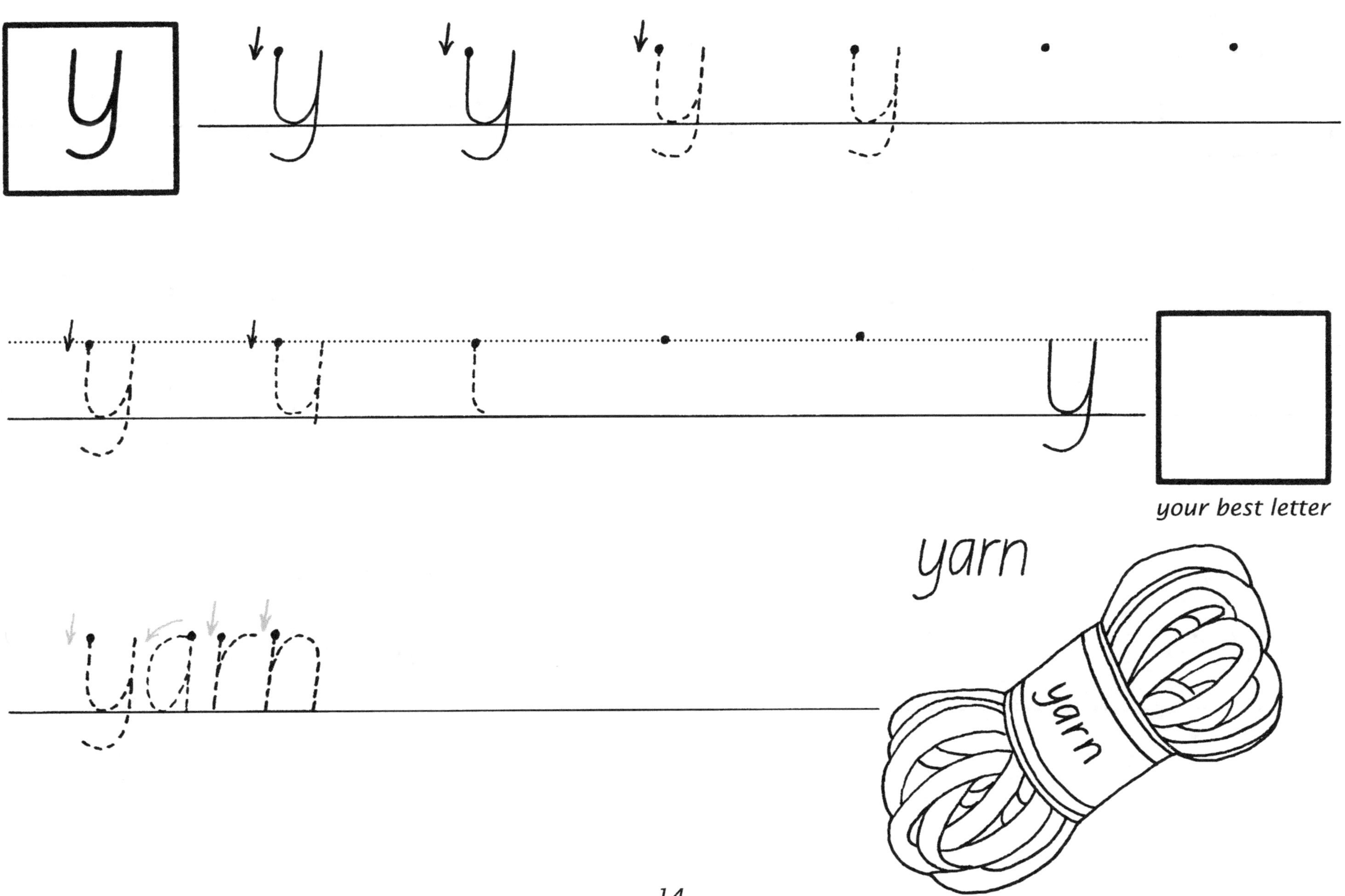

your best letter

yarn

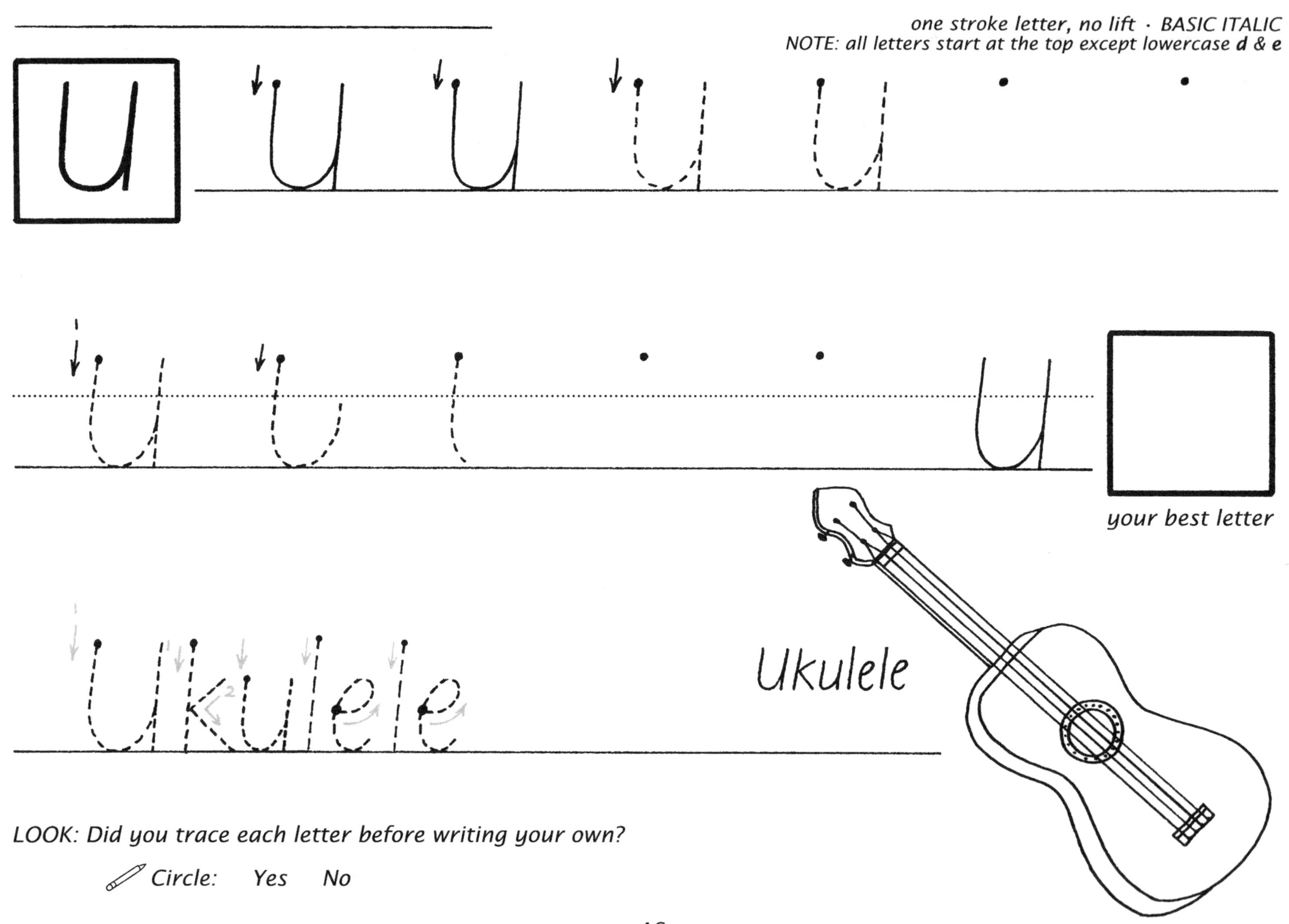

one stroke letter, no lift · BASIC ITALIC
NOTE: all letters start at the top except lowercase d & e
your best letter
Ukulele
LOOK: Did you trace each letter before writing your own?
Circle: Yes   No

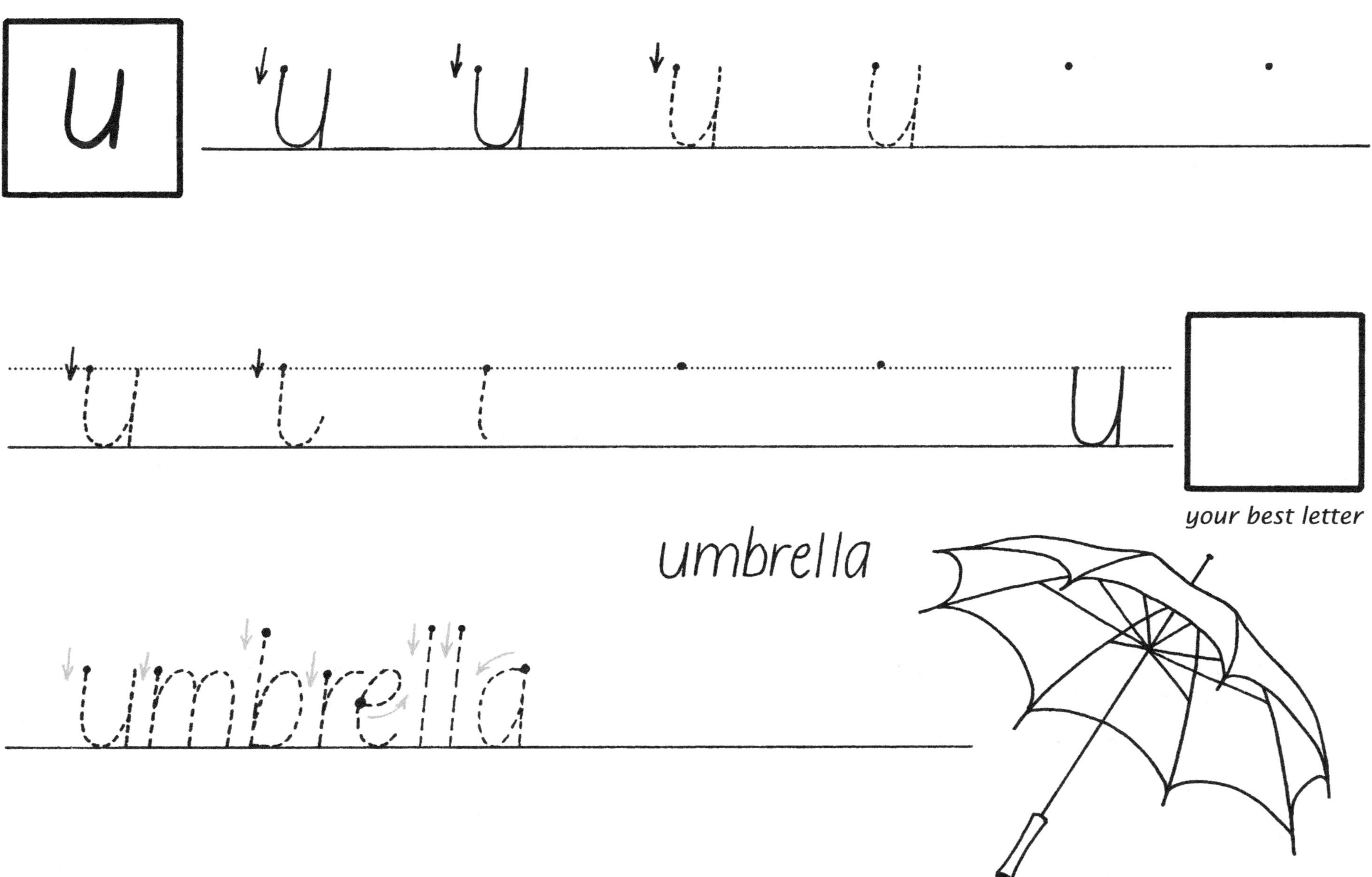

your best letter

umbrella

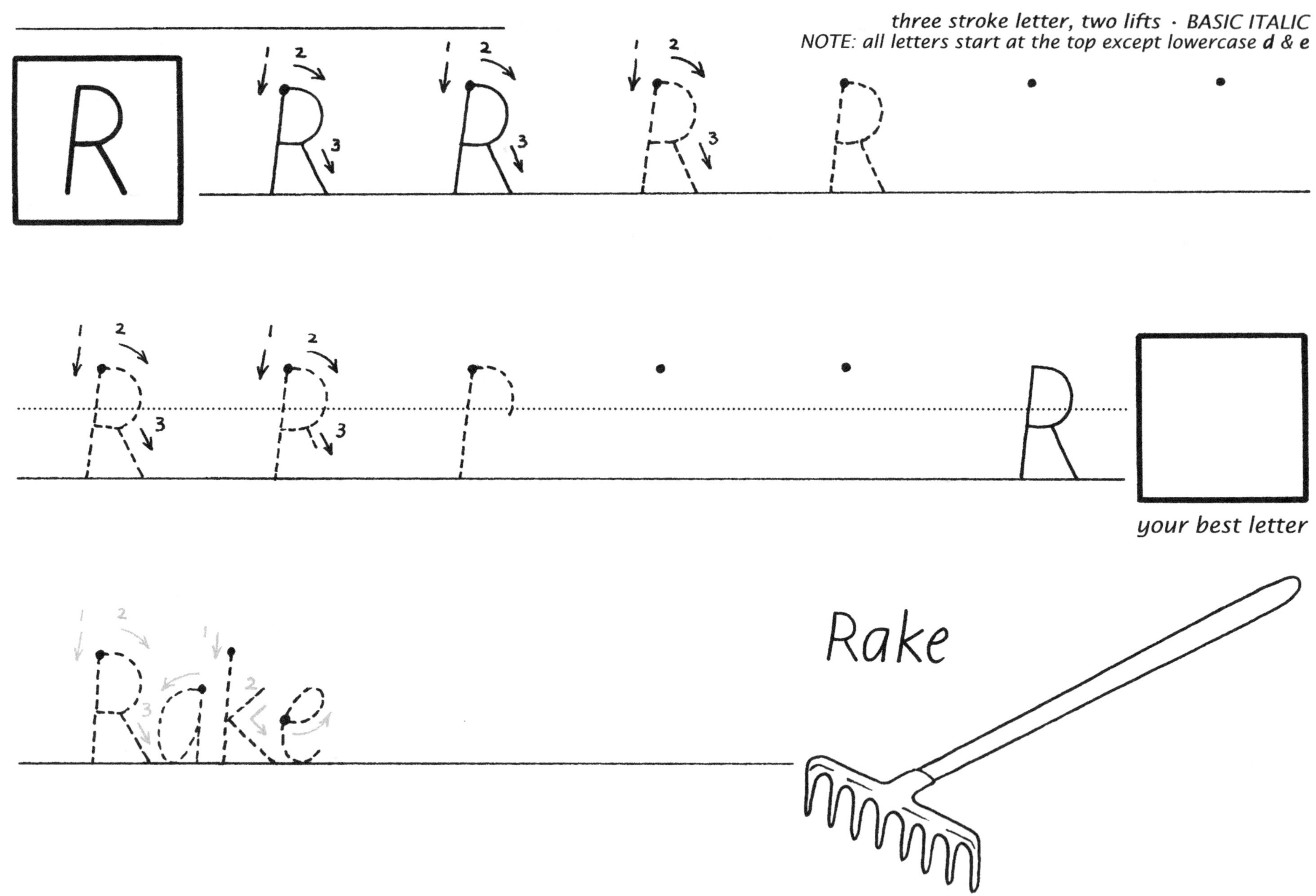

your best letter

Rake

LOOK: Did you start each letter at the top?   Circle: Yes   No

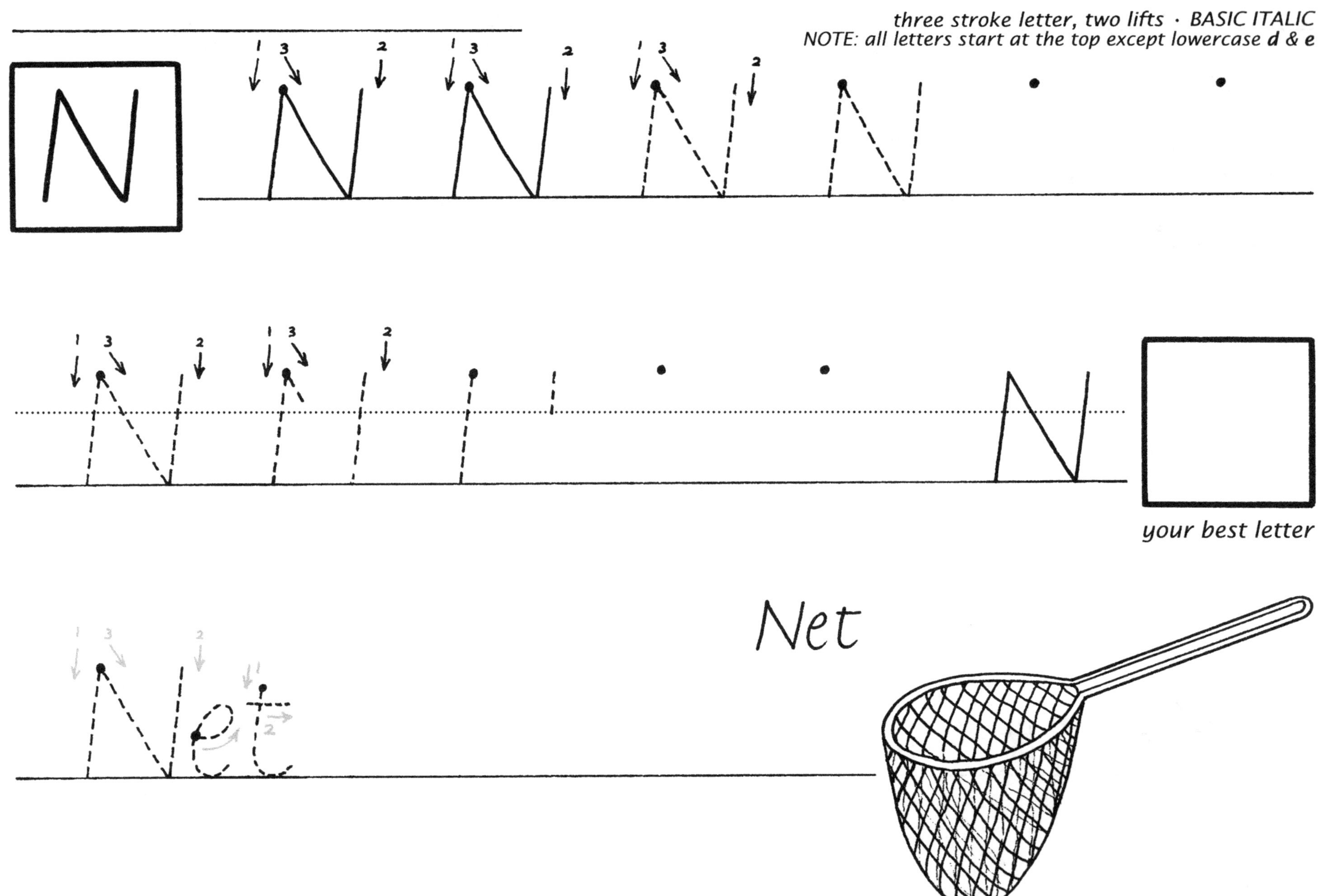

three stroke letter, two lifts · BASIC ITALIC
NOTE: all letters start at the top except lowercase d & e
your best letter
Net

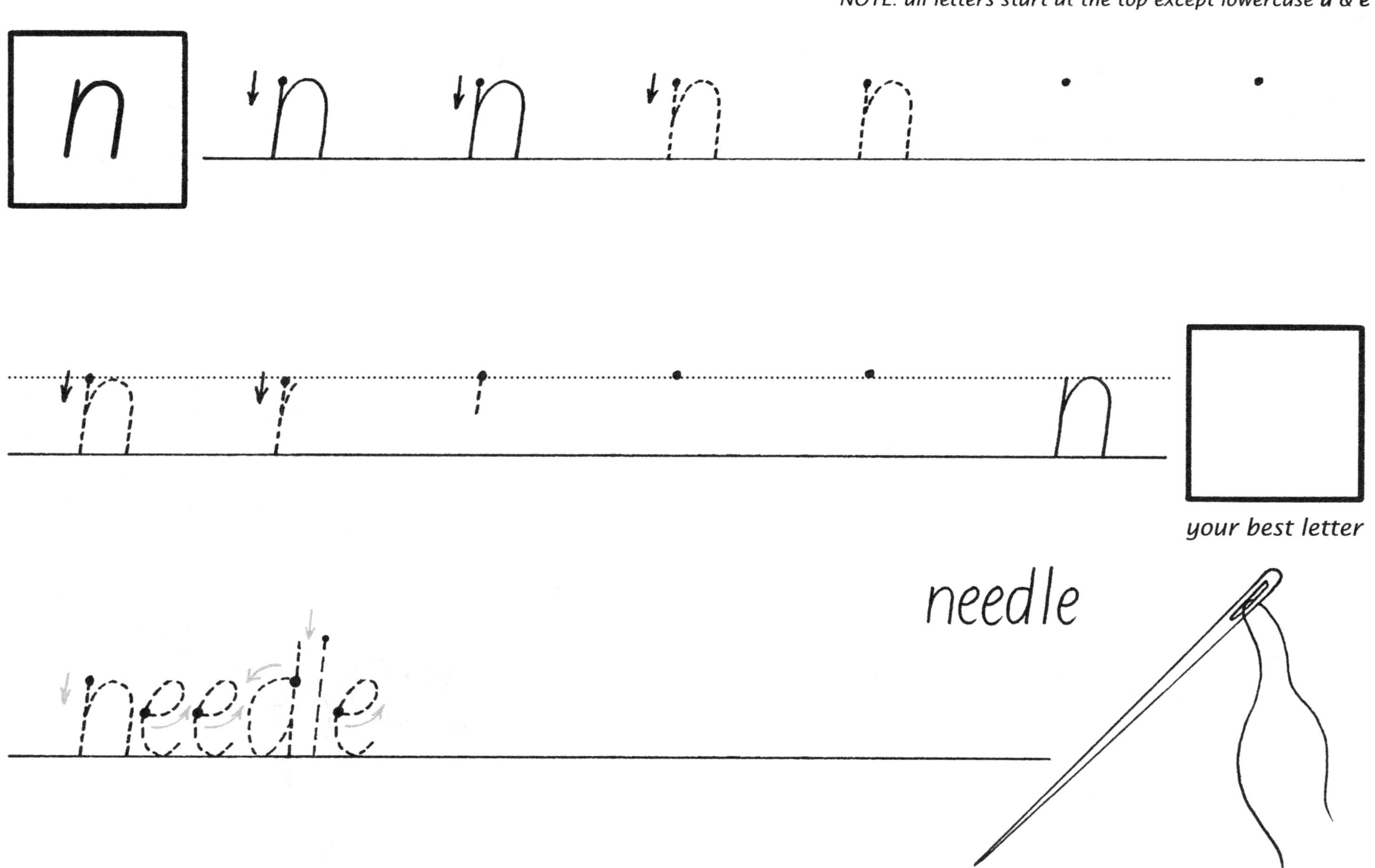

your best letter

needle

your best letter

Mittens

your best letter

mouse

LOOK: Did you start all letters at the top? Circle: Yes   No

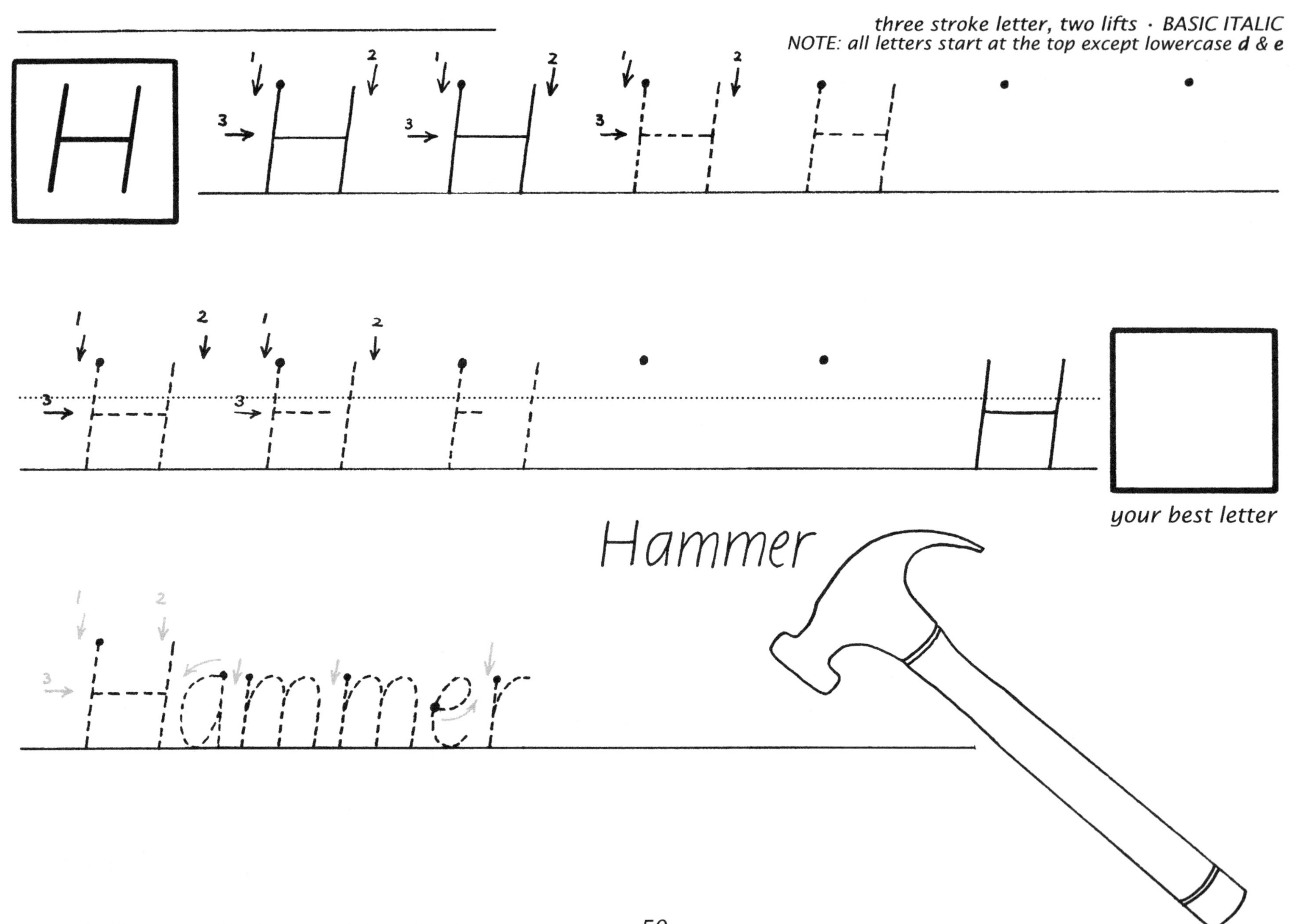

three stroke letter, two lifts · BASIC ITALIC
NOTE: all letters start at the top except lowercase d & e
1
2
3
your best letter
Hammer
Hammer

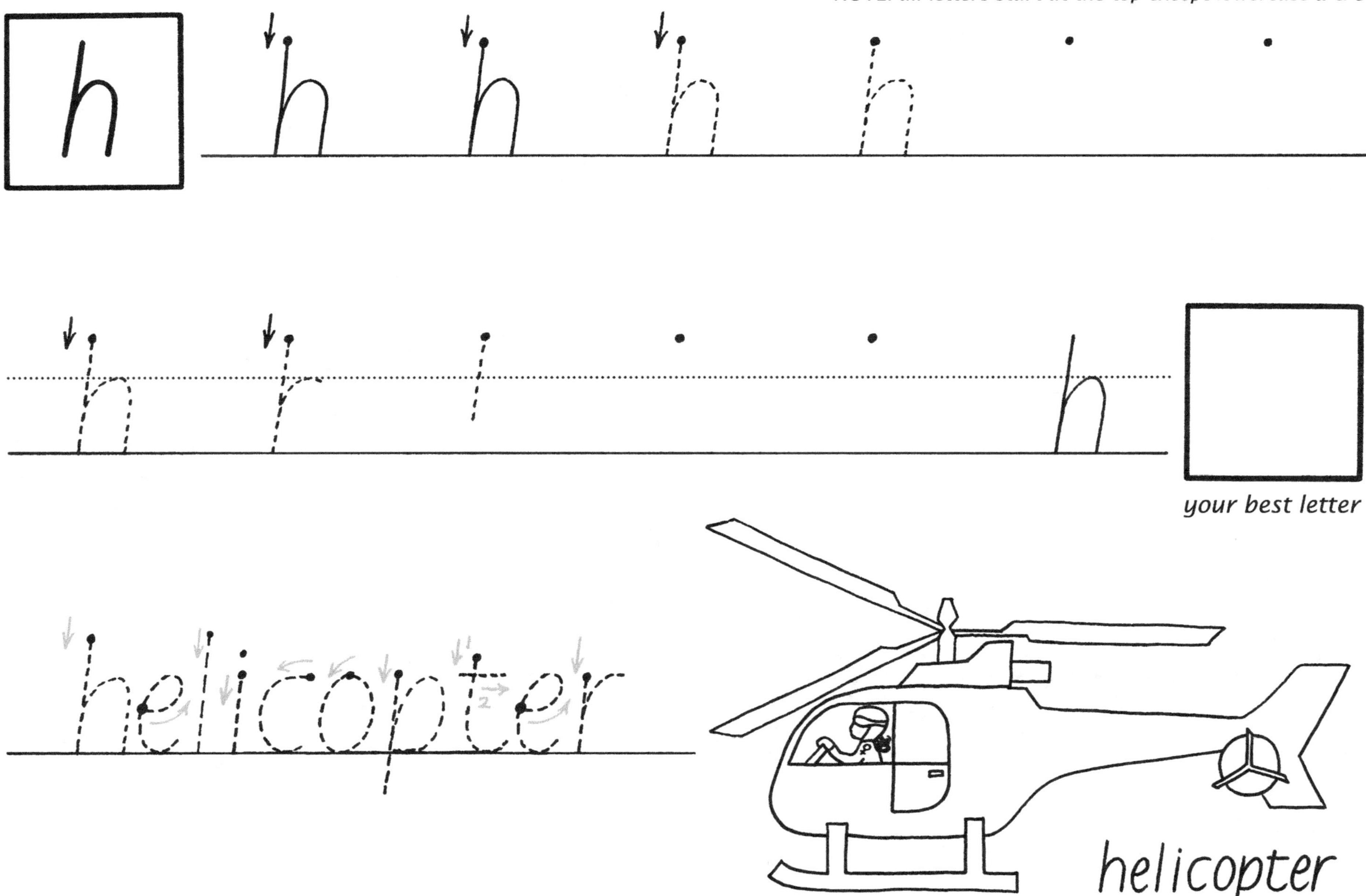

your best letter

helicopter

Zipper

your best letter

Zipper

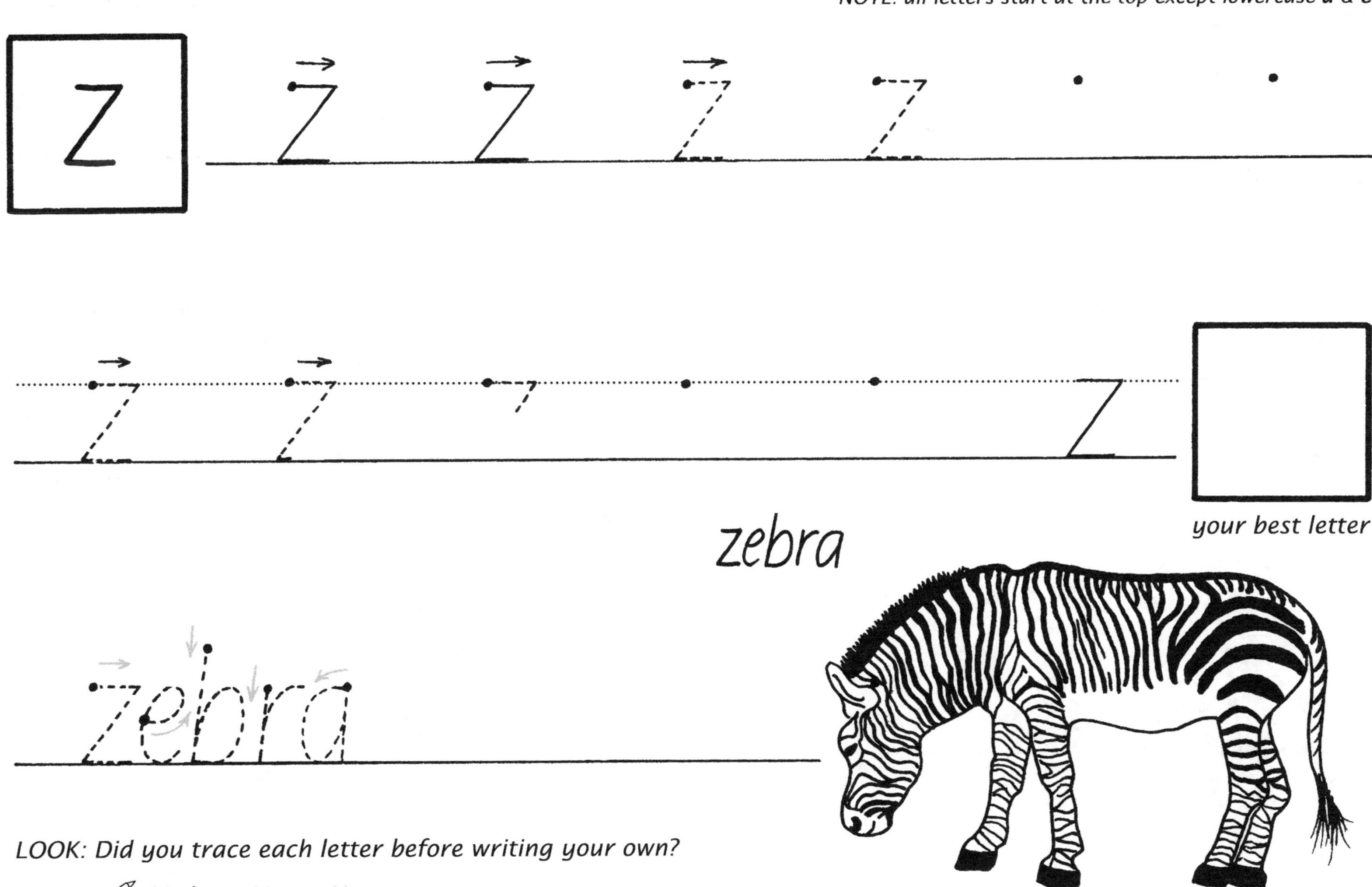

LOOK: Did you trace each letter before writing your own?

Circle: Yes   No

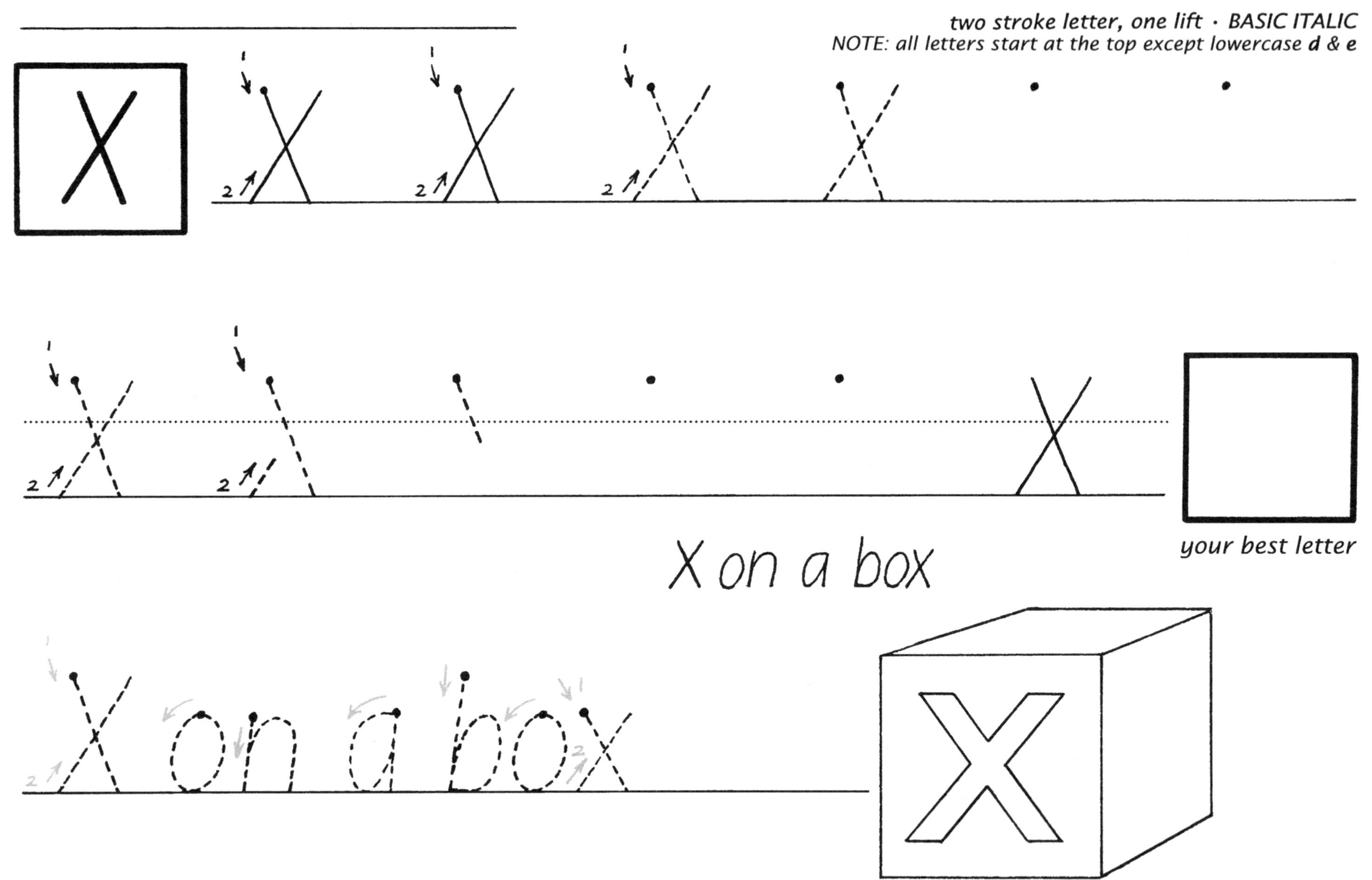

your best letter

X on a box

x in a box
your best letter
x in a box

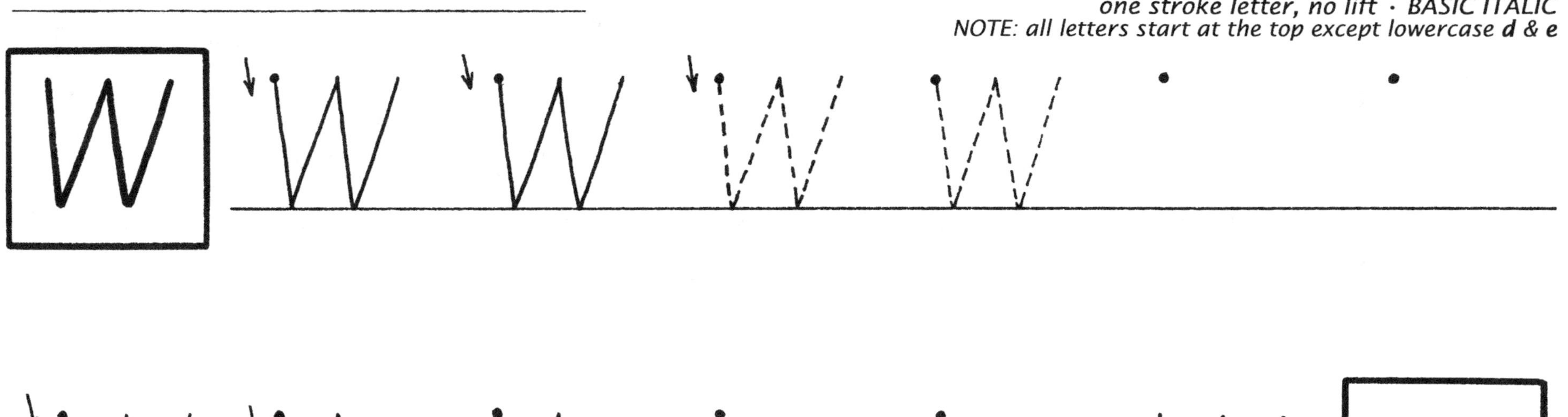

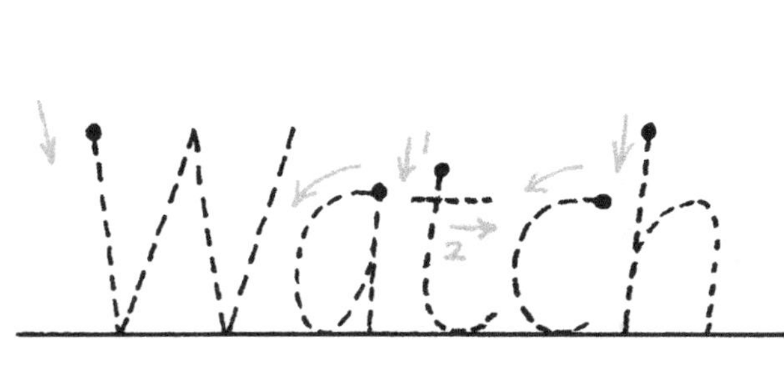

your best letter

Watch

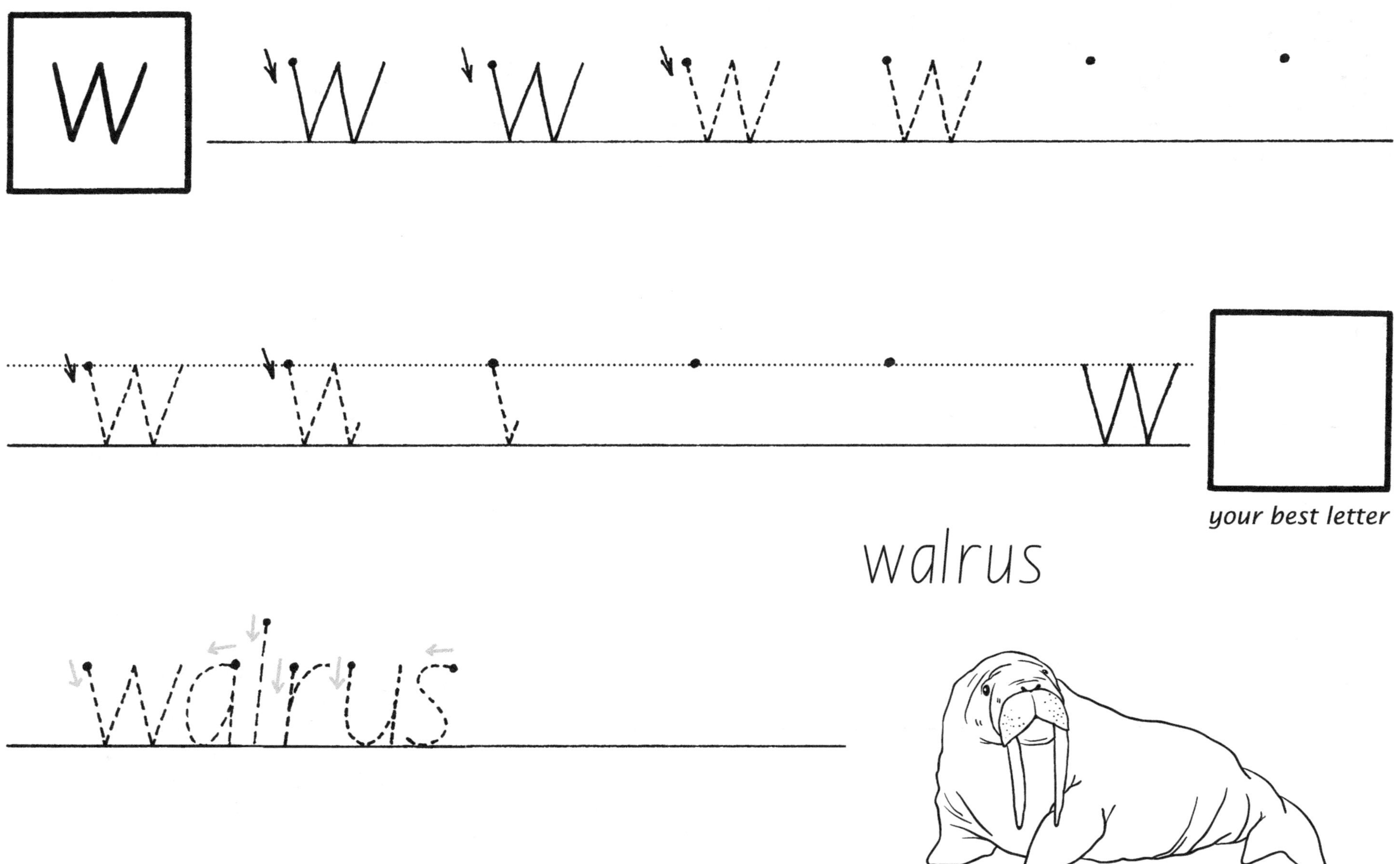

your best letter

walrus

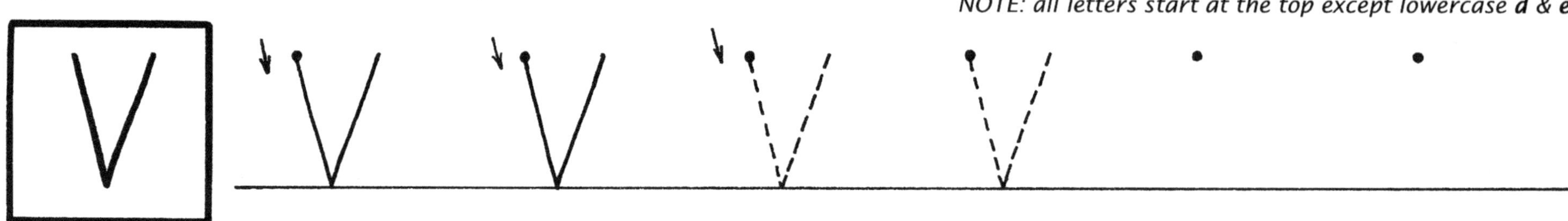

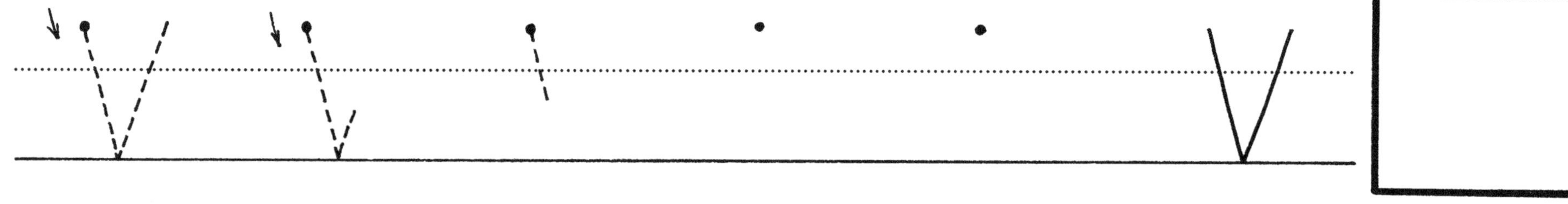

your best letter

Valentine

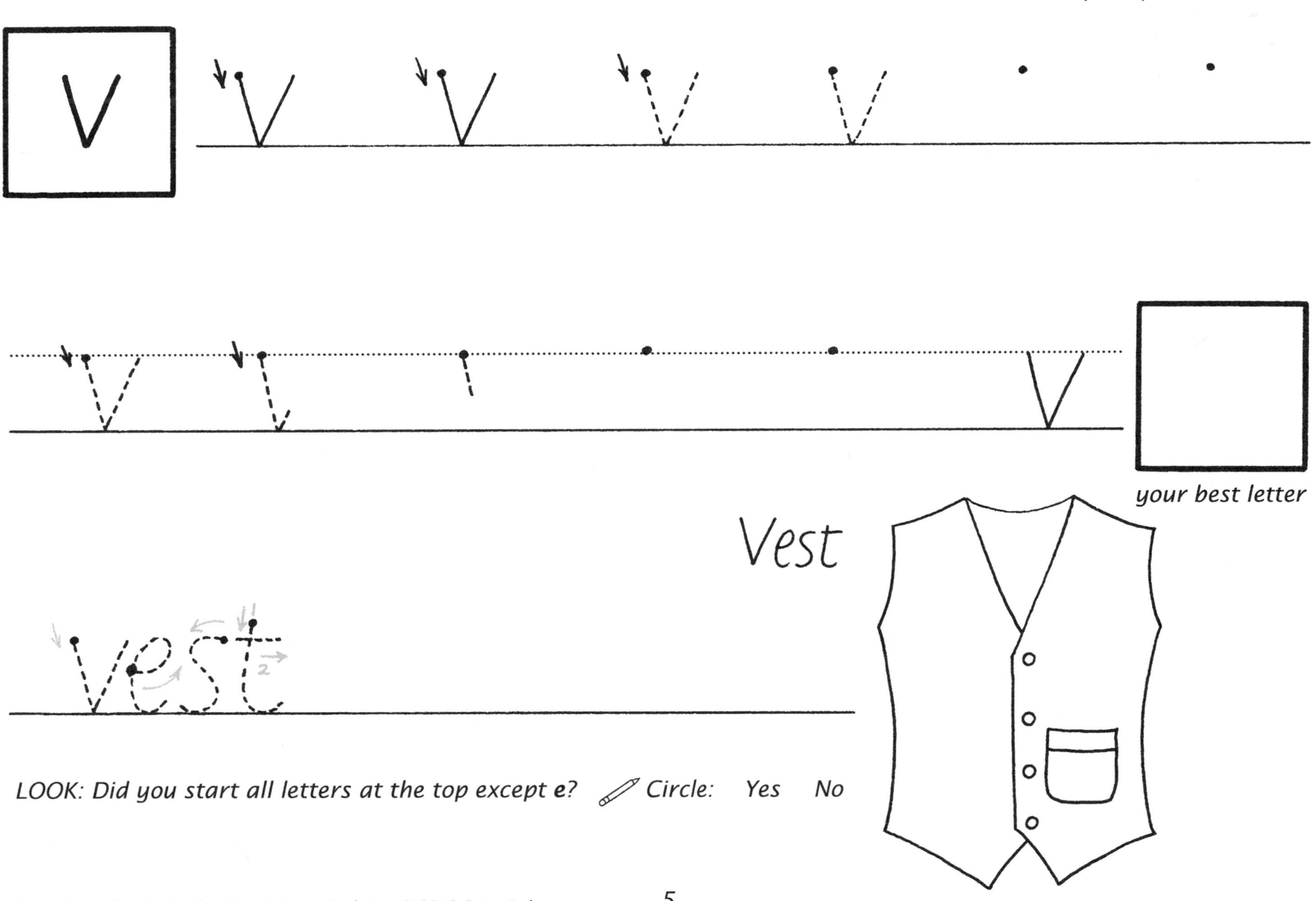

LOOK: Did you start all letters at the top except **e**? Circle: Yes   No

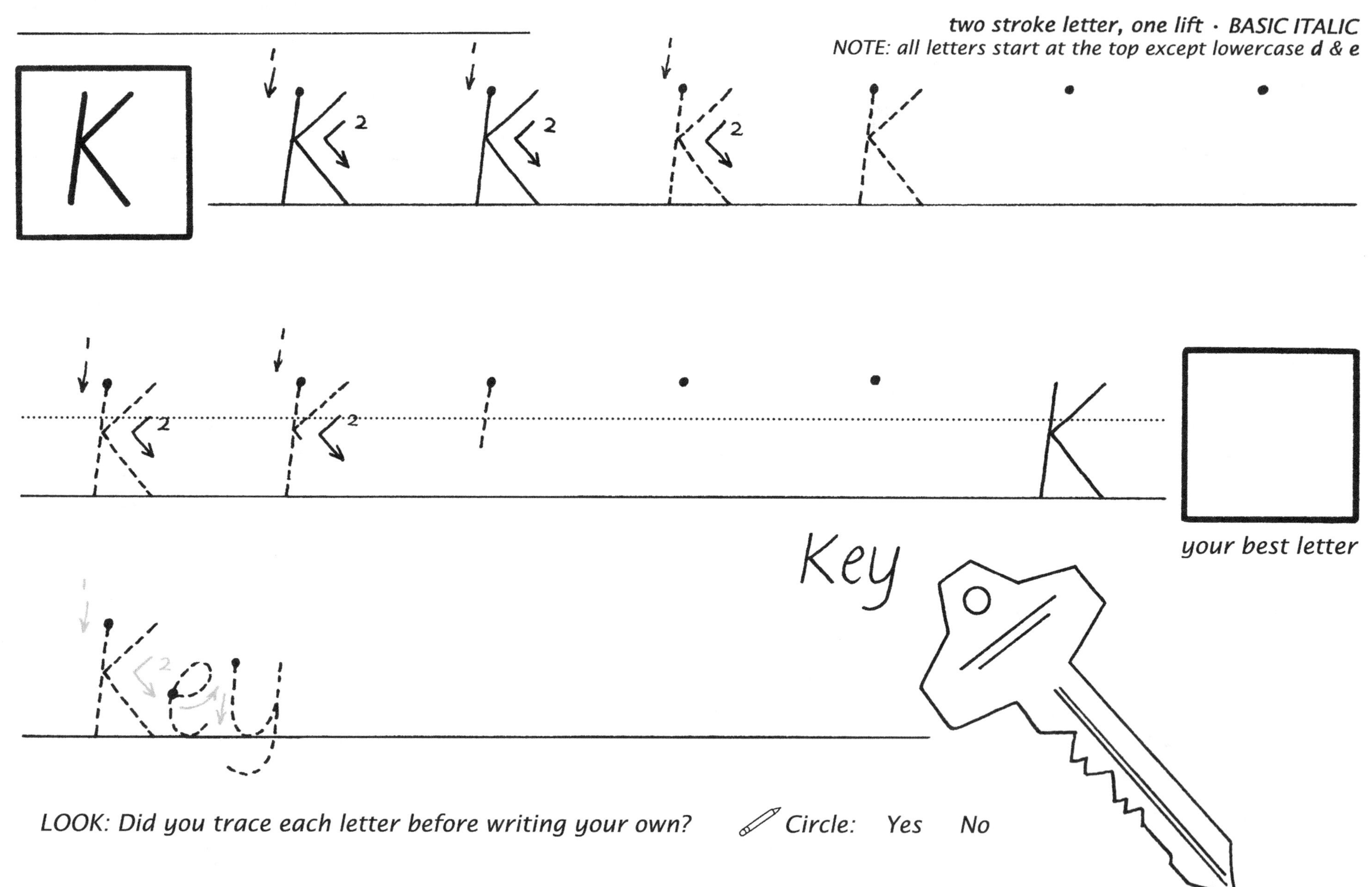

LOOK: Did you trace each letter before writing your own? Circle: Yes No

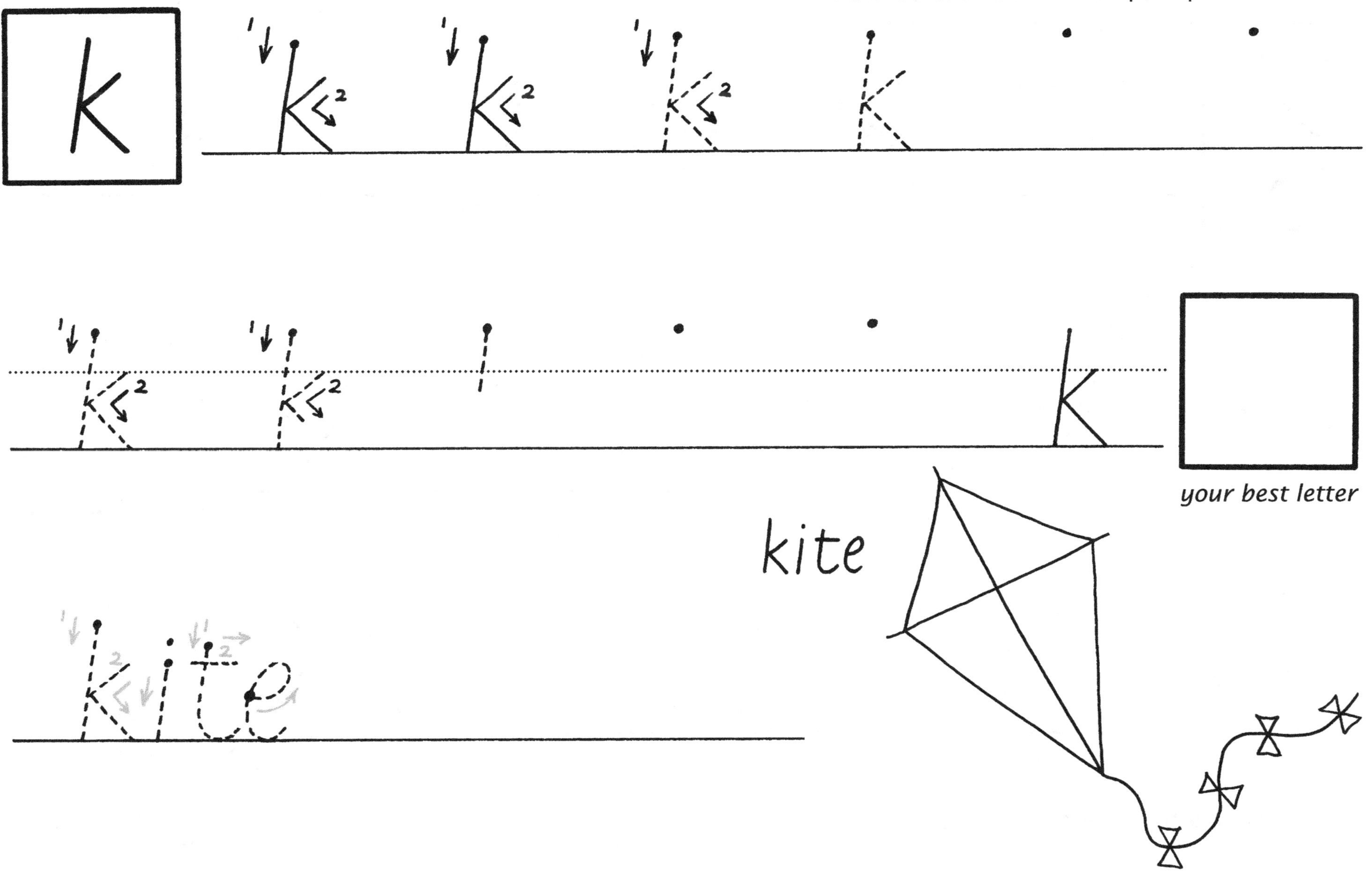

your best letter
kite

your best letter

Lock

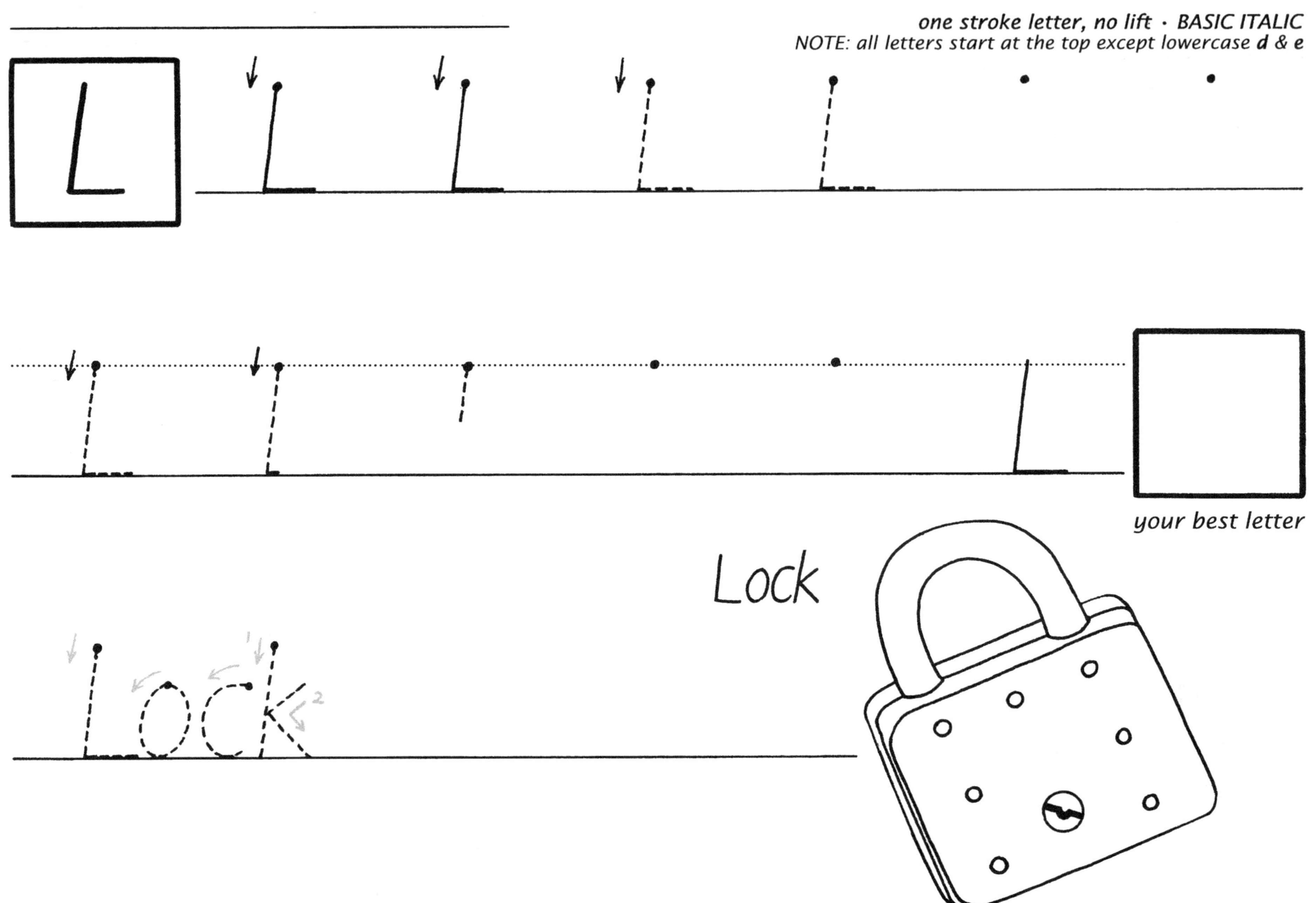

l

your best letter

lamb

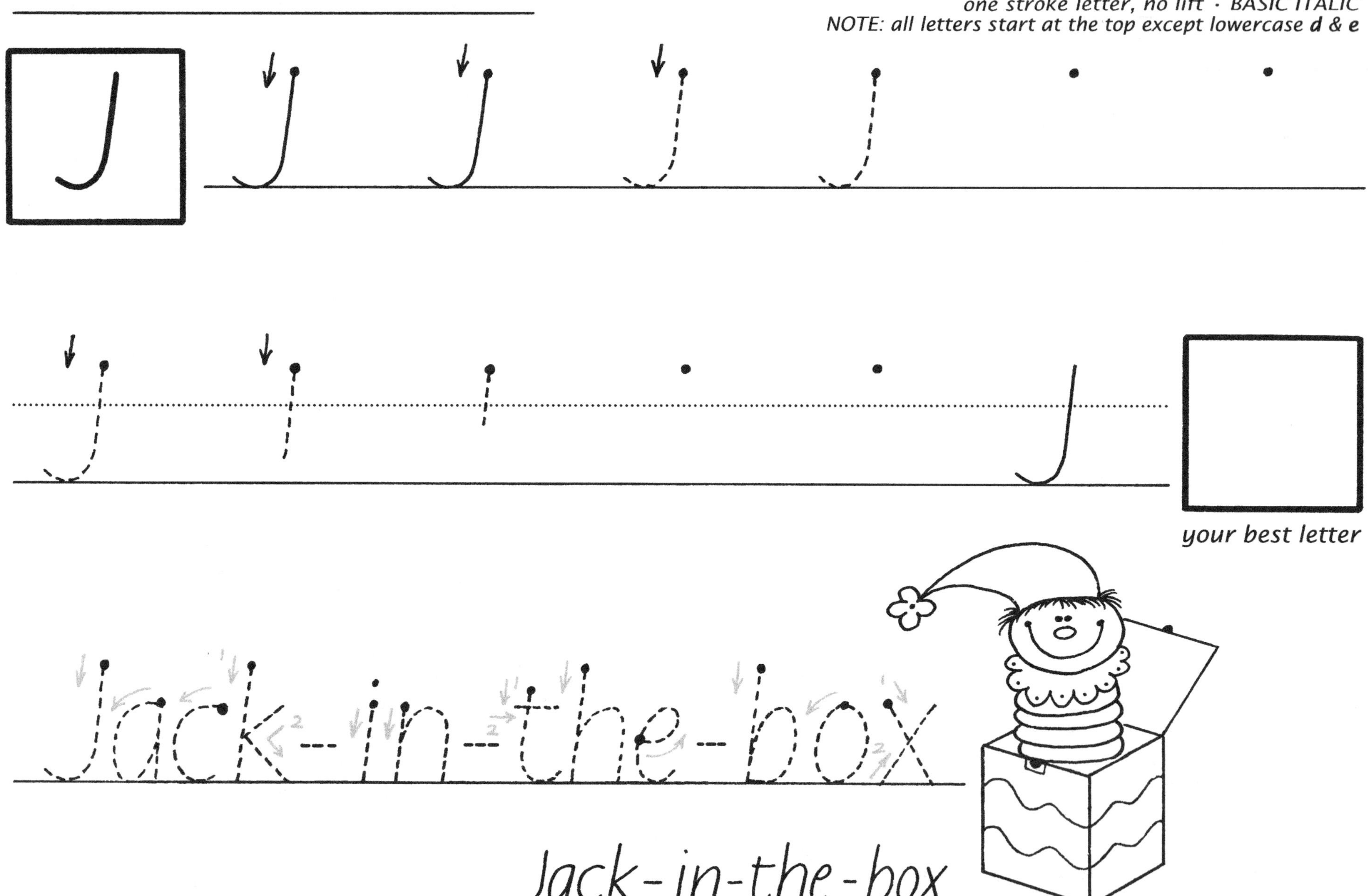

your best letter

Jack-in-the-box

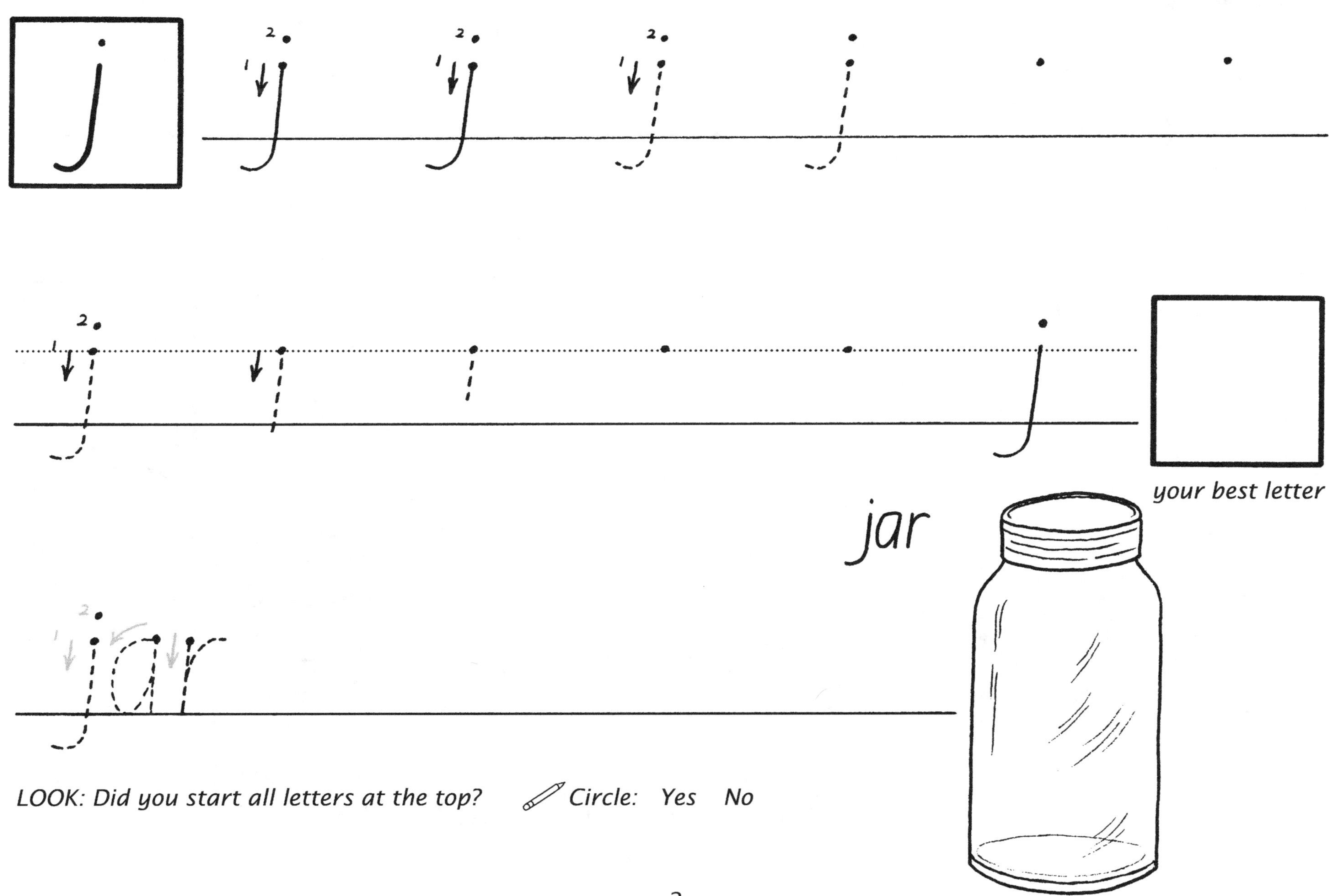

LOOK: Did you start all letters at the top?   Circle: Yes   No

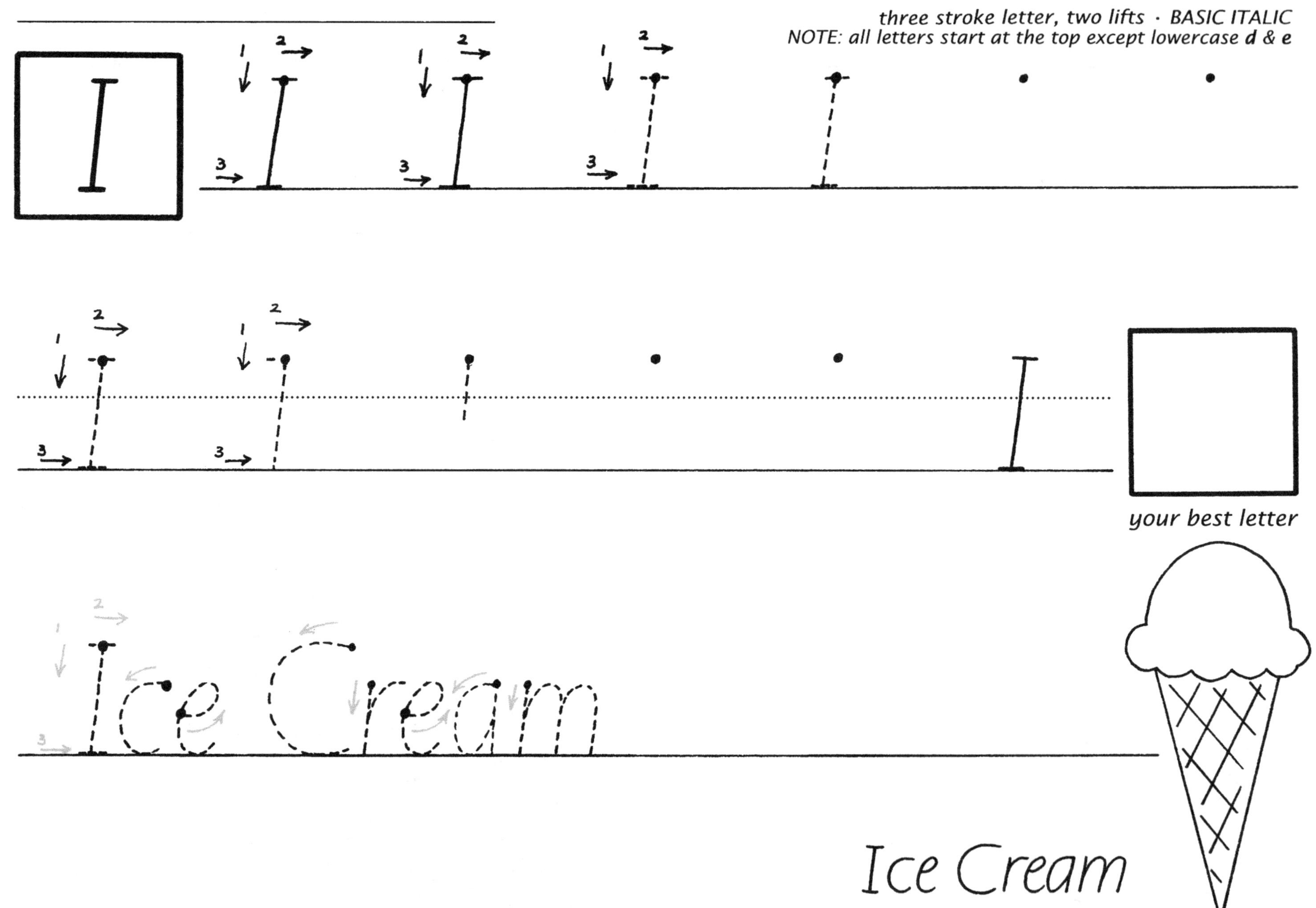

your best letter

Ice Cream

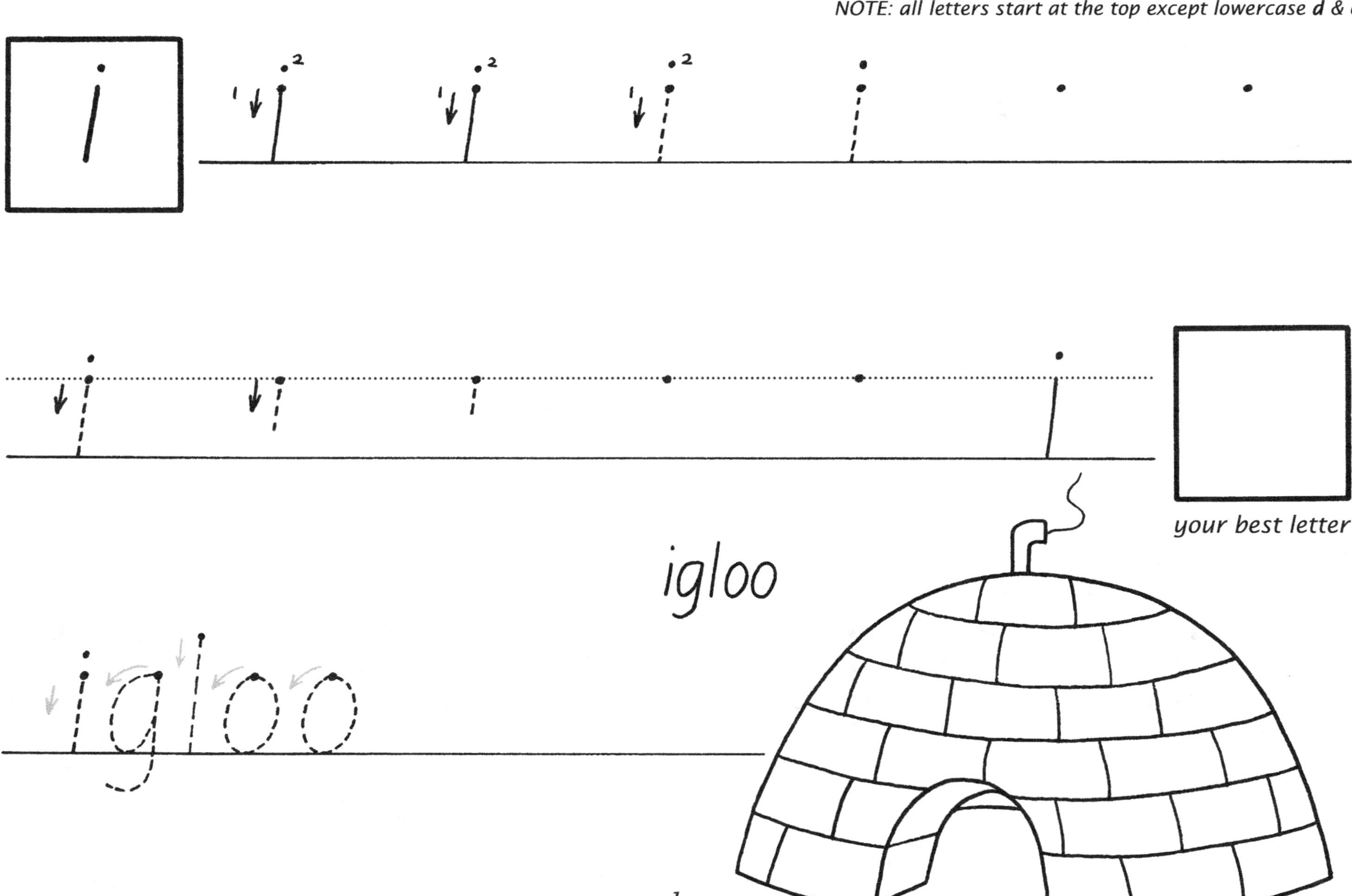

your best letter

igloo

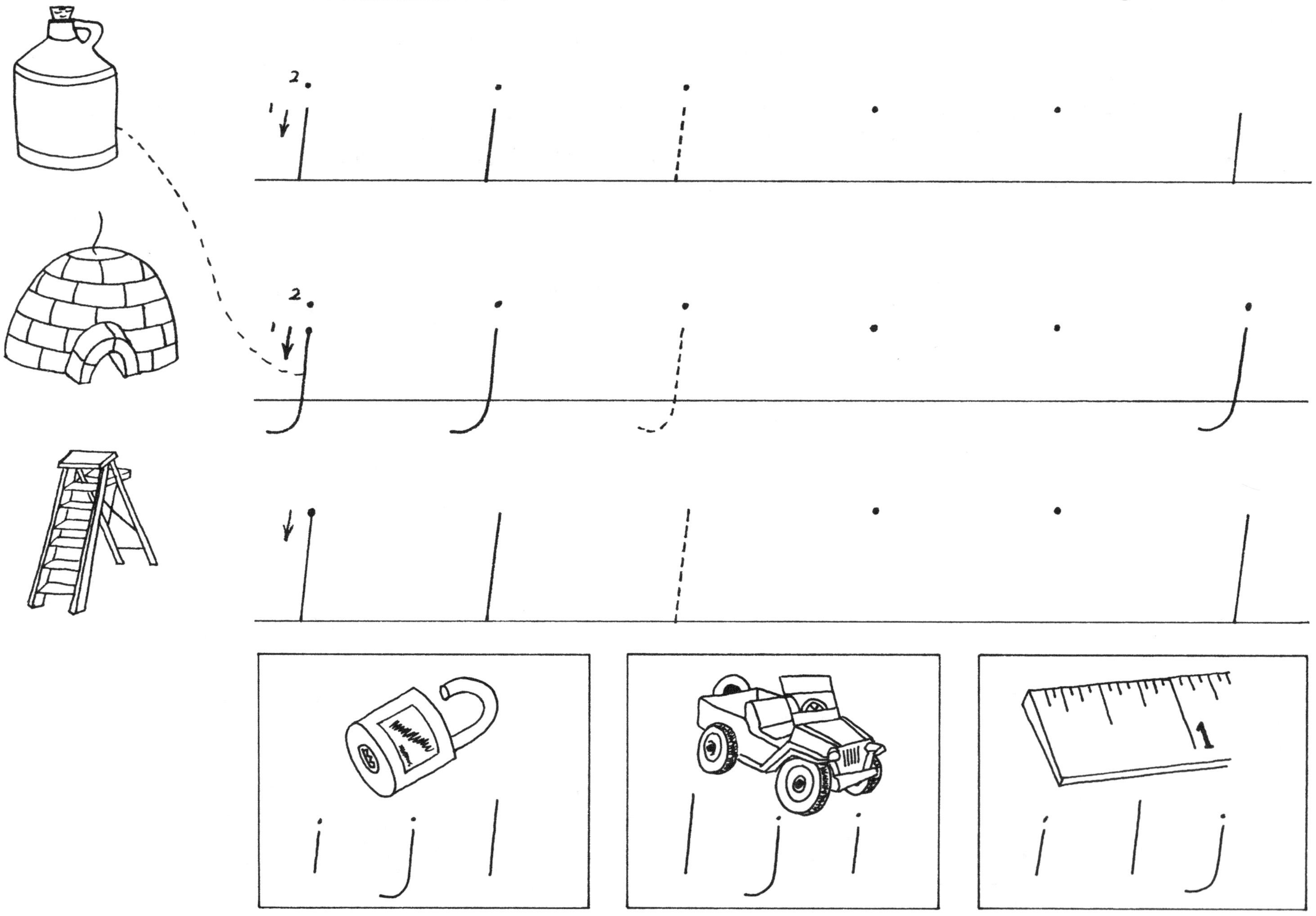

TOP THREE LINES: Ask the student to draw a line from the picture
to the letter that stands for the correct beginning sound.

BOTTOM THREE BOXES: Ask the student to circle the letter that
stands for the beginning sound of the picture.

BASIC SHAPES

Before the student begins writing in BOOK A, the authors recommend that the student practice the following shapes on unlined paper, one shape at a time. Allow the student to write each shape any size at first. Later, ask the student to write very large and very small forms of that same shape. We suggest the student also practice these shapes on a chalkboard and/or in cornmeal. (See INSTRUCTION MANUAL, "*Activity*," pp. 35 & 41.)

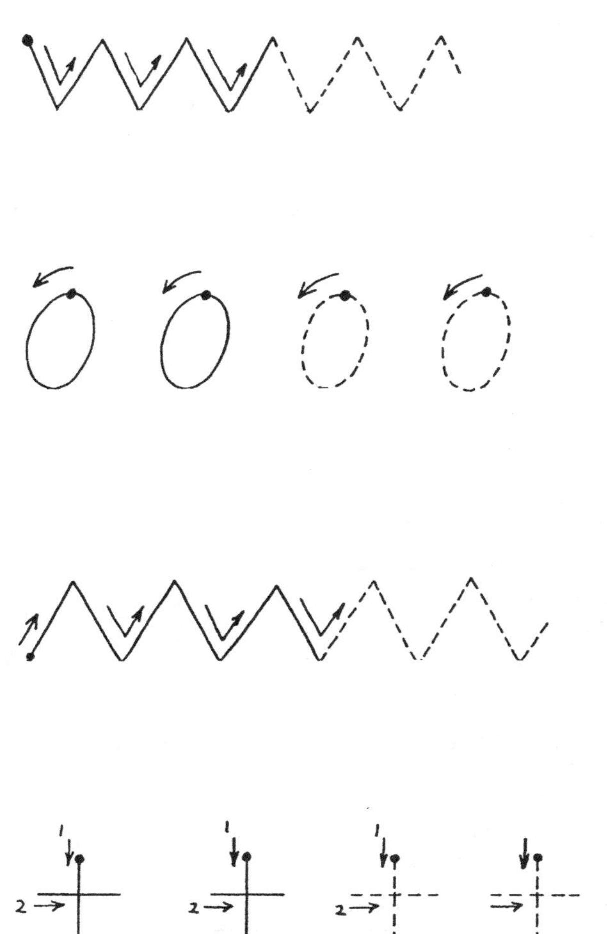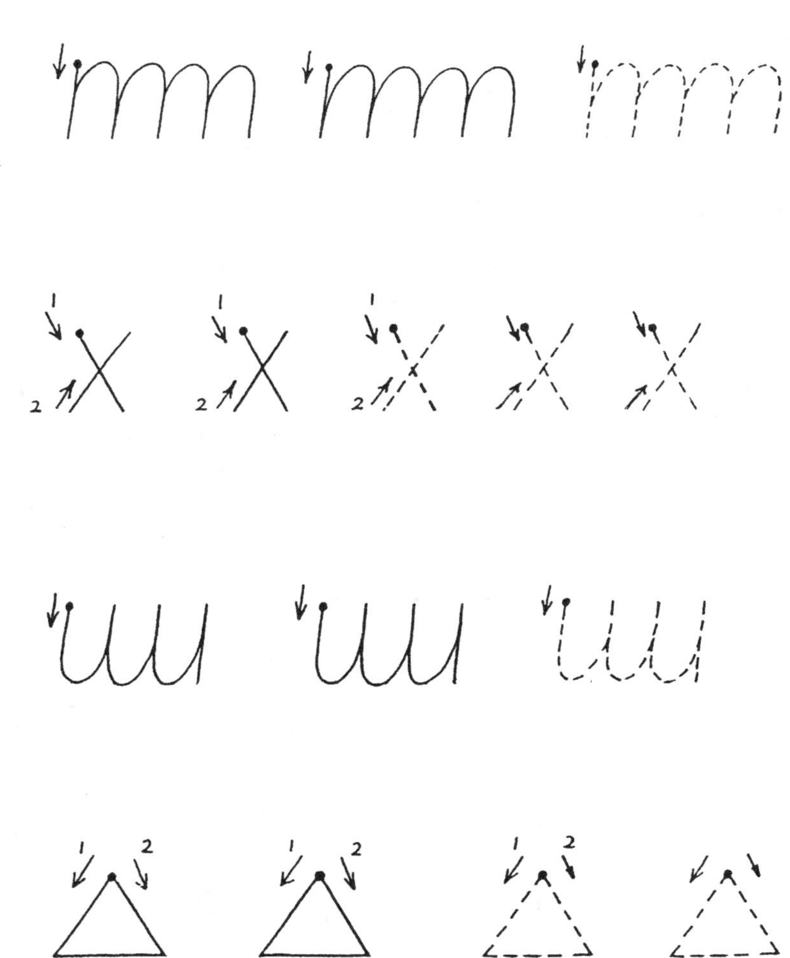

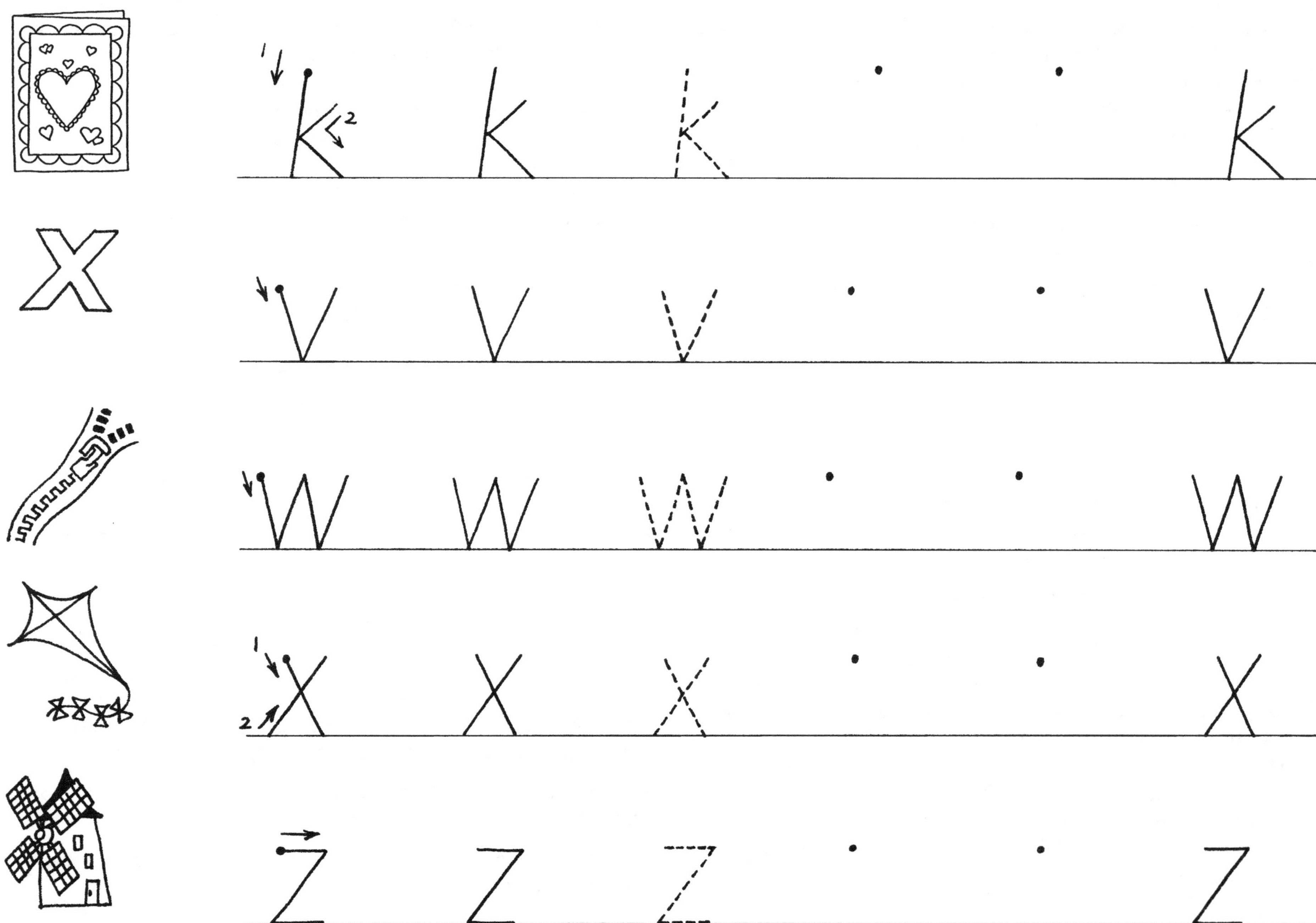

Ask the student to draw a line from the picture to the letter
that stands for the correct beginning sound.

THE BEGINNING WRITER

Learning how to write involves much more than learning to write letters. It is a sophisticated, complex process involving learning letterforms, learning how to space within and between words, and learning how to organize writing on a page. Research indicates that there exists an almost perfect correlation between measures evaluating the children's *awareness* of their fingers and the ability to *use* their fingers in precise manual skills.

Ways to determine manual ability

To assist young students increase awareness of their hands and fingers, and to help you, the teacher, evaluate students' manual skills, have your students perform these tasks:

1. Direct the students to touch each of their fingers to their thumb, in order, from the first to the little finger. (By the age of six years, most children should be able to complete this exercise using one or both hands at a time.)

2. Have the students connect two dots that are spaced approximately eight inches apart on a page. (Most children of five years can accomplish this. However, if the student draws beyond the second dot or draws an unusually shaky line when nearing the second dot, it may indicate potential deficiencies in handwriting skills.)

Ways to improve kinesthetic perception of the hands

1. Unstructured clay modeling facilitates a student's perception of his or her hands. Encourage the student to manipulate the clay in every possible way—squeezing, flattening, poking, making shapes, etc.

2. To heighten the student's perception of shape, use a box in which a variety of small objects are placed for the student to feel but not see.

   a. Ask the student to reach in the box and find an unseen object that matches the one he or she is looking at.

   b. Direct the student to locate in the box an object that you or another student has described.

   c. Ask the student to find two objects with similar characteristics—two fuzzy objects, two heavy objects, two small objects, etc.

3. Draw several circles on a sheet of paper. To determine the student's ability to aim the finger and hand and also to point, have the student place dots in the circles with a pencil, pen, or crayon. Vary the difficulty of this task by increasing or decreasing the size of the circles or increasing the rate at which the dots are made. (The student must be able to point at a given or imaginary point in order to begin the stroke of a letter.)

Ways to confirm hand-eye tracking skills

The ability to control continuous hand movements while drawing lines of varying difficulty is basic to handwriting. If you are able to detect problems as the student completes the following tasks and are able to obtain appropriate assistance for the student, subsequent difficulties may be avoided.

1. Demonstrate drawing parallel lines. Then direct the student to draw parallel lines of a given length, first at a relaxed pace then at a faster one.

2. Direct the student to draw two curved lines equal in distance from one another. Later require more difficult shapes that combine straight lines, angles, and/or curves.

3. Direct the student to connect numbered dots on a sheet of paper that require horizontal, vertical and lateral movements. Place the paper in front of the student, close to the dominant hand. Later, space the dots further apart and require the student to cross the midline of his or her body. This latter task may cause the neurologically challenged student some difficulty.

The above evaluative tasks may be of help in assisting the learning of handwriting and in discovering deficiencies.

(See INSTRUCTION MANUAL, p. 13, for more suggestions concerning the beginning writer.)

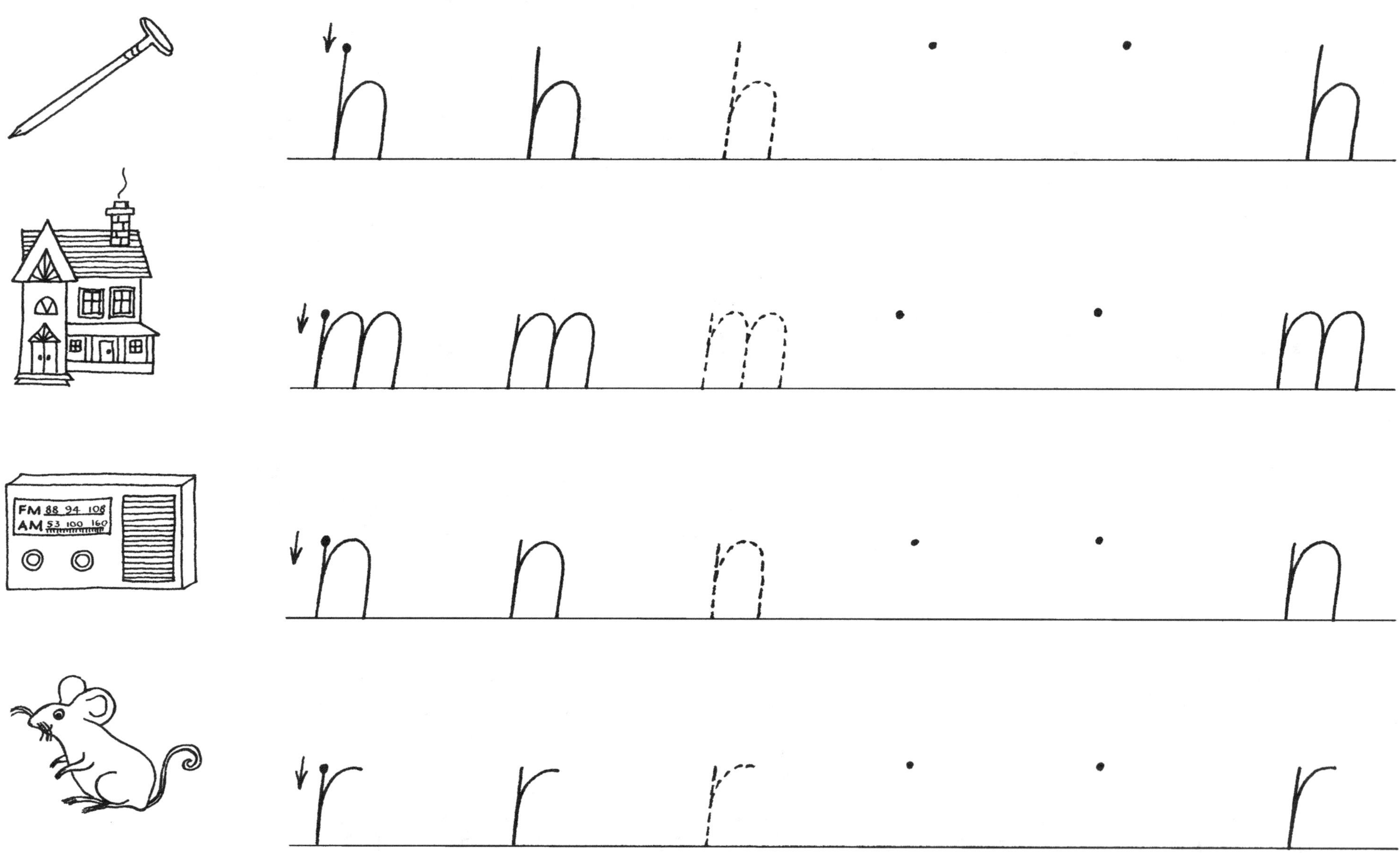

*Ask the student to draw a line from the picture to the letter
that stands for the correct beginning sound.*

BASIC ITALIC ALPHABET

All letters written in one stroke unless otherwise indicated.   *All letters start at the top except lowercase **d** and **e**.*

Aa Bb Cc Dd Ee Ff Gg

or

alternate 2-stroke e

Hh Ii Jj Kk Ll Mm

or

or

Nn Oo Pp Qq Rr Ss Tt

or

or

Uu Vv Ww Xx Yy Zz

0 1 2 3 4 5 6 7 8 9

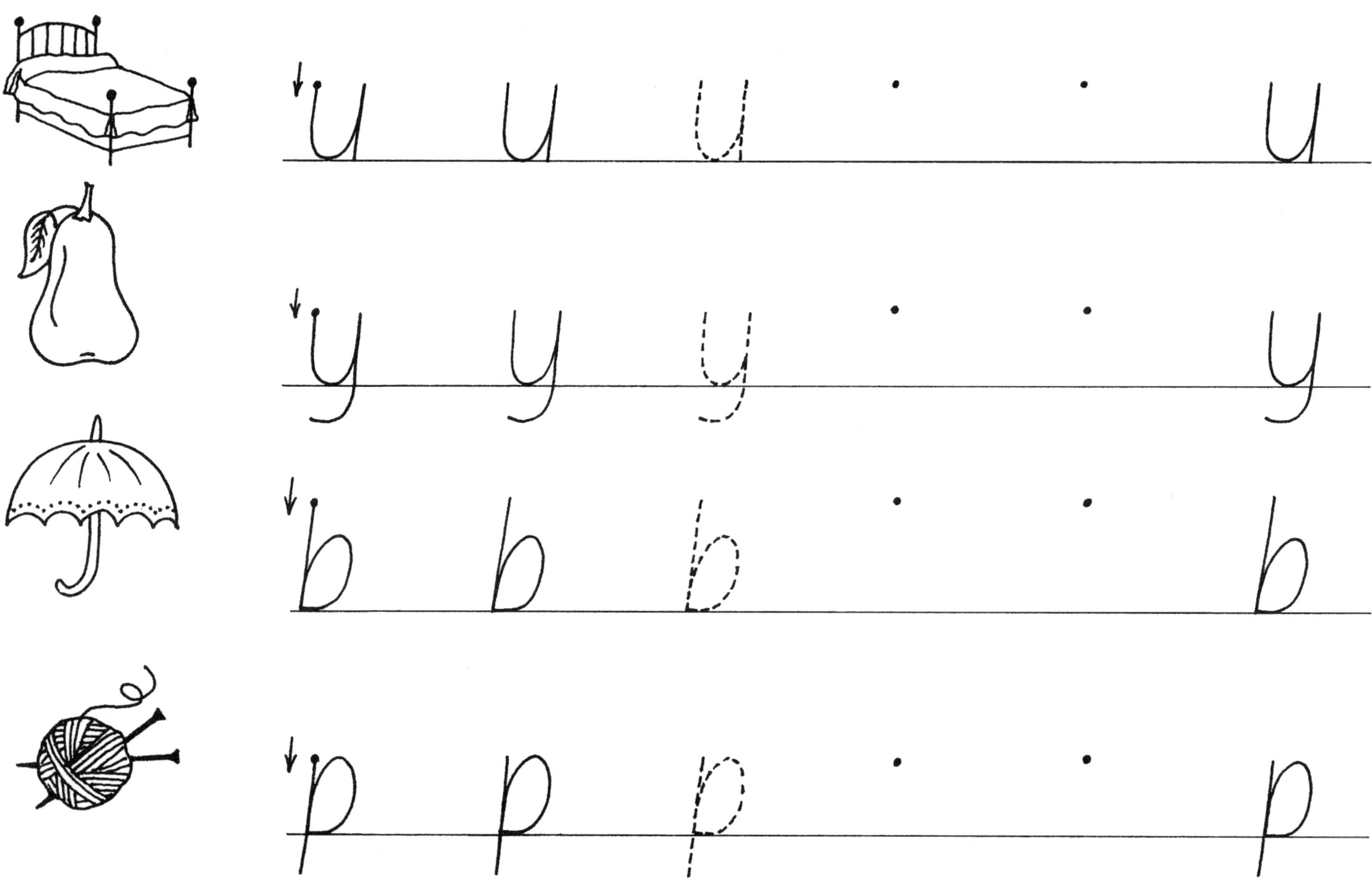

Ask the student to draw a line from the picture to the letter
that stands for the correct beginning sound.

GETTY-DUBAY™ HANDWRITING REMINDERS

PENCIL HOLD

Hold the pencil with the thumb and index finger, resting it on the middle finger. Rest the shaft of the pencil near the large knuckle. Hold the tool firmly and avoid pinching. To relax the hand, tap index finger on the pencil three times. Avoid "thumb wrap" and a "death grip".

PAPER POSITION

LEFT-HANDED: If the left-handed student writes with the wrist below the writing line, turn paper clockwise so it is slanted to the right, as illustrated.

If the left-handed student writes with a hook, with the wrist above the writing line, turn the paper counter-clockwise so it is slanted to the left, as illustrated. (Similar to right-handed position)

RIGHT-HANDED: If the student is right-handed, turn paper counter-clockwise so it is slanted to the left, as illustrated.

POSTURE

Rest feet flat on the floor and keep back comfortably straight without slumping. Rest forearms on writing surface. The student holds workbook or paper with the nonwriting hand so that the writing area is centered in the front of the student.

PRACTICE PAPER

Book A—Use unlined or lined paper together with workbooks.

MATERIALS

The *Getty-Dubay™ Italic Handwriting Series* workbooks, BOOKS A–G, and the INSTRUCTION MANUAL constitute a step-by-step program. Related materials consist of:

1. BLACKLINE MASTERS/WORKSHEETS - half sheets for introduction to, or review of, workbook pages.
2. CLASSROOM WALL CHARTS - basic & cursive italic.
3. DESK STRIPS - basic & cursive italic.

VOCABULARY

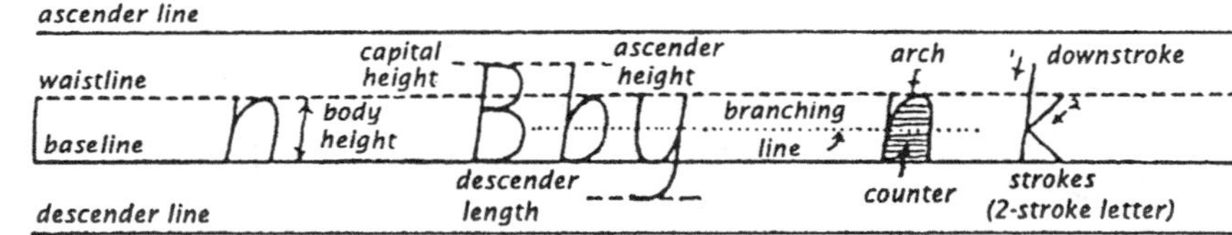

DIRECT INSTRUCTION

Several sessions of direct instruction each week are essential for a successful program. BOOK A – 5 to 10 minute sessions a day are recommended, see INSTRUCTION MANUAL, pp. 18-19

- SHAPE & STROKE SEQUENCE – teach basic italic in letter family groups, or according to the reading program in grade 1.
- SLOPE – encourage a consistent letter slope. Vertical letters (0° slope) may be the easiest to teach to beginning writers.
- SIZE – At first, allow students to write letters any size they wish on unlined paper, then introduce the workbook. A recommended progression through this book is one letter (lowercase and/or capital) per week.

SPACING

When young students are writing words, at first have them leave a space about the width of their two small fingers between words. As they become more proficient, they can leave less space.

ASSESSMENT

The *Getty-Dubay™ Italic Handwriting Series* provides a self-assessment process, LOOK, PLAN, PRACTICE, to enable the student to monitor progress. LOOK, step 1 of this process begins on some of the student pages in BOOK A. Assessment is the key to improving handwriting; in this book we introduce the first of three steps in the LOOK, PLAN, PRACTICE self-assessment process. The students look at their own writing and answer any questions on the page. The pencil indicates the student is to make a written response, generally by circling "yes" or "no". The teacher may encourage students to award themselves a star or a smiling face at the top of the page when they notice self-improvement.

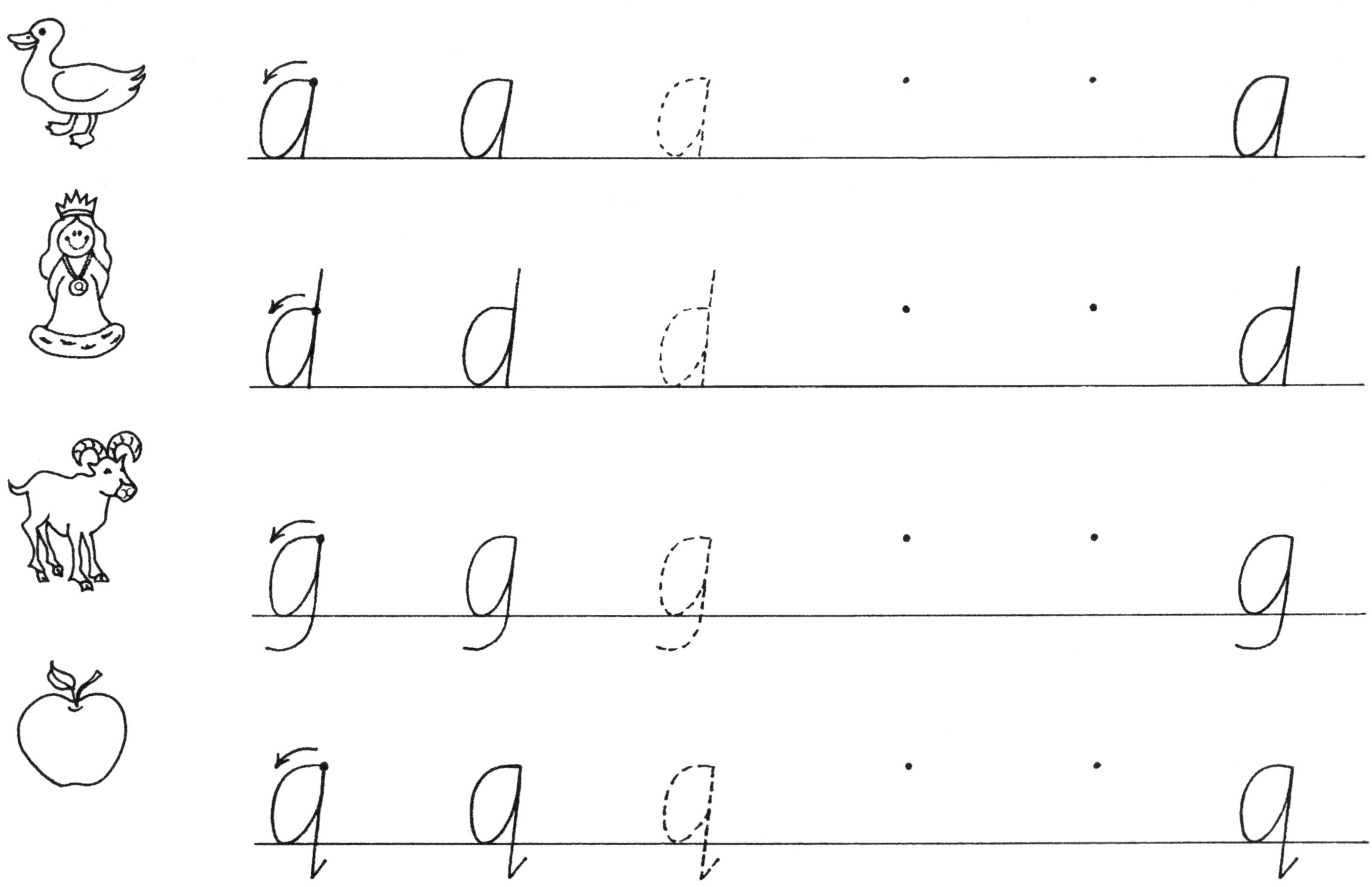

*Ask the student to draw a line from the picture to the letter
that stands for the correct beginning sound.*

INTRODUCTION

This is the first of seven workbooks providing instruction in basic italic handwriting. It is designed for the beginning student of handwriting and is recommended for preschool, kindergarten and/or early first grade (5 to 7 years of age).

The twenty-six lowercase letters and the twenty-six capitals are introduced one letter per page. Letters are arranged in the order of lowercase families, which group letters with similar strokes together and progress from simple to more complex forms. The matching capital letter occurs on the reverse of each lowercase page allowing introduction of both lowercase and capital together if preferred.

Each page is designed for the student to trace the models provided, write letters at the given dots, and to write a "best" letter in the empty box on each alphabet page. The standard writing tool is the pencil although other writing instruments such as the fiber tip pen may be used. When students are ready, they should trace the word describing the illustration on each letter page, following the dots and arrows.

It is essential that the instructor provide an understanding of the dot and the arrow to assist the writer in completing the pages successfully. The self-assessment method used in the *Getty-Dubay™ Italic Handwriting Series* enables students to monitor their individual progress. Step 1, LOOK, of the three-step LOOK, PLAN, PRACTICE format, is incorporated on 21 of the student pages. Students are asked to "LOOK" at their writing and affirm what is best. On the 21 pages with "LOOK" questions, students should circle their chosen answers. See INSTRUCTION MANUAL, PP. 13, 18 & 19.

The *Getty-Dubay™ Italic Handwriting Series* INSTRUCTION MANUAL is to be used in conjunction with this workbook. Explanations and in-depth descriptions of lowercase letters, capitals, joins, and numerals are presented in the manual, emphasizing shape, strokes, size, slope and spacing of the letters. Also included in the manual are: a rationale for italic handwriting, techniques for teaching and assessing handwriting, sequence of skills, handwriting activities, and a brief history of our alphabet.

BOOK B, basic italic, follows this workbook and is designed for the beginning reader. In the third book, BOOK C, basic italic letterforms are reinforced and cursive italic is introduced. BOOKS D, E, F, and G provide a complete basic italic and cursive italic handwriting program. BOOKS B, C, and/or D may also be suitable for the person learning English as a second language.

The format of this book was chosen to accommodate both the left- and right-handed writer. When open, the book fits easily on a small desk, and the writer is not encumbered with an additional page to the left or right. From day one, use a Getty-Dubay™ basic italic desk strip as a reminder. Blackline masters are designed for supplementary practice and are available for each workbook in the series. See www.handwritingsuccess.com for these supplementary materials.

You can guide children toward the challenge and delight in the writing process by reading to them, modeling handwriting, providing writing materials, and especially by building enthusiasm for the letters of our alphabet and for the written word.

·abcdefghijklmnopqrstuvwxyz·

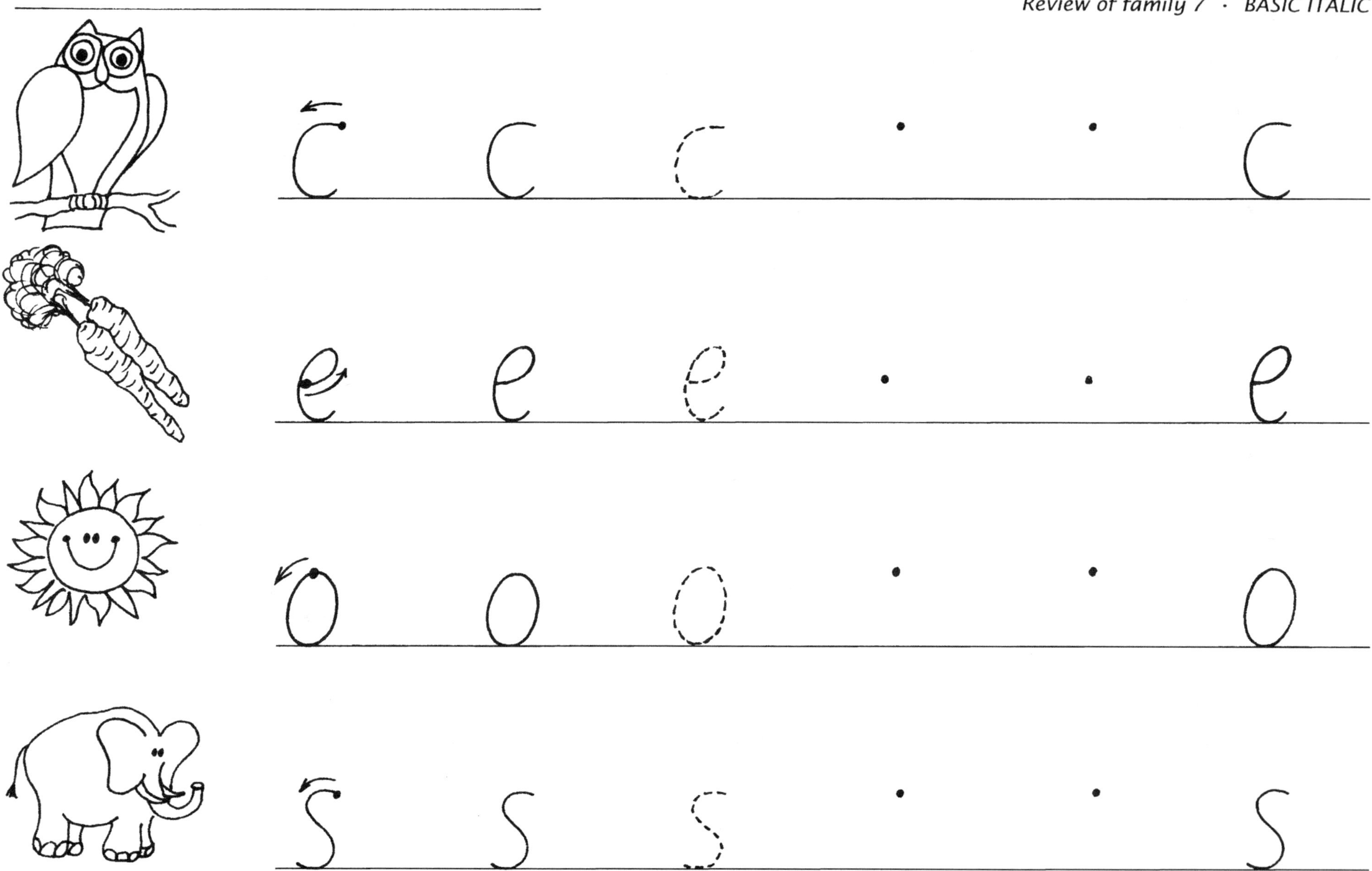

Ask the student to draw a line from the picture to the letter that stands for the correct beginning sound.

CONTENTS

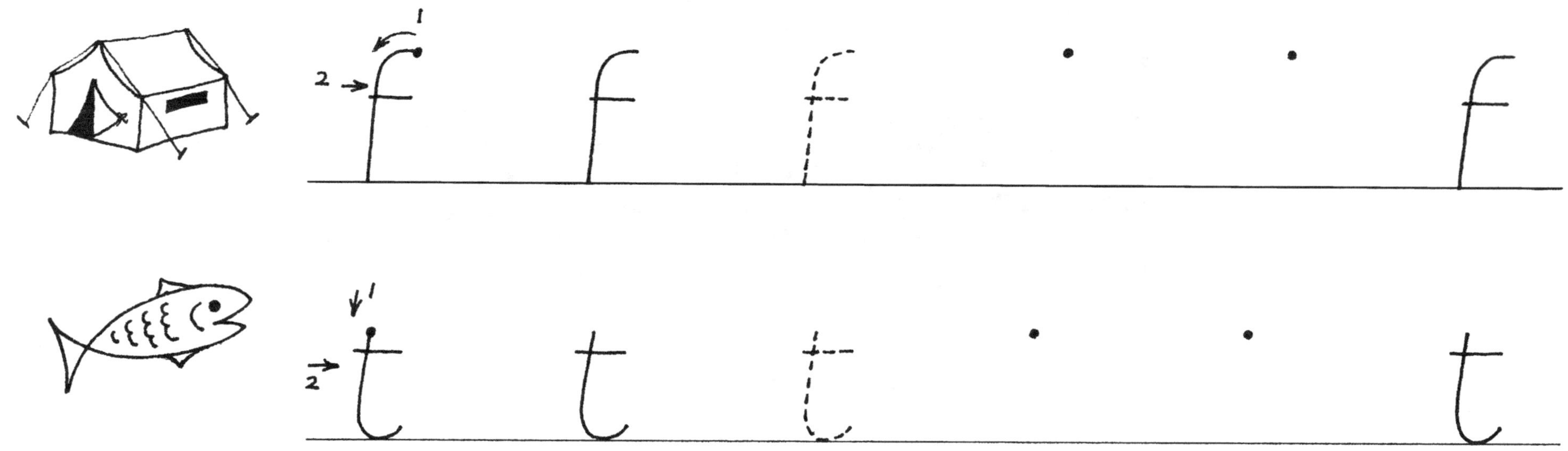

*TOP TWO LINES: Ask the student to draw a line from the picture
to the letter that stands for the correct beginning sound.*

*BOTTOM FOUR SQUARES: Ask the student to circle the letter that
stands for the beginning sound of the picture.*

by

Barbara Getty & Inga Dubay

GETTY-DUBAY™ ITALIC HANDWRITING SERIES

BOOK A ▪ Basic Italic
14 mm body height

BOOK B ▪ Basic Italic
11 mm body height, 9 mm

BOOK C ▪ Basic & Cursive Italic
9 mm, 6 mm body height   Introduction to Cursive Italic

BOOK D ▪ Basic & Cursive Italic
6 mm, 5 mm body height

BOOK E ▪ Basic & Cursive Italic
6 mm, 5 mm, 4 mm body height

BOOK F ▪ Basic & Cursive Italic
6 mm, 5 mm, 4 mm body height

BOOK G ▪ Basic & Cursive Italic
5 mm, 4 mm body height

INSTRUCTION MANUAL

BOOK A ▪ INTERNATIONAL EDITION

Copyright 2012 by Barbara M. Getty and Inga S. Dubay
ISBN 978-0-9827762-7-8

FOURTH EDITION
Copyright 2012 by Barbara M. Getty and Inga S. Dubay
THIRD EDITION
Copyright 1999 by Barbara M. Getty and Inga S. Dubay
SECOND EDITION
Copyright 1986 by Barbara M. Getty and Inga S. Dubay
REVISED EDITION
Copyright 1980 by Barbara M. Getty and Inga S. Dubay
FIRST EDITION
Copyright 1979 by Barbara M. Getty and Inga S. Dubay

All rights reserved. This text may not be reproduced in whole or in part without the express written permission of the copyright holder.

Published by Handwriting Success, LLC,
Portland, Oregon USA

www.handwritingsuccess.com

Printed at various locations around the world by IngramSpark.

Cover Design: Sinda Markham
Front cover picture: Flowers of the sunflower family in the Ochoco National Forest, Oregon, USA
Back cover pictures: Columbine flower, Golden-mantled squirrel

www.ingramcontent.com/pod-product-compliance
Lightning Source LLC
Chambersburg PA
CBHW081423210726
48464CB00020B/1370

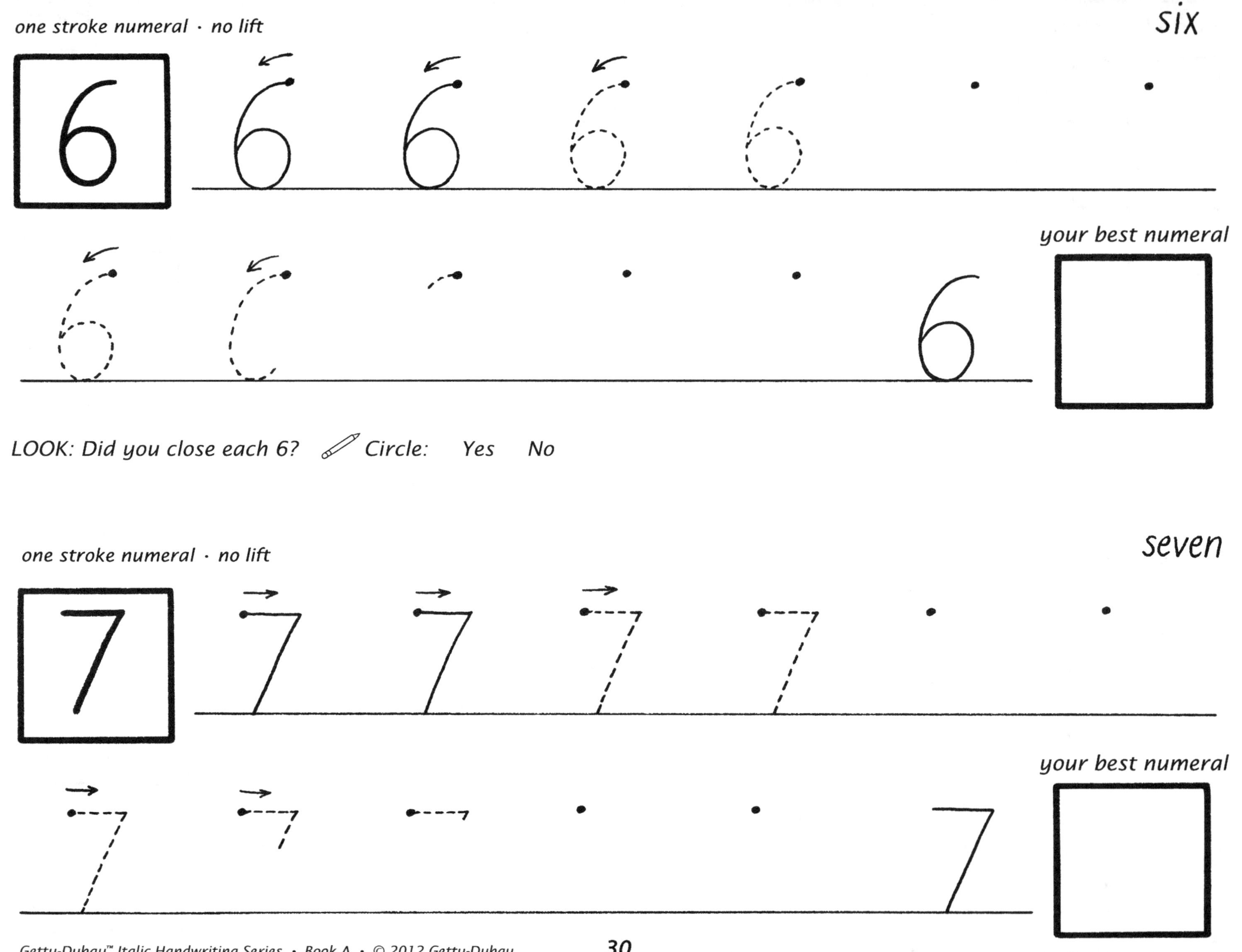

one stroke numeral · no lift
six
your best numeral
LOOK: Did you close each 6? Circle: Yes No
one stroke numeral · no lift
seven
your best numeral

four

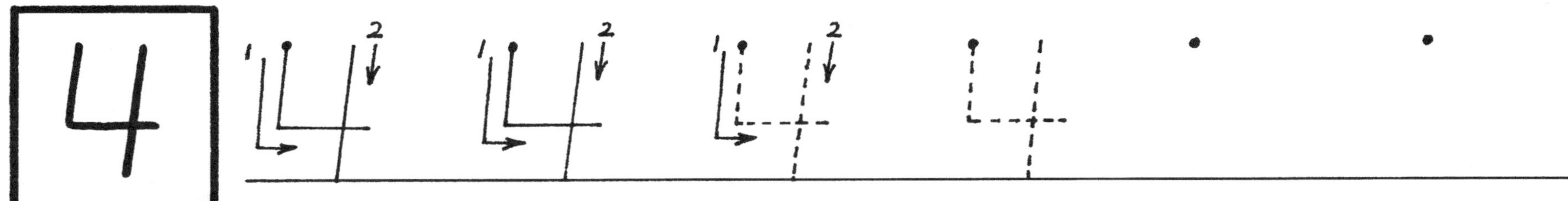

your best numeral

two stroke numeral · one lift

five

your best numeral

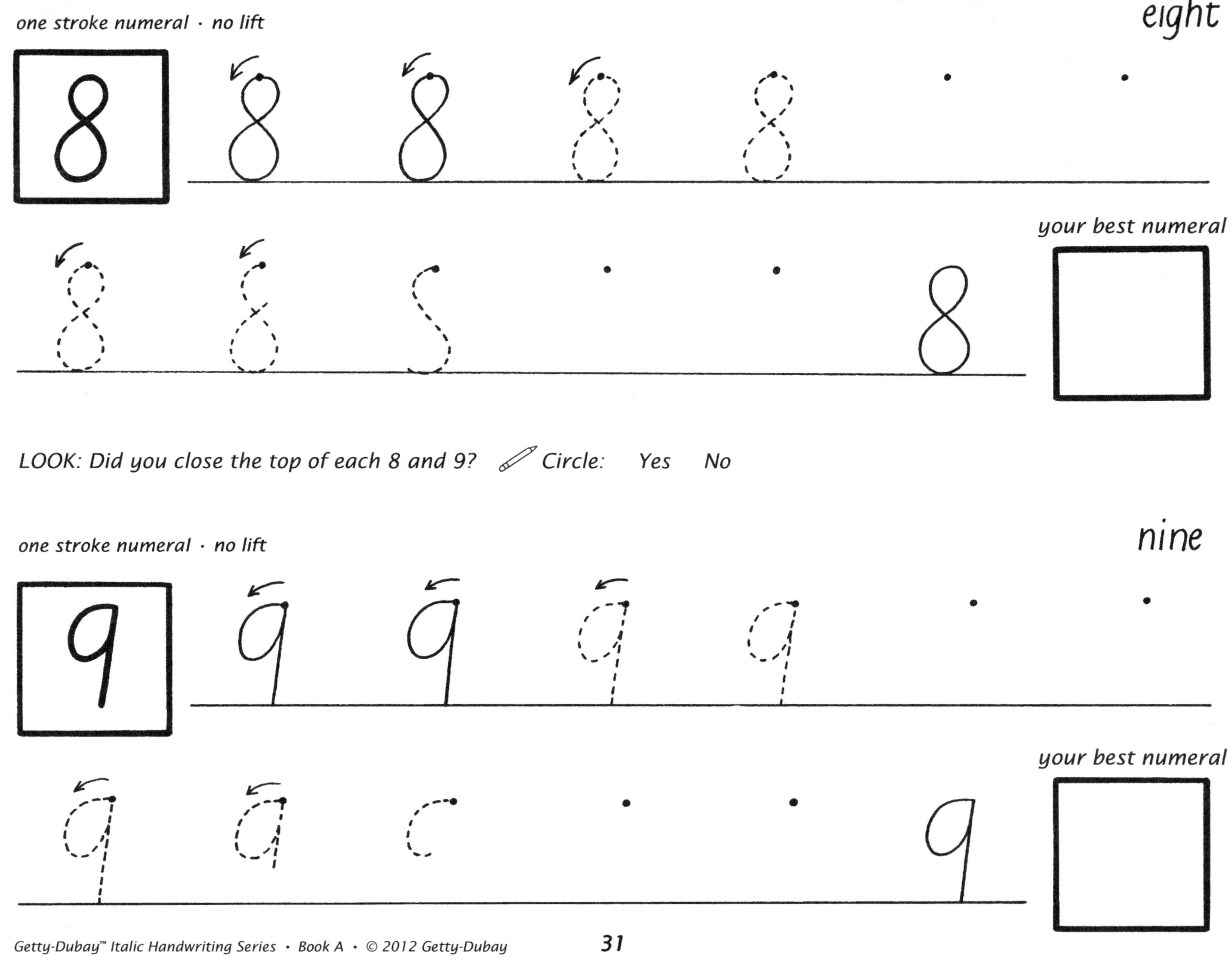

LOOK: Did you close the top of each 8 and 9?   Circle: Yes   No

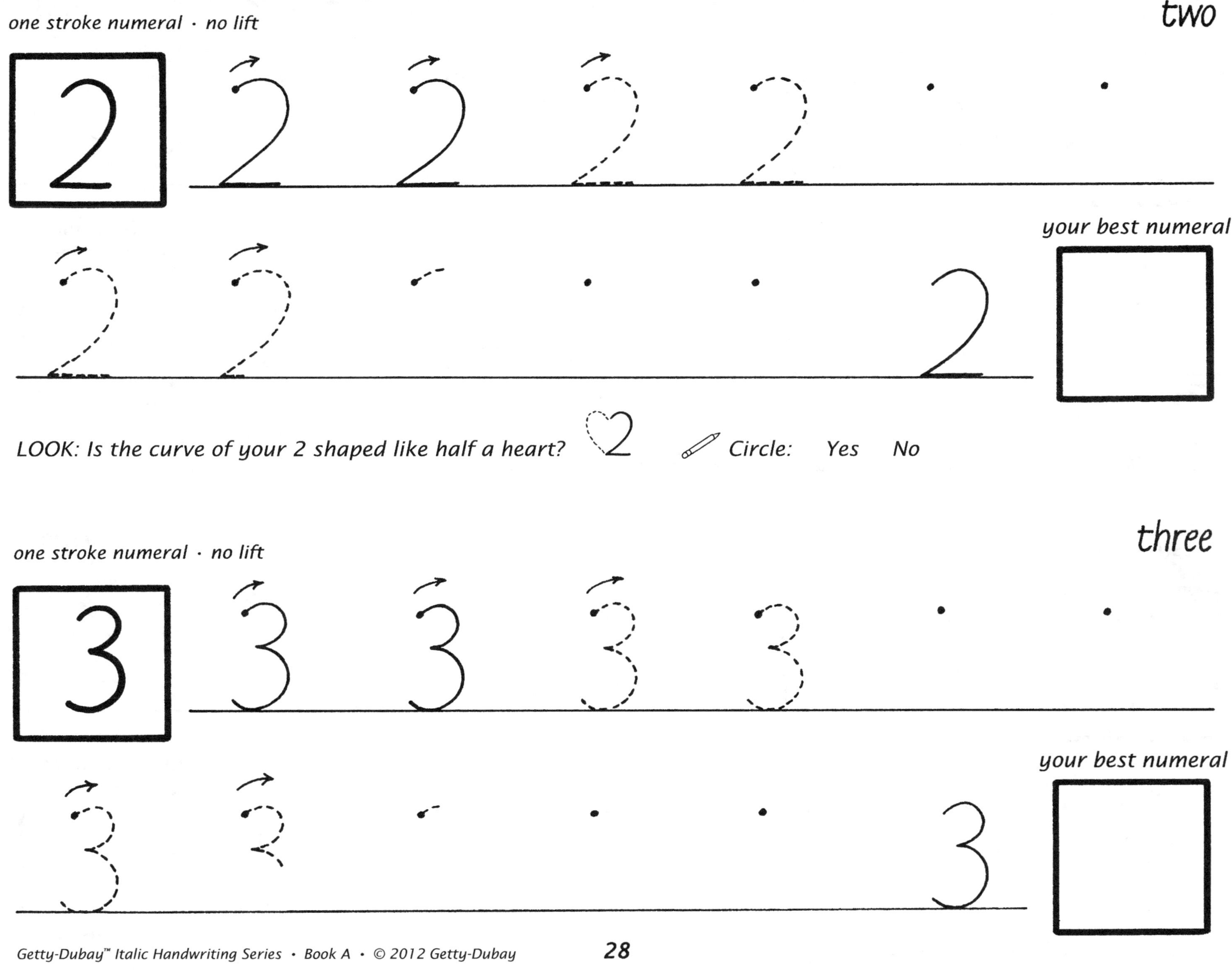

two
one stroke numeral · no lift
your best numeral
LOOK: Is the curve of your 2 shaped like half a heart?   Circle: Yes   No
three
one stroke numeral · no lift
your best numeral

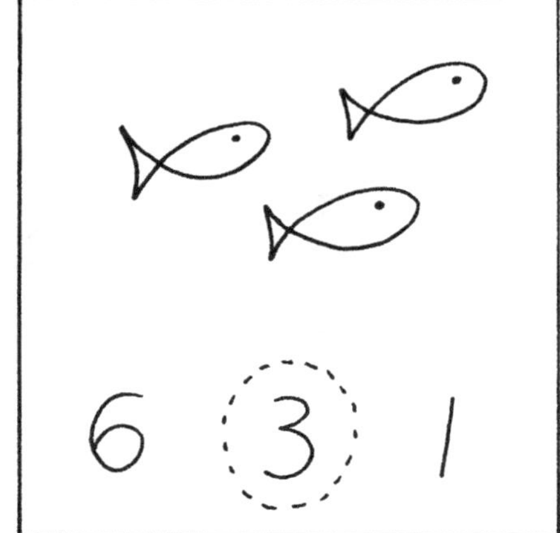

6 (3) 1

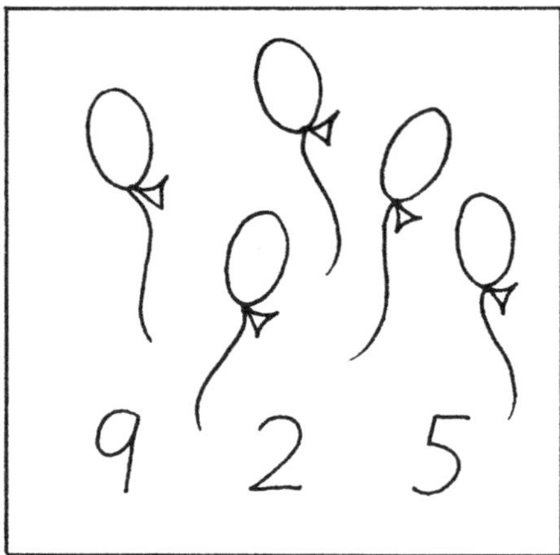

9 2 5

7 0 4

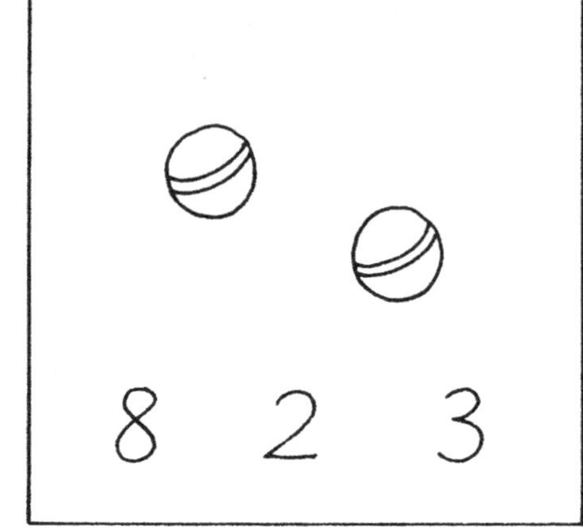

8 2 3

3 4 2

9 5 6

7 1 6

2 8 6

Ask the student to circle the numeral
that stands for the number of objects in the box.

one stroke numeral · no lift

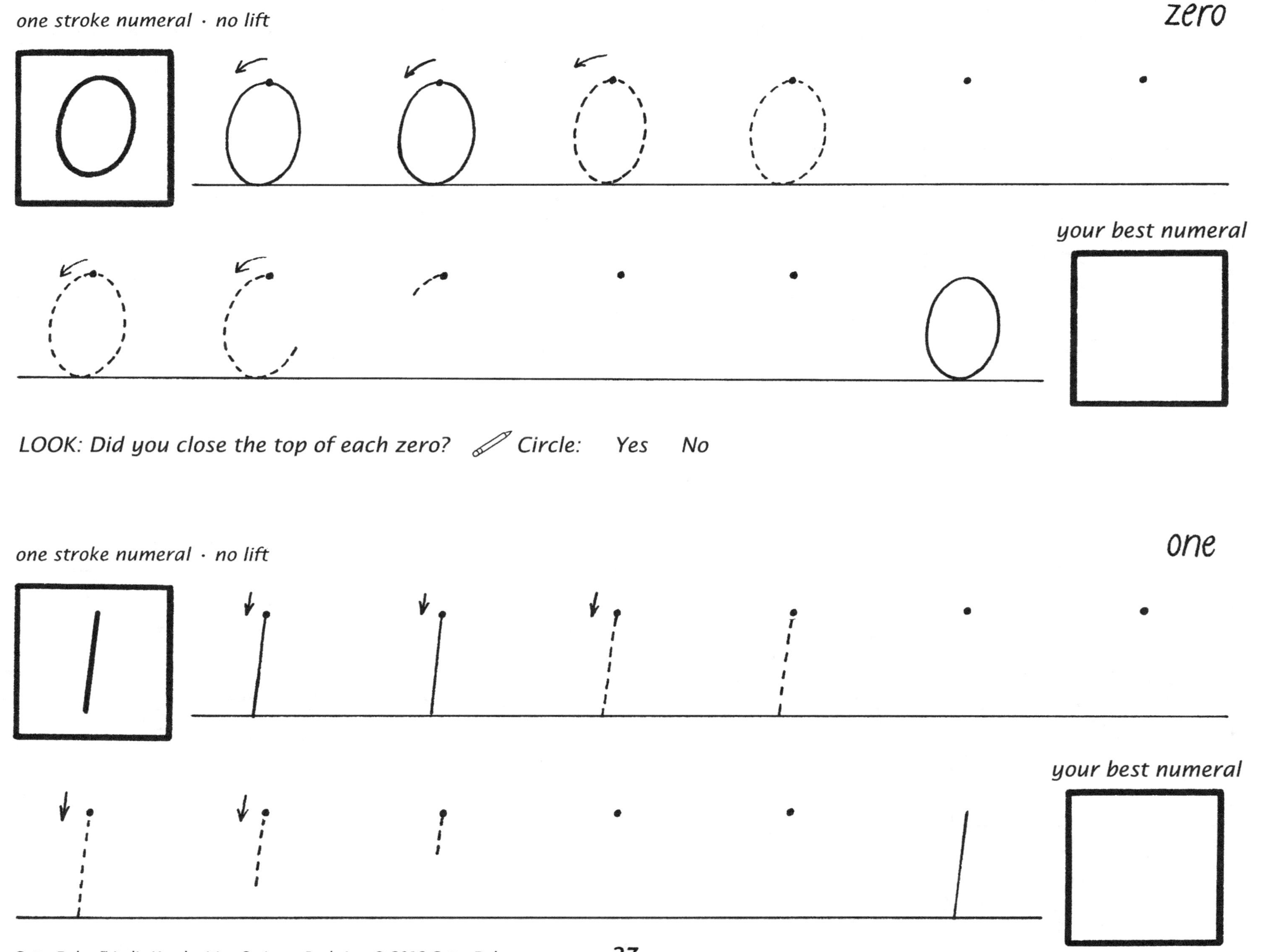

your best numeral

LOOK: Did you close the top of each zero? Circle: Yes No

one stroke numeral · no lift

one

your best numeral

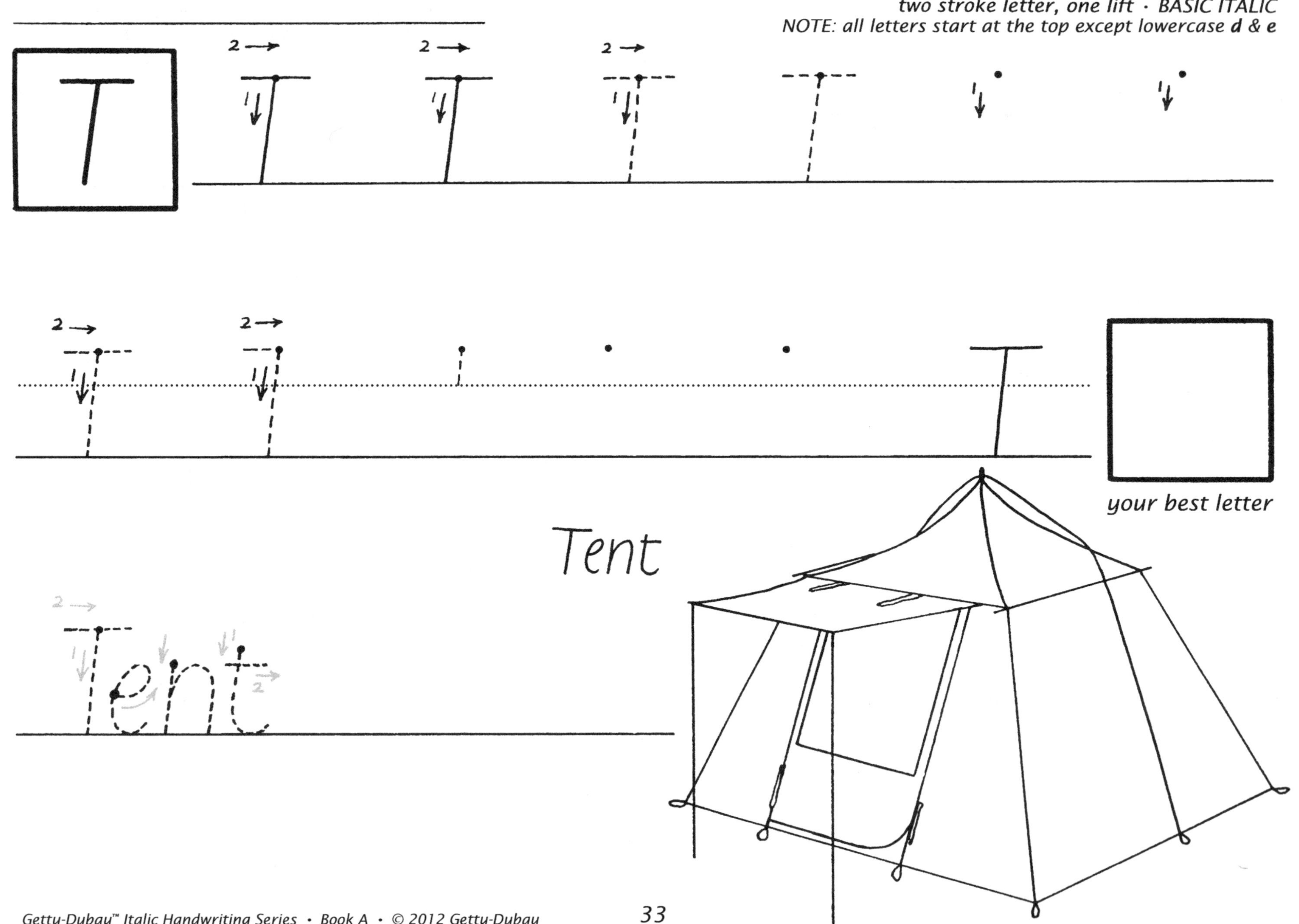

2 →
2 →
2 →
2 →
Tent
your best letter
Tent

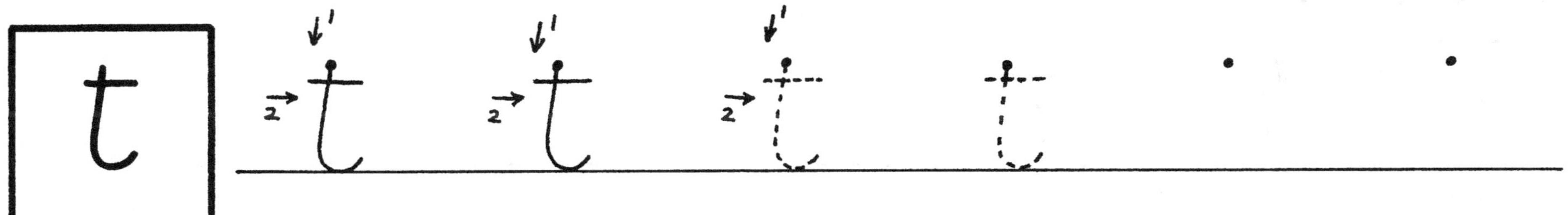

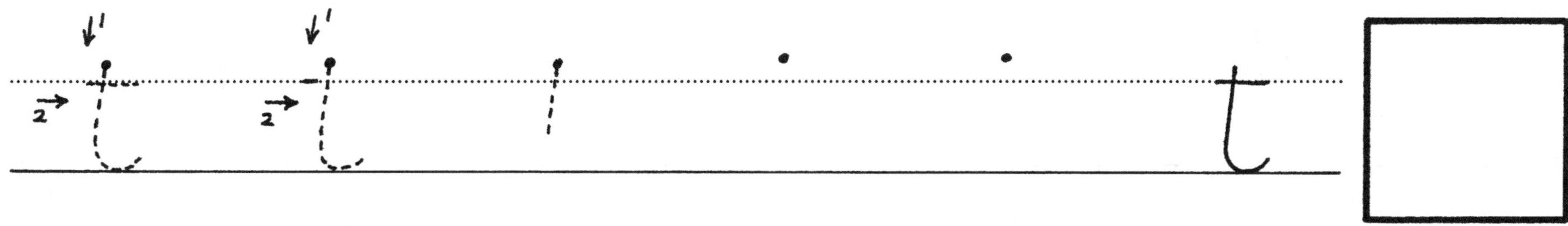

your best letter

turkey

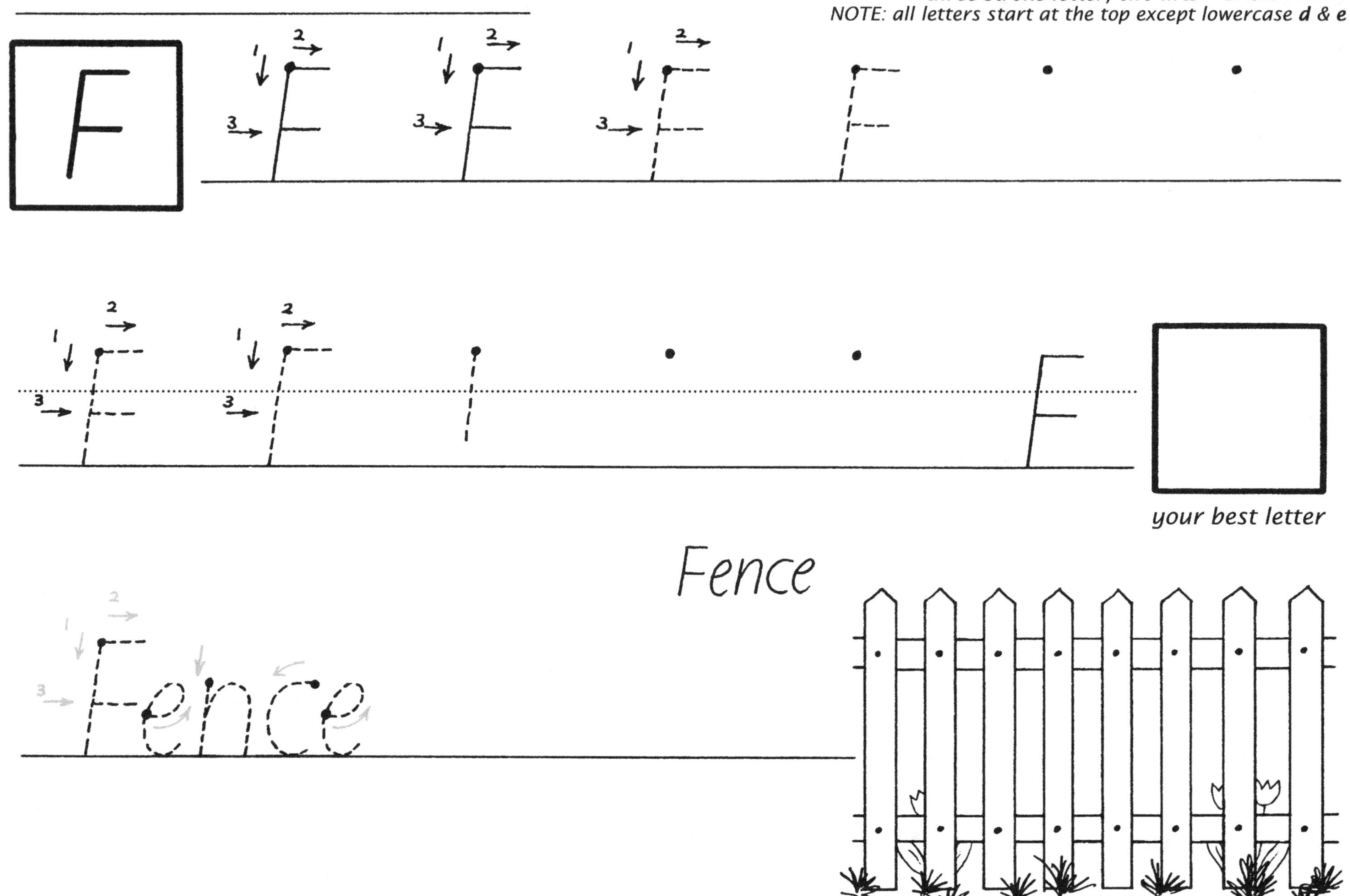

F
your best letter
Fence
Fence

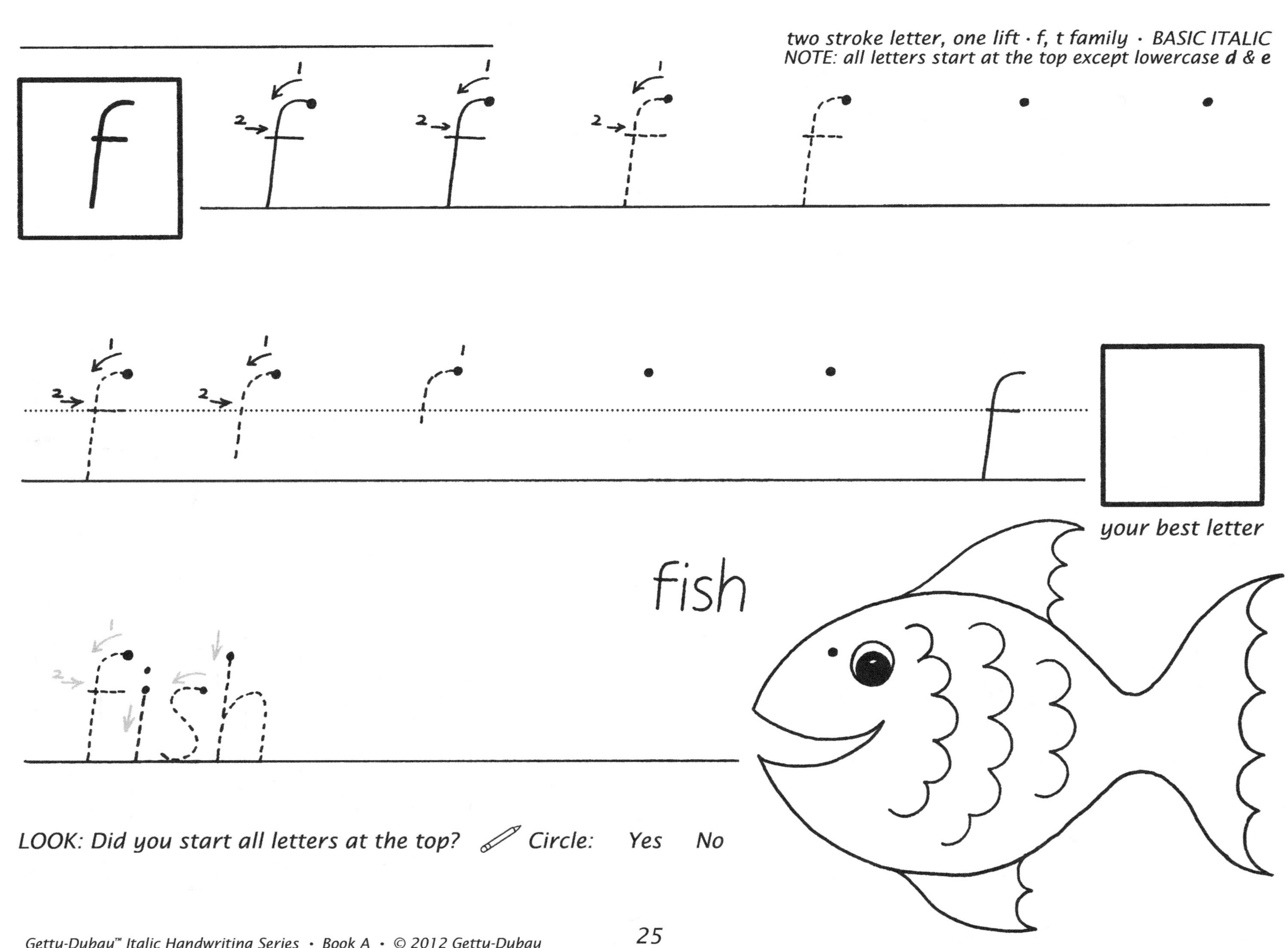

two stroke letter, one lift · f, t family · BASIC ITALIC
NOTE: all letters start at the top except lowercase d & e
your best letter
fish
LOOK: Did you start all letters at the top? Circle: Yes No

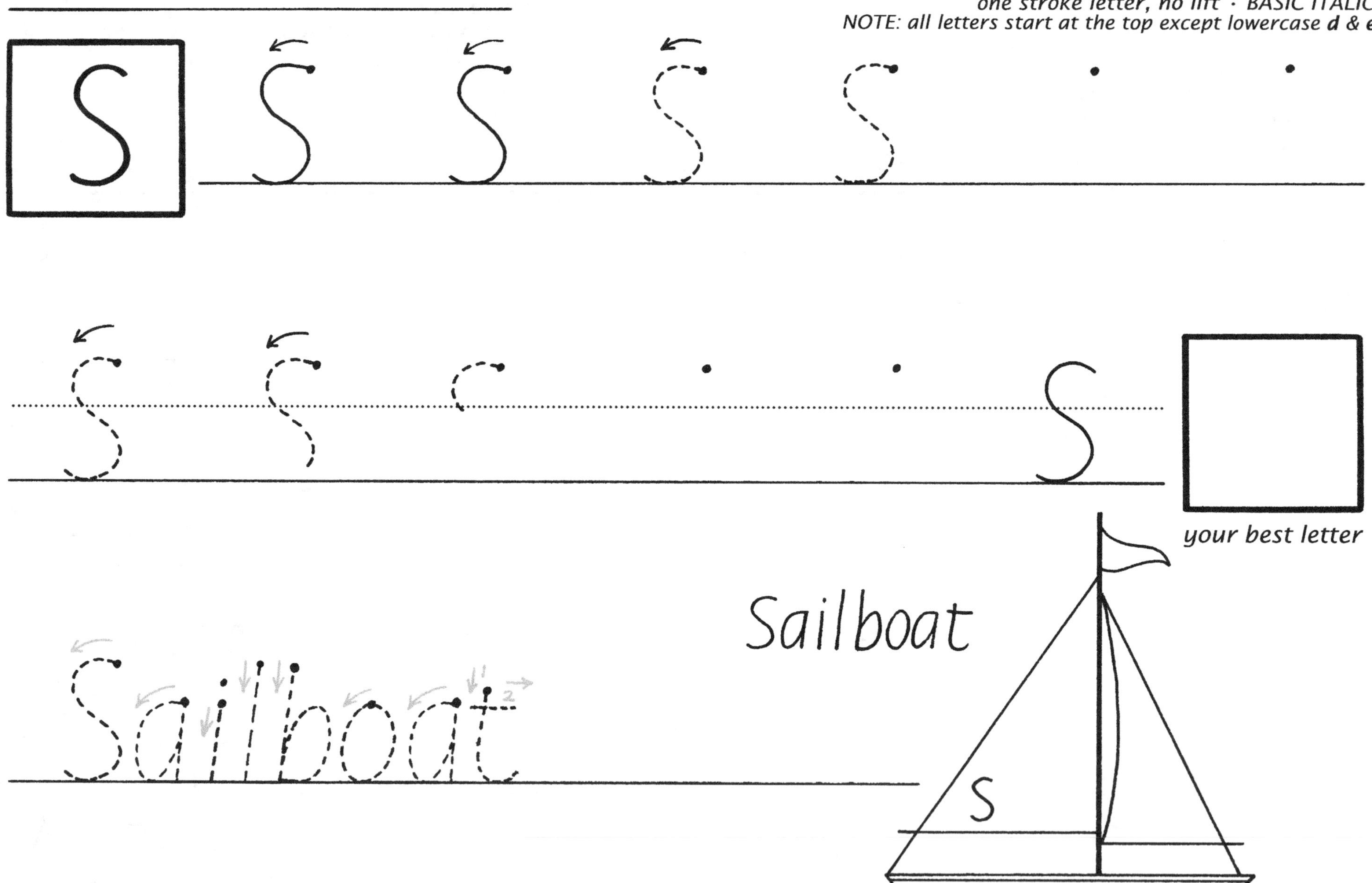

your best letter
Sailboat

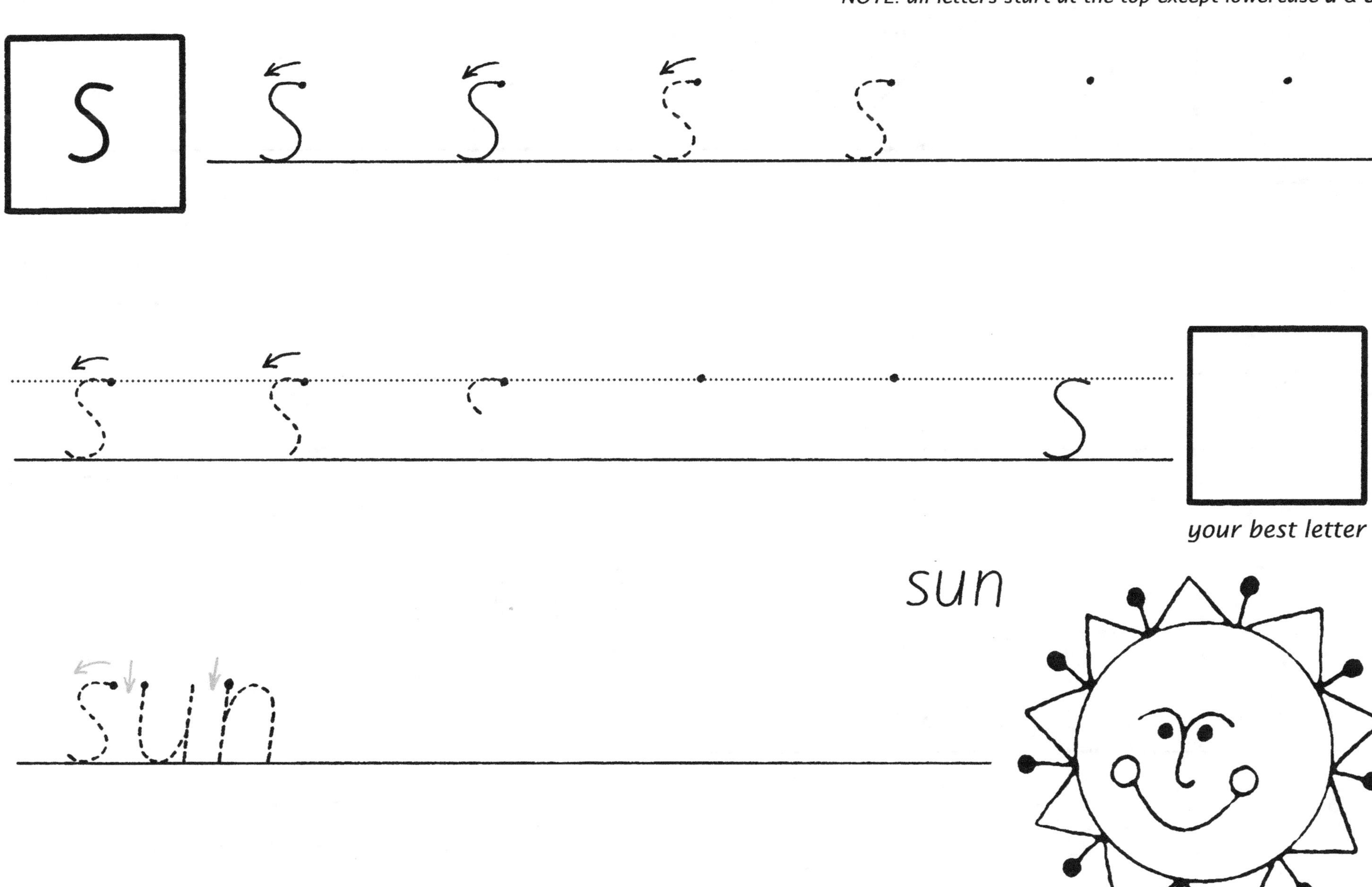

your best letter

sun

your best letter

LOOK: Did you trace each letter before writing your own?

Circle: Yes   No

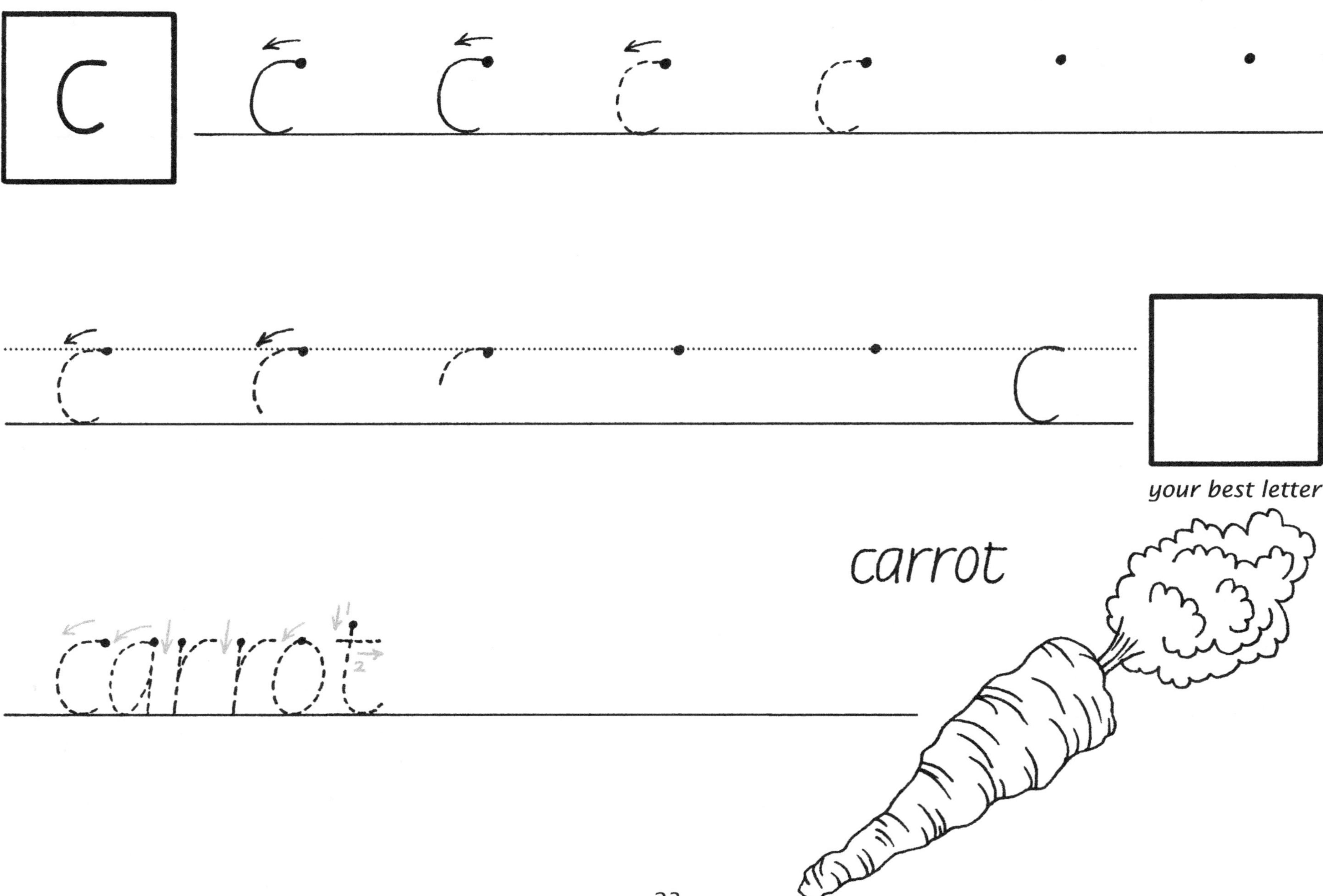

your best letter

carrot

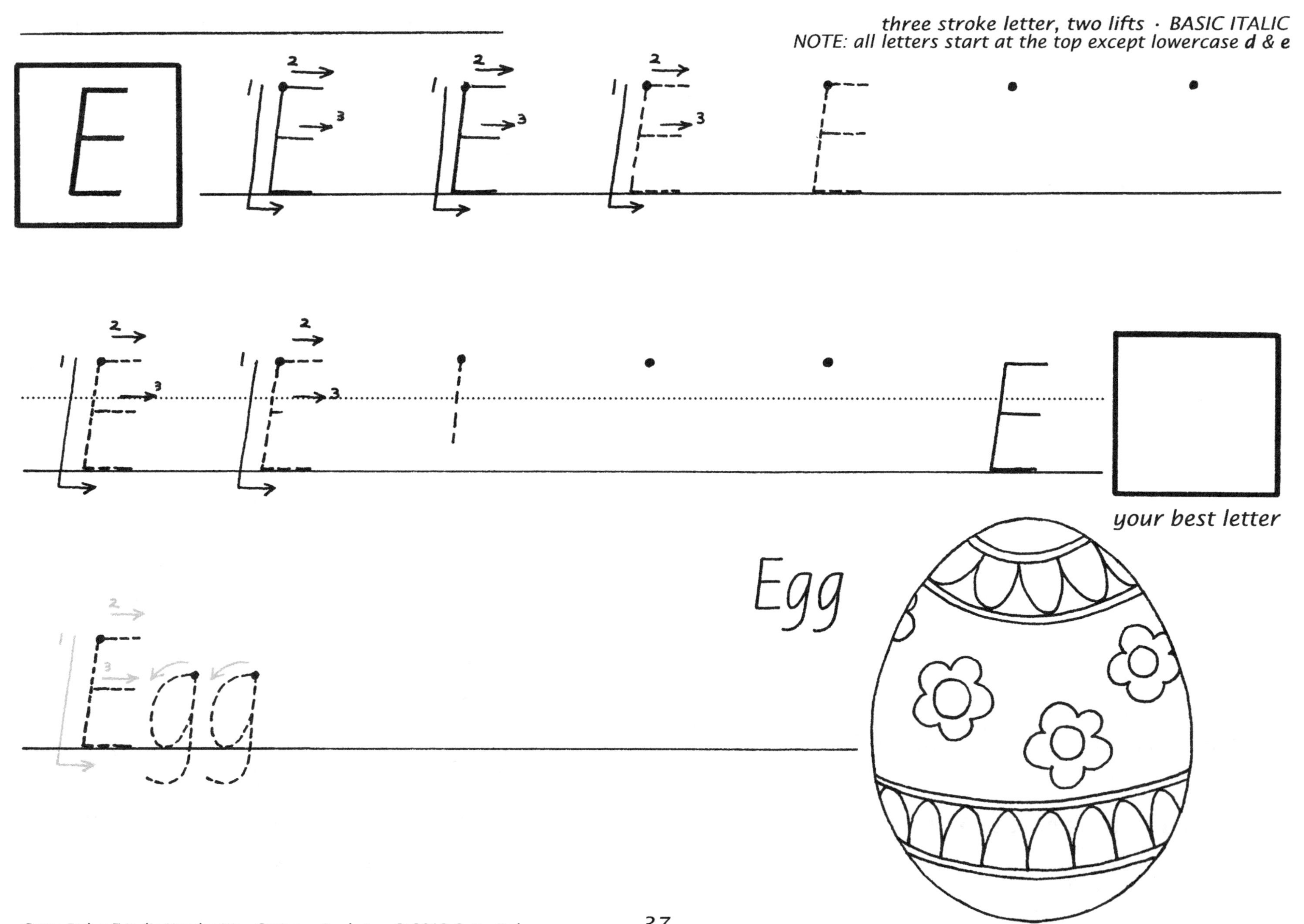

E
E
E
E
your best letter
Egg
Egg

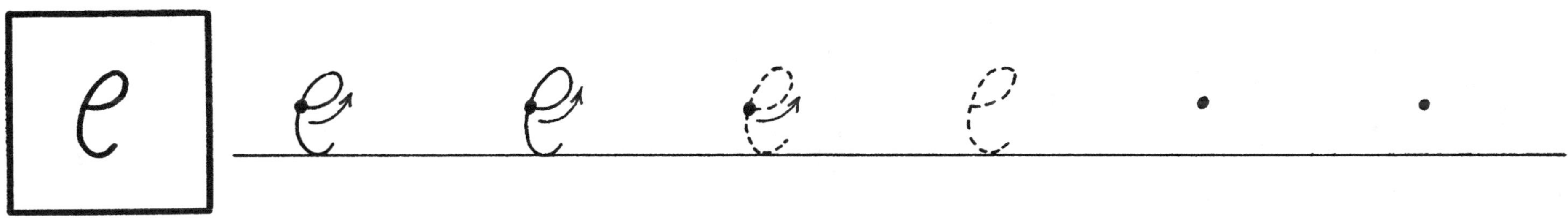

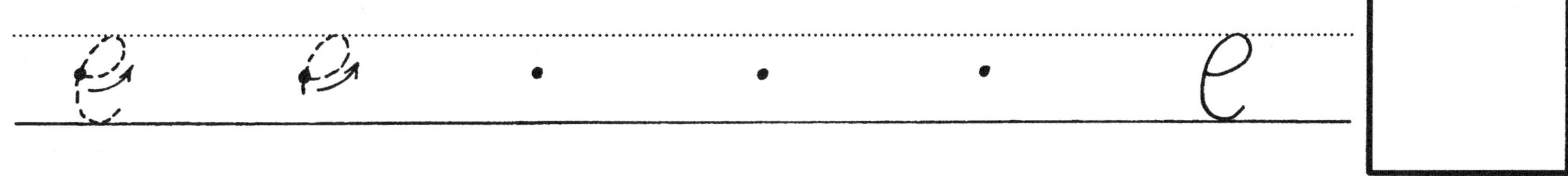

your best letter

elephant

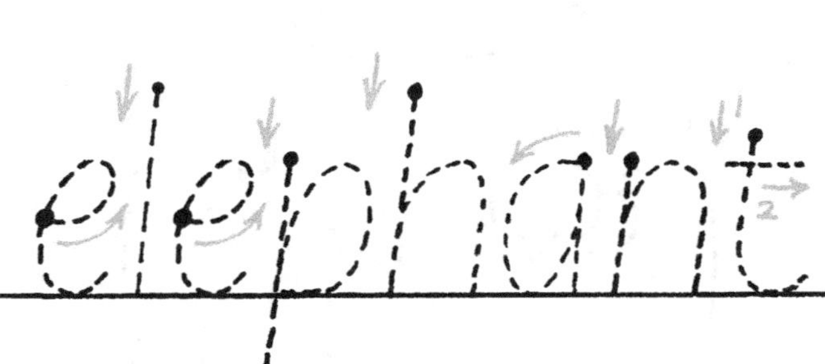

LOOK: Did you trace each **e** before writing your own?

Circle:　Yes　No

your best letter

Octagon

Octagon

LOOK: Did you close the top of each **O**? Circle: Yes   No

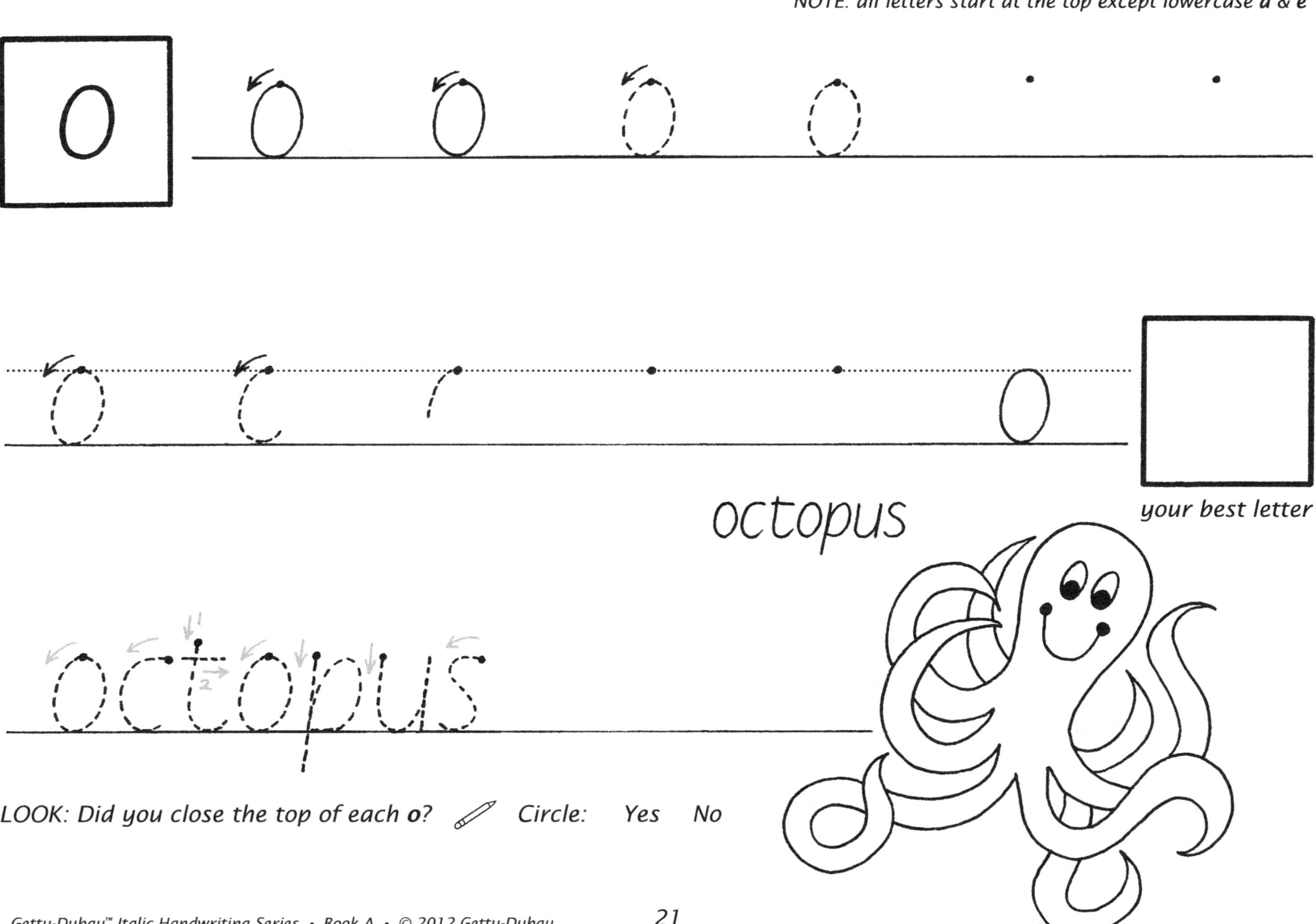

octopus

your best letter

LOOK: Did you close the top of each **o**? Circle: Yes No

your best letter

Peacock

your best letter

parrot

B   B   B   B

B   P   i

B

your best letter

Balloons

Balloons

b
butterfly
your best letter
butterfly

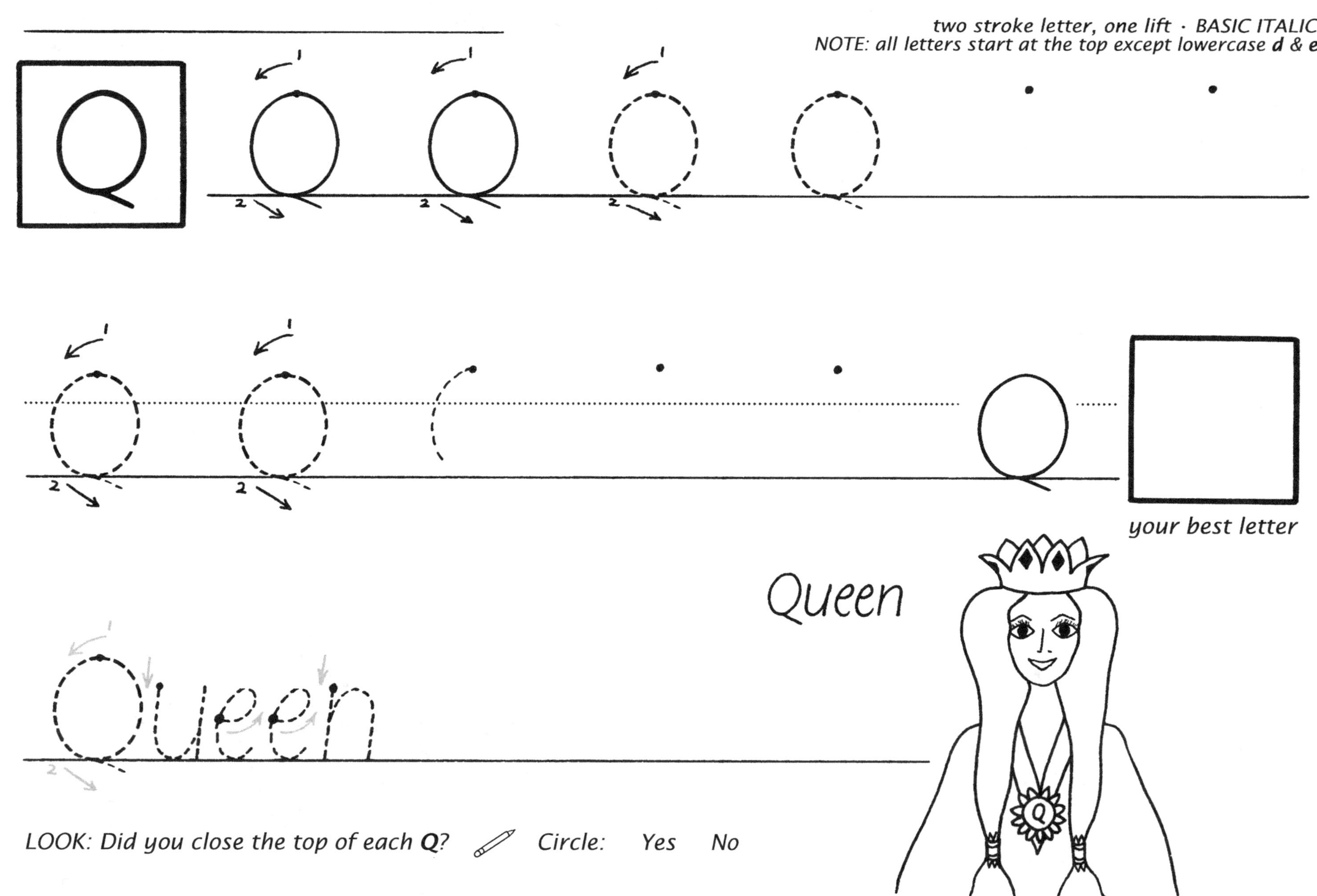

two stroke letter, one lift · BASIC ITALIC
NOTE: all letters start at the top except lowercase d & e
your best letter
Queen
Queen
LOOK: Did you close the top of each Q?   Circle: Yes   No

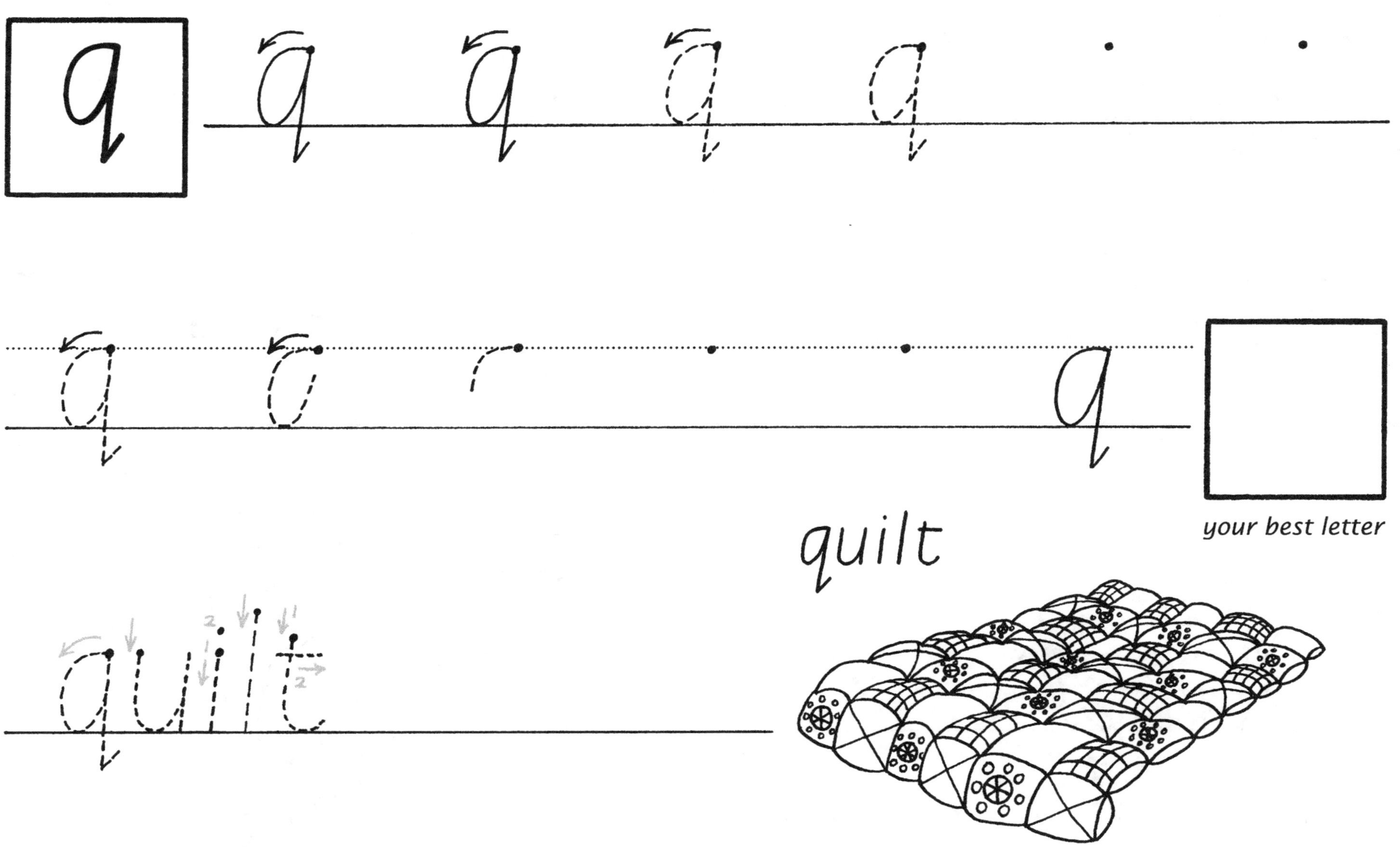

quilt

your best letter

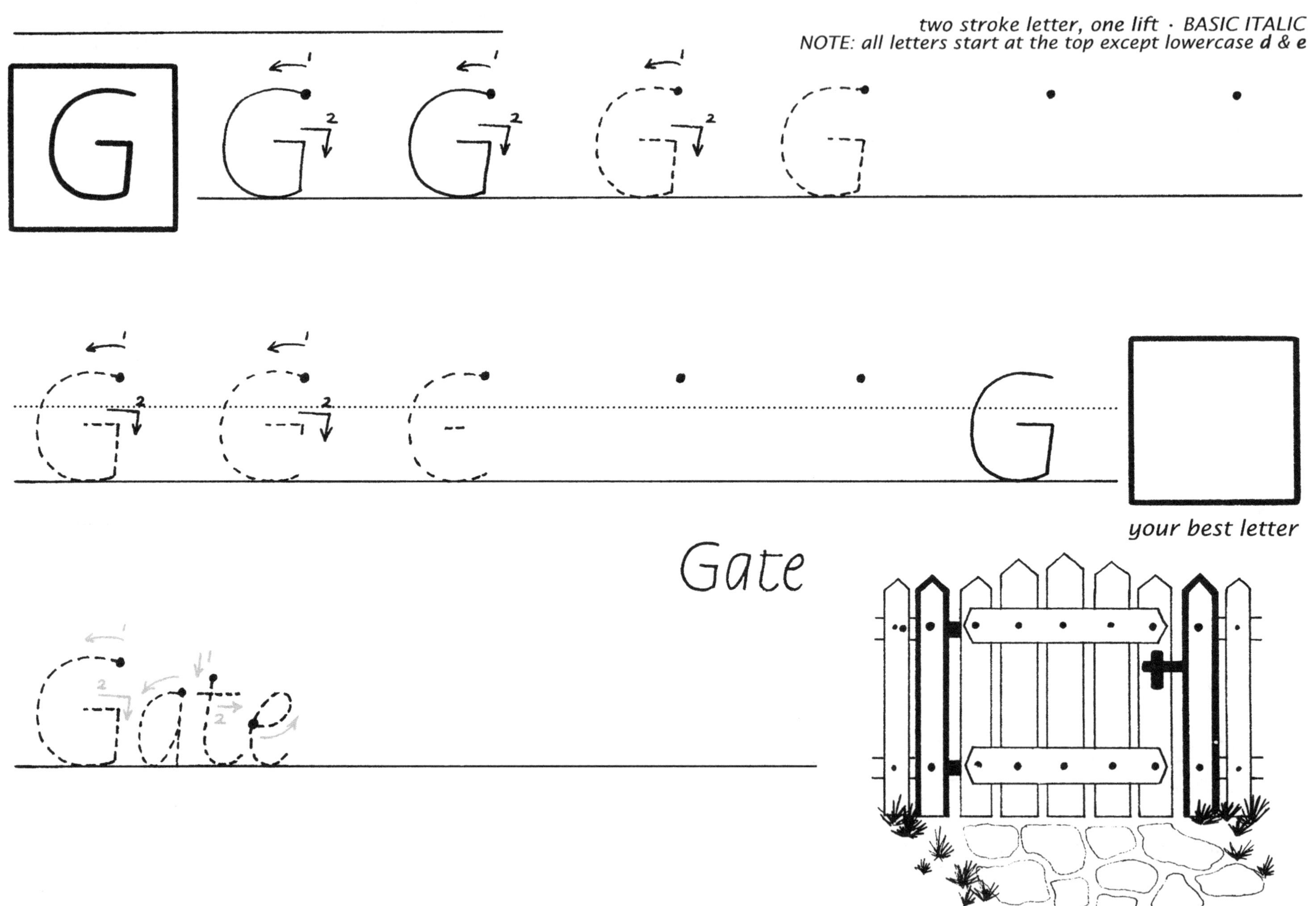

your best letter
Gate

LOOK: Did you trace each letter before writing your own?   Circle: Yes   No

your best letter

Dinosaur

your best letter
dog

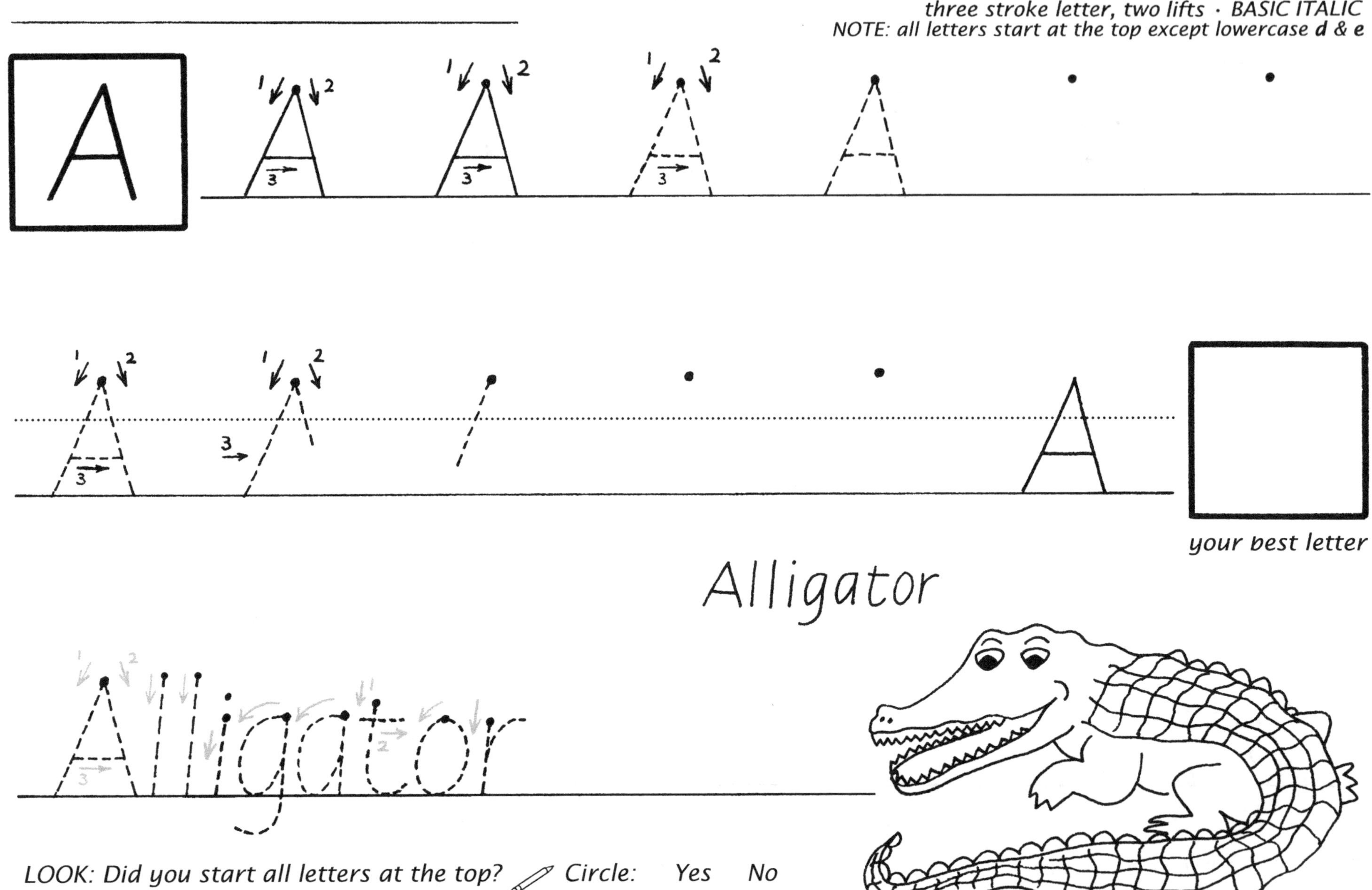

three stroke letter, two lifts · BASIC ITALIC
NOTE: all letters start at the top except lowercase d & e

your best letter

Alligator

LOOK: Did you start all letters at the top?   Circle: Yes   No

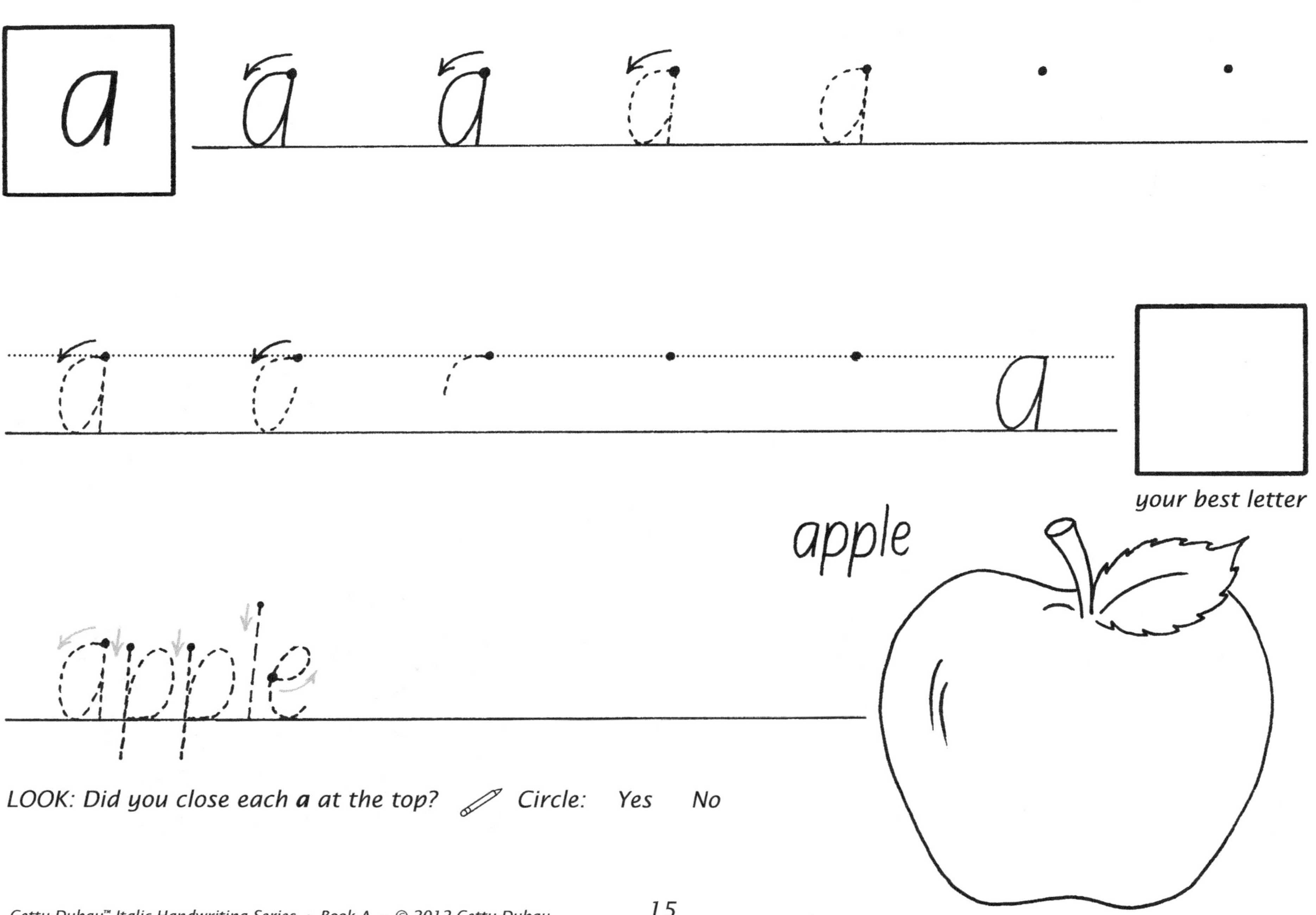

your best letter

apple

LOOK: Did you close each **a** at the top? Circle: Yes   No

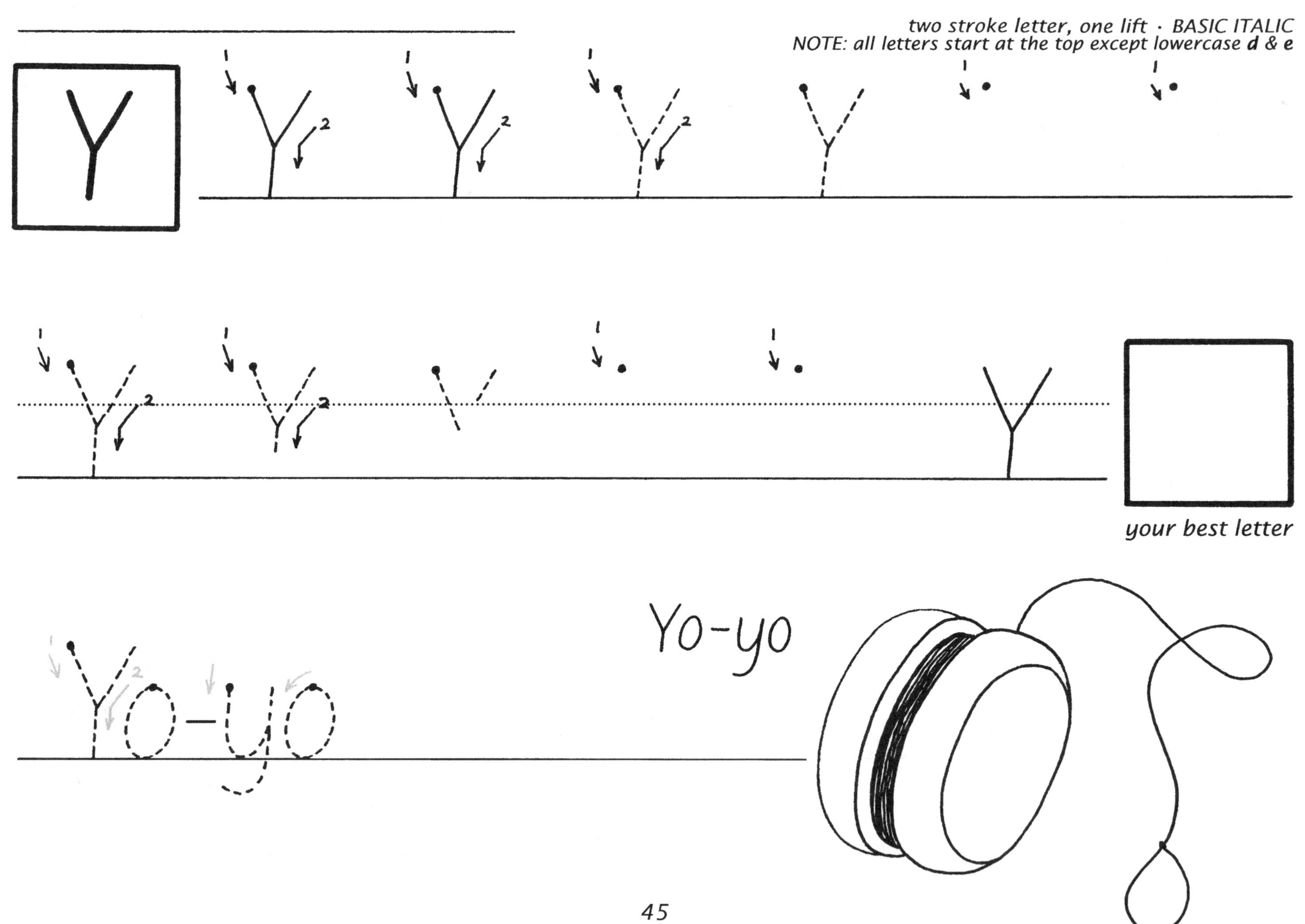

45

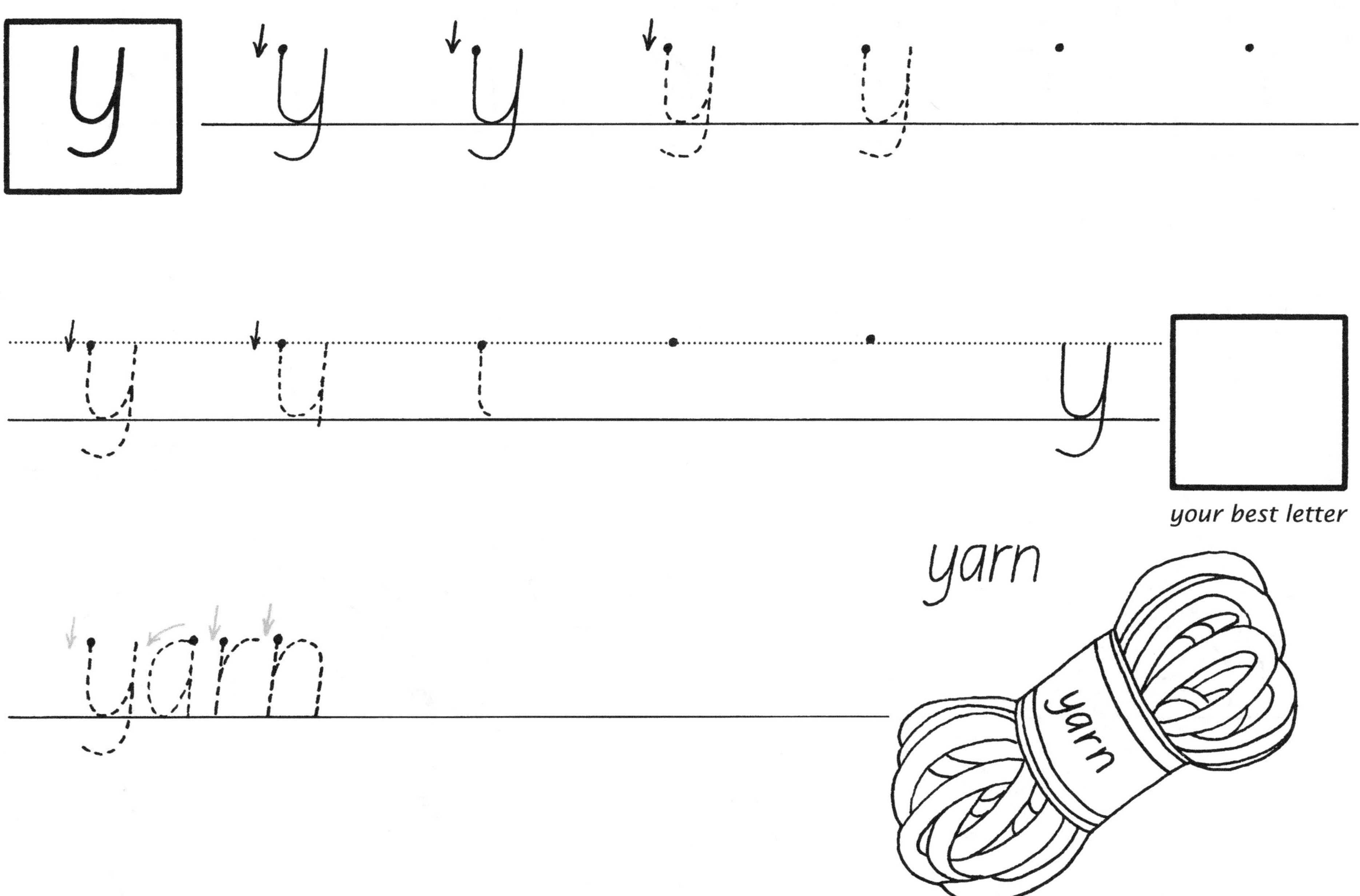

your best letter

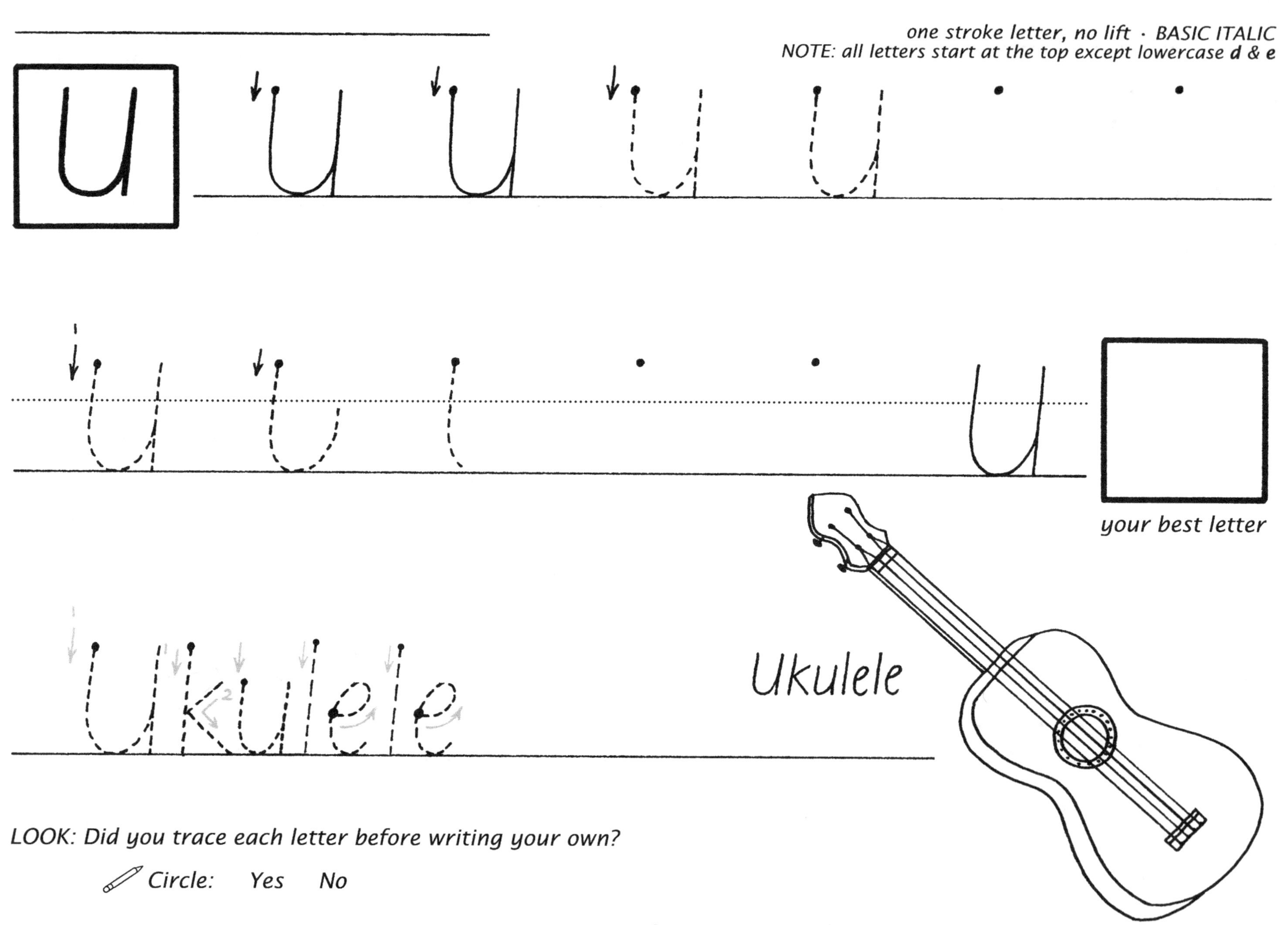

LOOK: Did you trace each letter before writing your own?

Circle: Yes   No

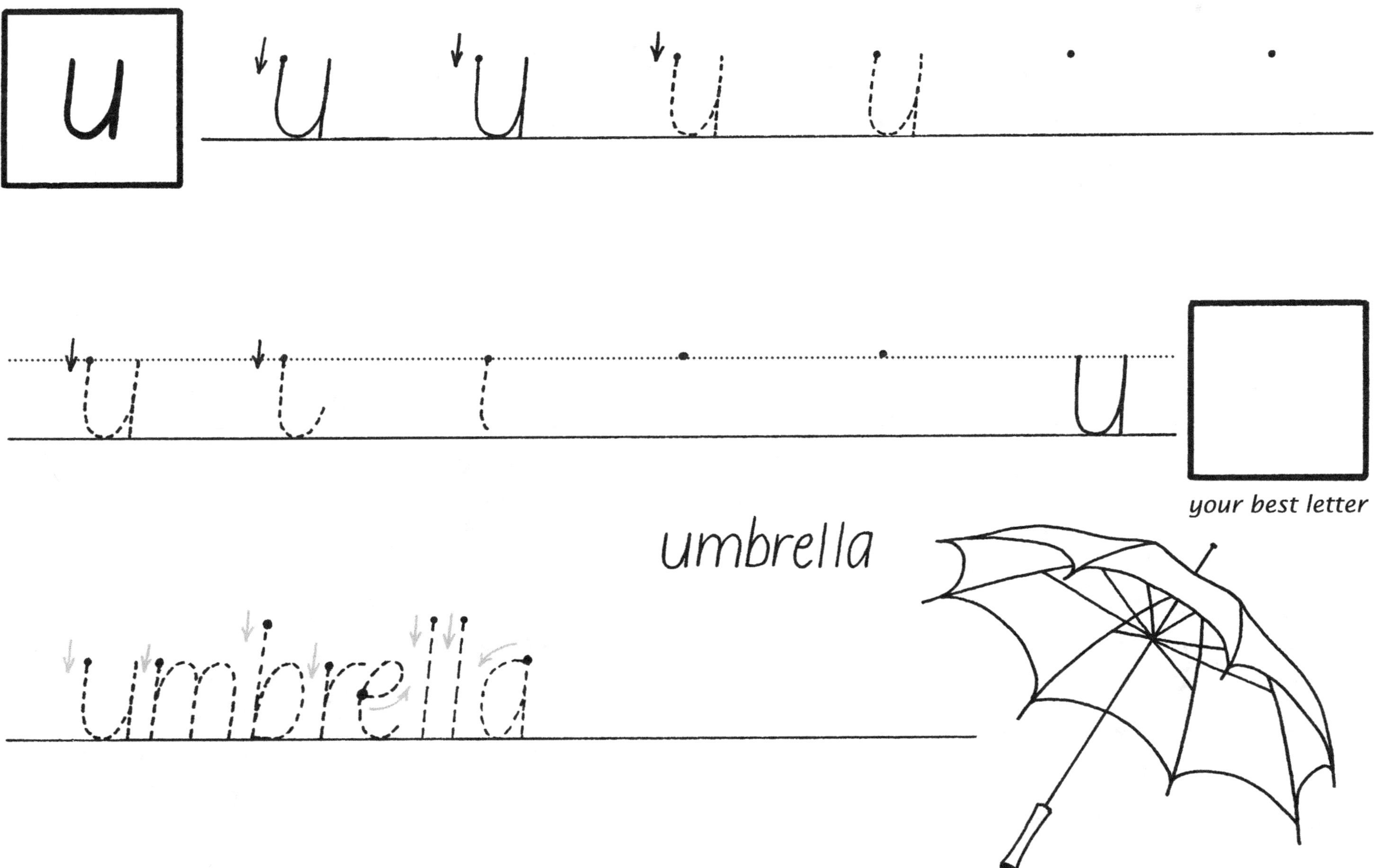

your best letter

umbrella

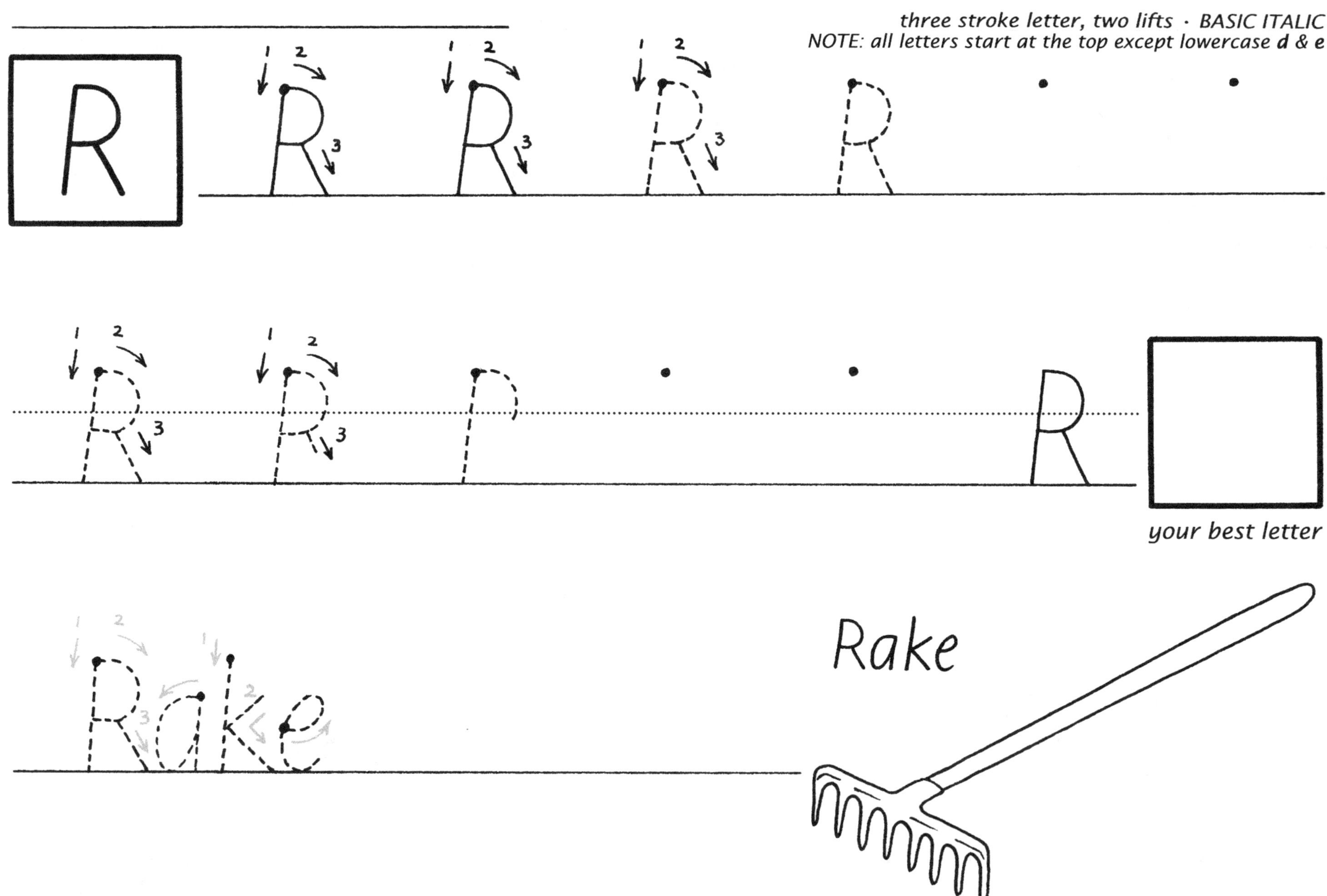

your best letter

Rake

LOOK: Did you start each letter at the top? Circle: Yes   No

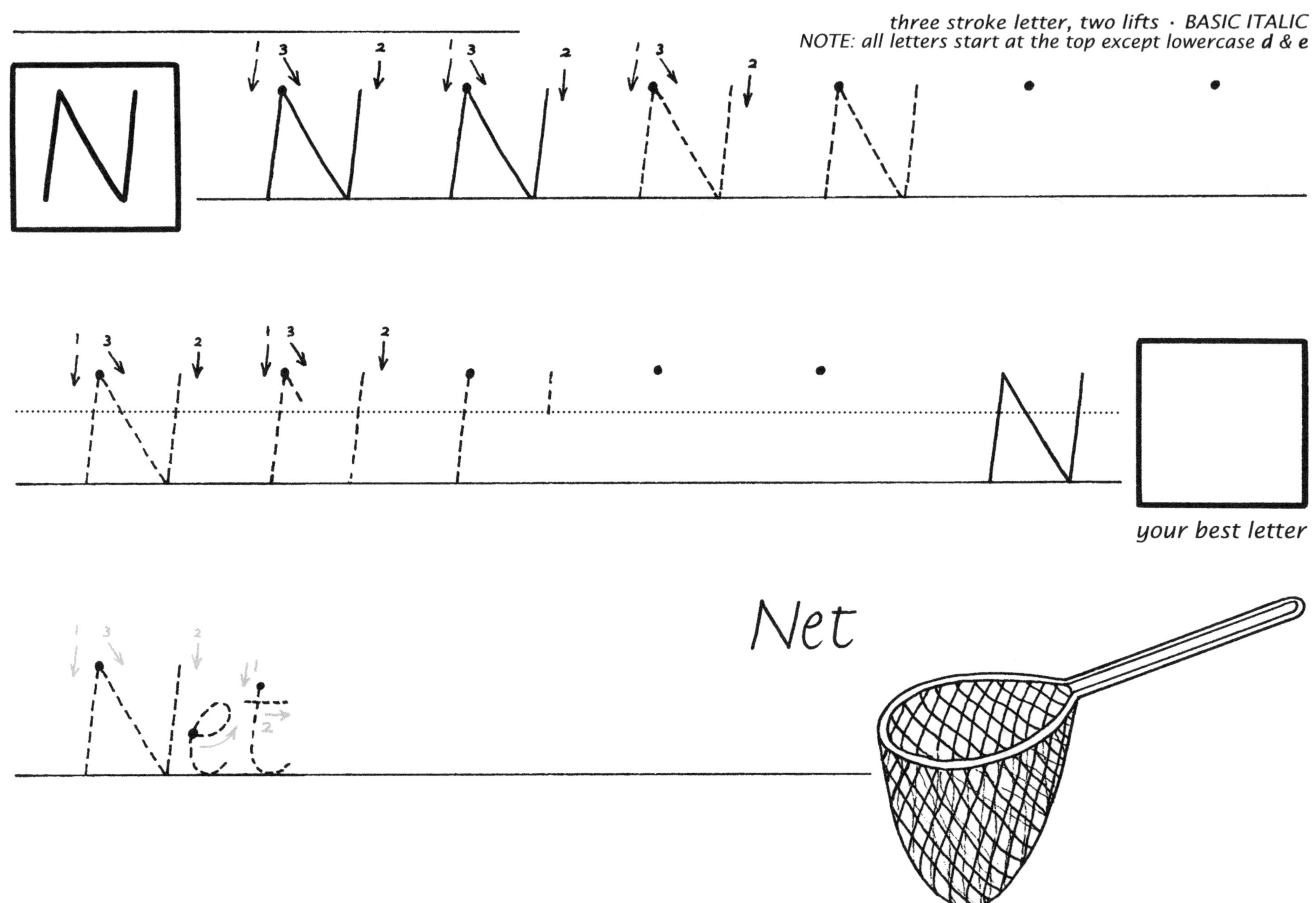
N
your best letter
Net

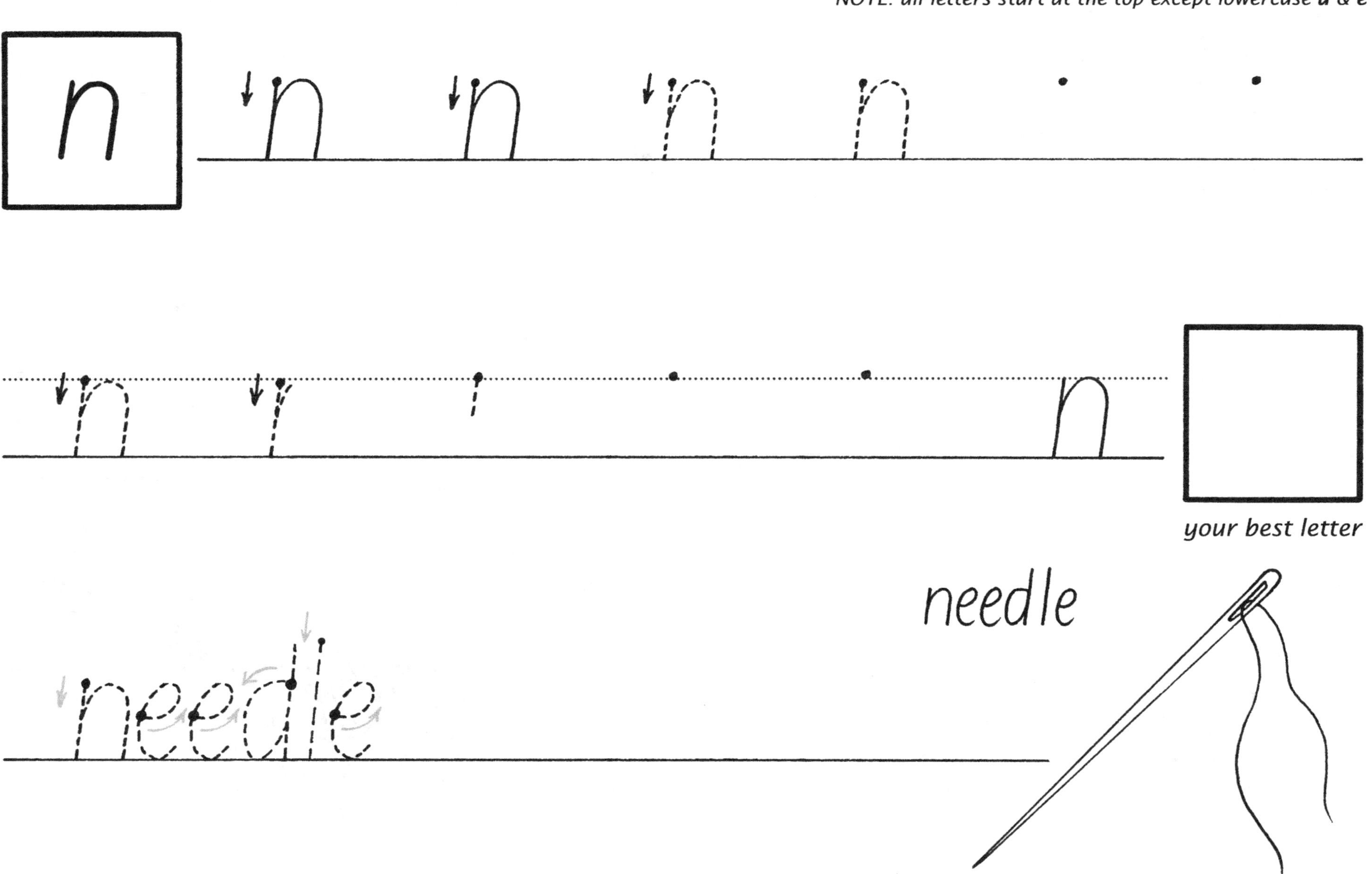

n
your best letter
needle
needle

your best letter

Mittens

m   'm 'm 'm m

'm 'r r   m

your best letter

mouse

mouse

LOOK: Did you start all letters at the top?   Circle: Yes   No

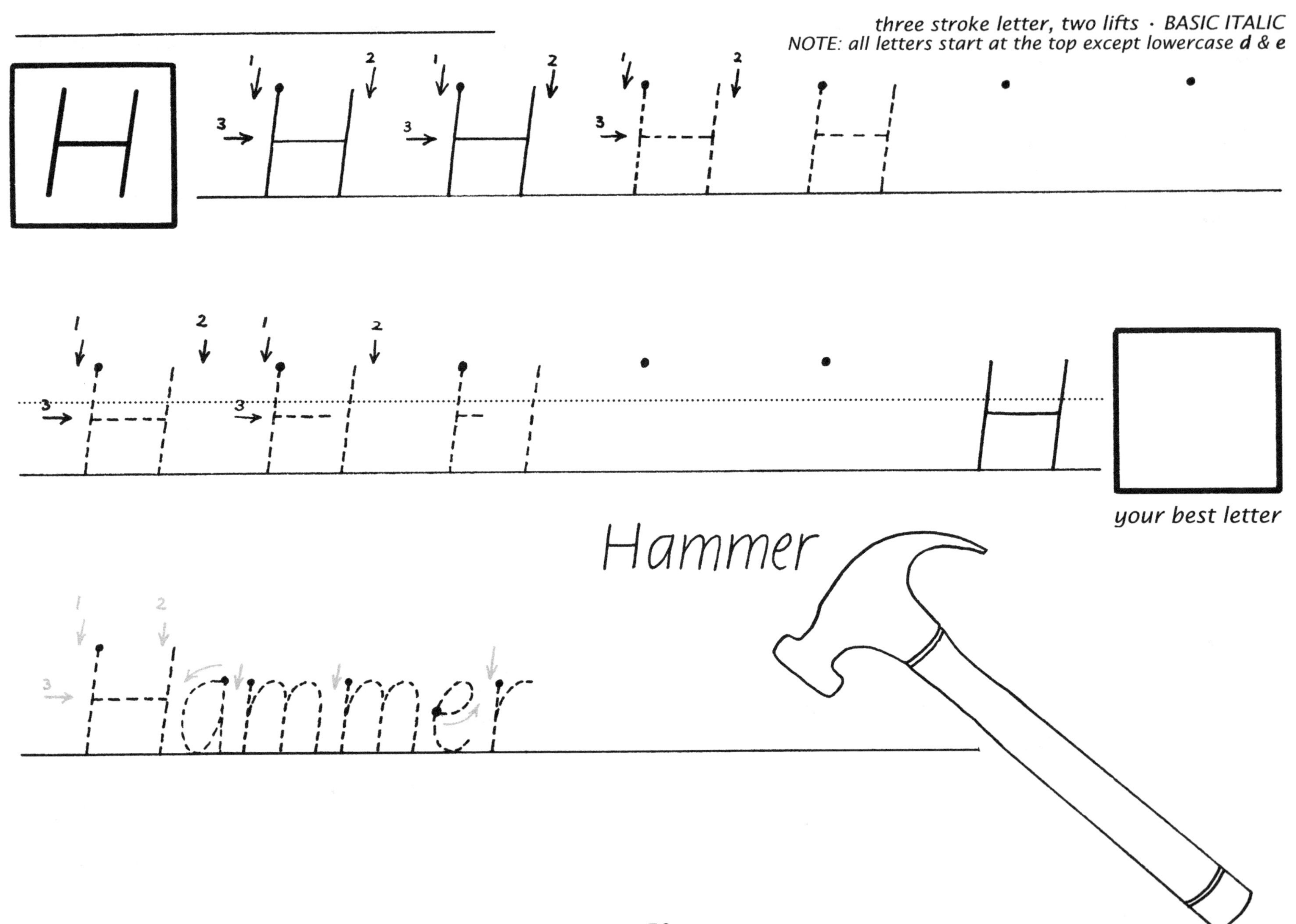

three stroke letter, two lifts · BASIC ITALIC
NOTE: all letters start at the top except lowercase d & e
your best letter
Hammer
Hammer

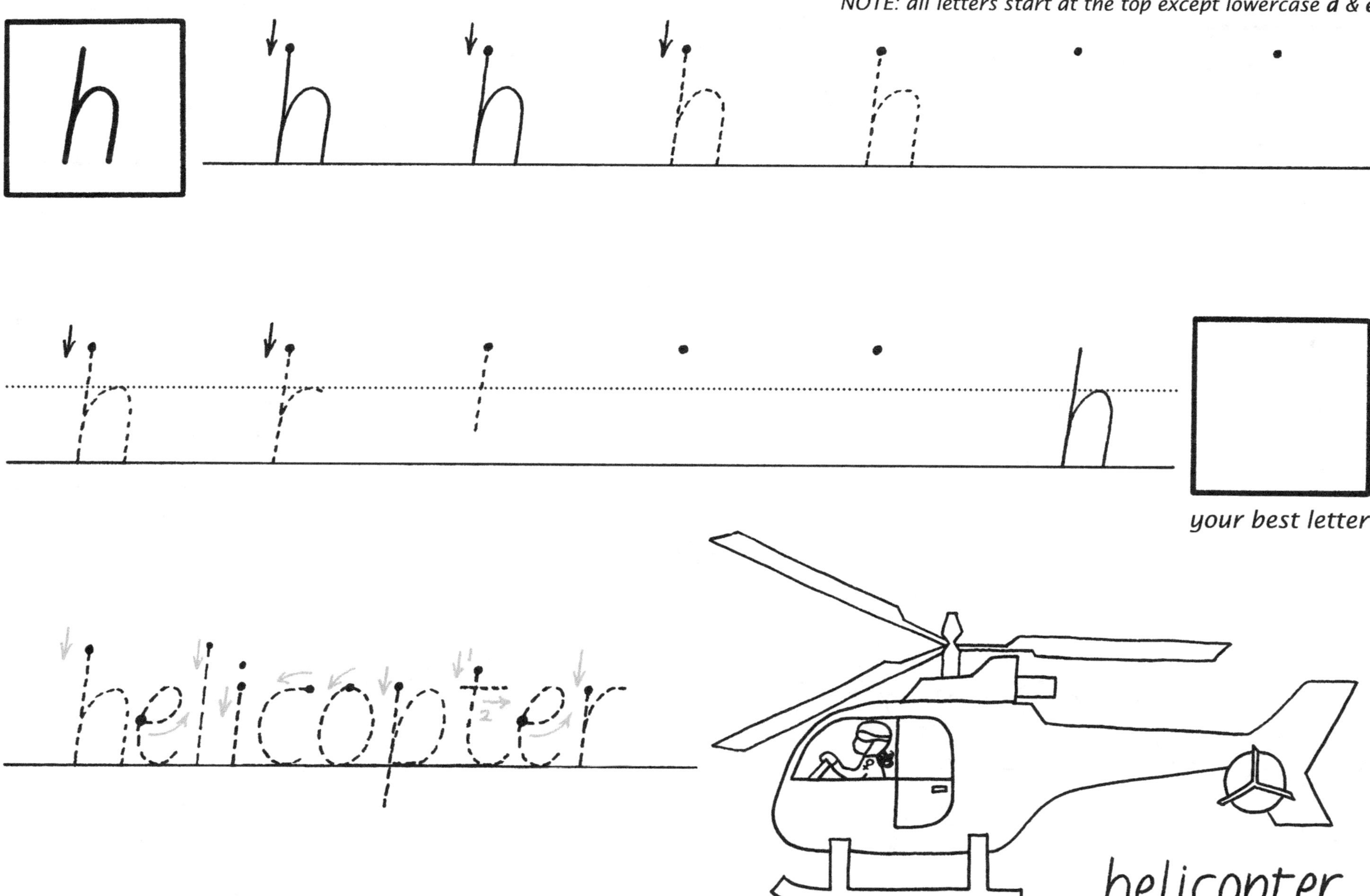

your best letter
helicopter

Zipper

your best letter

Zipper

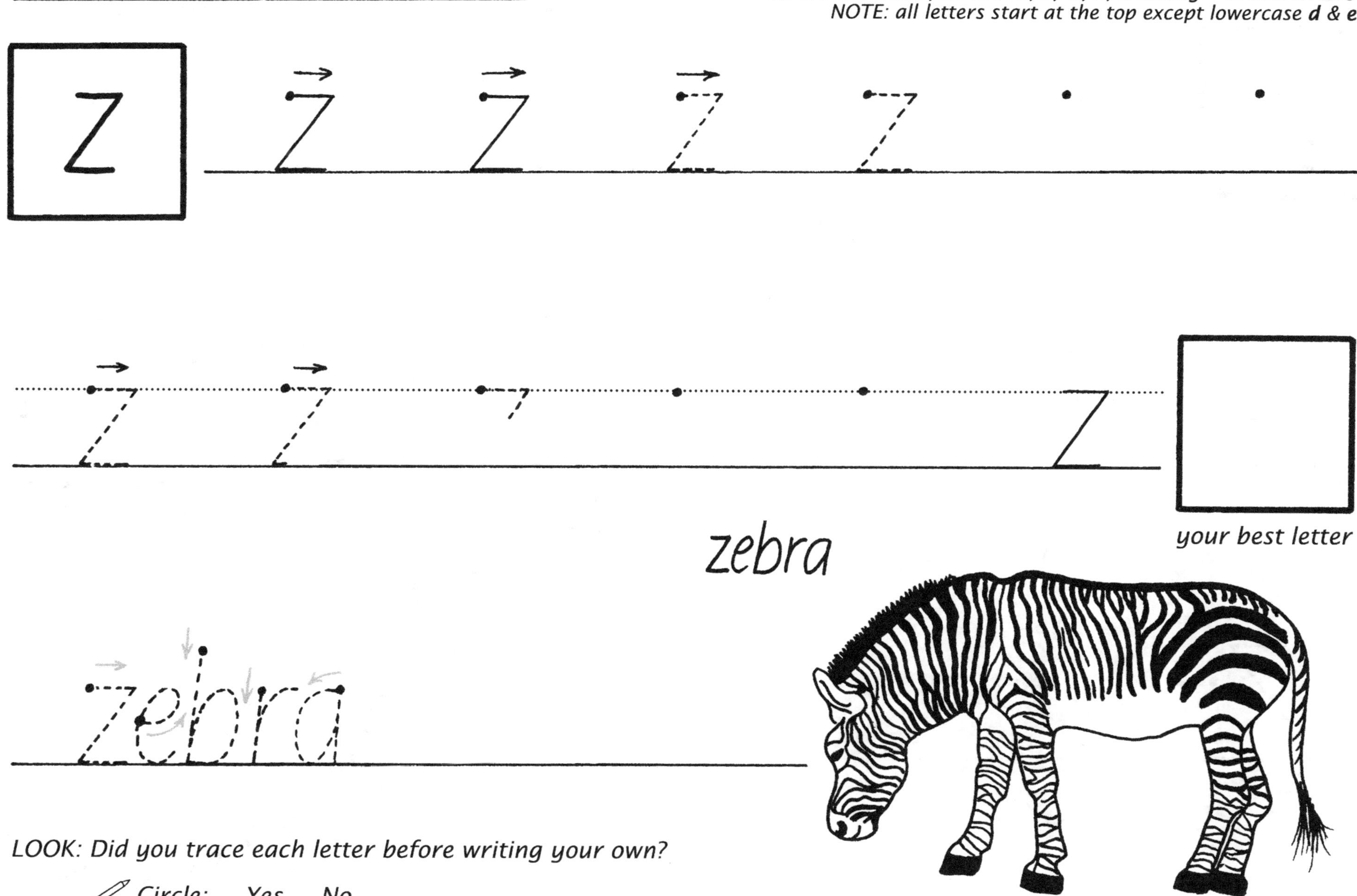

zebra

your best letter

LOOK: Did you trace each letter before writing your own?

Circle: Yes   No

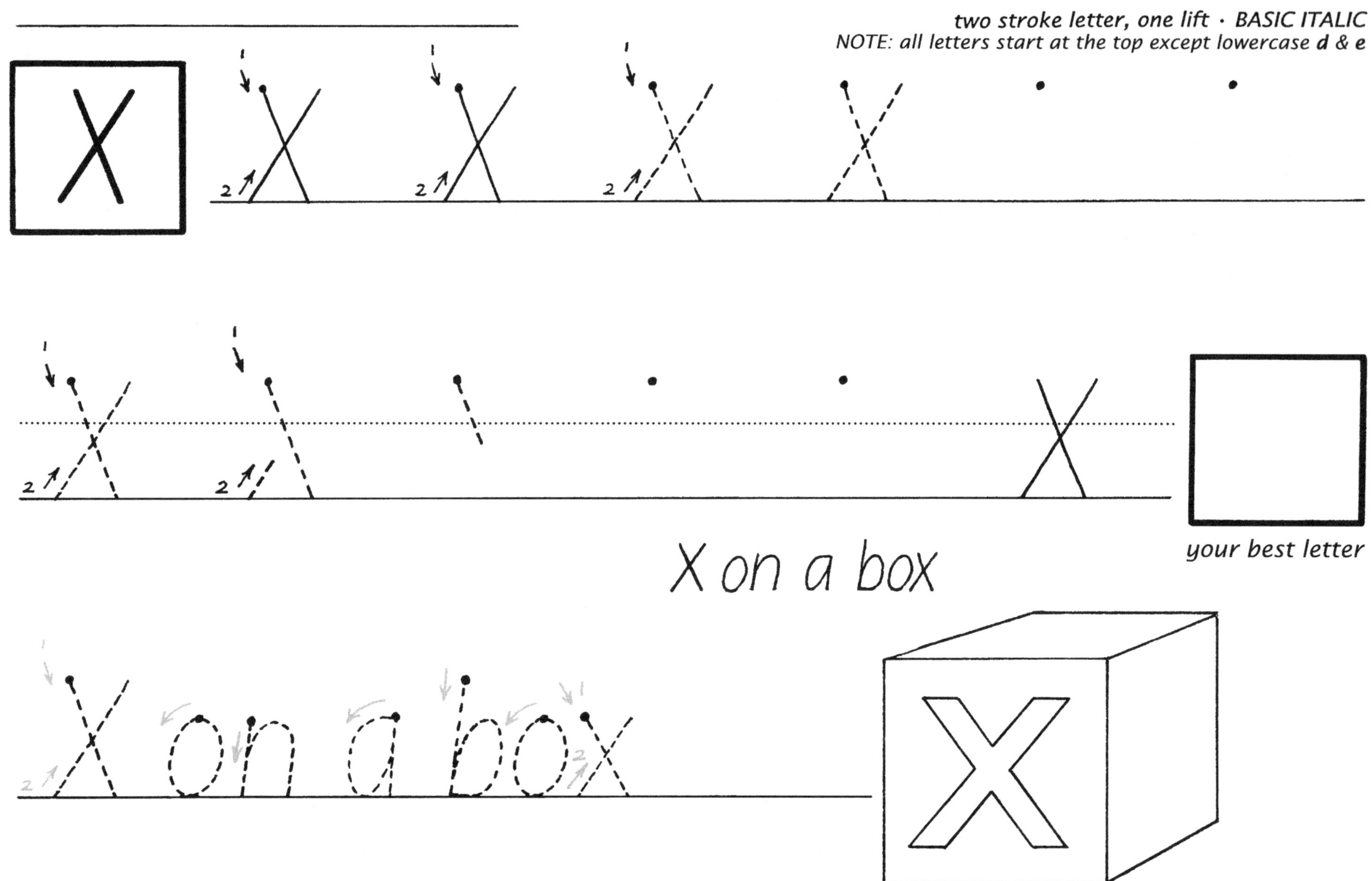

X on a box
your best letter
X on a box

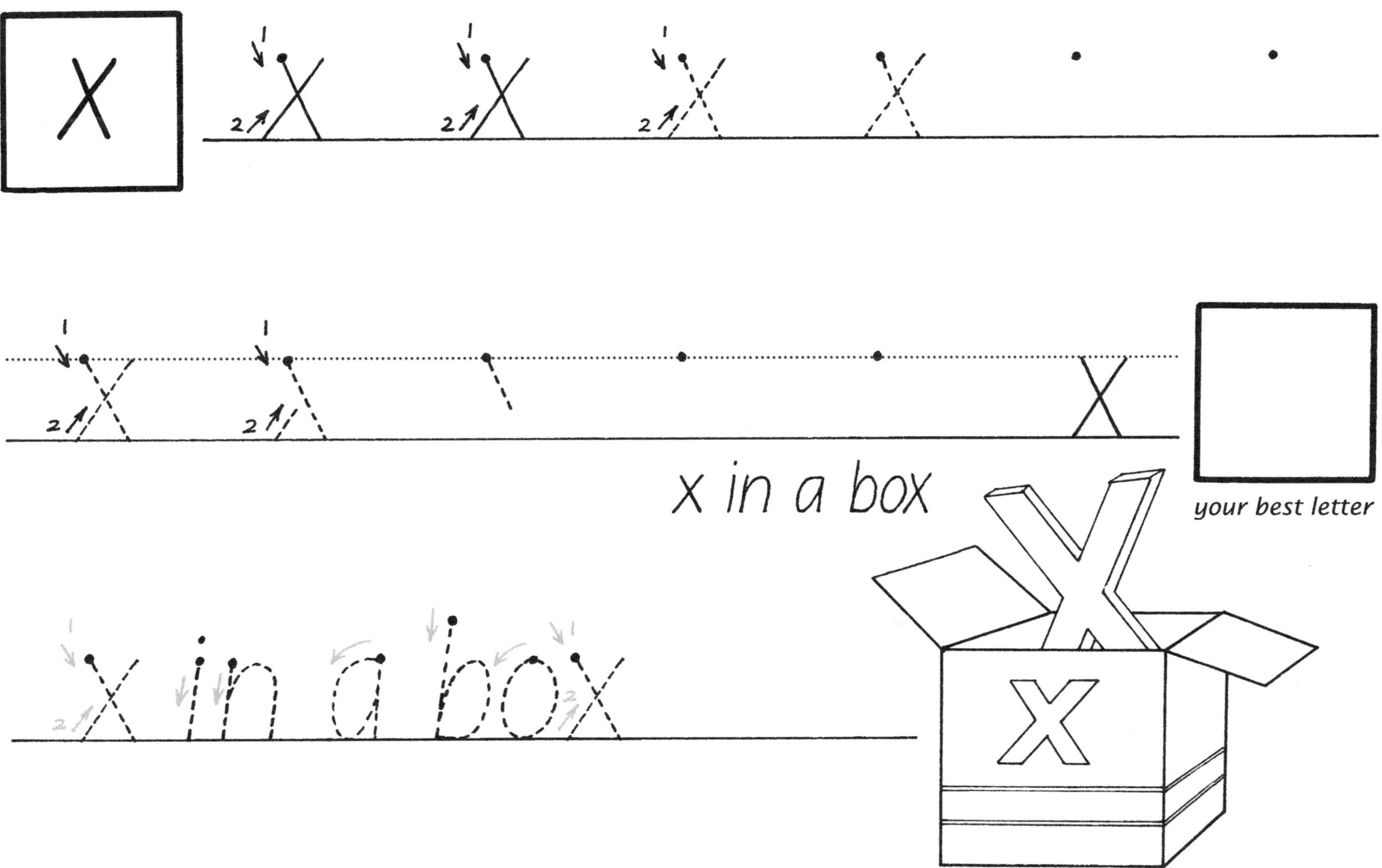

x in a box
your best letter
x in a box

W

your best letter

Watch

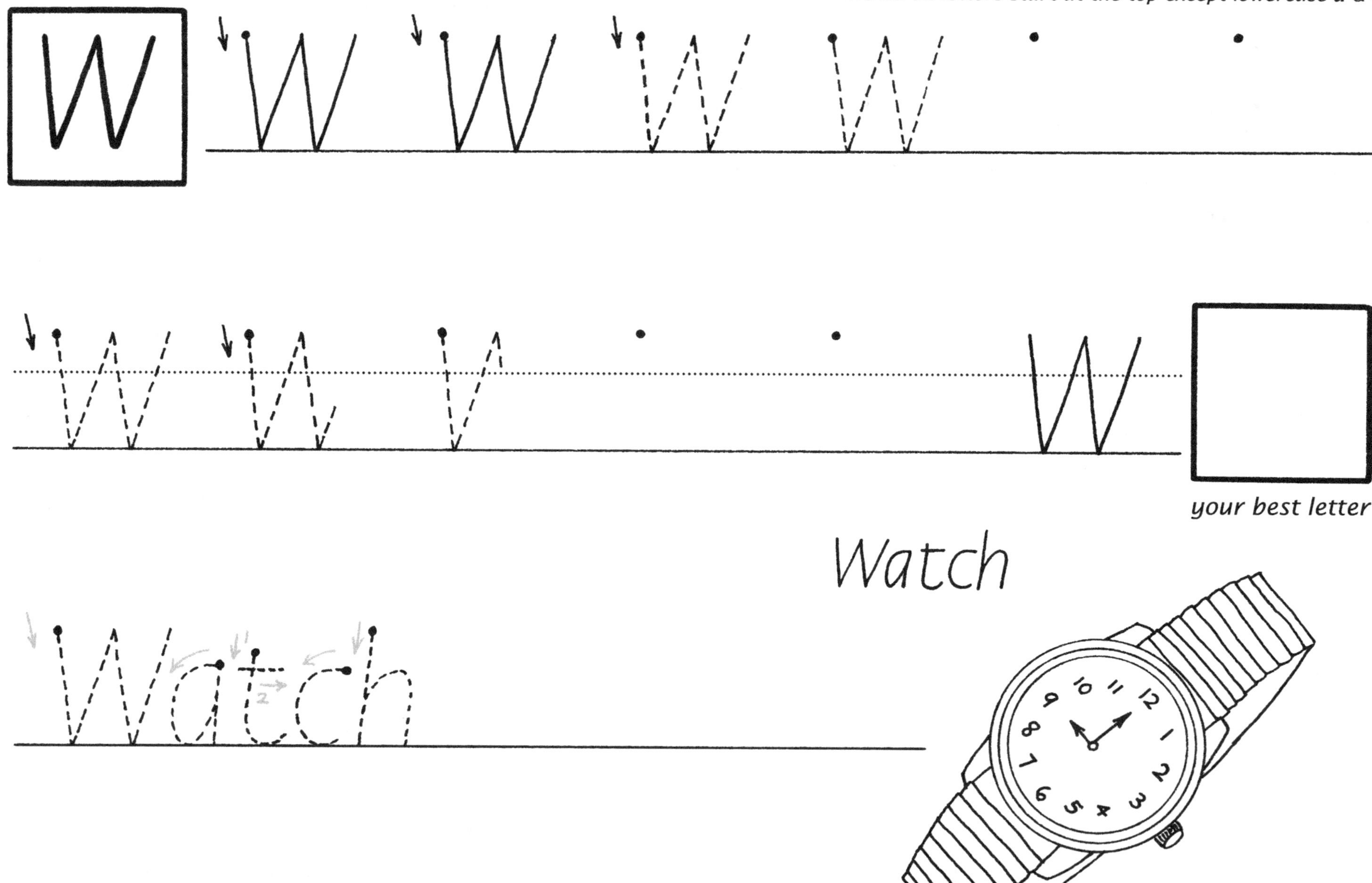

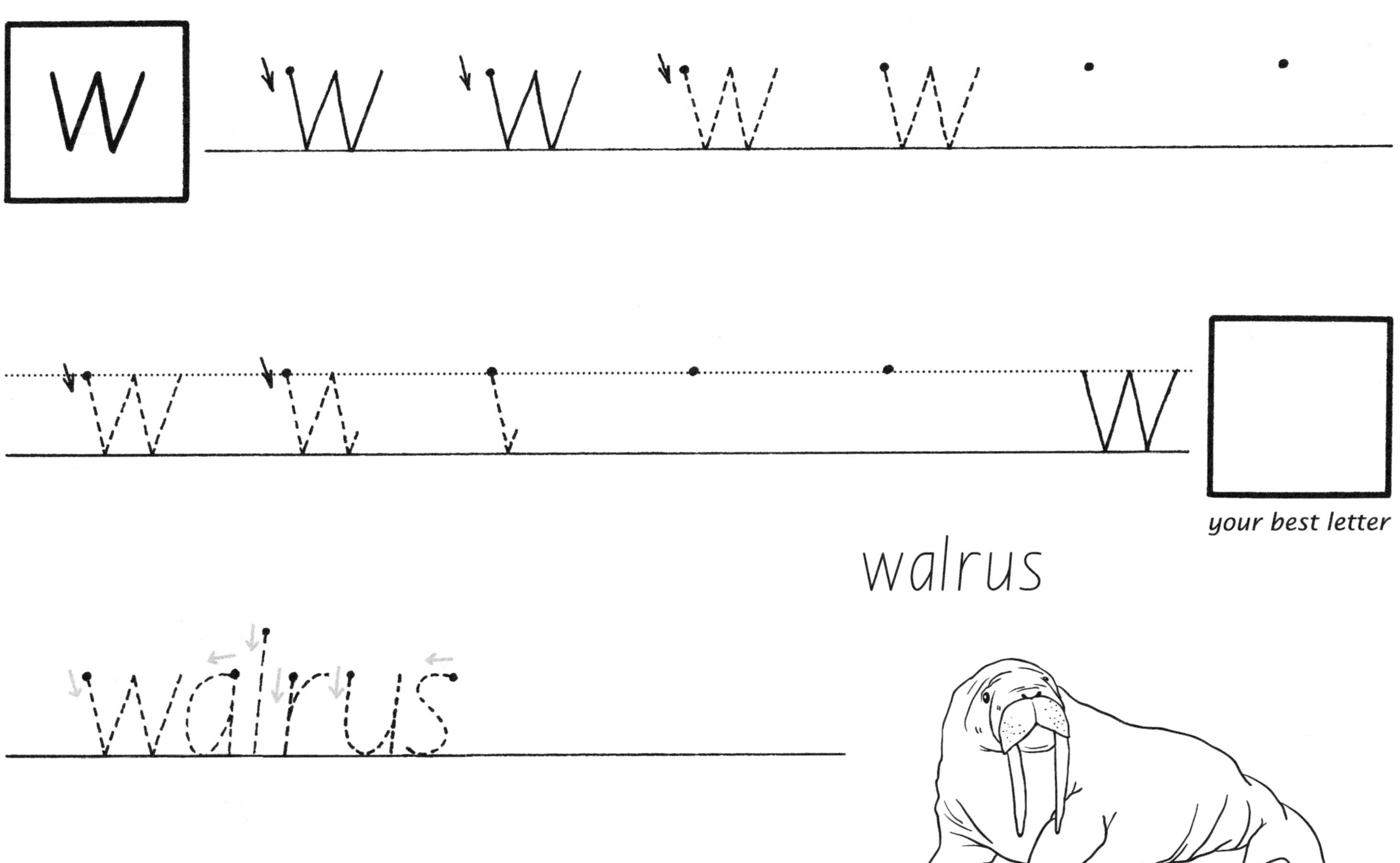

your best letter

walrus

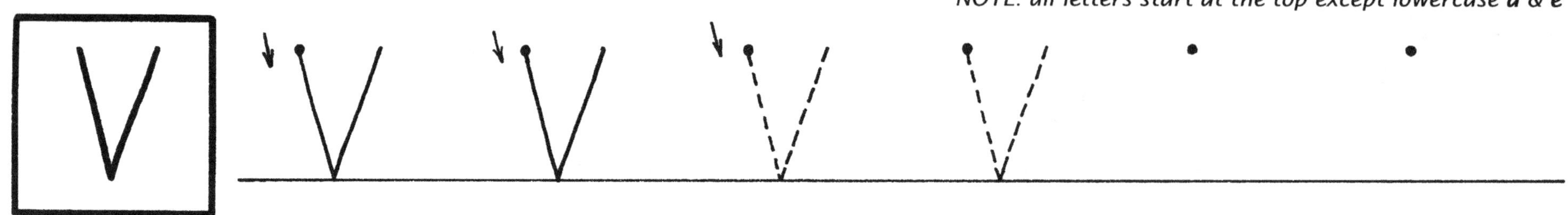

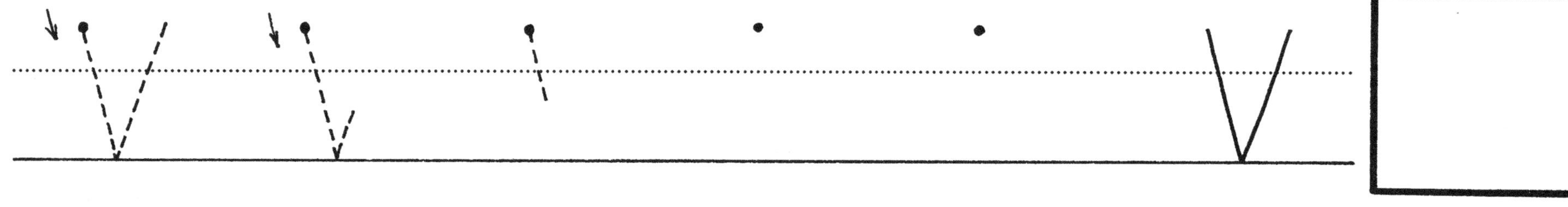

your best letter

Valentine

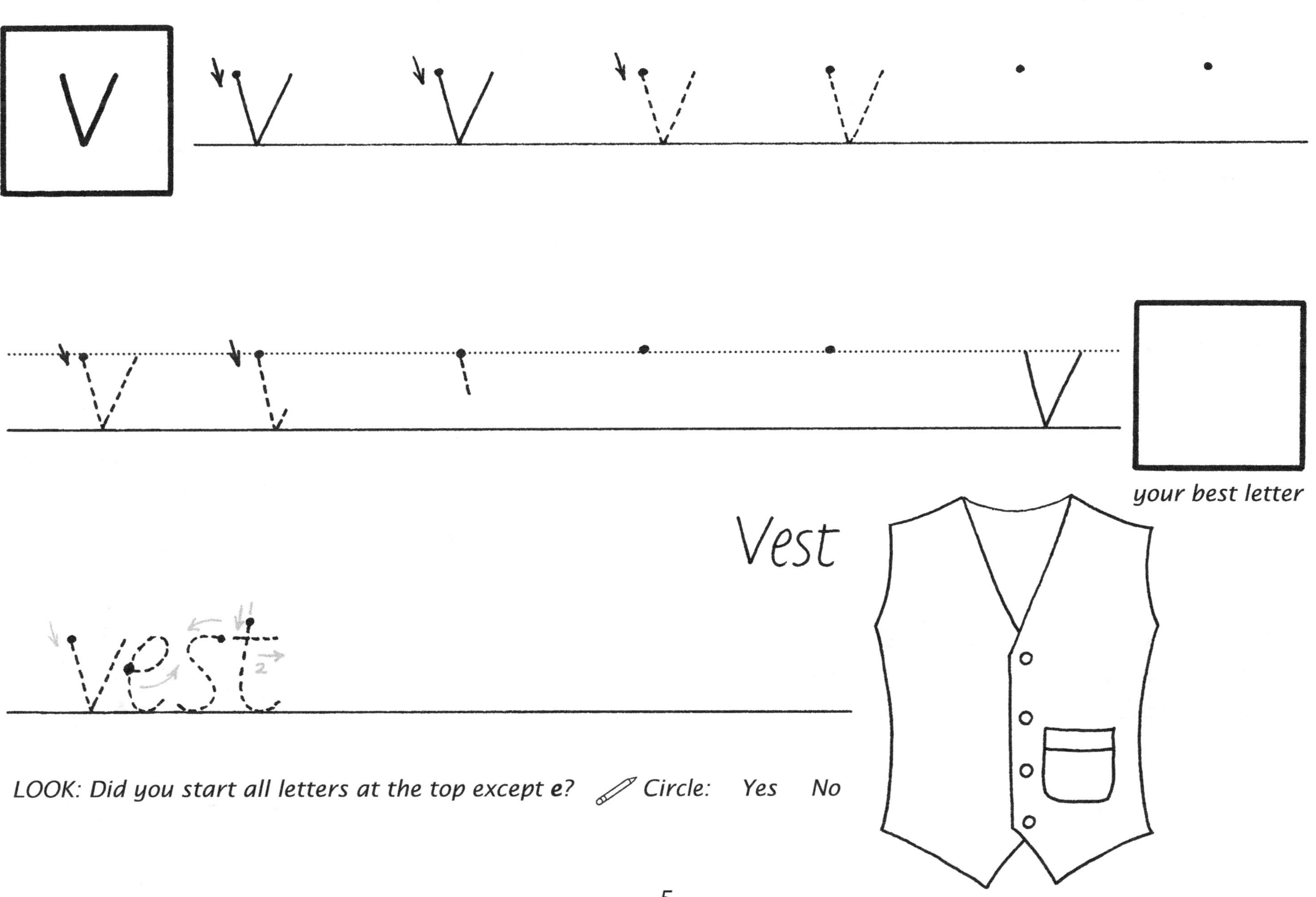

LOOK: Did you start all letters at the top except *e*? Circle: Yes   No

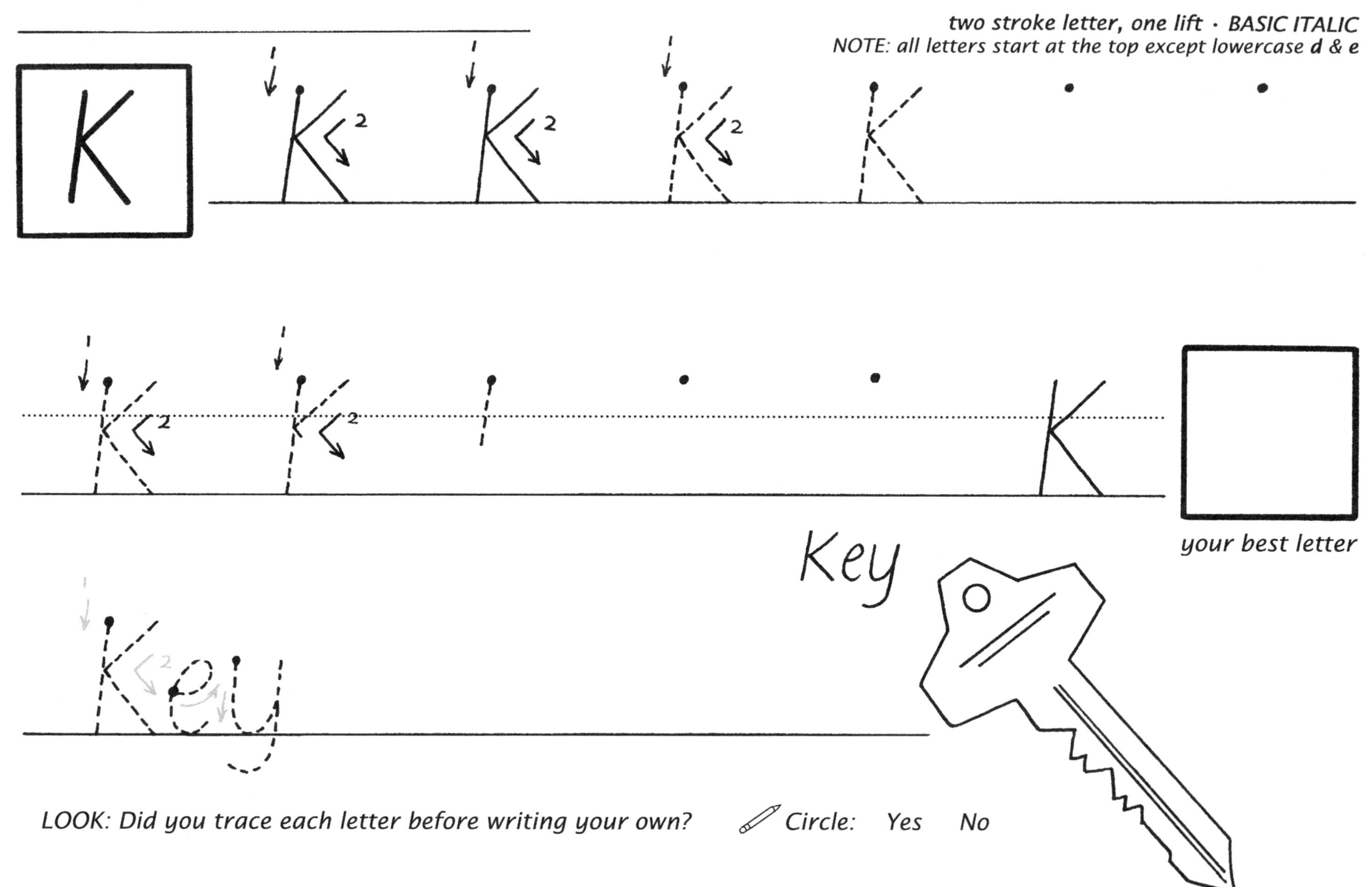

LOOK: Did you trace each letter before writing your own?   Circle: Yes   No

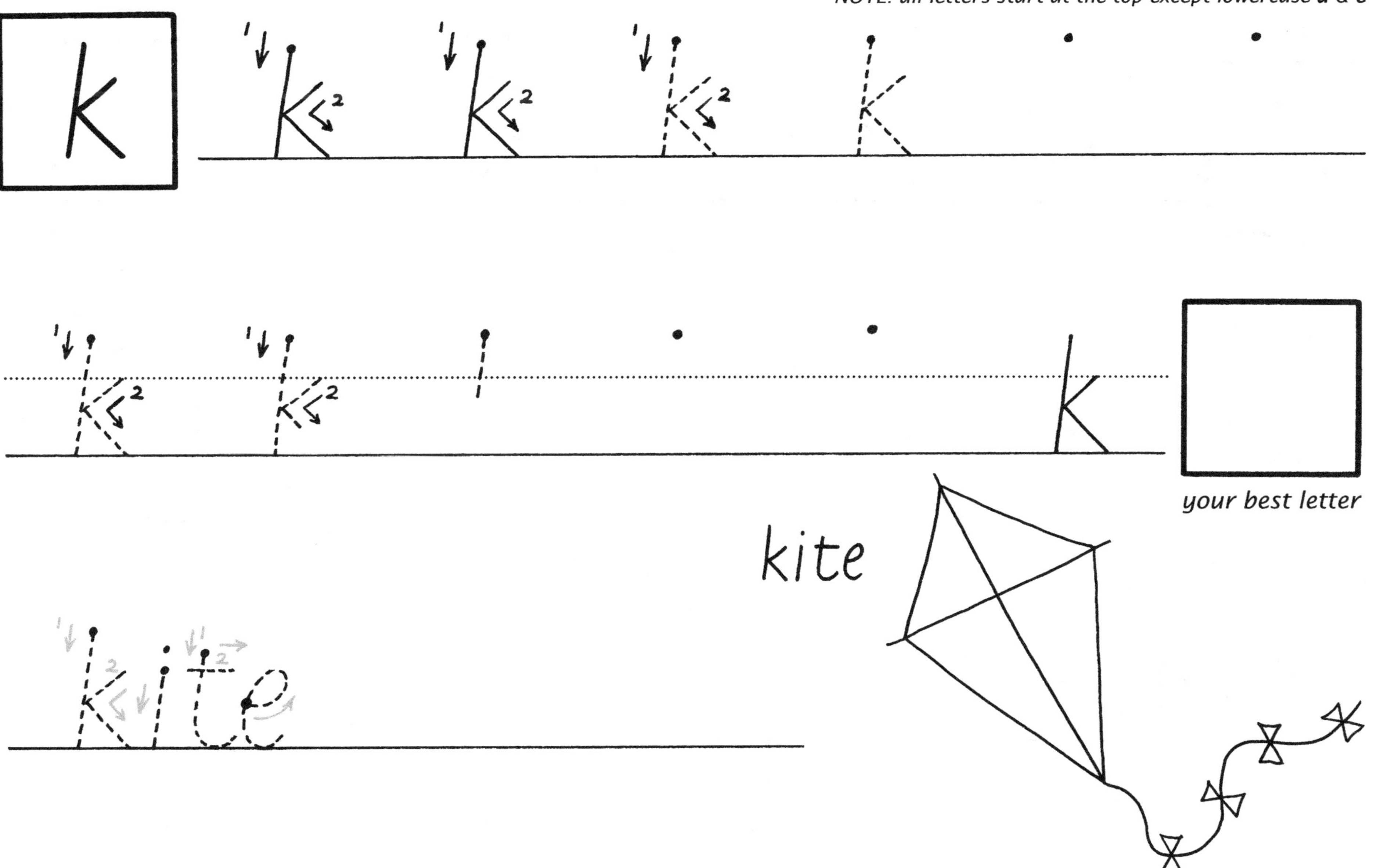

two stroke letter, one lift · k, v, w, x, z family · BASIC ITALIC
NOTE: all letters start at the top except lowercase d & e
your best letter
kite

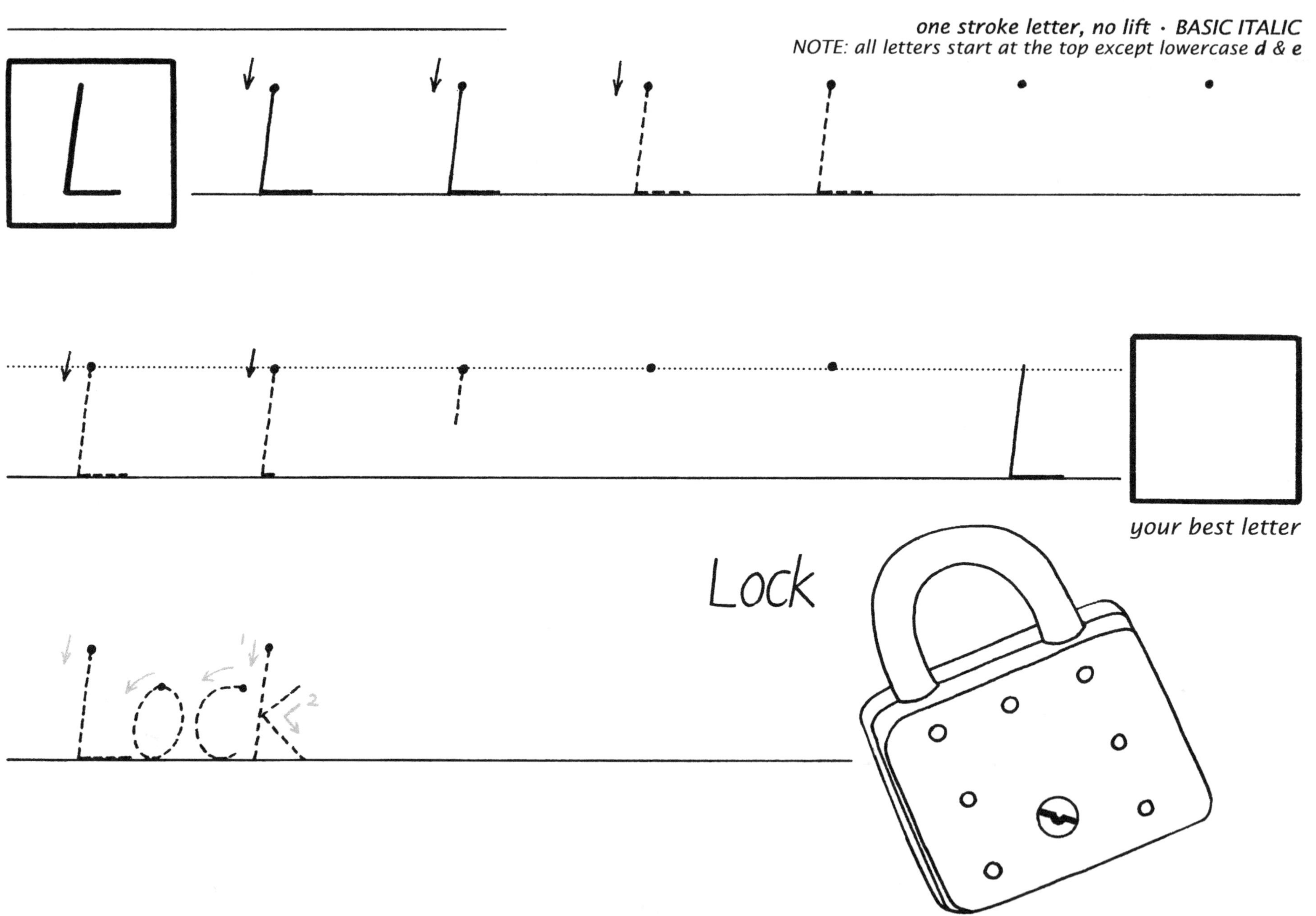

your best letter

Lock

your best letter

lamb

lamb

J

your best letter

Jack-in-the-box

Jack-in-the-box

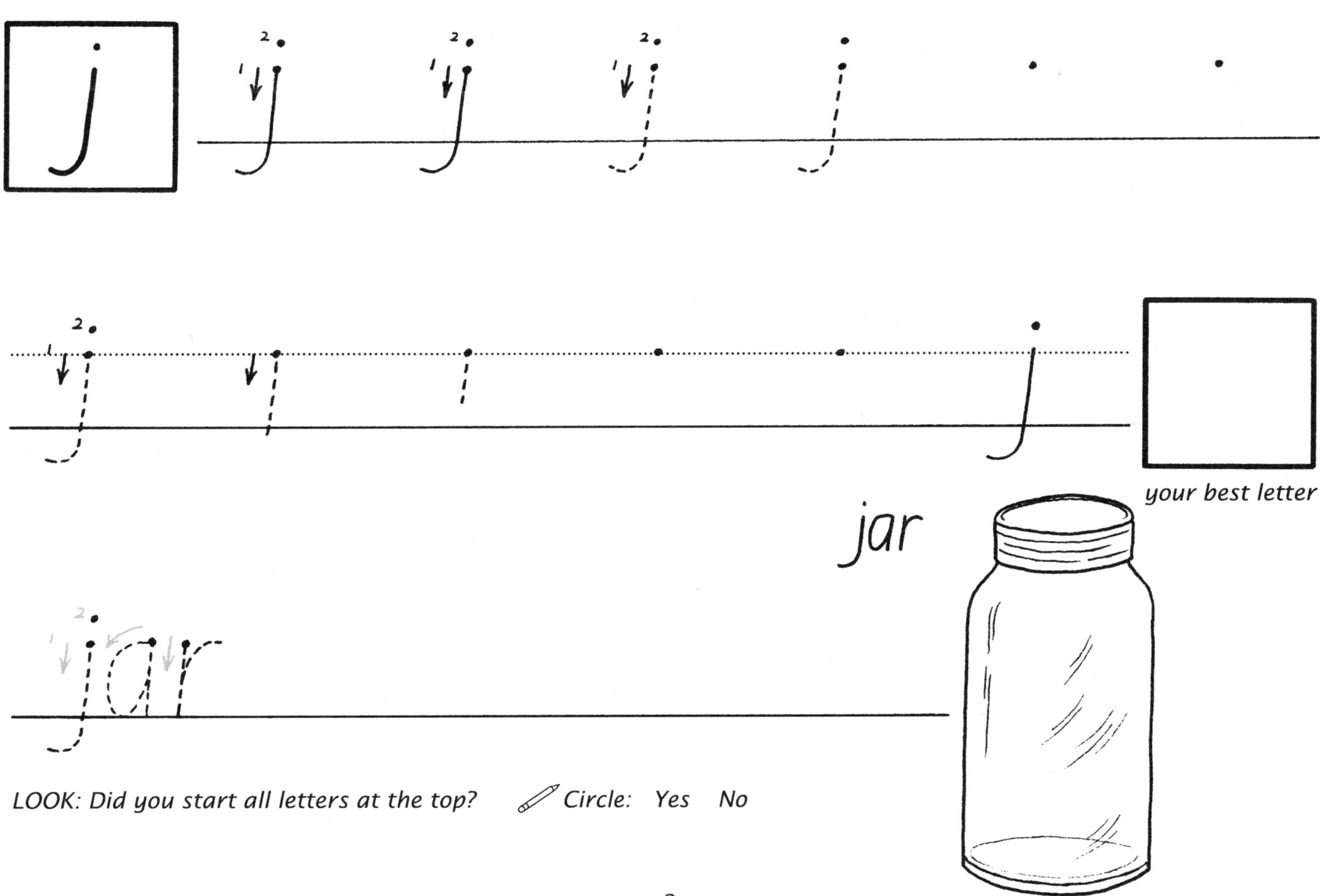

LOOK: Did you start all letters at the top?   Circle: Yes   No

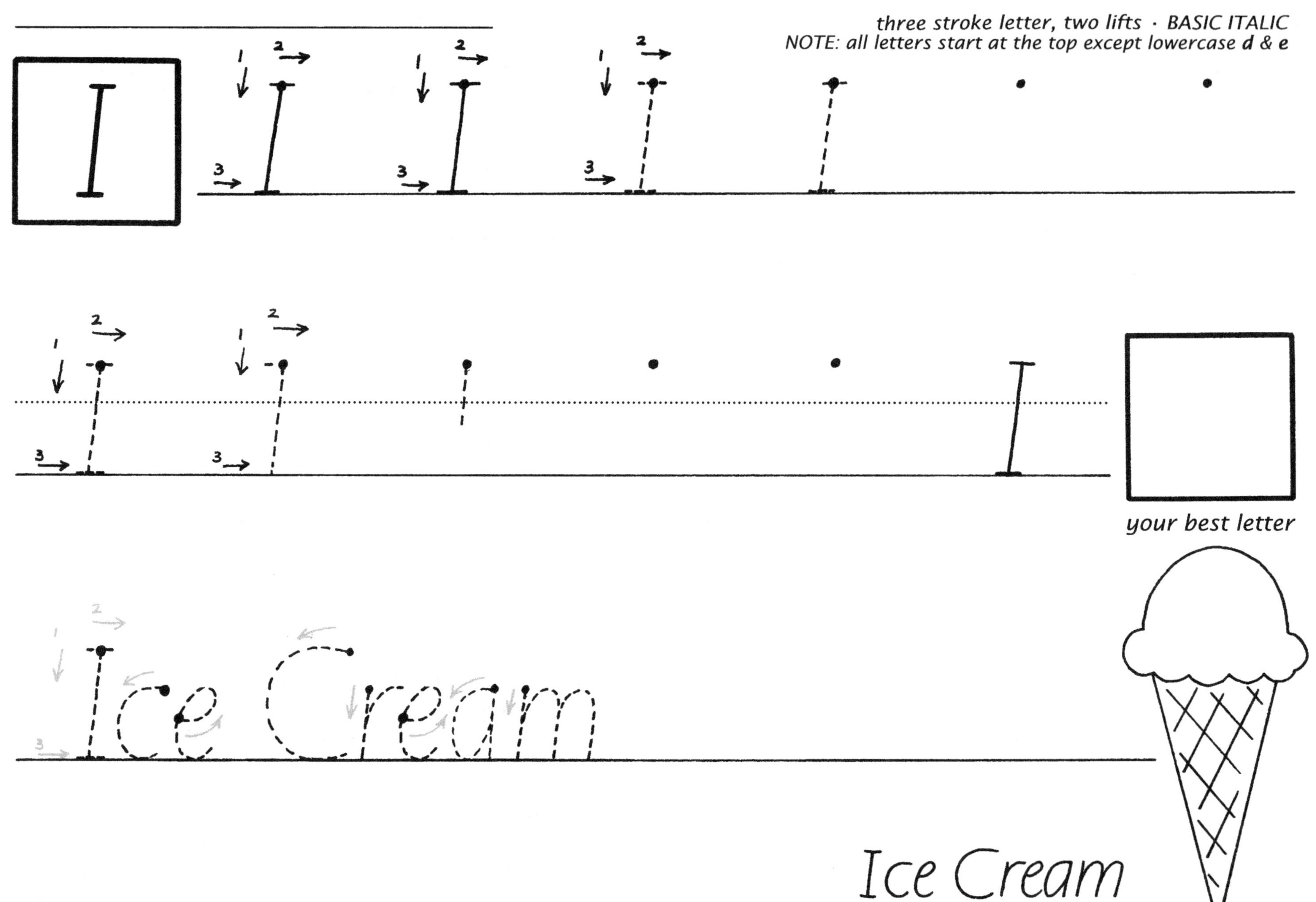

I
your best letter
Ice Cream

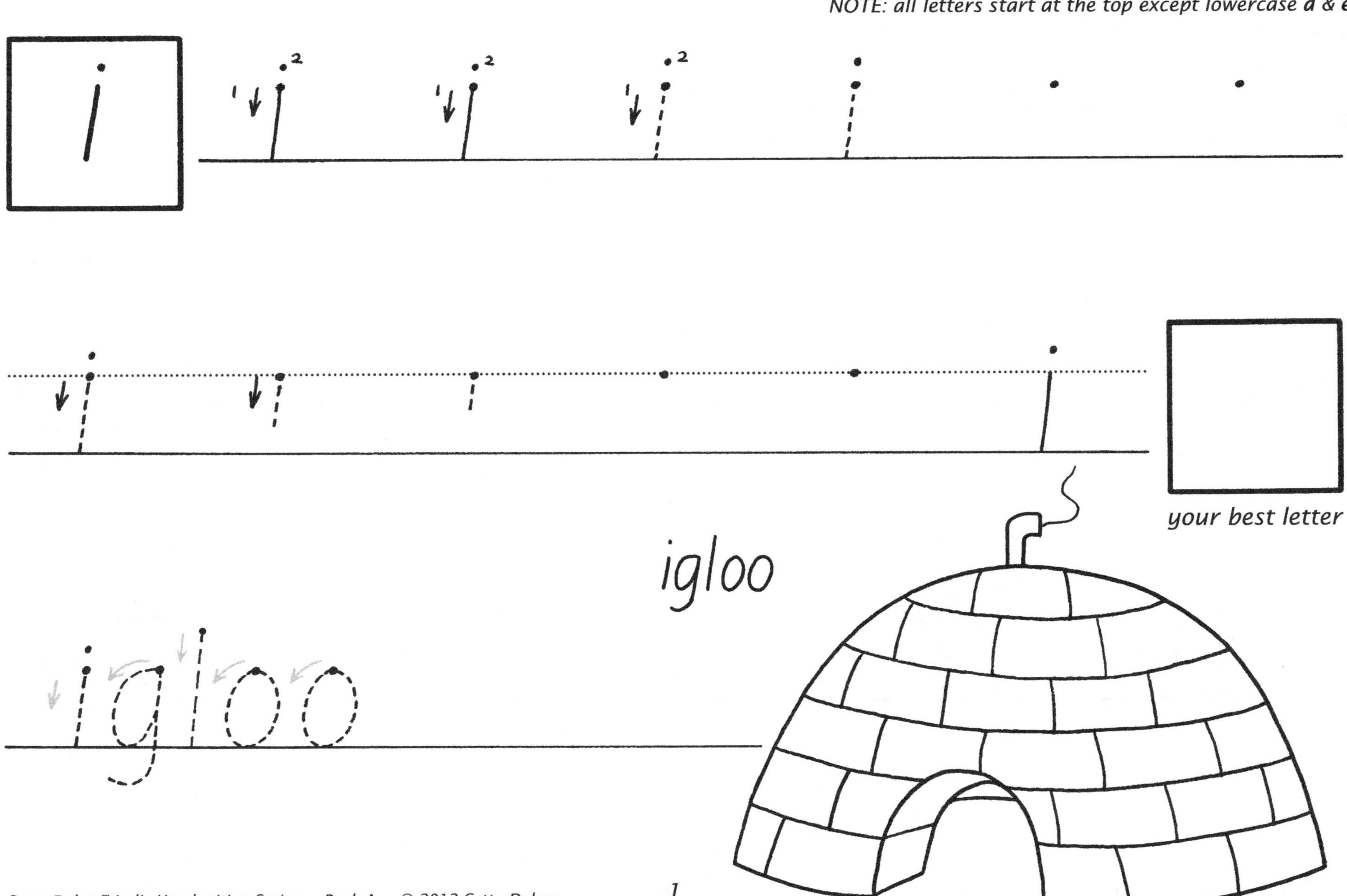

your best letter

igloo

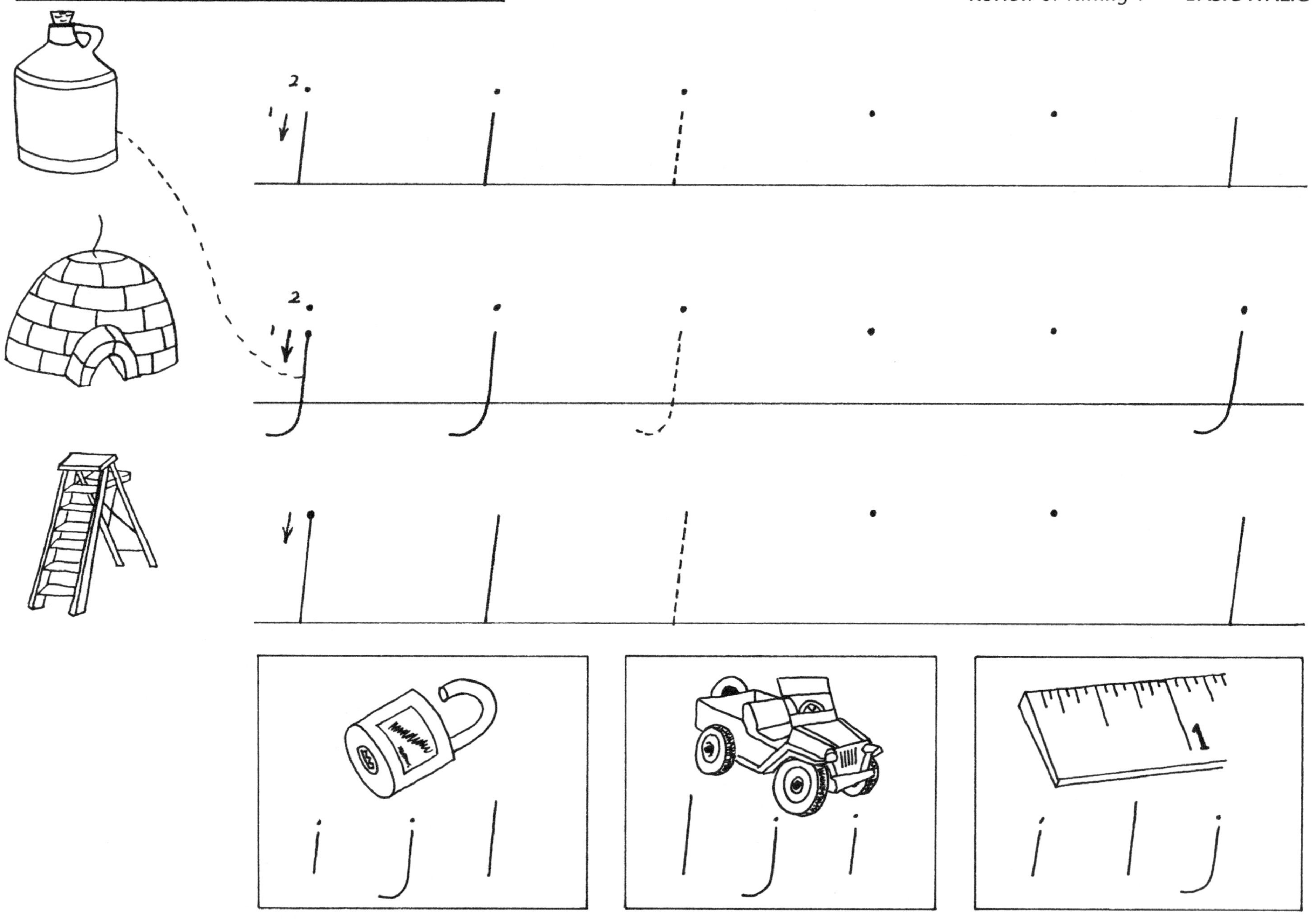

TOP THREE LINES: *Ask the student to draw a line from the picture to the letter that stands for the correct beginning sound.*

BOTTOM THREE BOXES: *Ask the student to circle the letter that stands for the beginning sound of the picture.*

Getty-Dubay™ Italic Handwriting Series · Book A · © 2012 Getty-Dubay

BASIC SHAPES

Before the student begins writing in BOOK A, the authors recommend that the student practice the following shapes on unlined paper, one shape at a time. Allow the student to write each shape any size at first. Later, ask the student to write very large and very small forms of that same shape. We suggest the student also practice these shapes on a chalkboard and/or in cornmeal. (See INSTRUCTION MANUAL, "*Activity*," pp. 35 & 41.)

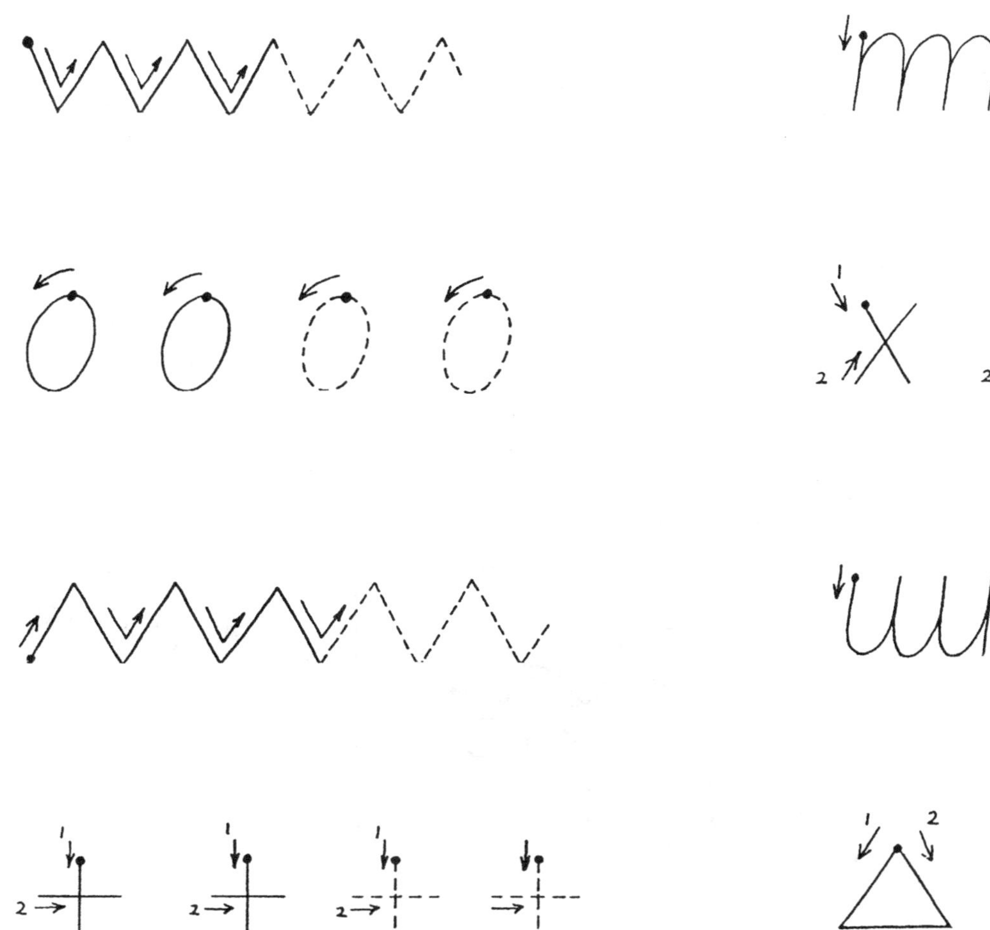

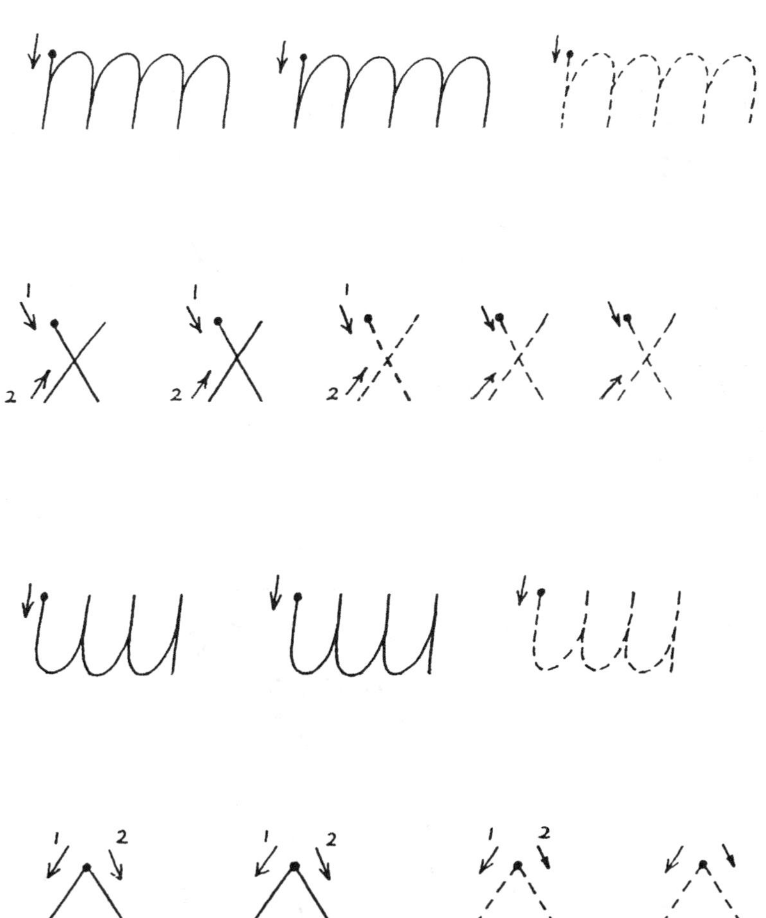

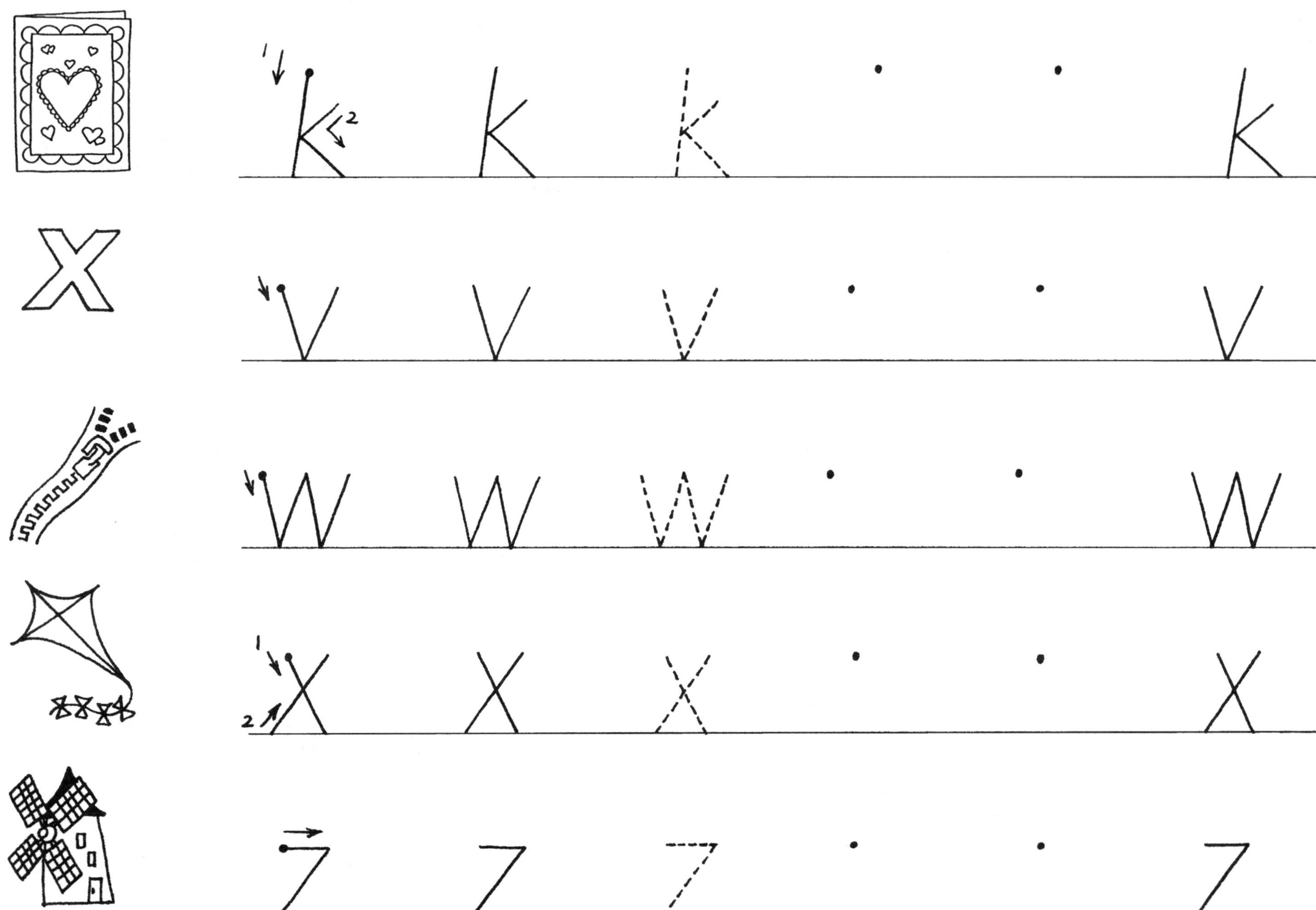

Ask the student to draw a line from the picture to the letter
that stands for the correct beginning sound.

Getty-Dubay™ Italic Handwriting Series · Book A · © 2012 Getty-Dubay

THE BEGINNING WRITER

Learning how to write involves much more than learning to write letters. It is a sophisticated, complex process involving learning letterforms, learning how to space within and between words, and learning how to organize writing on a page. Research indicates that there exists an almost perfect correlation between measures evaluating the children's *awareness* of their fingers and the ability to *use* their fingers in precise manual skills.

Ways to determine manual ability

To assist young students increase awareness of their hands and fingers, and to help you, the teacher, evaluate students' manual skills, have your students perform these tasks:

1. Direct the students to touch each of their fingers to their thumb, in order, from the first to the little finger. (By the age of six years, most children should be able to complete this exercise using one or both hands at a time.)

2. Have the students connect two dots that are spaced approximately eight inches apart on a page. (Most children of five years can accomplish this. However, if the student draws beyond the second dot or draws an unusually shaky line when nearing the second dot, it may indicate potential deficiencies in handwriting skills.)

Ways to improve kinesthetic perception of the hands

1. Unstructured clay modeling facilitates a student's perception of his or her hands. Encourage the student to manipulate the clay in every possible way—squeezing, flattening, poking, making shapes, etc.

2. To heighten the student's perception of shape, use a box in which a variety of small objects are placed for the student to feel but not see.

   a. Ask the student to reach in the box and find an unseen object that matches the one he or she is looking at.

   b. Direct the student to locate in the box an object that you or another student has described.

   c. Ask the student to find two objects with similar characteristics— two fuzzy objects, two heavy objects, two small objects, etc.

3. Draw several circles on a sheet of paper. To determine the student's ability to aim the finger and hand and also to point, have the student place dots in the circles with a pencil, pen, or crayon. Vary the difficulty of this task by increasing or decreasing the size of the circles or increasing the rate at which the dots are made. (The student must be able to point at a given or imaginary point in order to begin the stroke of a letter.)

Ways to confirm hand-eye tracking skills

The ability to control continuous hand movements while drawing lines of varying difficulty is basic to handwriting. If you are able to detect problems as the student completes the following tasks and are able to obtain appropriate assistance for the student, subsequent difficulties may be avoided.

1. Demonstrate drawing parallel lines. Then direct the student to draw parallel lines of a given length, first at a relaxed pace then at a faster one.

2. Direct the student to draw two curved lines equal in distance from one another. Later require more difficult shapes that combine straight lines, angles, and/or curves.

3. Direct the student to connect numbered dots on a sheet of paper that require horizontal, vertical and lateral movements. Place the paper in front of the student, close to the dominant hand. Later, space the dots further apart and require the student to cross the midline of his or her body. This latter task may cause the neuro-logically challenged student some difficulty.

The above evaluative tasks may be of help in assisting the learning of handwriting and in discovering deficiencies.

(See INSTRUCTION MANUAL, p. 13, for more suggestions concerning the beginning writer.)

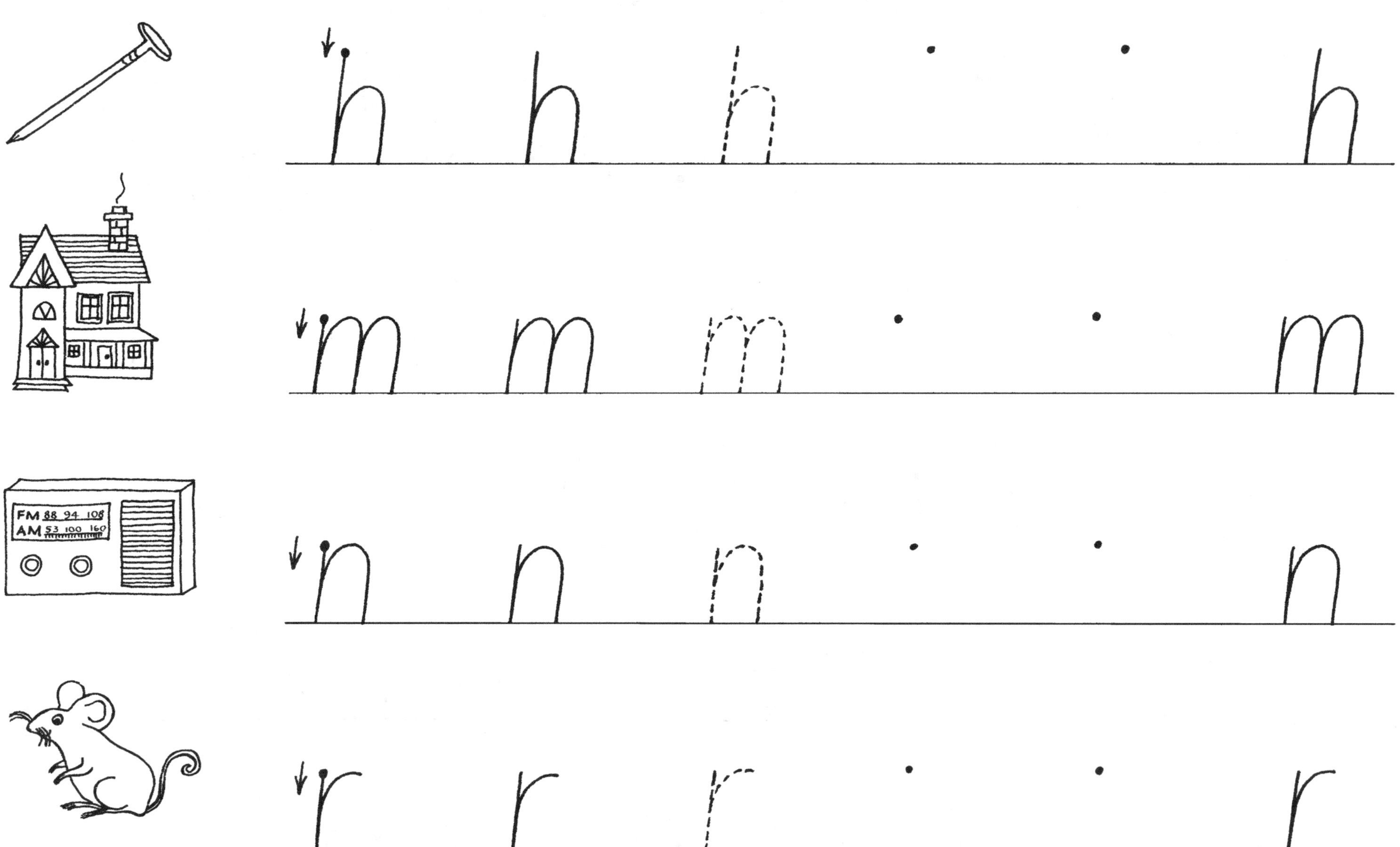

Ask the student to draw a line from the picture to the letter
that stands for the correct beginning sound.

BASIC ITALIC ALPHABET

All letters written in one stroke unless otherwise indicated.   *All letters start at the top except lowercase **d** and **e**.*

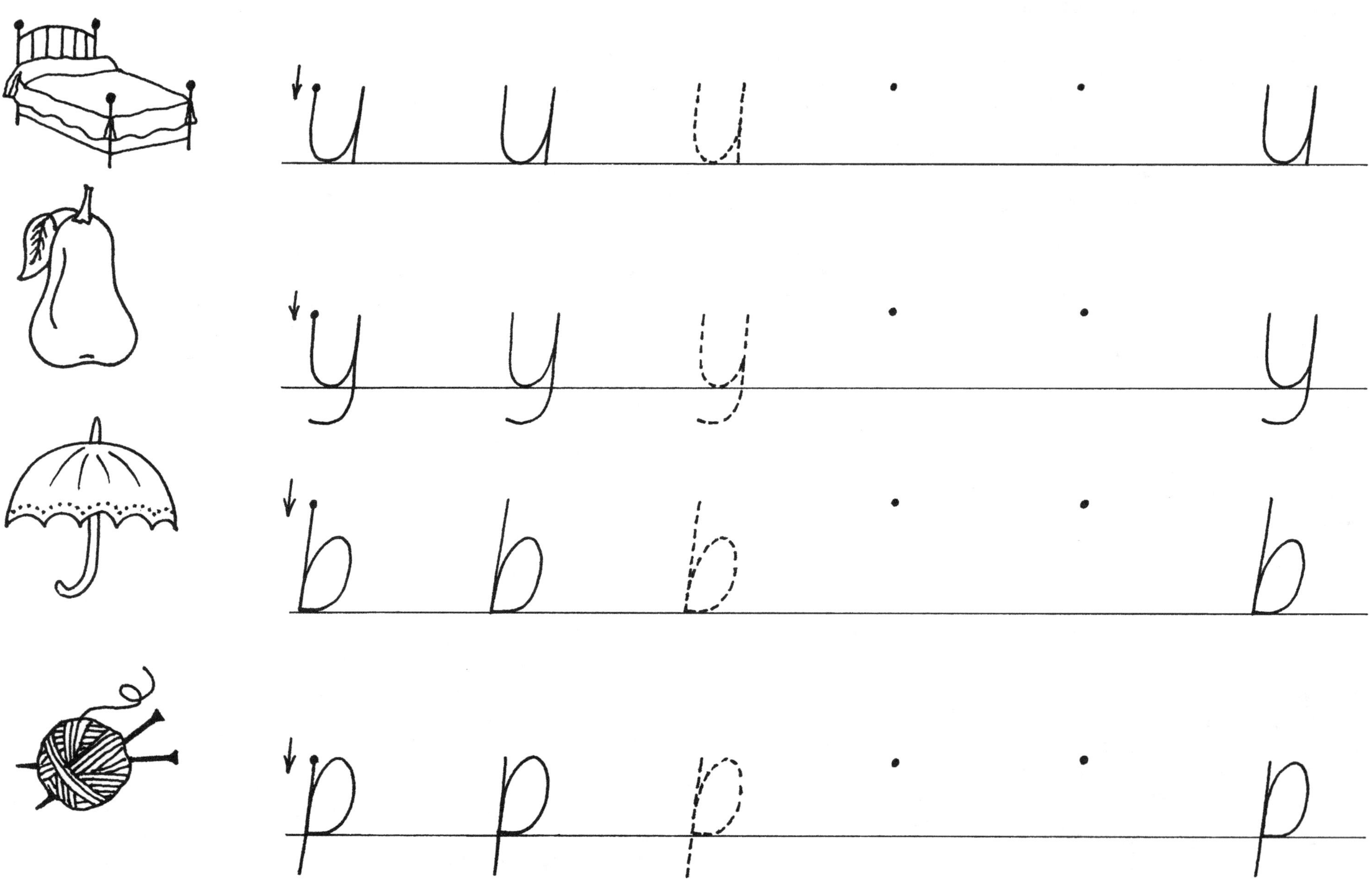

Ask the student to draw a line from the picture to the letter
that stands for the correct beginning sound.

GETTY-DUBAY™ HANDWRITING REMINDERS

PENCIL HOLD

Hold the pencil with the thumb and index finger, resting it on the middle finger. Rest the shaft of the pencil near the large knuckle. Hold the tool firmly and avoid pinching. To relax the hand, tap index finger on the pencil three times. Avoid "thumb wrap" and a "death grip".

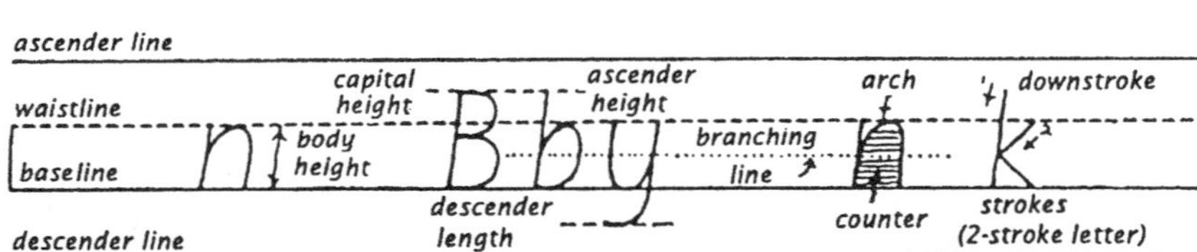

PAPER POSITION

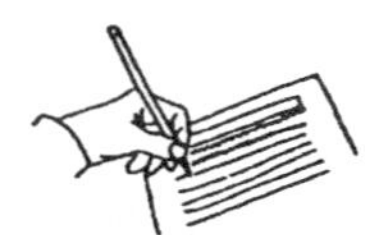

LEFT-HANDED: If the left-handed student writes with the wrist below the writing line, turn paper clockwise so it is slanted to the right, as illustrated.

If the left-handed student writes with a hook, with the wrist above the writing line, turn the paper counter-clockwise so it is slanted to the left, as illustrated. (Similar to right-handed position)

RIGHT-HANDED: If the student is right-handed, turn paper counter-clockwise so it is slanted to the left, as illustrated.

POSTURE

Rest feet flat on the floor and keep back comfortably straight without slumping. Rest forearms on writing surface. The student holds workbook or paper with the nonwriting hand so that the writing area is centered in the front of the student.

PRACTICE PAPER

Book A—Use unlined or lined paper together with workbooks.

MATERIALS

The *Getty-Dubay™ Italic Handwriting Series* workbooks, BOOKS A-G, and the INSTRUCTION MANUAL constitute a step-by-step program. Related materials consist of:

1. BLACKLINE MASTERS/WORKSHEETS - half sheets for introduction to, or review of, workbook pages.
2. CLASSROOM WALL CHARTS - basic & cursive italic.
3. DESK STRIPS - basic & cursive italic.

VOCABULARY

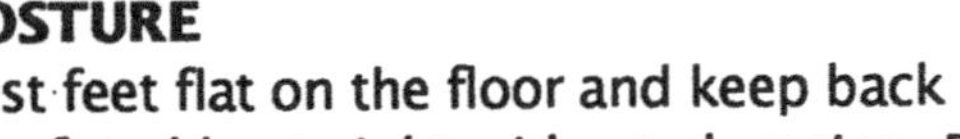
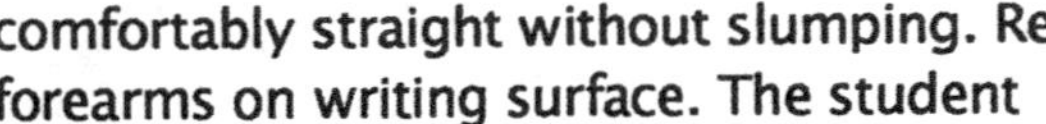
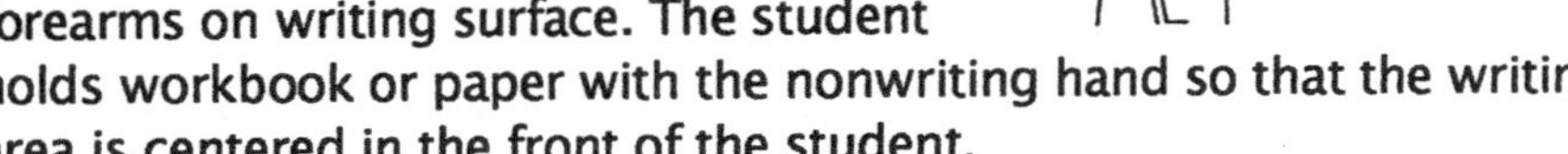

DIRECT INSTRUCTION

Several sessions of direct instruction each week are essential for a successful program. BOOK A – 5 to 10 minute sessions a day are recommended, see INSTRUCTION MANUAL, pp. 18-19

- SHAPE & STROKE SEQUENCE – teach basic italic in letter family groups, or according to the reading program in grade 1.
- SLOPE – encourage a consistent letter slope. Vertical letters (0° slope) may be the easiest to teach to beginning writers.
- SIZE – At first, allow students to write letters any size they wish on unlined paper, then introduce the workbook. A recommended progression through this book is one letter (lowercase and/or capital) per week.

SPACING

When young students are writing words, at first have them leave a space about the width of their two small fingers between words. As they become more proficient, they can leave less space.

ASSESSMENT

The *Getty-Dubay™ Italic Handwriting Series* provides a self-assessment process, LOOK, PLAN, PRACTICE, to enable the student to monitor progress. LOOK, step 1 of this process begins on some of the student pages in BOOK A. Assessment is the key to improving handwriting; in this book we introduce the first of three steps in the LOOK, PLAN, PRACTICE self-assessment process. The students look at their own writing and answer any questions on the page. The pencil indicates the student is to make a written response, generally by circling "yes" or "no". The teacher may encourage students to award themselves a star or a smiling face at the top of the page when they notice self-improvement.

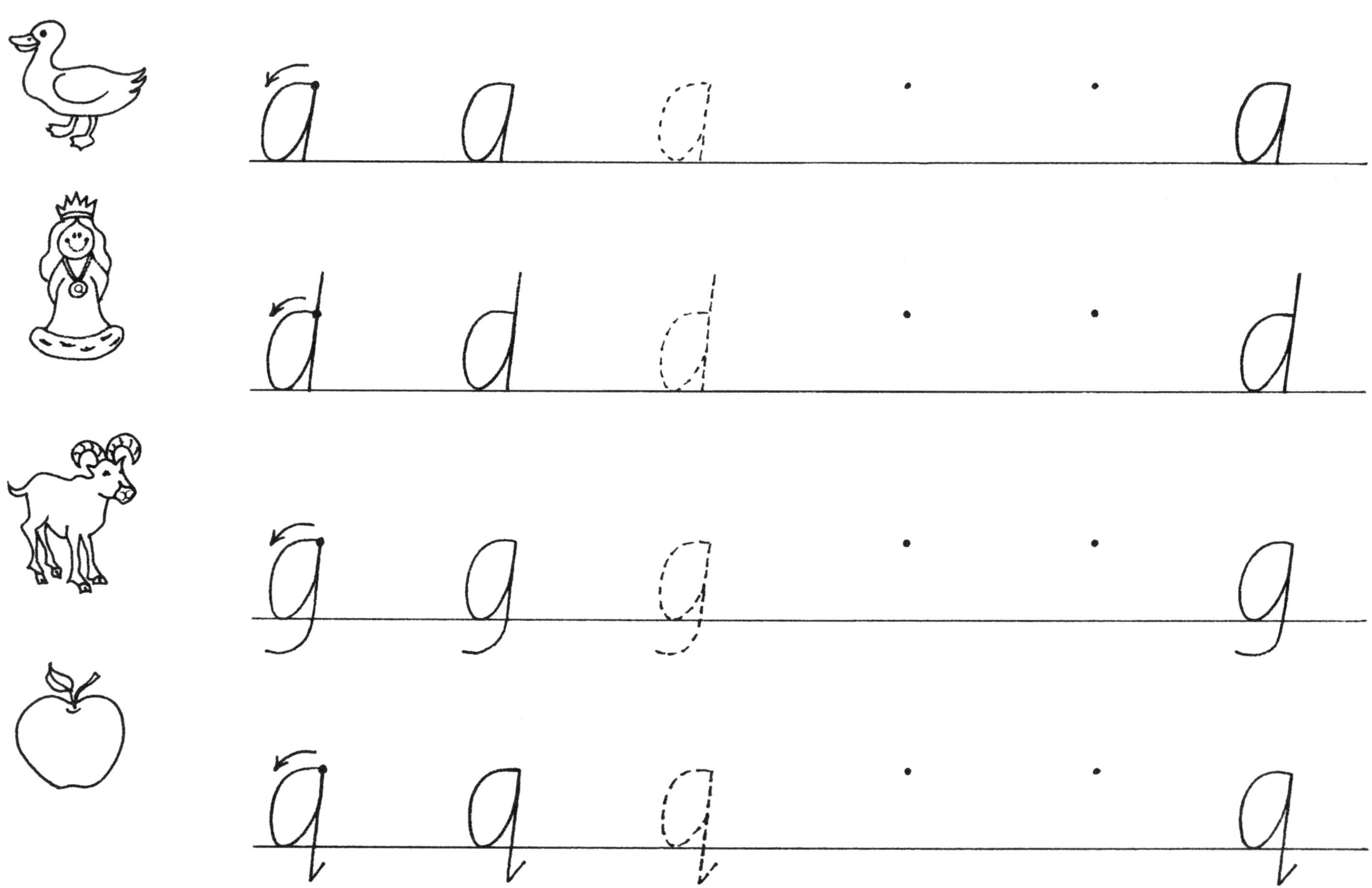

Ask the student to draw a line from the picture to the letter that stands for the correct beginning sound.

INTRODUCTION

This is the first of seven workbooks providing instruction in basic italic handwriting. It is designed for the beginning student of handwriting and is recommended for preschool, kindergarten and/or early first grade (5 to 7 years of age).

The twenty-six lowercase letters and the twenty-six capitals are introduced one letter per page. Letters are arranged in the order of lowercase families, which group letters with similar strokes together and progress from simple to more complex forms. The matching capital letter occurs on the reverse of each lowercase page allowing introduction of both lowercase and capital together if preferred.

Each page is designed for the student to trace the models provided, write letters at the given dots, and to write a "best" letter in the empty box on each alphabet page. The standard writing tool is the pencil although other writing instruments such as the fiber tip pen may be used. When students are ready, they should trace the word describing the illustration on each letter page, following the dots and arrows.

It is essential that the instructor provide an understanding of the dot and the arrow to assist the writer in completing the pages successfully. The self-assessment method used in the *Getty-Dubay™ Italic Handwriting Series* enables students to monitor their individual progress. Step 1, LOOK, of the three-step LOOK, PLAN, PRACTICE format, is incorporated on 21 of the student pages. Students are asked to "LOOK" at their writing and affirm what is best. On the 21 pages with "LOOK" questions, students should circle their chosen answers. See INSTRUCTION MANUAL, PP. 13, 18 & 19.

The *Getty-Dubay™ Italic Handwriting Series* INSTRUCTION MANUAL is to be used in conjunction with this workbook. Explanations and in-depth descriptions of lowercase letters, capitals, joins, and numerals are presented in the manual, emphasizing shape, strokes, size, slope and spacing of the letters. Also included in the manual are: a rationale for italic handwriting, techniques for teaching and assessing handwriting, sequence of skills, handwriting activities, and a brief history of our alphabet.

BOOK B, basic italic, follows this workbook and is designed for the beginning reader. In the third book, BOOK C, basic italic letterforms are reinforced and cursive italic is introduced. BOOKS D, E, F, and G provide a complete basic italic and cursive italic handwriting program. BOOKS B, C, and/or D may also be suitable for the person learning English as a second language.

The format of this book was chosen to accommodate both the left- and right-handed writer. When open, the book fits easily on a small desk, and the writer is not encumbered with an additional page to the left or right. From day one, use a Getty-Dubay™ basic italic desk strip as a reminder. Blackline masters are designed for supplementary practice and are available for each workbook in the series. See www.handwritingsuccess.com for these supplementary materials.

You can guide children toward the challenge and delight in the writing process by reading to them, modeling handwriting, providing writing materials, and especially by building enthusiasm for the letters of our alphabet and for the written word.

·abcdefghijklmnopqrstuvwxyz·

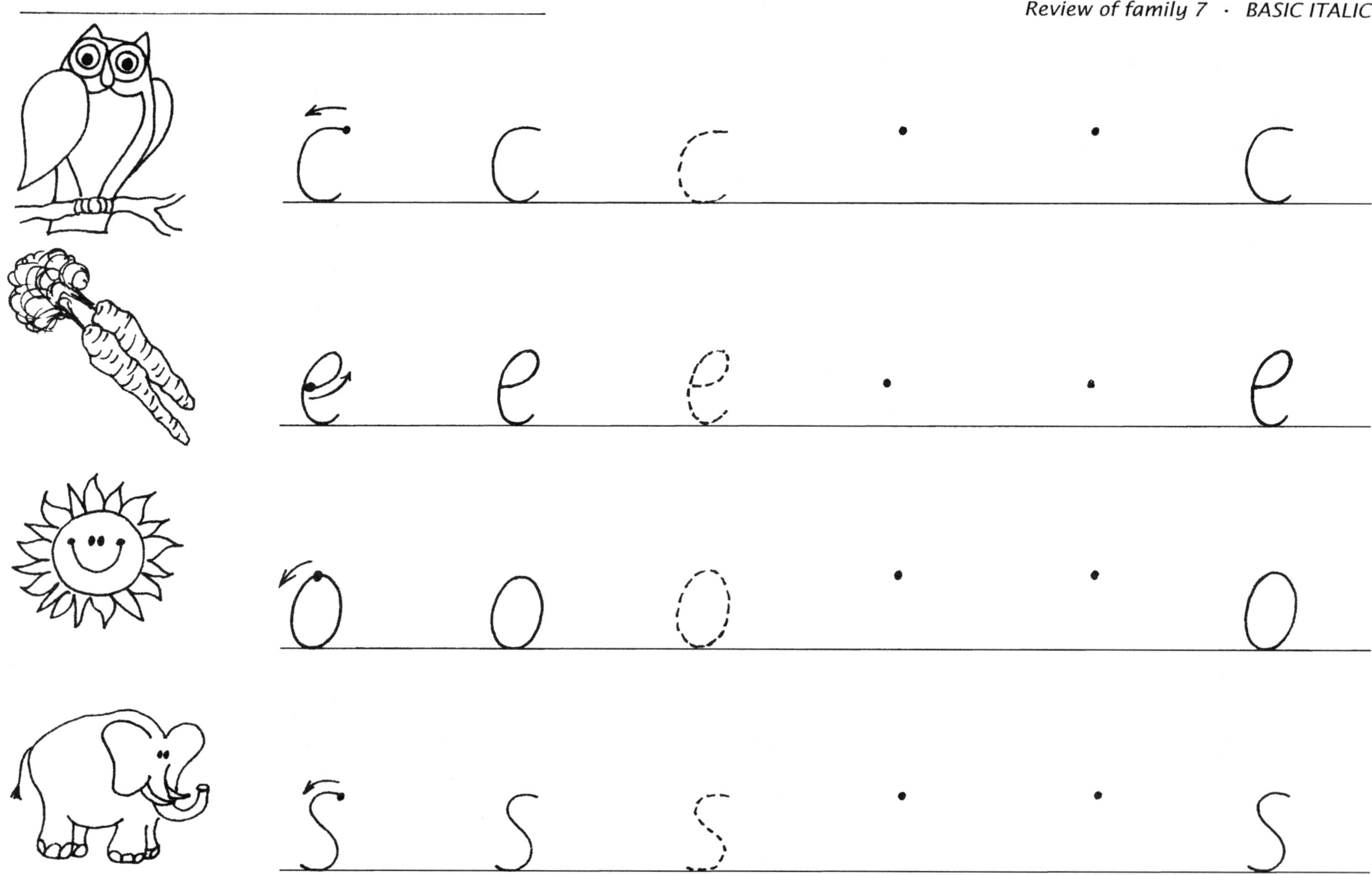

Ask the student to draw a line from the picture to the letter
that stands for the correct beginning sound.

CONTENTS

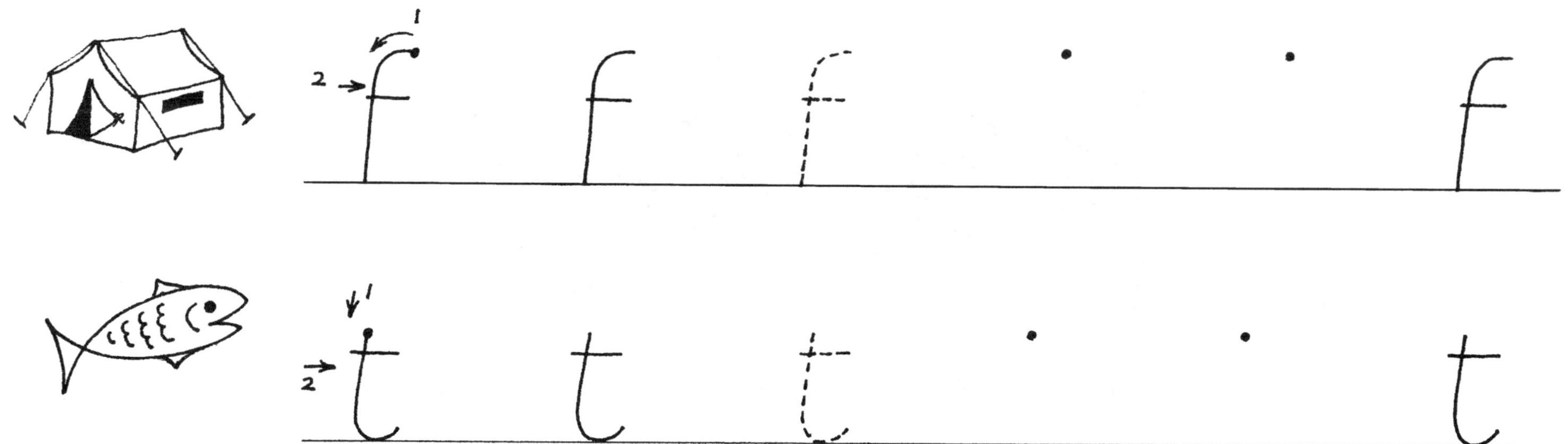

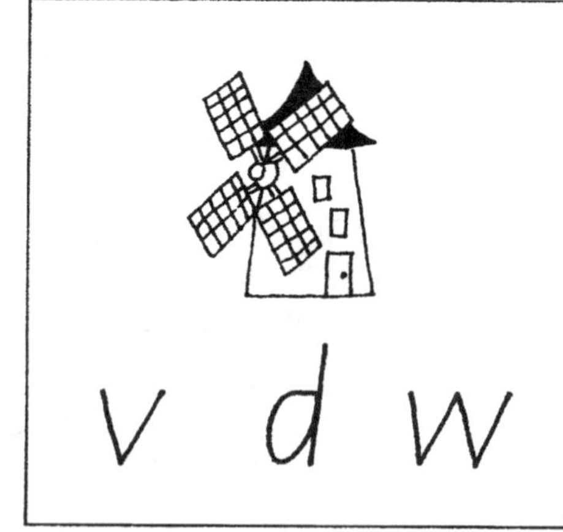

*TOP TWO LINES: Ask the student to draw a line from the picture
to the letter that stands for the correct beginning sound.*

*BOTTOM FOUR SQUARES: Ask the student to circle the letter that
stands for the beginning sound of the picture.*

by

Barbara Getty & Inga Dubay

GETTY-DUBAY™ ITALIC HANDWRITING SERIES

BOOK A ▪ Basic Italic
14 mm body height

BOOK B ▪ Basic Italic
11 mm body height, 9 mm

BOOK C ▪ Basic & Cursive Italic
9 mm, 6 mm body height   Introduction to Cursive Italic

BOOK D ▪ Basic & Cursive Italic
6 mm, 5 mm body height

BOOK E ▪ Basic & Cursive Italic
6 mm, 5 mm, 4 mm body height

BOOK F ▪ Basic & Cursive Italic
6 mm, 5 mm, 4 mm body height

BOOK G ▪ Basic & Cursive Italic
5 mm, 4 mm body height

INSTRUCTION MANUAL

BOOK A ▪ INTERNATIONAL EDITION

Copyright 2012 by Barbara M. Getty and Inga S. Dubay
ISBN 978-0-9827762-7-8

FOURTH EDITION
Copyright 2012 by Barbara M. Getty and Inga S. Dubay
THIRD EDITION
Copyright 1999 by Barbara M. Getty and Inga S. Dubay
SECOND EDITION
Copyright 1986 by Barbara M. Getty and Inga S. Dubay
REVISED EDITION
Copyright 1980 by Barbara M. Getty and Inga S. Dubay
FIRST EDITION
Copyright 1979 by Barbara M. Getty and Inga S. Dubay

All rights reserved. This text may not be reproduced in whole or in part without the express written permission of the copyright holder.

Published by Handwriting Success, LLC,
Portland, Oregon USA

www.handwritingsuccess.com

Printed at various locations around the world by IngramSpark.

Cover Design: Sinda Markham
Front cover picture: Flowers of the sunflower family in the Ochoco National Forest, Oregon, USA
Back cover pictures: Columbine flower, Golden-mantled squirrel

www.ingramcontent.com/pod-product-compliance
Lightning Source LLC
Chambersburg PA
CBHW081423210726
48464CB00020B/1370

six

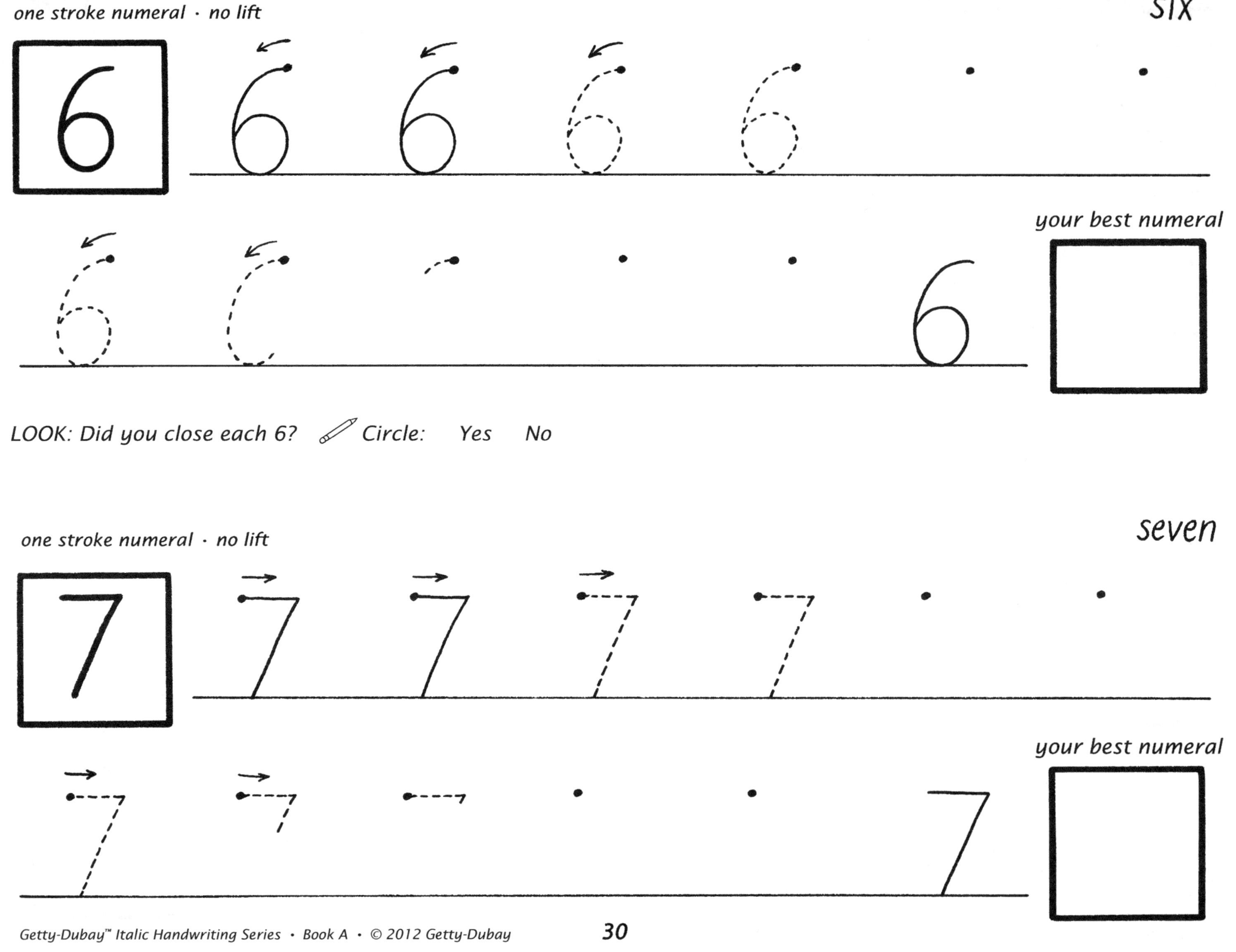

your best numeral

LOOK: Did you close each 6? Circle: Yes   No

one stroke numeral · no lift

seven

your best numeral

two stroke numeral · one lift
four
your best numeral

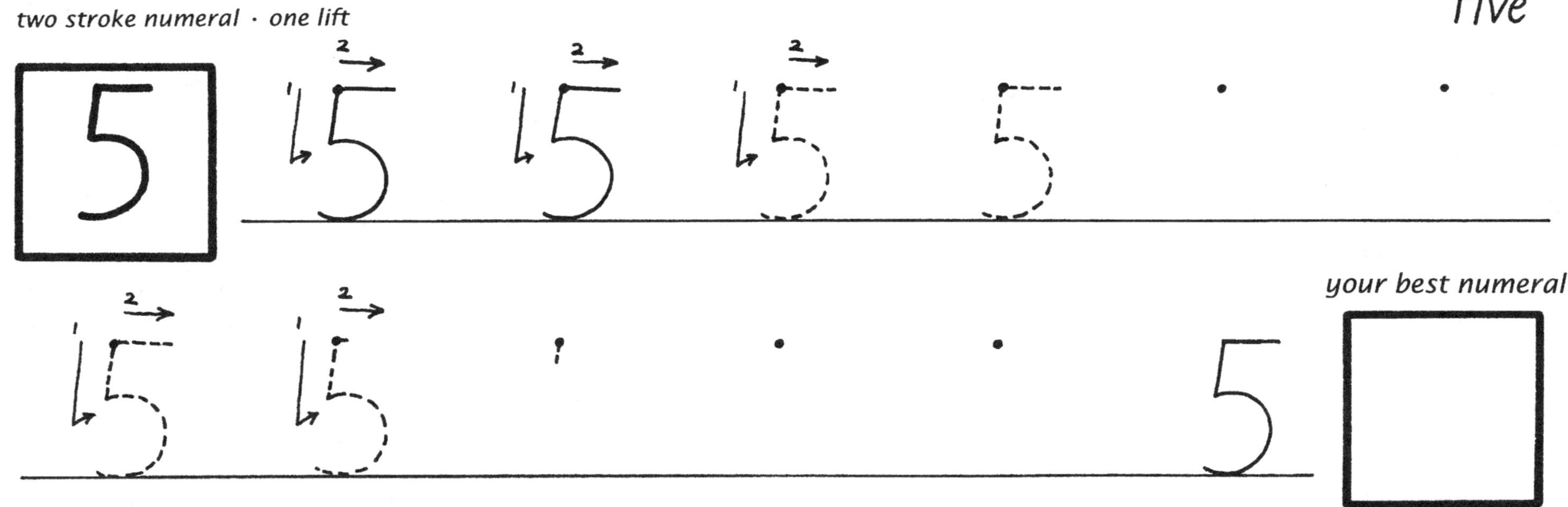

two stroke numeral · one lift
five
your best numeral

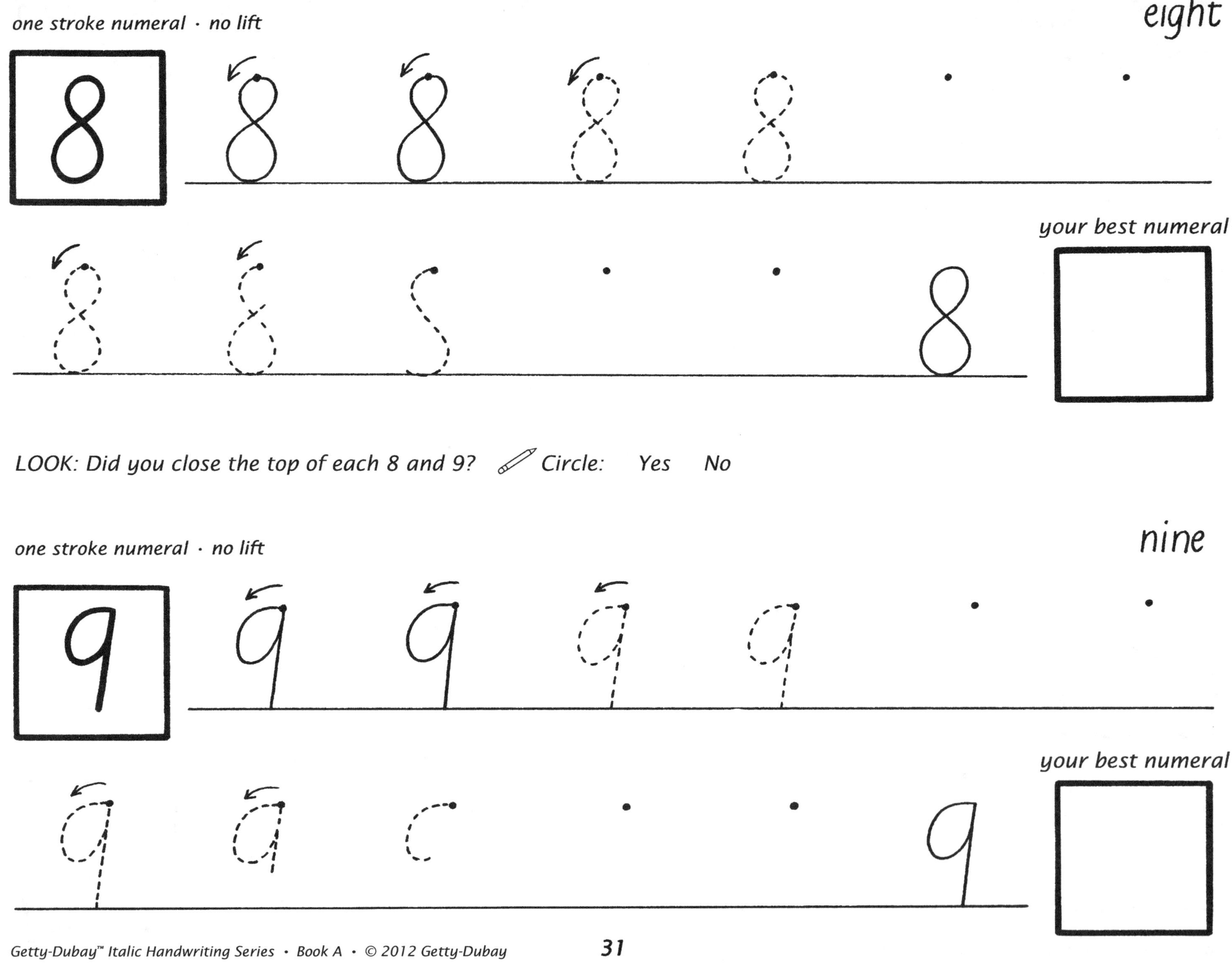

one stroke numeral · no lift

your best numeral

LOOK: Did you close the top of each 8 and 9?   Circle: Yes   No

one stroke numeral · no lift

nine

your best numeral

one stroke numeral · no lift

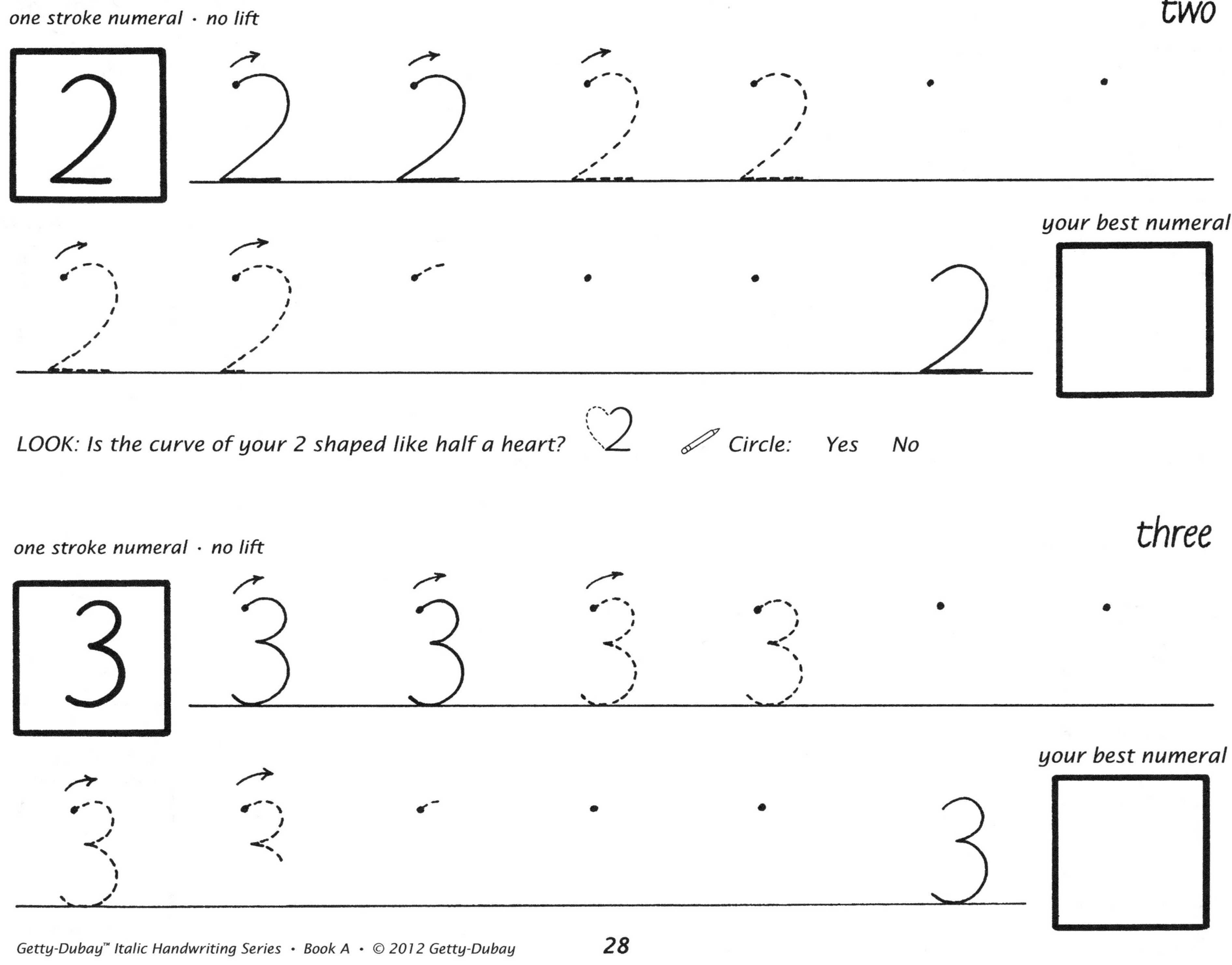

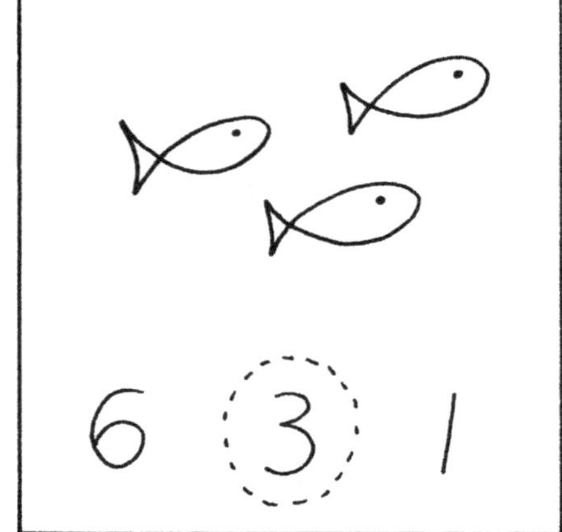

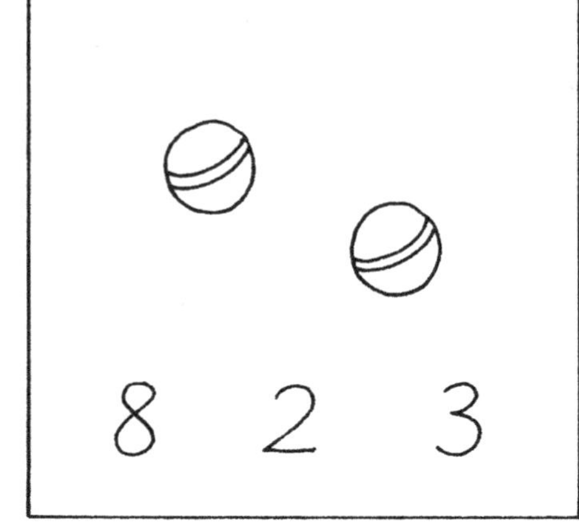

Ask the student to circle the numeral
that stands for the number of objects in the box.

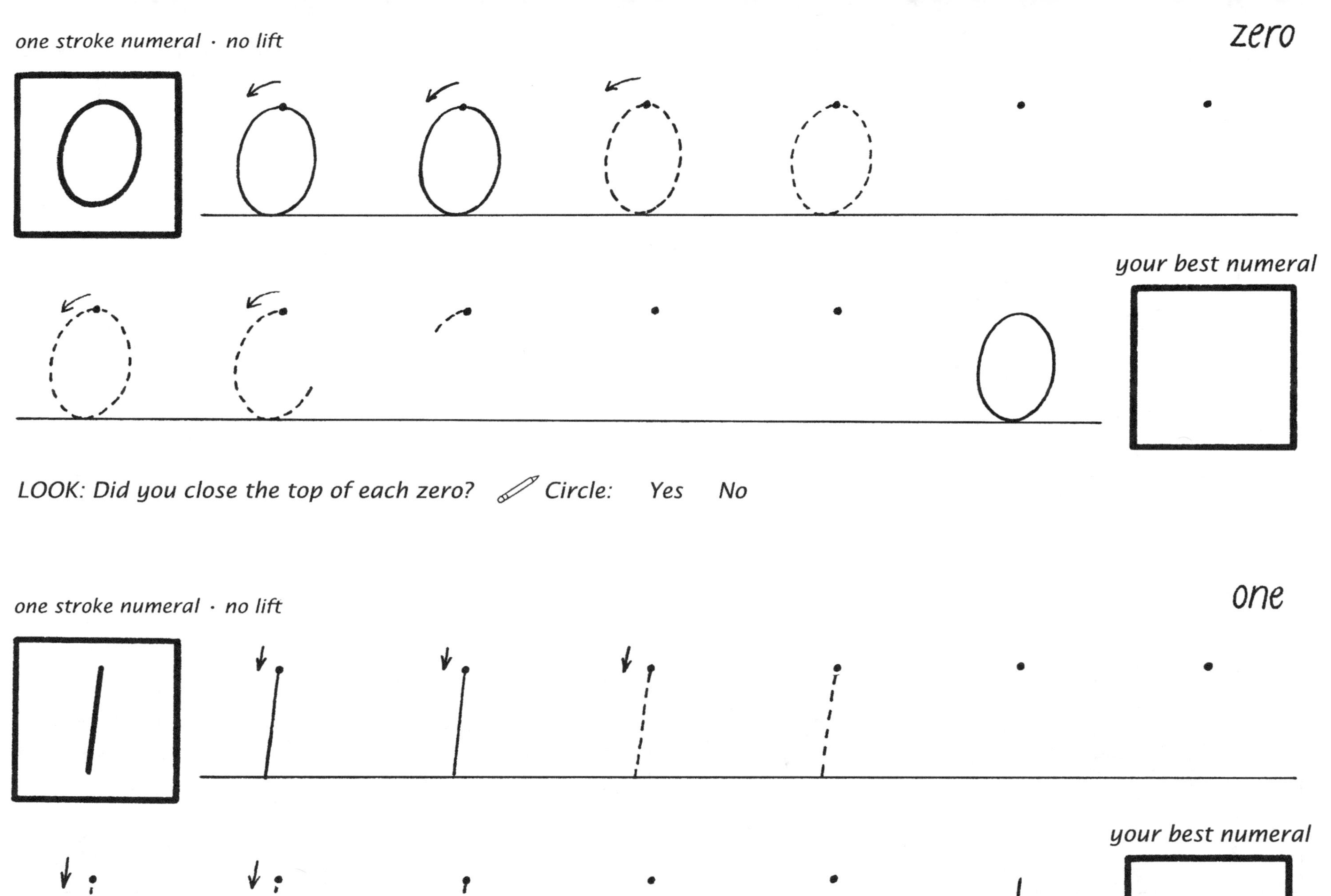

LOOK: Did you close the top of each zero?   Circle: Yes   No

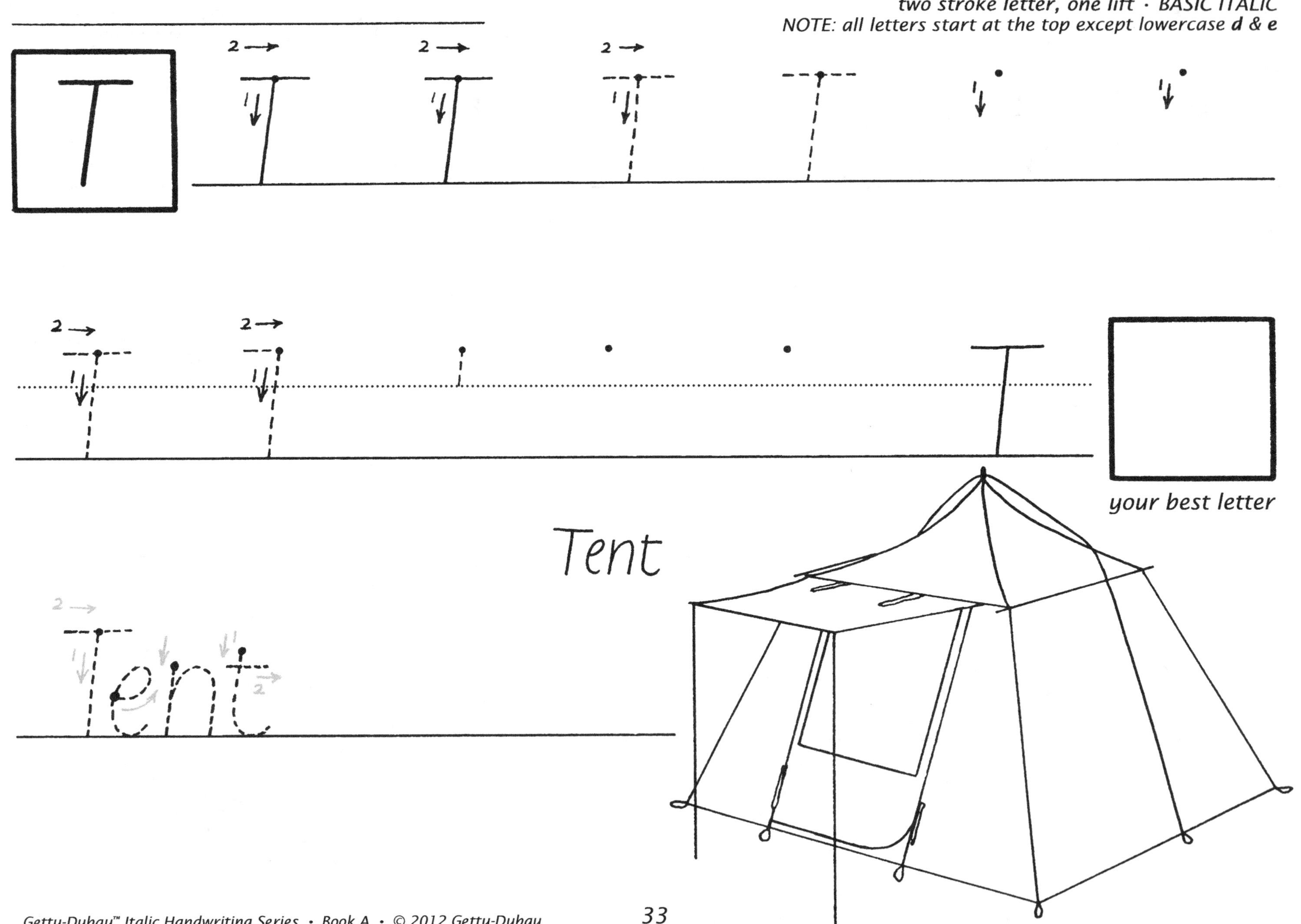

T
2→
2→
2→
2→
2→
your best letter
Tent
Tent

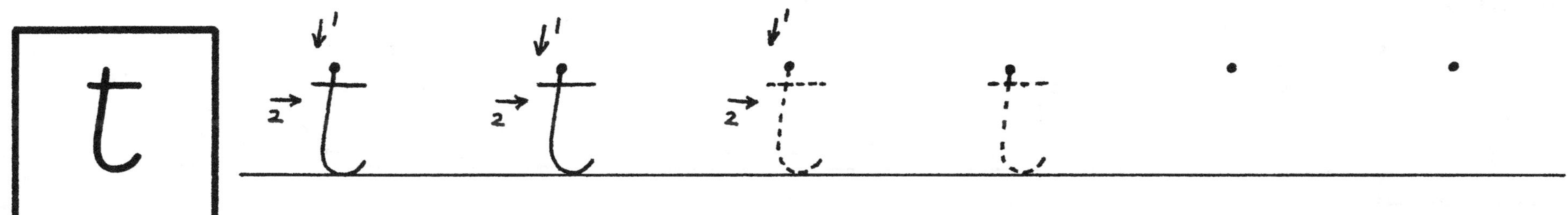

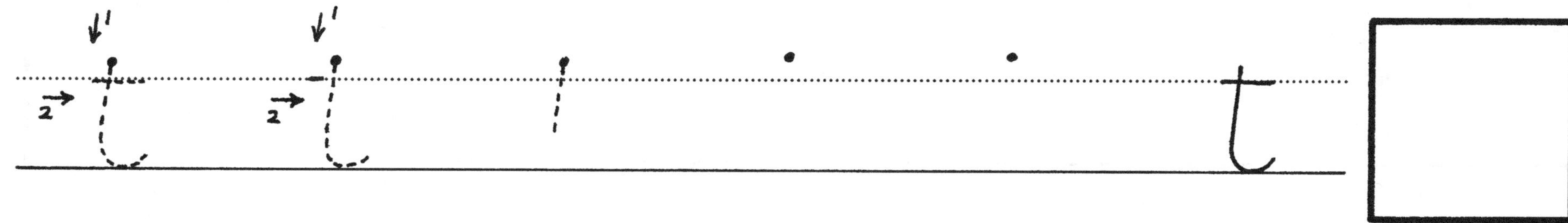

your best letter

turkey

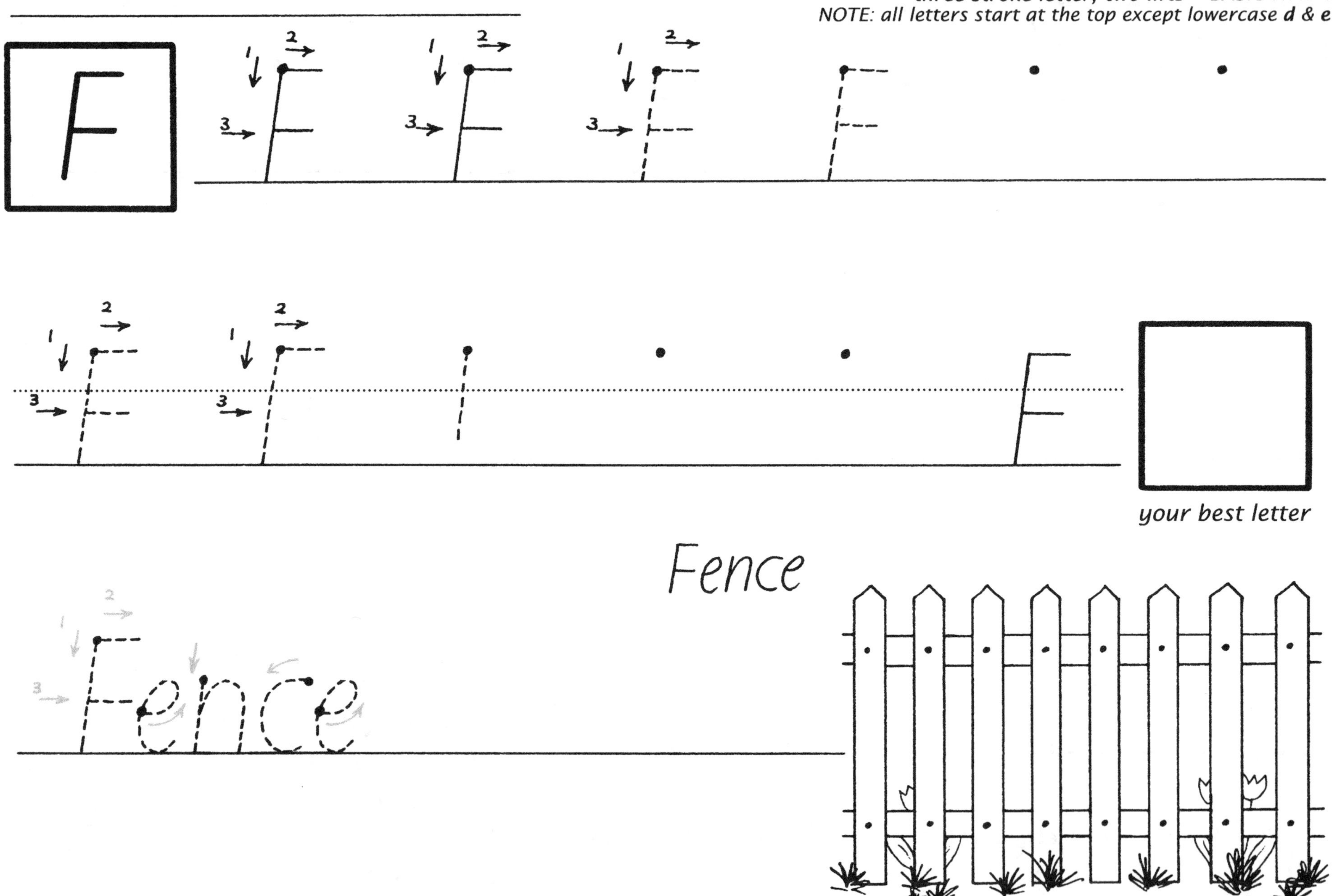

your best letter
Fence

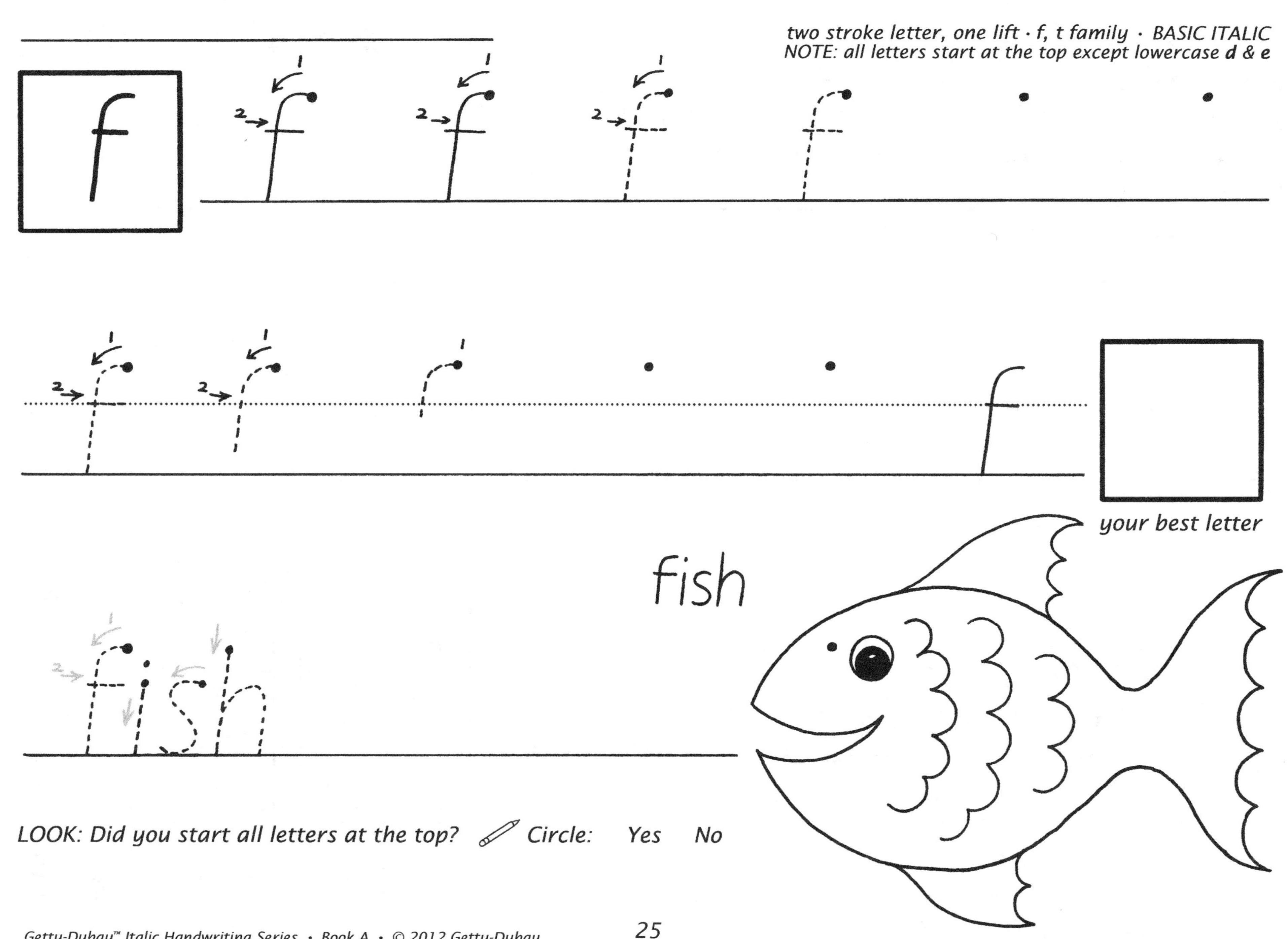

two stroke letter, one lift · f, t family · BASIC ITALIC
NOTE: all letters start at the top except lowercase d & e

your best letter

fish

LOOK: Did you start all letters at the top?   Circle: Yes   No

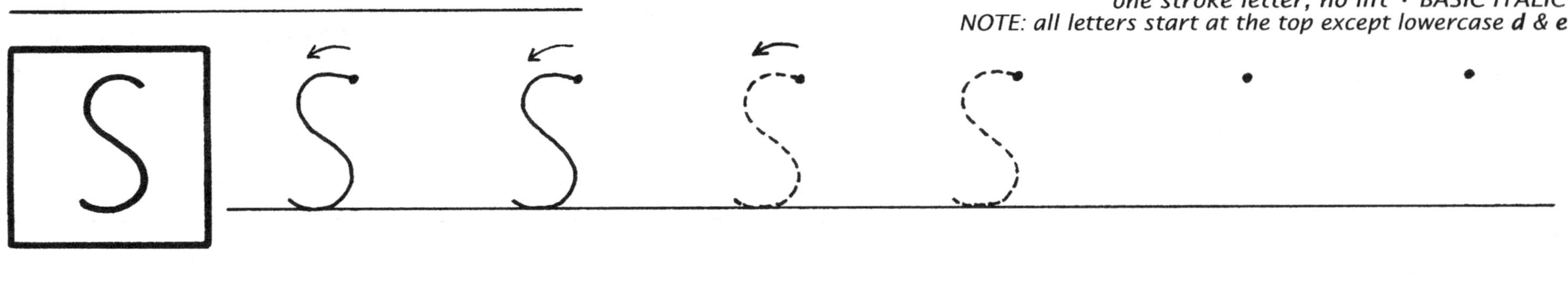

your best letter

Sailboat

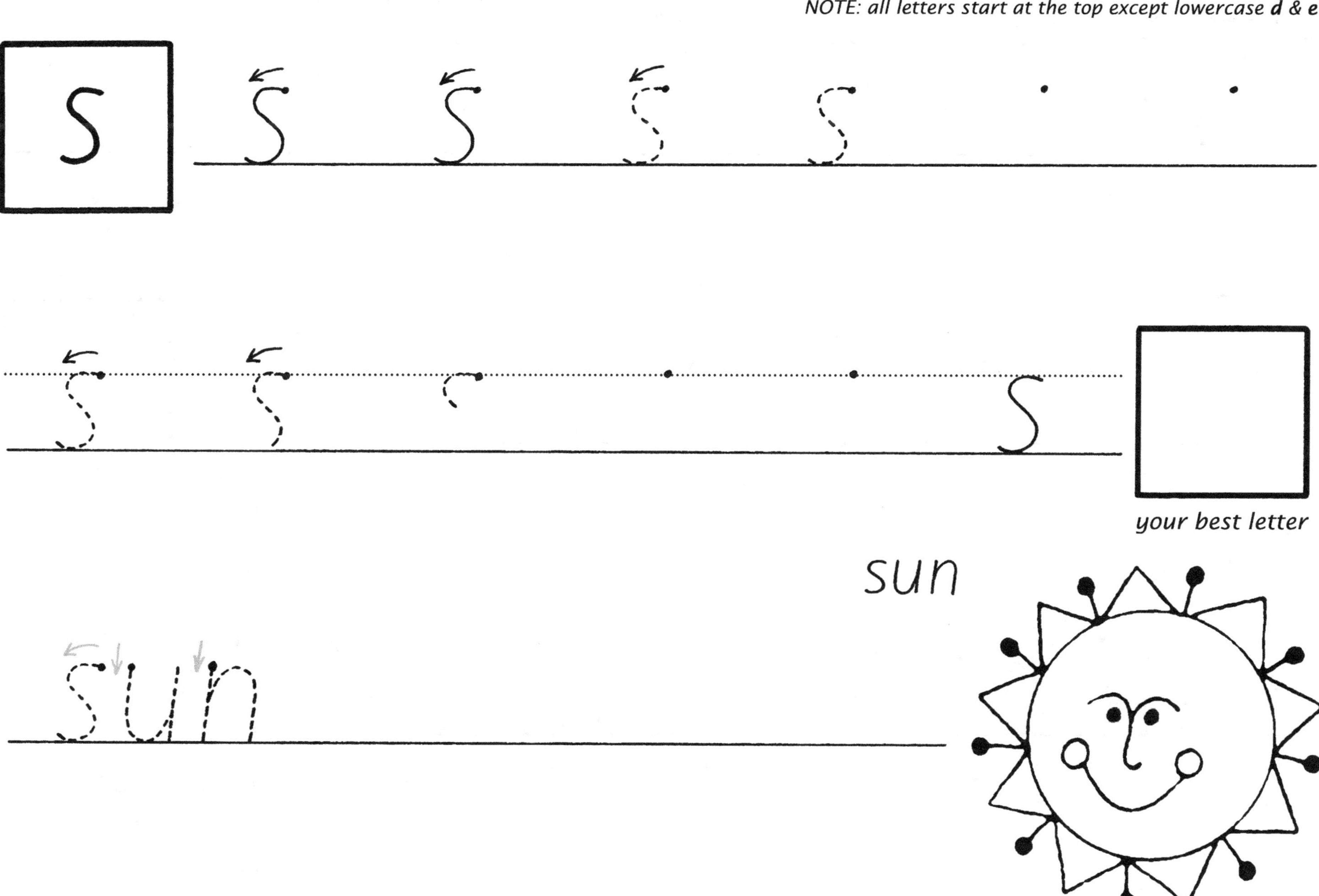

your best letter

sun

LOOK: Did you trace each letter before writing your own?

✐ Circle: Yes   No

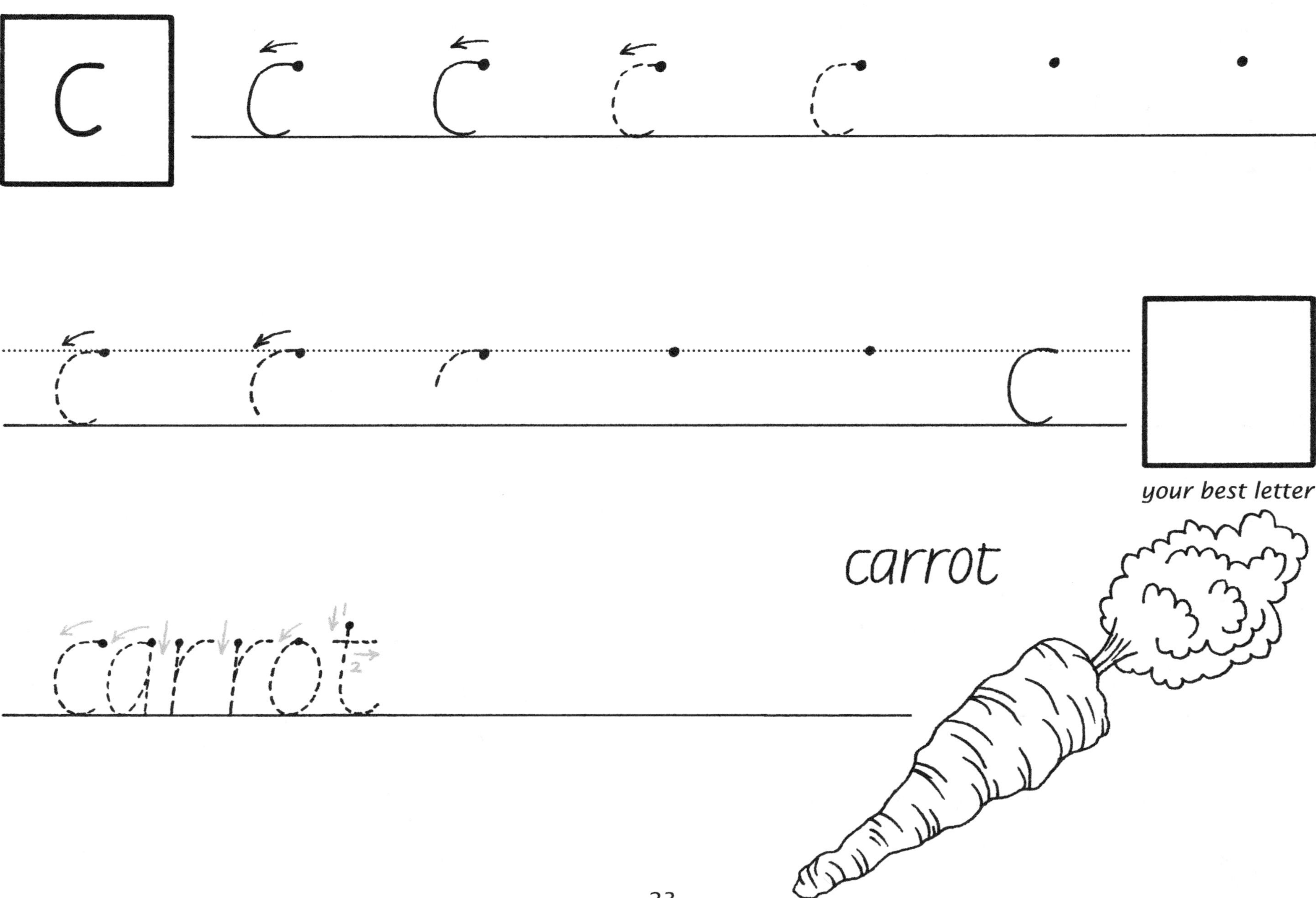

C
your best letter
carrot
carrot

E

your best letter

Egg

your best letter

elephant

LOOK: Did you trace each **e** before writing your own?

Circle: Yes   No

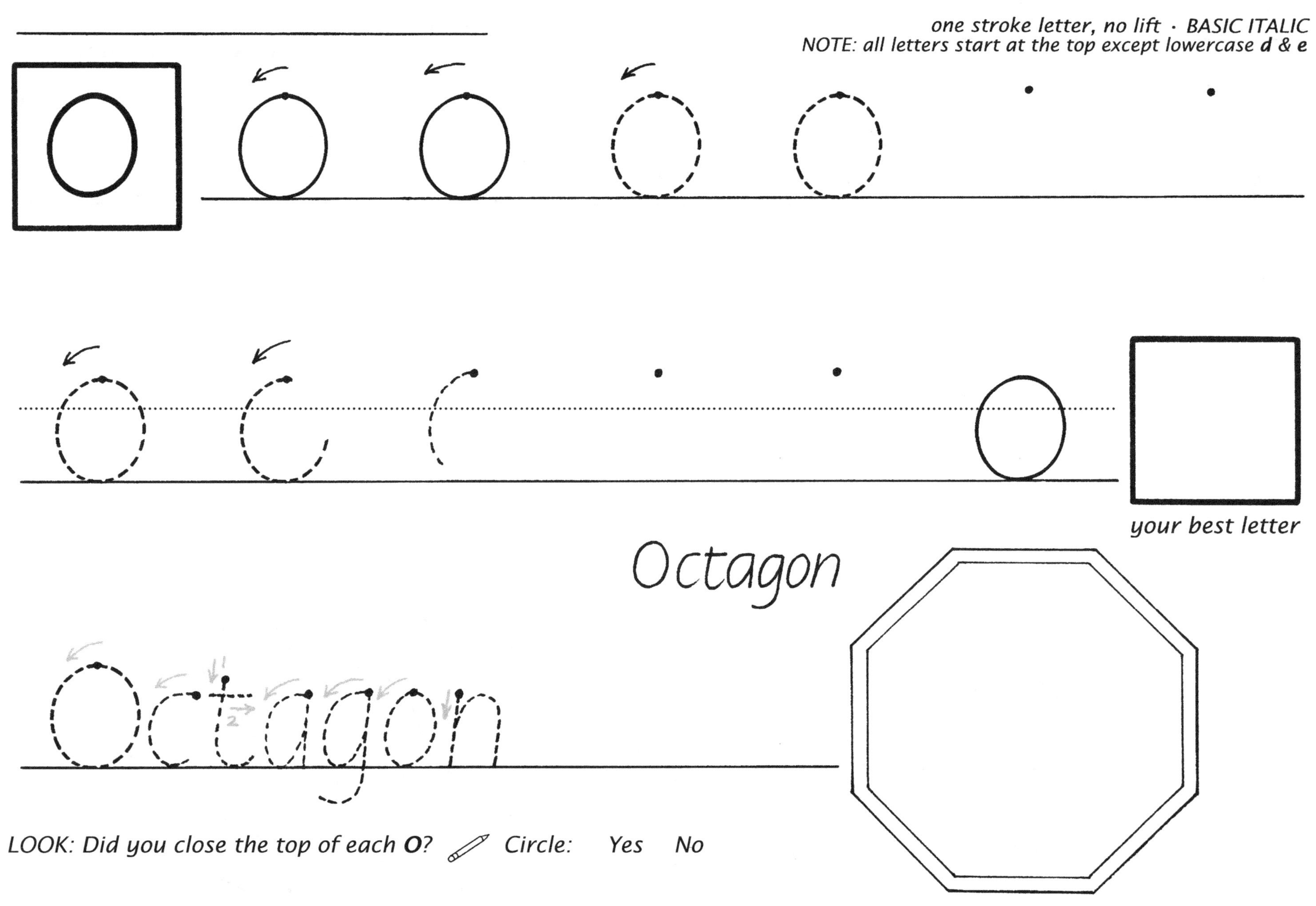

LOOK: Did you close the top of each **O**?   Circle: Yes   No

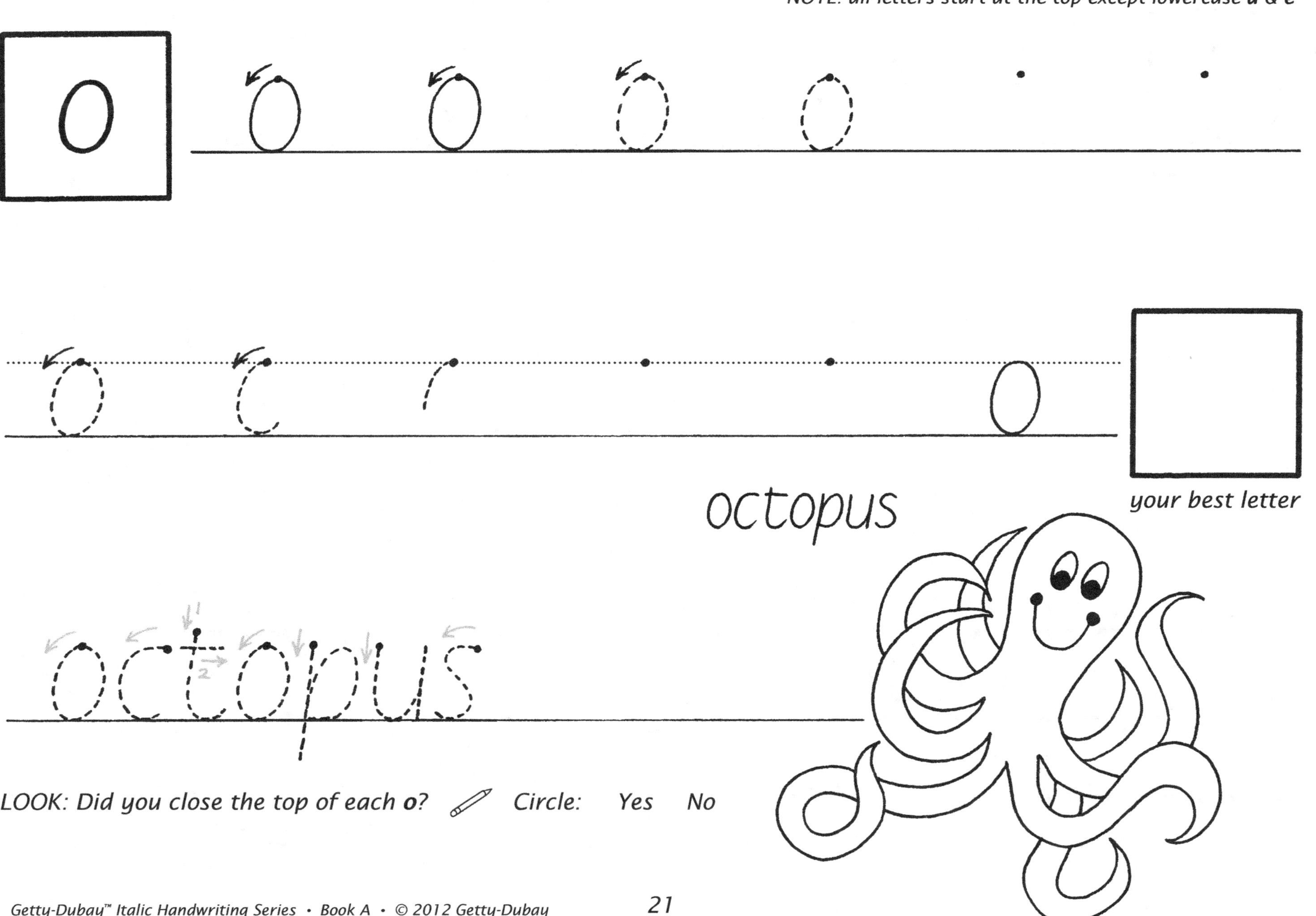

octopus

your best letter

octopus

LOOK: Did you close the top of each **o**? Circle: Yes   No

your best letter

Peacock

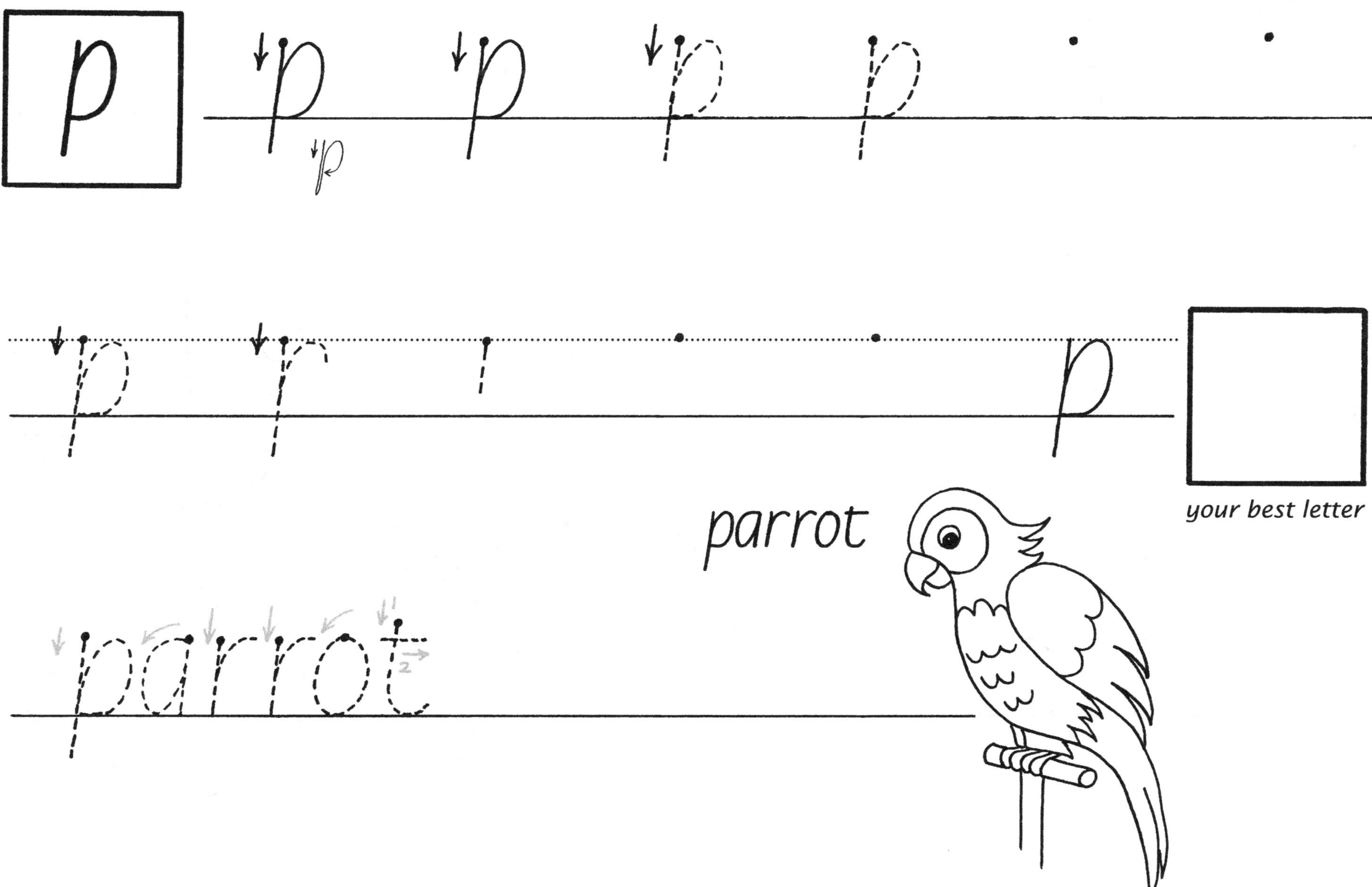

parrot

B

2
1

2
1

2
1

·

·

2
1

2
1

·

·

·

B

your best letter

Balloons

Balloons

your best letter

butterfly

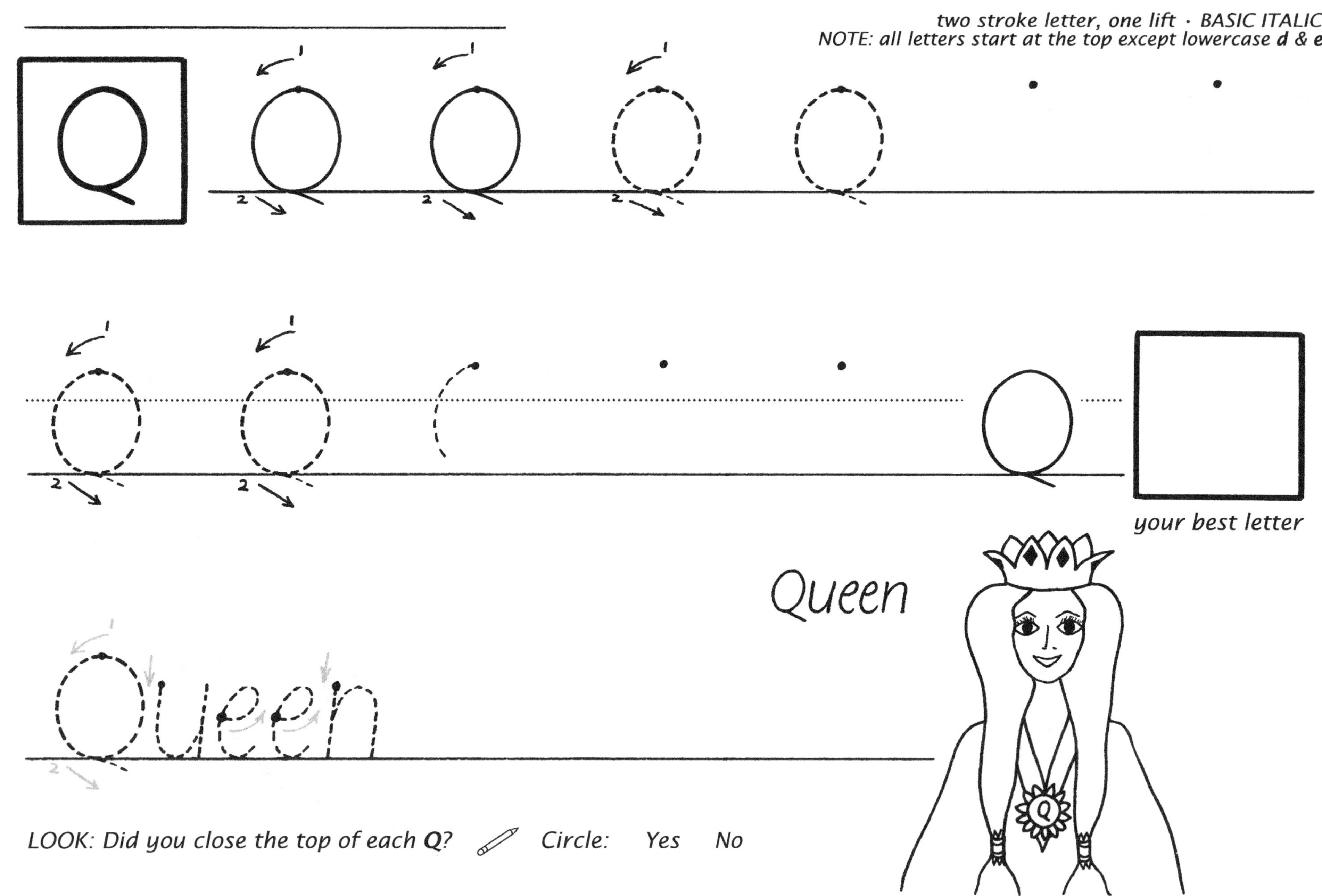

two stroke letter, one lift · BASIC ITALIC
NOTE: all letters start at the top except lowercase *d & e*

your best letter

Queen

LOOK: Did you close the top of each Q?   Circle: Yes   No

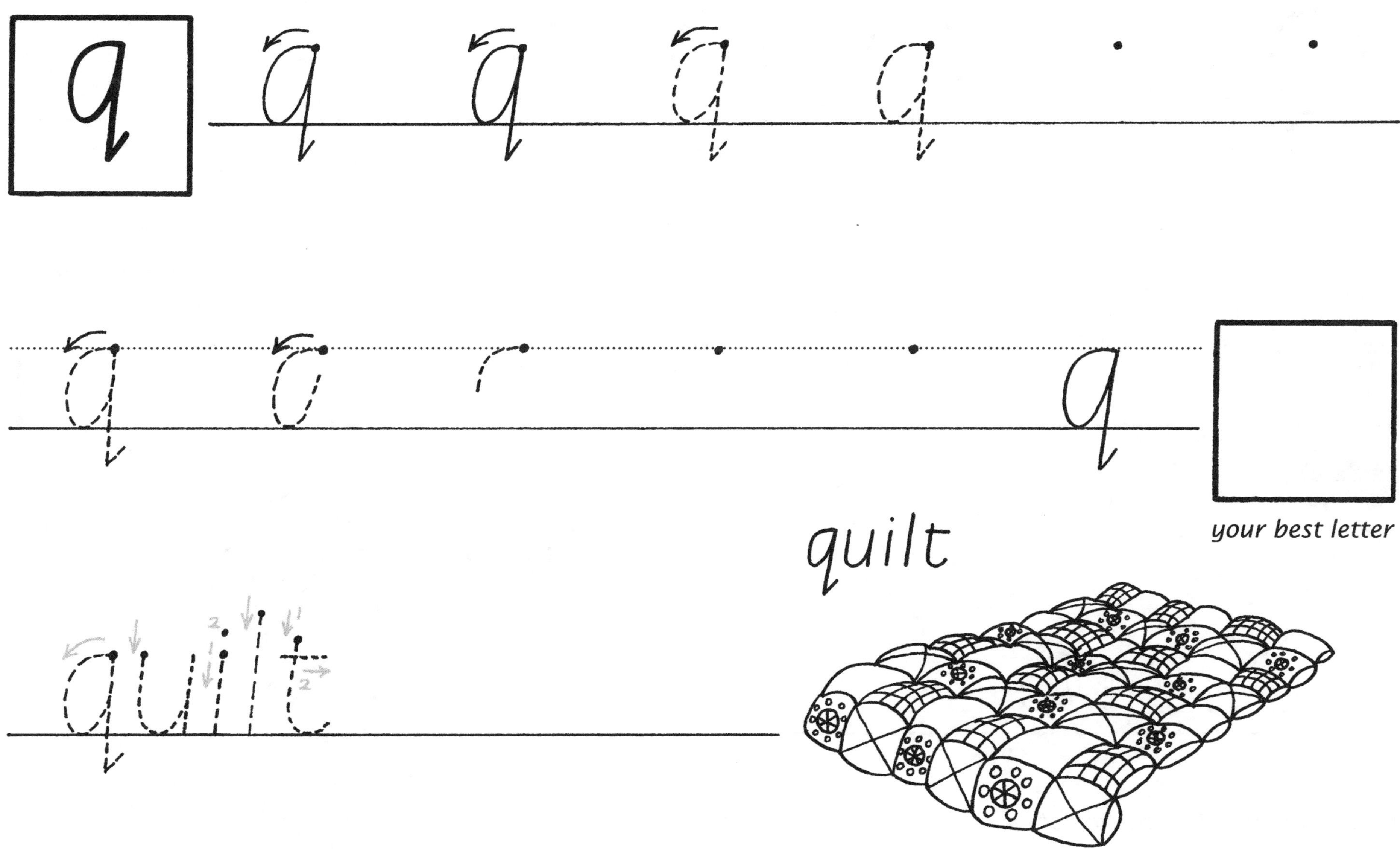

your best letter

quilt

G

G G G G

G G G G

your best letter

Gate

Gate

your best letter

goat

LOOK: Did you trace each letter before writing your own?   Circle: Yes   No

your best letter

Dinosaur

your best letter

dog

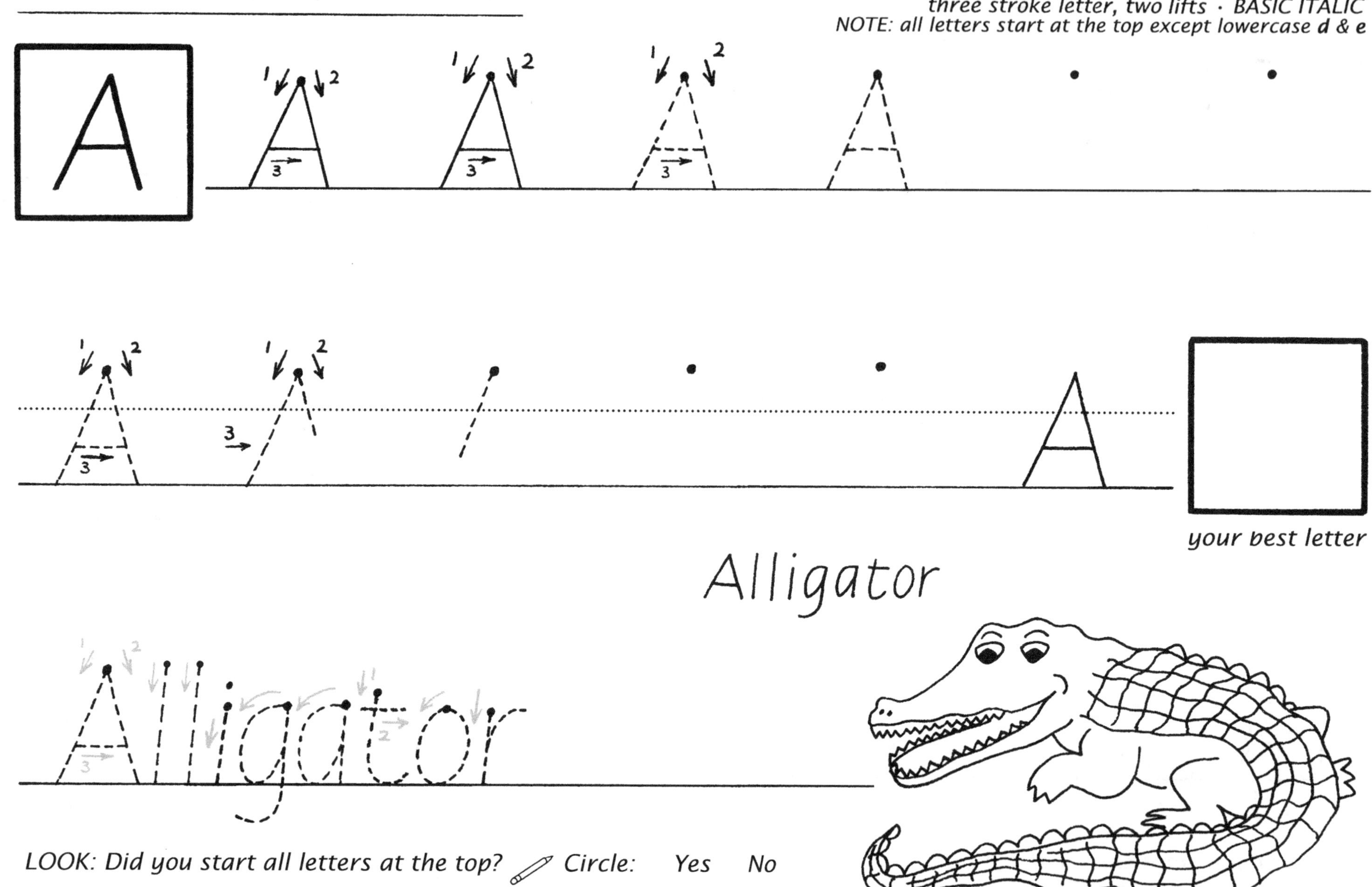

your best letter

Alligator

LOOK: Did you start all letters at the top? Circle: Yes   No

LOOK: Did you close each **a** at the top? Circle: Yes   No

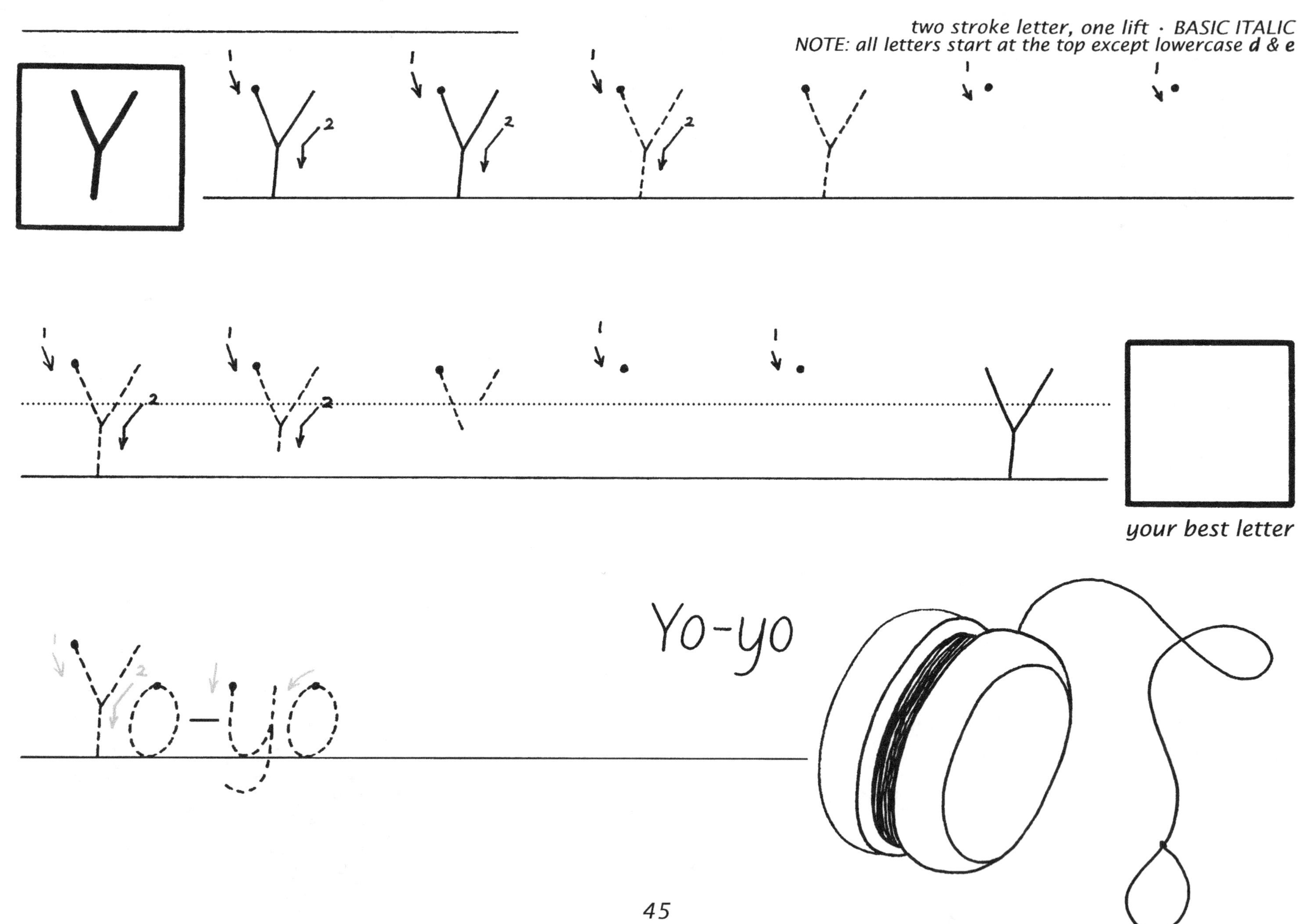

Getty-Dubay™ Italic Handwriting Series · Book A · © 2012 Getty-Dubay

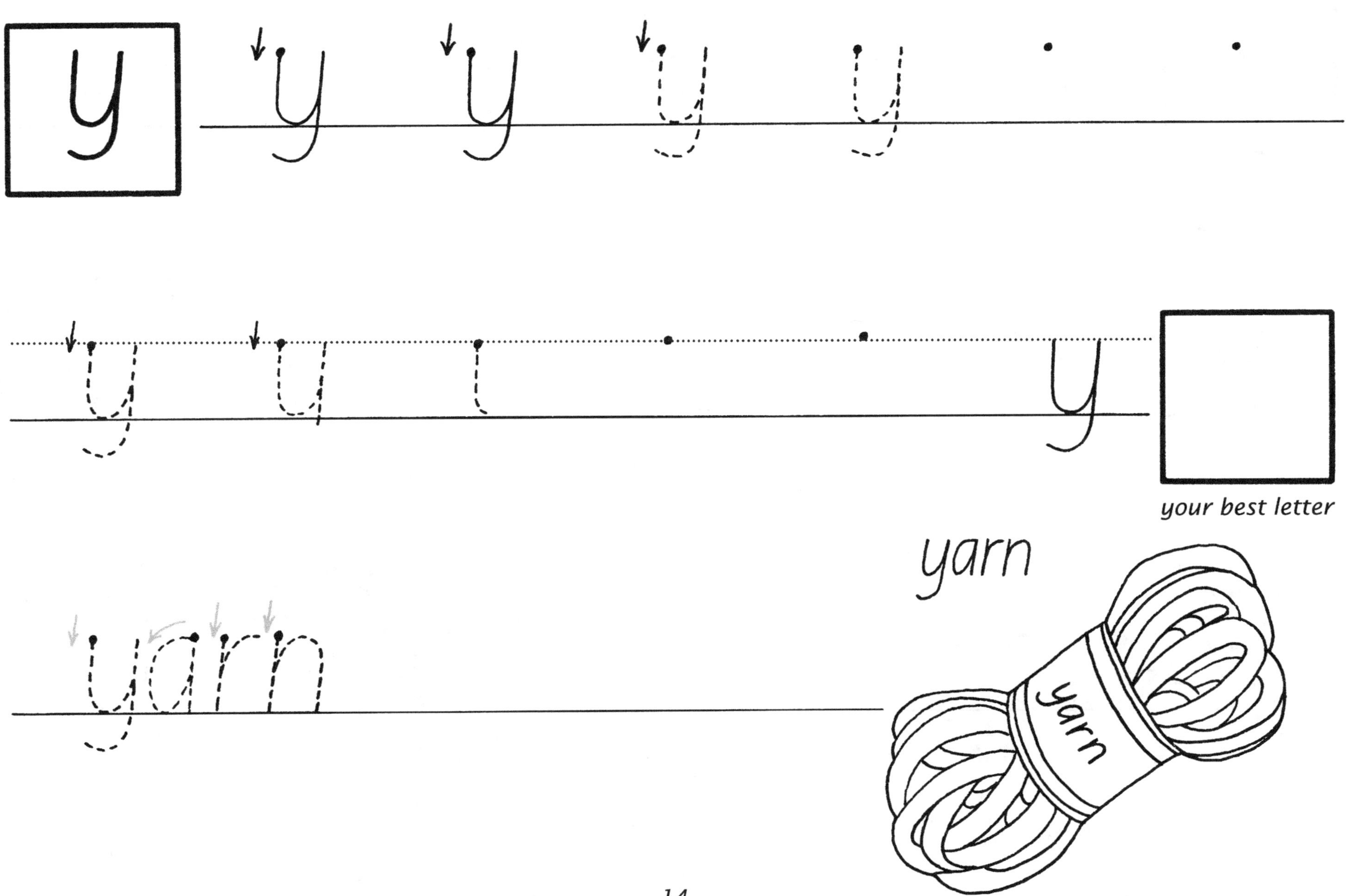

your best letter

yarn

your best letter

Ukulele

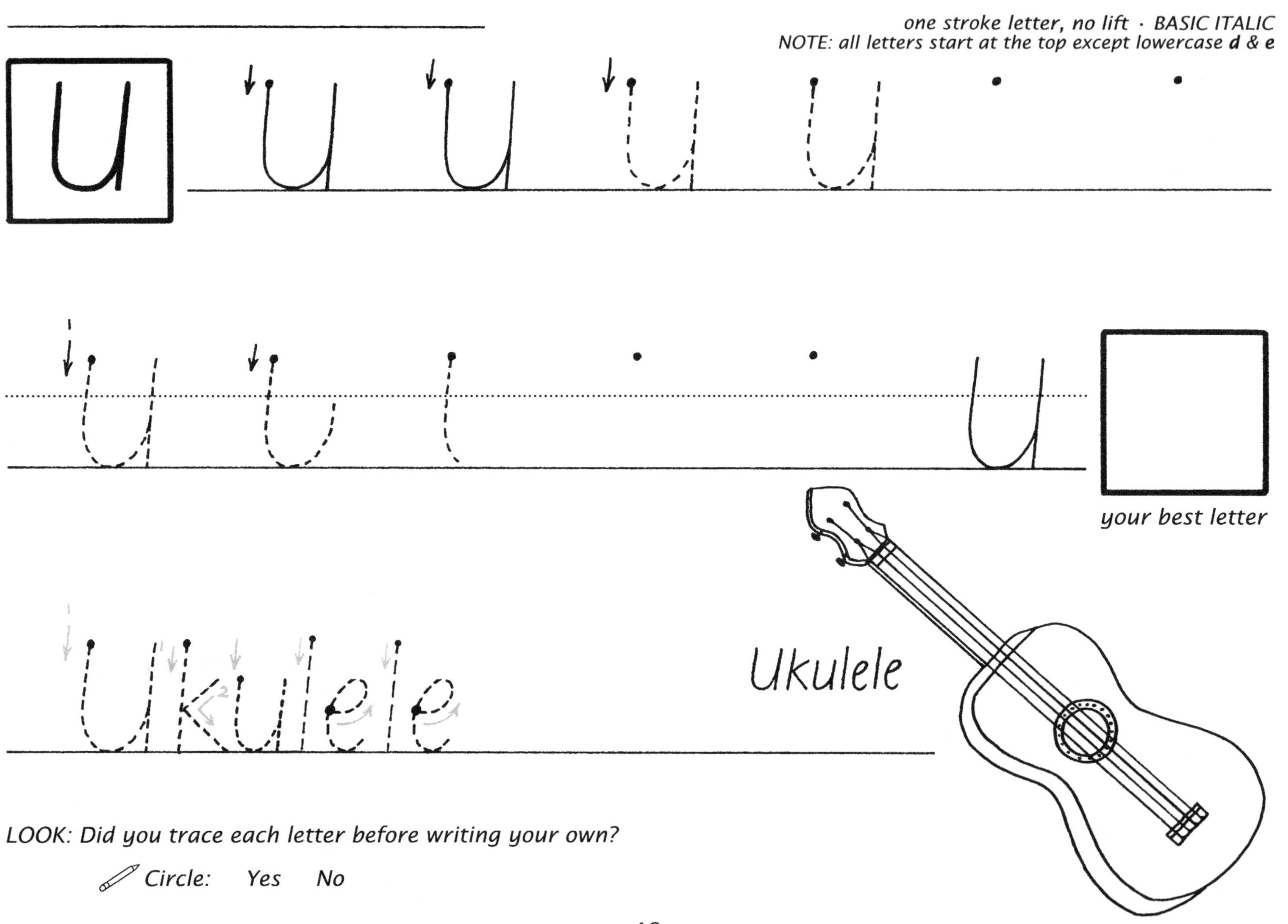

LOOK: Did you trace each letter before writing your own?

✎ Circle: Yes   No

u

your best letter

umbrella

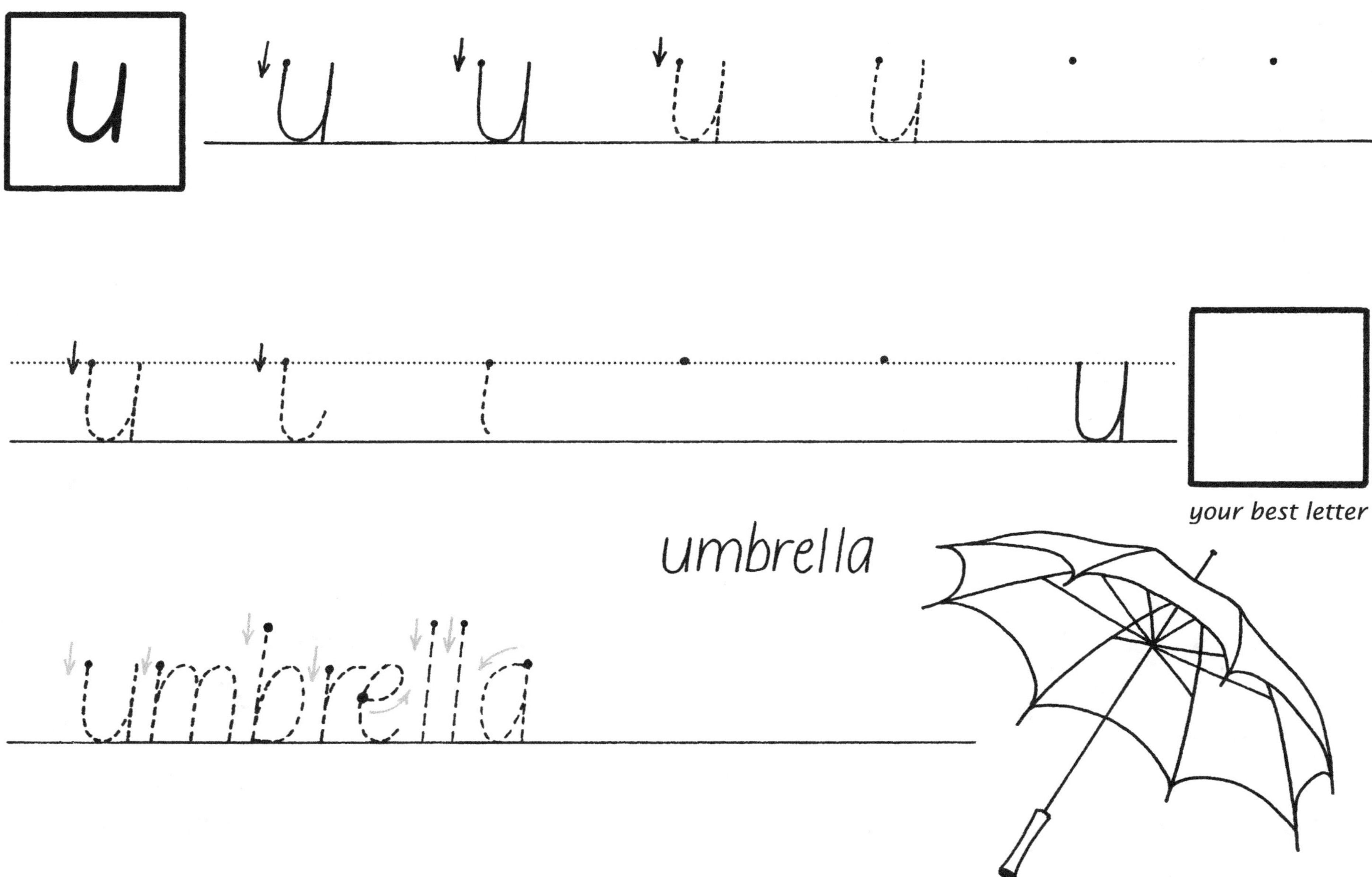

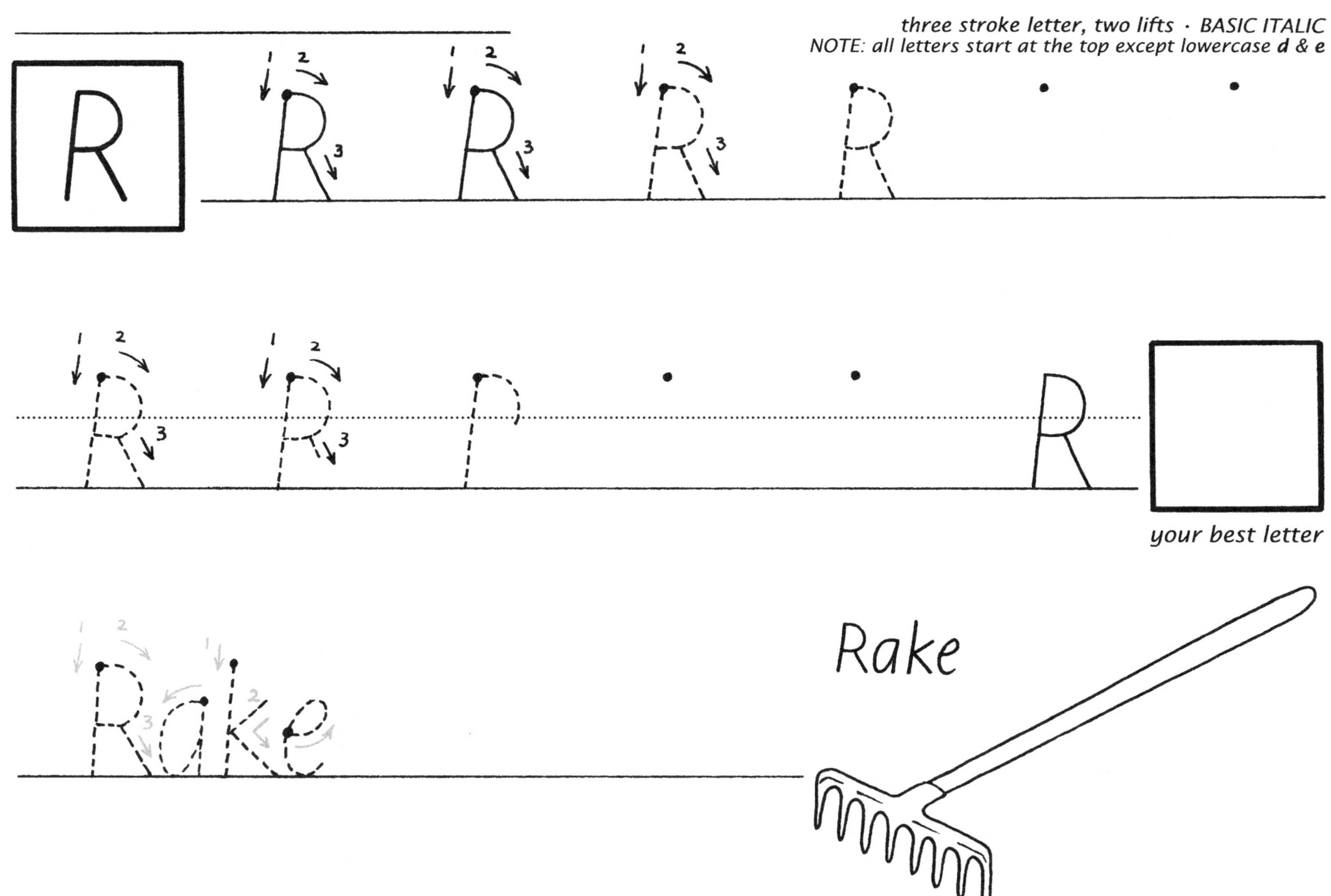

your best letter
Rake

LOOK: Did you start each letter at the top? ✏ Circle: Yes No

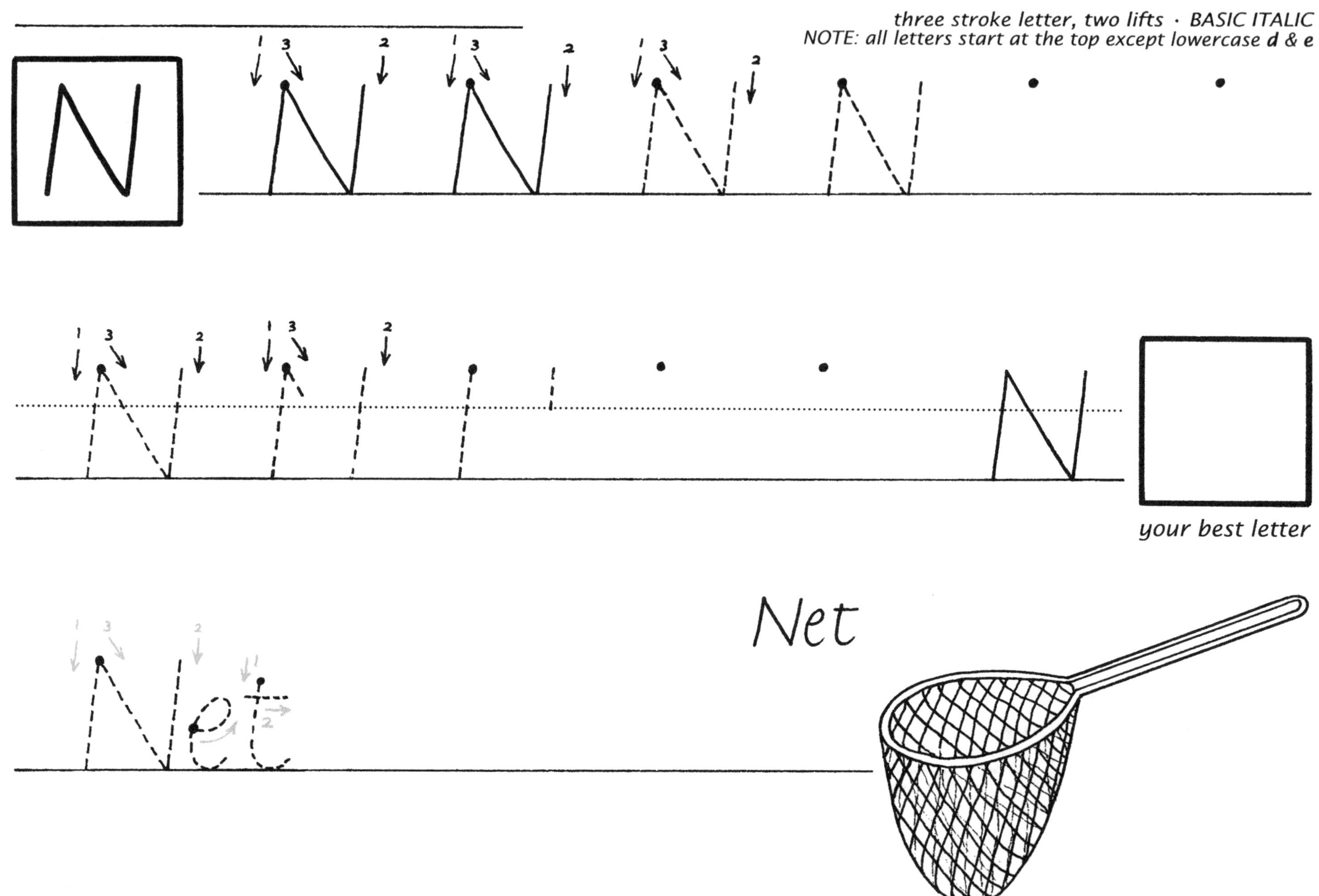

three stroke letter, two lifts · BASIC ITALIC
NOTE: all letters start at the top except lowercase d & e
N
your best letter
Net

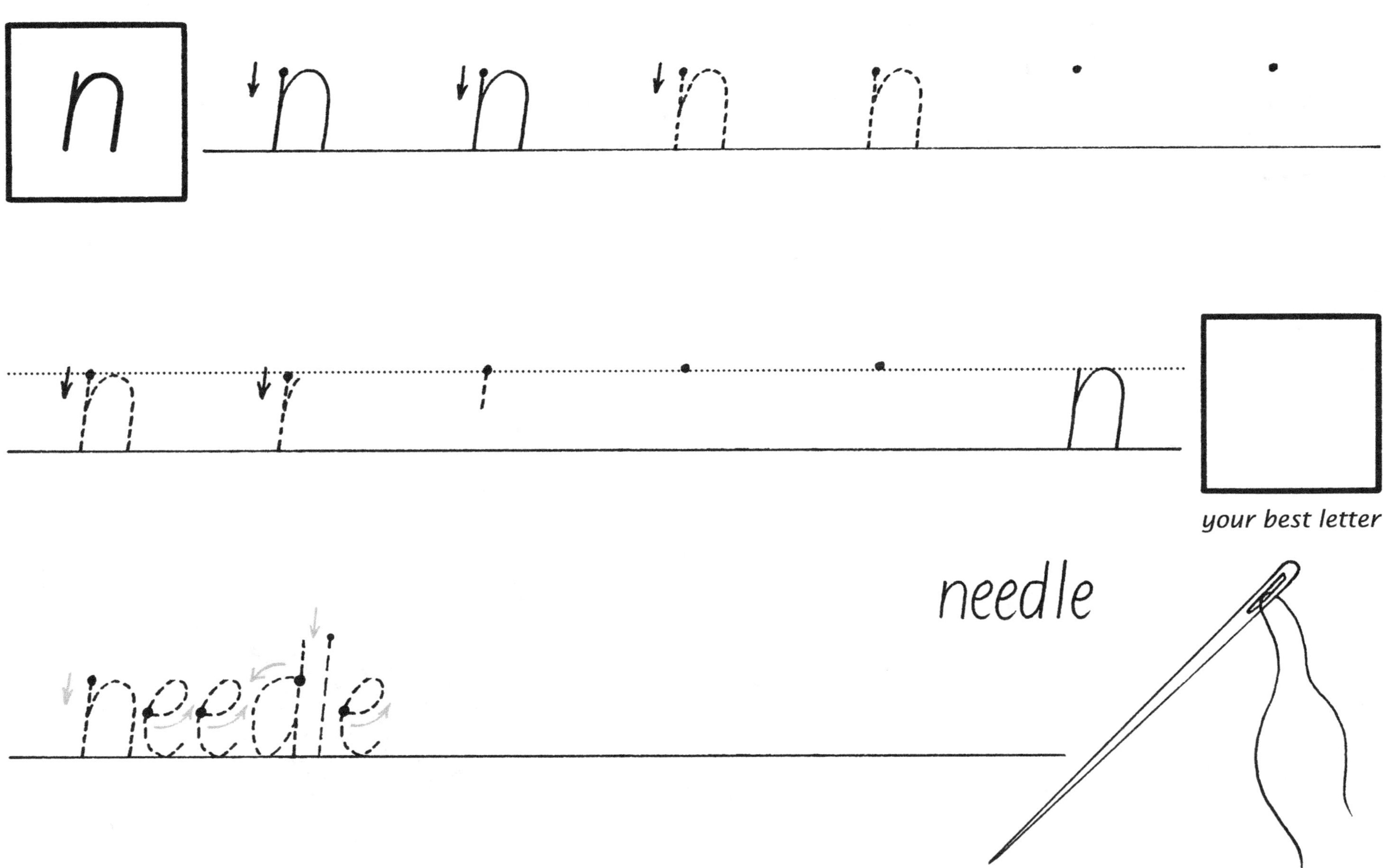

your best letter

needle

your best letter

Mittens

LOOK: Did you start all letters at the top?   Circle: Yes   No

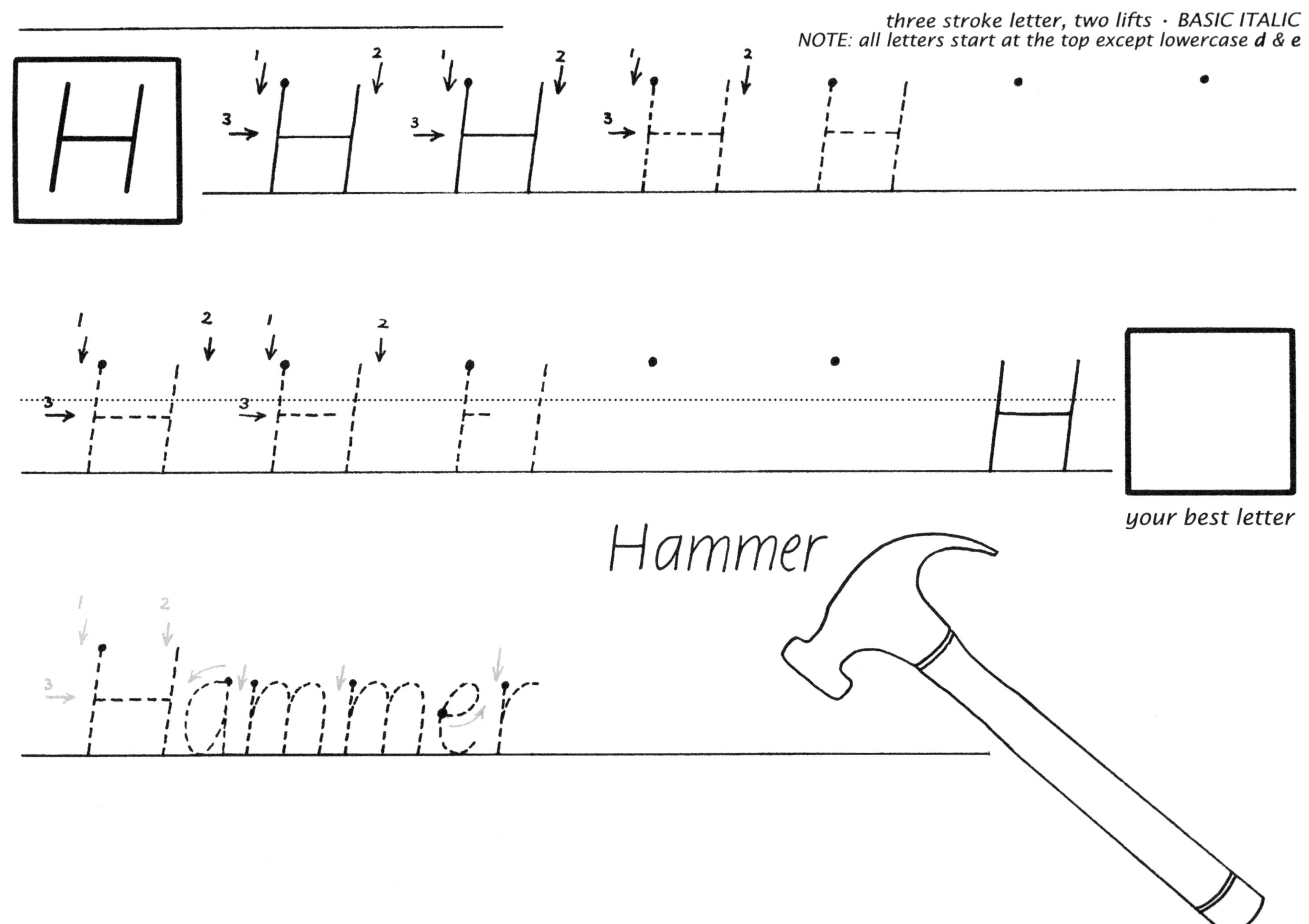
your best letter
Hammer

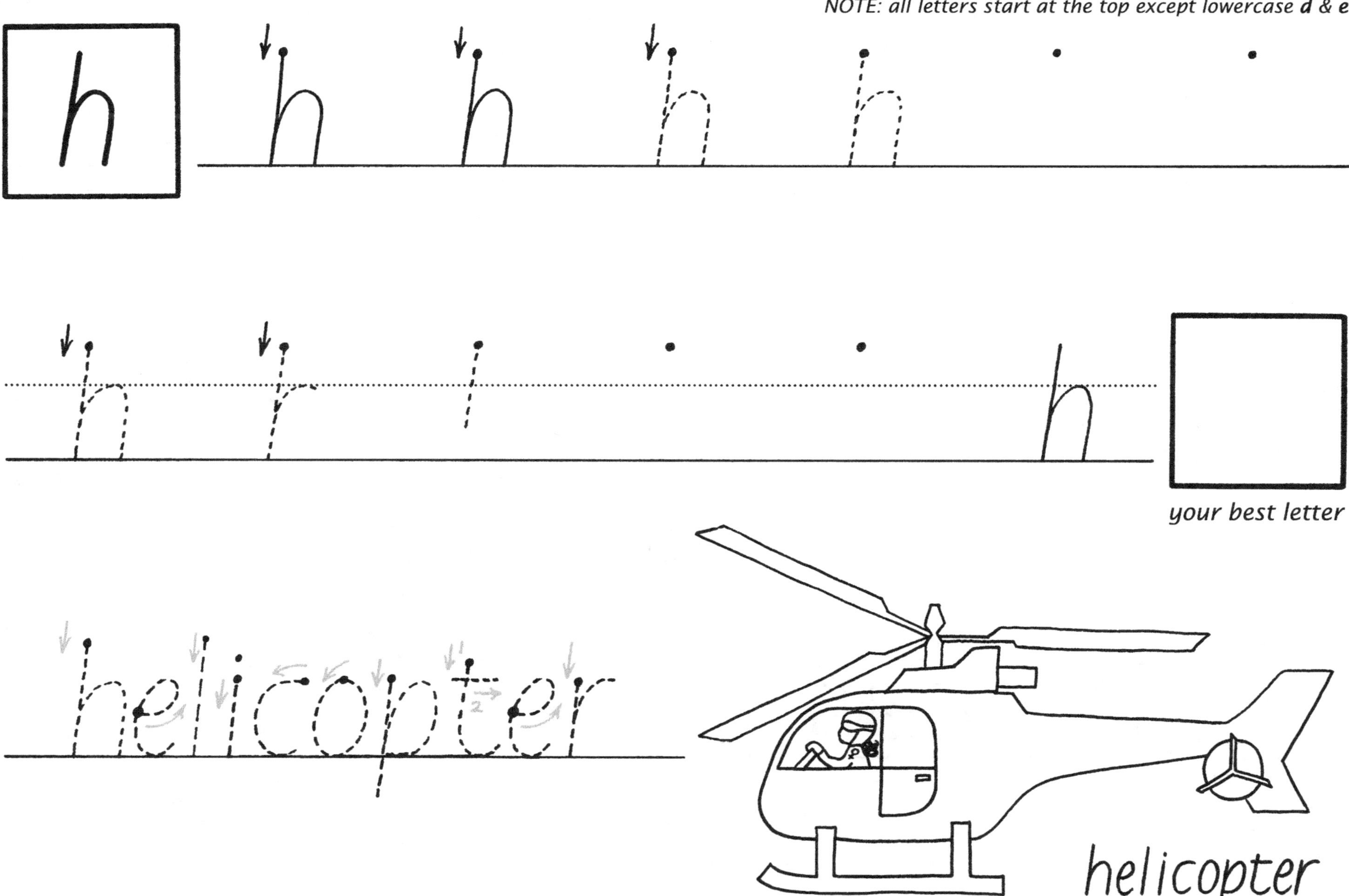

your best letter

helicopter

Z

Zipper

your best letter

Zipper

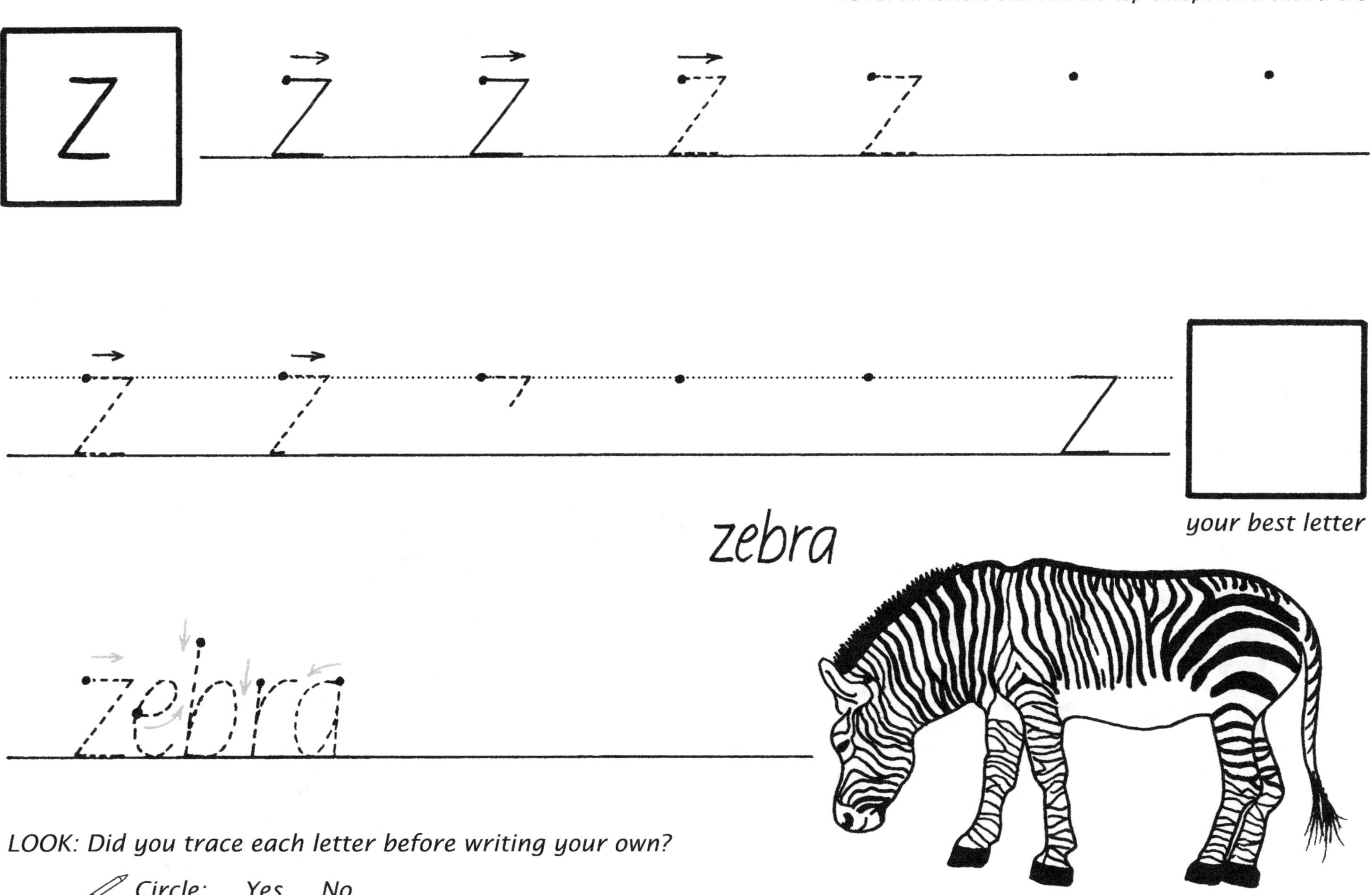

zebra

your best letter

LOOK: Did you trace each letter before writing your own?

Circle: Yes   No

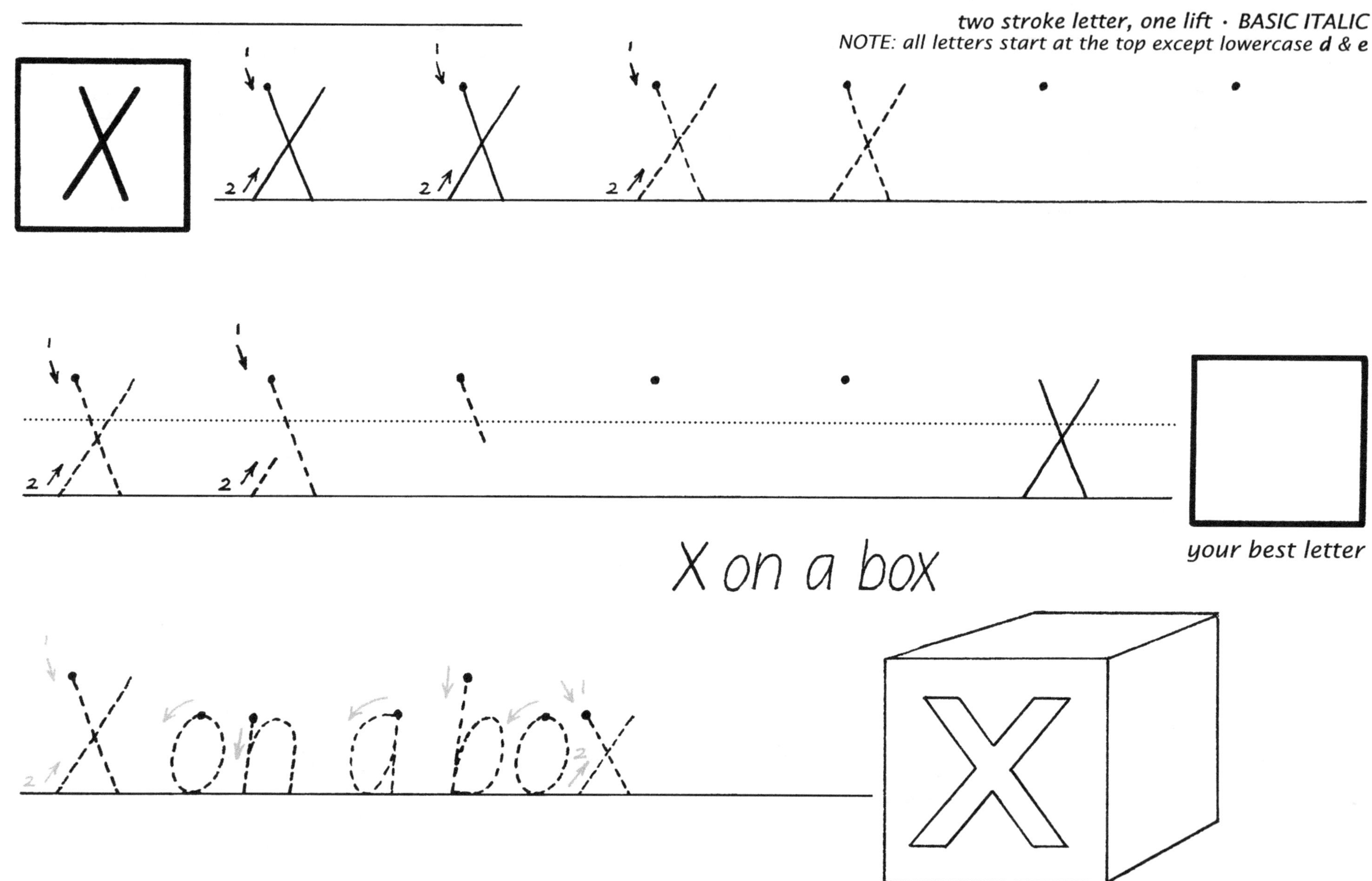

your best letter

X on a box

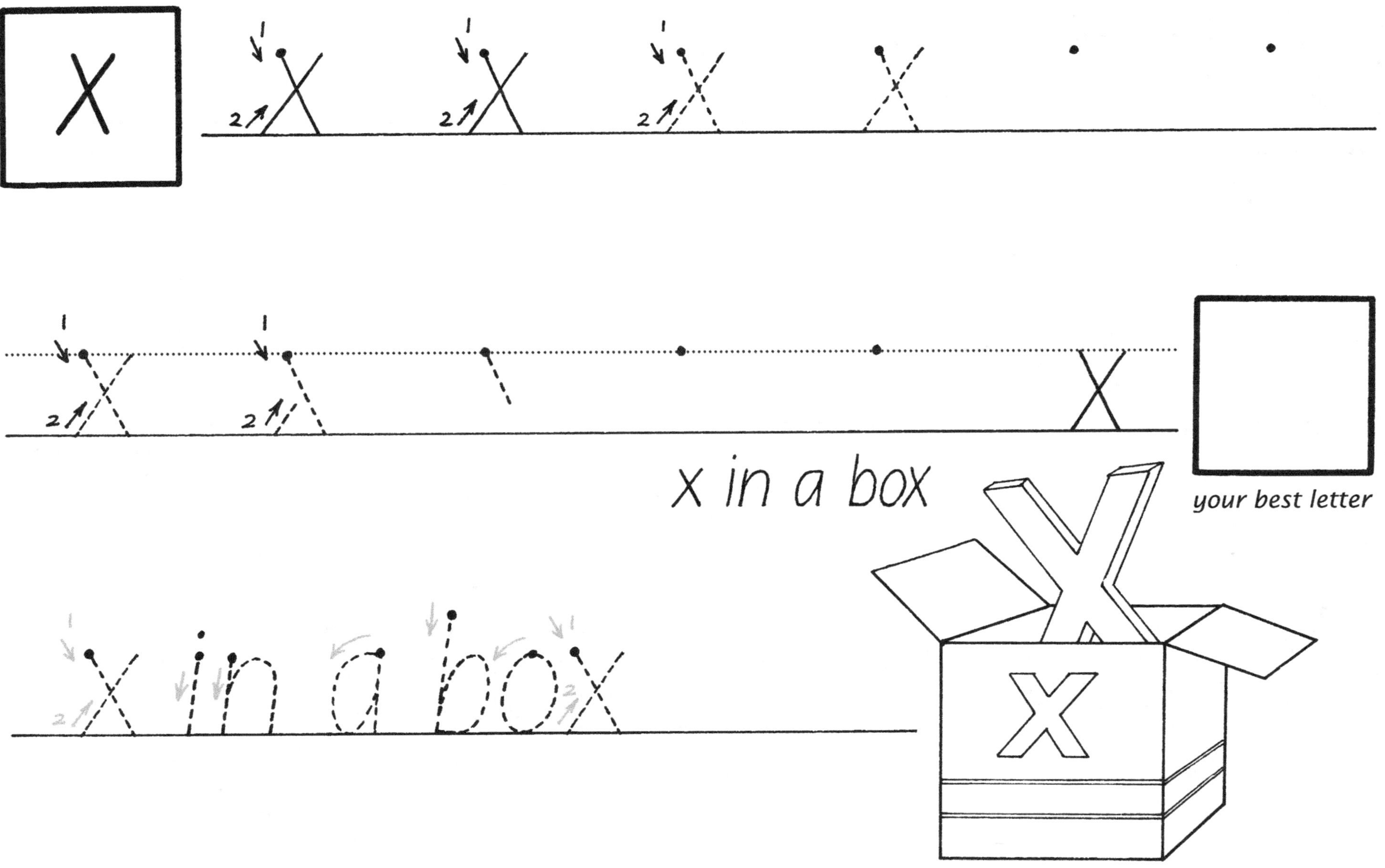
x in a box
your best letter
x in a box

your best letter

Watch

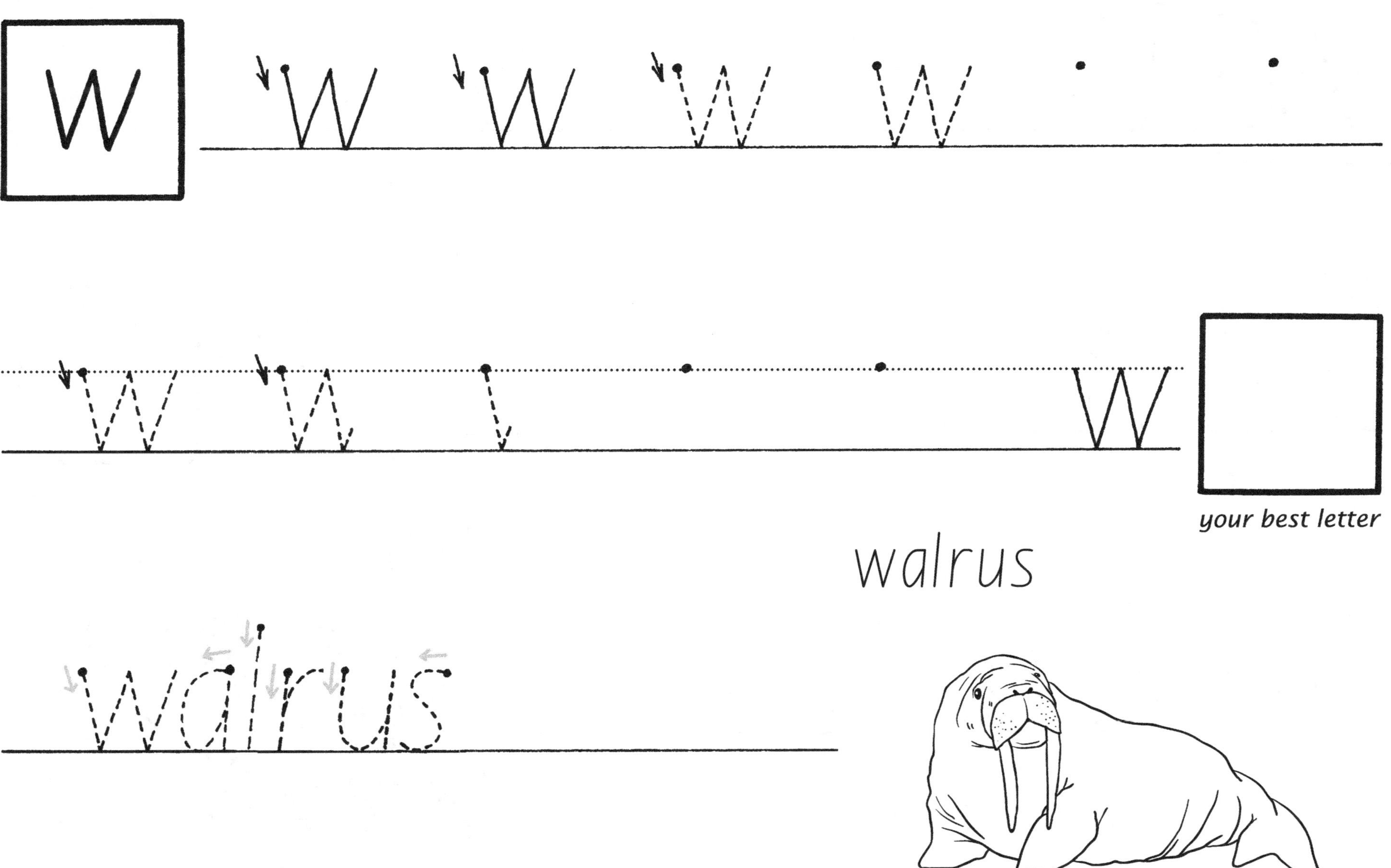

your best letter

walrus

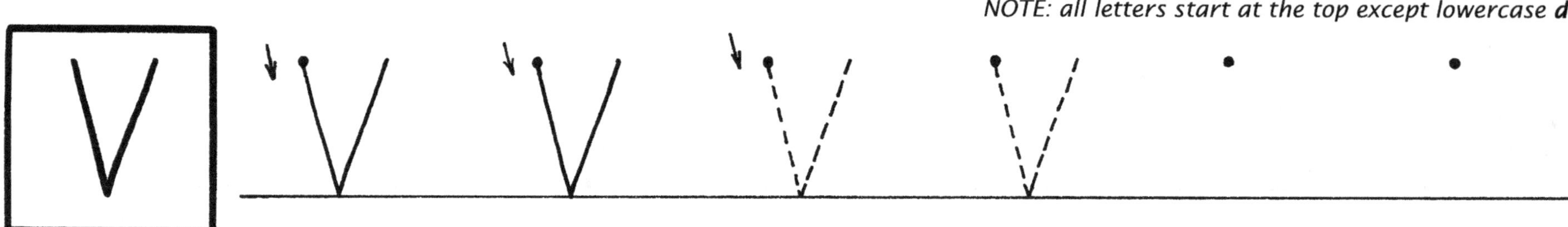

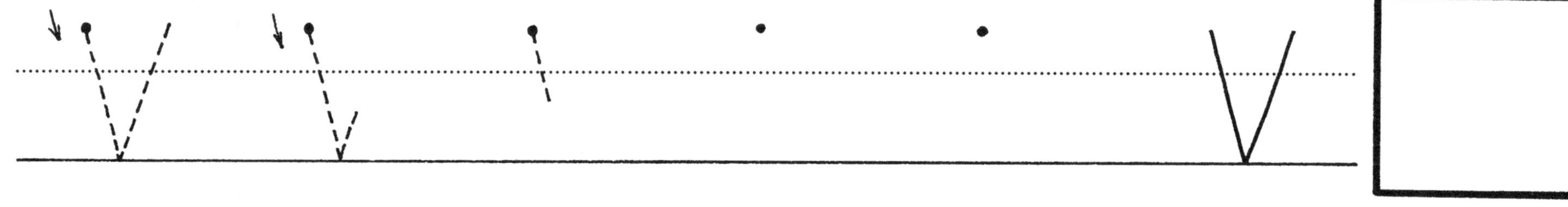

your best letter

Valentine

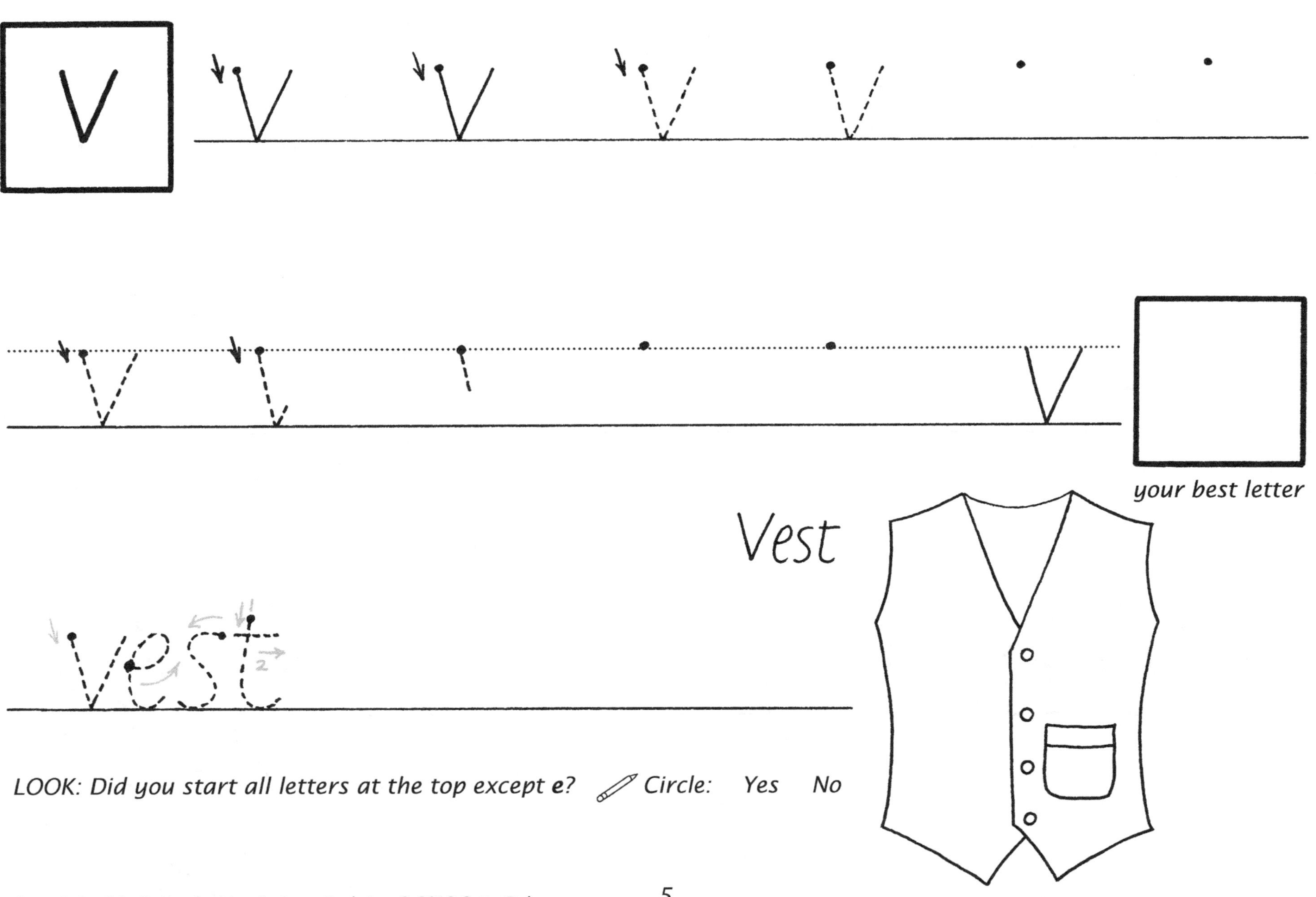

LOOK: Did you start all letters at the top except *e*?   Circle: Yes   No

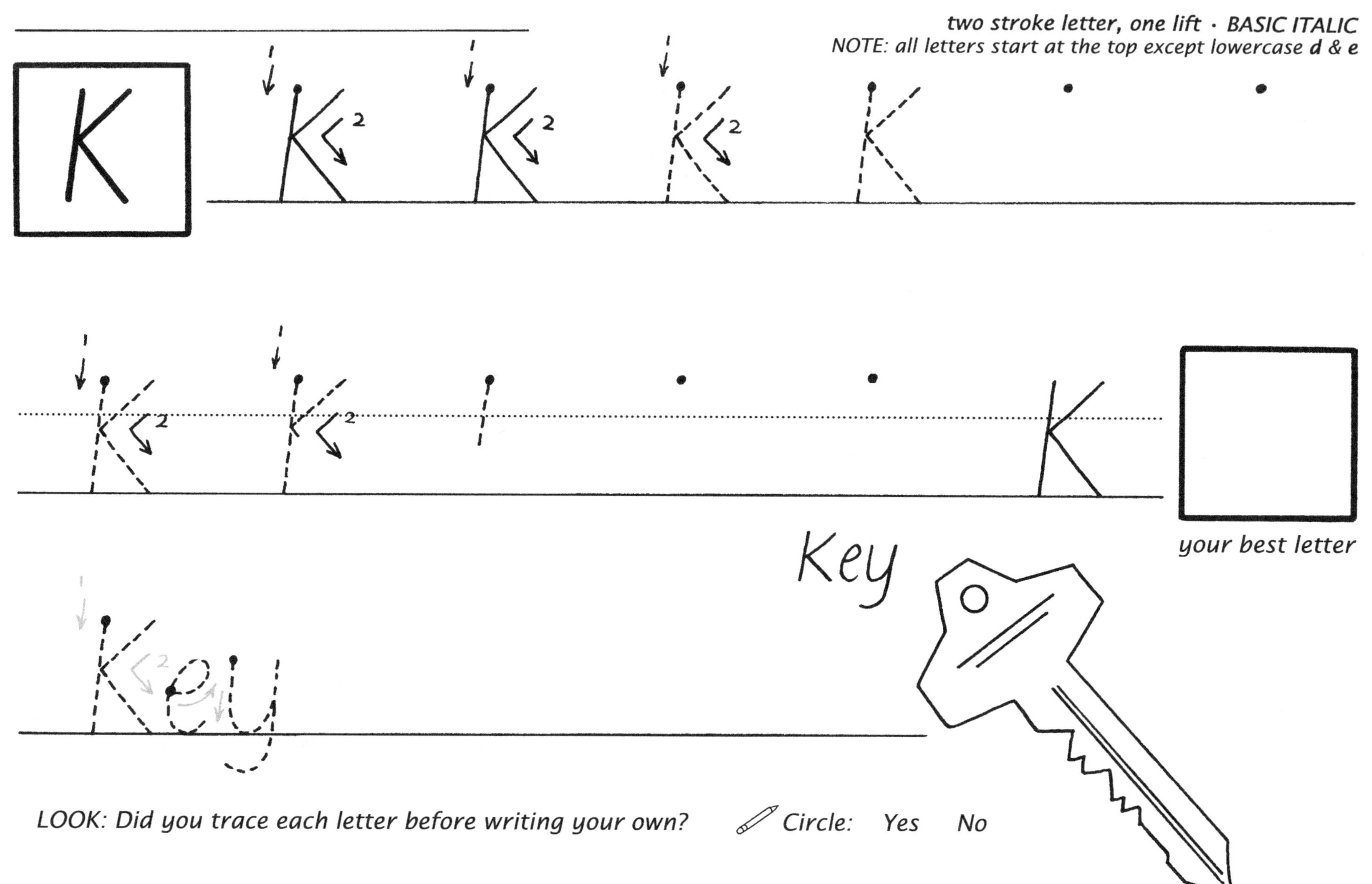

LOOK: Did you trace each letter before writing your own?   Circle: Yes   No

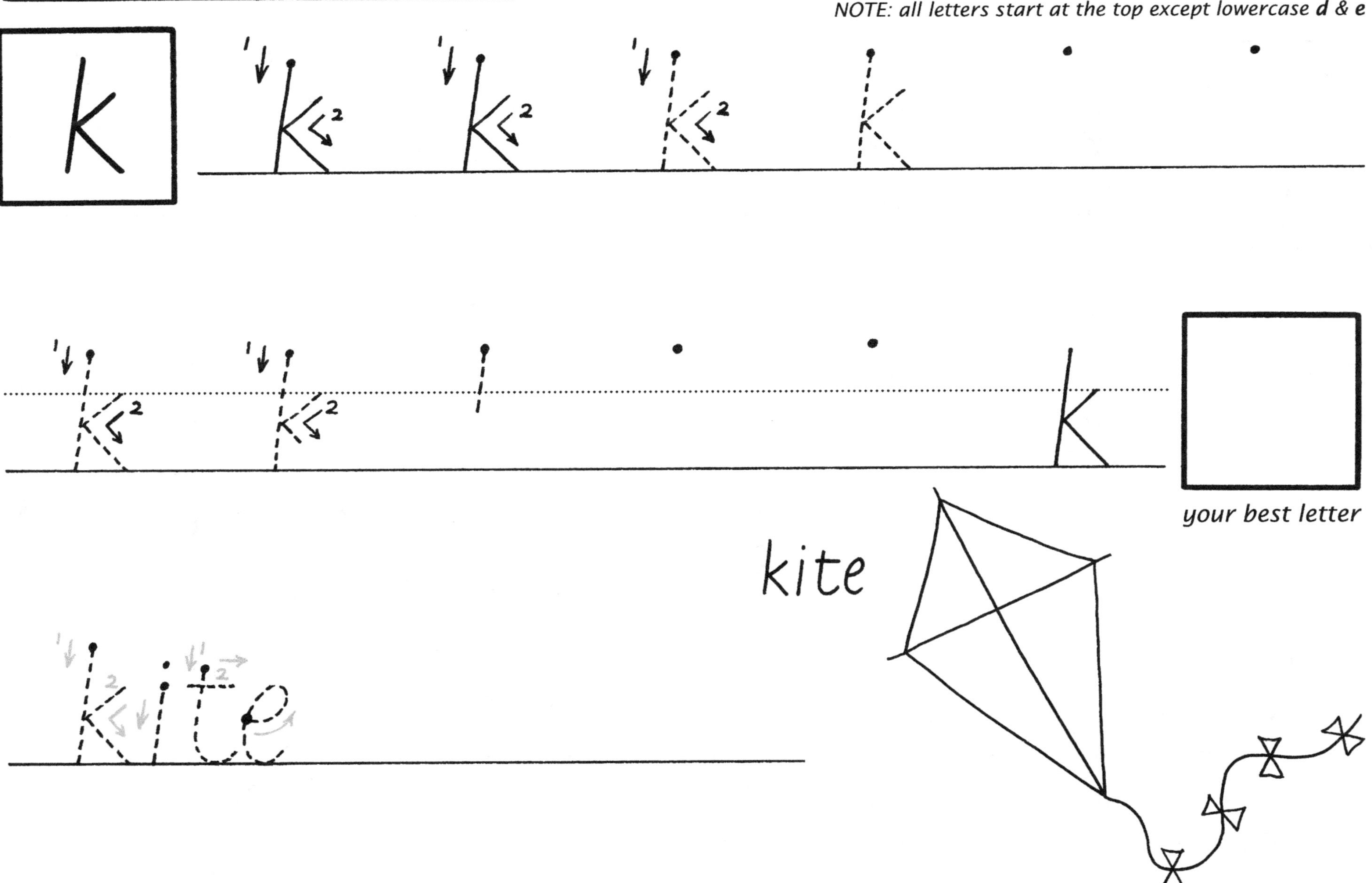

two stroke letter, one lift · k, v, w, x, z family · BASIC ITALIC
NOTE: all letters start at the top except lowercase d & e
your best letter
kite

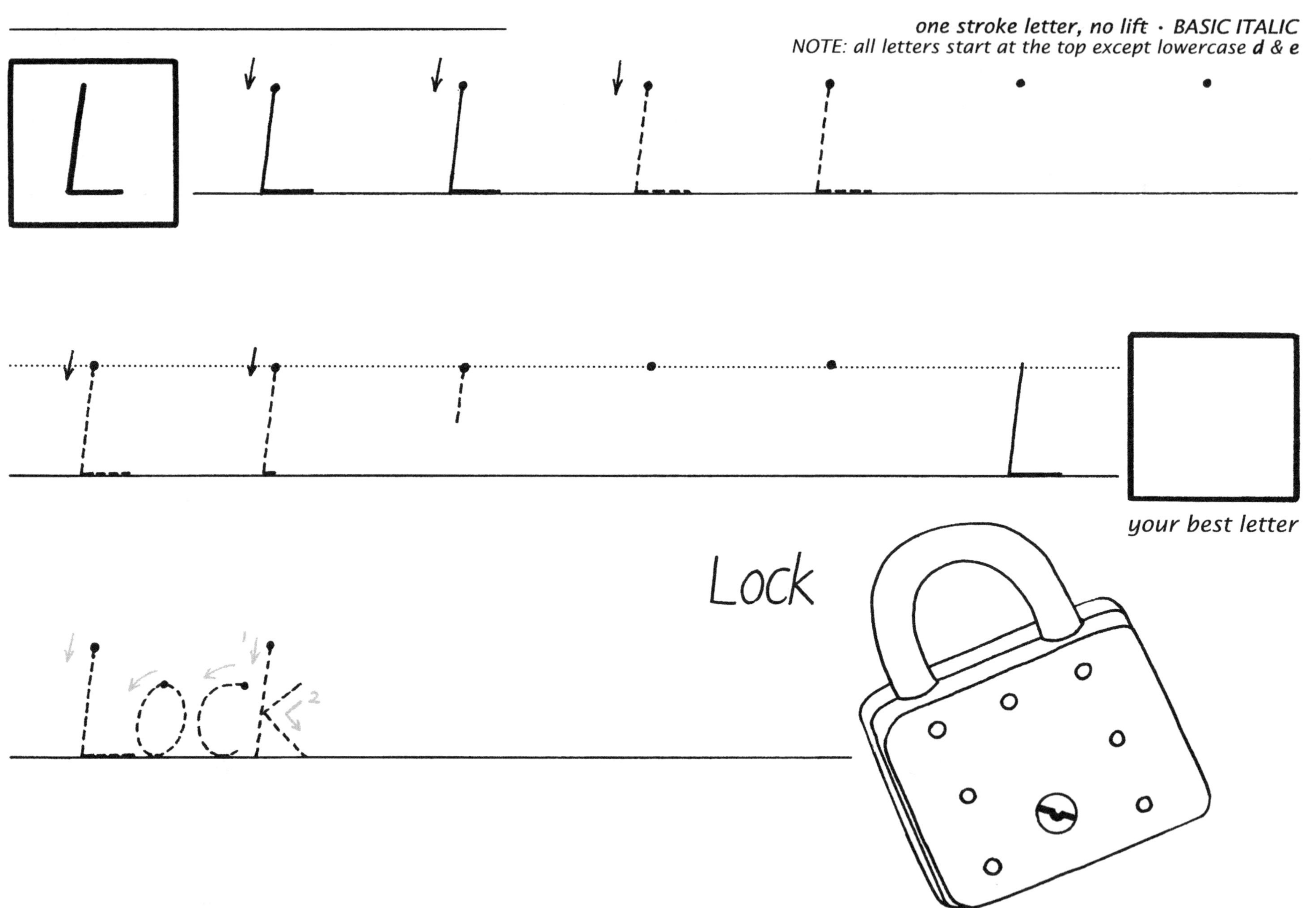

one stroke letter, no lift · BASIC ITALIC
NOTE: all letters start at the top except lowercase *d* & *e*
your best letter
Lock

your best letter

lamb

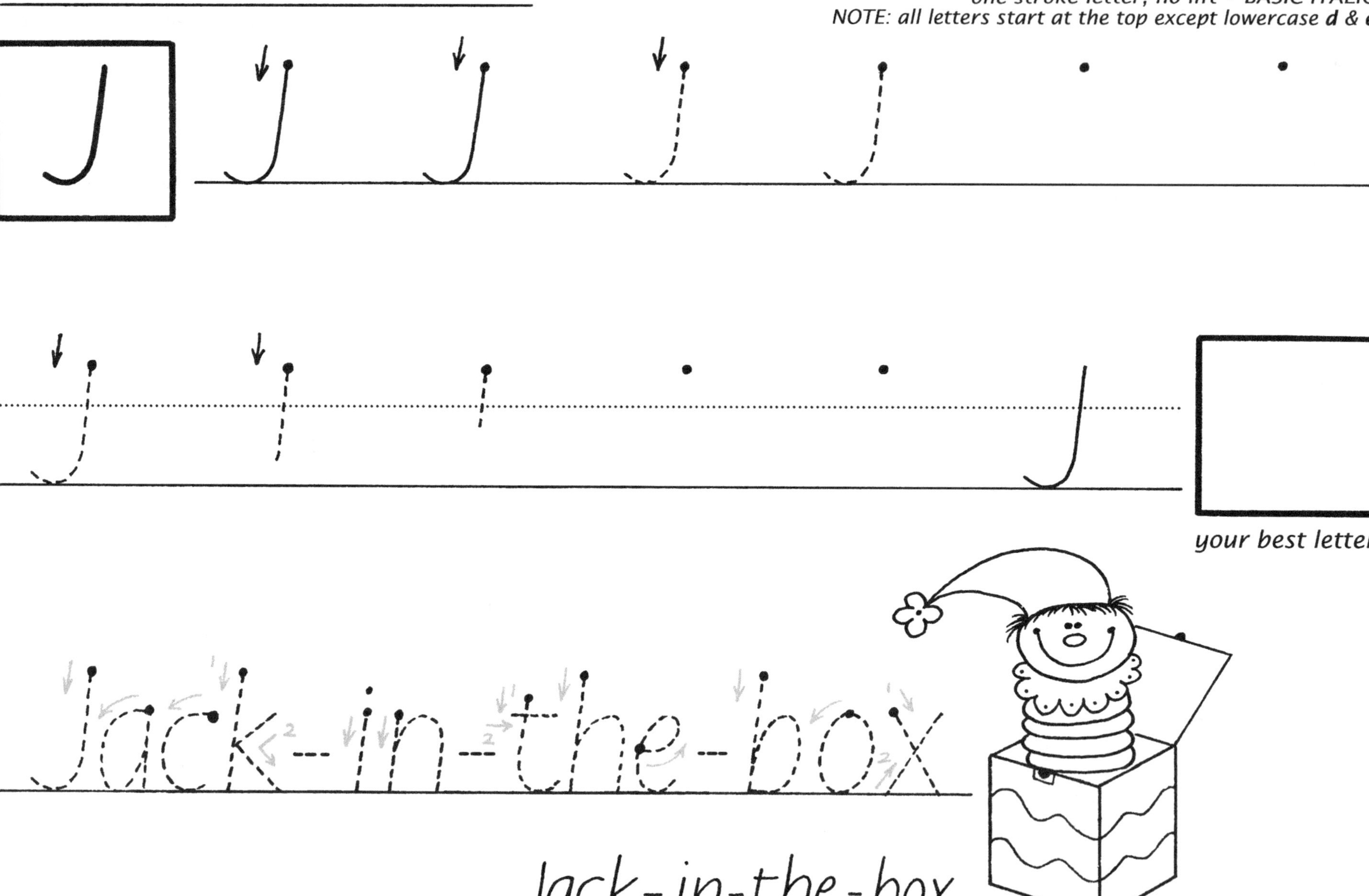

your best letter

Jack-in-the-box

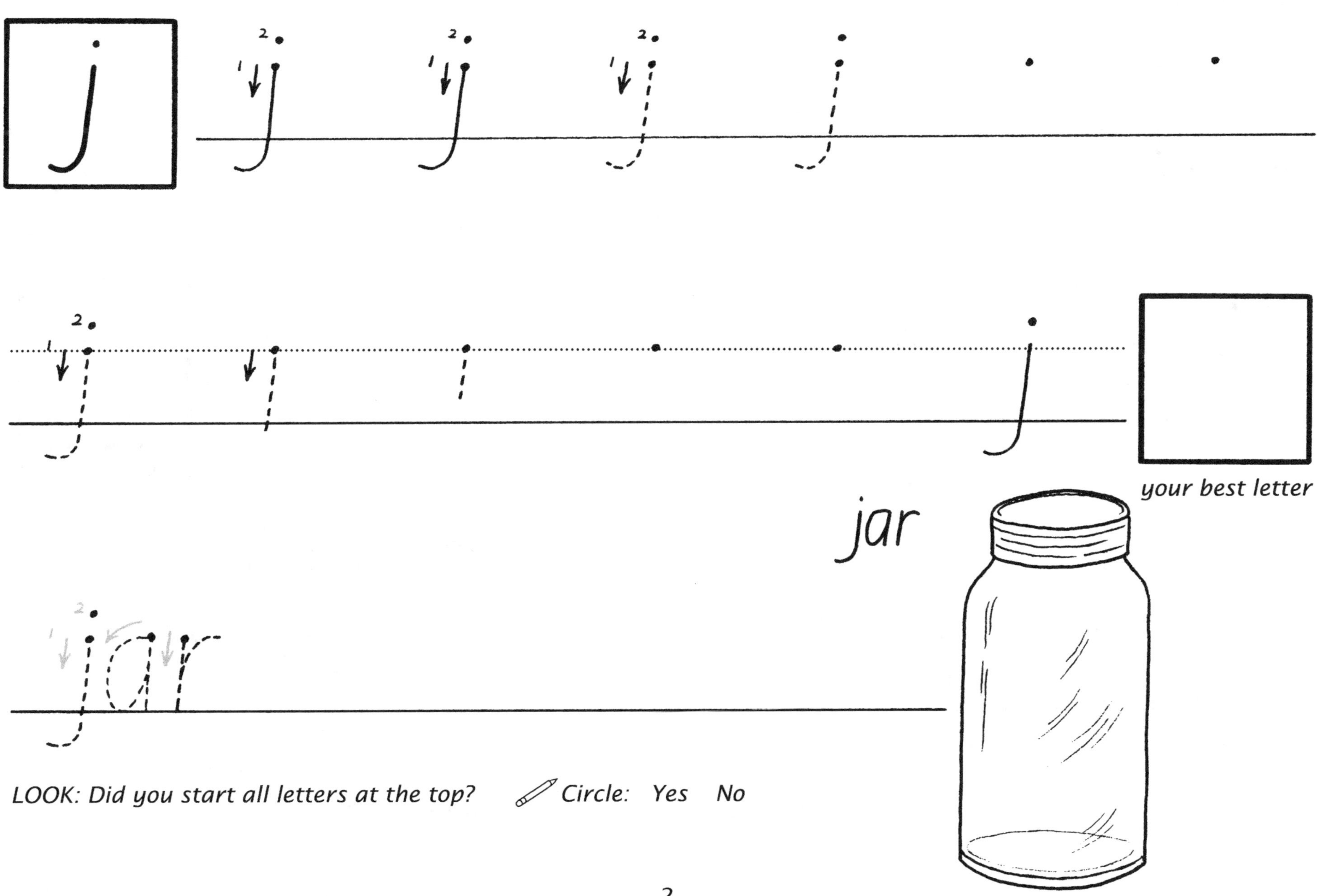

LOOK: Did you start all letters at the top?   Circle: Yes   No

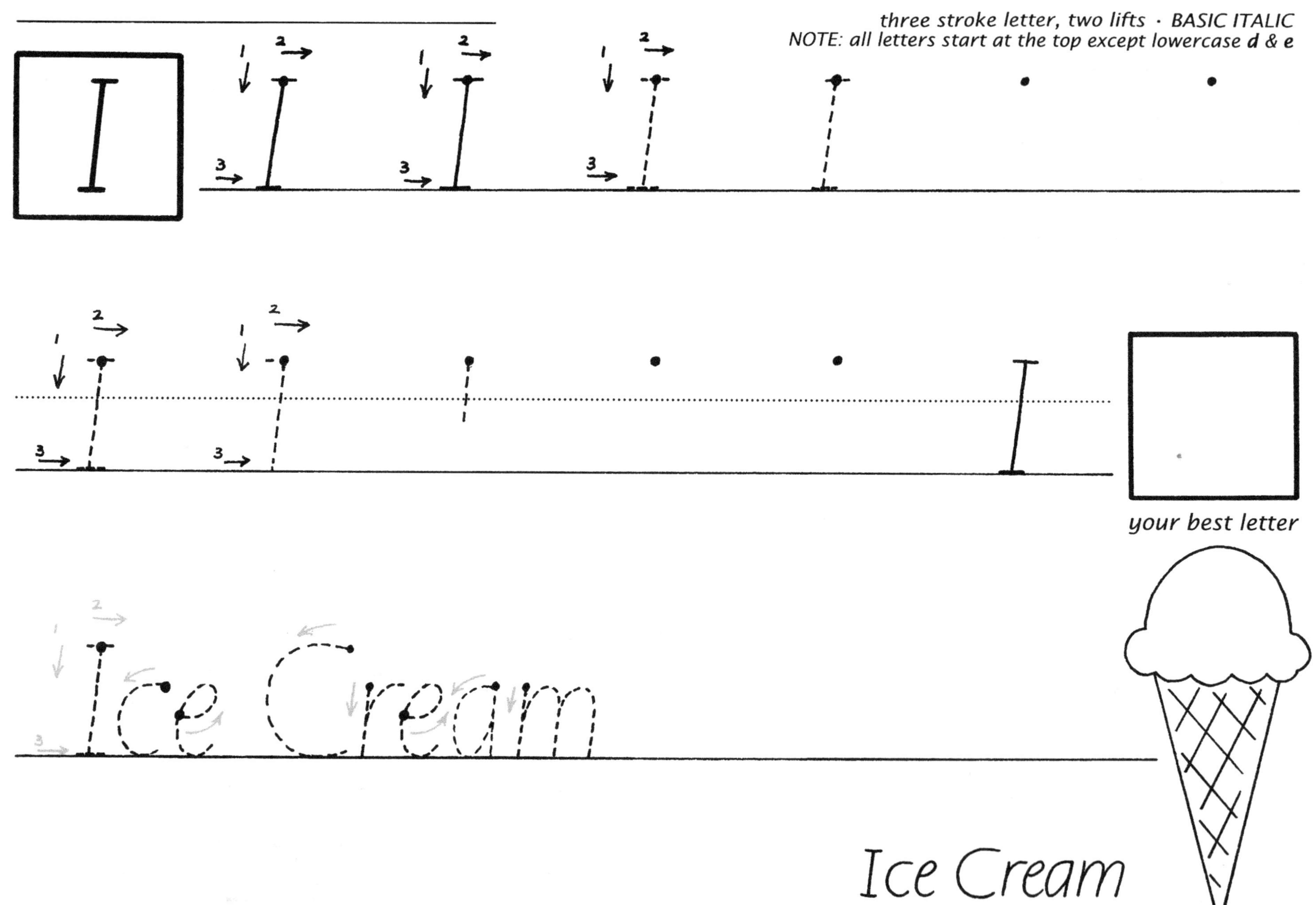
your best letter
Ice Cream
Ice Cream

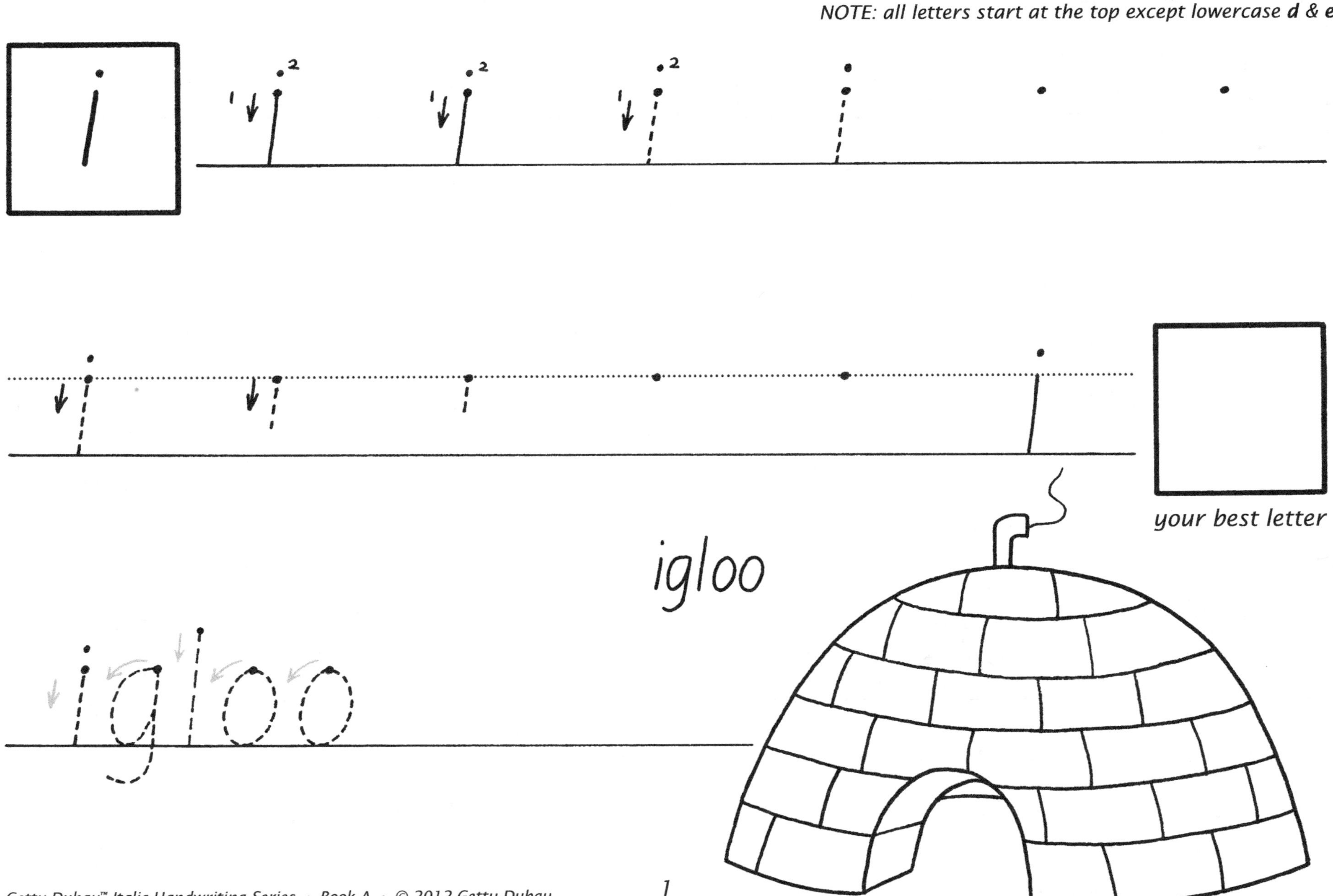

your best letter

igloo

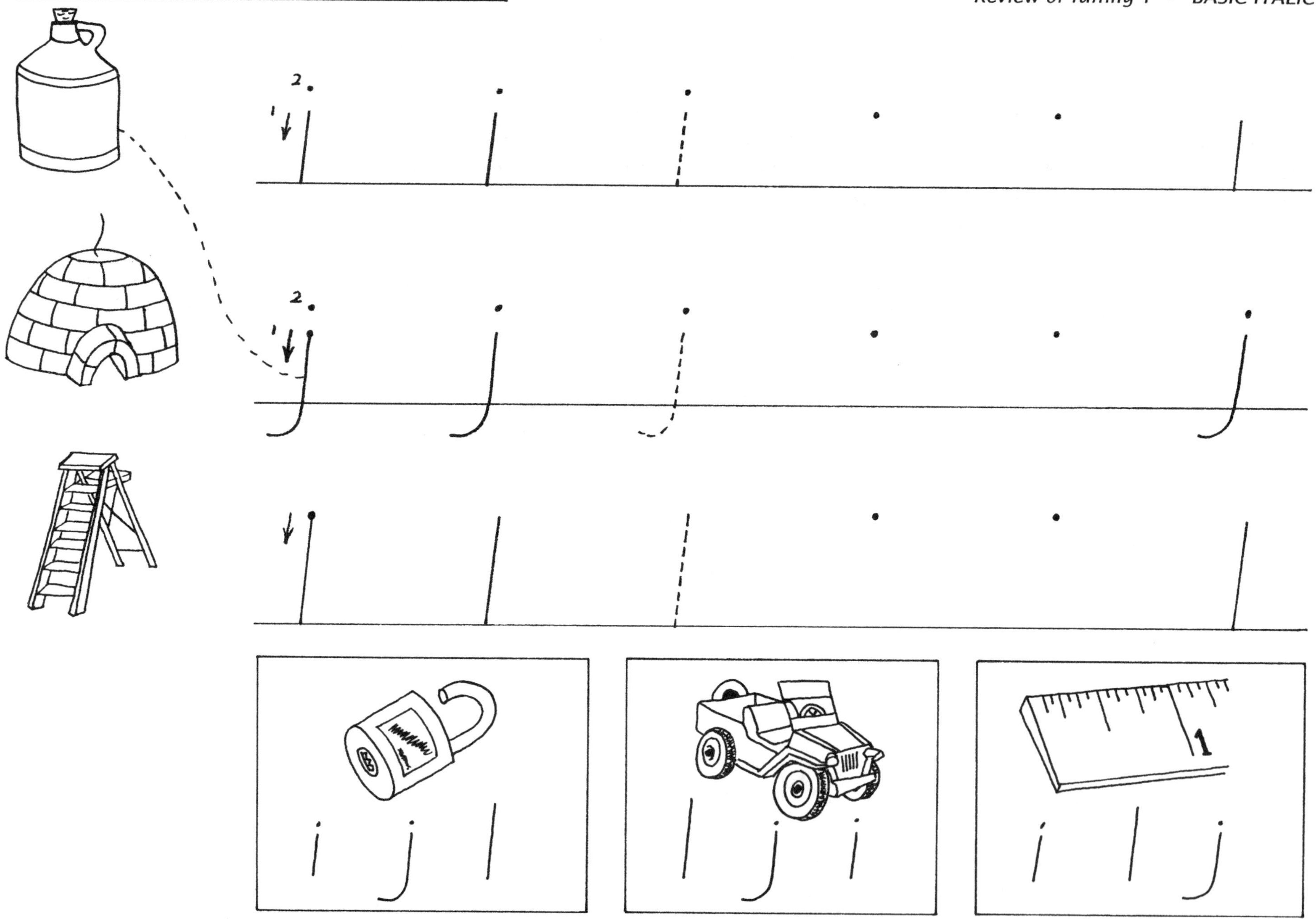

TOP THREE LINES: Ask the student to draw a line from the picture
to the letter that stands for the correct beginning sound.

BOTTOM THREE BOXES: Ask the student to circle the letter that
stands for the beginning sound of the picture.

BASIC SHAPES

Before the student begins writing in BOOK A, the authors recommend that the student practice the following shapes on unlined paper, one shape at a time. Allow the student to write each shape any size at first. Later, ask the student to write very large and very small forms of that same shape. We suggest the student also practice these shapes on a chalkboard and/or in cornmeal. (See INSTRUCTION MANUAL, "*Activity*," pp. 35 & 41.)

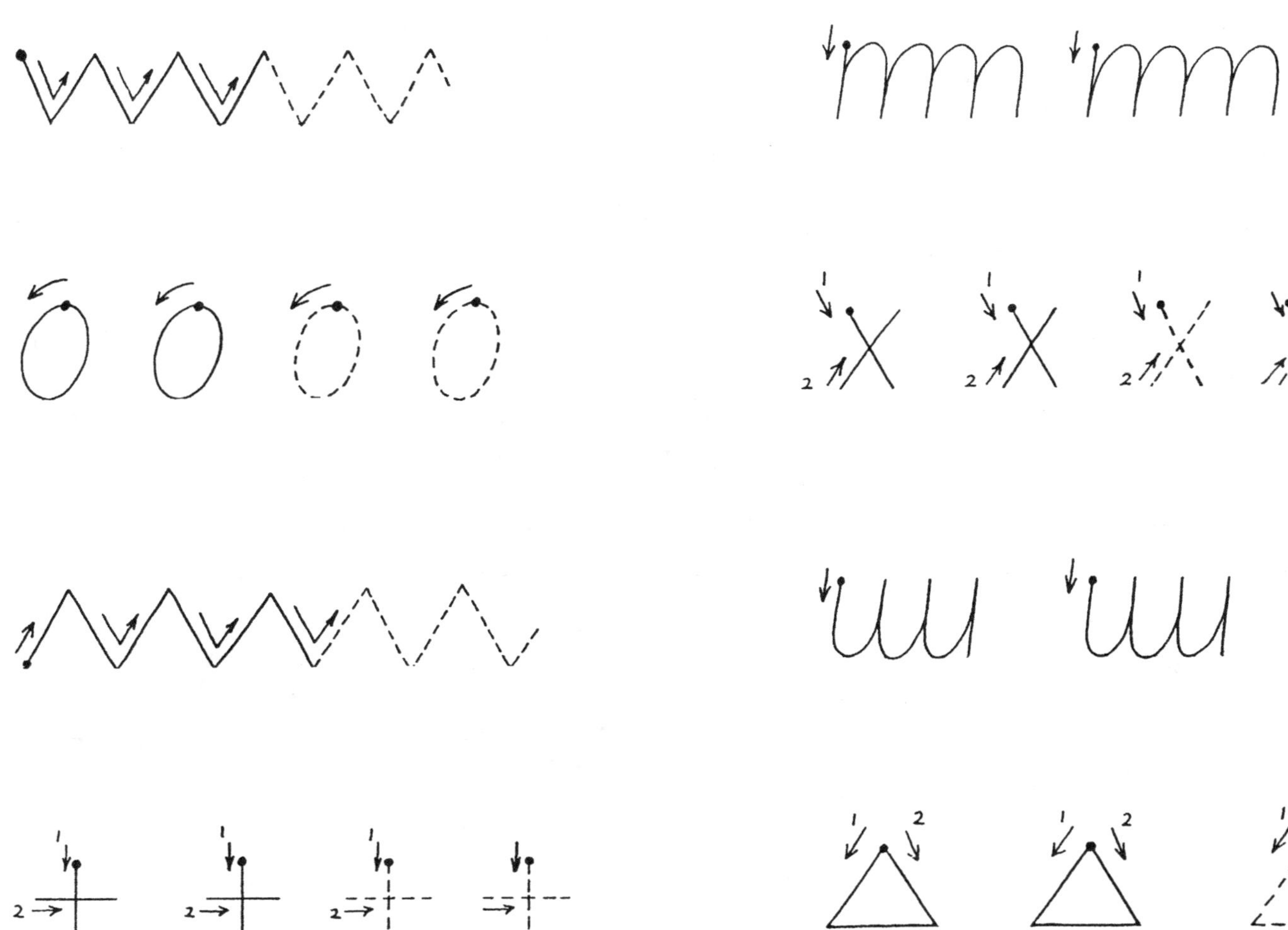

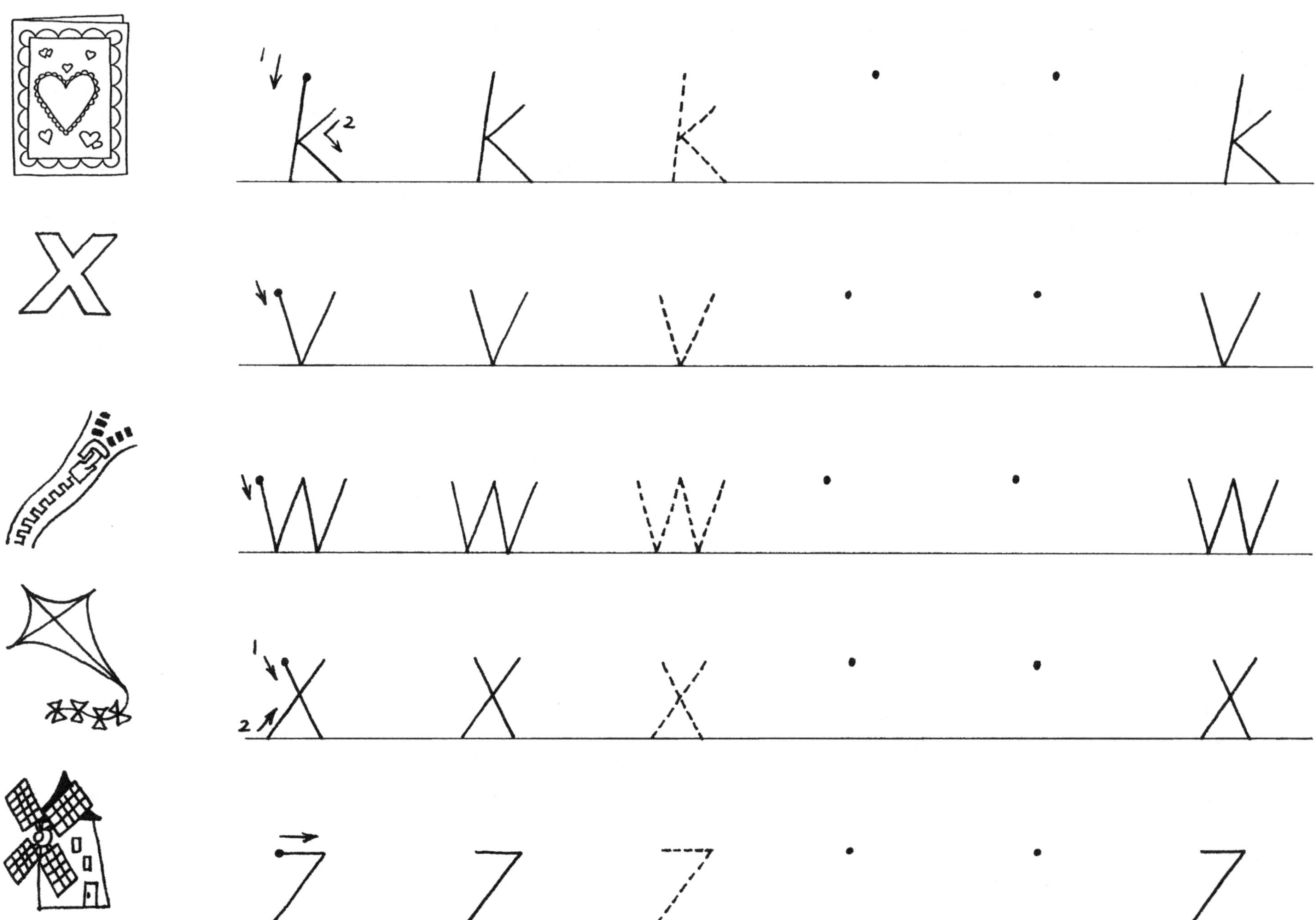

*Ask the student to draw a line from the picture to the letter
that stands for the correct beginning sound.*

Getty-Dubay™ Italic Handwriting Series · Book A · © 2012 Getty-Dubay

Learning how to write involves much more than learning to write letters. It is a sophisticated, complex process involving learning letterforms, learning how to space within and between words, and learning how to organize writing on a page. Research indicates that there exists an almost perfect correlation between measures evaluating the children's *awareness* of their fingers and the ability to *use* their fingers in precise manual skills.

Ways to determine manual ability

To assist young students increase awareness of their hands and fingers, and to help you, the teacher, evaluate students' manual skills, have your students perform these tasks:

1. Direct the students to touch each of their fingers to their thumb, in order, from the first to the little finger. (By the age of six years, most children should be able to complete this exercise using one or both hands at a time.)

2. Have the students connect two dots that are spaced approximately eight inches apart on a page. (Most children of five years can accomplish this. However, if the student draws beyond the second dot or draws an unusually shaky line when nearing the second dot, it may indicate potential deficiencies in handwriting skills.)

Ways to improve kinesthetic perception of the hands

1. Unstructured clay modeling facilitates a student's perception of his or her hands. Encourage the student to manipulate the clay in every possible way—squeezing, flattening, poking, making shapes, etc.

2. To heighten the student's perception of shape, use a box in which a variety of small objects are placed for the student to feel but not see.

   a. Ask the student to reach in the box and find an unseen object that matches the one he or she is looking at.

   b. Direct the student to locate in the box an object that you or another student has described.

   c. Ask the student to find two objects with similar characteristics—two fuzzy objects, two heavy objects, two small objects, etc.

3. Draw several circles on a sheet of paper. To determine the student's ability to aim the finger and hand and also to point, have the student place dots in the circles with a pencil, pen, or crayon. Vary the difficulty of this task by increasing or decreasing the size of the circles or increasing the rate at which the dots are made. (The student must be able to point at a given or imaginary point in order to begin the stroke of a letter.)

Ways to confirm hand-eye tracking skills

The ability to control continuous hand movements while drawing lines of varying difficulty is basic to handwriting. If you are able to detect problems as the student completes the following tasks and are able to obtain appropriate assistance for the student, subsequent difficulties may be avoided.

1. Demonstrate drawing parallel lines. Then direct the student to draw parallel lines of a given length, first at a relaxed pace then at a faster one.

2. Direct the student to draw two curved lines equal in distance from one another. Later require more difficult shapes that combine straight lines, angles, and/or curves.

3. Direct the student to connect numbered dots on a sheet of paper that require horizontal, vertical and lateral movements. Place the paper in front of the student, close to the dominant hand. Later, space the dots further apart and require the student to cross the midline of his or her body. This latter task may cause the neuro-logically challenged student some difficulty.

The above evaluative tasks may be of help in assisting the learning of handwriting and in discovering deficiencies.

(See INSTRUCTION MANUAL, p. 13, for more suggestions concerning the beginning writer.)

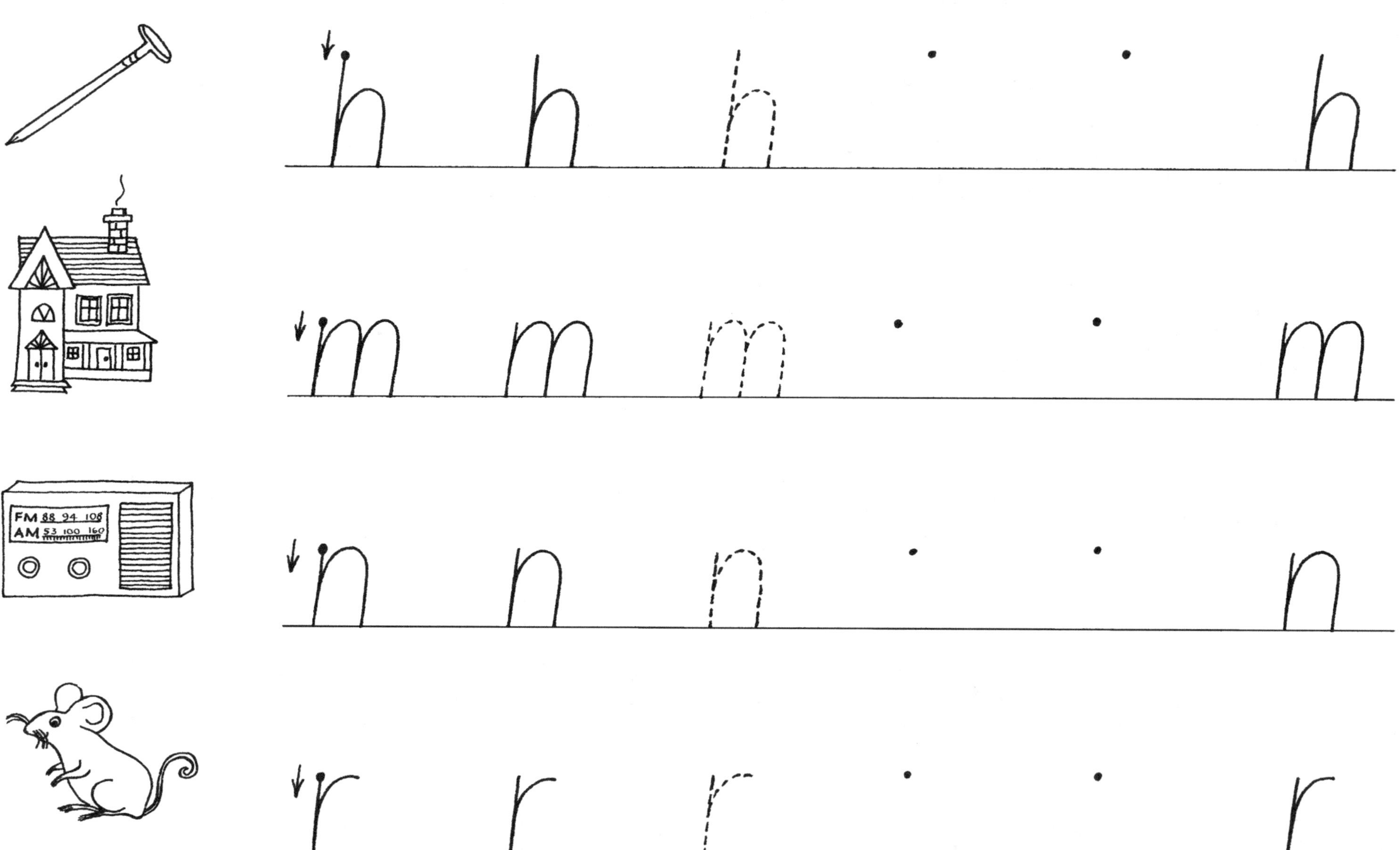

Ask the student to draw a line from the picture to the letter
that stands for the correct beginning sound.

GETTY-DUBAY™ ITALIC HANDWRITING SERIES
BASIC ITALIC ALPHABET

All letters written in one stroke unless otherwise indicated.   *All letters start at the top except lowercase **d** and **e**.*

Aa Bb Cc Dd Ee Ff Gg

alternate 2-stroke e

Hh Ii Jj Kk Ll Mm

Nn Oo Pp Qq Rr Ss Tt

Uu Vv Ww Xx Yy Zz

0 1 2 3 4 5 6 7 8 9

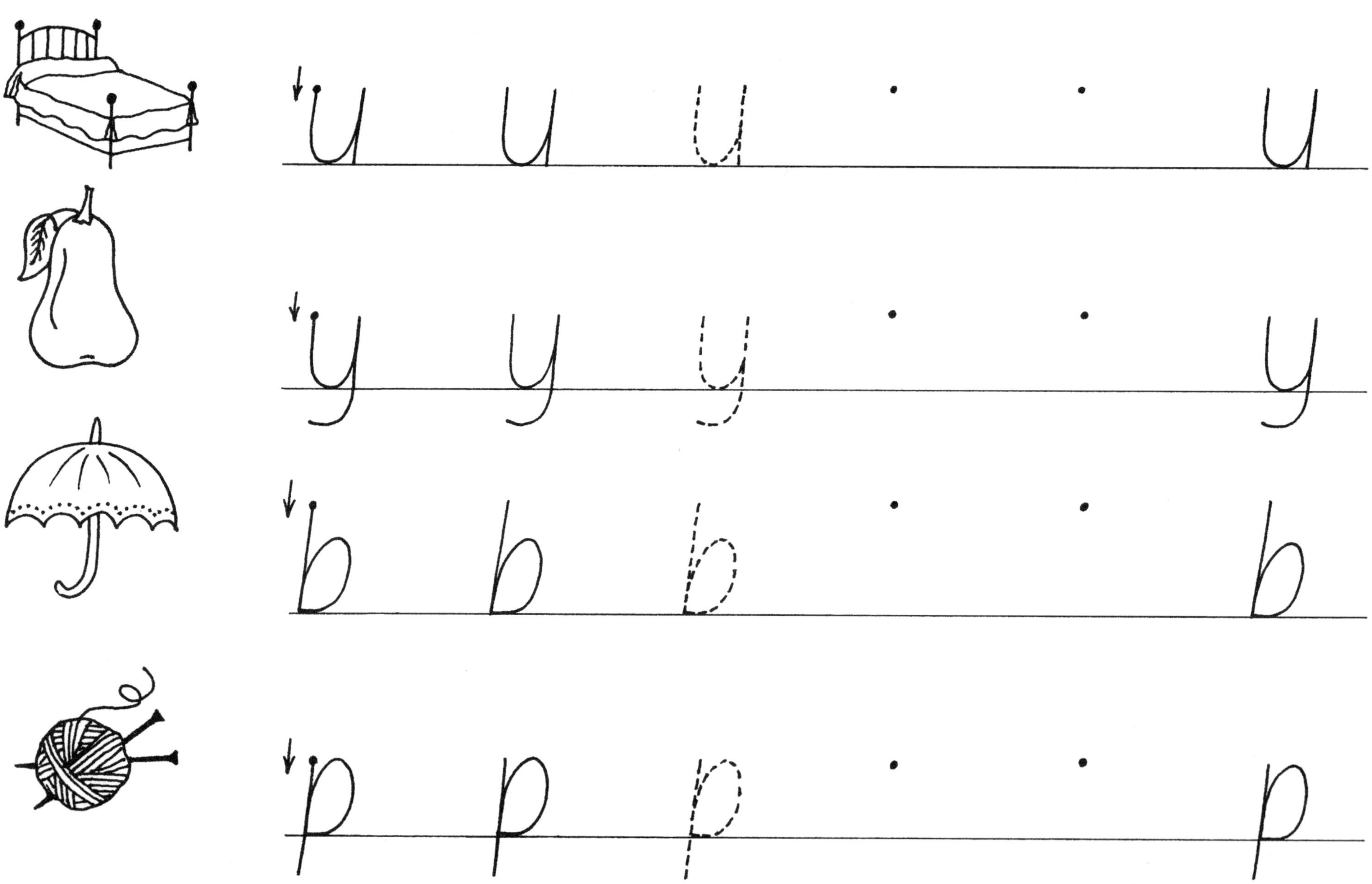

Ask the student to draw a line from the picture to the letter
that stands for the correct beginning sound.

GETTY-DUBAY™ HANDWRITING REMINDERS

PENCIL HOLD

Hold the pencil with the thumb and index finger, resting it on the middle finger. Rest the shaft of the pencil near the large knuckle. Hold the tool firmly and avoid pinching. To relax the hand, tap index finger on the pencil three times. Avoid "thumb wrap" and a "death grip".

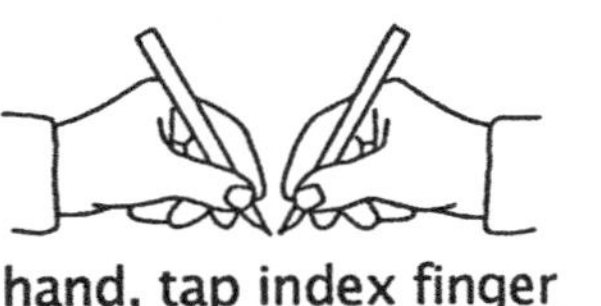

PAPER POSITION

LEFT-HANDED: If the left-handed student writes with the wrist below the writing line, turn paper clockwise so it is slanted to the right, as illustrated.

If the left-handed student writes with a hook, with the wrist above the writing line, turn the paper counter-clockwise so it is slanted to the left, as illustrated. (Similar to right-handed position)

RIGHT-HANDED: If the student is right-handed, turn paper counter-clockwise so it is slanted to the left, as illustrated.

POSTURE

Rest feet flat on the floor and keep back comfortably straight without slumping. Rest forearms on writing surface. The student holds workbook or paper with the nonwriting hand so that the writing area is centered in the front of the student.

PRACTICE PAPER

Book A—Use unlined or lined paper together with workbooks.

MATERIALS

The *Getty-Dubay™ Italic Handwriting Series* workbooks, BOOKS A–G, and the INSTRUCTION MANUAL constitute a step-by-step program. Related materials consist of:

1. BLACKLINE MASTERS/WORKSHEETS - half sheets for introduction to, or review of, workbook pages.
2. CLASSROOM WALL CHARTS - basic & cursive italic.
3. DESK STRIPS - basic & cursive italic.

VOCABULARY

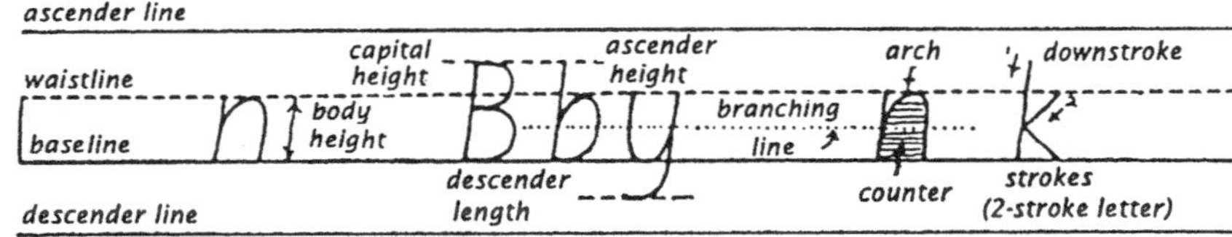

DIRECT INSTRUCTION

Several sessions of direct instruction each week are essential for a successful program. BOOK A – 5 to 10 minute sessions a day are recommended, see INSTRUCTION MANUAL, pp. 18-19

- SHAPE & STROKE SEQUENCE – teach basic italic in letter family groups, or according to the reading program in grade 1.
- SLOPE – encourage a consistent letter slope. Vertical letters (0° slope) may be the easiest to teach to beginning writers.
- SIZE – At first, allow students to write letters any size they wish on unlined paper, then introduce the workbook. A recommended progression through this book is one letter (lowercase and/or capital) per week.

SPACING

When young students are writing words, at first have them leave a space about the width of their two small fingers between words. As they become more proficient, they can leave less space.

ASSESSMENT

The *Getty-Dubay™ Italic Handwriting Series* provides a self-assessment process, LOOK, PLAN, PRACTICE, to enable the student to monitor progress. LOOK, step 1 of this process begins on some of the student pages in BOOK A. Assessment is the key to improving handwriting; in this book we introduce the first of three steps in the LOOK, PLAN, PRACTICE self-assessment process. The students look at their own writing and answer any questions on the page. The pencil indicates the student is to make a written response, generally by circling "yes" or "no". The teacher may encourage students to award themselves a star or a smiling face at the top of the page when they notice self-improvement.

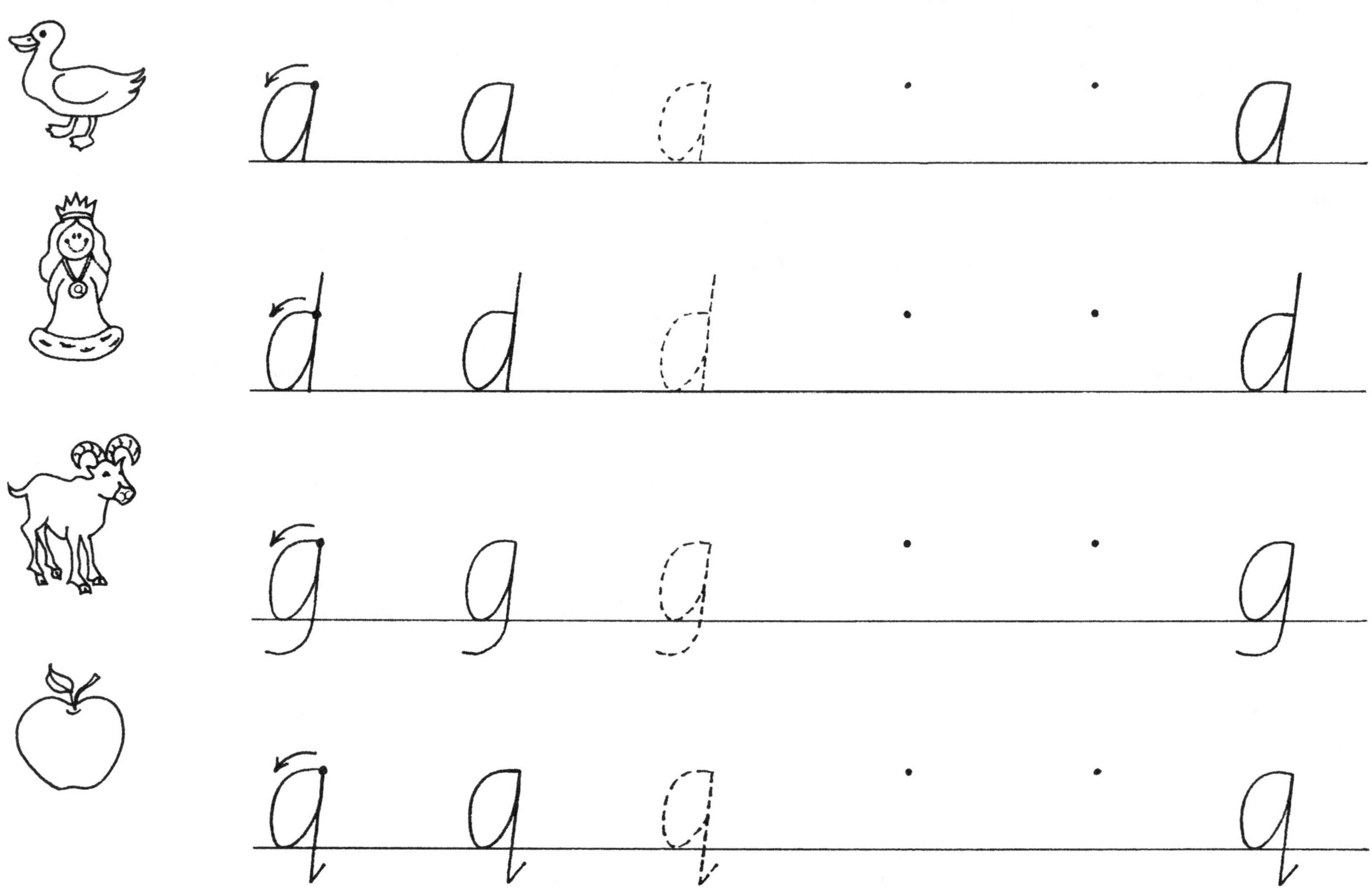

Ask the student to draw a line from the picture to the letter
that stands for the correct beginning sound.

INTRODUCTION

This is the first of seven workbooks providing instruction in basic italic handwriting. It is designed for the beginning student of handwriting and is recommended for preschool, kindergarten and/or early first grade (5 to 7 years of age).

The twenty-six lowercase letters and the twenty-six capitals are introduced one letter per page. Letters are arranged in the order of lowercase families, which group letters with similar strokes together and progress from simple to more complex forms. The matching capital letter occurs on the reverse of each lowercase page allowing introduction of both lowercase and capital together if preferred.

Each page is designed for the student to trace the models provided, write letters at the given dots, and to write a "best" letter in the empty box on each alphabet page. The standard writing tool is the pencil although other writing instruments such as the fiber tip pen may be used. When students are ready, they should trace the word describing the illustration on each letter page, following the dots and arrows.

It is essential that the instructor provide an understanding of the dot and the arrow to assist the writer in completing the pages successfully. The self-assessment method used in the *Getty-Dubay* *Italic Handwriting Series* enables students to monitor their individual progress. Step 1, LOOK, of the three-step LOOK, PLAN, PRACTICE format, is incorporated on 21 of the student pages. Students are asked to "LOOK" at their writing and affirm what is best. On the 21 pages with "LOOK" questions, students should circle their chosen answers. See INSTRUCTION MANUAL, PP. 13, 18 & 19.

The *Getty-Dubay™ Italic Handwriting Series* INSTRUCTION MANUAL is to be used in conjunction with this workbook. Explanations and in-depth descriptions of lowercase letters, capitals, joins, and numerals are presented in the manual, emphasizing shape, strokes, size, slope and spacing of the letters. Also included in the manual are: a rationale for italic handwriting, techniques for teaching and assessing handwriting, sequence of skills, handwriting activities, and a brief history of our alphabet.

BOOK B, basic italic, follows this workbook and is designed for the beginning reader. In the third book, BOOK C, basic italic letterforms are reinforced and cursive italic is introduced. BOOKS D, E, F, and G provide a complete basic italic and cursive italic handwriting program. BOOKS B, C, and/or D may also be suitable for the person learning English as a second language.

The format of this book was chosen to accommodate both the left- and right-handed writer. When open, the book fits easily on a small desk, and the writer is not encumbered with an additional page to the left or right. From day one, use a Getty-Dubay™ basic italic desk strip as a reminder. Blackline masters are designed for supplementary practice and are available for each workbook in the series. See www.handwritingsuccess.com for these supplementary materials.

You can guide children toward the challenge and delight in the writing process by reading to them, modeling handwriting, providing writing materials, and especially by building enthusiasm for the letters of our alphabet and for the written word.

· abcdefghijklmnopqrstuvwxyz ·

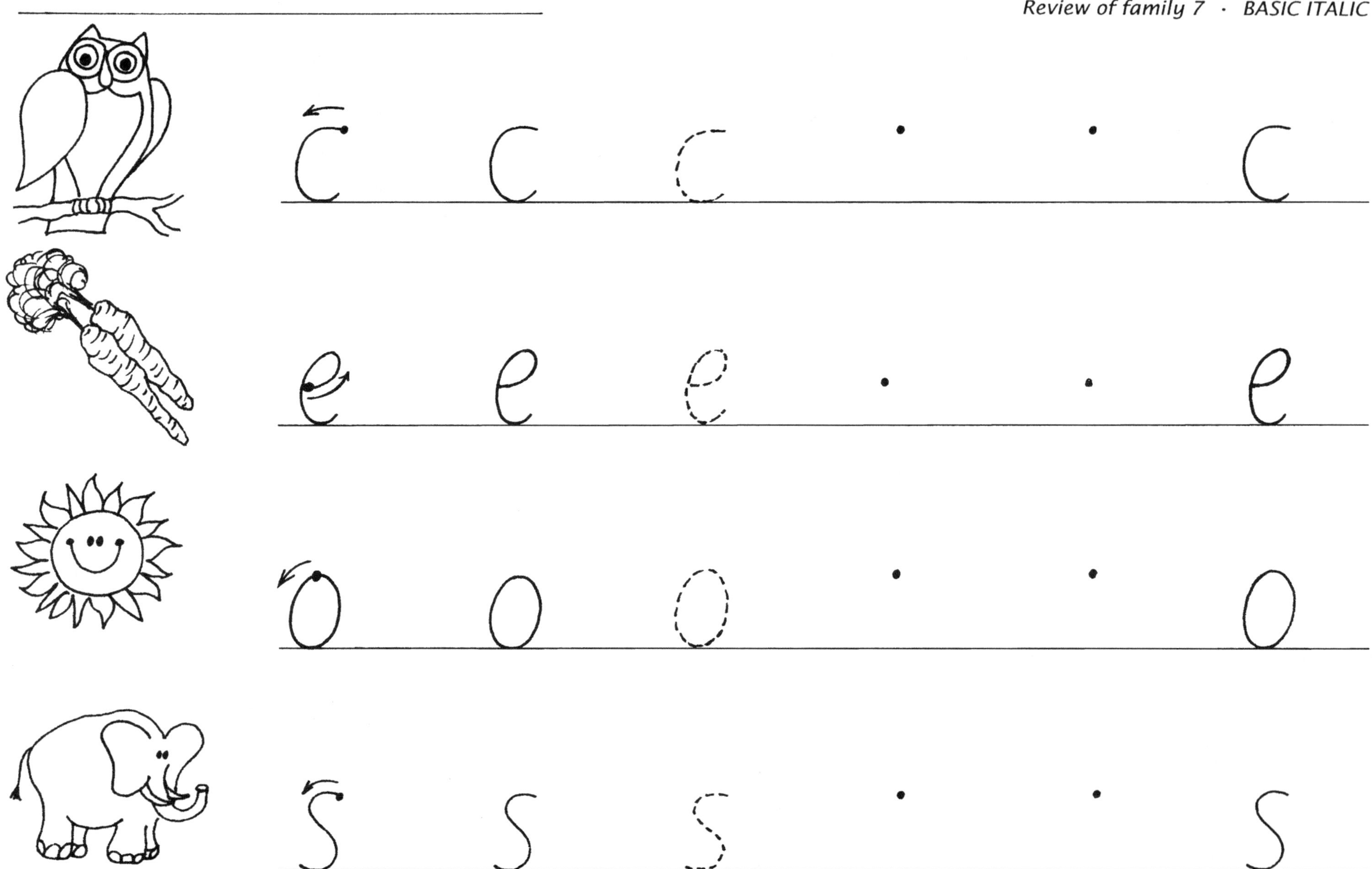

Ask the student to draw a line from the picture to the letter
that stands for the correct beginning sound.

CONTENTS

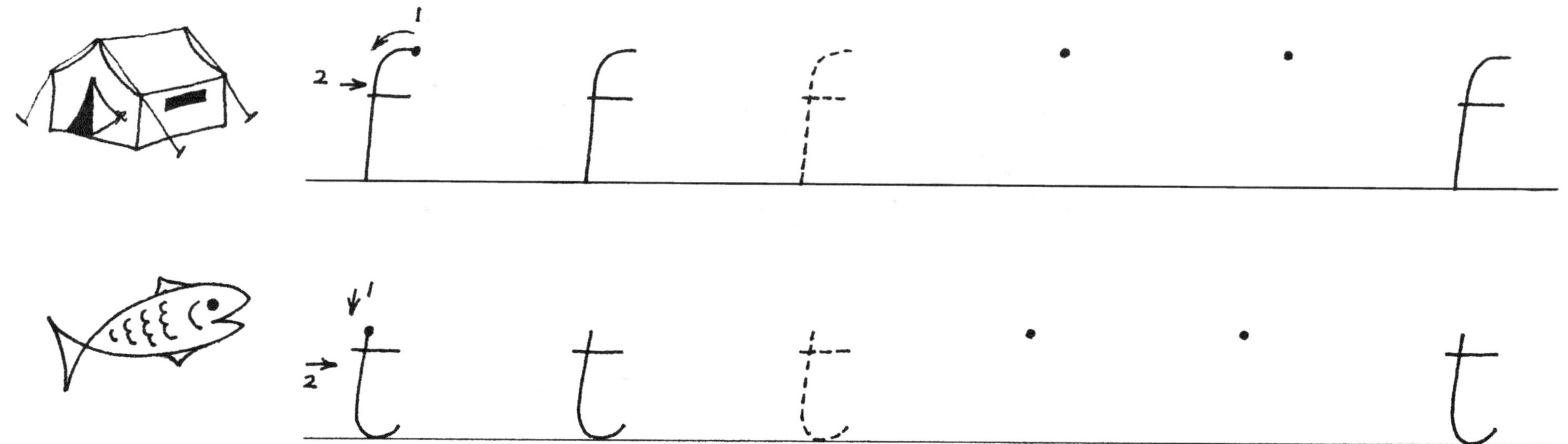

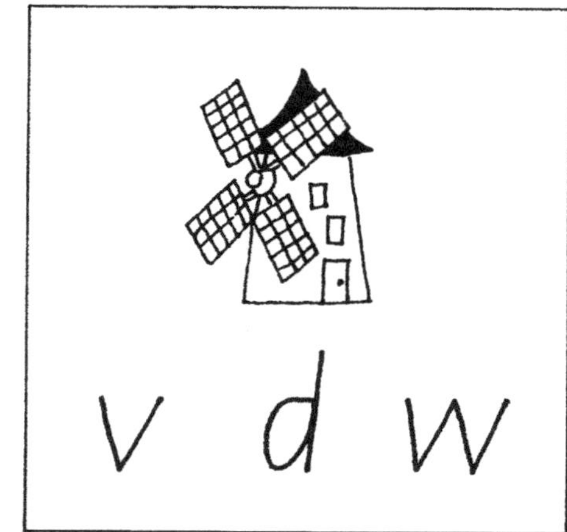

TOP TWO LINES: Ask the student to draw a line from the picture to the letter that stands for the correct beginning sound.

BOTTOM FOUR SQUARES: Ask the student to circle the letter that stands for the beginning sound of the picture.

by

Barbara Getty & Inga Dubay

GETTY-DUBAY™ ITALIC HANDWRITING SERIES

BOOK A ▪ Basic Italic
14 mm body height

BOOK B ▪ Basic Italic
11 mm body height, 9 mm

BOOK C ▪ Basic & Cursive Italic
9 mm, 6 mm body height   Introduction to Cursive Italic

BOOK D ▪ Basic & Cursive Italic
6 mm, 5 mm body height

BOOK E ▪ Basic & Cursive Italic
6 mm, 5 mm, 4 mm body height

BOOK F ▪ Basic & Cursive Italic
6 mm, 5 mm, 4 mm body height

BOOK G ▪ Basic & Cursive Italic
5 mm, 4 mm body height

INSTRUCTION MANUAL

BOOK A ▪ INTERNATIONAL EDITION
Copyright 2012 by Barbara M. Getty and Inga S. Dubay
ISBN 978-0-9827762-7-8

FOURTH EDITION
Copyright 2012 by Barbara M. Getty and Inga S. Dubay
THIRD EDITION
Copyright 1999 by Barbara M. Getty and Inga S. Dubay
SECOND EDITION
Copyright 1986 by Barbara M. Getty and Inga S. Dubay
REVISED EDITION
Copyright 1980 by Barbara M. Getty and Inga S. Dubay
FIRST EDITION
Copyright 1979 by Barbara M. Getty and Inga S. Dubay

All rights reserved. This text may not be reproduced in whole or in part without the express written permission of the copyright holder.

Published by Handwriting Success, LLC,
Portland, Oregon USA

www.handwritingsuccess.com

Printed at various locations around the world by IngramSpark.

Cover Design: Sinda Markham
Front cover picture: Flowers of the sunflower family in the Ochoco National Forest, Oregon, USA
Back cover pictures: Columbine flower, Golden-mantled squirrel

www.ingramcontent.com/pod-product-compliance
Lightning Source LLC
Chambersburg PA
CBHW081423210726
48464CB00020B/1370

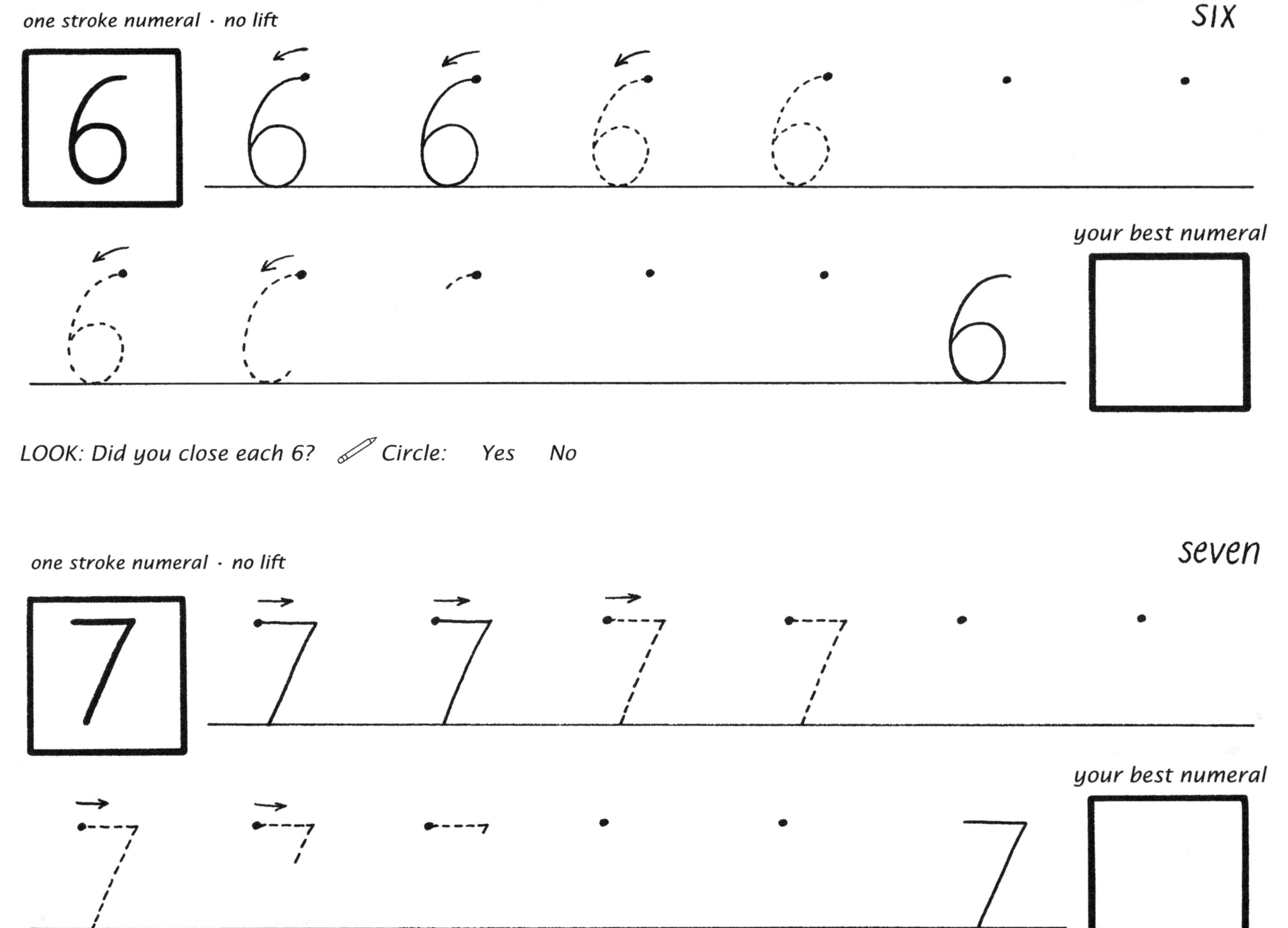

one stroke numeral · no lift
your best numeral
LOOK: Did you close each 6?   Circle: Yes   No
one stroke numeral · no lift
seven
your best numeral

two stroke numeral · one lift

your best numeral

two stroke numeral · one lift

your best numeral

one stroke numeral · no lift
eight
your best numeral
nine
one stroke numeral · no lift
your best numeral
LOOK: Did you close the top of each 8 and 9?   Circle: Yes   No

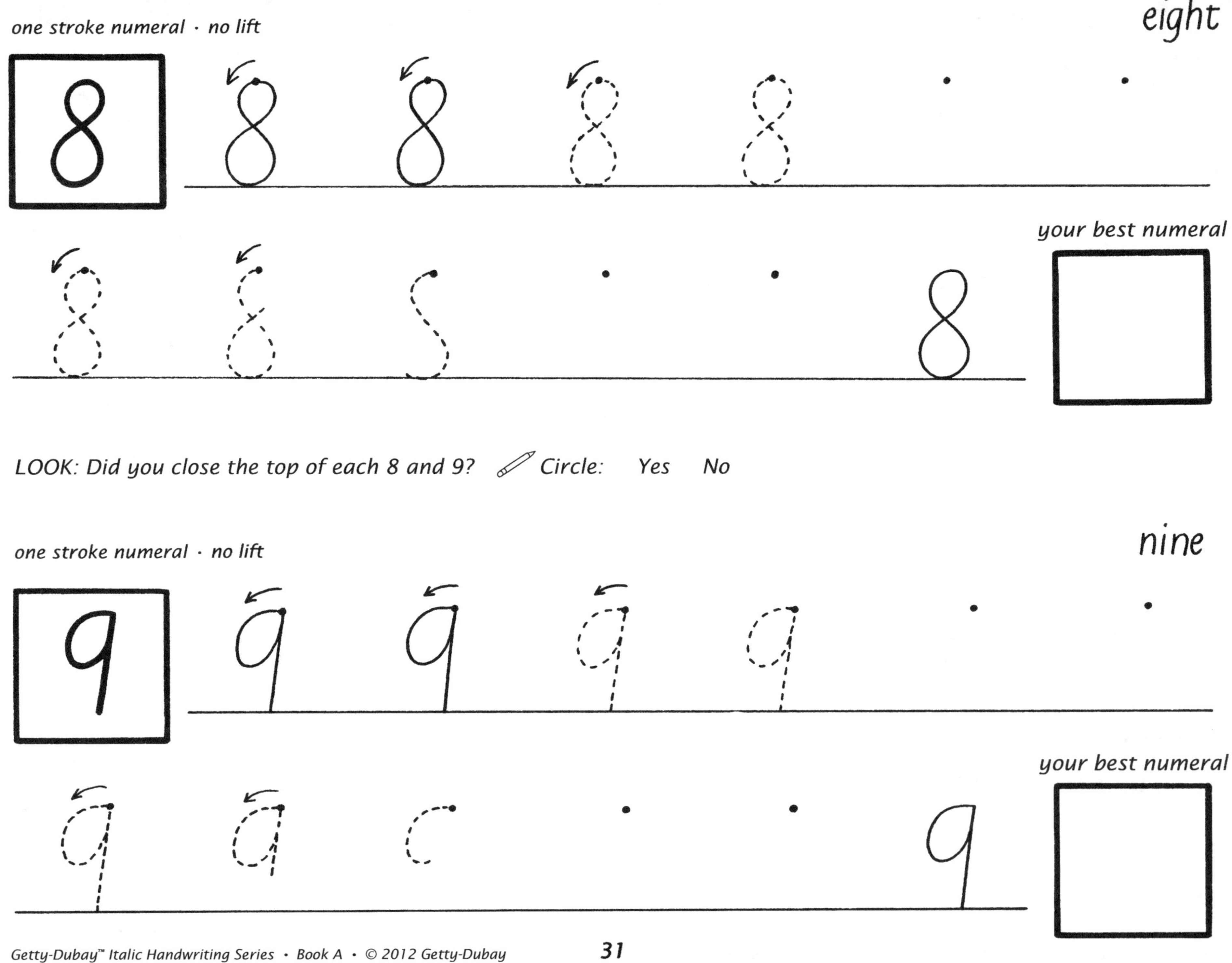

one stroke numeral · no lift

your best numeral

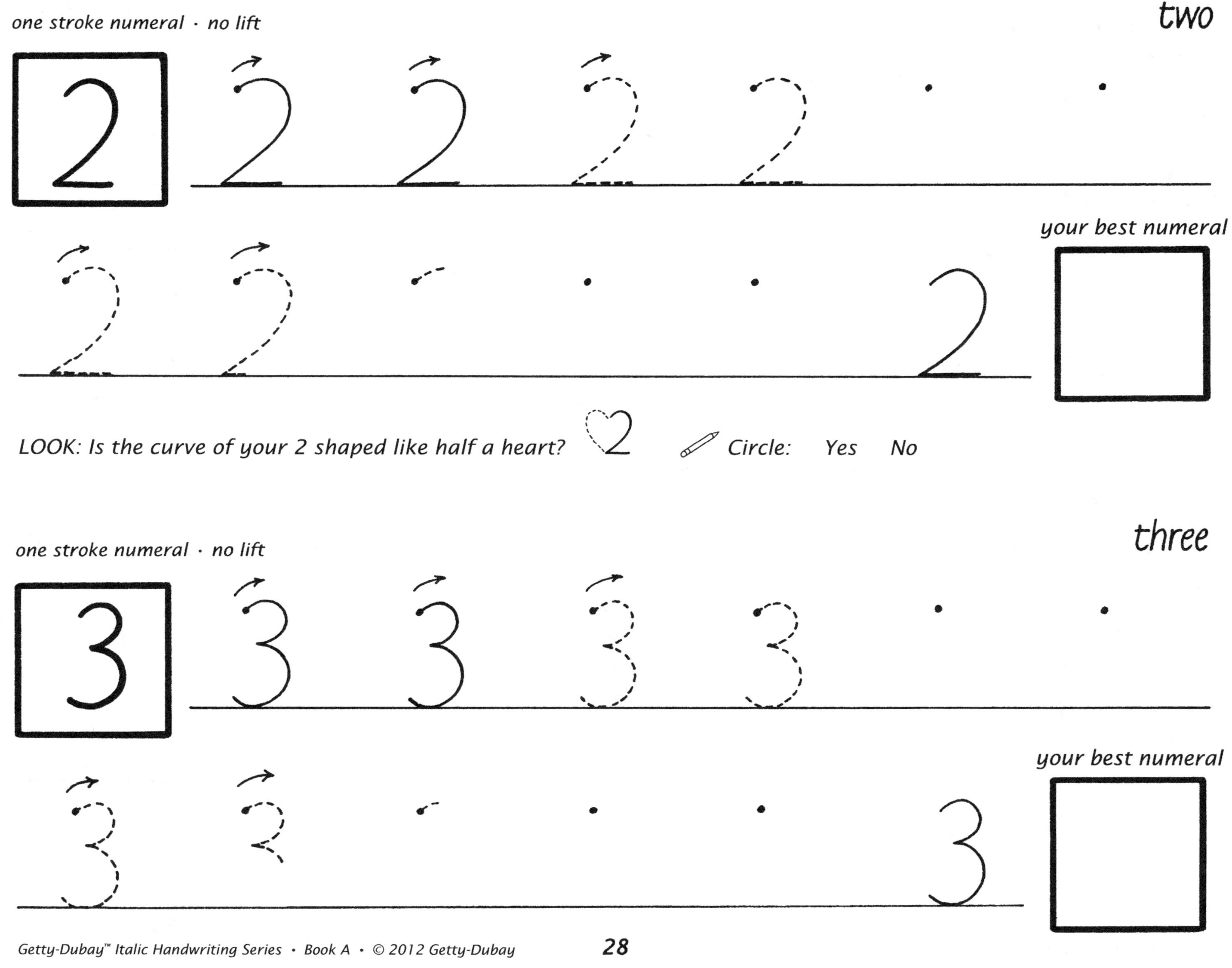

LOOK: Is the curve of your 2 shaped like half a heart? ✏ Circle: Yes   No

three

one stroke numeral · no lift

your best numeral

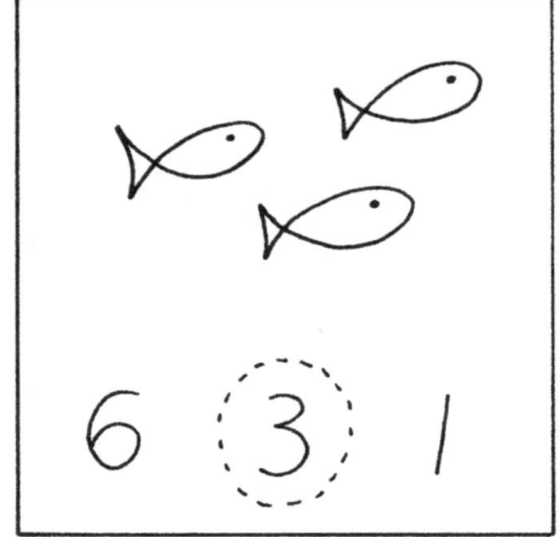

6   3   1

9   2   5

7   0   4

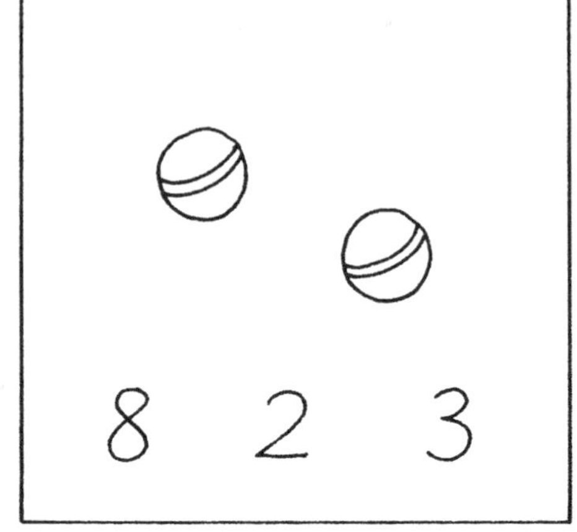

8   2   3

3   4   2

9   5   6

7   1   6

2   8   6

*Ask the student to circle the numeral
that stands for the number of objects in the box.*

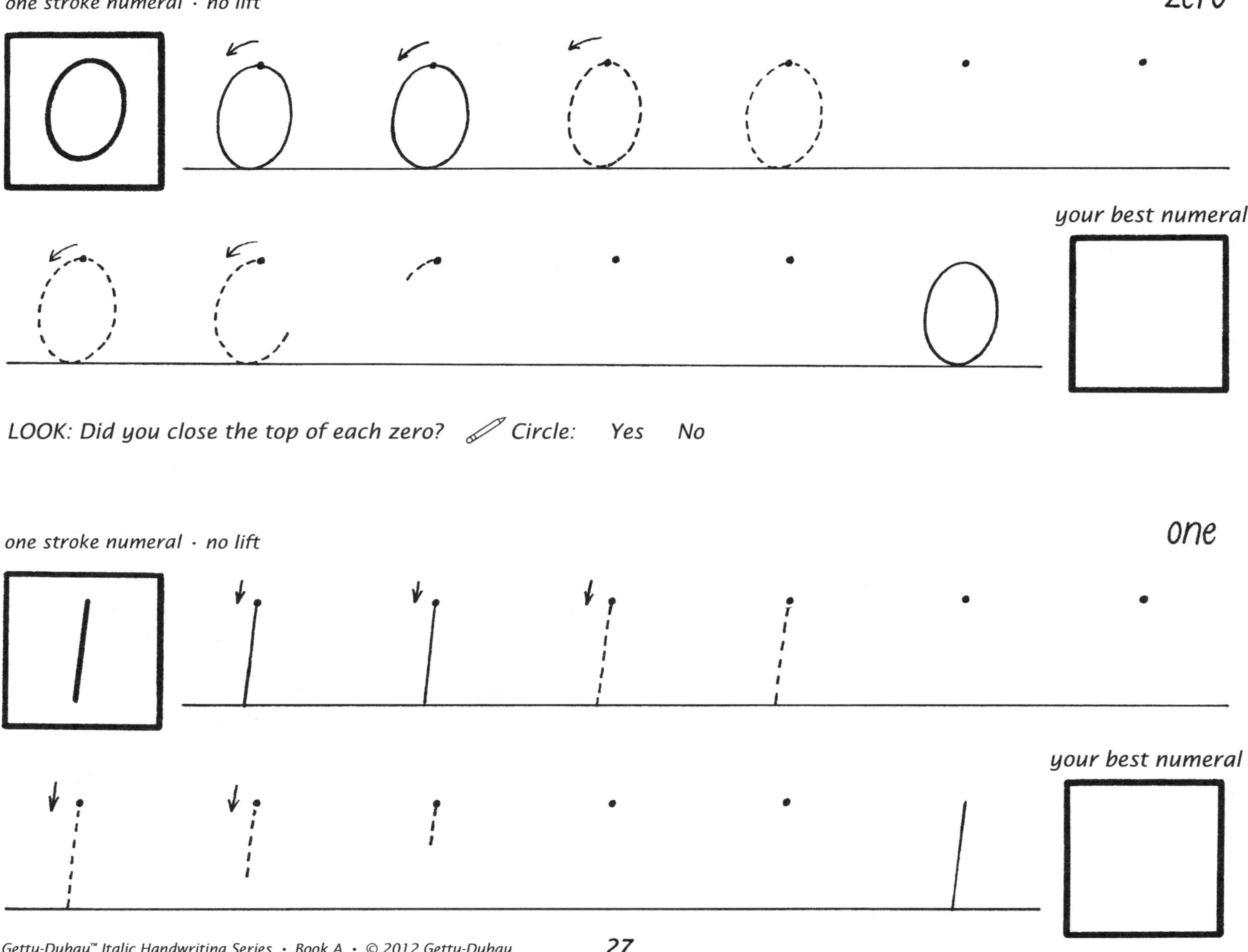

one stroke numeral · no lift
zero
your best numeral
LOOK: Did you close the top of each zero?   Circle: Yes   No
one stroke numeral · no lift
one
your best numeral

T

your best letter

Tent

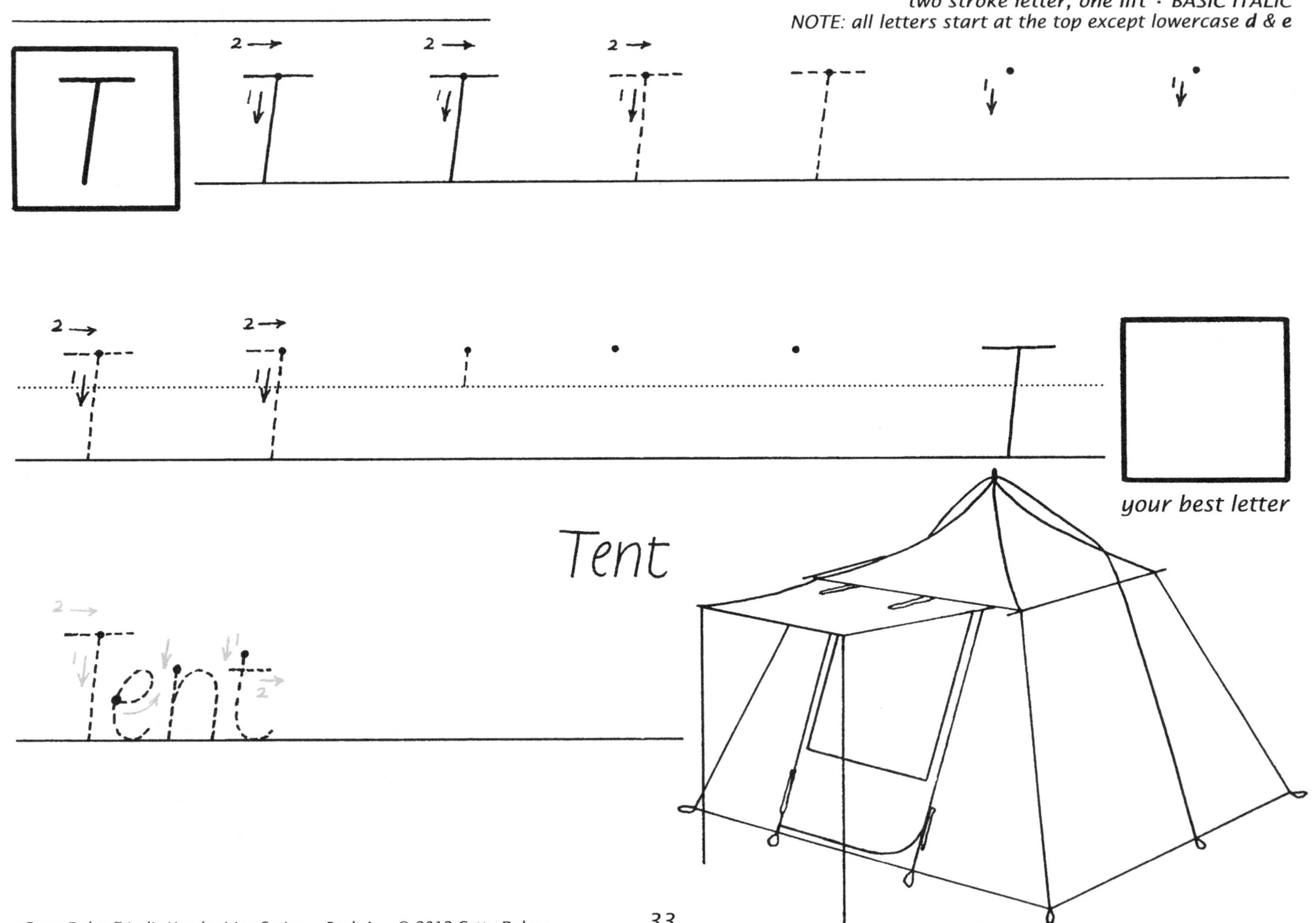

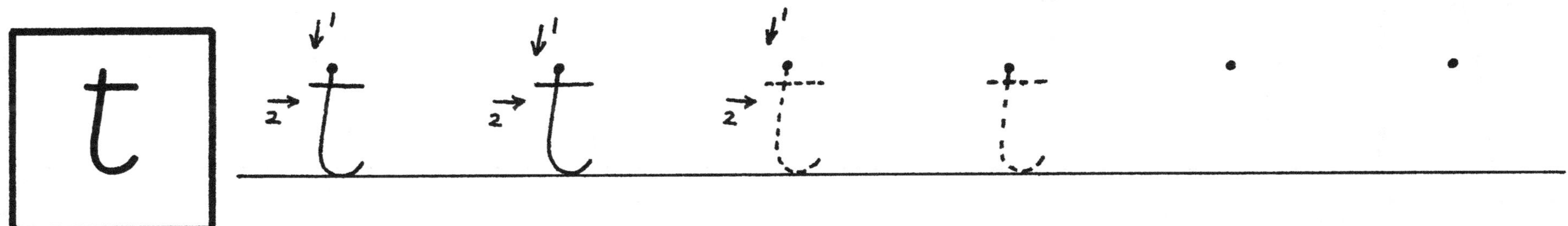

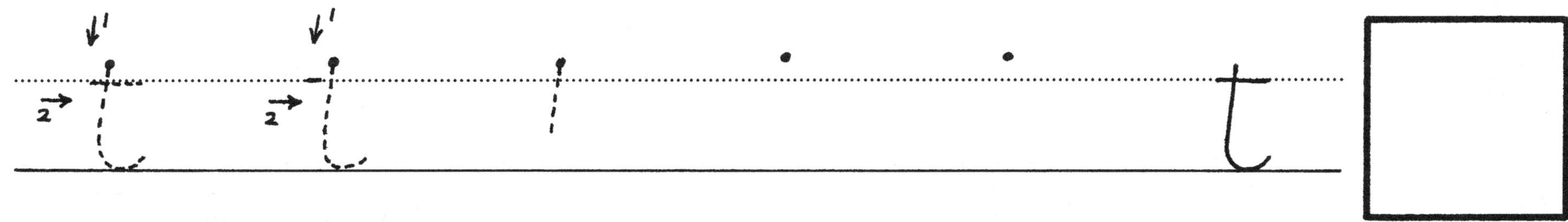

your best letter

turkey

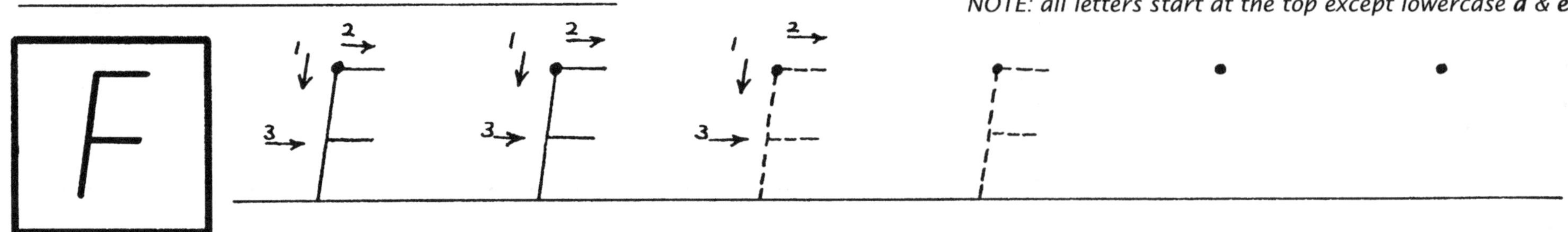

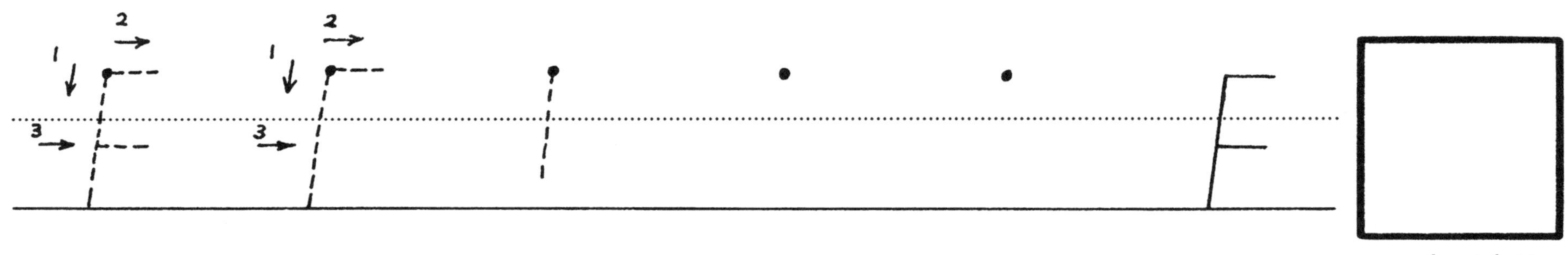

your best letter

Fence

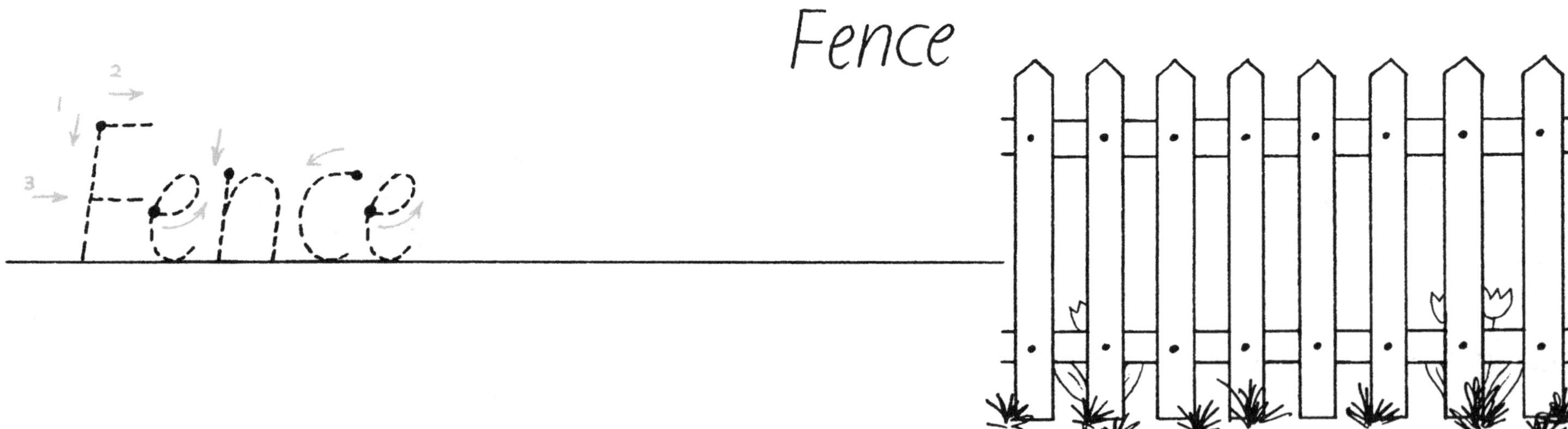

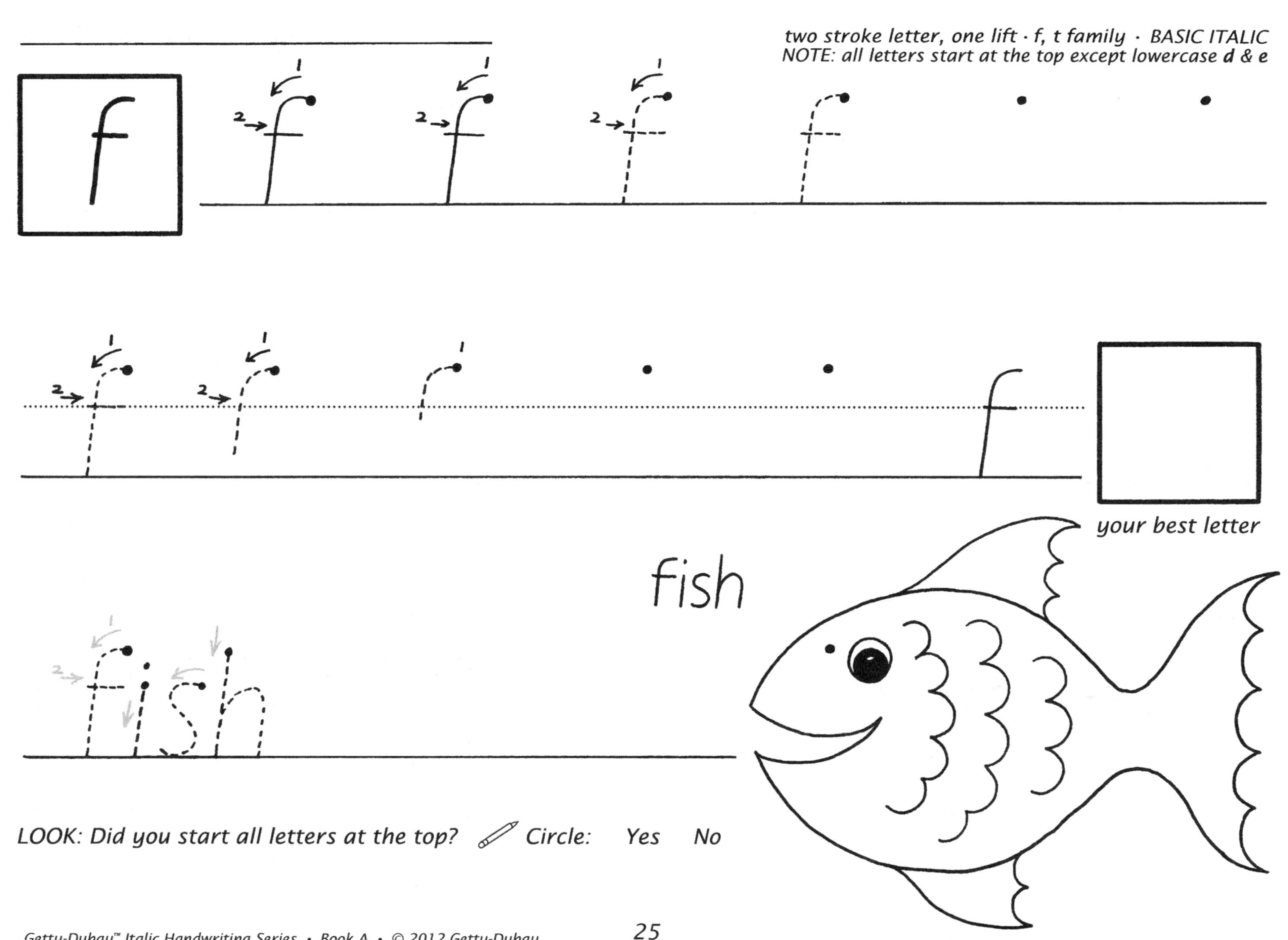

LOOK: Did you start all letters at the top? Circle: Yes   No

your best letter

Sailboat

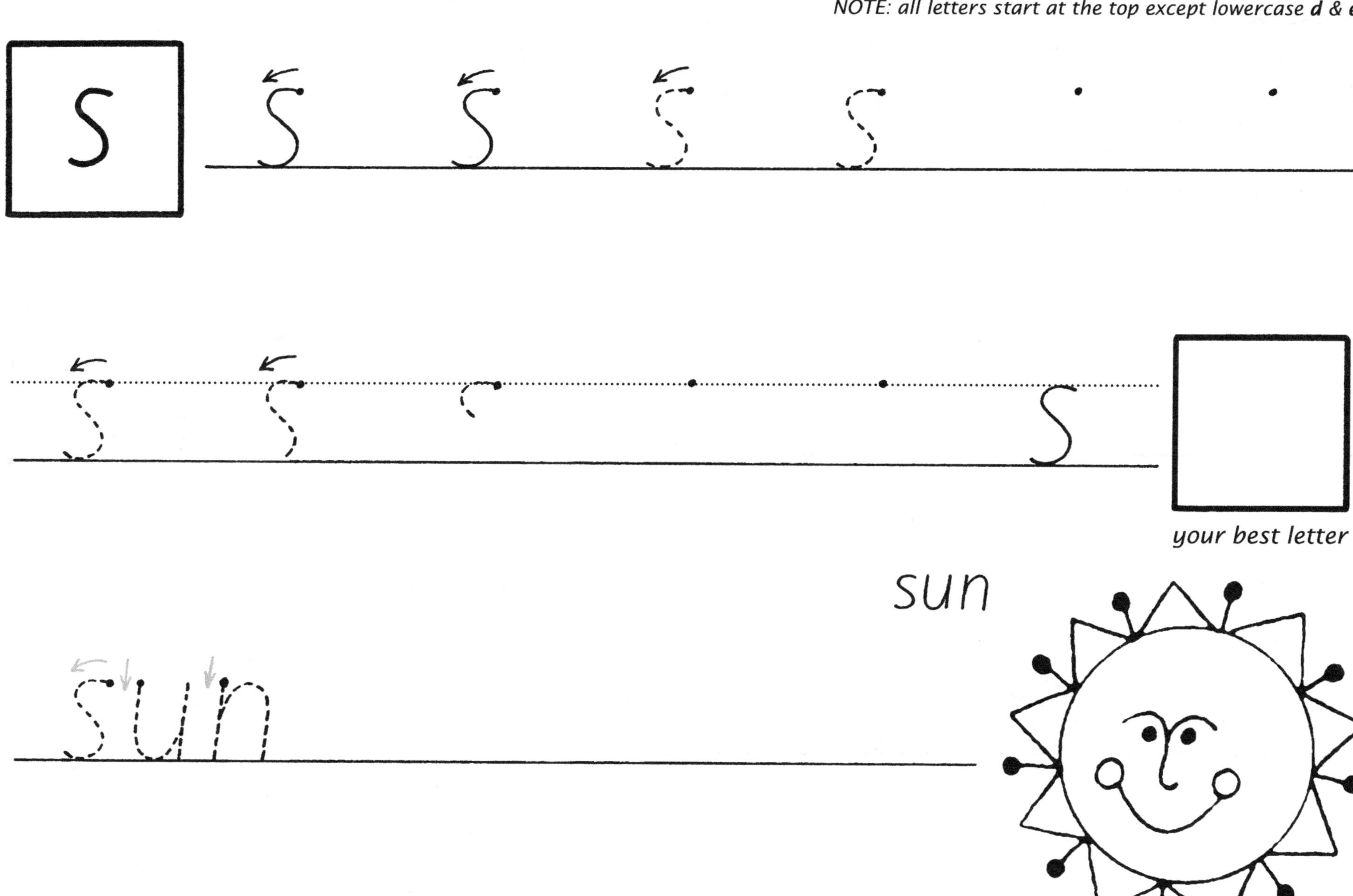

your best letter
sun
sun

one stroke letter, no lift · BASIC ITALIC
NOTE: all letters start at the top except lowercase d & e
your best letter
Cow
LOOK: Did you trace each letter before writing your own?
Circle: Yes   No

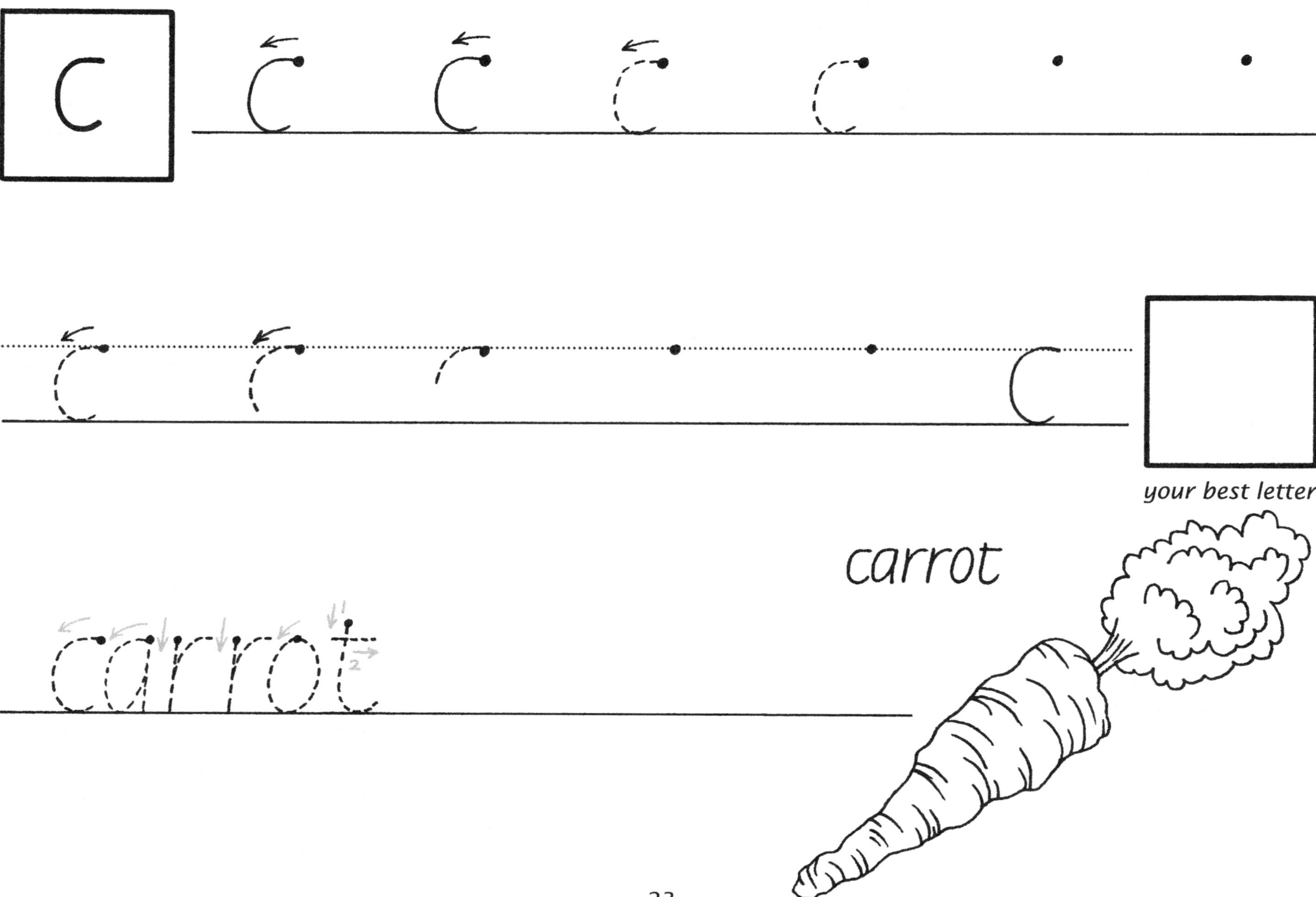

your best letter

carrot

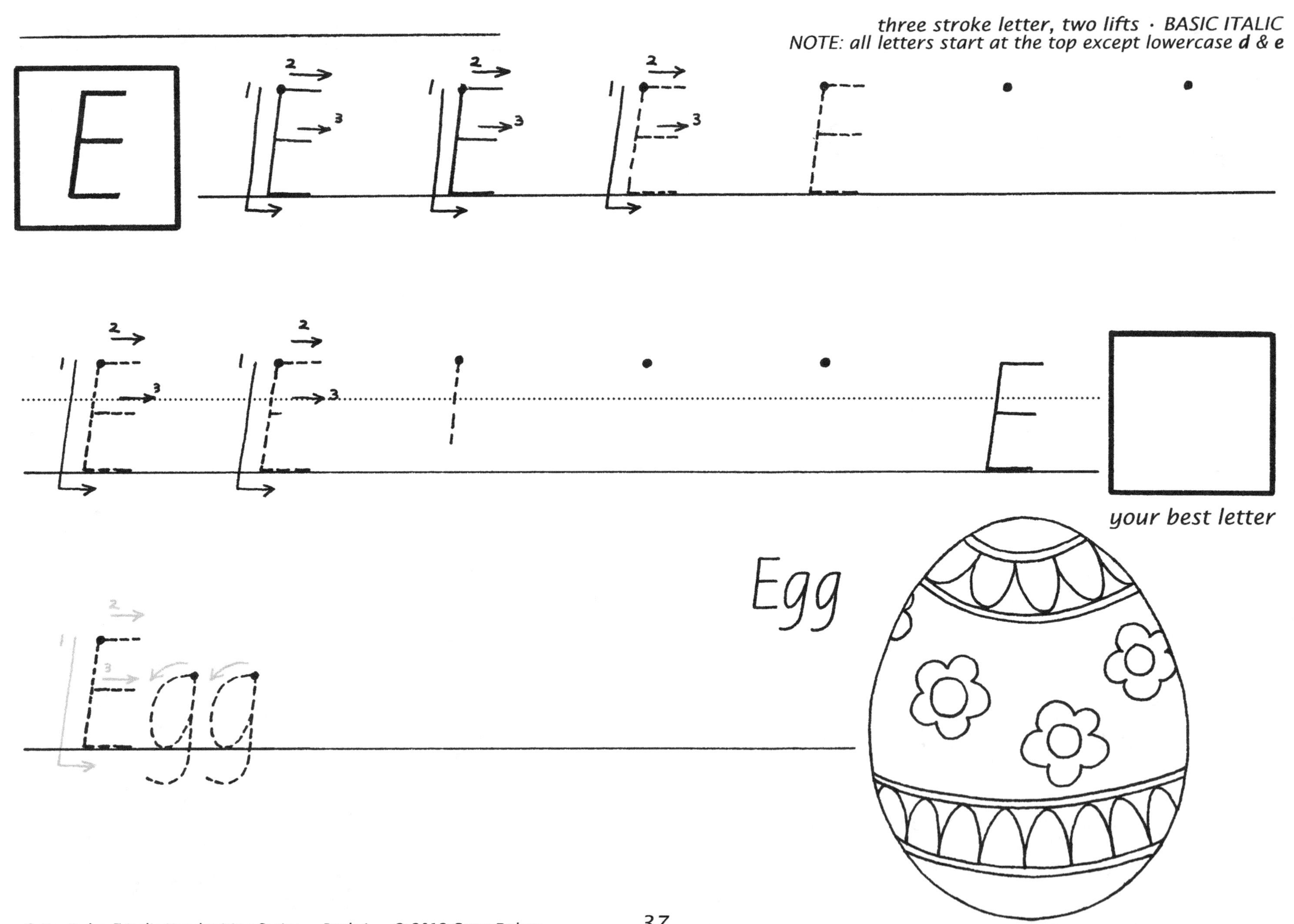

E
your best letter
Egg
Egg

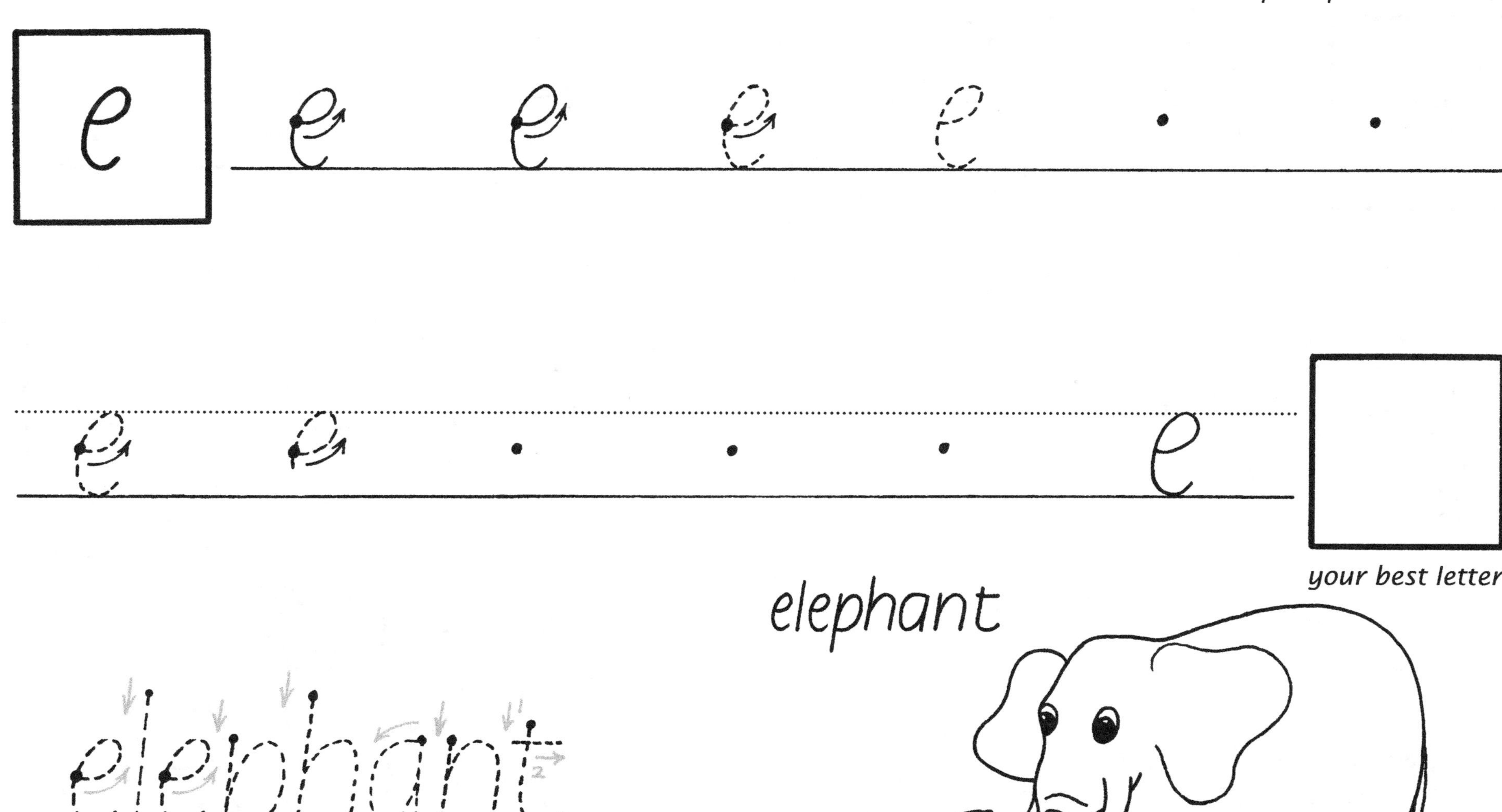

LOOK: Did you trace each **e** before writing your own?

Circle: Yes   No

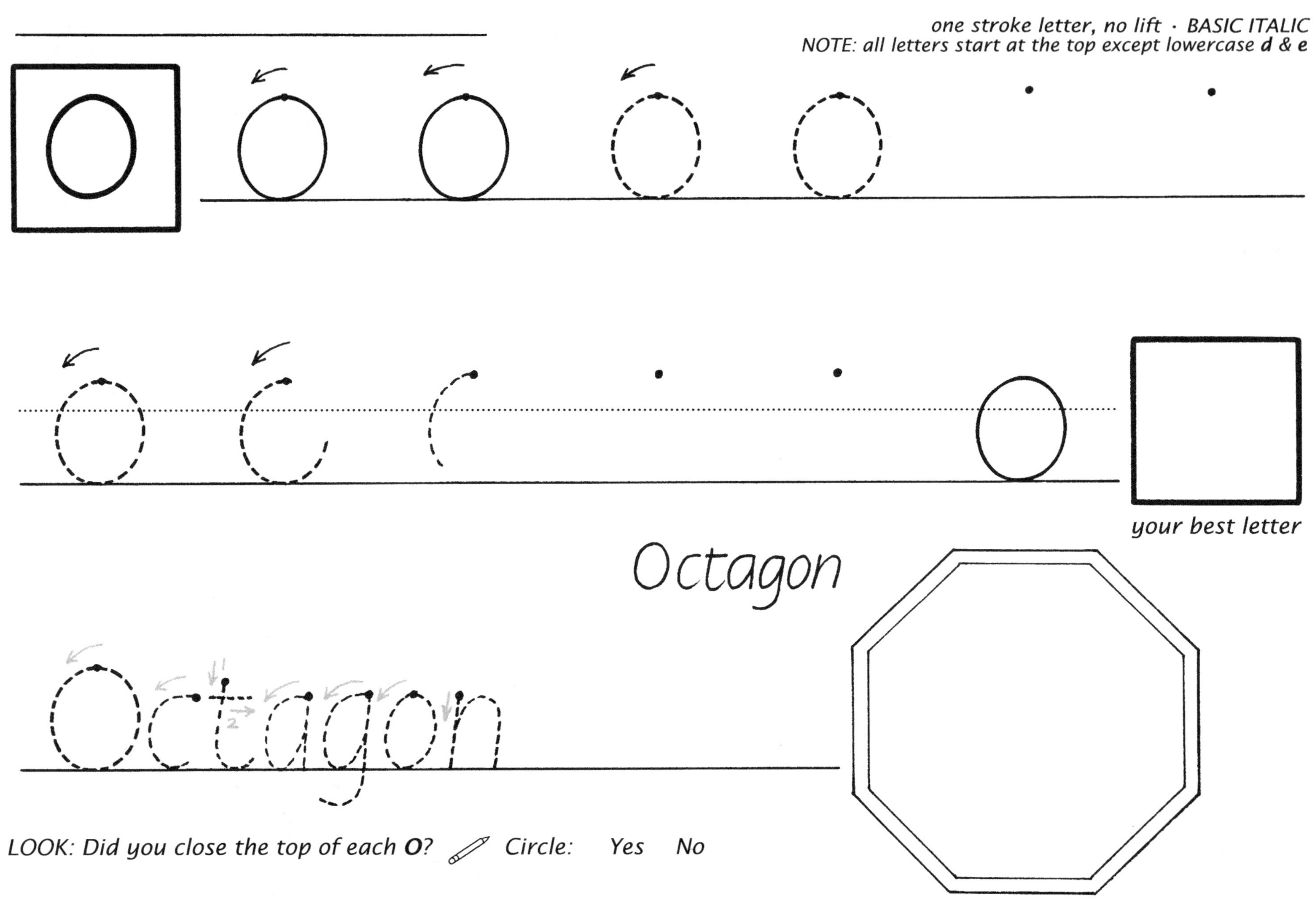

one stroke letter, no lift · BASIC ITALIC
NOTE: all letters start at the top except lowercase d & e
your best letter
Octagon
LOOK: Did you close the top of each O? Circle: Yes   No

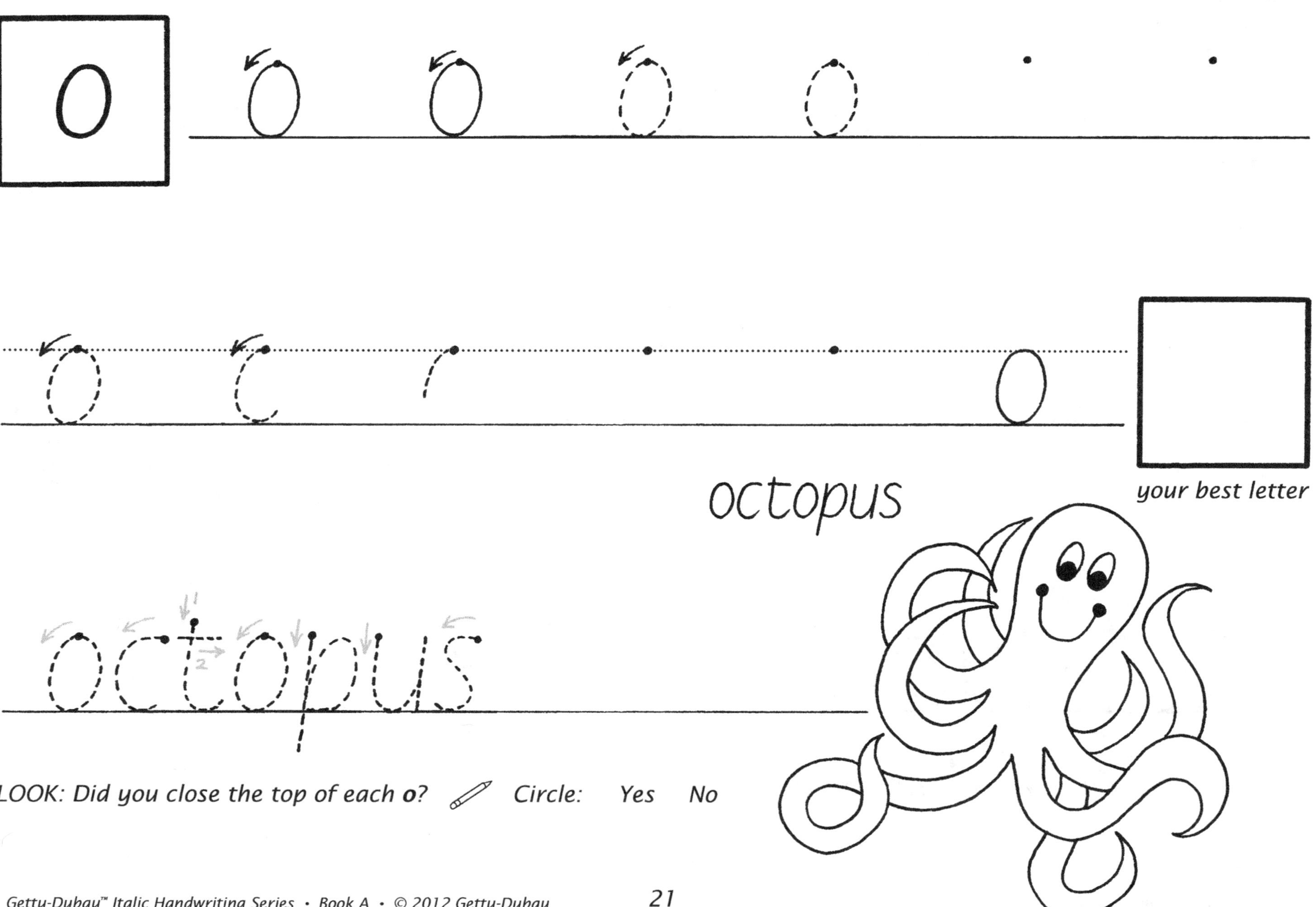

LOOK: Did you close the top of each *o*?   Circle: Yes   No

your best letter

Peacock

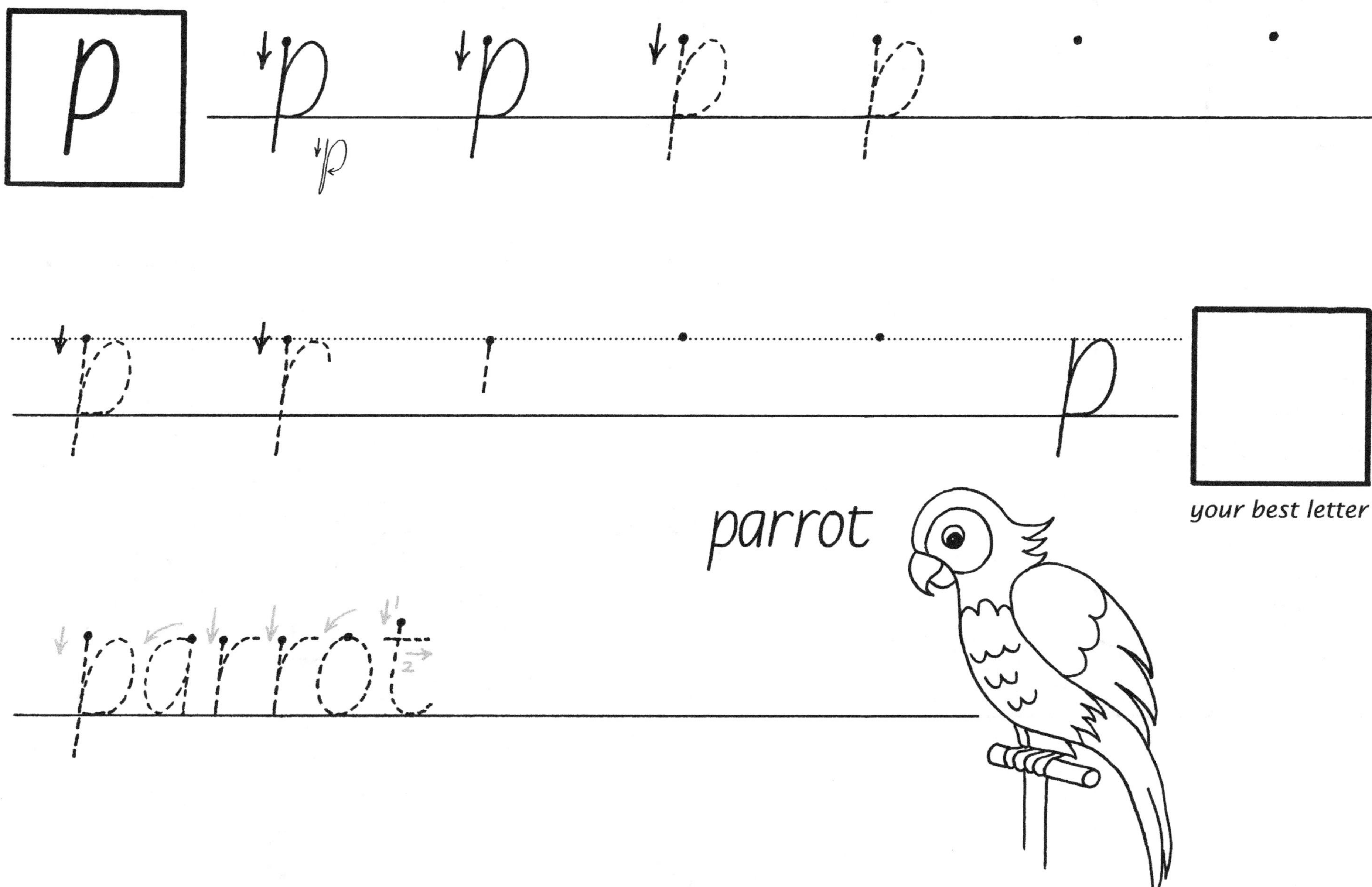

parrot
parrot
your best letter

B

your best letter

Balloons

Balloons

your best letter

butterfly

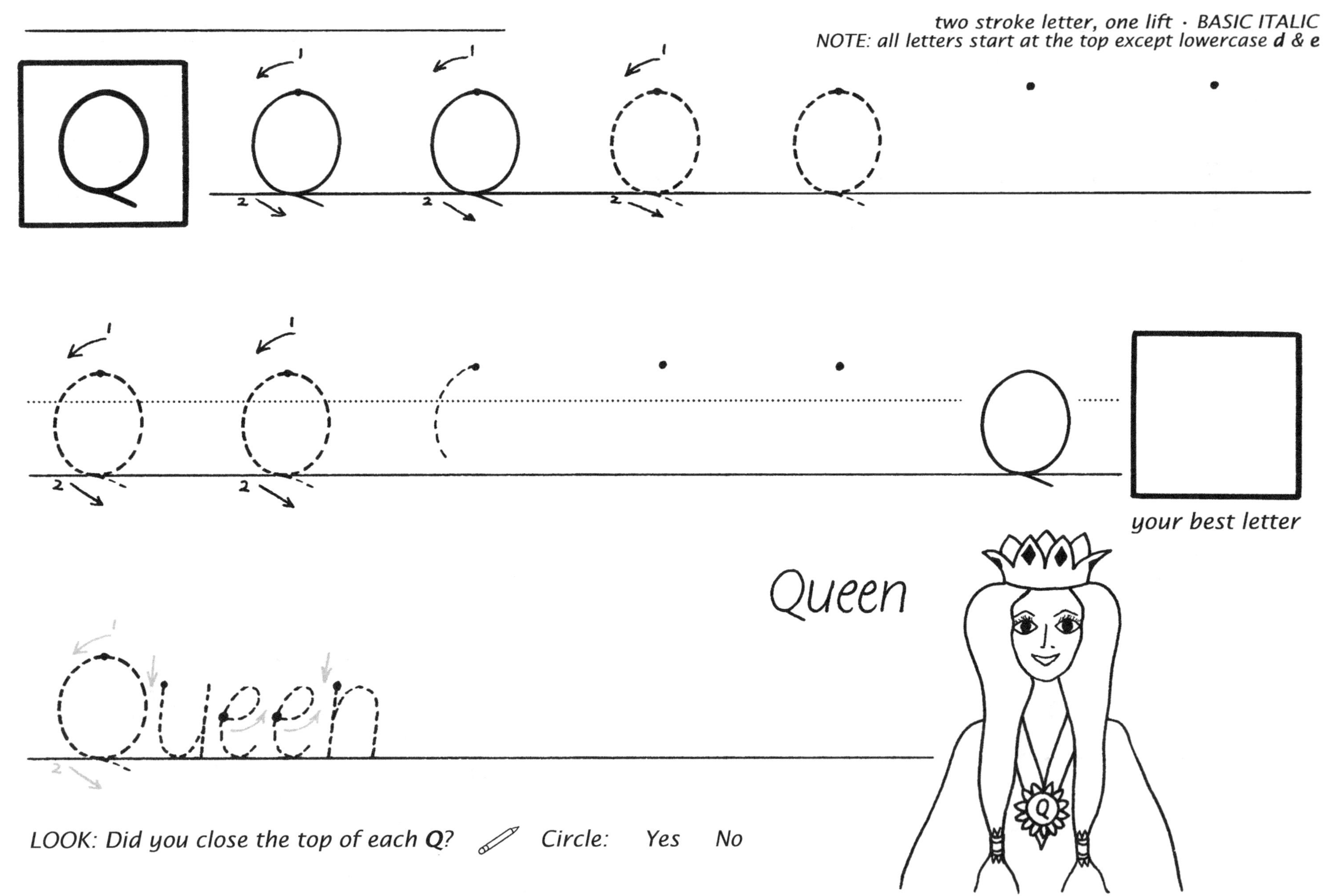

your best letter

Queen

LOOK: Did you close the top of each **Q**?   Circle: Yes   No

q

quilt

your best letter

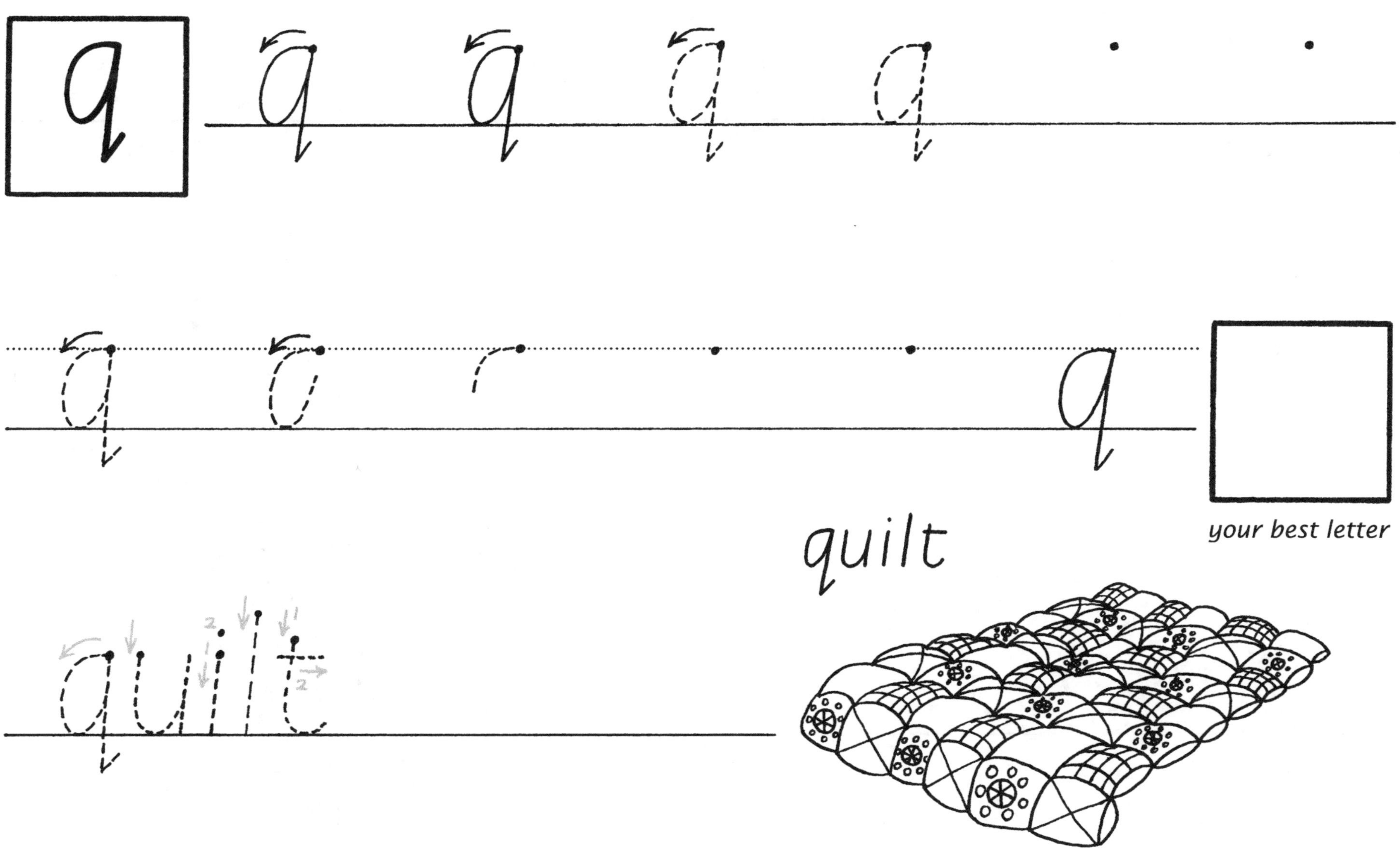

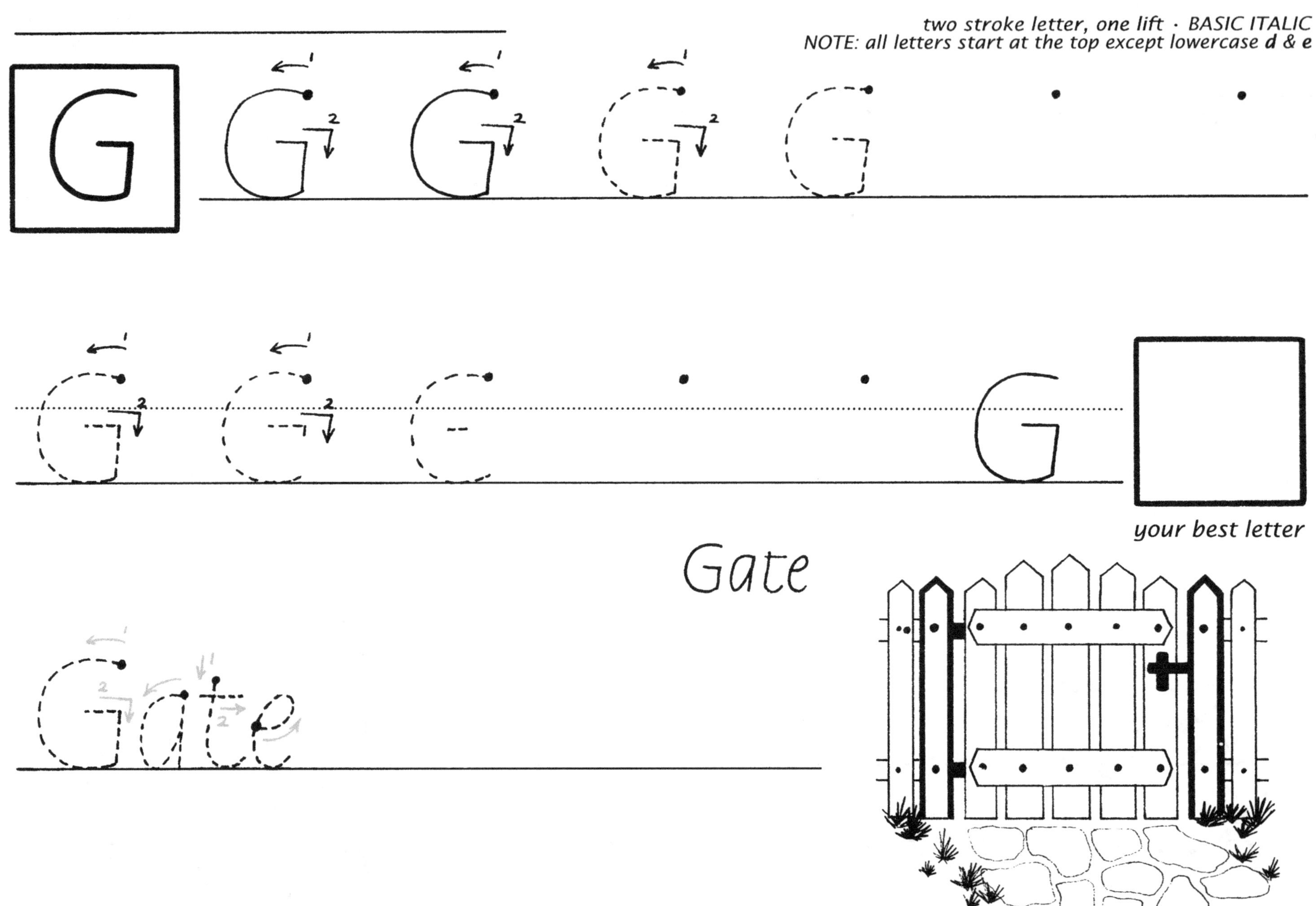
G
your best letter
Gate

LOOK: Did you trace each letter before writing your own? Circle: Yes   No

your best letter

Dinosaur

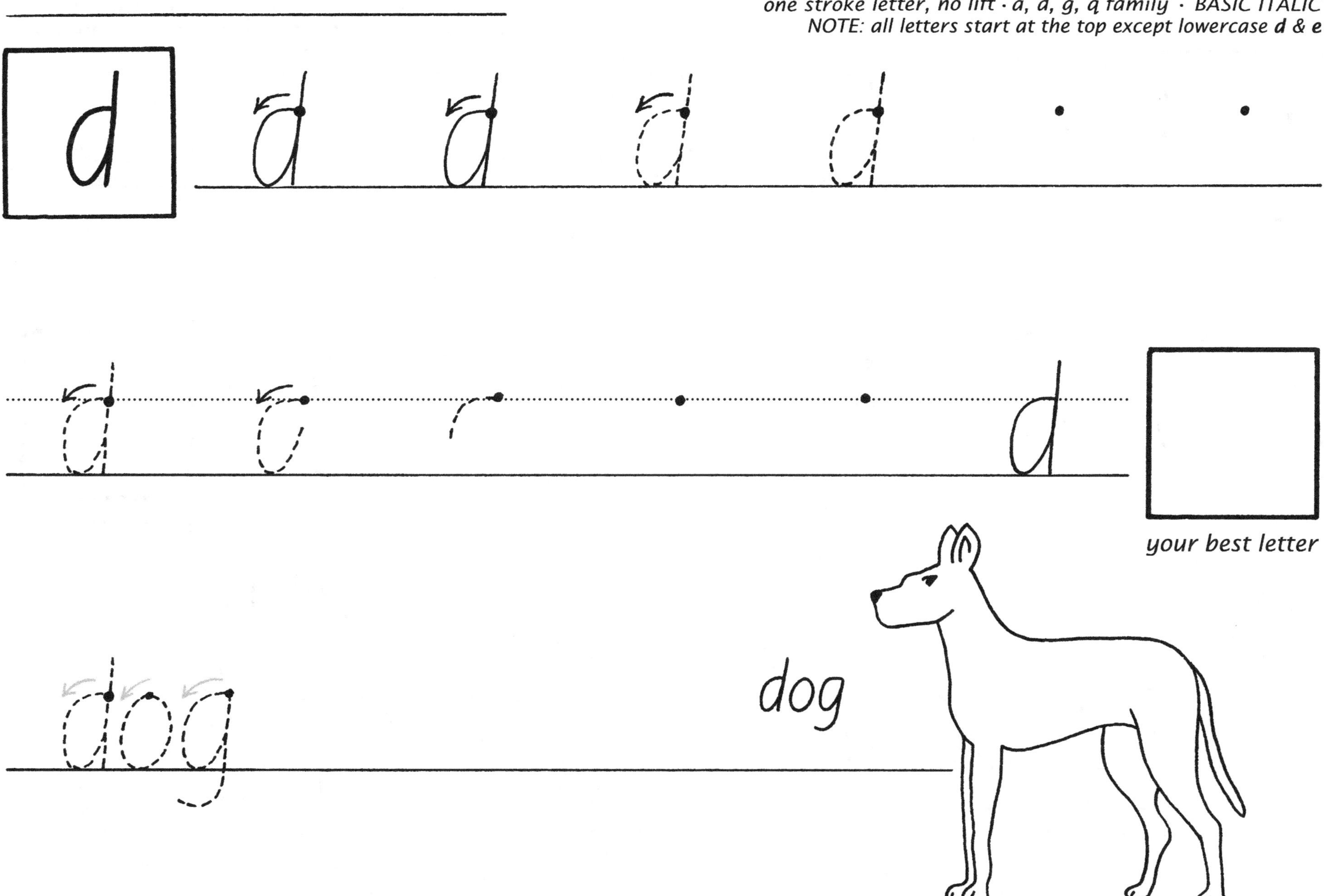

your best letter
dog

your best letter

Alligator

LOOK: Did you start all letters at the top? Circle: Yes   No

LOOK: Did you close each **a** at the top? Circle: Yes   No

your best letter

Yo-yo

Getty-Dubay™ Italic Handwriting Series · Book A · © 2012 Getty-Dubay

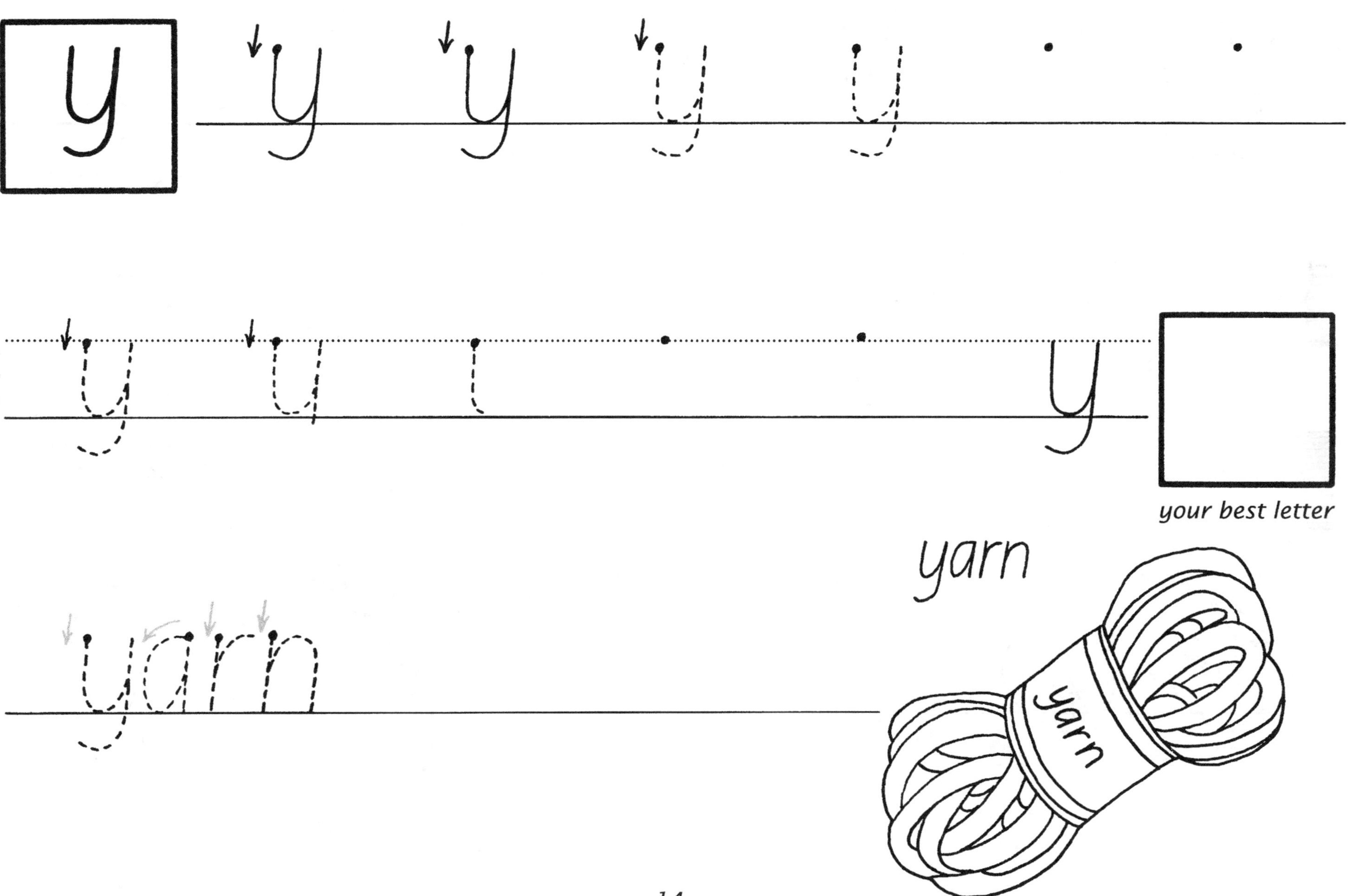

your best letter

yarn

u

your best letter

Ukulele

LOOK: Did you trace each letter before writing your own?

Circle: Yes   No

u

your best letter

umbrella

three stroke letter, two lifts · BASIC ITALIC
NOTE: all letters start at the top except lowercase *d & e*

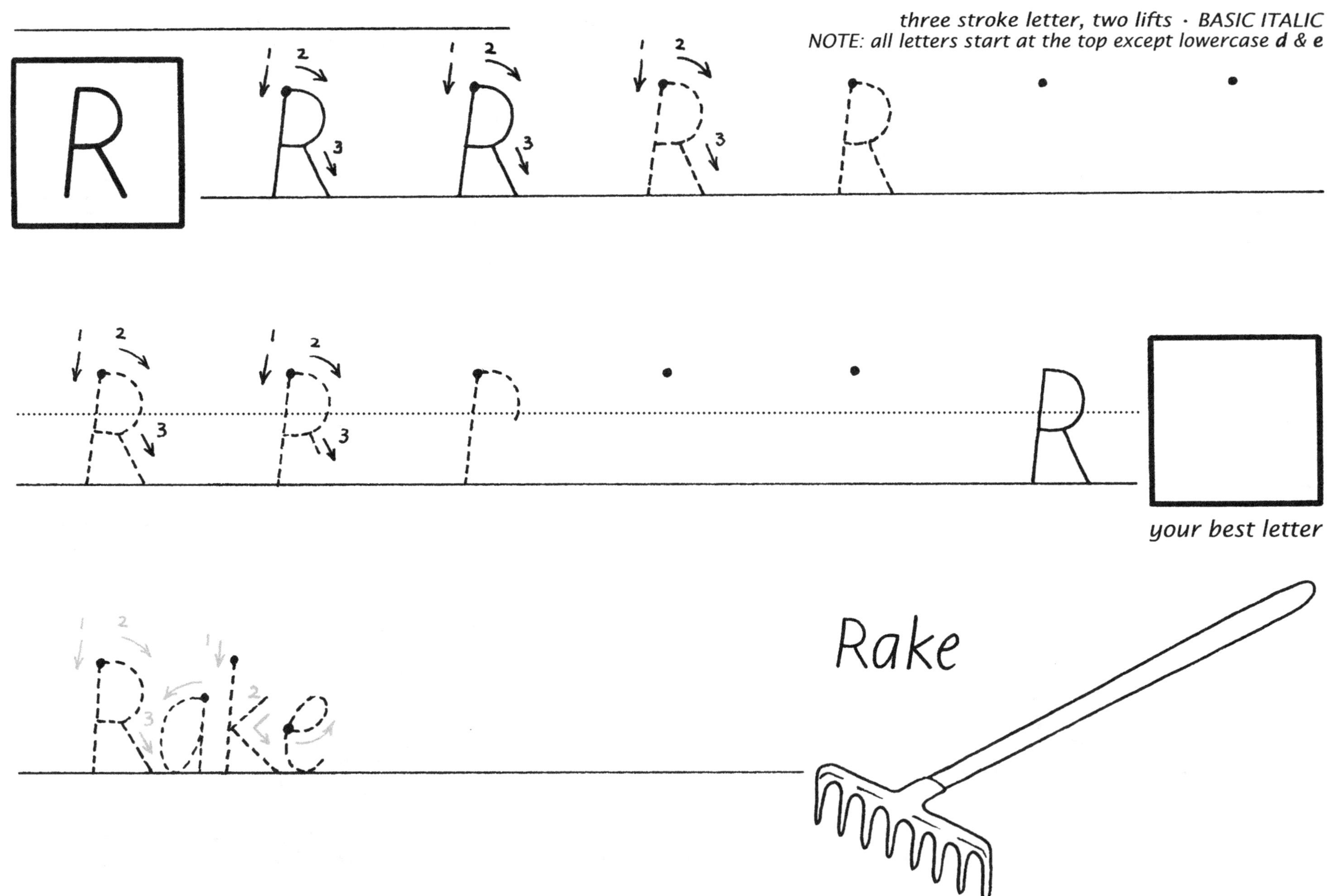

your best letter
Rake

your best letter

rabbit

LOOK: Did you start each letter at the top?   ✏ Circle: Yes   No

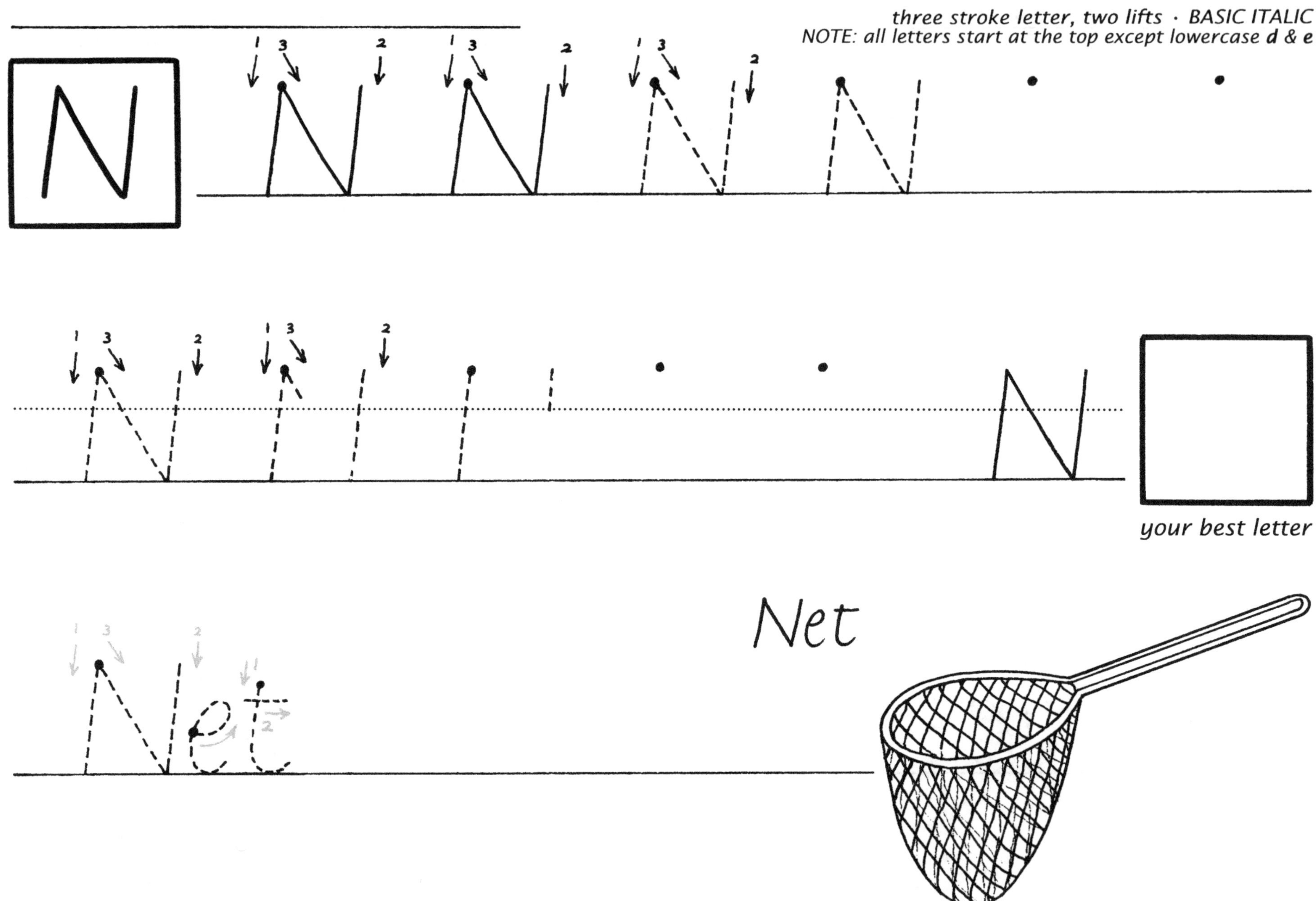

your best letter

Net

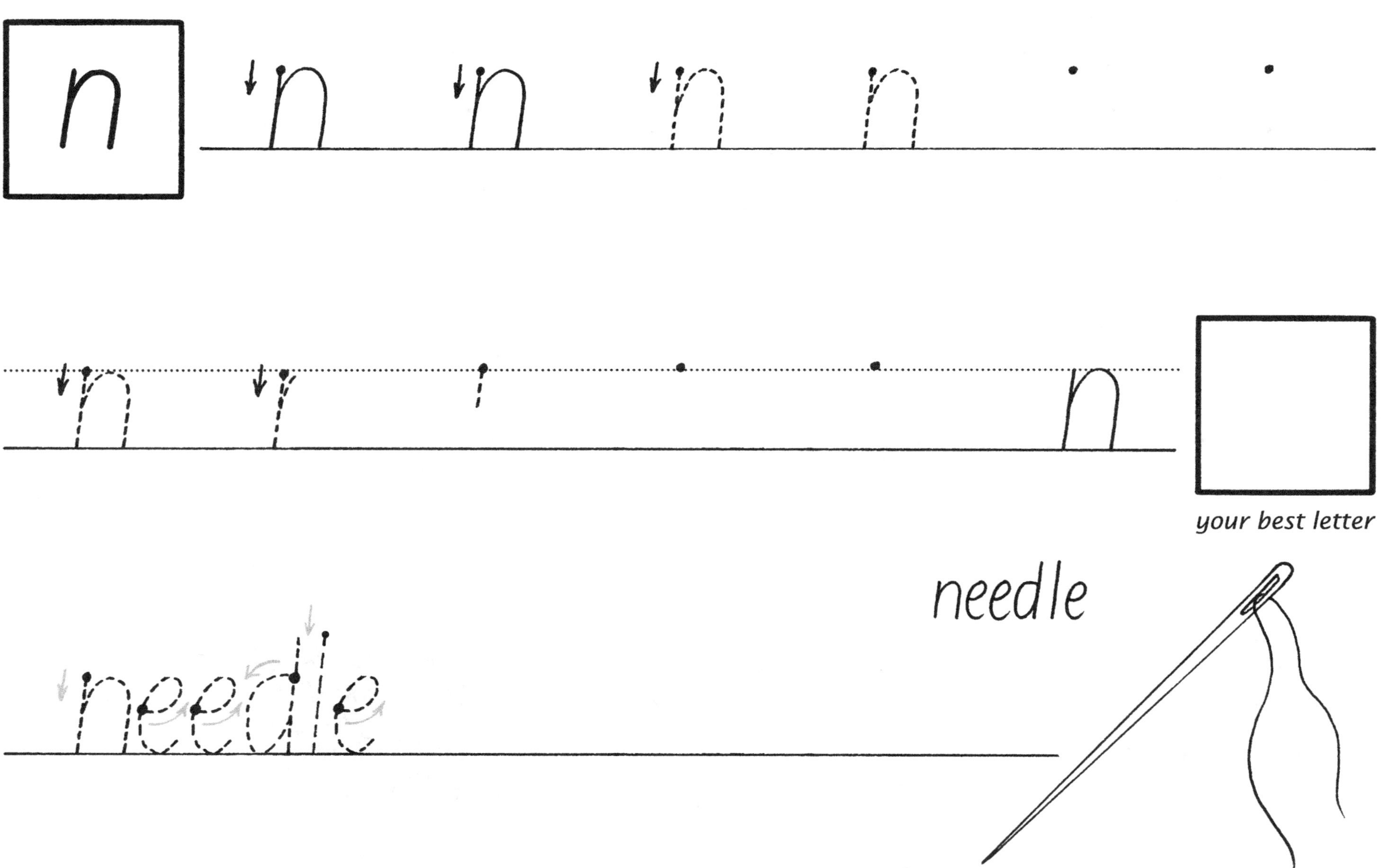

your best letter
needle

your best letter

Mittens

your best letter

mouse

LOOK: Did you start all letters at the top?   Circle: Yes   No

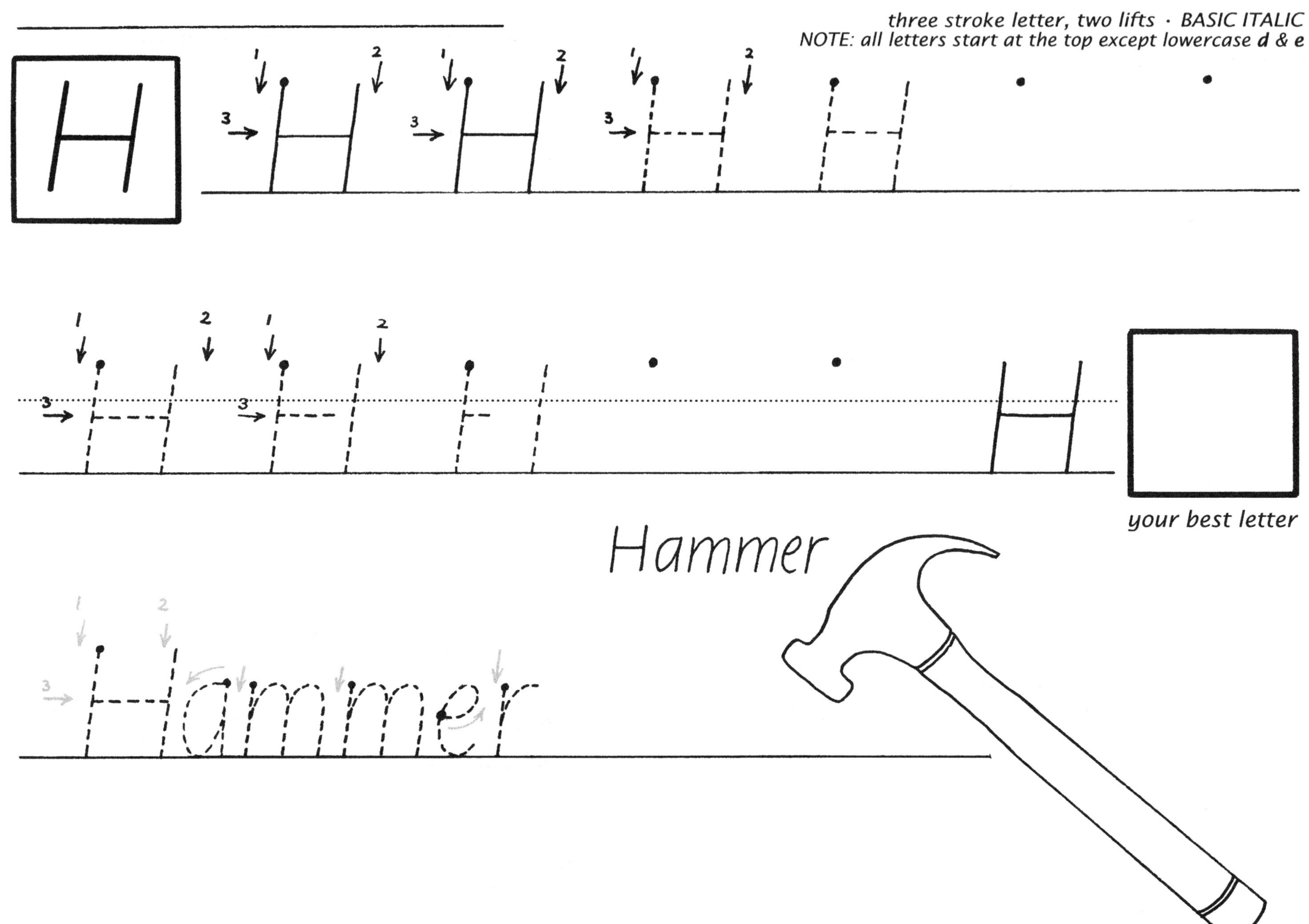

three stroke letter, two lifts · BASIC ITALIC
NOTE: all letters start at the top except lowercase d & e
your best letter
Hammer

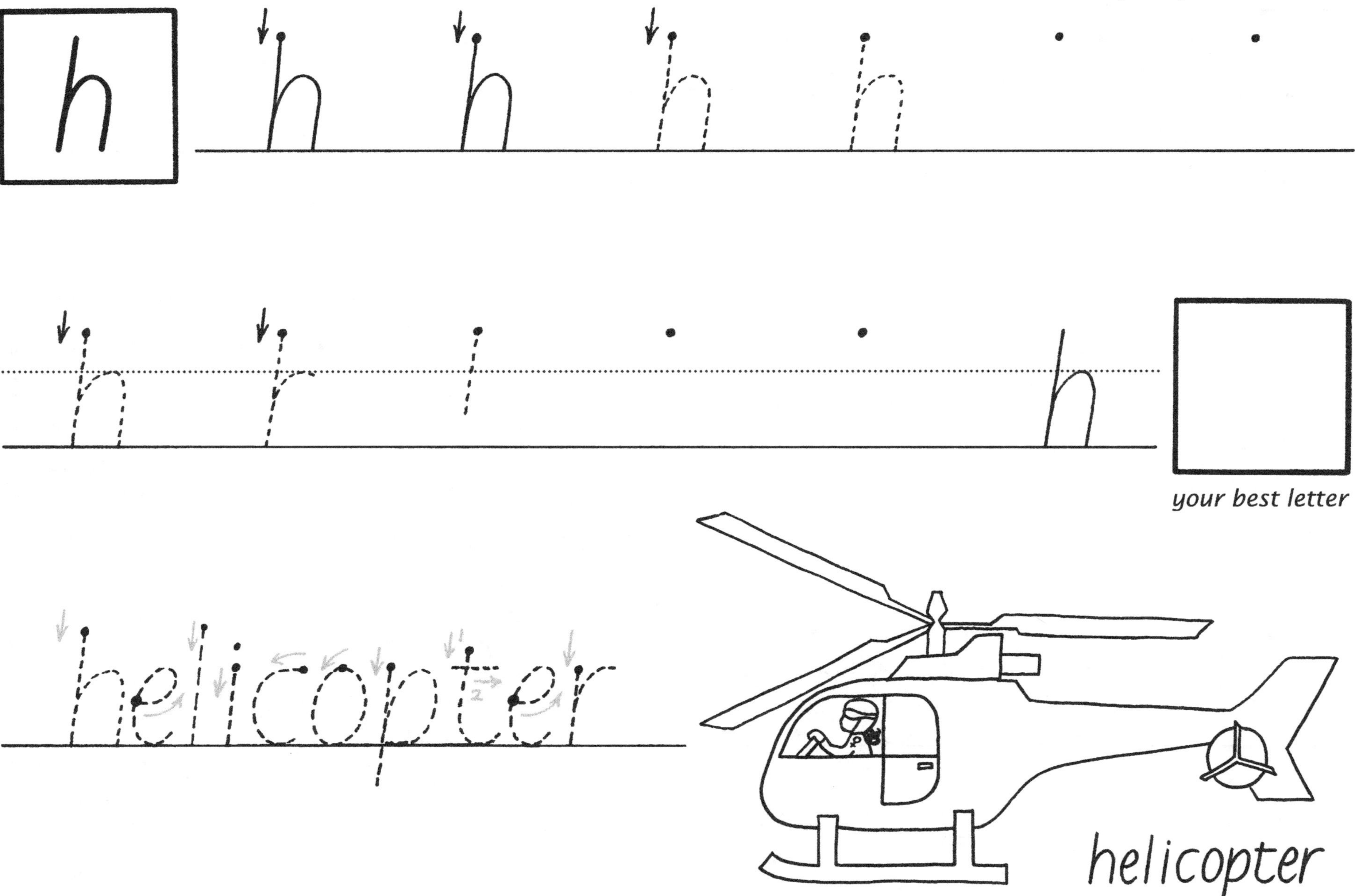

h

r   i

your best letter

helicopter

Zipper

your best letter

Zipper

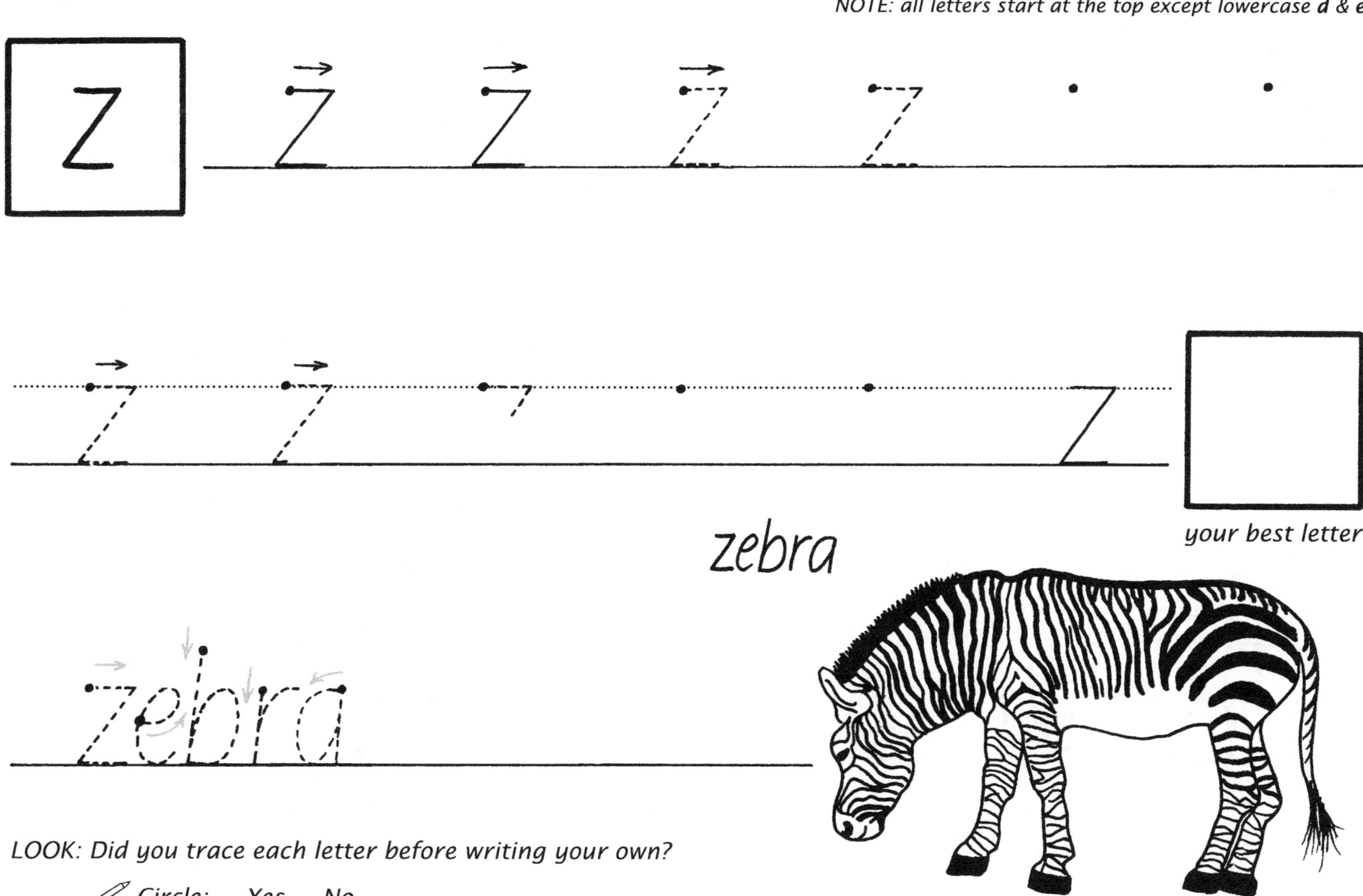

zebra

your best letter

LOOK: Did you trace each letter before writing your own?

✏ Circle: Yes No

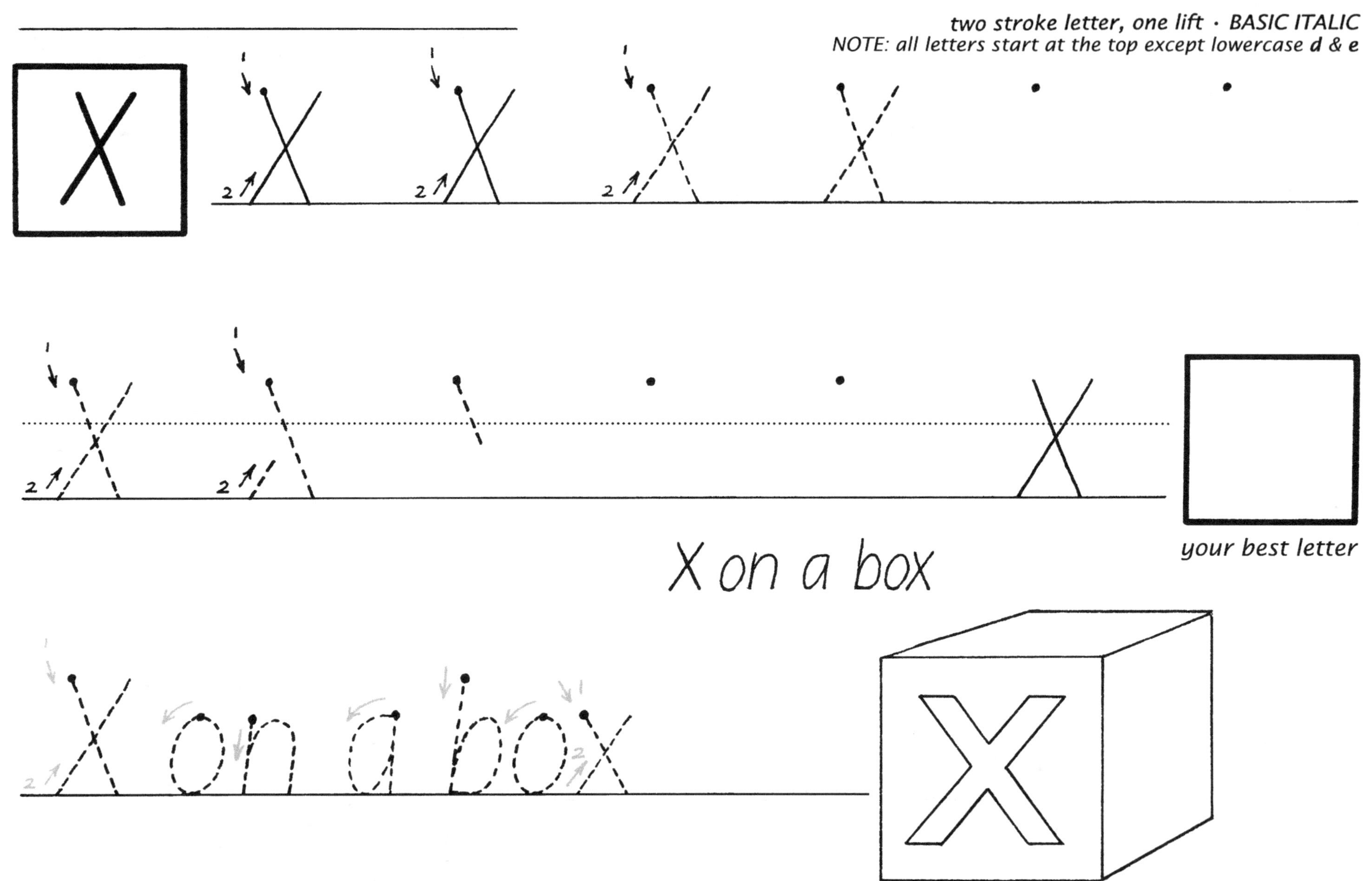

your best letter

X on a box

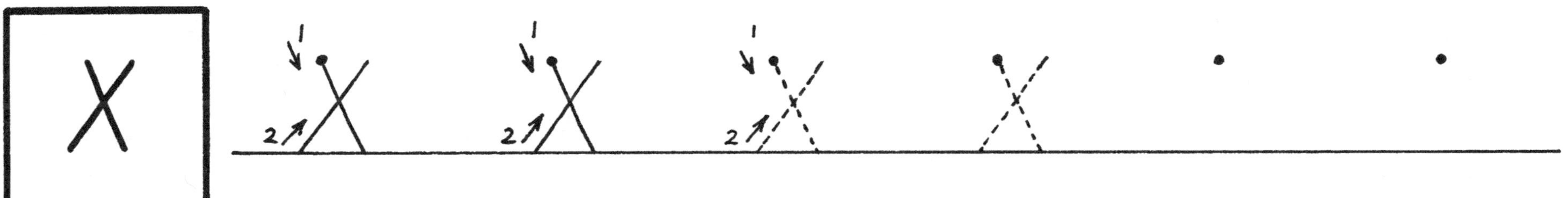

x in a box

your best letter

x in a box

W W W W W W W

W W V W

your best letter

Watch

Watch

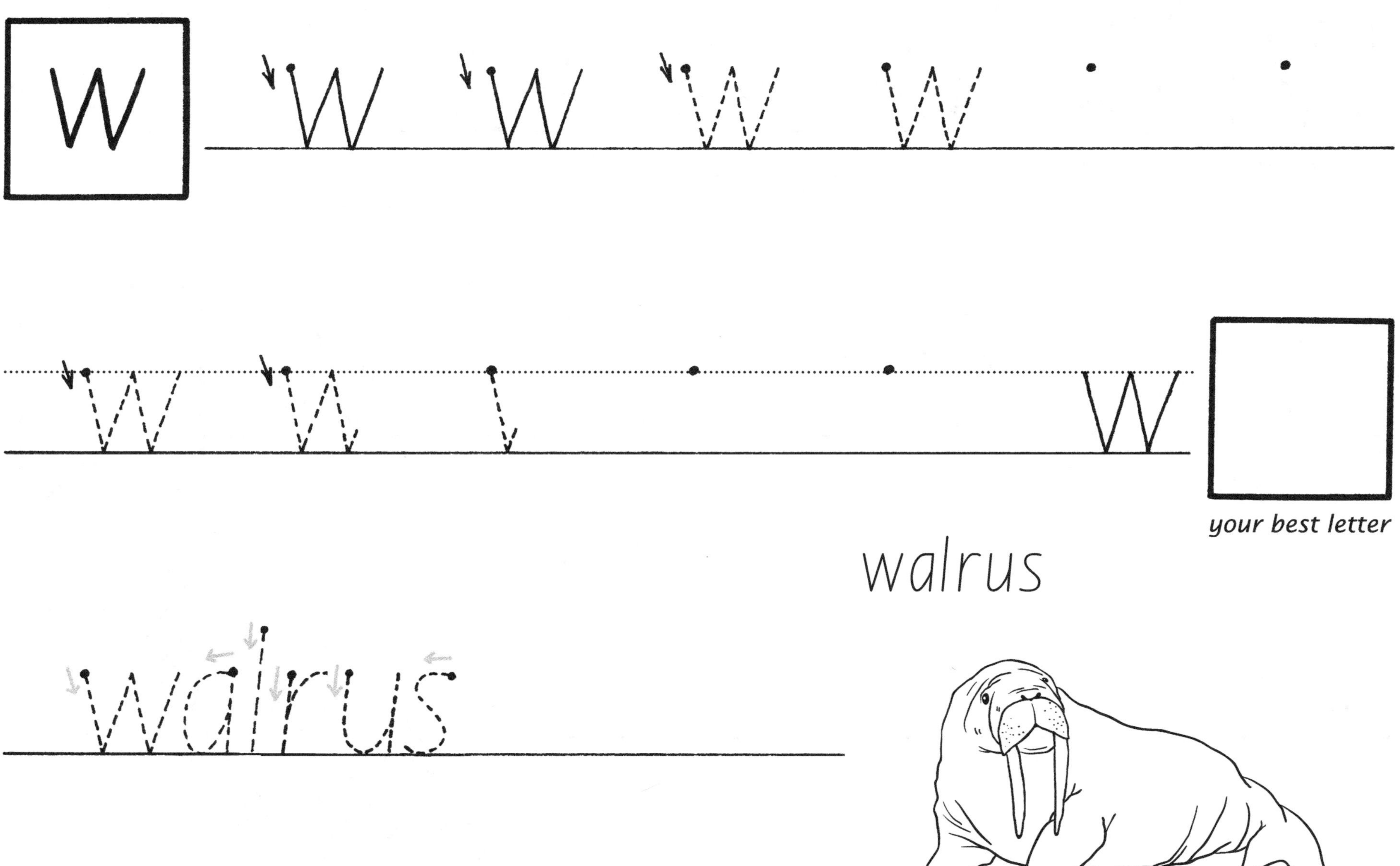

your best letter

walrus

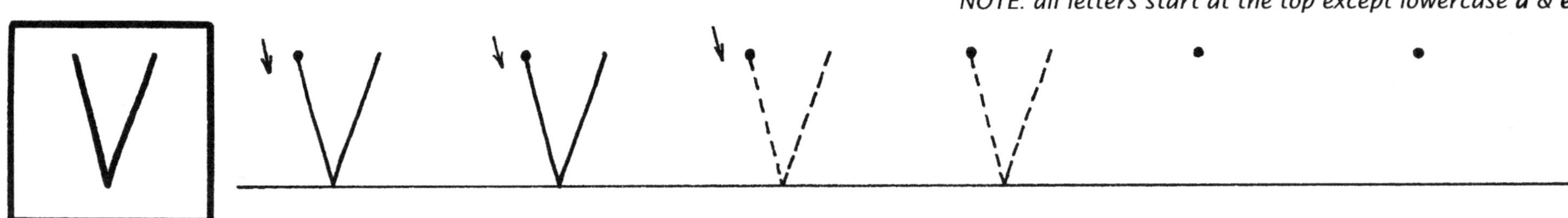

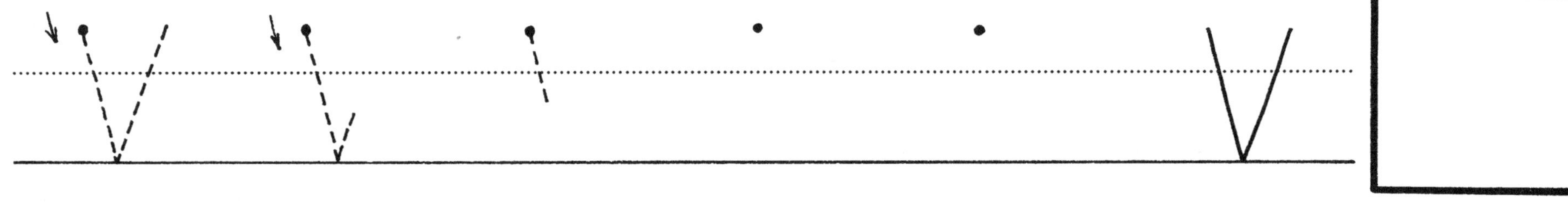

your best letter

Valentine

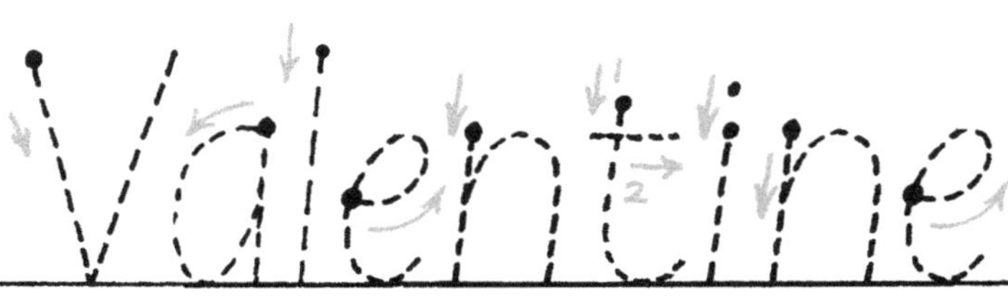

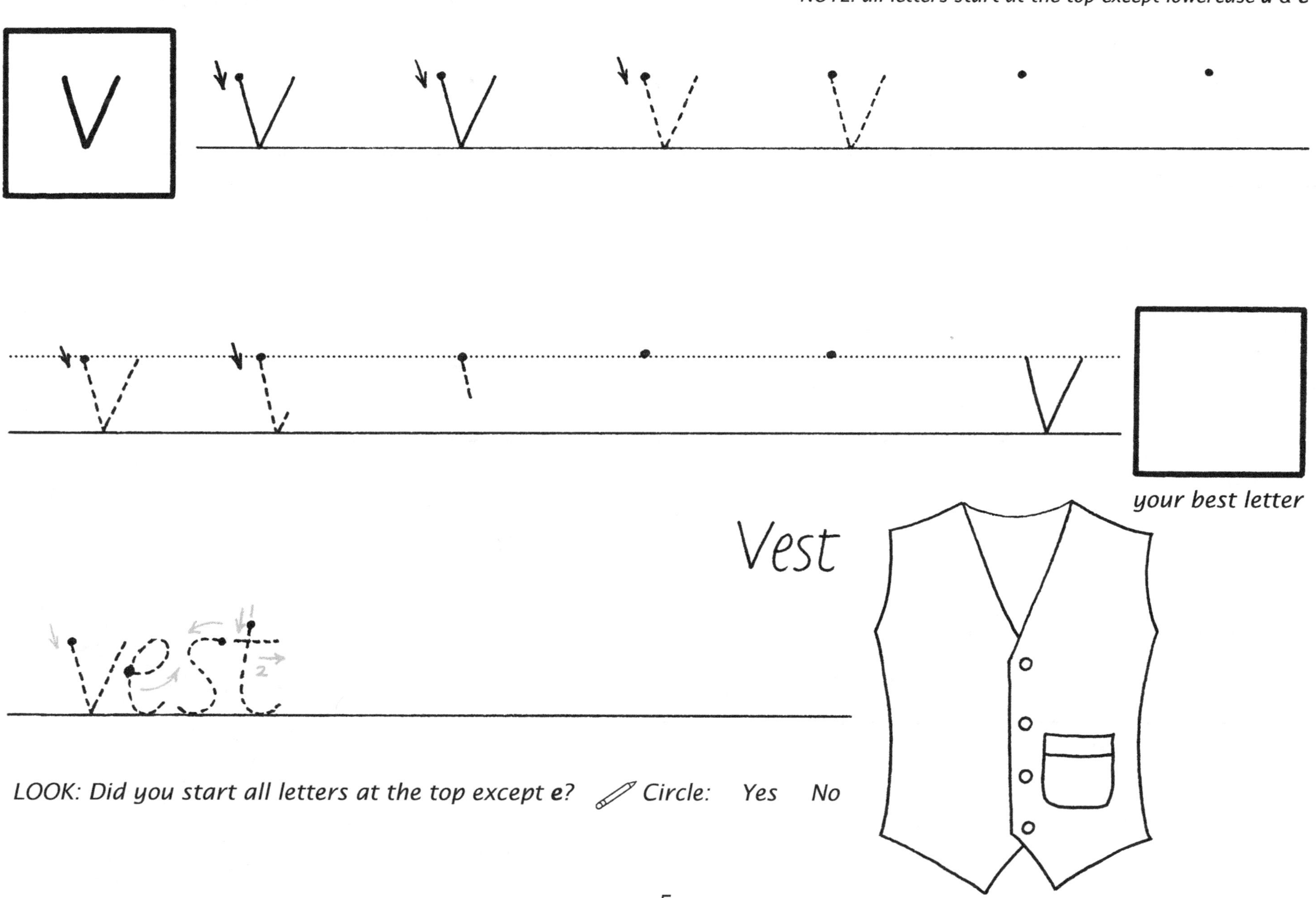

LOOK: Did you start all letters at the top except **e**? Circle: Yes   No

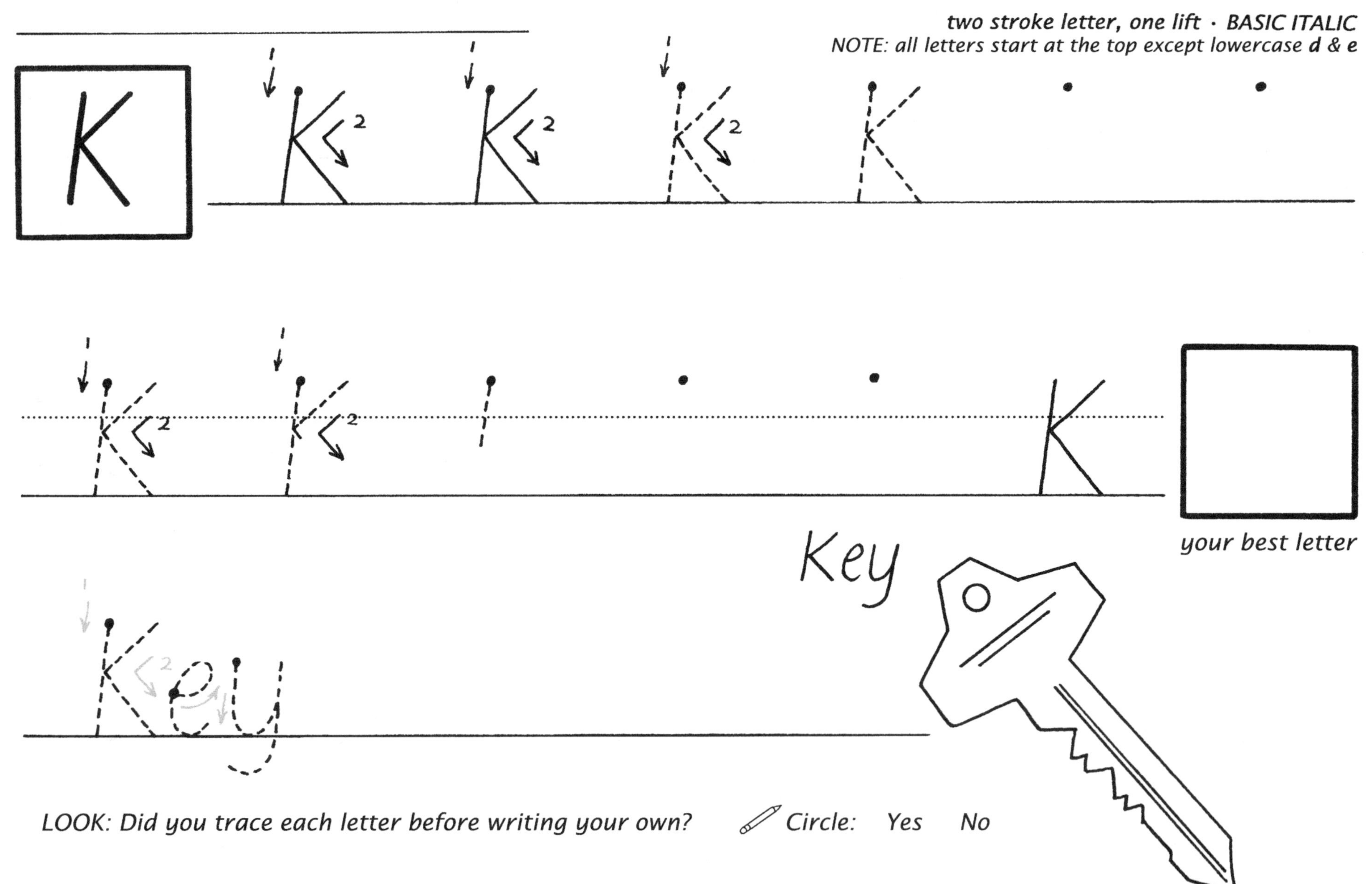

LOOK: Did you trace each letter before writing your own?   Circle: Yes   No

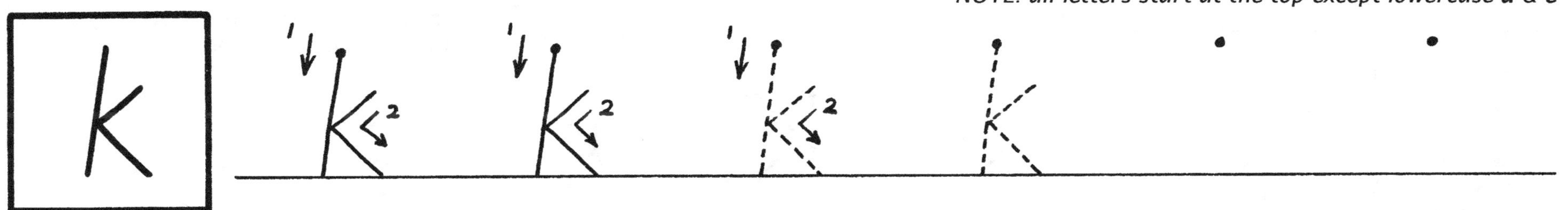

your best letter

kite

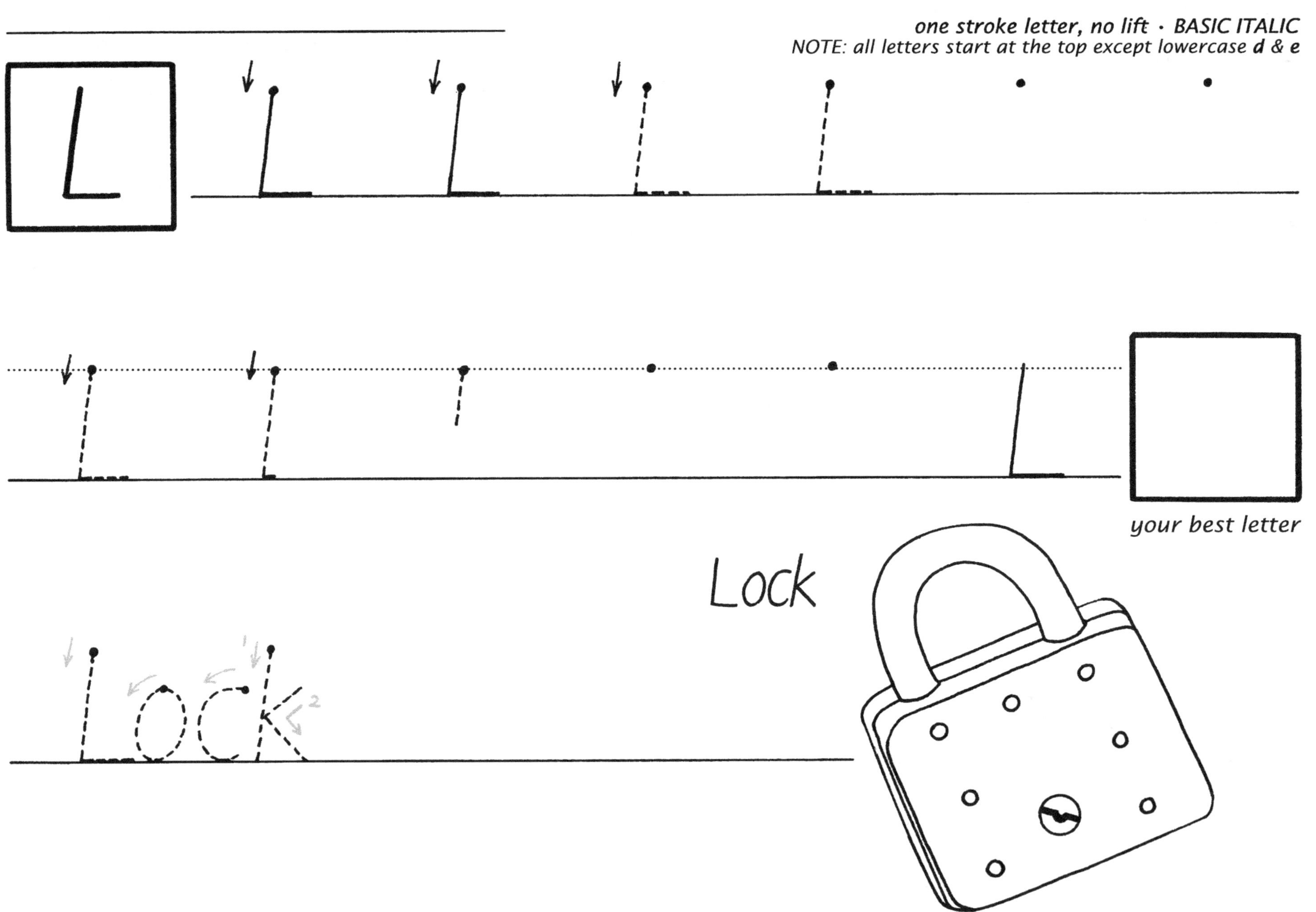

your best letter
Lock
Lock

your best letter

lamb

J

your best letter

Jack-in-the-box

your best letter

jar

LOOK: Did you start all letters at the top?   Circle: Yes   No

three stroke letter, two lifts · BASIC ITALIC
NOTE: all letters start at the top except lowercase d & e
your best letter
Ice Cream

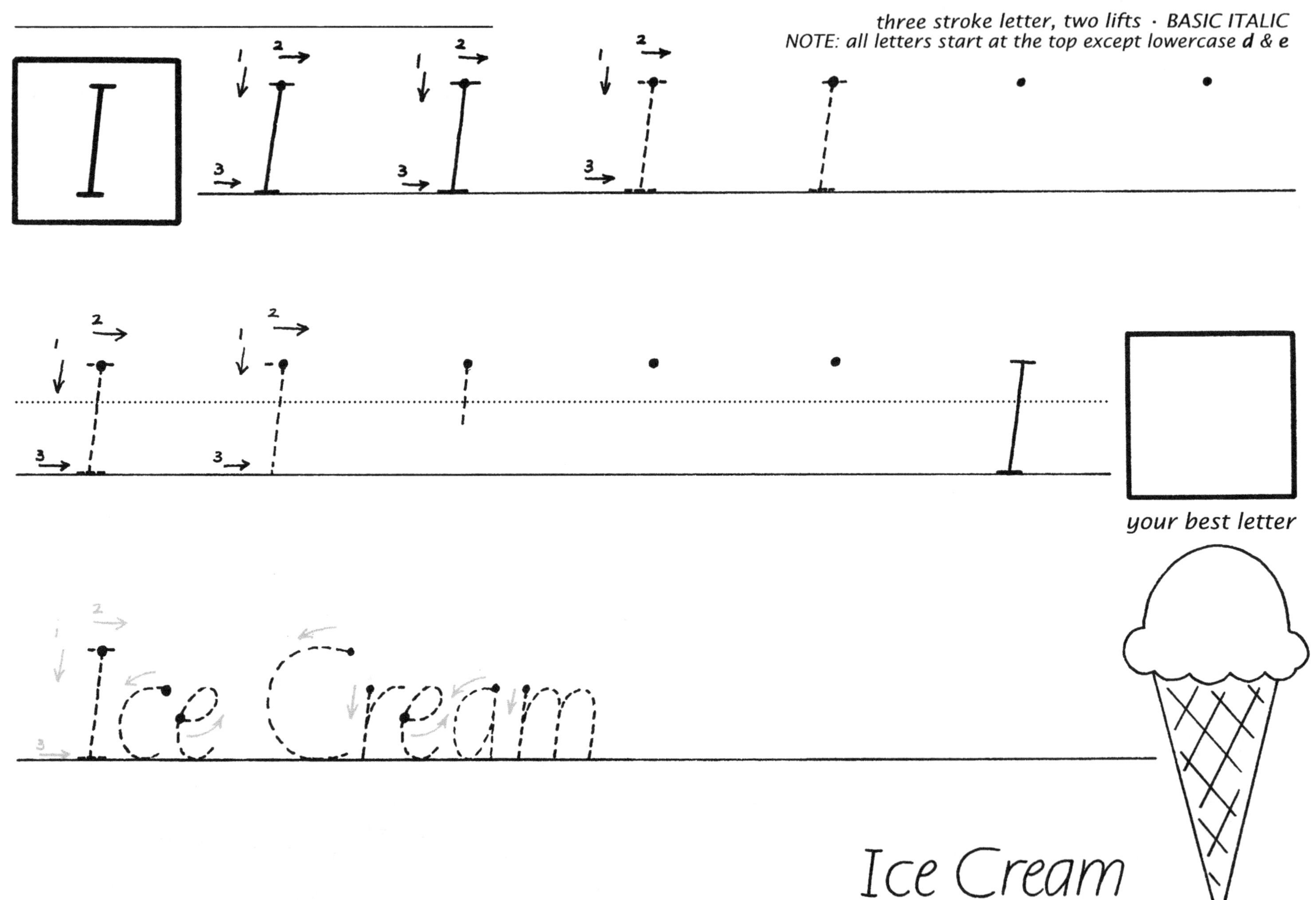

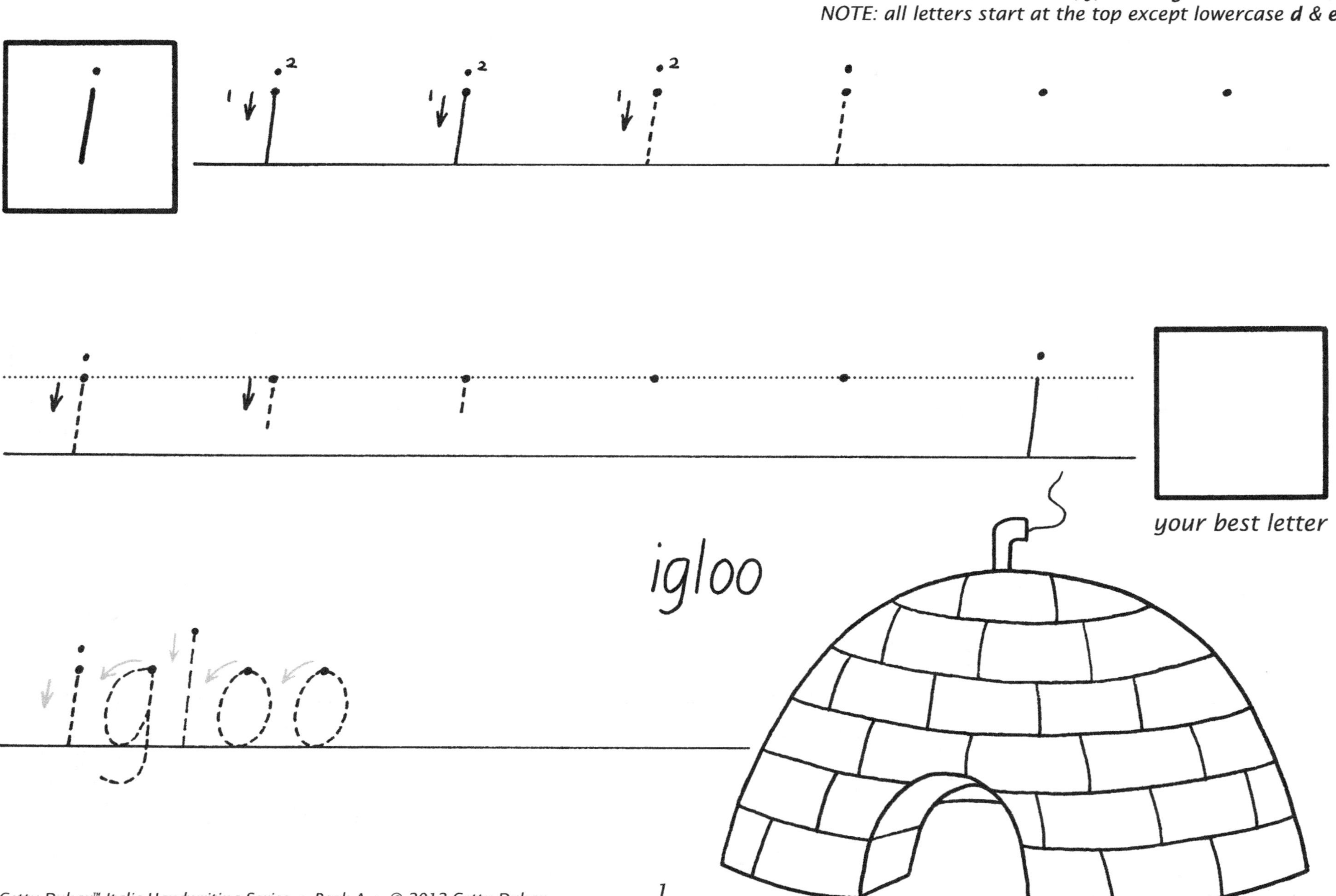

your best letter

igloo

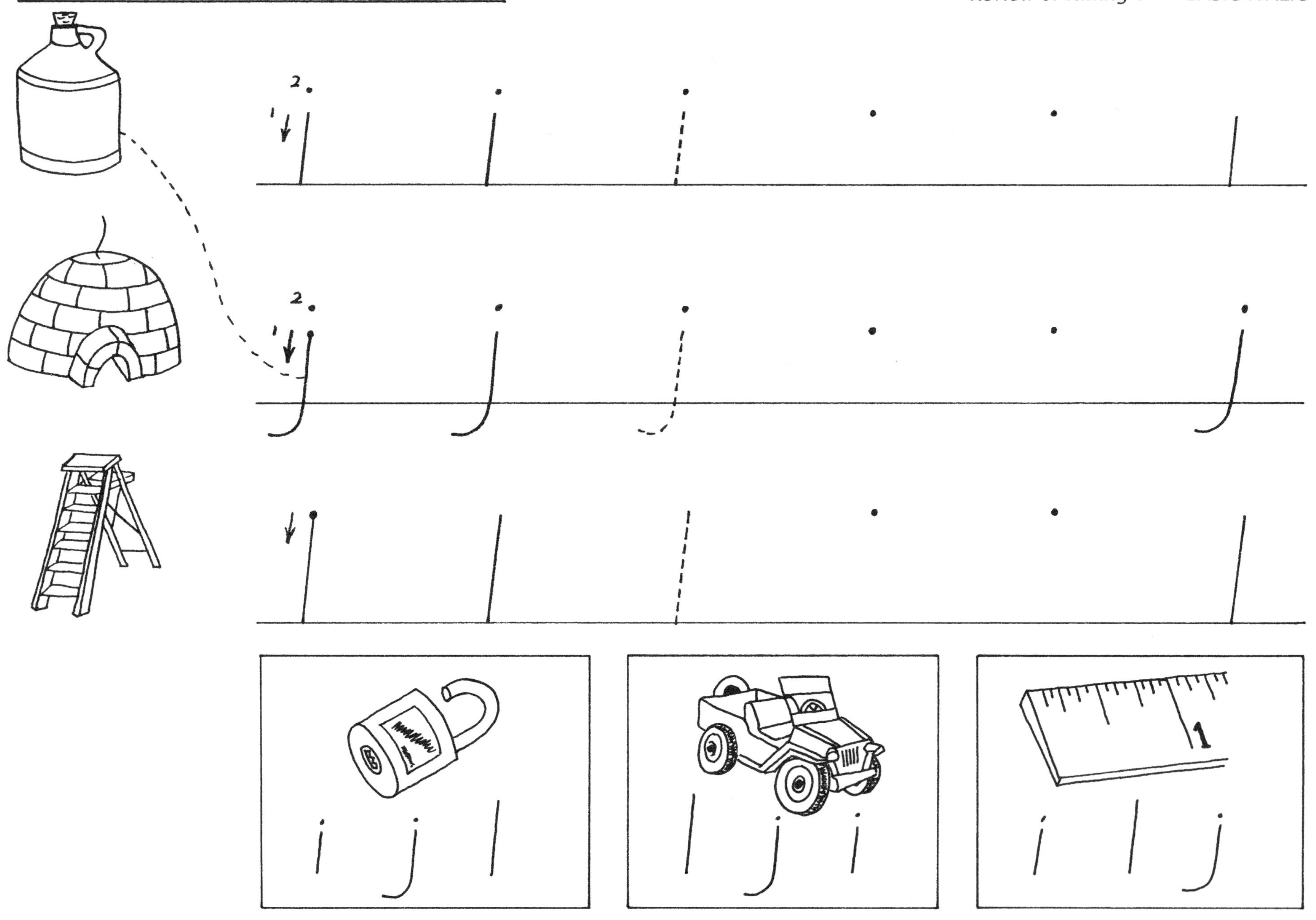

TOP THREE LINES: *Ask the student to draw a line from the picture to the letter that stands for the correct beginning sound.*

BOTTOM THREE BOXES: *Ask the student to circle the letter that stands for the beginning sound of the picture.*

BASIC SHAPES

Before the student begins writing in BOOK A, the authors recommend that the student practice the following shapes on unlined paper, one shape at a time. Allow the student to write each shape any size at first. Later, ask the student to write very large and very small forms of that same shape. We suggest the student also practice these shapes on a chalkboard and/or in cornmeal. (See INSTRUCTION MANUAL, "*Activity*," pp. 35 & 41.)

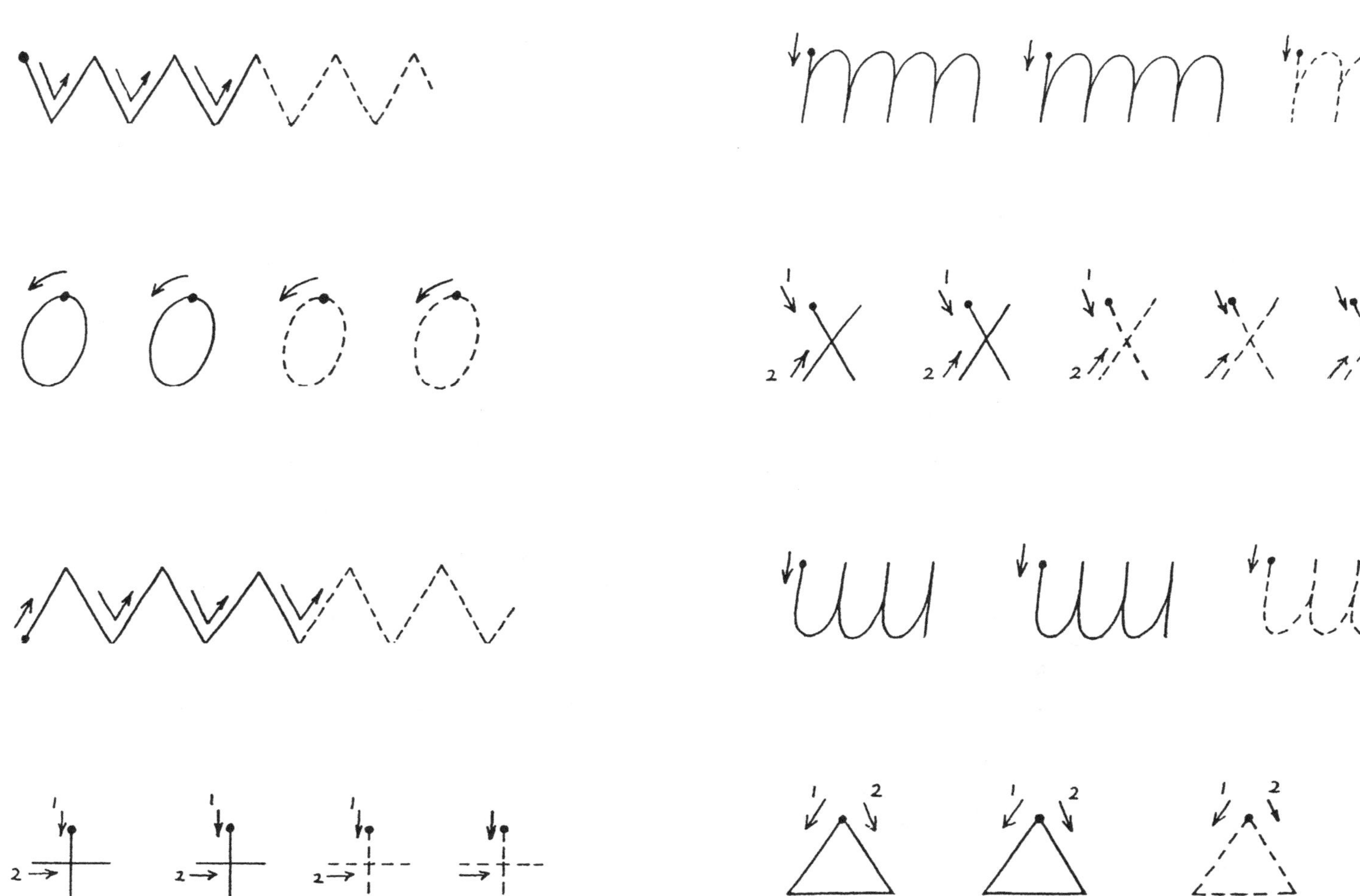

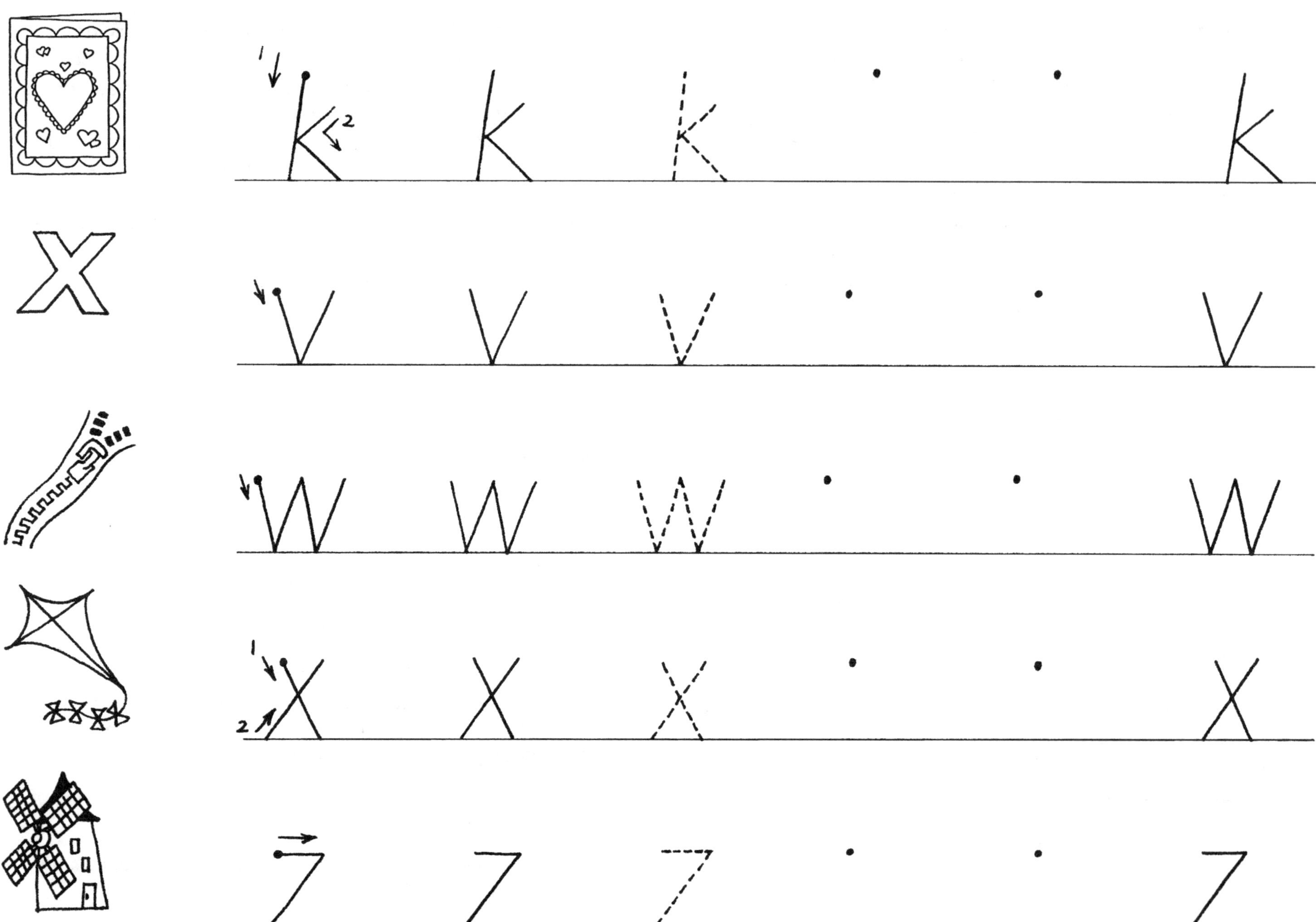

*Ask the student to draw a line from the picture to the letter
that stands for the correct beginning sound.*

THE BEGINNING WRITER

Learning how to write involves much more than learning to write letters. It is a sophisticated, complex process involving learning letterforms, learning how to space within and between words, and learning how to organize writing on a page. Research indicates that there exists an almost perfect correlation between measures evaluating the children's *awareness* of their fingers and the ability to *use* their fingers in precise manual skills.

Ways to determine manual ability

To assist young students increase awareness of their hands and fingers, and to help you, the teacher, evaluate students' manual skills, have your students perform these tasks:

1. Direct the students to touch each of their fingers to their thumb, in order, from the first to the little finger. (By the age of six years, most children should be able to complete this exercise using one or both hands at a time.)

2. Have the students connect two dots that are spaced approximately eight inches apart on a page. (Most children of five years can accomplish this. However, if the student draws beyond the second dot or draws an unusually shaky line when nearing the second dot, it may indicate potential deficiencies in handwriting skills.)

Ways to improve kinesthetic perception of the hands

1. Unstructured clay modeling facilitates a student's perception of his or her hands. Encourage the student to manipulate the clay in every possible way—squeezing, flattening, poking, making shapes, etc.

2. To heighten the student's perception of shape, use a box in which a variety of small objects are placed for the student to feel but not see.

   a. Ask the student to reach in the box and find an unseen object that matches the one he or she is looking at.

   b. Direct the student to locate in the box an object that you or another student has described.

   c. Ask the student to find two objects with similar characteristics—two fuzzy objects, two heavy objects, two small objects, etc.

3. Draw several circles on a sheet of paper. To determine the student's ability to aim the finger and hand and also to point, have the student place dots in the circles with a pencil, pen, or crayon. Vary the difficulty of this task by increasing or decreasing the size of the circles or increasing the rate at which the dots are made. (The student must be able to point at a given or imaginary point in order to begin the stroke of a letter.)

Ways to confirm hand-eye tracking skills

The ability to control continuous hand movements while drawing lines of varying difficulty is basic to handwriting. If you are able to detect problems as the student completes the following tasks and are able to obtain appropriate assistance for the student, subsequent difficulties may be avoided.

1. Demonstrate drawing parallel lines. Then direct the student to draw parallel lines of a given length, first at a relaxed pace then at a faster one.

2. Direct the student to draw two curved lines equal in distance from one another. Later require more difficult shapes that combine straight lines, angles, and/or curves.

3. Direct the student to connect numbered dots on a sheet of paper that require horizontal, vertical and lateral movements. Place the paper in front of the student, close to the dominant hand. Later, space the dots further apart and require the student to cross the midline of his or her body. This latter task may cause the neurologically challenged student some difficulty.

The above evaluative tasks may be of help in assisting the learning of handwriting and in discovering deficiencies.

(See INSTRUCTION MANUAL, p. 13, for more suggestions concerning the beginning writer.)

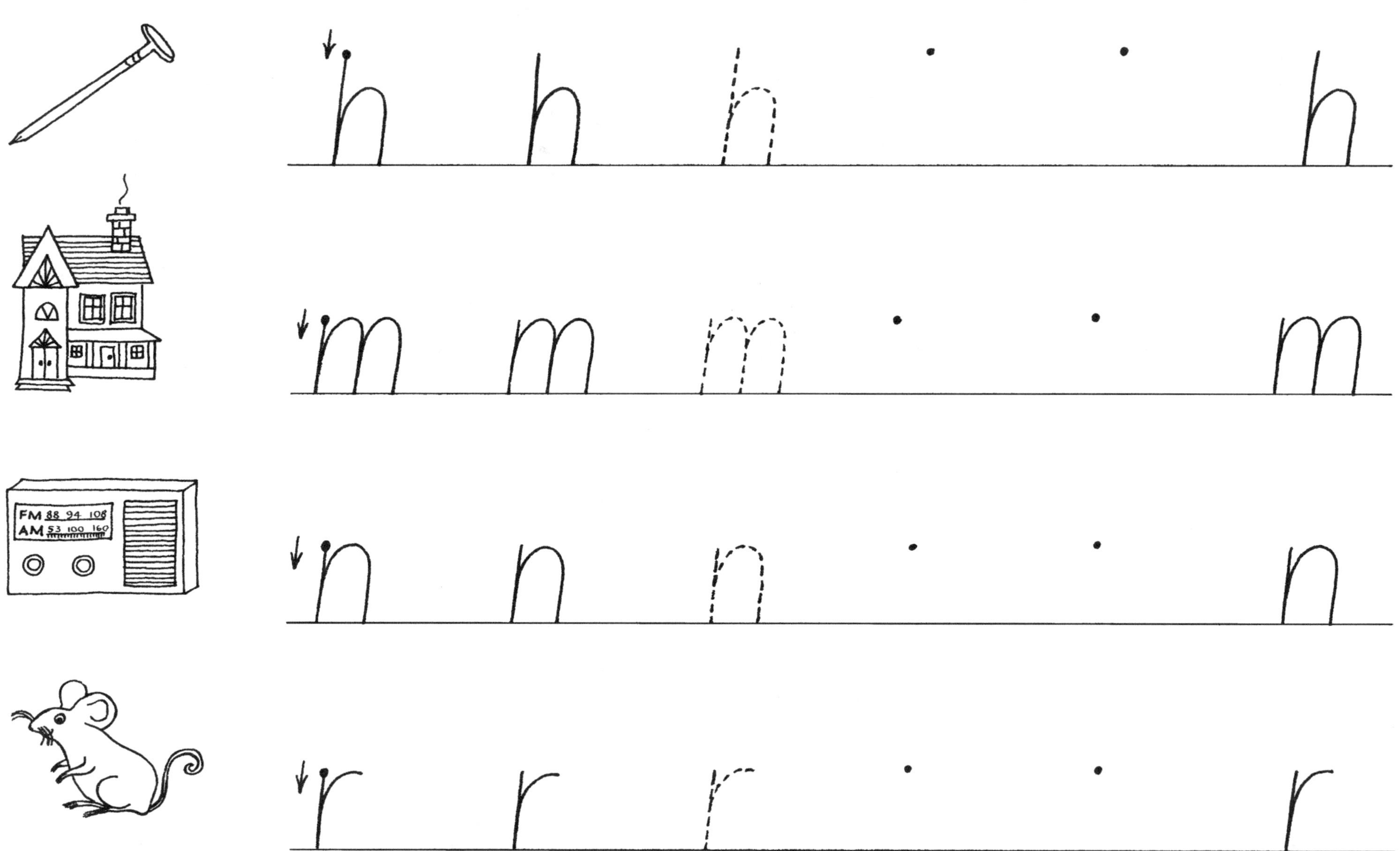

Ask the student to draw a line from the picture to the letter
that stands for the correct beginning sound.

BASIC ITALIC ALPHABET

All letters written in one stroke unless otherwise indicated. *All letters start at the top except lowercase **d** and **e**.*

Aa Bb Cc Dd Ee Ff Gg

or

alternate
2-stroke e

Hh Ii Jj Kk Ll Mm

or   or

Nn Oo Pp Qq Rr Ss Tt

or   or

Uu Vv Ww Xx Yy Zz

0 1 2 3 4 5 6 7 8 9

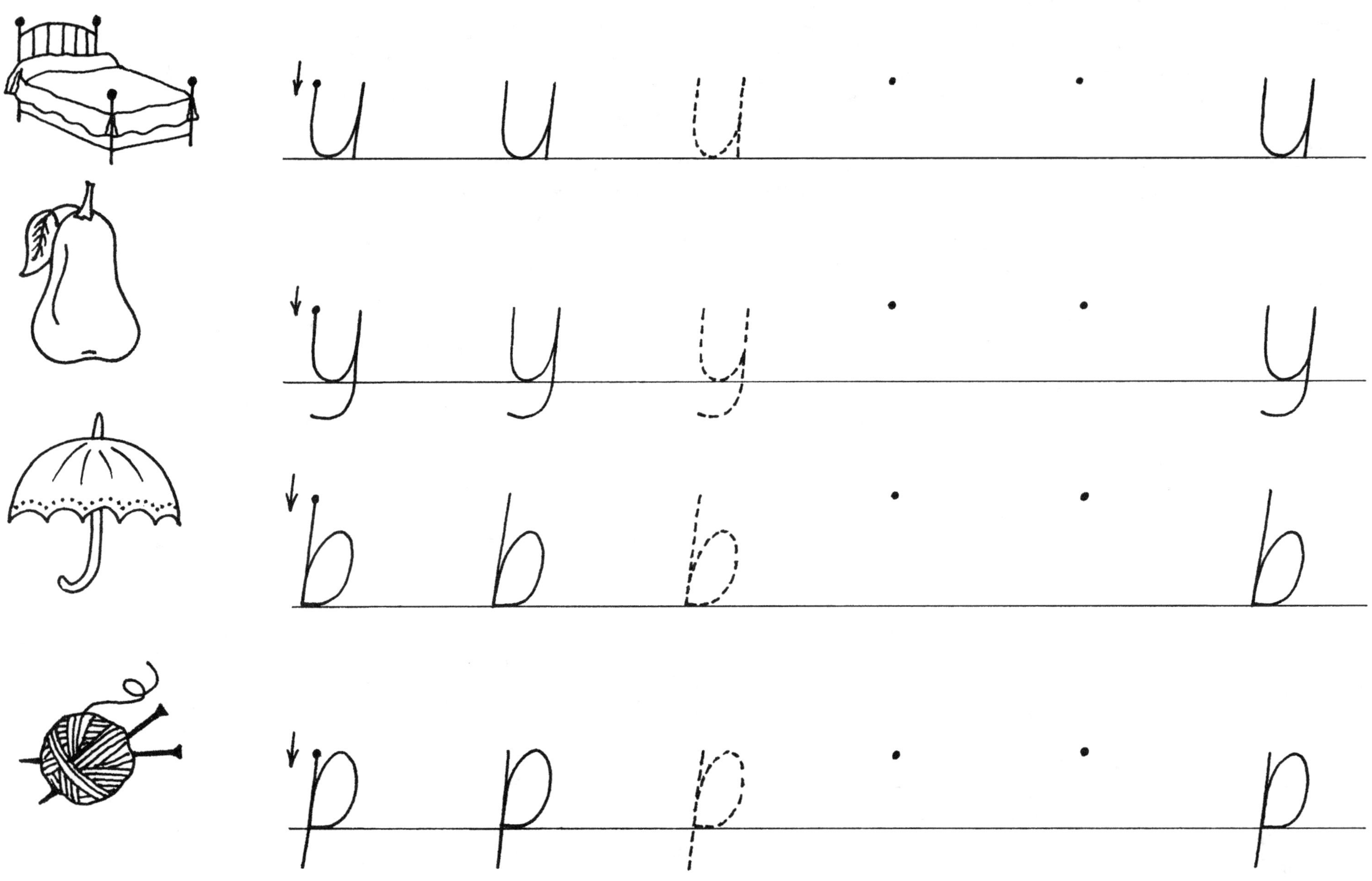

Ask the student to draw a line from the picture to the letter
that stands for the correct beginning sound.

GETTY-DUBAY™ HANDWRITING REMINDERS

PENCIL HOLD

Hold the pencil with the thumb and index finger, resting it on the middle finger. Rest the shaft of the pencil near the large knuckle. Hold the tool firmly and avoid pinching. To relax the hand, tap index finger on the pencil three times. Avoid "thumb wrap" and a "death grip".

PAPER POSITION

LEFT-HANDED: If the left-handed student writes with the wrist below the writing line, turn paper clockwise so it is slanted to the right, as illustrated.
If the left-handed student writes with a hook, with the wrist above the writing line, turn the paper counter-clockwise so it is slanted to the left, as illustrated. (Similar to right-handed position)

RIGHT-HANDED: If the student is right-handed, turn paper counter-clockwise so it is slanted to the left, as illustrated. 

POSTURE

Rest feet flat on the floor and keep back comfortably straight without slumping. Rest forearms on writing surface. The student  holds workbook or paper with the nonwriting hand so that the writing area is centered in the front of the student.

PRACTICE PAPER

Book A—Use unlined or lined paper together with workbooks.

MATERIALS

The *Getty-Dubay™ Italic Handwriting Series* workbooks, BOOKS A-G, and the INSTRUCTION MANUAL constitute a step-by-step program. Related materials consist of:

1. BLACKLINE MASTERS/WORKSHEETS - half sheets for introduction to, or review of, workbook pages.
2. CLASSROOM WALL CHARTS - basic & cursive italic.
3. DESK STRIPS - basic & cursive italic.

VOCABULARY

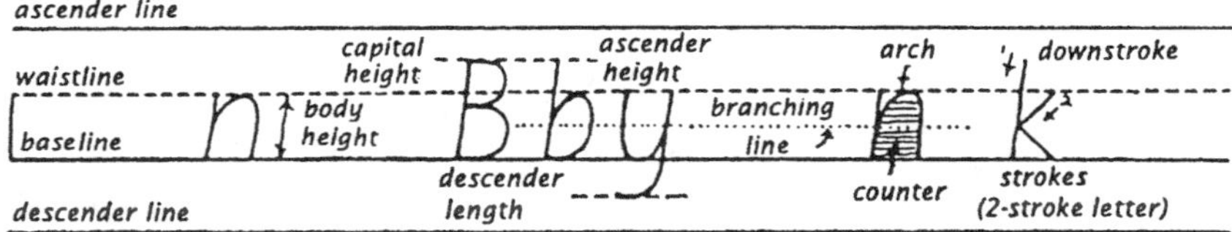

DIRECT INSTRUCTION

Several sessions of direct instruction each week are essential for a successful program. BOOK A – 5 to 10 minute sessions a day are recommended, see INSTRUCTION MANUAL, pp. 18-19

- SHAPE & STROKE SEQUENCE – teach basic italic in letter family groups, or according to the reading program in grade 1.
- SLOPE – encourage a consistent letter slope. Vertical letters (0° slope) may be the easiest to teach to beginning writers.
- SIZE – At first, allow students to write letters any size they wish on unlined paper, then introduce the workbook. A recommended progression through this book is one letter (lowercase and/or capital) per week.

SPACING

When young students are writing words, at first have them leave a space about the width of their two small fingers between words. As they become more proficient, they can leave less space.

ASSESSMENT

The *Getty-Dubay™ Italic Handwriting Series* provides a self-assessment process, LOOK, PLAN, PRACTICE, to enable the student to monitor progress. LOOK, step 1 of this process begins on some of the student pages in BOOK A. Assessment is the key to improving handwriting; in this book we introduce the first of three steps in the LOOK, PLAN, PRACTICE self-assessment process. The students look at their own writing and answer any questions on the page. The pencil indicates the student is to make a written response, generally by circling "yes" or "no". The teacher may encourage students to award themselves a star or a smiling face at the top of the page when they notice self-improvement.

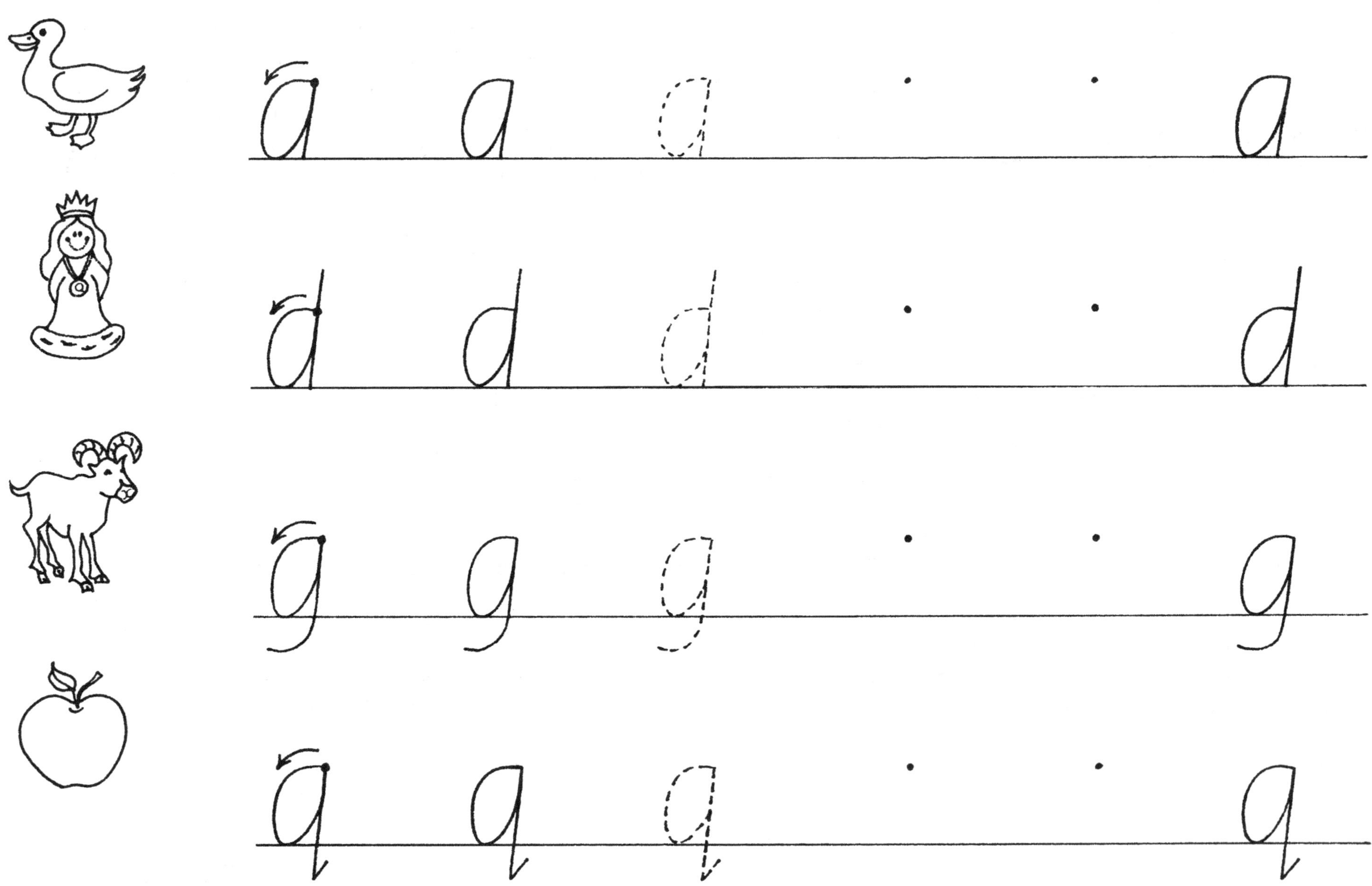

*Ask the student to draw a line from the picture to the letter
that stands for the correct beginning sound.*

INTRODUCTION

This is the first of seven workbooks providing instruction in basic italic handwriting. It is designed for the beginning student of handwriting and is recommended for preschool, kindergarten and/or early first grade (5 to 7 years of age).

The twenty-six lowercase letters and the twenty-six capitals are introduced one letter per page. Letters are arranged in the order of lowercase families, which group letters with similar strokes together and progress from simple to more complex forms. The matching capital letter occurs on the reverse of each lowercase page allowing introduction of both lowercase and capital together if preferred.

Each page is designed for the student to trace the models provided, write letters at the given dots, and to write a "best" letter in the empty box on each alphabet page. The standard writing tool is the pencil although other writing instruments such as the fiber tip pen may be used. When students are ready, they should trace the word describing the illustration on each letter page, following the dots and arrows.

It is essential that the instructor provide an understanding of the dot and the arrow to assist the writer in completing the pages successfully. The self-assessment method used in the *Getty-Dubay™ Italic Handwriting Series* enables students to monitor their individual progress. Step 1, LOOK, of the three-step LOOK, PLAN, PRACTICE format, is incorporated on 21 of the student pages. Students are asked to "LOOK" at their writing and affirm what is best. On the 21 pages with "LOOK" questions, students should circle their chosen answers. See INSTRUCTION MANUAL, PP. 13, 18 & 19.

The *Getty-Dubay™ Italic Handwriting Series* INSTRUCTION MANUAL is to be used in conjunction with this workbook. Explanations and in-depth descriptions of lowercase letters, capitals, joins, and numerals are presented in the manual, emphasizing shape, strokes, size, slope and spacing of the letters. Also included in the manual are: a rationale for italic handwriting, techniques for teaching and assessing handwriting, sequence of skills, handwriting activities, and a brief history of our alphabet.

BOOK B, basic italic, follows this workbook and is designed for the beginning reader. In the third book, BOOK C, basic italic letterforms are reinforced and cursive italic is introduced. BOOKS D, E, F, and G provide a complete basic italic and cursive italic handwriting program. BOOKS B, C, and/or D may also be suitable for the person learning English as a second language.

The format of this book was chosen to accommodate both the left- and right-handed writer. When open, the book fits easily on a small desk, and the writer is not encumbered with an additional page to the left or right. From day one, use a Getty-Dubay™ basic italic desk strip as a reminder. Blackline masters are designed for supplementary practice and are available for each workbook in the series. See www.handwritingsuccess.com for these supplementary materials.

You can guide children toward the challenge and delight in the writing process by reading to them, modeling handwriting, providing writing materials, and especially by building enthusiasm for the letters of our alphabet and for the written word.

·abcdefghijklmnopqrstuvwxyz·

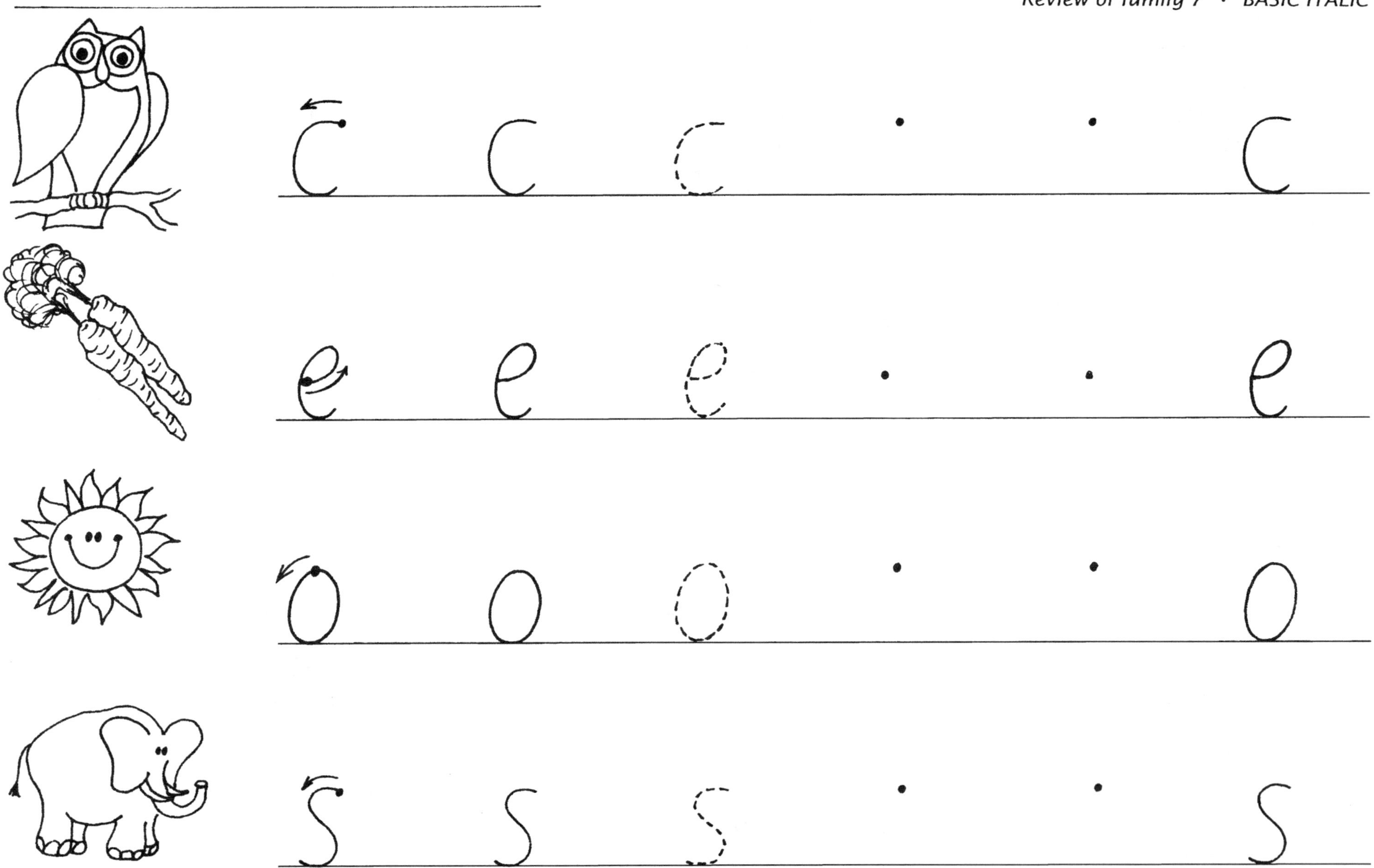

Ask the student to draw a line from the picture to the letter that stands for the correct beginning sound.

CONTENTS

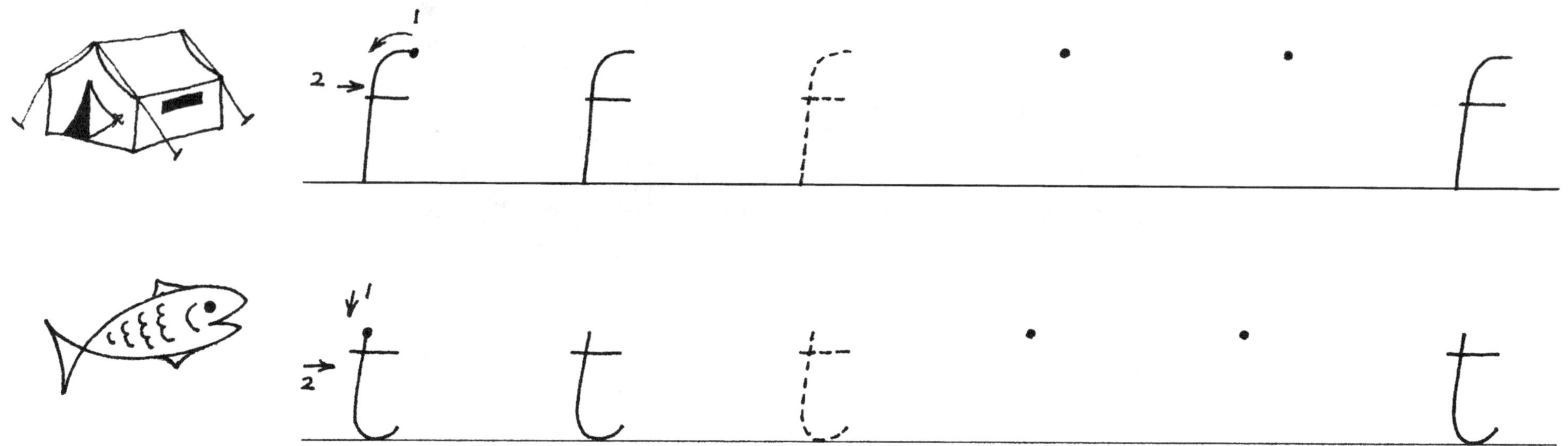

*TOP TWO LINES: Ask the student to draw a line from the picture
to the letter that stands for the correct beginning sound.*

*BOTTOM FOUR SQUARES: Ask the student to circle the letter that
stands for the beginning sound of the picture.*

by

Barbara Getty & Inga Dubay

GETTY-DUBAY™ ITALIC HANDWRITING SERIES

BOOK A ■ Basic Italic
14 mm body height

BOOK B ■ Basic Italic
11 mm body height, 9 mm

BOOK C ■ Basic & Cursive Italic
9 mm, 6 mm body height   Introduction to Cursive Italic

BOOK D ■ Basic & Cursive Italic
6 mm, 5 mm body height

BOOK E ■ Basic & Cursive Italic
6 mm, 5 mm, 4 mm body height

BOOK F ■ Basic & Cursive Italic
6 mm, 5 mm, 4 mm body height

BOOK G ■ Basic & Cursive Italic
5 mm, 4 mm body height

INSTRUCTION MANUAL

BOOK A ■ INTERNATIONAL EDITION

Copyright 2012 by Barbara M. Getty and Inga S. Dubay
ISBN 978-0-9827762-7-8

FOURTH EDITION
Copyright 2012 by Barbara M. Getty and Inga S. Dubay
THIRD EDITION
Copyright 1999 by Barbara M. Getty and Inga S. Dubay
SECOND EDITION
Copyright 1986 by Barbara M. Getty and Inga S. Dubay
REVISED EDITION
Copyright 1980 by Barbara M. Getty and Inga S. Dubay
FIRST EDITION
Copyright 1979 by Barbara M. Getty and Inga S. Dubay

All rights reserved. This text may not be reproduced in whole or in part without the express written permission of the copyright holder.

Published by Handwriting Success, LLC,
Portland, Oregon USA

www.handwritingsuccess.com

Printed at various locations around the world by IngramSpark.

Cover Design: Sinda Markham
Front cover picture: Flowers of the sunflower family in the Ochoco National Forest, Oregon, USA
Back cover pictures: Columbine flower, Golden-mantled squirrel

one stroke numeral · no lift

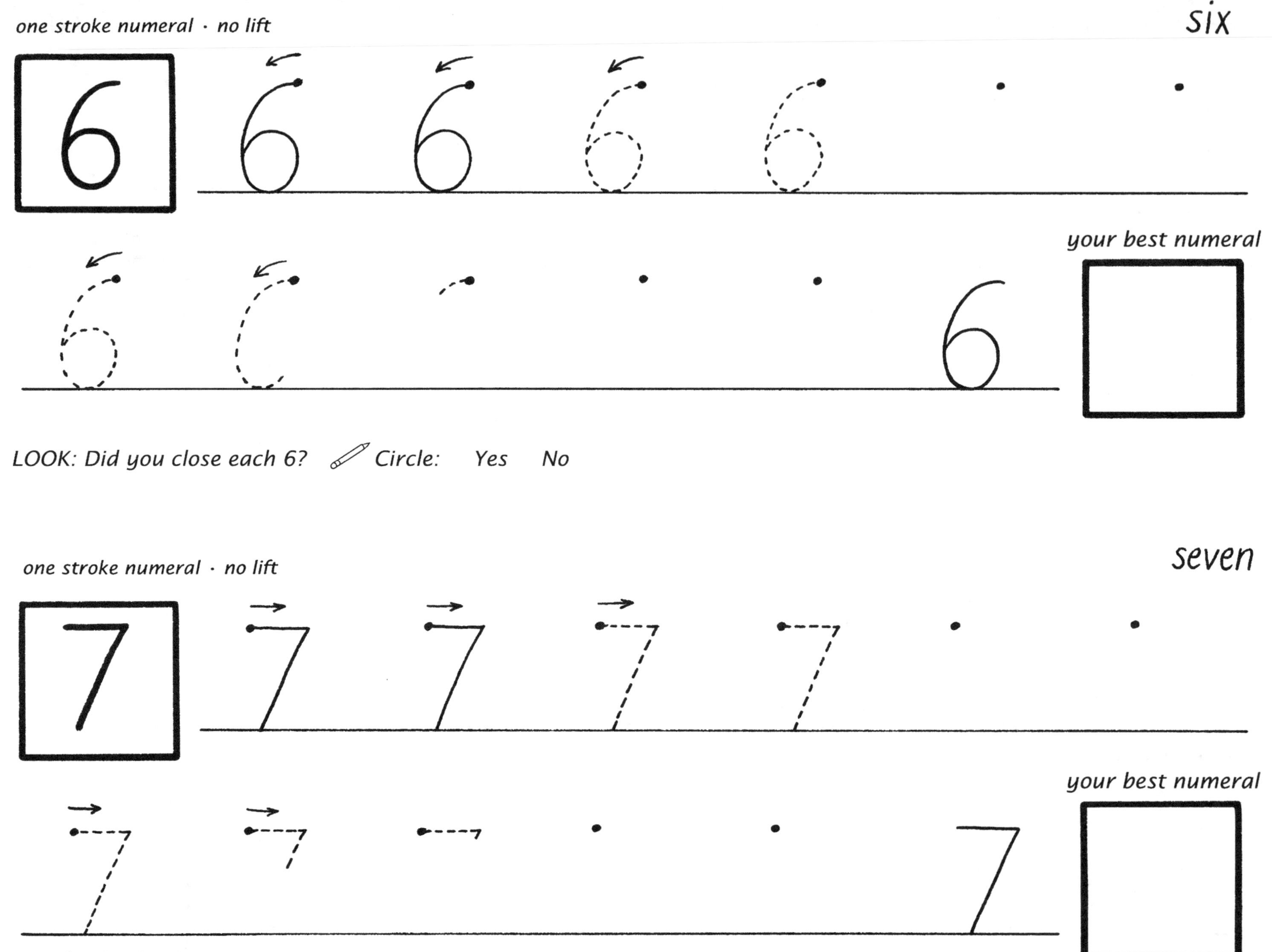

your best numeral

LOOK: Did you close each 6? Circle: Yes   No

one stroke numeral · no lift

seven

your best numeral

four

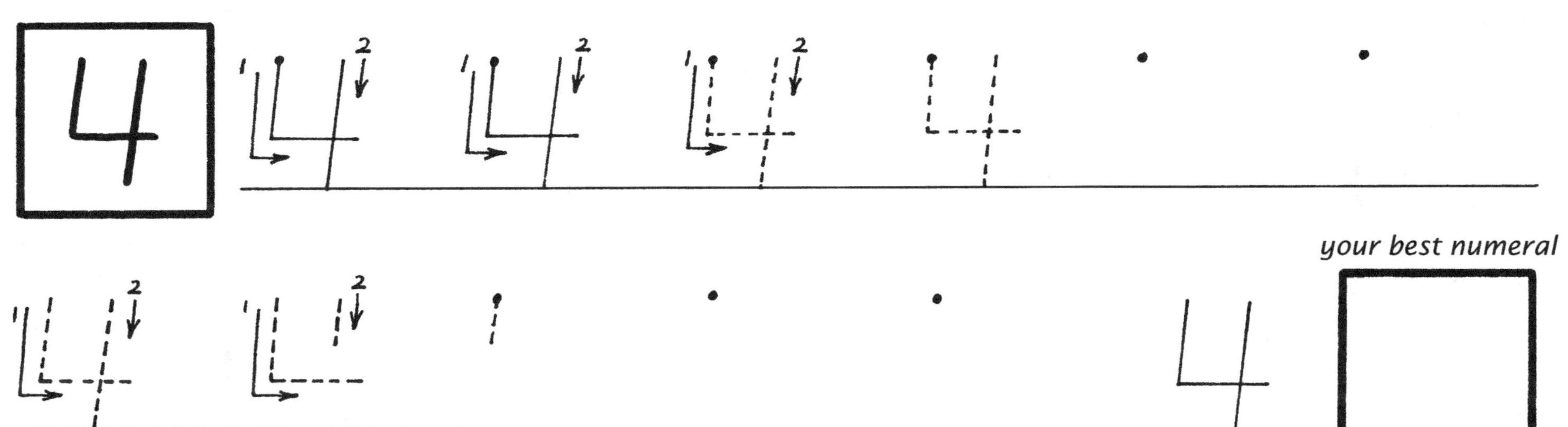

your best numeral

two stroke numeral · one lift

five

your best numeral

eight

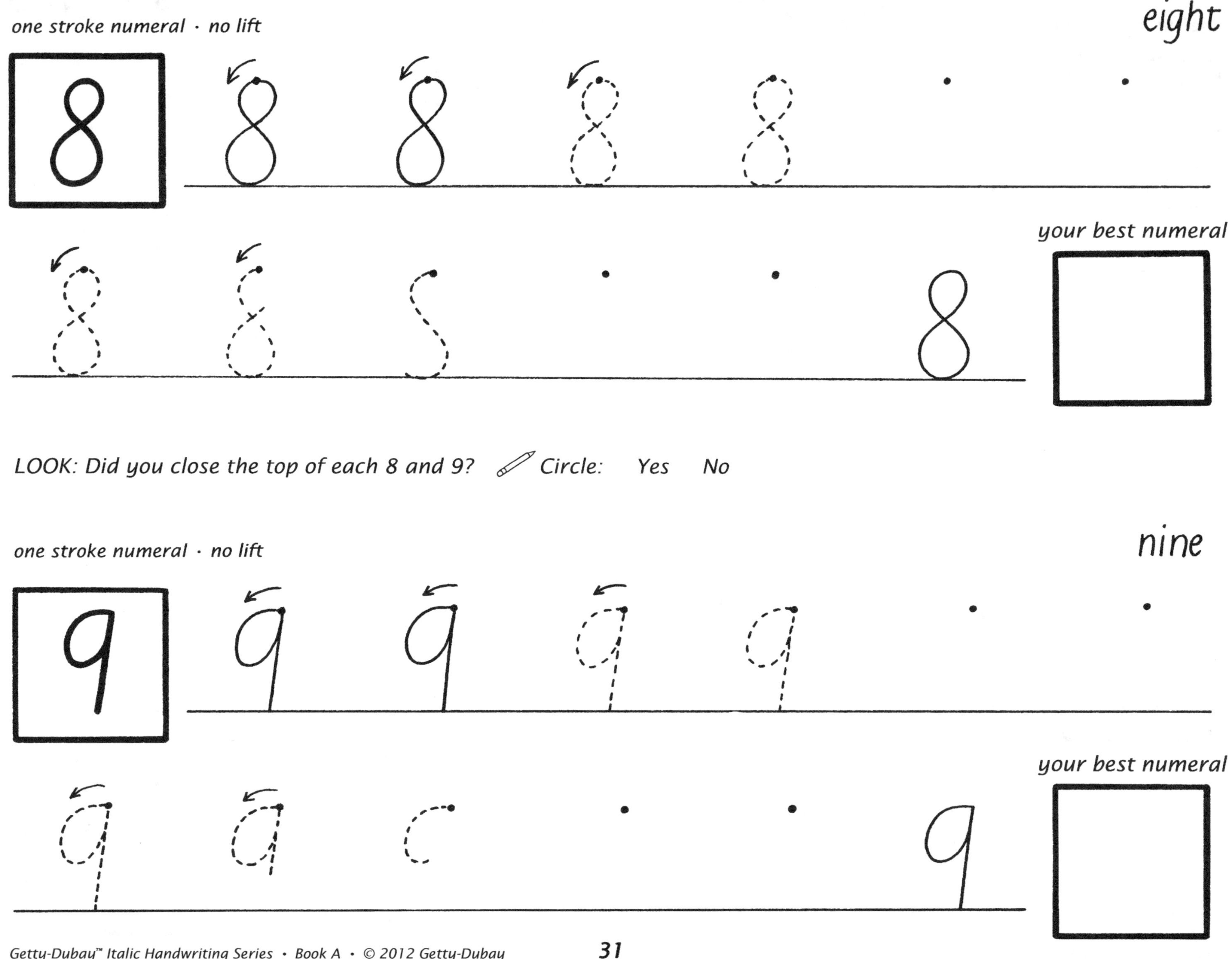

your best numeral

LOOK: Did you close the top of each 8 and 9?   Circle: Yes   No

one stroke numeral · no lift

nine

your best numeral

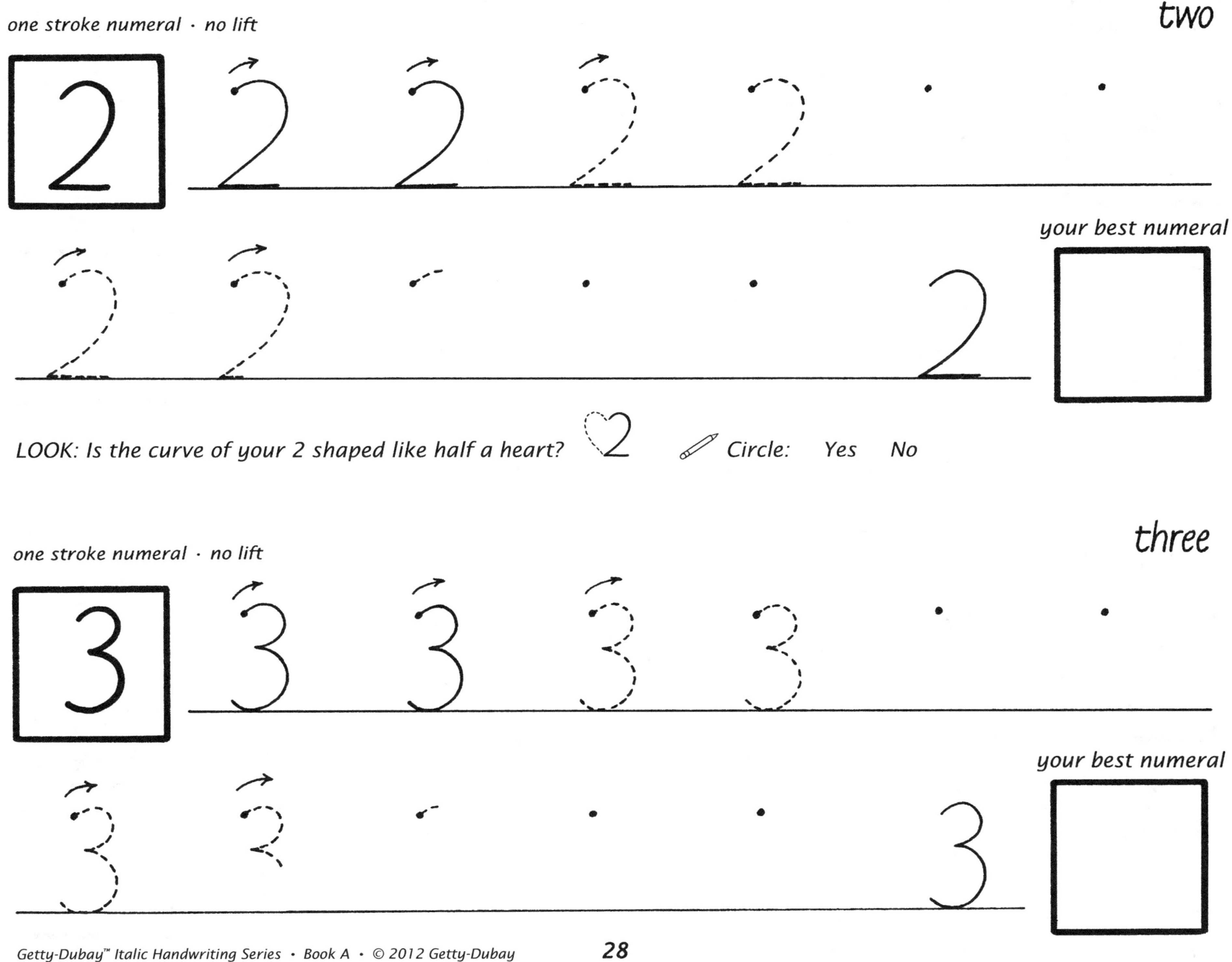

one stroke numeral · no lift
two
your best numeral
LOOK: Is the curve of your 2 shaped like half a heart? Circle: Yes No
one stroke numeral · no lift
three
your best numeral

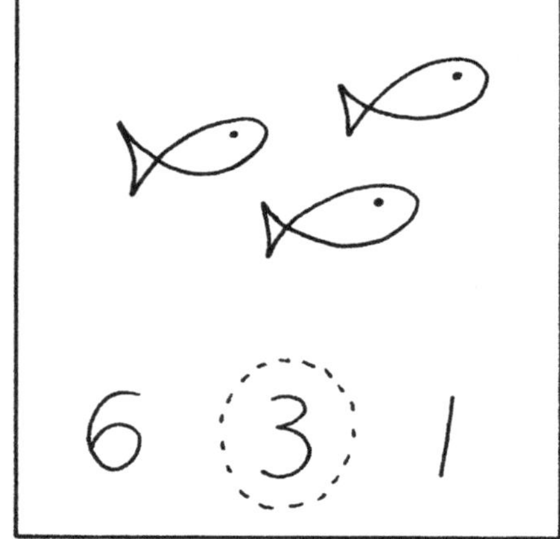

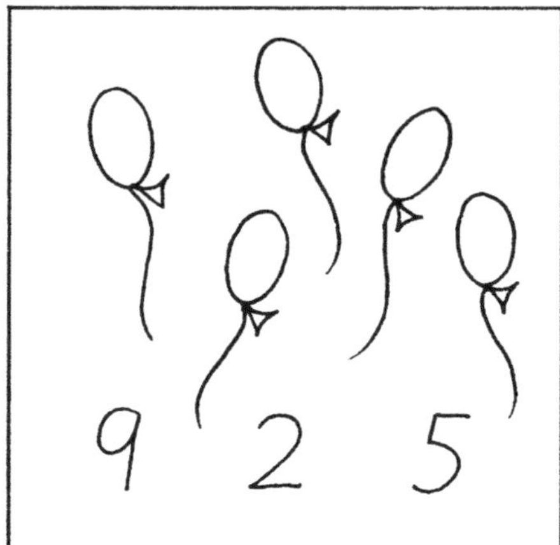

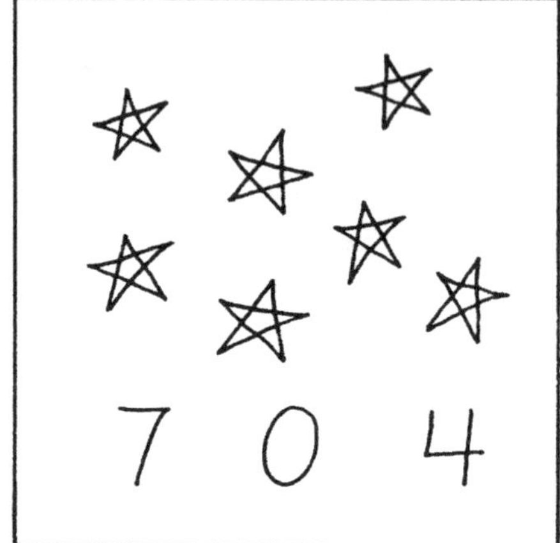

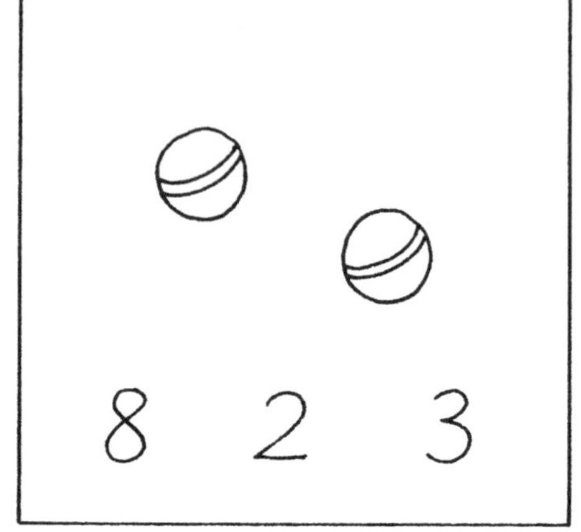

Ask the student to circle the numeral
that stands for the number of objects in the box.

32

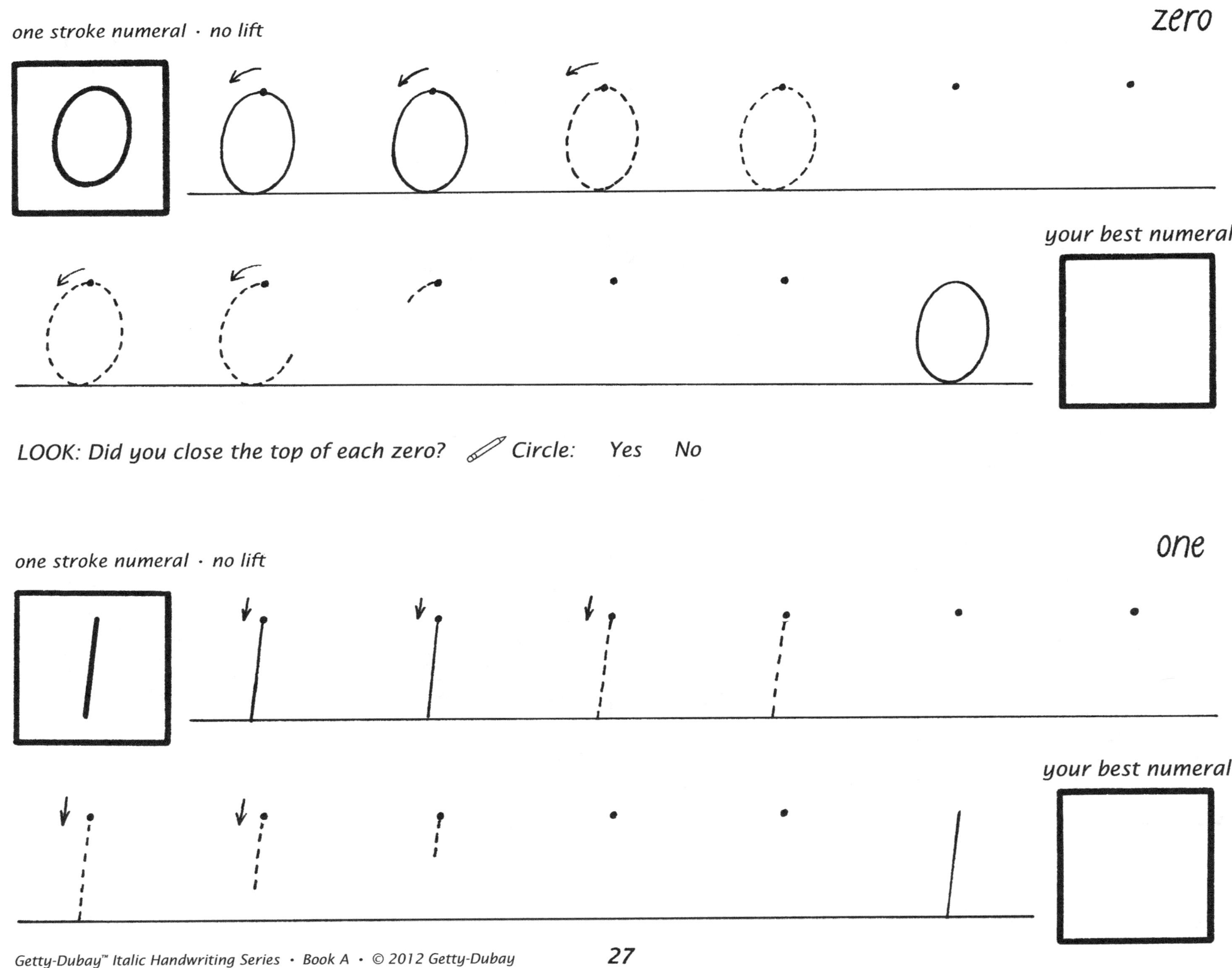

one stroke numeral · no lift
zero
your best numeral
LOOK: Did you close the top of each zero?   Circle: Yes   No
one stroke numeral · no lift
one
your best numeral

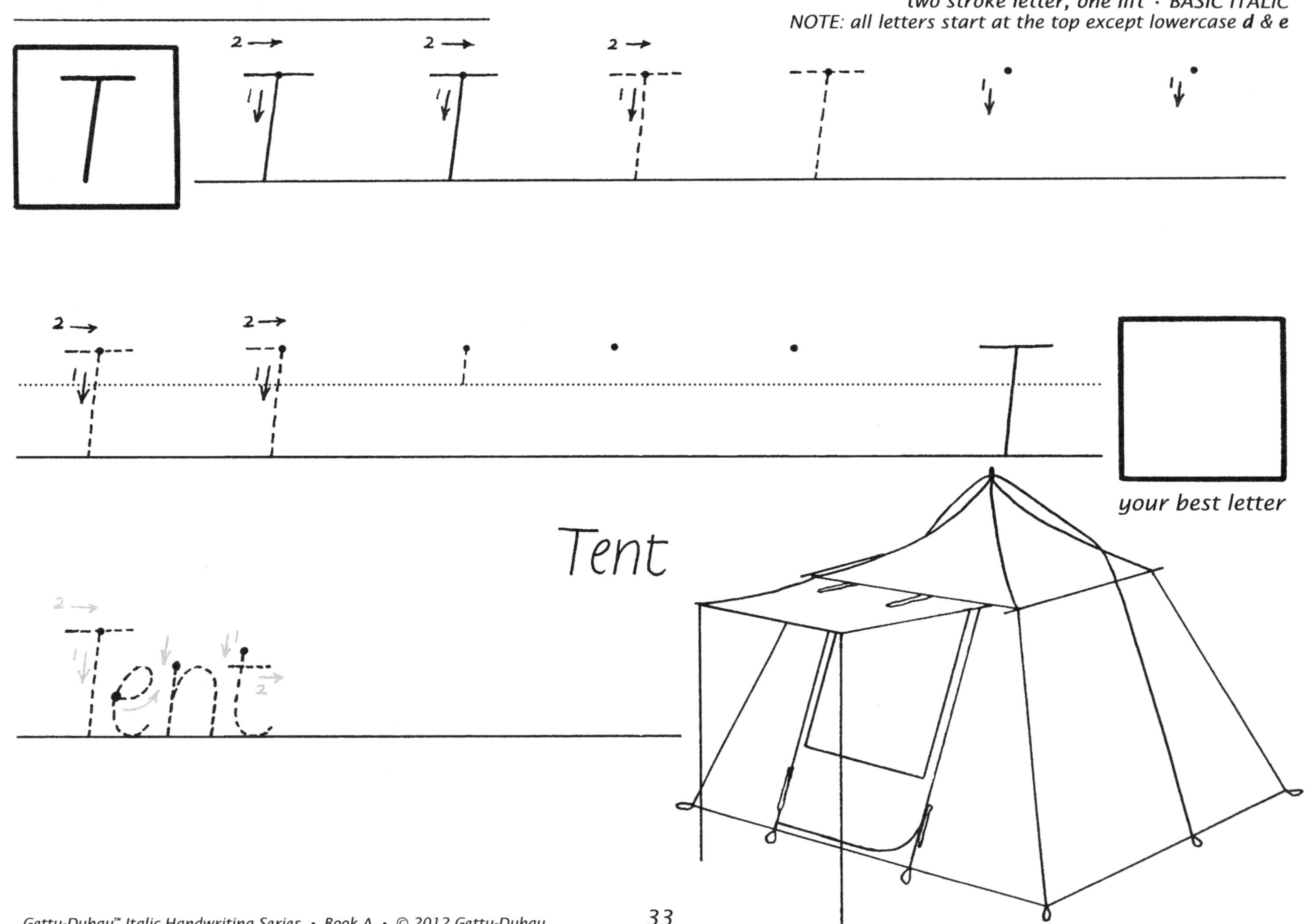

T
2
2
2
2
2
2
your best letter
Tent
Tent

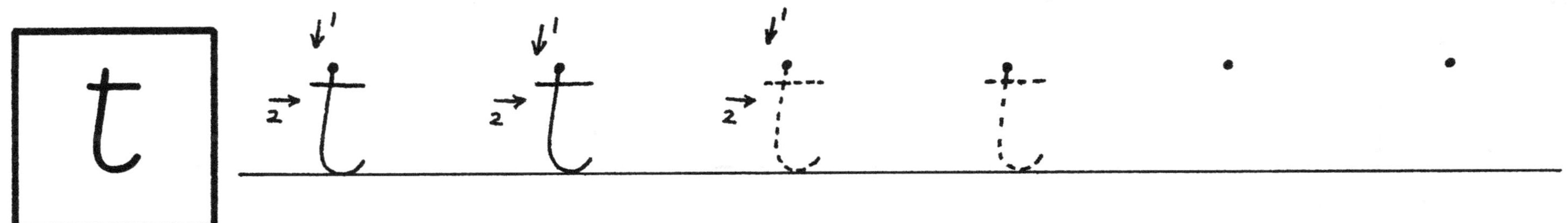

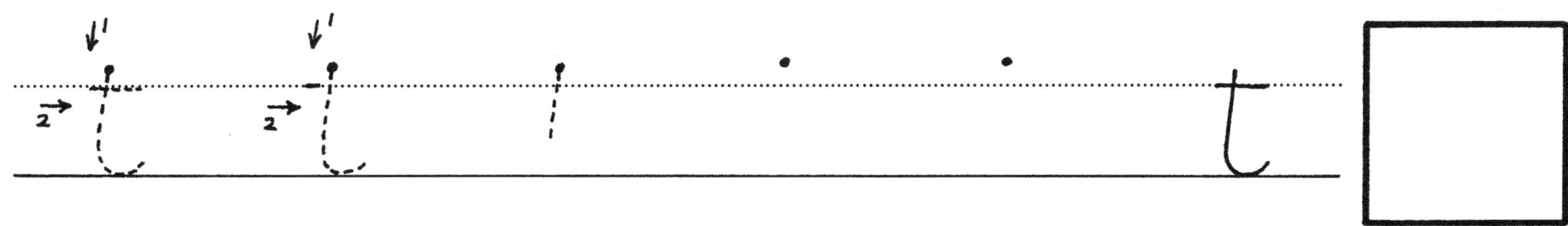

your best letter

turkey

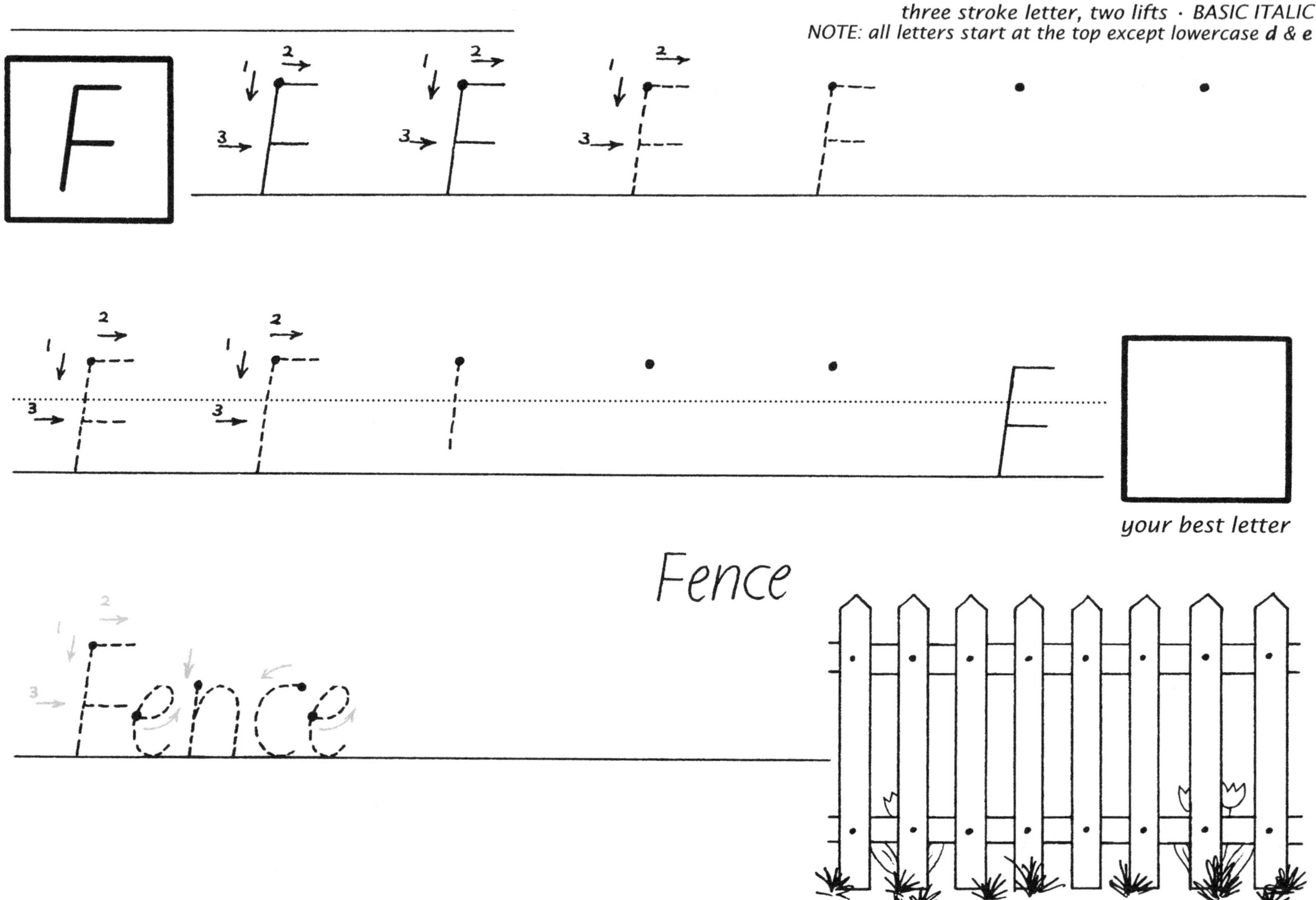

three stroke letter, two lifts · BASIC ITALIC
NOTE: all letters start at the top except lowercase d & e
F
1
2
3
your best letter
Fence
Fence

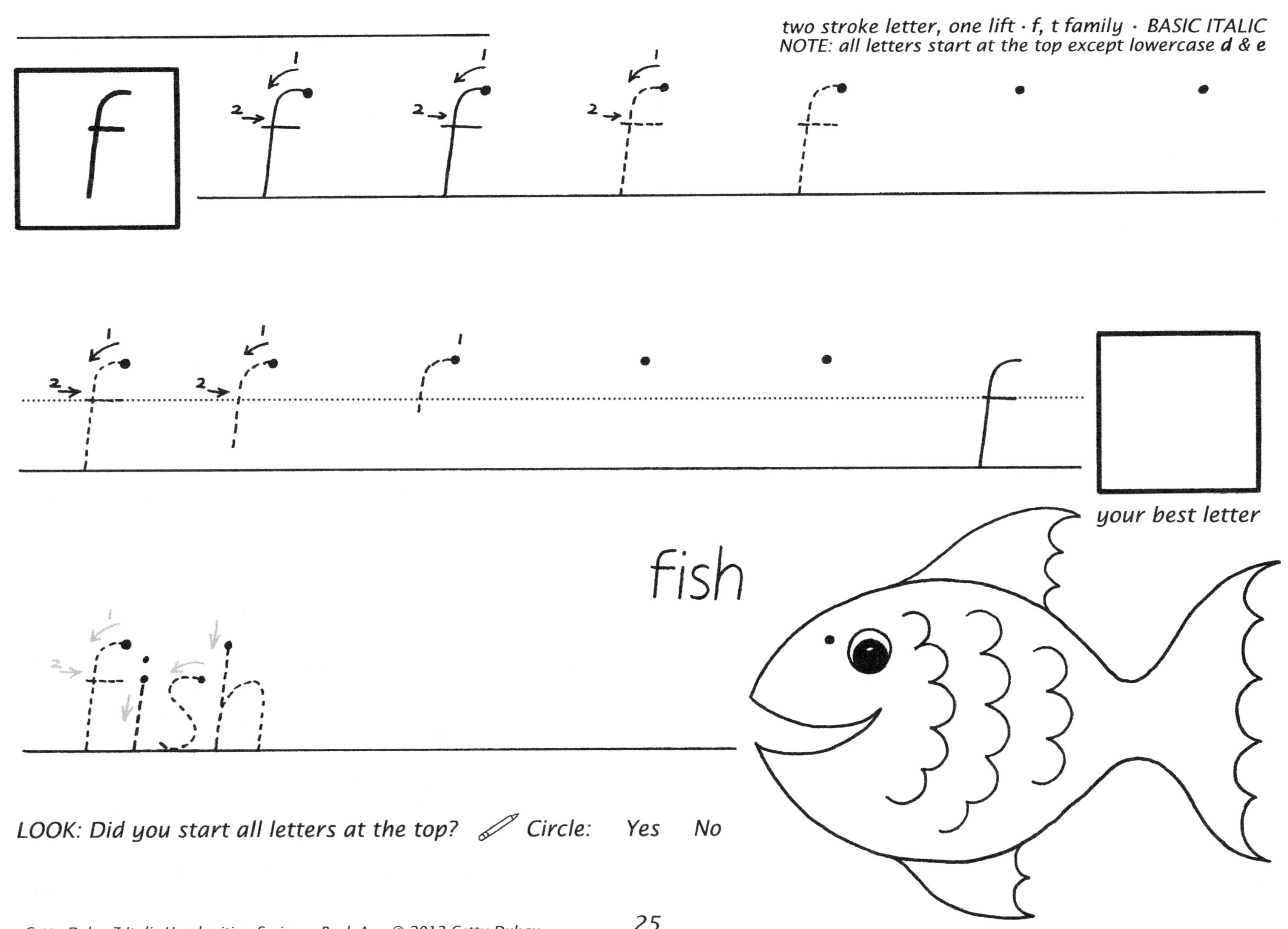

two stroke letter, one lift · f, t family · BASIC ITALIC
NOTE: all letters start at the top except lowercase d & e
f
1
2
your best letter
fish
fish
LOOK: Did you start all letters at the top? Circle: Yes   No

your best letter

Sailboat

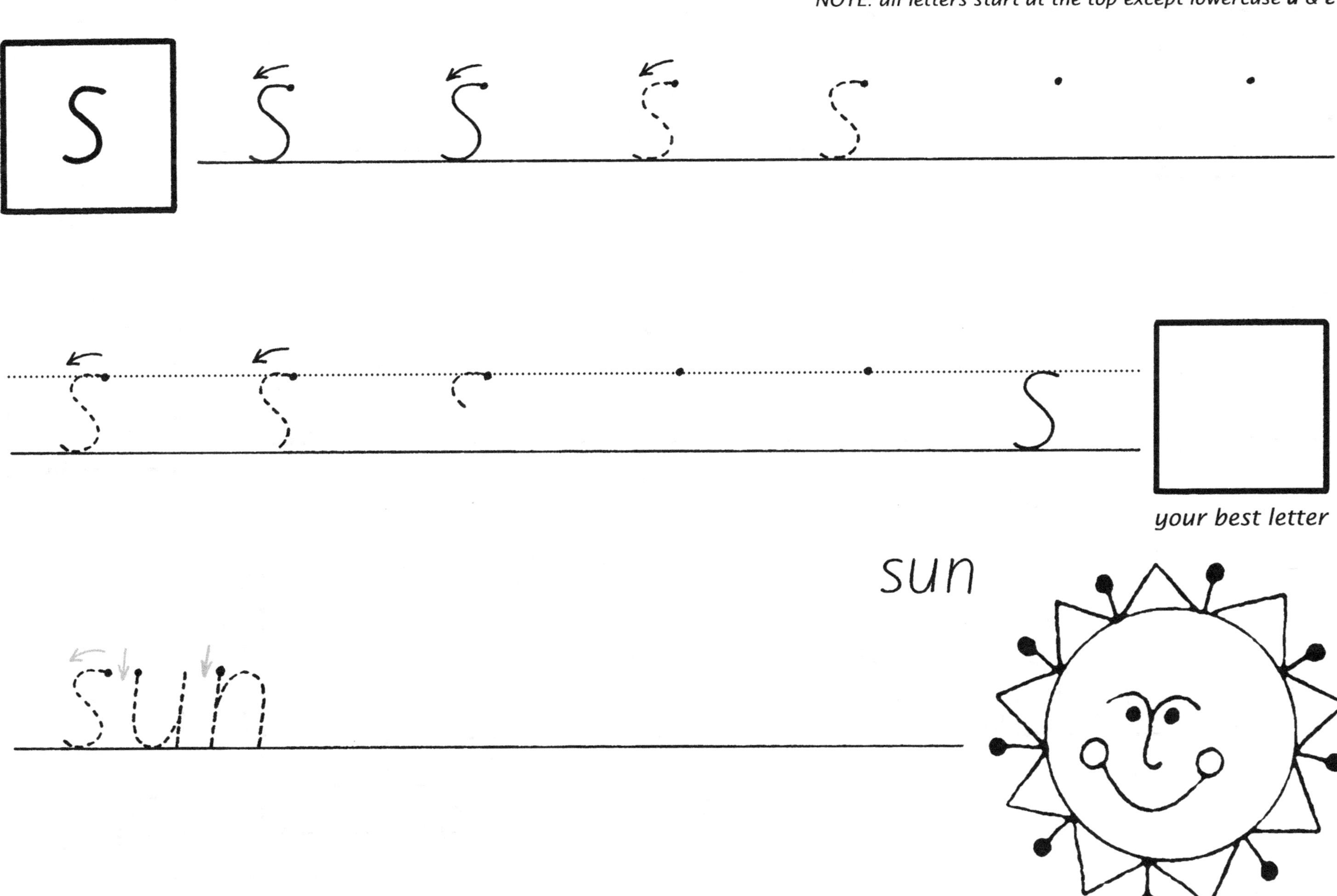
your best letter
sun

C

your best letter

Cow

LOOK: Did you trace each letter before writing your own?

Circle: Yes   No

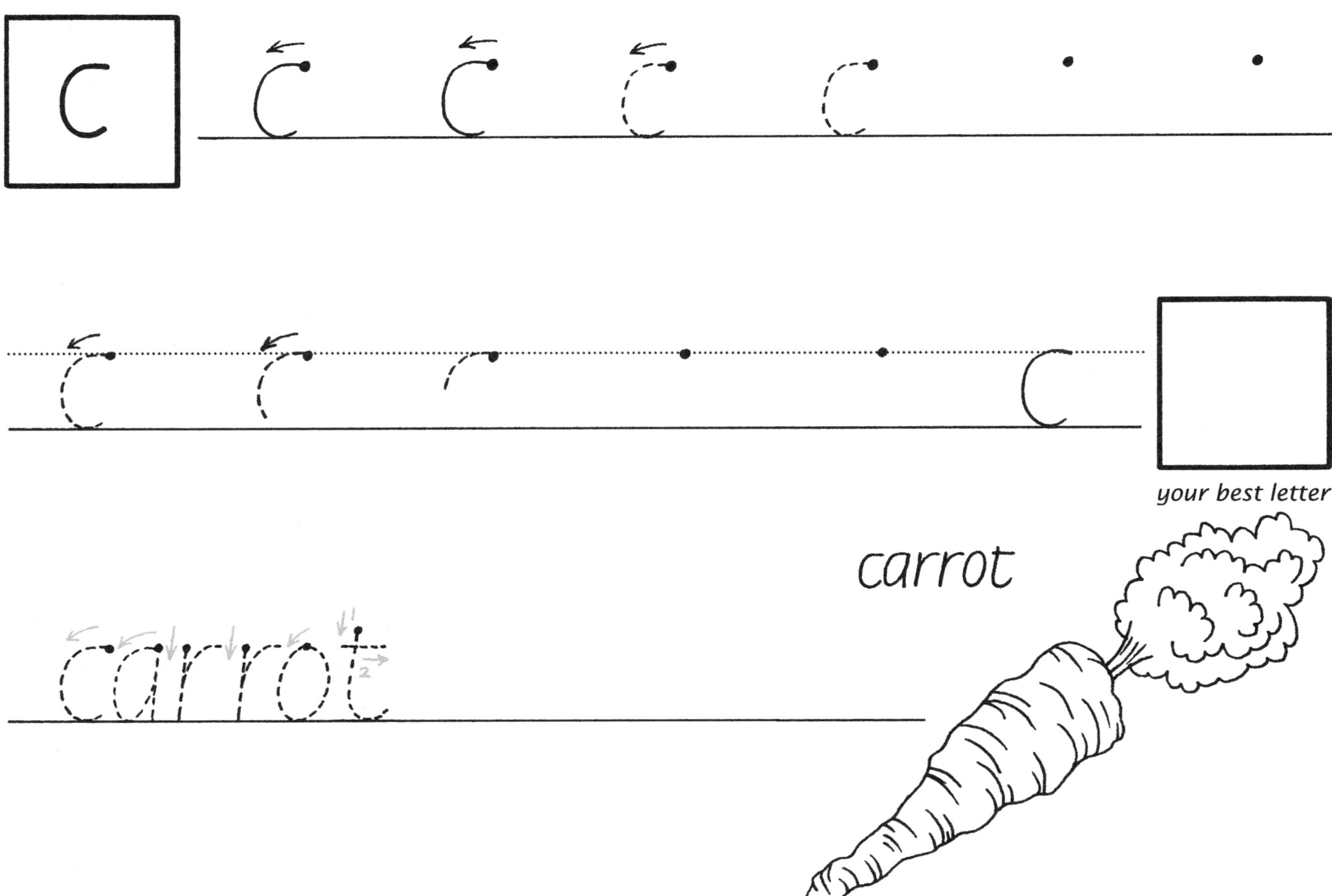

C
your best letter
carrot
carrot

E

your best letter

Egg

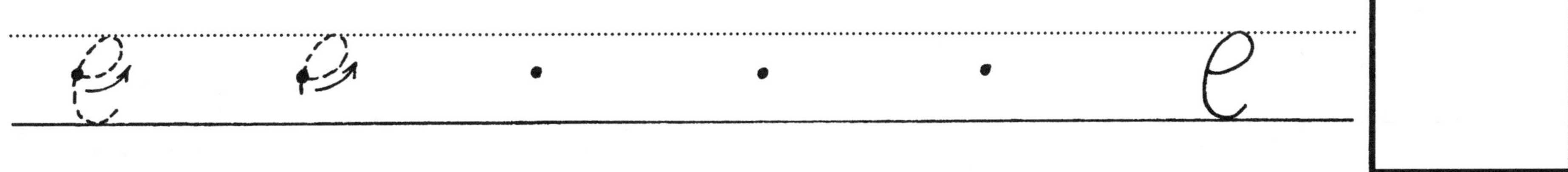

your best letter

elephant

LOOK: Did you trace each **e** before writing your own?

Circle: Yes   No

your best letter

Octagon

Octagon

LOOK: Did you close the top of each **O**? Circle: Yes   No

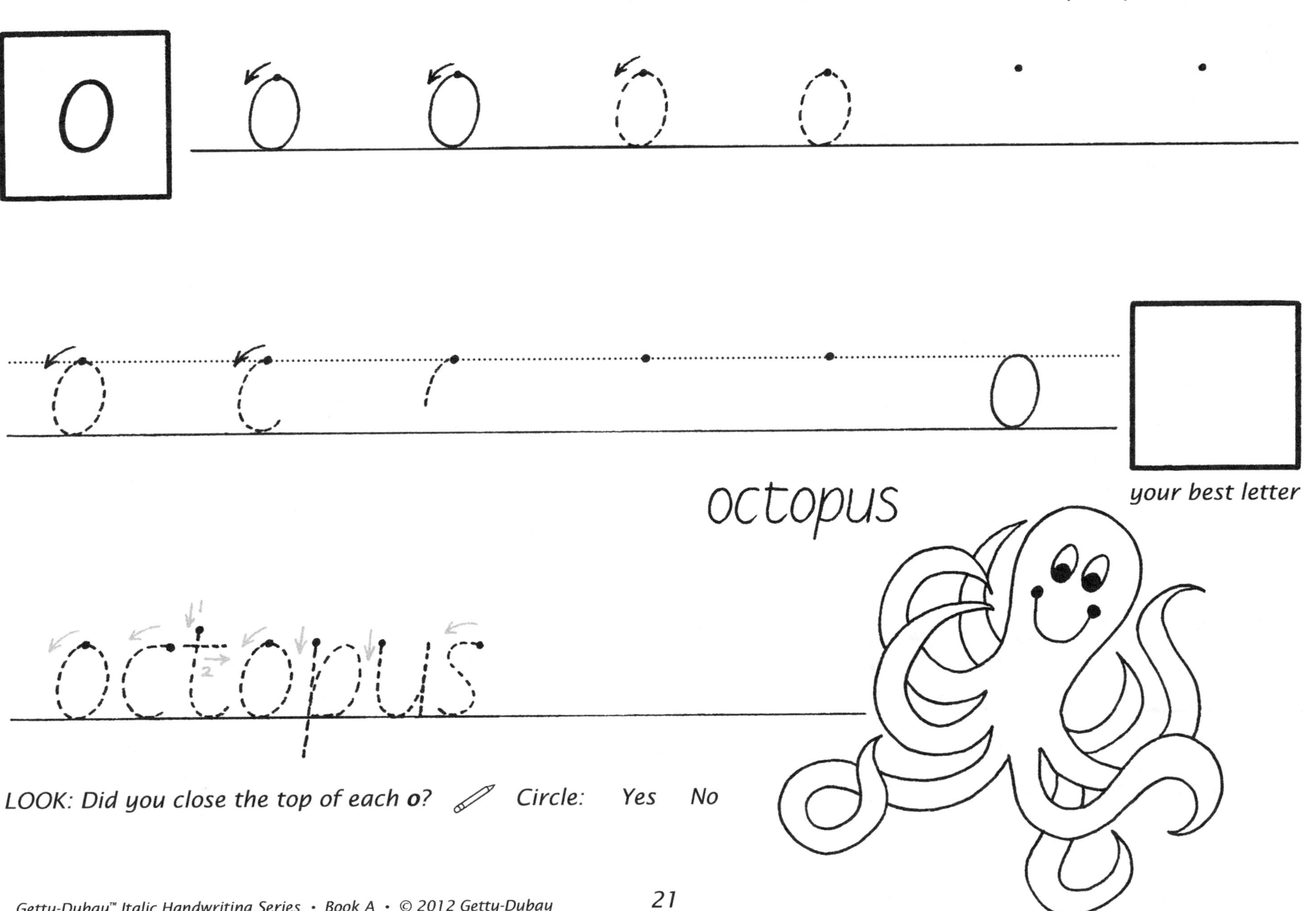

octopus

your best letter

LOOK: Did you close the top of each **o**? Circle: Yes No

your best letter

Peacock

your best letter

parrot

B

your best letter

Balloons

Balloons

your best letter

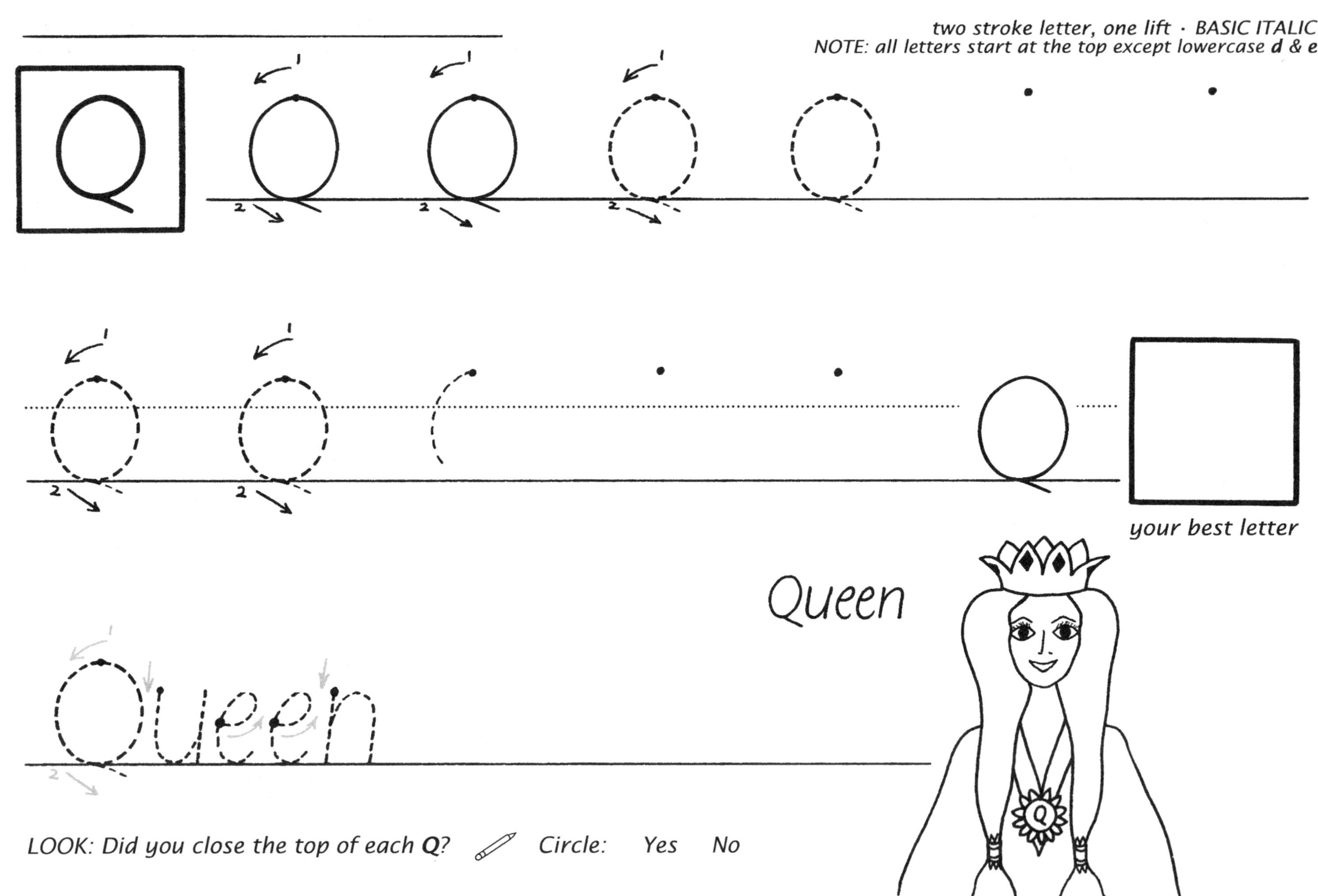

two stroke letter, one lift · BASIC ITALIC
NOTE: all letters start at the top except lowercase d & e
1
2
your best letter
Queen
LOOK: Did you close the top of each Q?   Circle: Yes   No

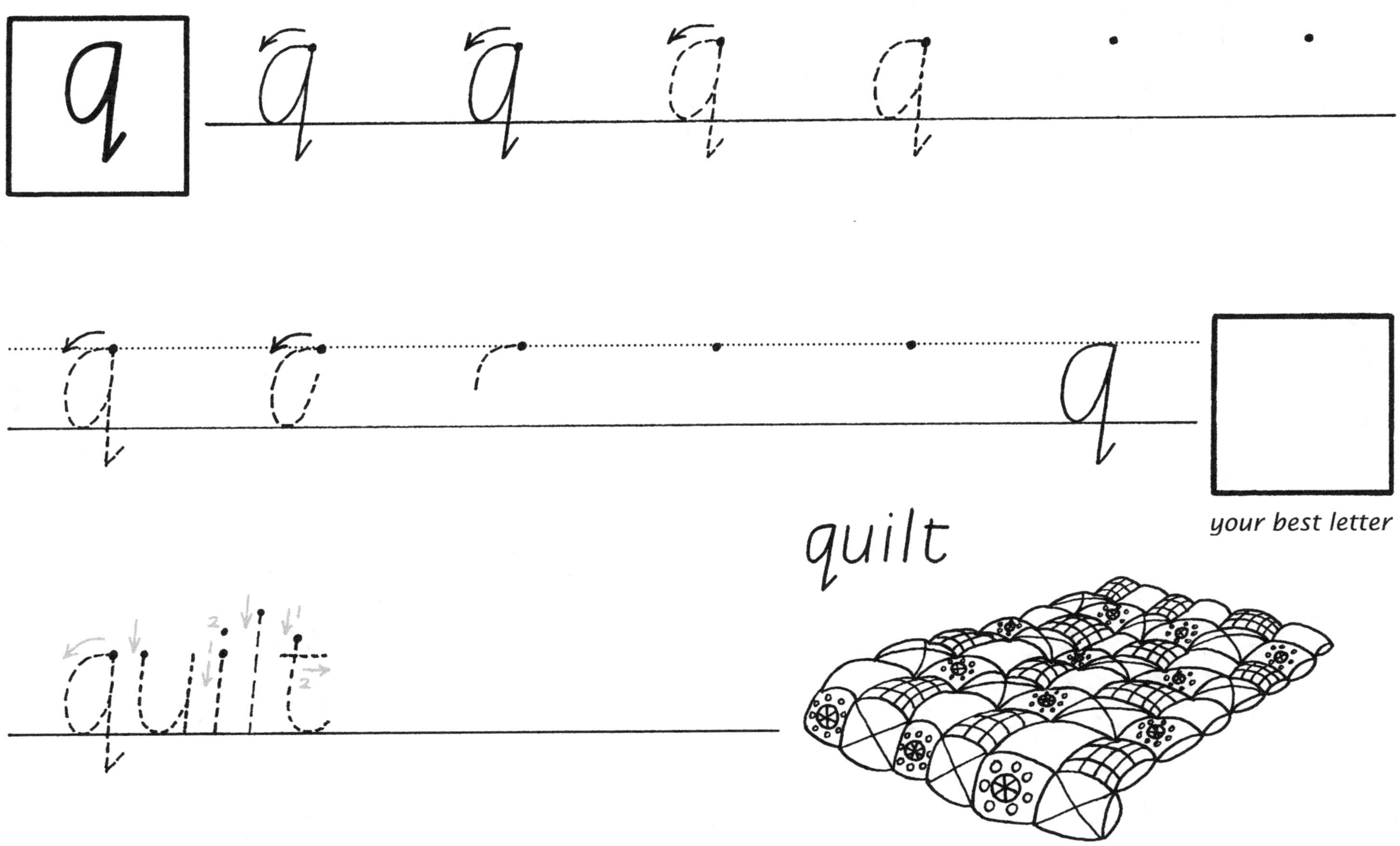

your best letter

quilt

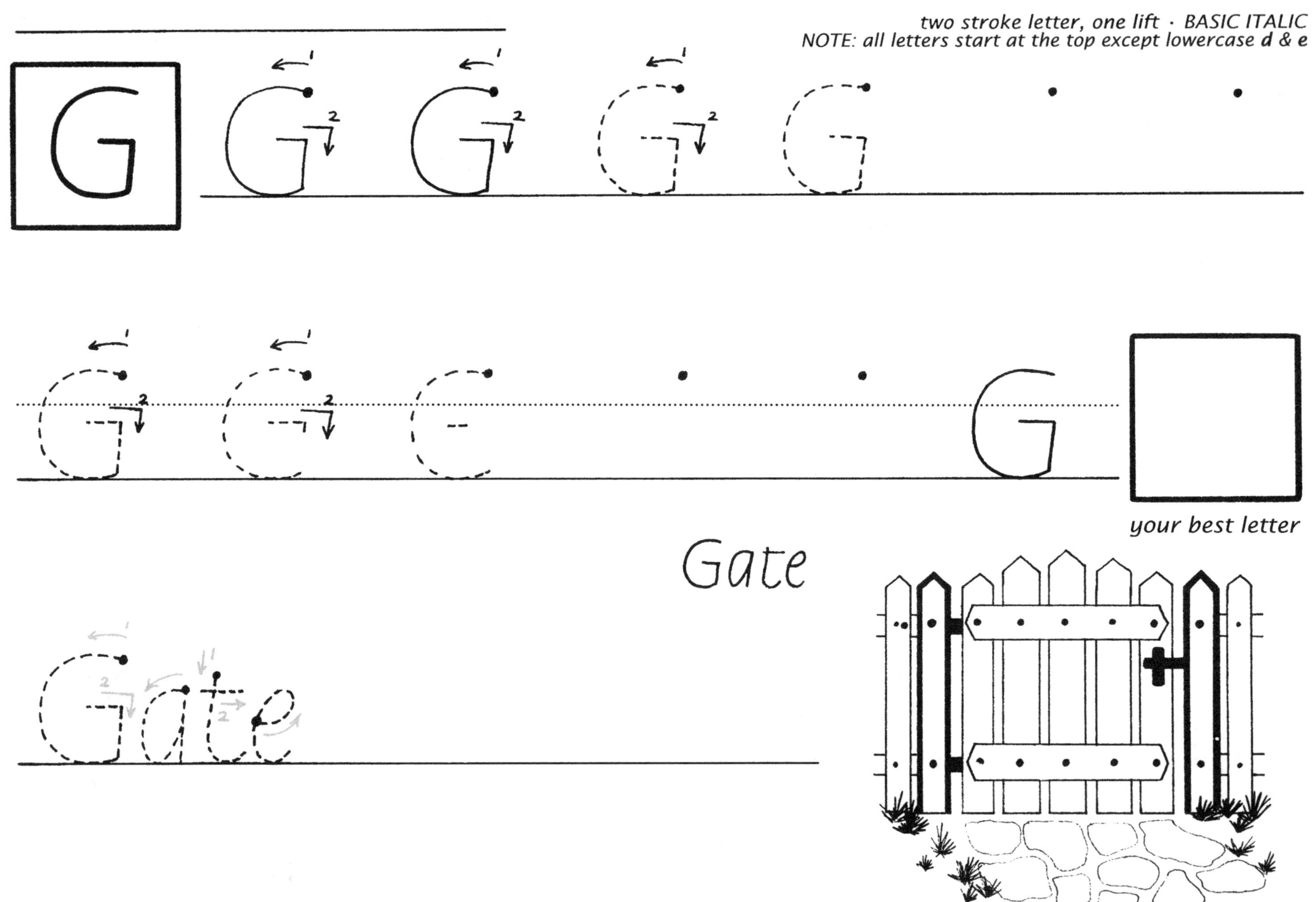

your best letter

Gate

LOOK: Did you trace each letter before writing your own?   Circle: Yes   No

two stroke letter, one lift · BASIC ITALIC
NOTE: all letters start at the top except lowercase d & e
your best letter
Dinosaur

your best letter
dog

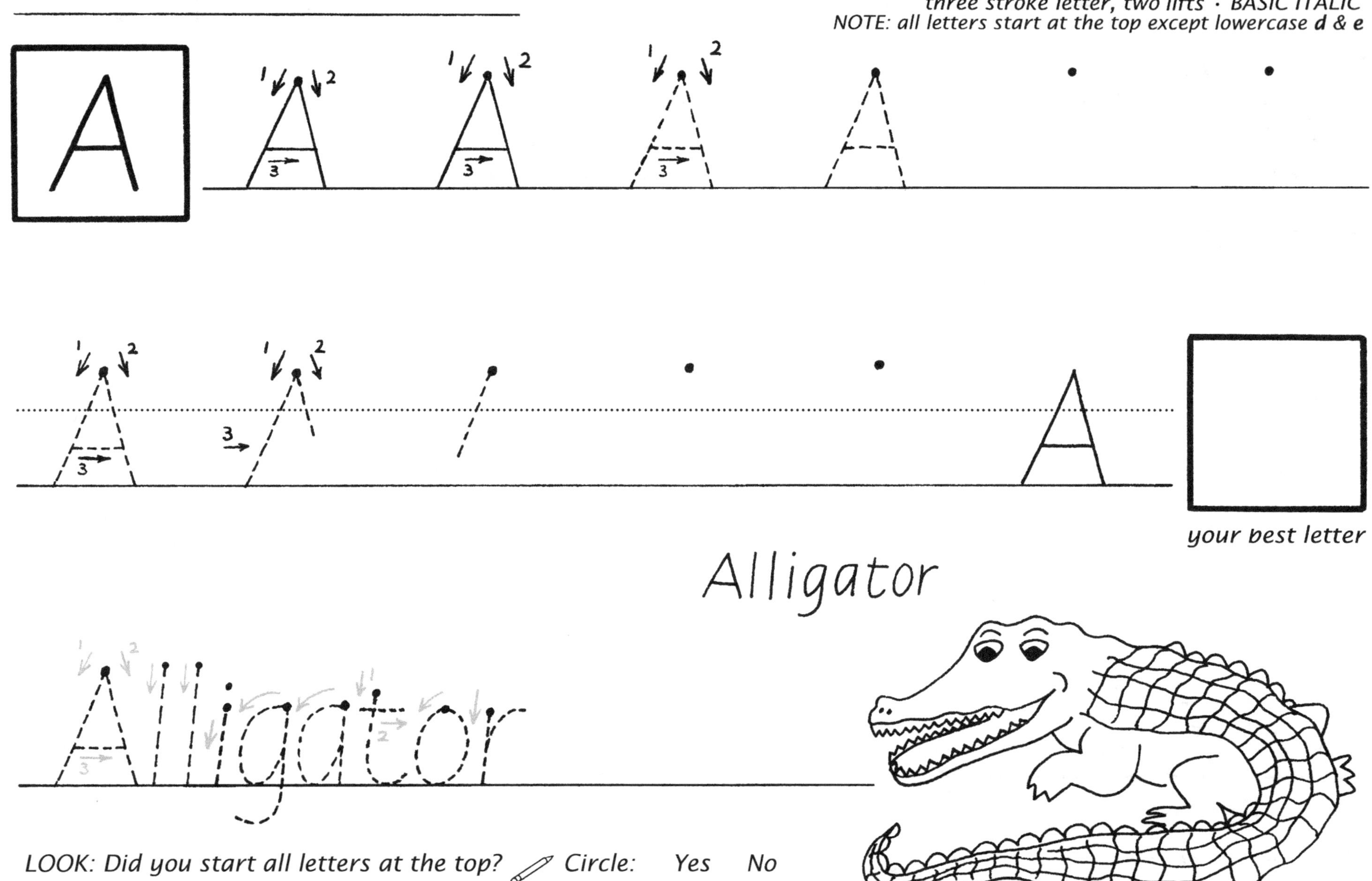

your best letter

Alligator

LOOK: Did you start all letters at the top? ✏ Circle: Yes   No

LOOK: Did you close each **a** at the top?   Circle: Yes   No

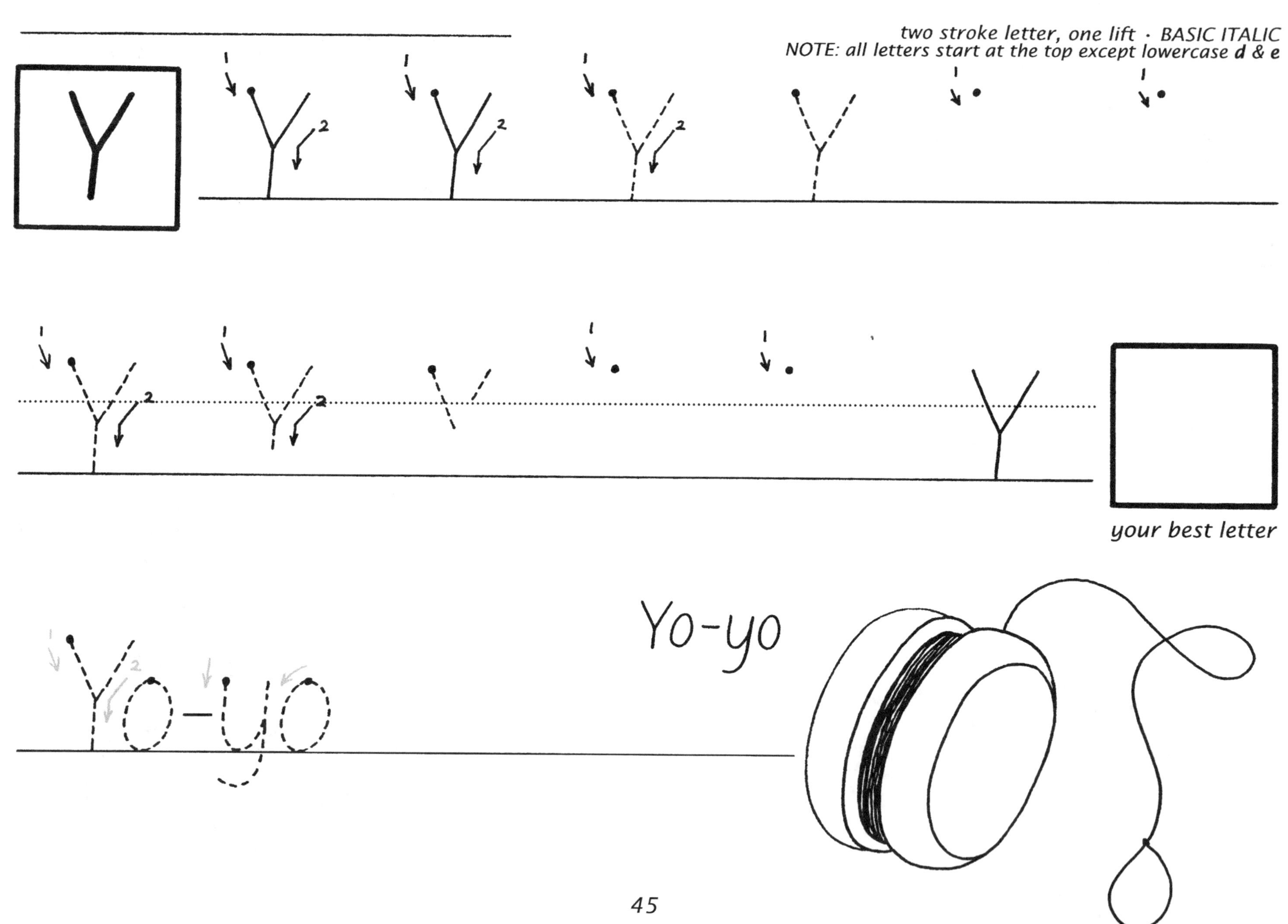

Getty-Dubay™ Italic Handwriting Series · Book A · © 2012 Getty-Dubay

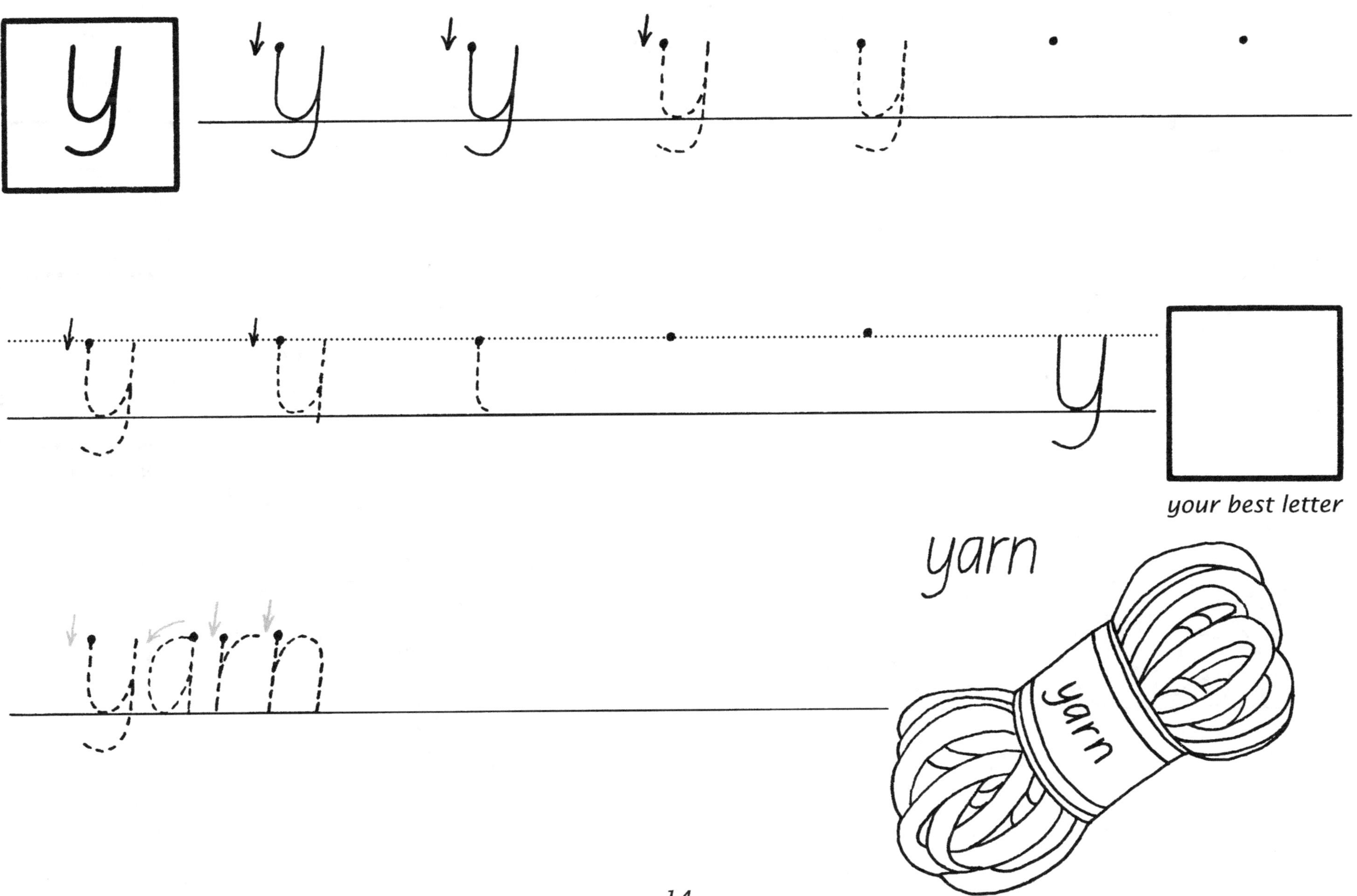

your best letter

yarn

U

your best letter

Ukulele

LOOK: Did you trace each letter before writing your own?

Circle: Yes   No

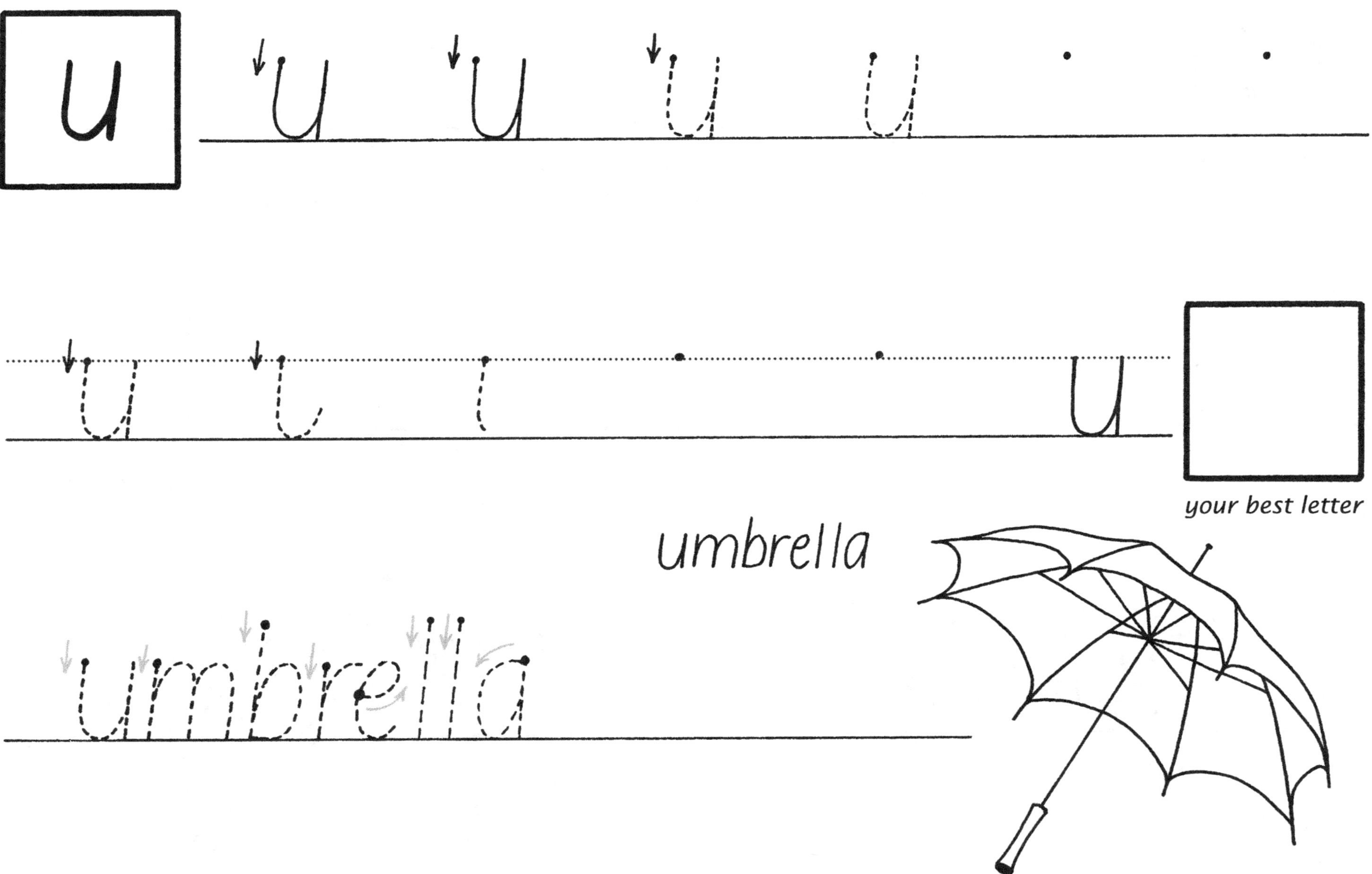

u
your best letter
umbrella
umbrella

three stroke letter, two lifts · BASIC ITALIC
NOTE: all letters start at the top except lowercase d & e

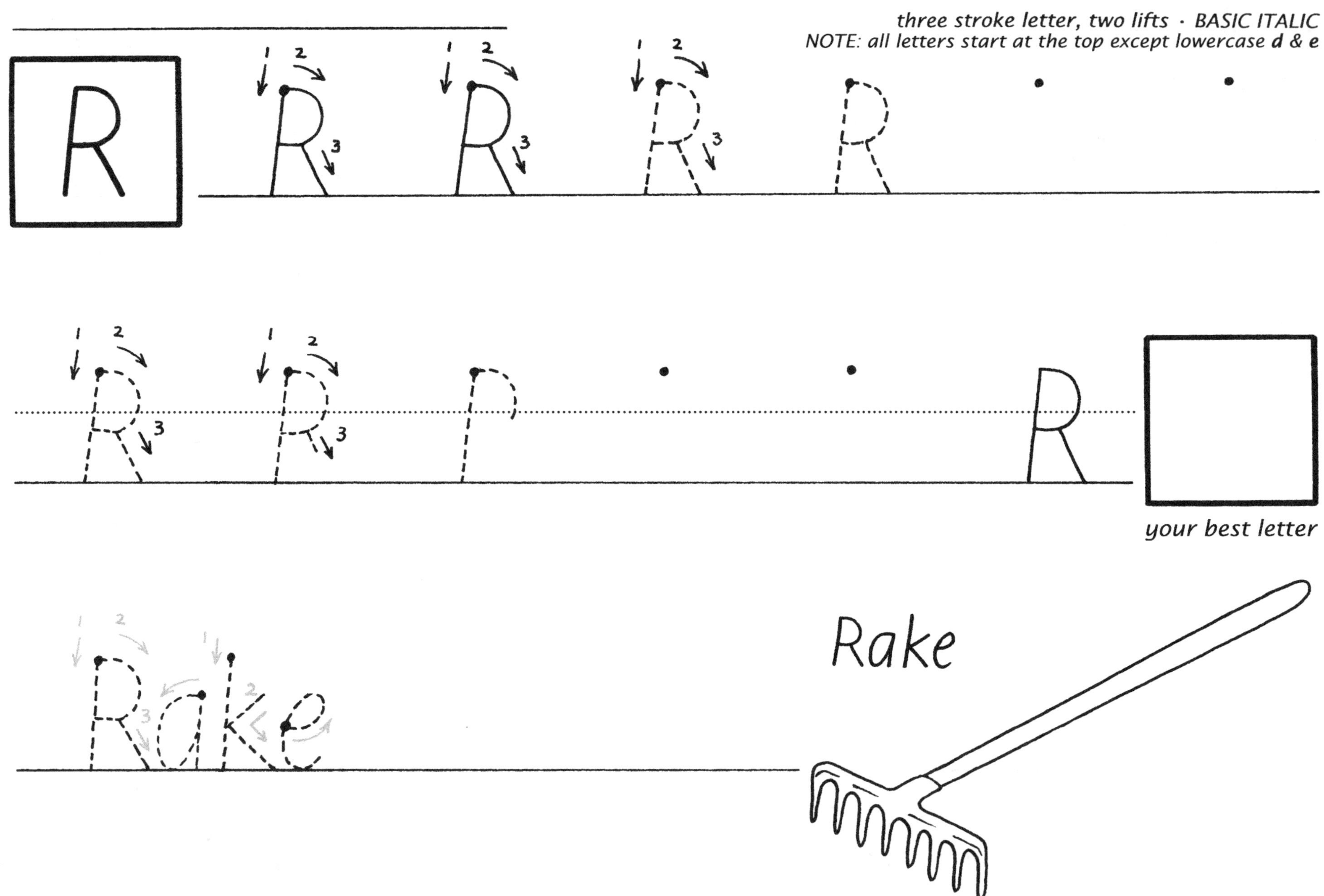

your best letter

Rake

r

your best letter

rabbit

LOOK: Did you start each letter at the top?   Circle: Yes   No

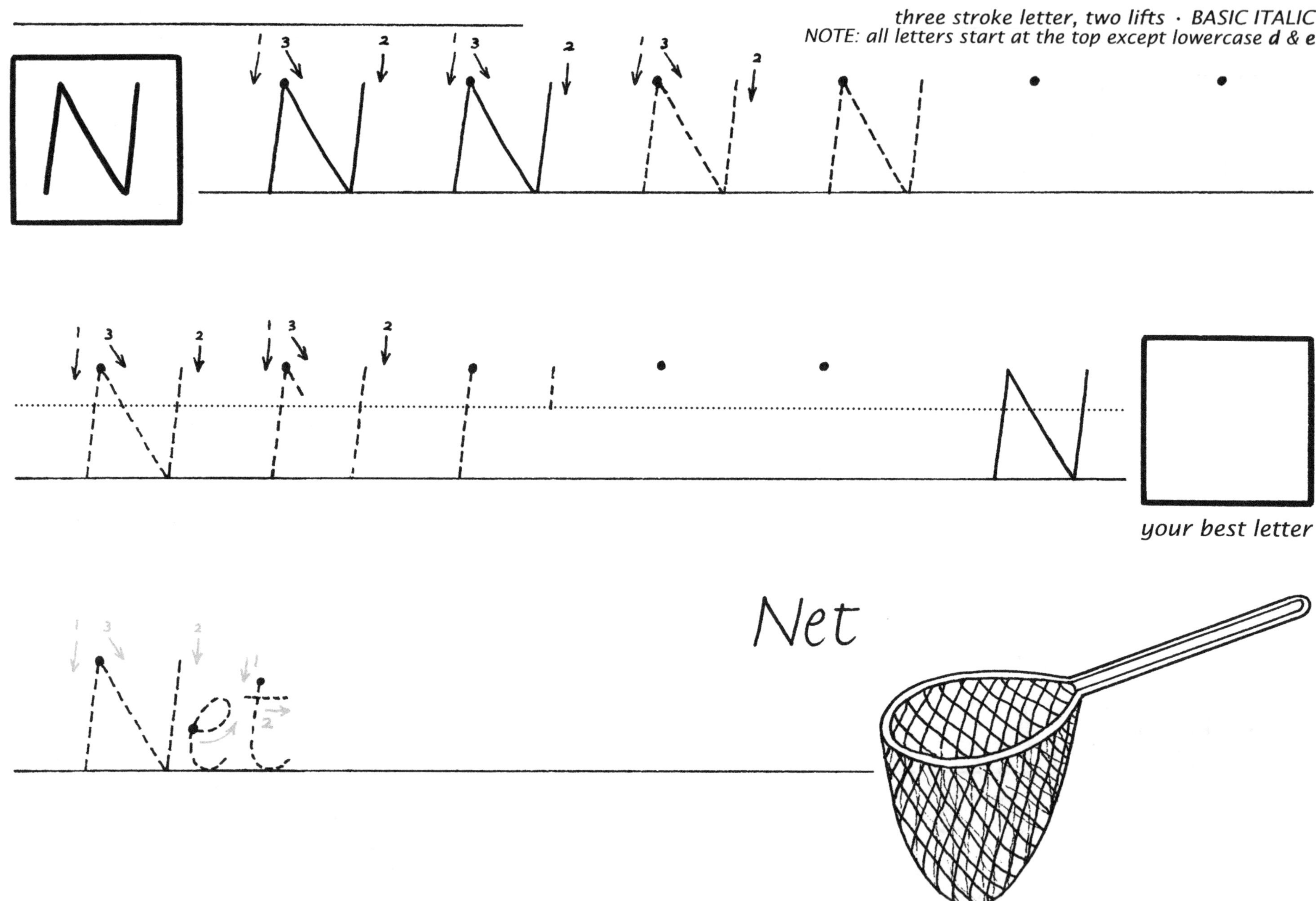

your best letter

Net

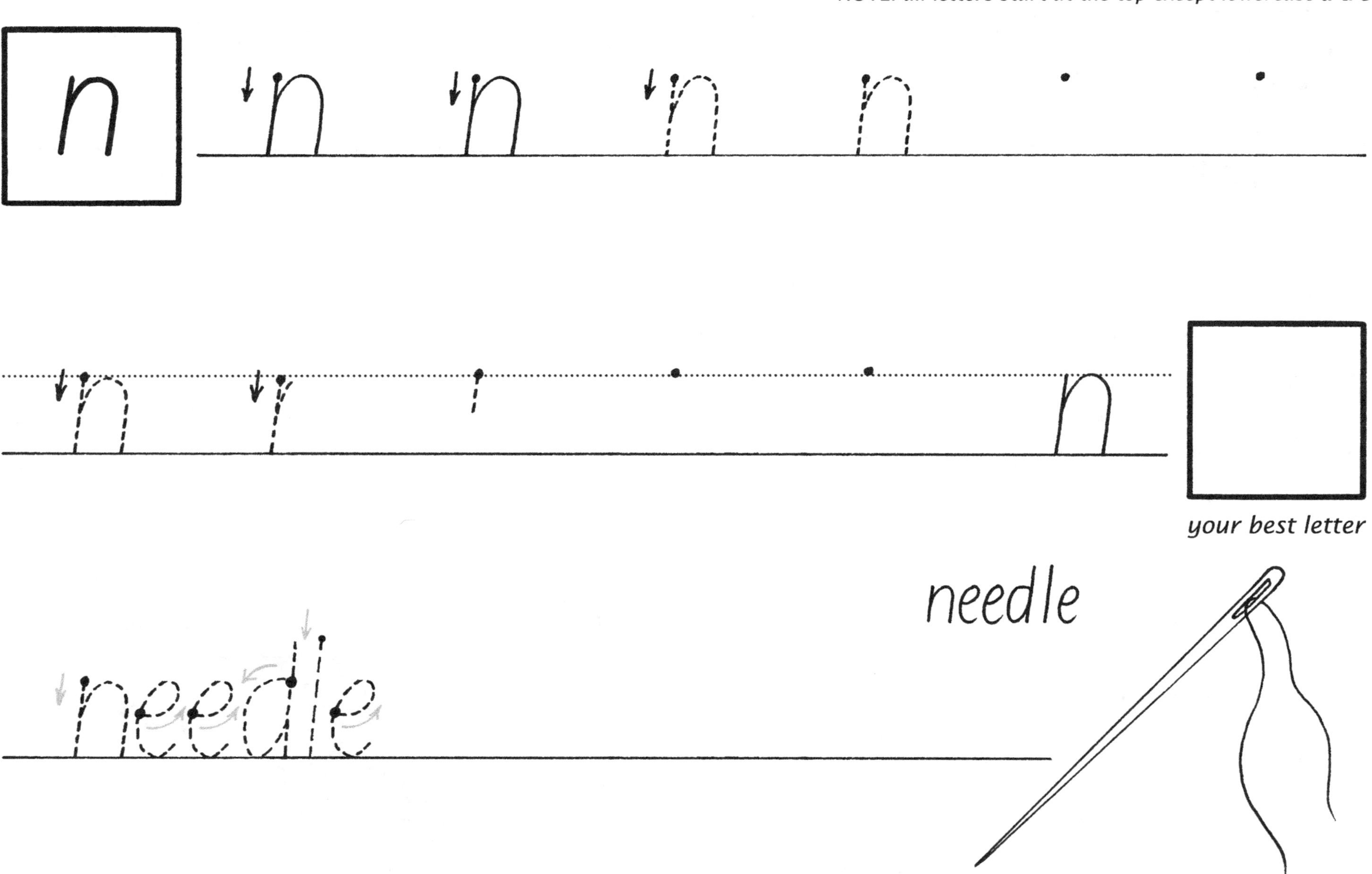

your best letter
needle

your best letter

Mittens

LOOK: Did you start all letters at the top?   Circle: Yes   No

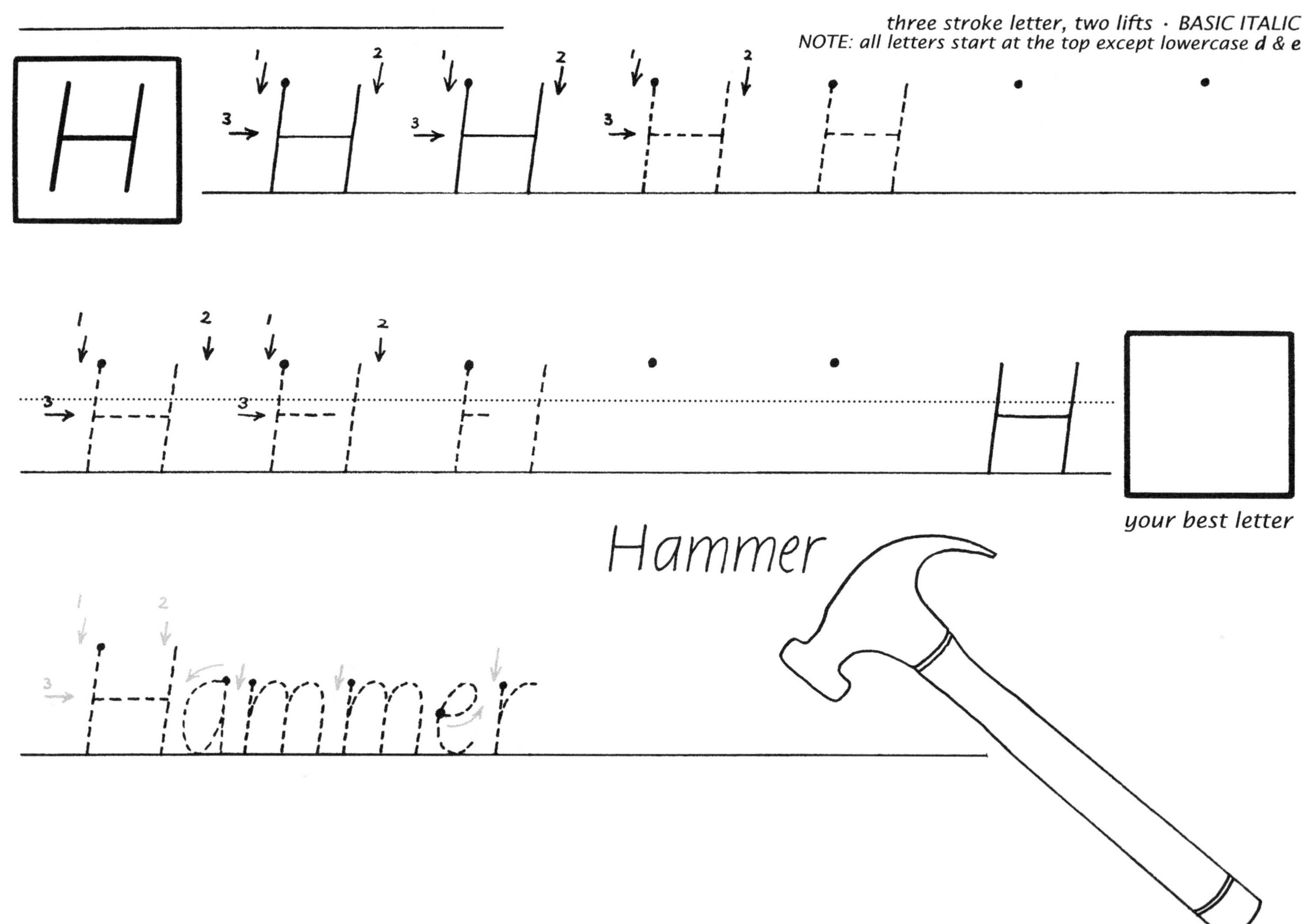

three stroke letter, two lifts · BASIC ITALIC
NOTE: all letters start at the top except lowercase d & e
your best letter
Hammer

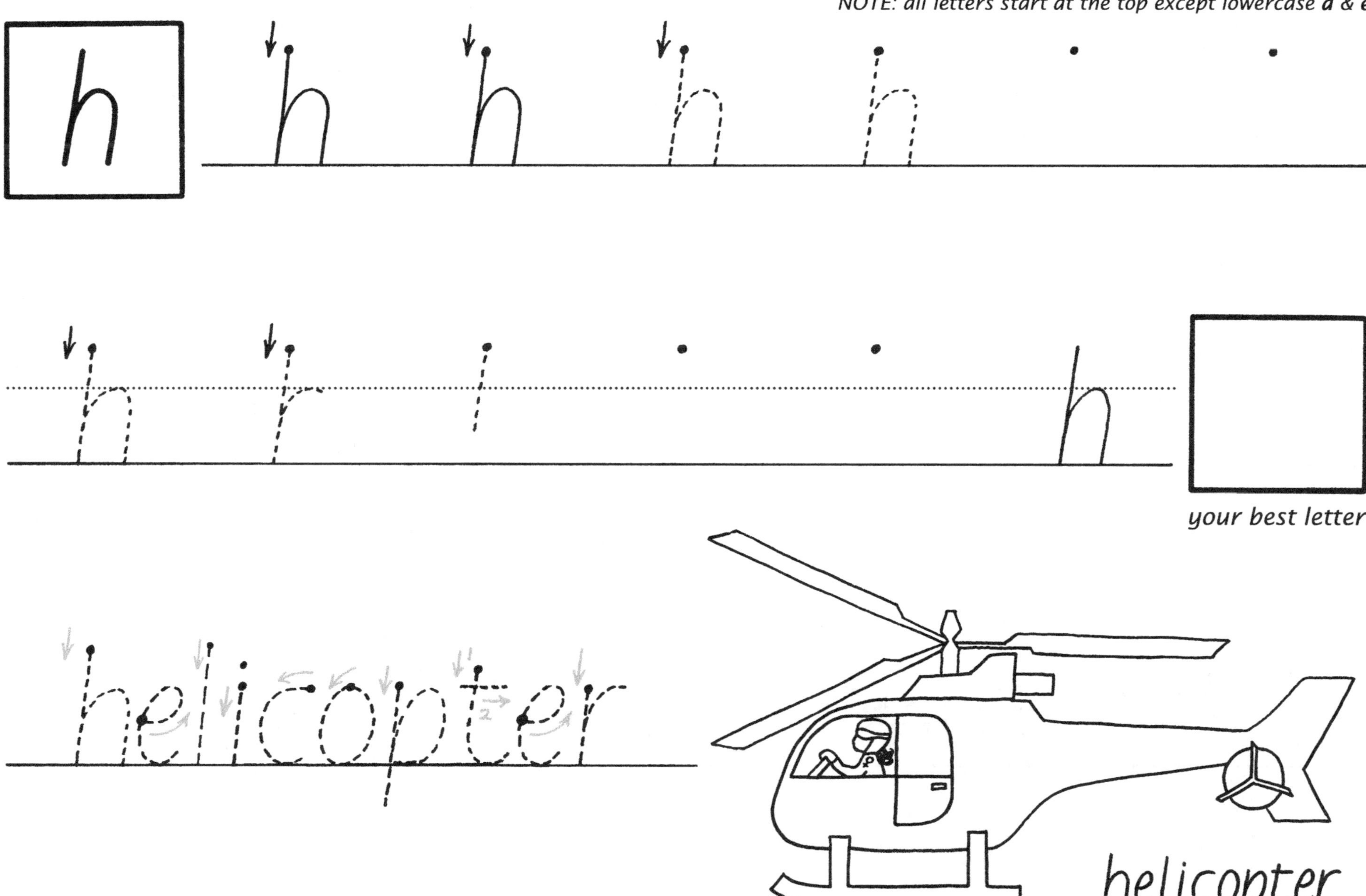

your best letter

helicopter

Zipper

your best letter

Zipper

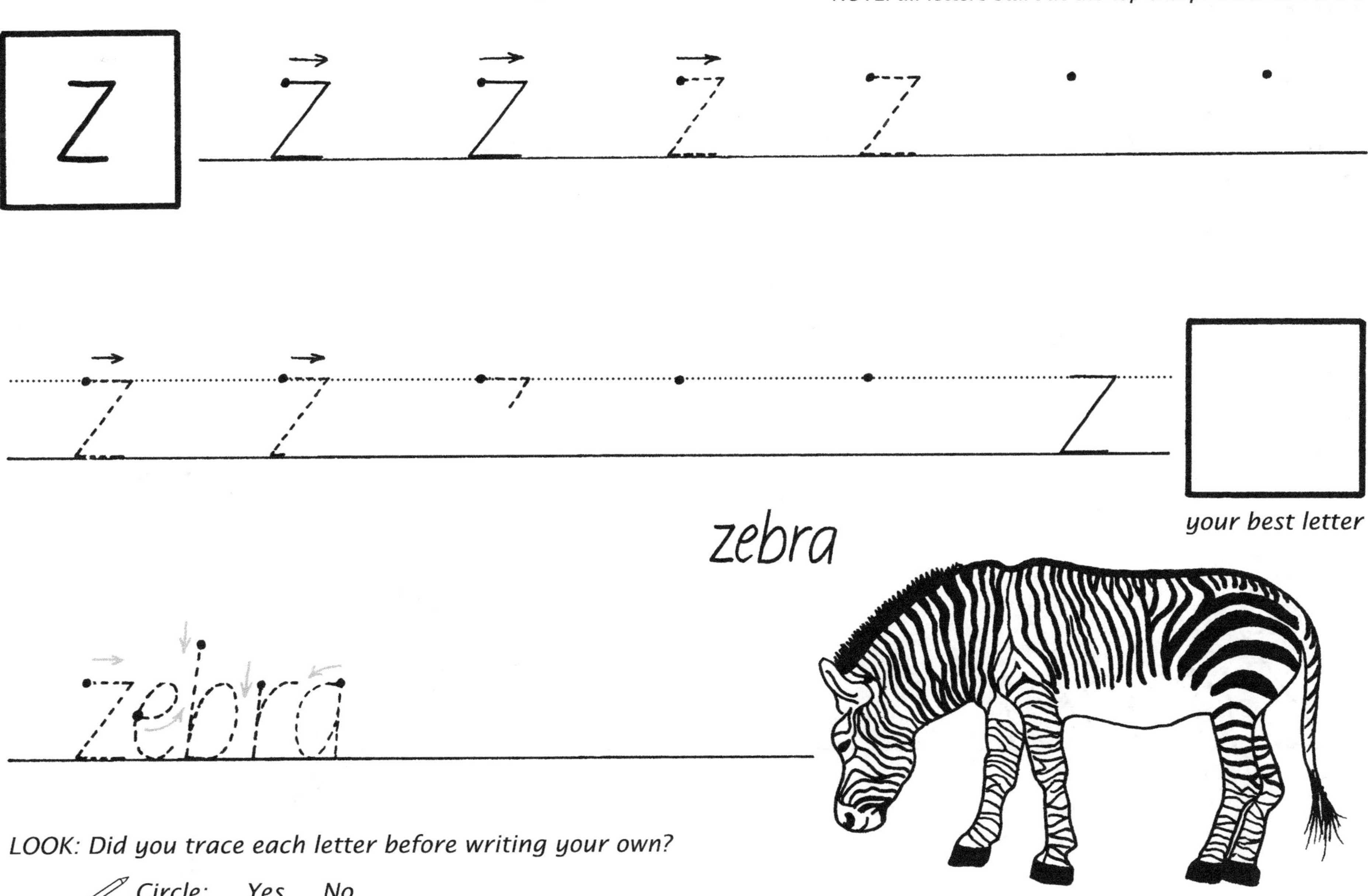

your best letter

zebra

LOOK: Did you trace each letter before writing your own?

Circle: Yes   No

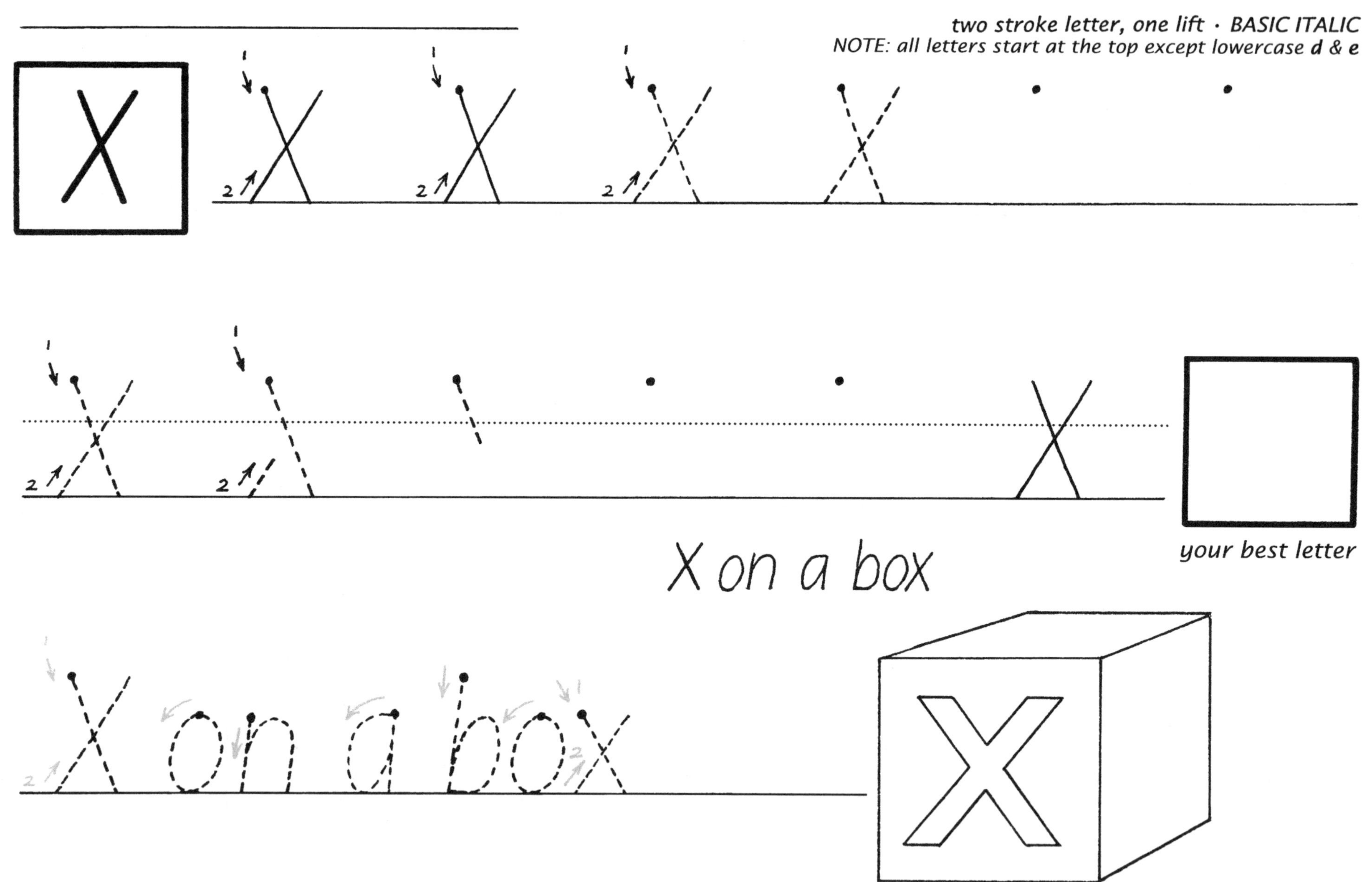

X on a box
your best letter
X on a box

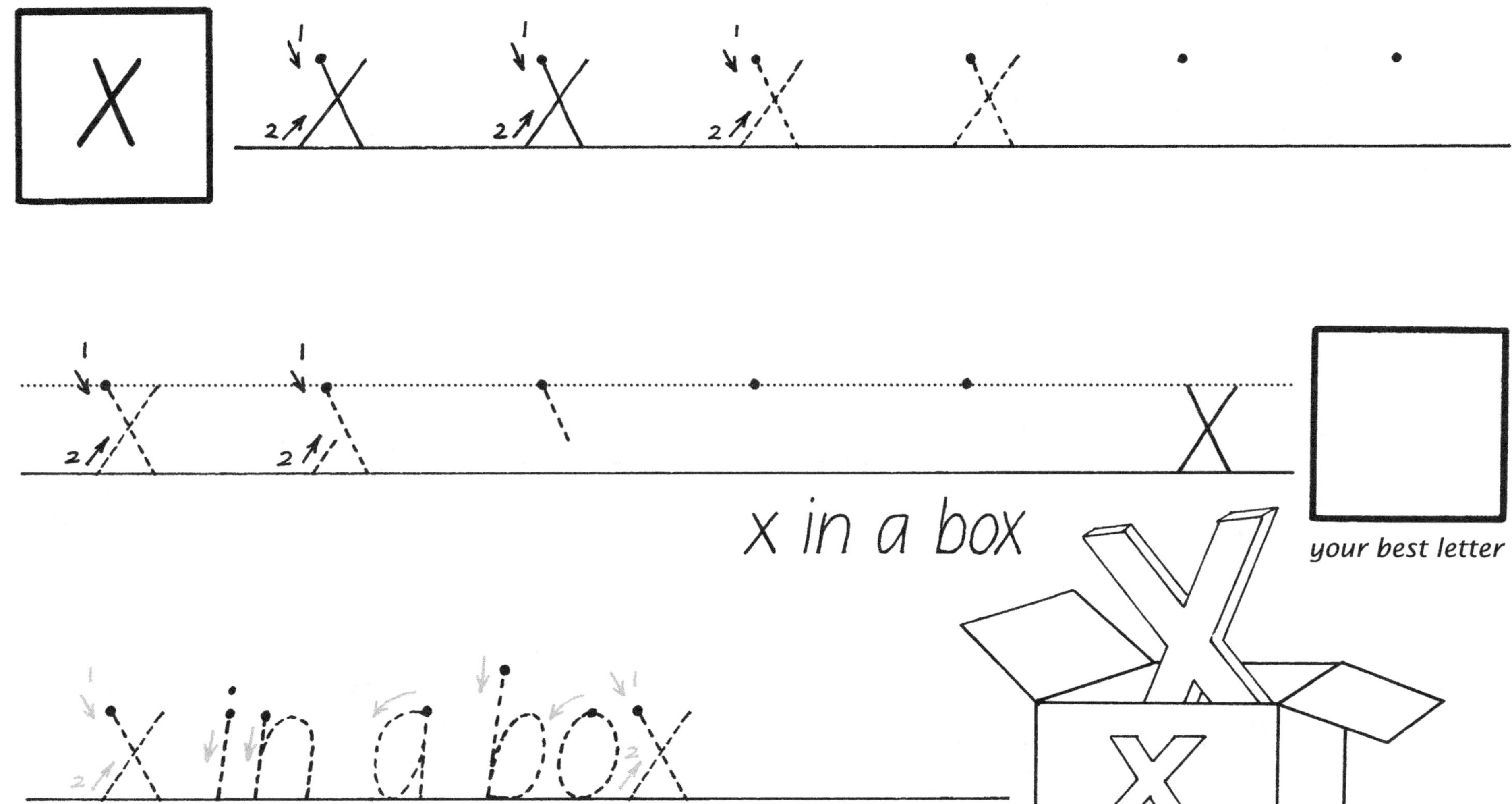
x in a box
your best letter
x in a box

your best letter

Watch

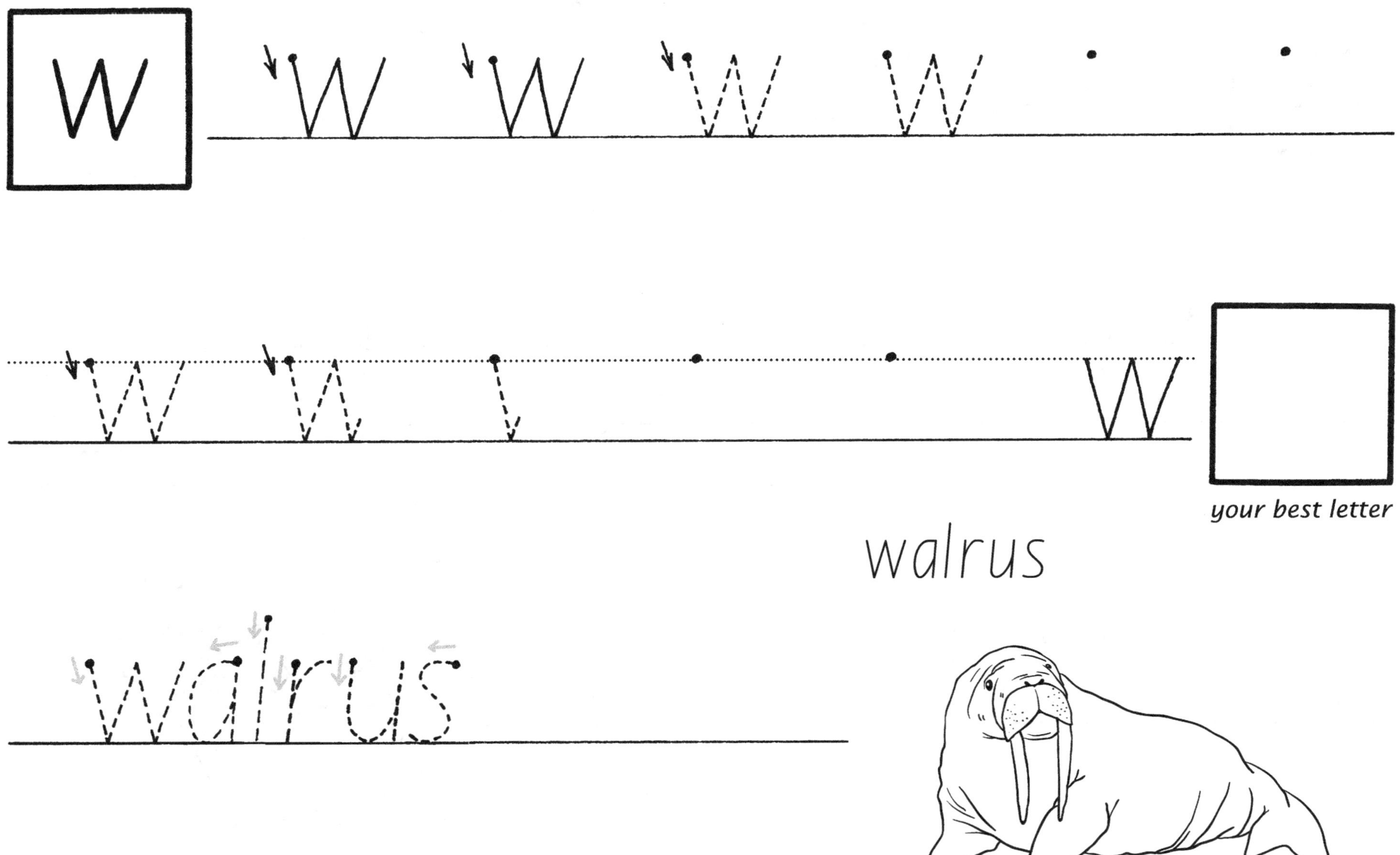

your best letter

walrus

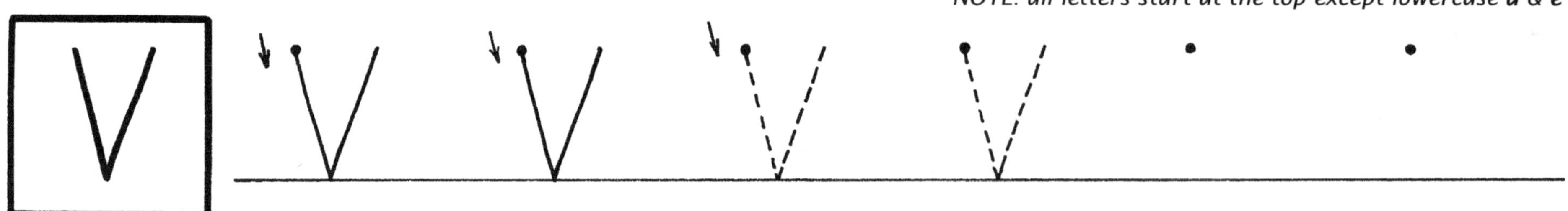

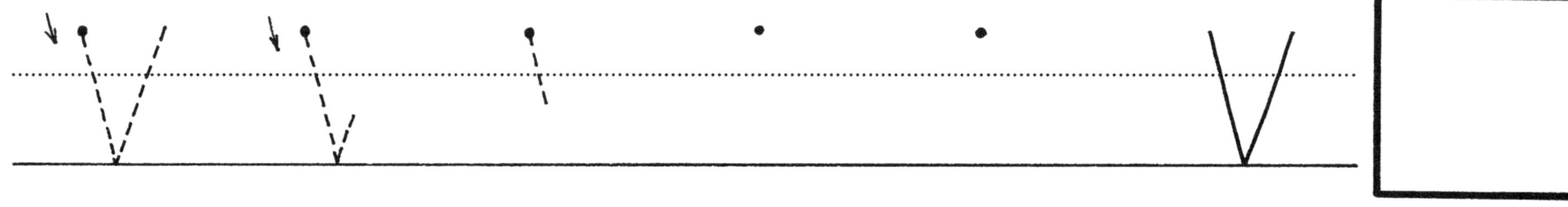

your best letter

Valentine

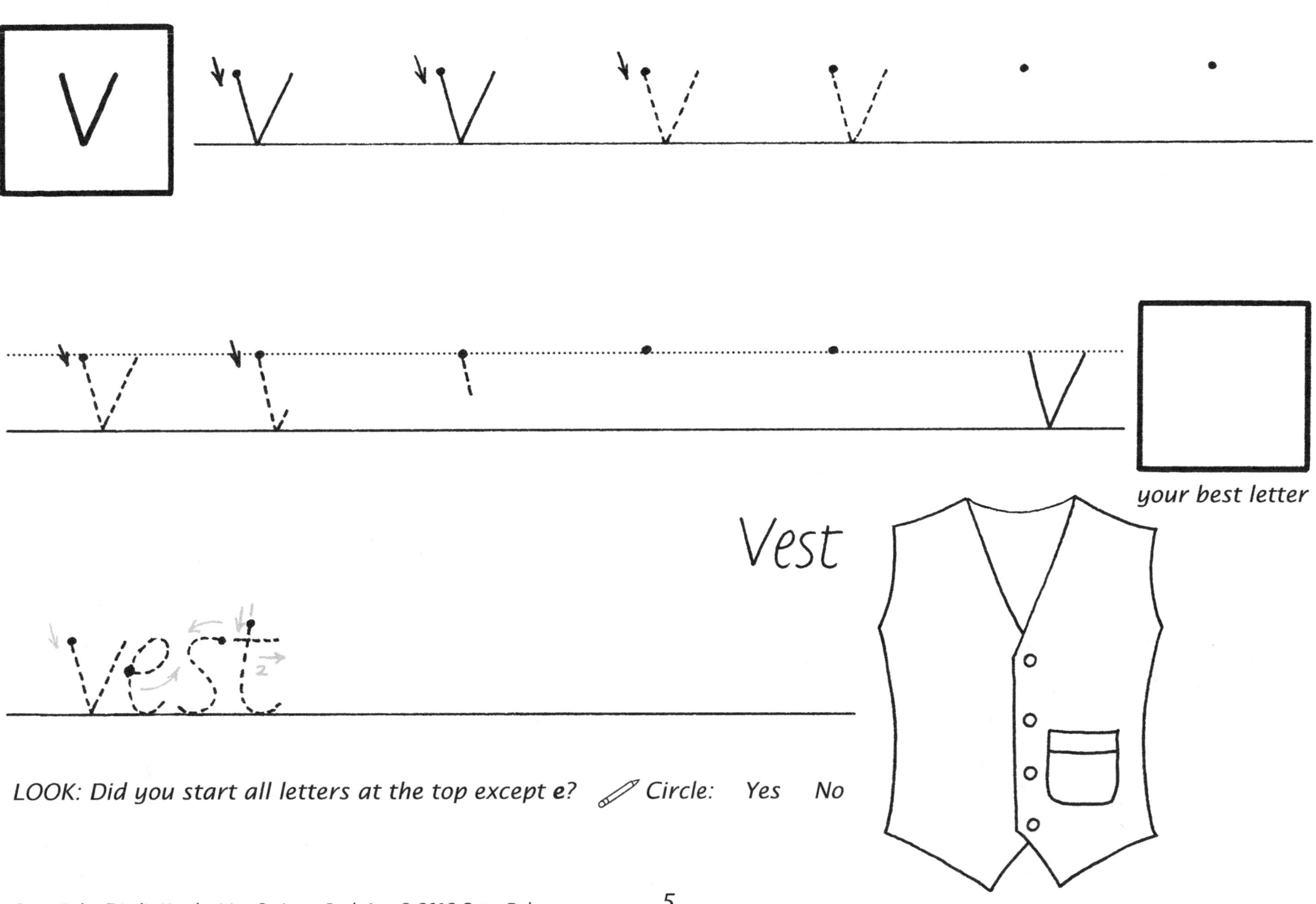

your best letter

Vest

LOOK: Did you start all letters at the top except *e*? Circle: Yes   No

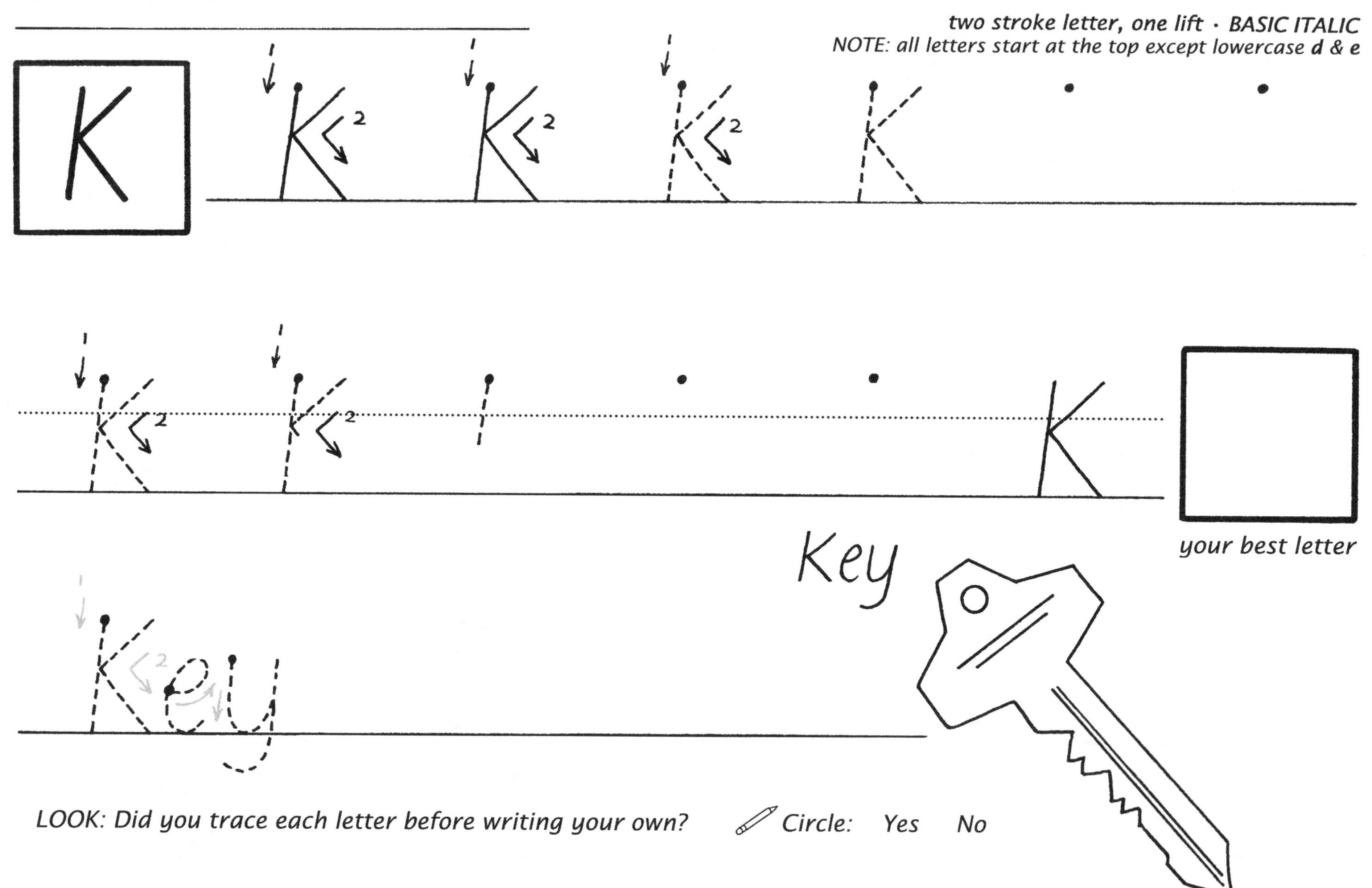

LOOK: Did you trace each letter before writing your own?   Circle: Yes   No

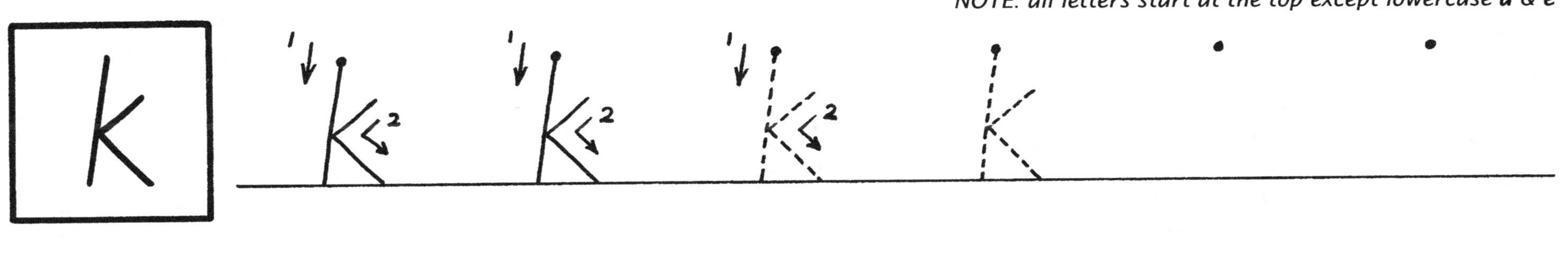

k

your best letter

kite

kite

one stroke letter, no lift · BASIC ITALIC
NOTE: all letters start at the top except lowercase *d* & *e*

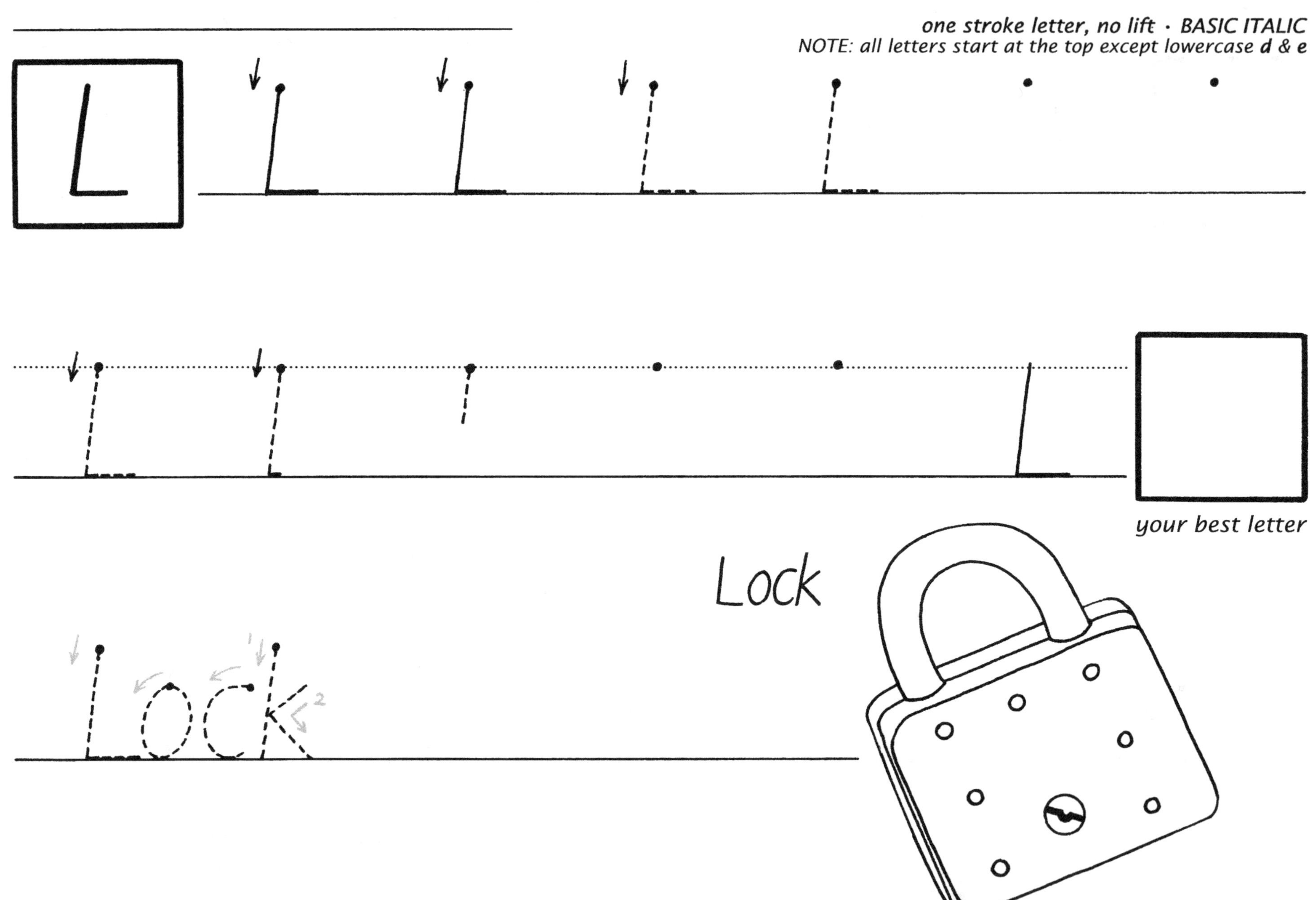

your best letter
Lock
Lock

your best letter

lamb

lamb

your best letter

Jack-in-the-box

Jack-in-the-box

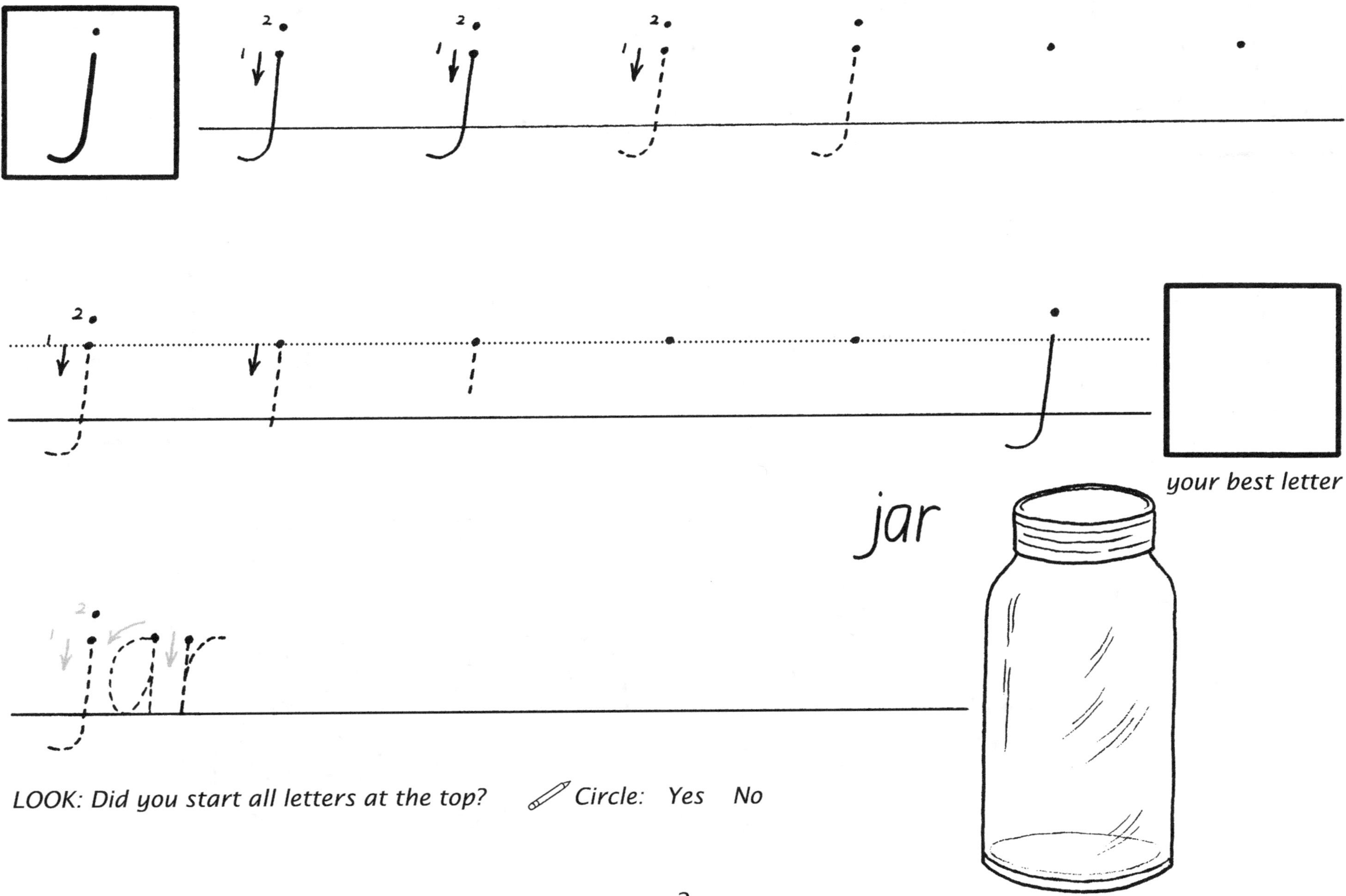

your best letter

jar

LOOK: Did you start all letters at the top?   Circle: Yes   No

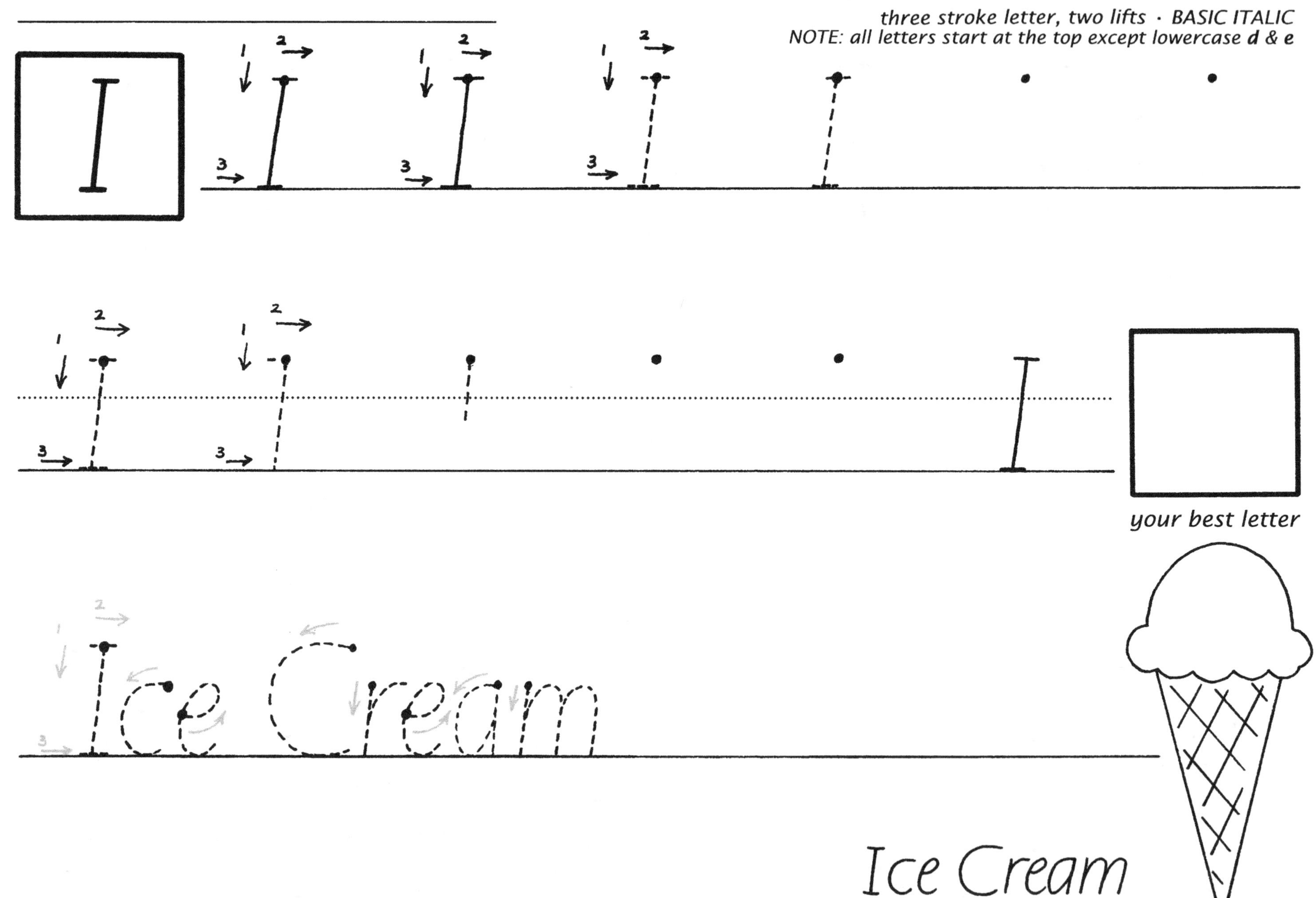

three stroke letter, two lifts · BASIC ITALIC
NOTE: all letters start at the top except lowercase d & e
your best letter
Ice Cream

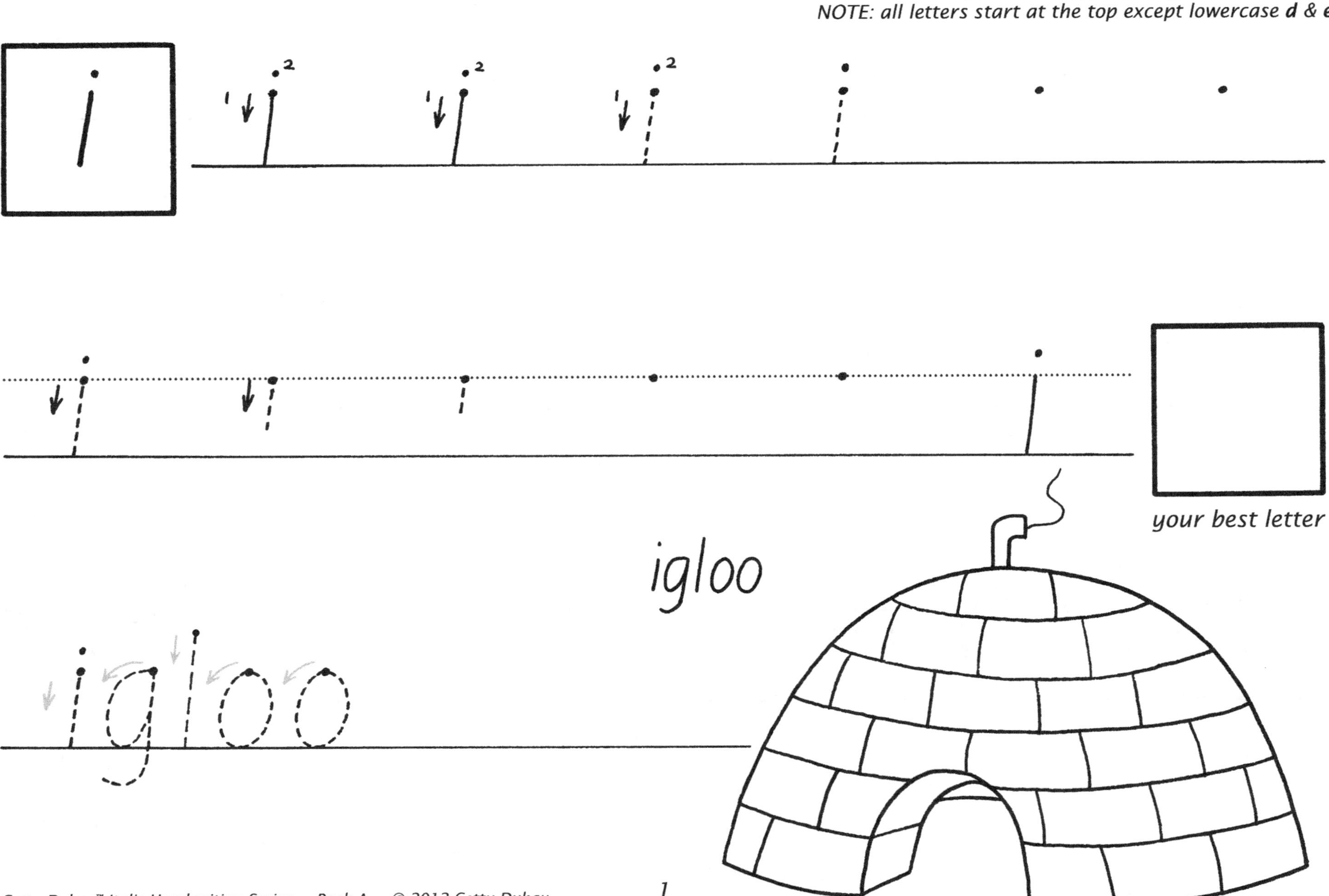

your best letter

igloo

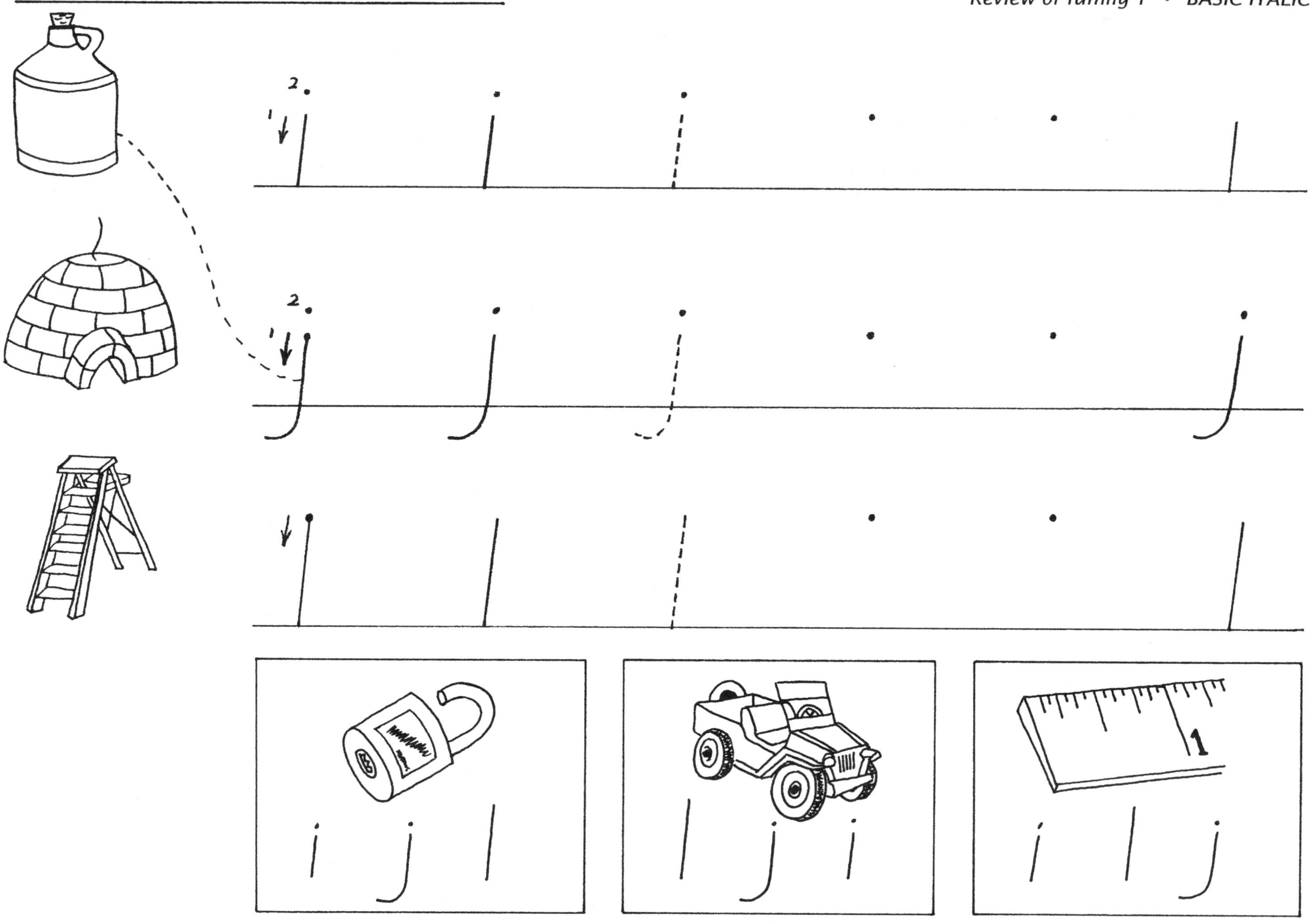

TOP THREE LINES: Ask the student to draw a line from the picture to the letter that stands for the correct beginning sound.

BOTTOM THREE BOXES: Ask the student to circle the letter that stands for the beginning sound of the picture.

Before the student begins writing in BOOK A, the authors recommend that the student practice the following shapes on unlined paper, one shape at a time. Allow the student to write each shape any size at first. Later, ask the student to write very large and very small forms of that same shape. We suggest the student also practice these shapes on a chalkboard and/or in cornmeal. (See INSTRUCTION MANUAL, "*Activity*," pp. 35 & 41.)

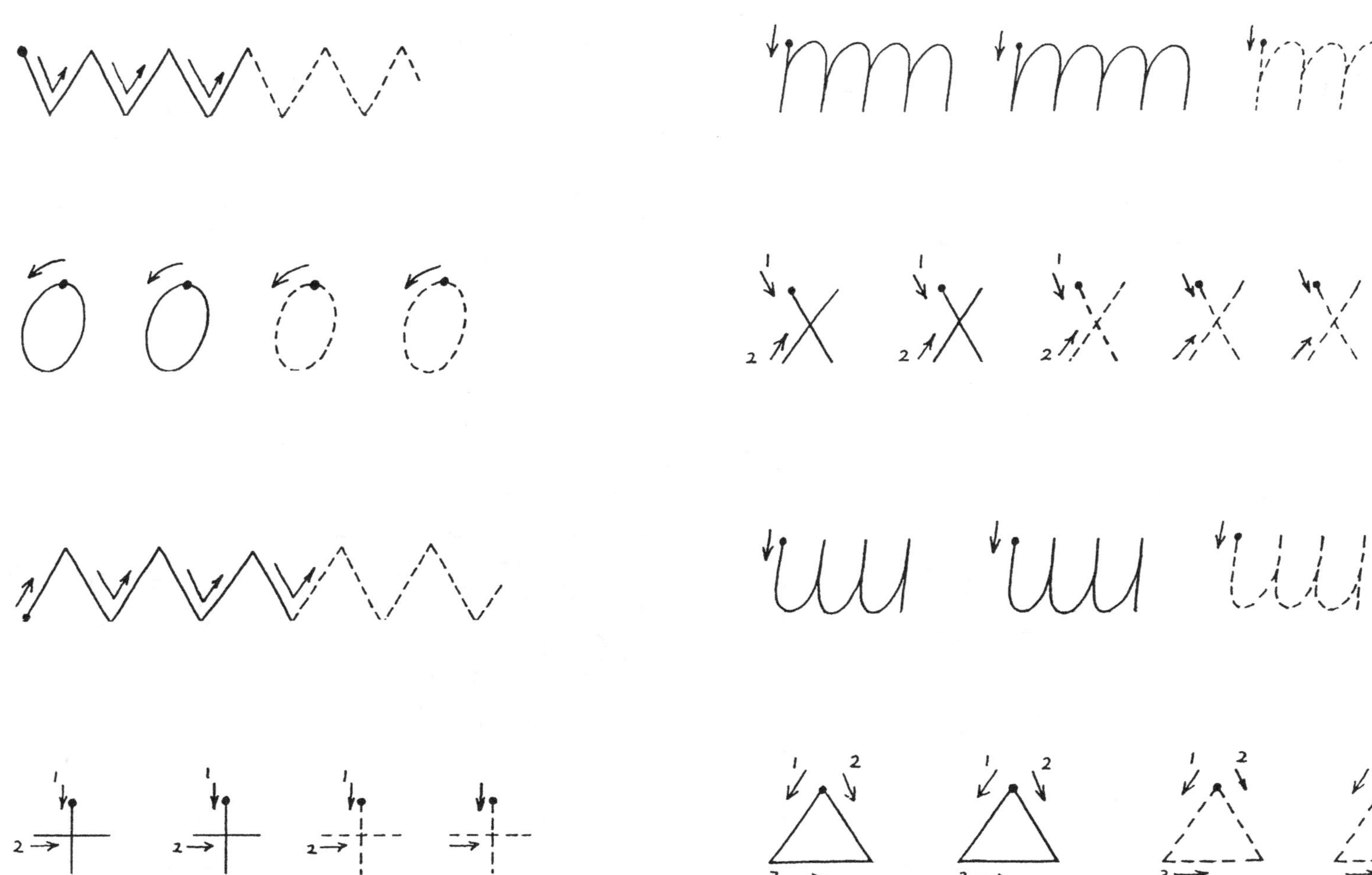

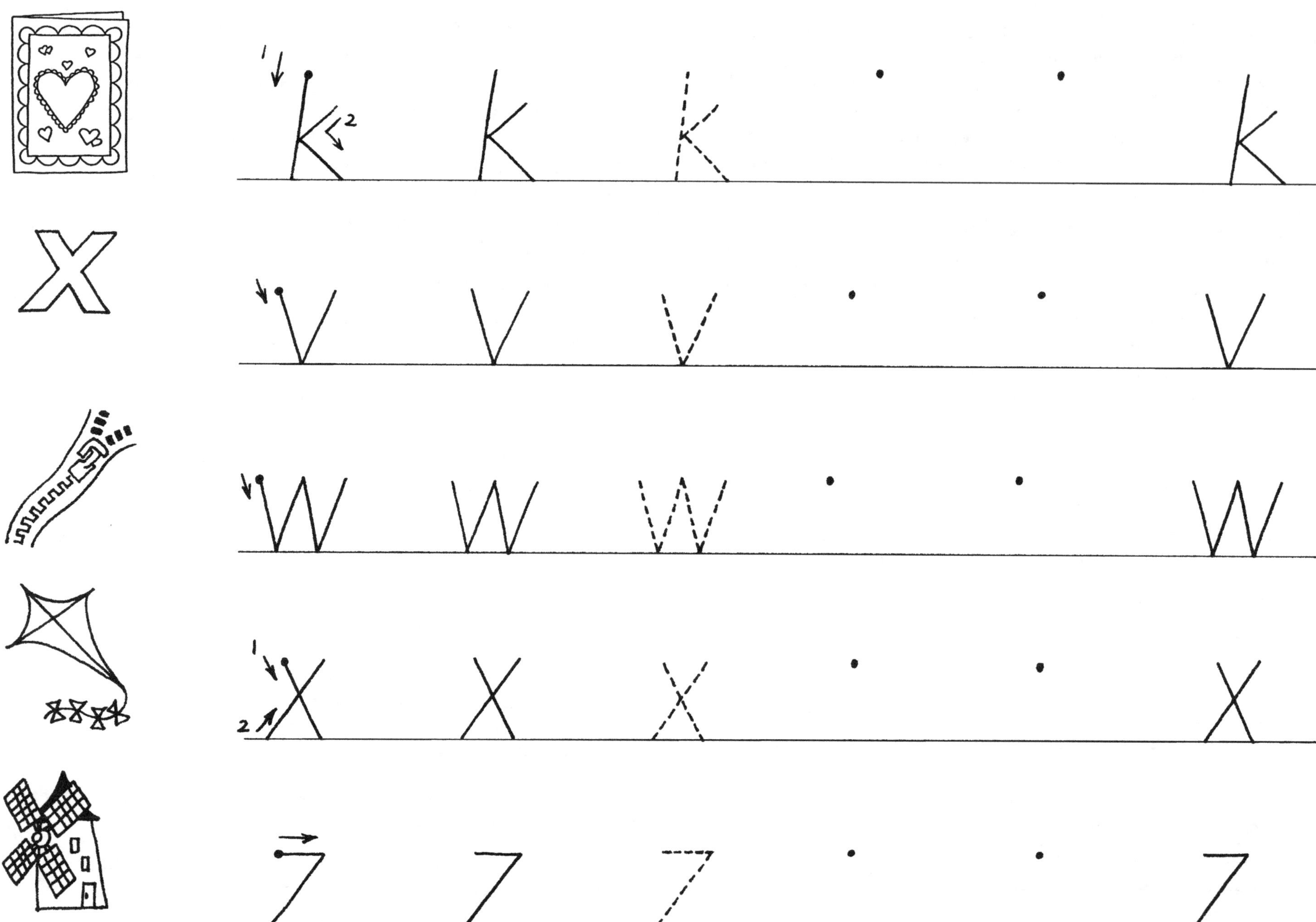

*Ask the student to draw a line from the picture to the letter
that stands for the correct beginning sound.*

THE BEGINNING WRITER

Learning how to write involves much more than learning to write letters. It is a sophisticated, complex process involving learning letterforms, learning how to space within and between words, and learning how to organize writing on a page. Research indicates that there exists an almost perfect correlation between measures evaluating the children's *awareness* of their fingers and the ability to *use* their fingers in precise manual skills.

Ways to determine manual ability

To assist young students increase awareness of their hands and fingers, and to help you, the teacher, evaluate students' manual skills, have your students perform these tasks:

1. Direct the students to touch each of their fingers to their thumb, in order, from the first to the little finger. (By the age of six years, most children should be able to complete this exercise using one or both hands at a time.)

2. Have the students connect two dots that are spaced approximately eight inches apart on a page. (Most children of five years can accomplish this. However, if the student draws beyond the second dot or draws an unusually shaky line when nearing the second dot, it may indicate potential deficiencies in handwriting skills.)

Ways to improve kinesthetic perception of the hands

1. Unstructured clay modeling facilitates a student's perception of his or her hands. Encourage the student to manipulate the clay in every possible way—squeezing, flattening, poking, making shapes, etc.

2. To heighten the student's perception of shape, use a box in which a variety of small objects are placed for the student to feel but not see.

   a. Ask the student to reach in the box and find an unseen object that matches the one he or she is looking at.

   b. Direct the student to locate in the box an object that you or another student has described.

   c. Ask the student to find two objects with similar characteristics— two fuzzy objects, two heavy objects, two small objects, etc.

3. Draw several circles on a sheet of paper. To determine the student's ability to aim the finger and hand and also to point, have the student place dots in the circles with a pencil, pen, or crayon. Vary the difficulty of this task by increasing or decreasing the size of the circles or increasing the rate at which the dots are made. (The student must be able to point at a given or imaginary point in order to begin the stroke of a letter.)

Ways to confirm hand-eye tracking skills

The ability to control continuous hand movements while drawing lines of varying difficulty is basic to handwriting. If you are able to detect problems as the student completes the following tasks and are able to obtain appropriate assistance for the student, subsequent difficulties may be avoided.

1. Demonstrate drawing parallel lines. Then direct the student to draw parallel lines of a given length, first at a relaxed pace then at a faster one.

2. Direct the student to draw two curved lines equal in distance from one another. Later require more difficult shapes that combine straight lines, angles, and/or curves.

3. Direct the student to connect numbered dots on a sheet of paper that require horizontal, vertical and lateral movements. Place the paper in front of the student, close to the dominant hand. Later, space the dots further apart and require the student to cross the midline of his or her body. This latter task may cause the neuro-logically challenged student some difficulty.

The above evaluative tasks may be of help in assisting the learning of handwriting and in discovering deficiencies.

(See INSTRUCTION MANUAL, p. 13, for more suggestions concerning the beginning writer.)

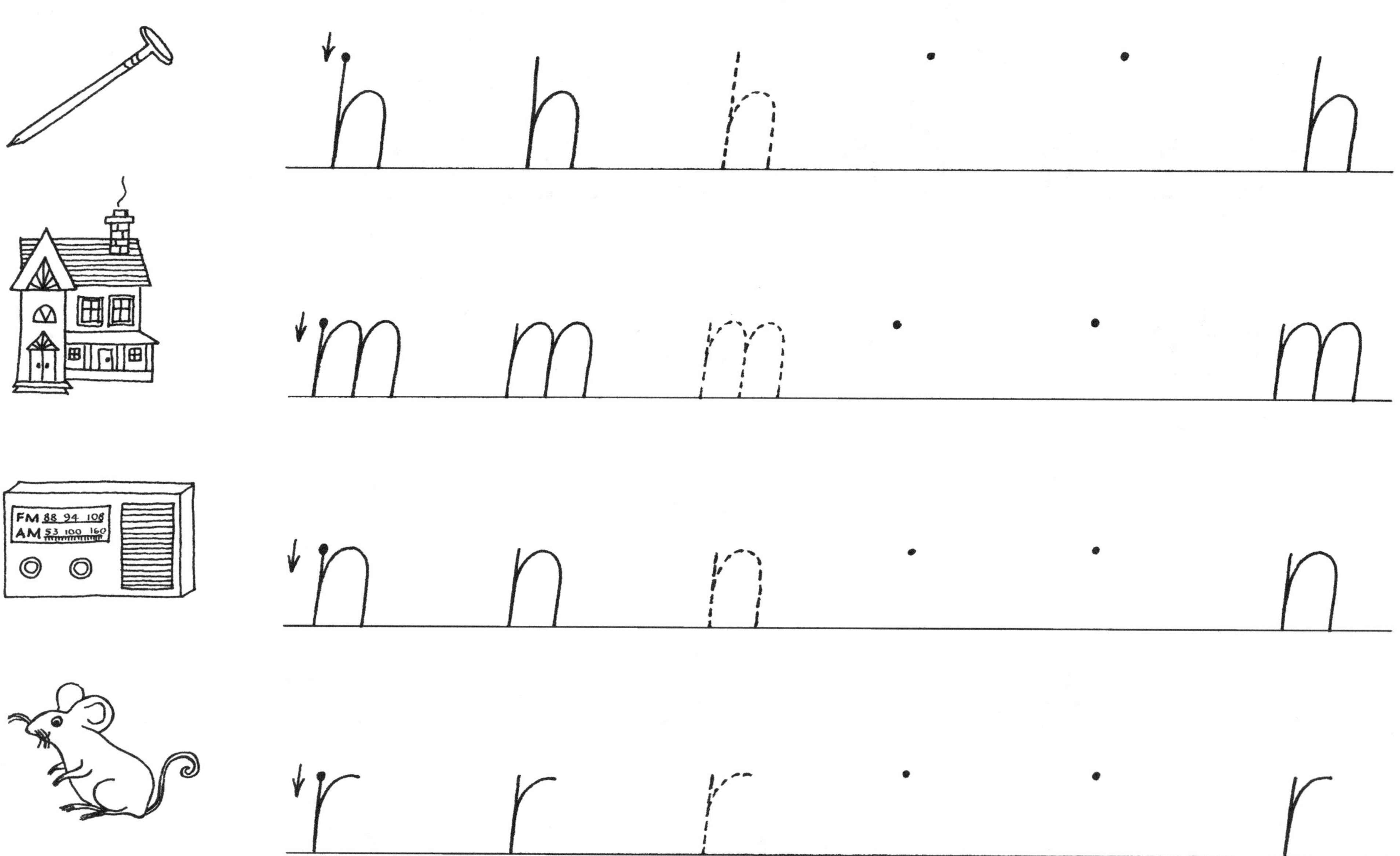

Ask the student to draw a line from the picture to the letter
that stands for the correct beginning sound.

BASIC ITALIC ALPHABET

All letters written in one stroke unless otherwise indicated.   *All letters start at the top except lowercase **d** and **e**.*

Aa Bb Cc Dd Ee Ff Gg

or

alternate 2-stroke e

Hh Ii Jj Kk Ll Mm

or   or

Nn Oo Pp Qq Rr Ss Tt

or   or

Uu Vv Ww Xx Yy Zz

0 1 2 3 4 5 6 7 8 9

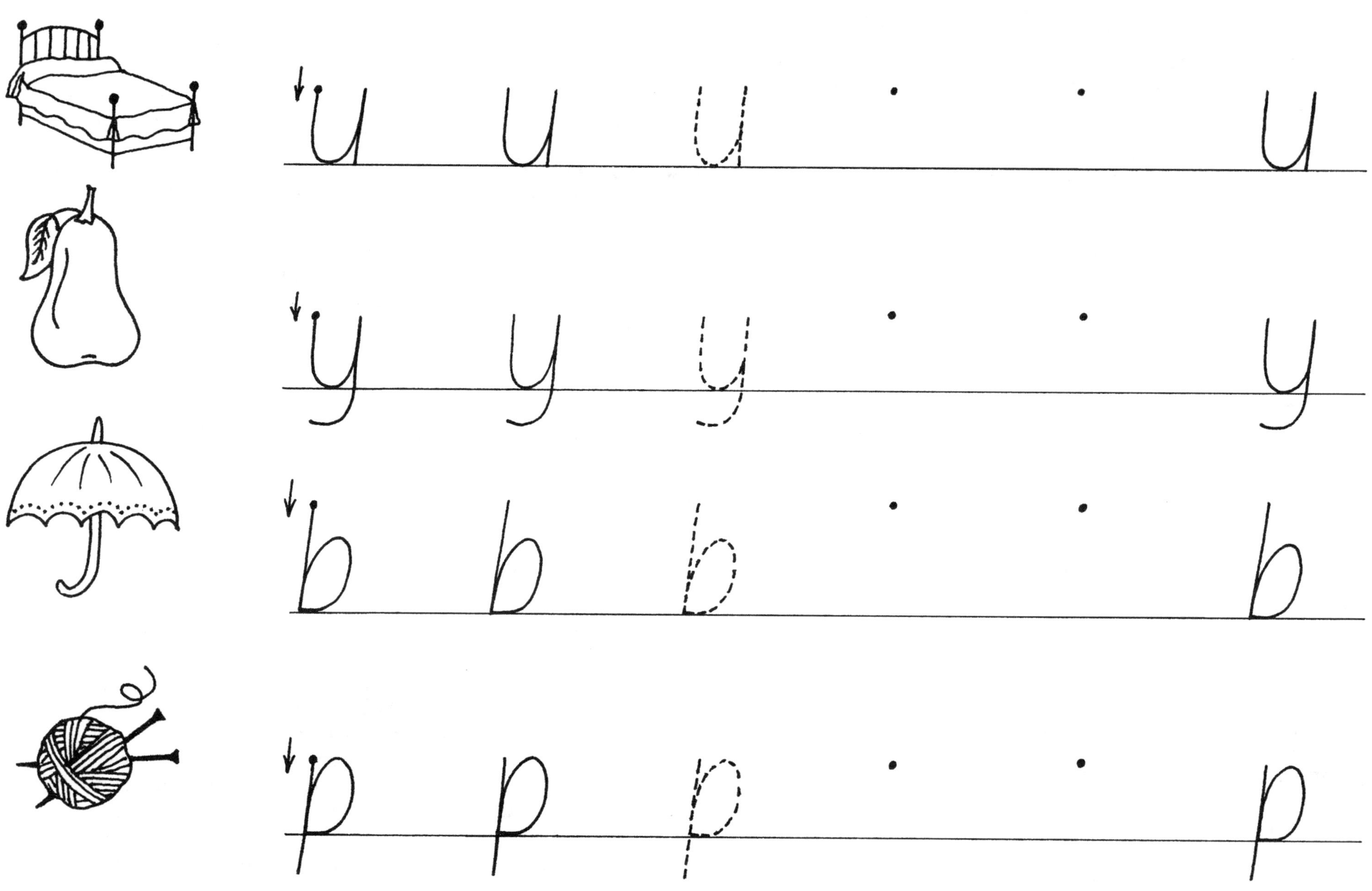

Ask the student to draw a line from the picture to the letter
that stands for the correct beginning sound.

GETTY-DUBAY™ HANDWRITING REMINDERS

PENCIL HOLD

Hold the pencil with the thumb and index finger, resting it on the middle finger. Rest the shaft of the pencil near the large knuckle. Hold the tool firmly and avoid pinching. To relax the hand, tap index finger on the pencil three times. Avoid "thumb wrap" and a "death grip".

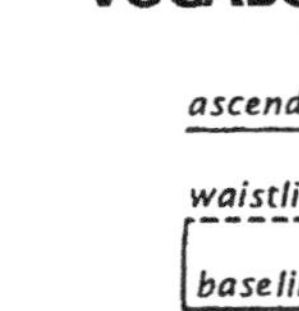

PAPER POSITION

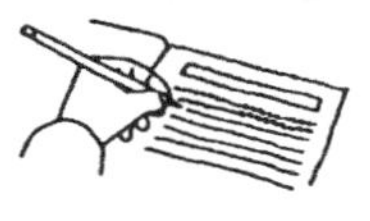

LEFT-HANDED: If the left-handed student writes with the wrist below the writing line, turn paper clockwise so it is slanted to the right, as illustrated.
If the left-handed student writes with a hook, with the wrist above the writing line, turn the paper counter-clockwise so it is slanted to the left, as illustrated. (Similar to right-handed position)

RIGHT-HANDED: If the student is right-handed, turn paper counter-clockwise so it is slanted to the left, as illustrated.

POSTURE

Rest feet flat on the floor and keep back comfortably straight without slumping. Rest forearms on writing surface. The student holds workbook or paper with the nonwriting hand so that the writing area is centered in the front of the student.

PRACTICE PAPER

Book A—Use unlined or lined paper together with workbooks.

MATERIALS

The *Getty-Dubay™ Italic Handwriting Series* workbooks, BOOKS A-G, and the INSTRUCTION MANUAL constitute a step-by-step program. Related materials consist of:

1. BLACKLINE MASTERS/WORKSHEETS - half sheets for introduction to, or review of, workbook pages.
2. CLASSROOM WALL CHARTS - basic & cursive italic.
3. DESK STRIPS - basic & cursive italic.

VOCABULARY

DIRECT INSTRUCTION

Several sessions of direct instruction each week are essential for a successful program. BOOK A – 5 to 10 minute sessions a day are recommended, see INSTRUCTION MANUAL, pp. 18-19

- SHAPE & STROKE SEQUENCE – teach basic italic in letter family groups, or according to the reading program in grade 1.

- SLOPE – encourage a consistent letter slope. Vertical letters (0° slope) may be the easiest to teach to beginning writers.

- SIZE – At first, allow students to write letters any size they wish on unlined paper, then introduce the workbook. A recommended progression through this book is one letter (lowercase and/or capital) per week.

SPACING

When young students are writing words, at first have them leave a space about the width of their two small fingers between words. As they become more proficient, they can leave less space.

ASSESSMENT

The *Getty-Dubay™ Italic Handwriting Series* provides a self-assessment process, LOOK, PLAN, PRACTICE, to enable the student to monitor progress. LOOK, step 1 of this process begins on some of the student pages in BOOK A. Assessment is the key to improving handwriting; in this book we introduce the first of three steps in the LOOK, PLAN, PRACTICE self-assessment process. The students look at their own writing and answer any questions on the page. The pencil indicates the student is to make a written response, generally by circling "yes" or "no". The teacher may encourage students to award themselves a star or a smiling face at the top of the page when they notice self-improvement.

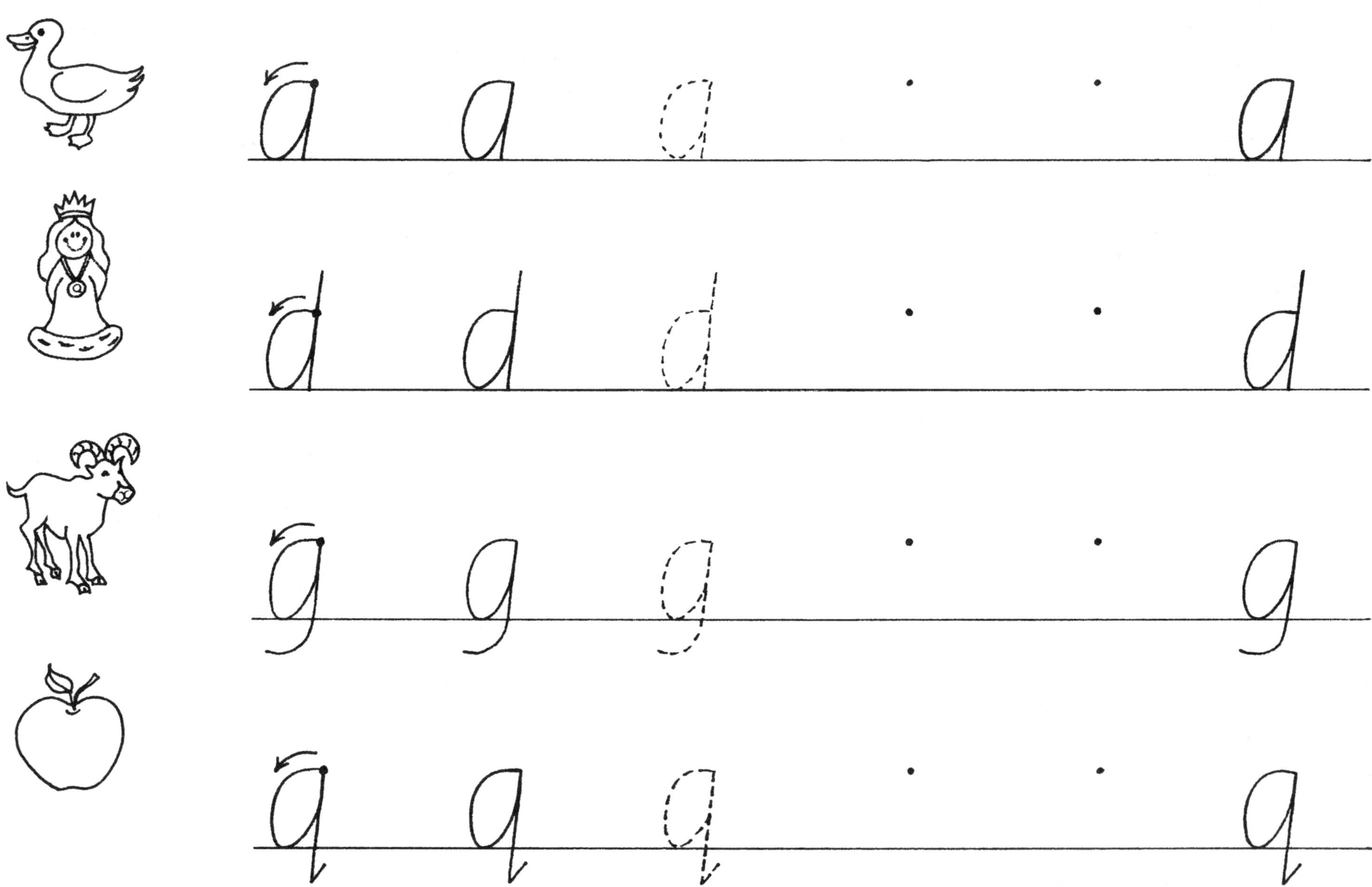

Ask the student to draw a line from the picture to the letter
that stands for the correct beginning sound.

INTRODUCTION

This is the first of seven workbooks providing instruction in basic italic handwriting. It is designed for the beginning student of handwriting and is recommended for preschool, kindergarten and/or early first grade (5 to 7 years of age).

The twenty-six lowercase letters and the twenty-six capitals are introduced one letter per page. Letters are arranged in the order of lowercase families, which group letters with similar strokes together and progress from simple to more complex forms. The matching capital letter occurs on the reverse of each lowercase page allowing introduction of both lowercase and capital together if preferred.

Each page is designed for the student to trace the models provided, write letters at the given dots, and to write a "best" letter in the empty box on each alphabet page. The standard writing tool is the pencil although other writing instruments such as the fiber tip pen may be used. When students are ready, they should trace the word describing the illustration on each letter page, following the dots and arrows.

It is essential that the instructor provide an understanding of the dot and the arrow to assist the writer in completing the pages successfully. The self-assessment method used in the *Getty-Dubay* *Italic Handwriting Series* enables students to monitor their individual progress. Step 1, LOOK, of the three-step LOOK, PLAN, PRACTICE format, is incorporated on 21 of the student pages. Students are asked to "LOOK" at their writing and affirm what is best. On the 21 pages with "LOOK" questions, students should circle their chosen answers. See INSTRUCTION MANUAL, PP. 13, 18 & 19.

The *Getty-Dubay™ Italic Handwriting Series* INSTRUCTION MANUAL is to be used in conjunction with this workbook. Explanations and in-depth descriptions of lowercase letters, capitals, joins, and numerals are presented in the manual, emphasizing shape, strokes, size, slope and spacing of the letters. Also included in the manual are: a rationale for italic handwriting, techniques for teaching and assessing handwriting, sequence of skills, handwriting activities, and a brief history of our alphabet.

BOOK B, basic italic, follows this workbook and is designed for the beginning reader. In the third book, BOOK C, basic italic letterforms are reinforced and cursive italic is introduced. BOOKS D, E, F, and G provide a complete basic italic and cursive italic handwriting program. BOOKS B, C, and/or D may also be suitable for the person learning English as a second language.

The format of this book was chosen to accommodate both the left- and right-handed writer. When open, the book fits easily on a small desk, and the writer is not encumbered with an additional page to the left or right. From day one, use a Getty-Dubay™ basic italic desk strip as a reminder. Blackline masters are designed for supplementary practice and are available for each workbook in the series. See www.handwritingsuccess.com for these supplementary materials.

You can guide children toward the challenge and delight in the writing process by reading to them, modeling handwriting, providing writing materials, and especially by building enthusiasm for the letters of our alphabet and for the written word.

· abcdefghijklmnopqrstuvwxyz ·

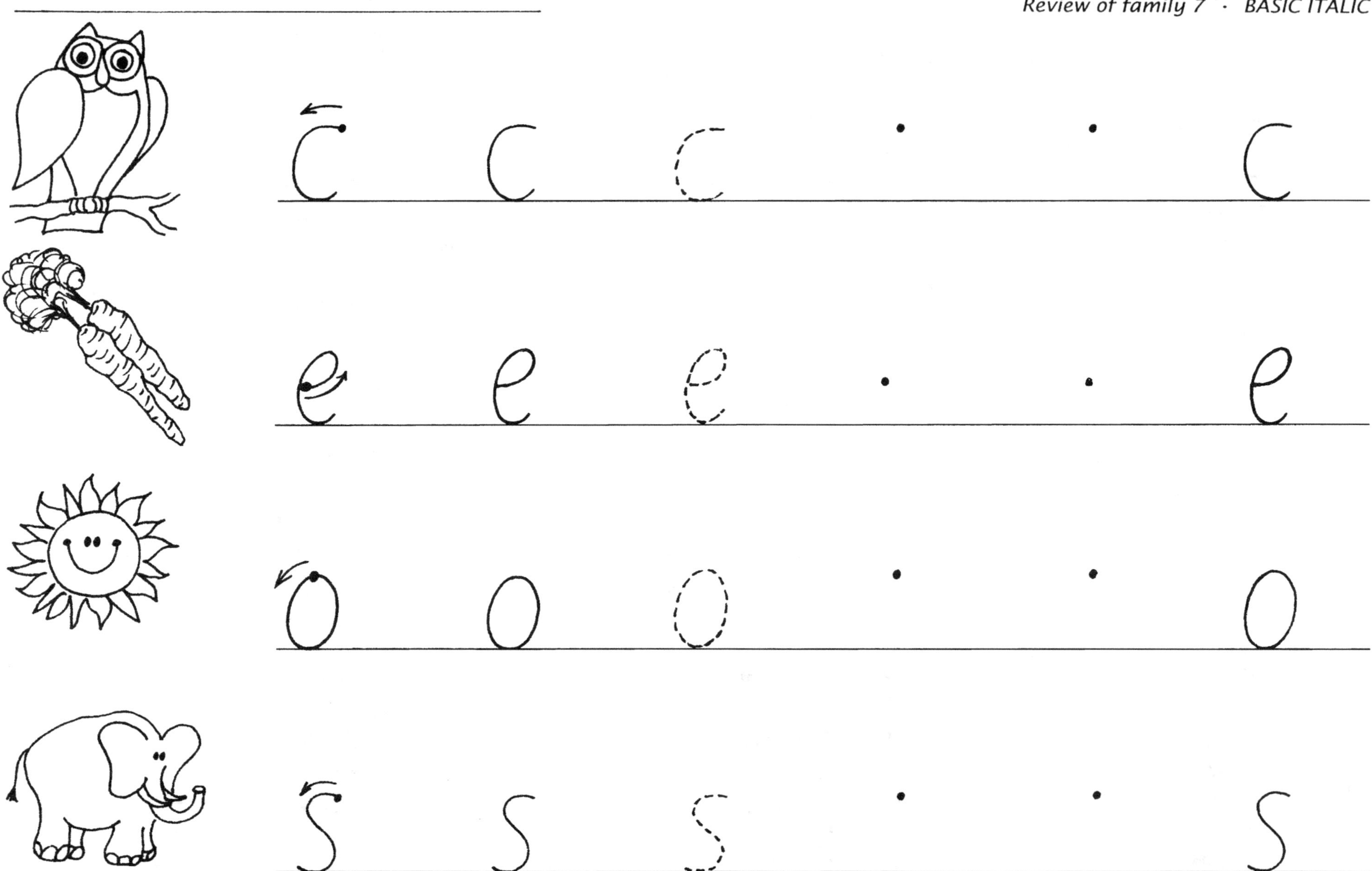

Ask the student to draw a line from the picture to the letter that stands for the correct beginning sound.

CONTENTS

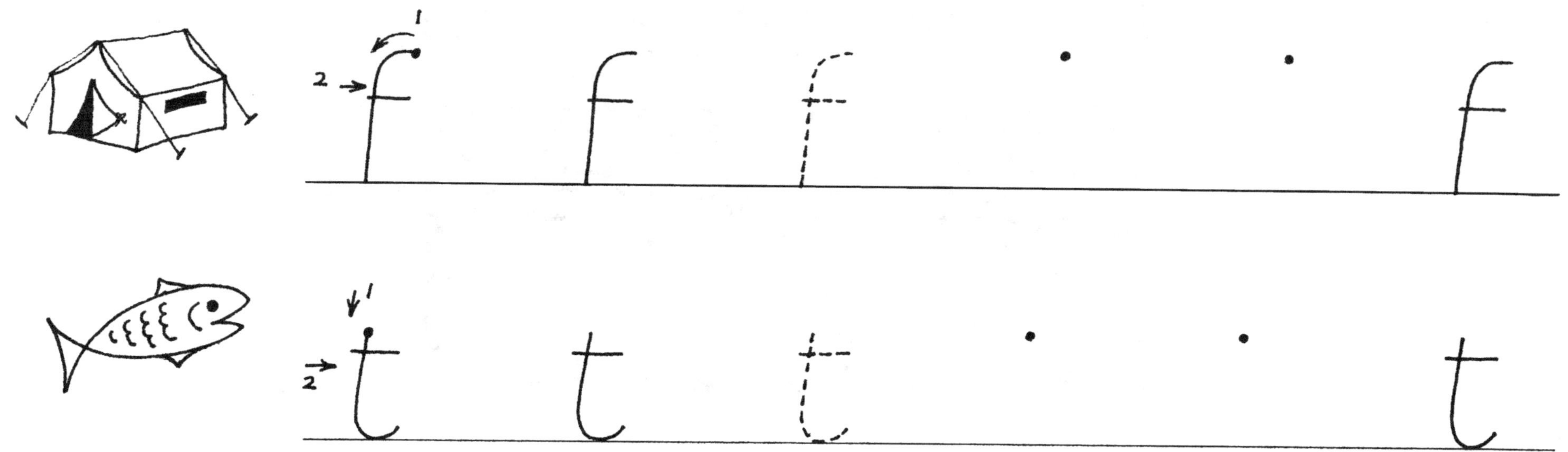

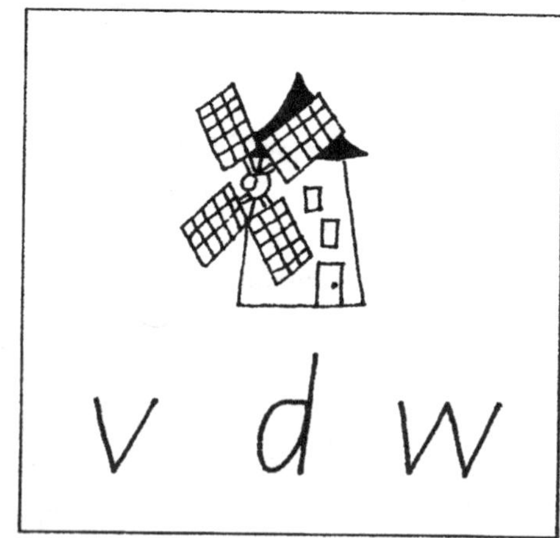

TOP TWO LINES: Ask the student to draw a line from the picture
   to the letter that stands for the correct beginning sound.

BOTTOM FOUR SQUARES: Ask the student to circle the letter that
   stands for the beginning sound of the picture.

by
Barbara Getty & Inga Dubay

GETTY-DUBAY™ ITALIC HANDWRITING SERIES

BOOK A ▪ Basic Italic
14 mm body height

BOOK B ▪ Basic Italic
11 mm body height, 9 mm

BOOK C ▪ Basic & Cursive Italic
9 mm, 6 mm body height   Introduction to Cursive Italic

BOOK D ▪ Basic & Cursive Italic
6 mm, 5 mm body height

BOOK E ▪ Basic & Cursive Italic
6 mm, 5 mm, 4 mm body height

BOOK F ▪ Basic & Cursive Italic
6 mm, 5 mm, 4 mm body height

BOOK G ▪ Basic & Cursive Italic
5 mm, 4 mm body height

INSTRUCTION MANUAL

BOOK A ▪ INTERNATIONAL EDITION
Copyright 2012 by Barbara M. Getty and Inga S. Dubay
ISBN 978-0-9827762-7-8

FOURTH EDITION
Copyright 2012 by Barbara M. Getty and Inga S. Dubay
THIRD EDITION
Copyright 1999 by Barbara M. Getty and Inga S. Dubay
SECOND EDITION
Copyright 1986 by Barbara M. Getty and Inga S. Dubay
REVISED EDITION
Copyright 1980 by Barbara M. Getty and Inga S. Dubay
FIRST EDITION
Copyright 1979 by Barbara M. Getty and Inga S. Dubay

All rights reserved. This text may not be reproduced in whole or in part without the express written permission of the copyright holder.

Published by Handwriting Success, LLC,
Portland, Oregon USA

www.handwritingsuccess.com

Printed at various locations around the world by IngramSpark.

Cover Design: Sinda Markham
Front cover picture: Flowers of the sunflower family in the Ochoco National Forest, Oregon, USA
Back cover pictures: Columbine flower, Golden-mantled squirrel

www.ingramcontent.com/pod-product-compliance
Lightning Source LLC
Chambersburg PA
CBHW081423210726
48464CB00020B/1370

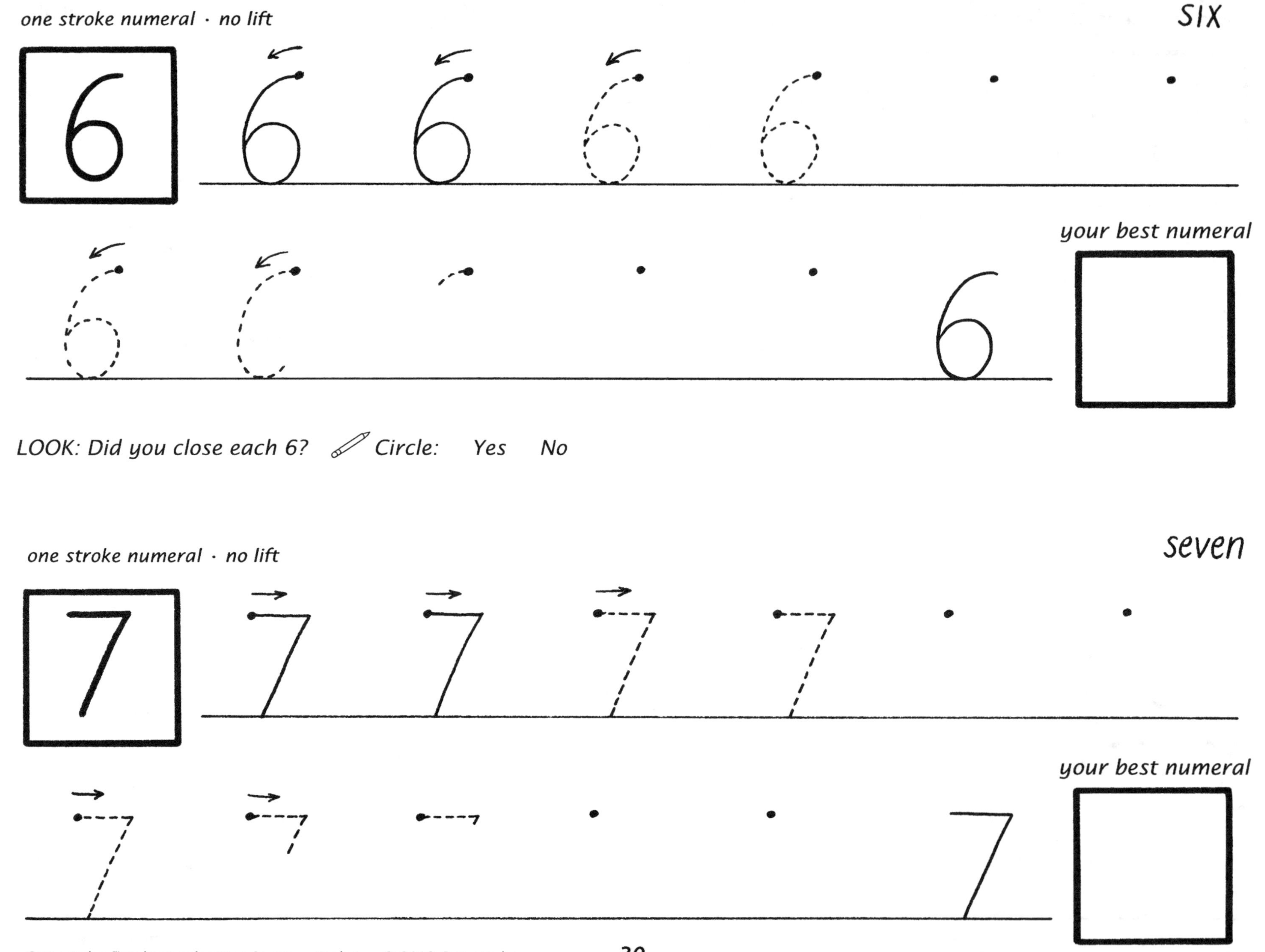

one stroke numeral · no lift
six
6 6 6 6 6
your best numeral
6 6 6
LOOK: Did you close each 6?   Circle: Yes   No
one stroke numeral · no lift
seven
7 7 7 7
your best numeral
7 7

four

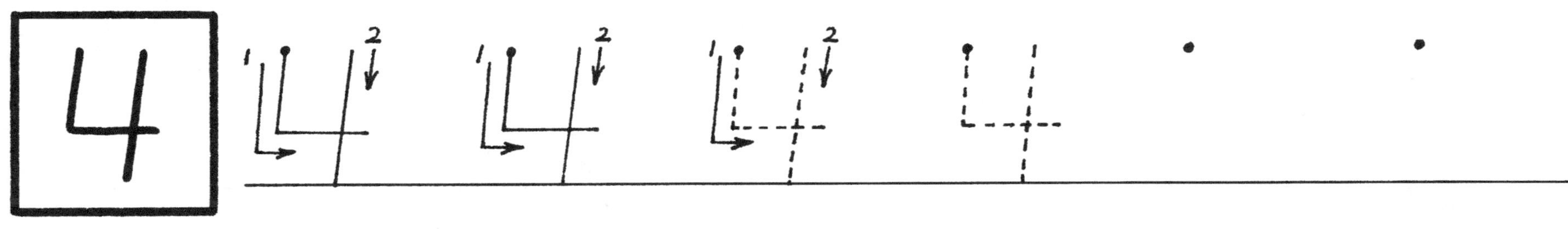

your best numeral

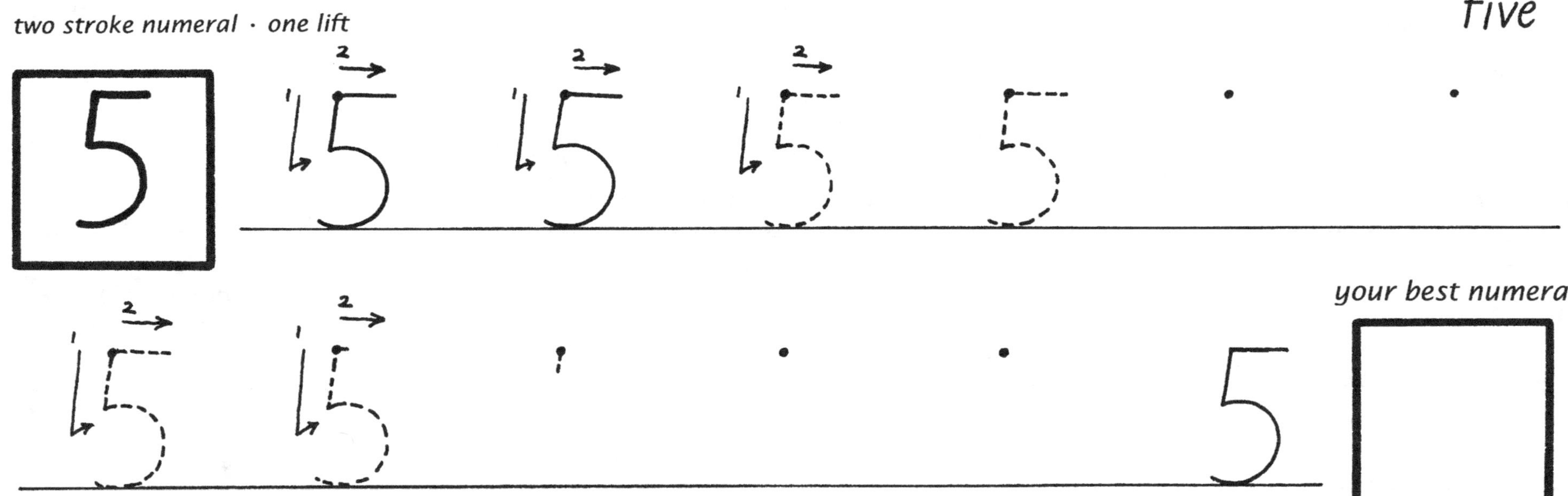

five

your best numeral

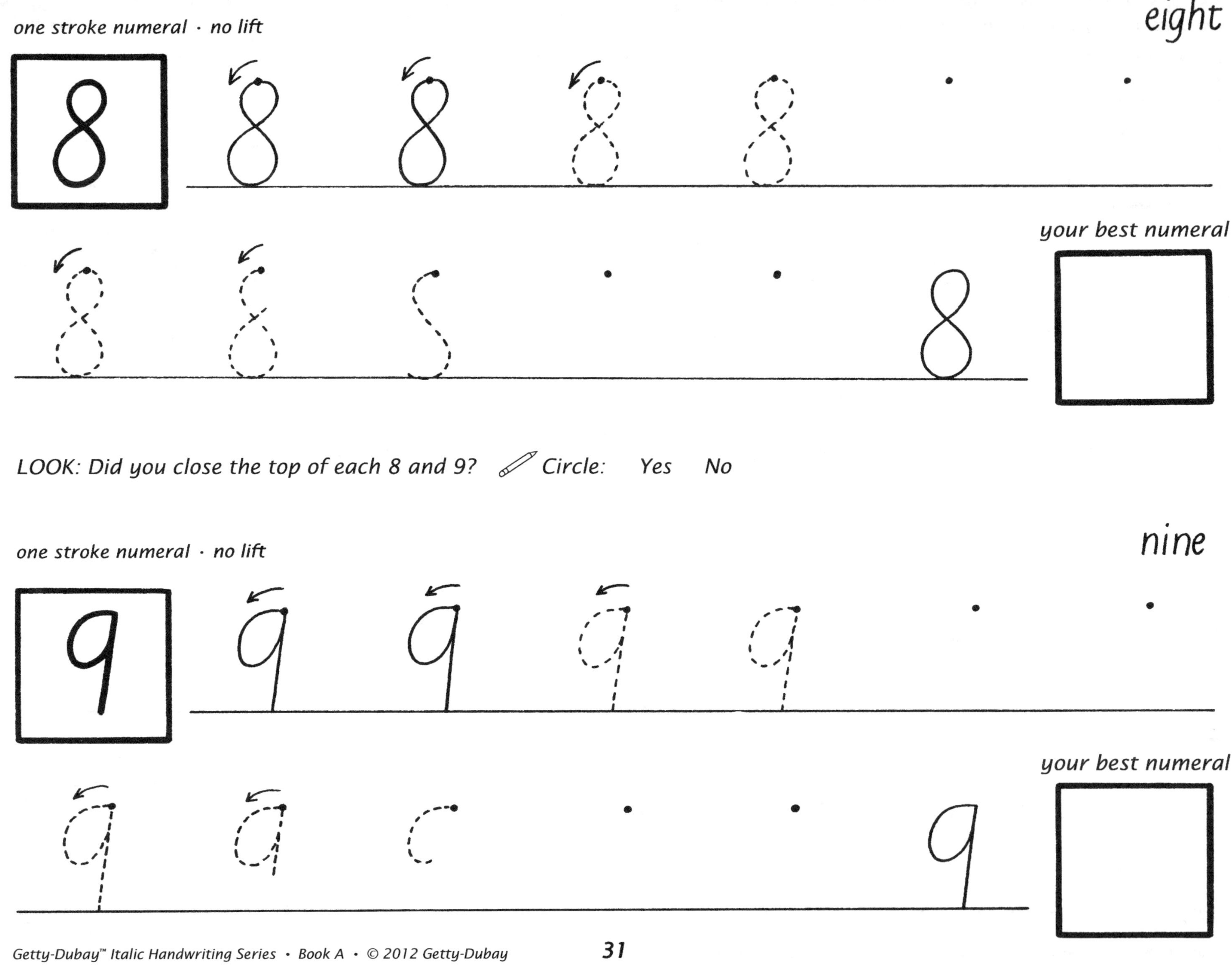

one stroke numeral · no lift
eight
your best numeral
LOOK: Did you close the top of each 8 and 9?   Circle: Yes   No
one stroke numeral · no lift
nine
your best numeral

one stroke numeral · no lift

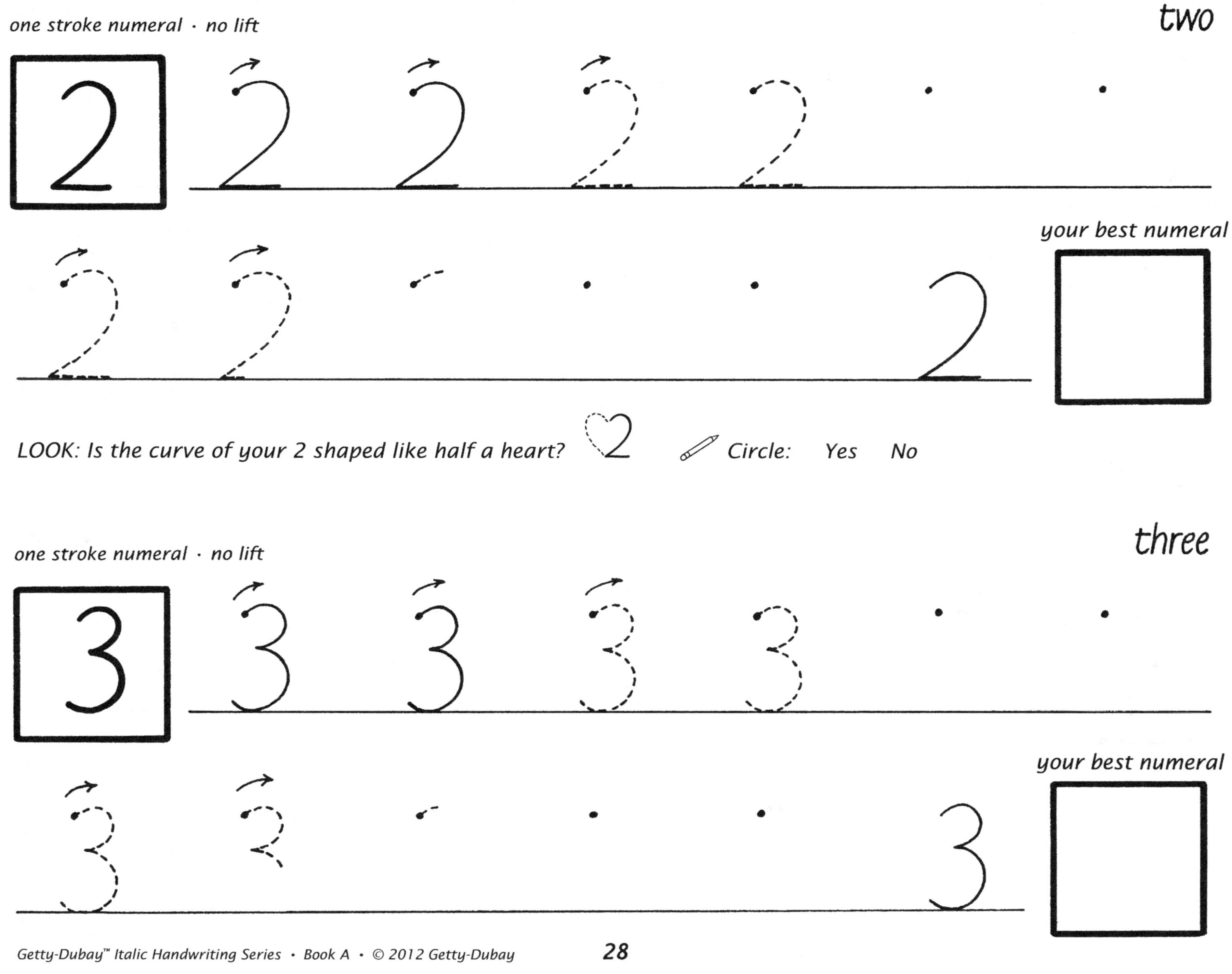

your best numeral

LOOK: Is the curve of your 2 shaped like half a heart?   Circle: Yes   No

one stroke numeral · no lift

your best numeral

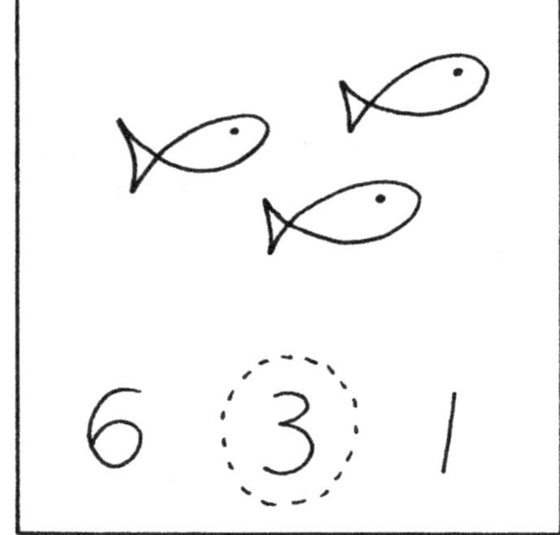

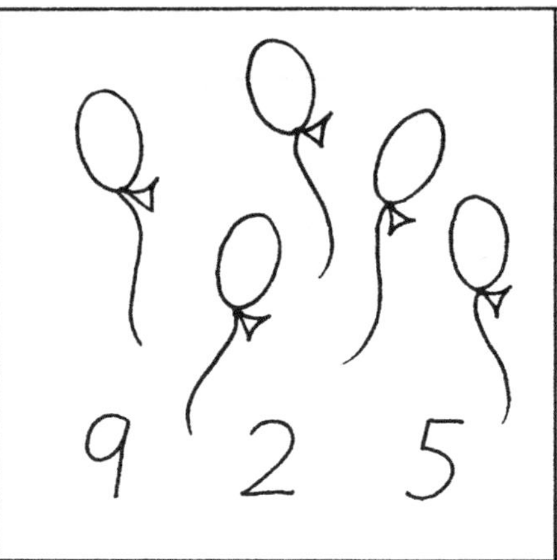

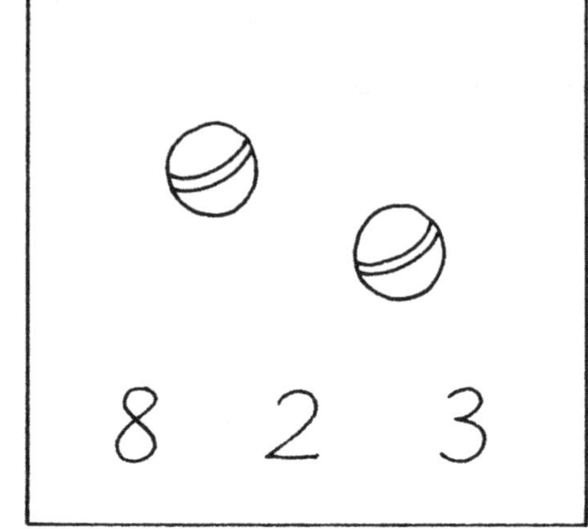

Ask the student to circle the numeral
that stands for the number of objects in the box.

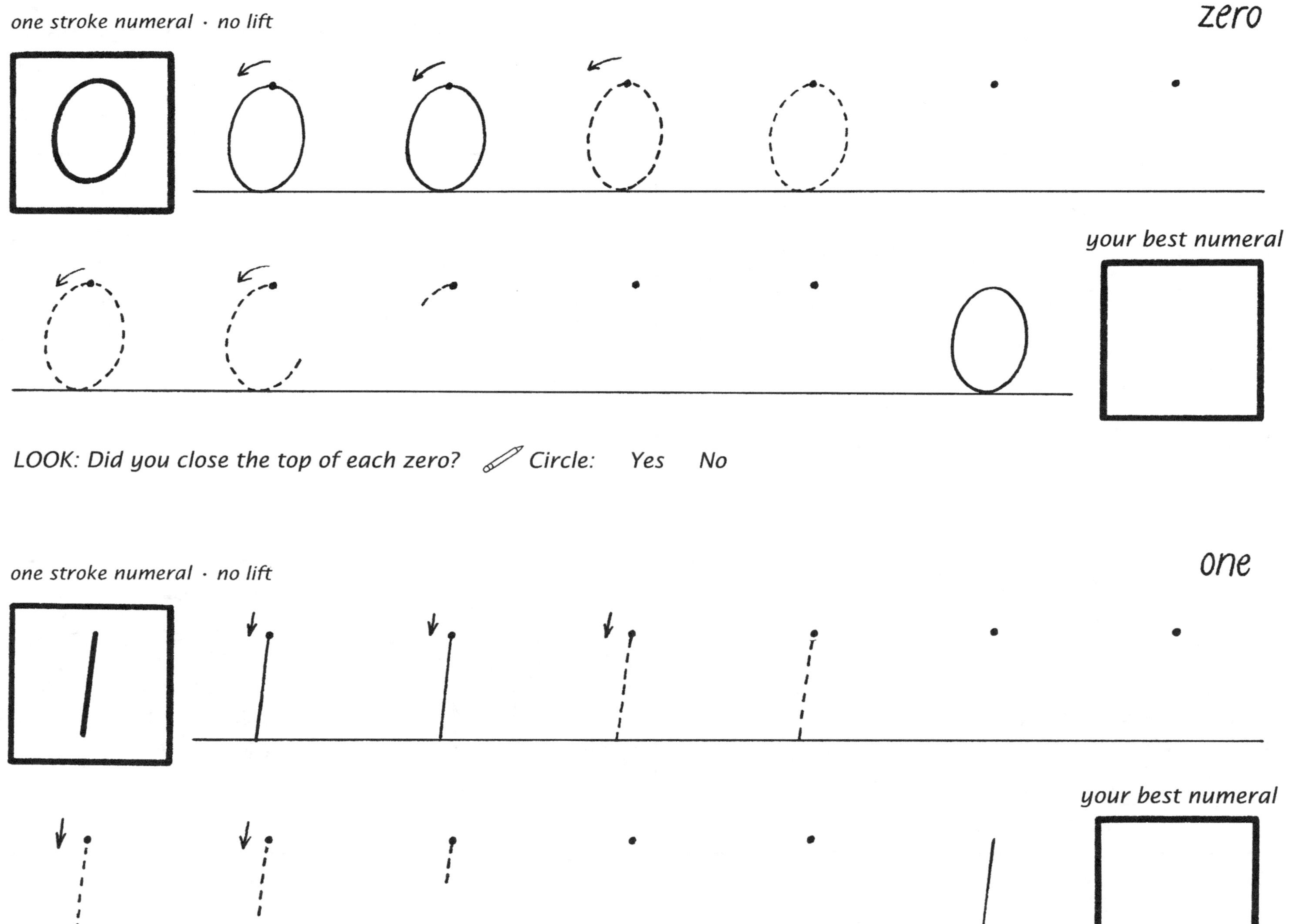

your best numeral

LOOK: Did you close the top of each zero? Circle: Yes   No

one stroke numeral · no lift

one

your best numeral

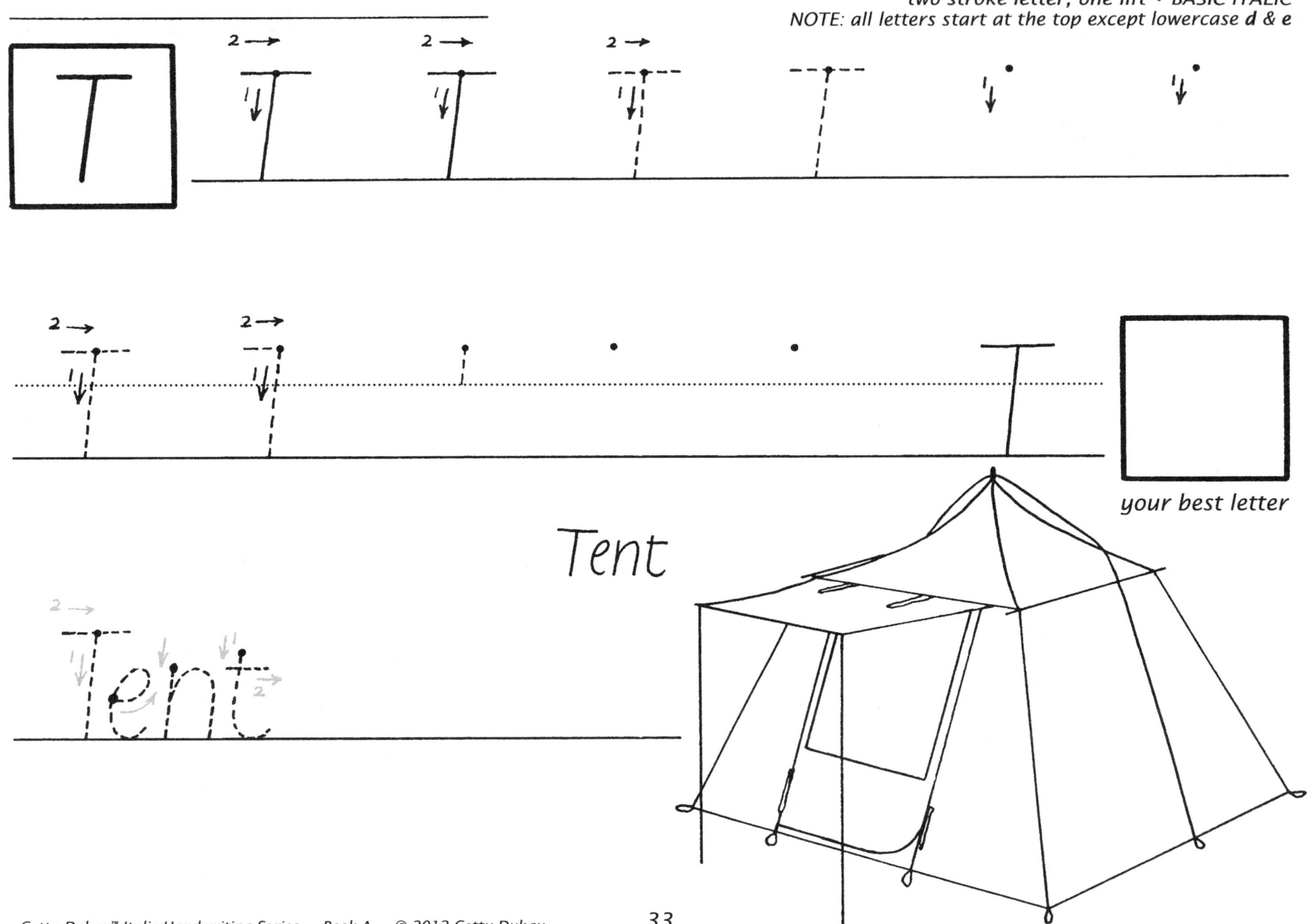

T
2 →
2 →
2 →
2 →
your best letter
Tent
Tent

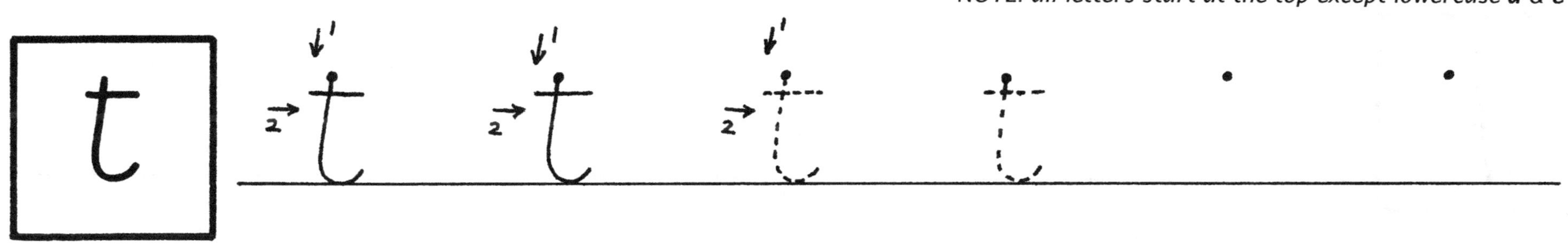

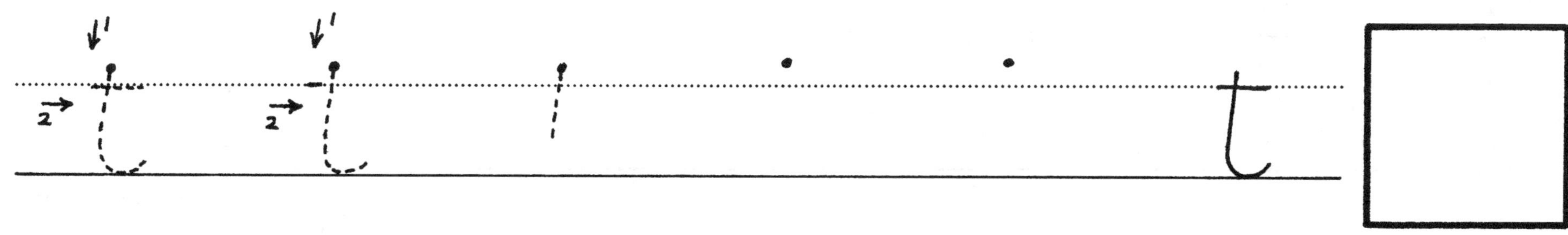

your best letter

turkey

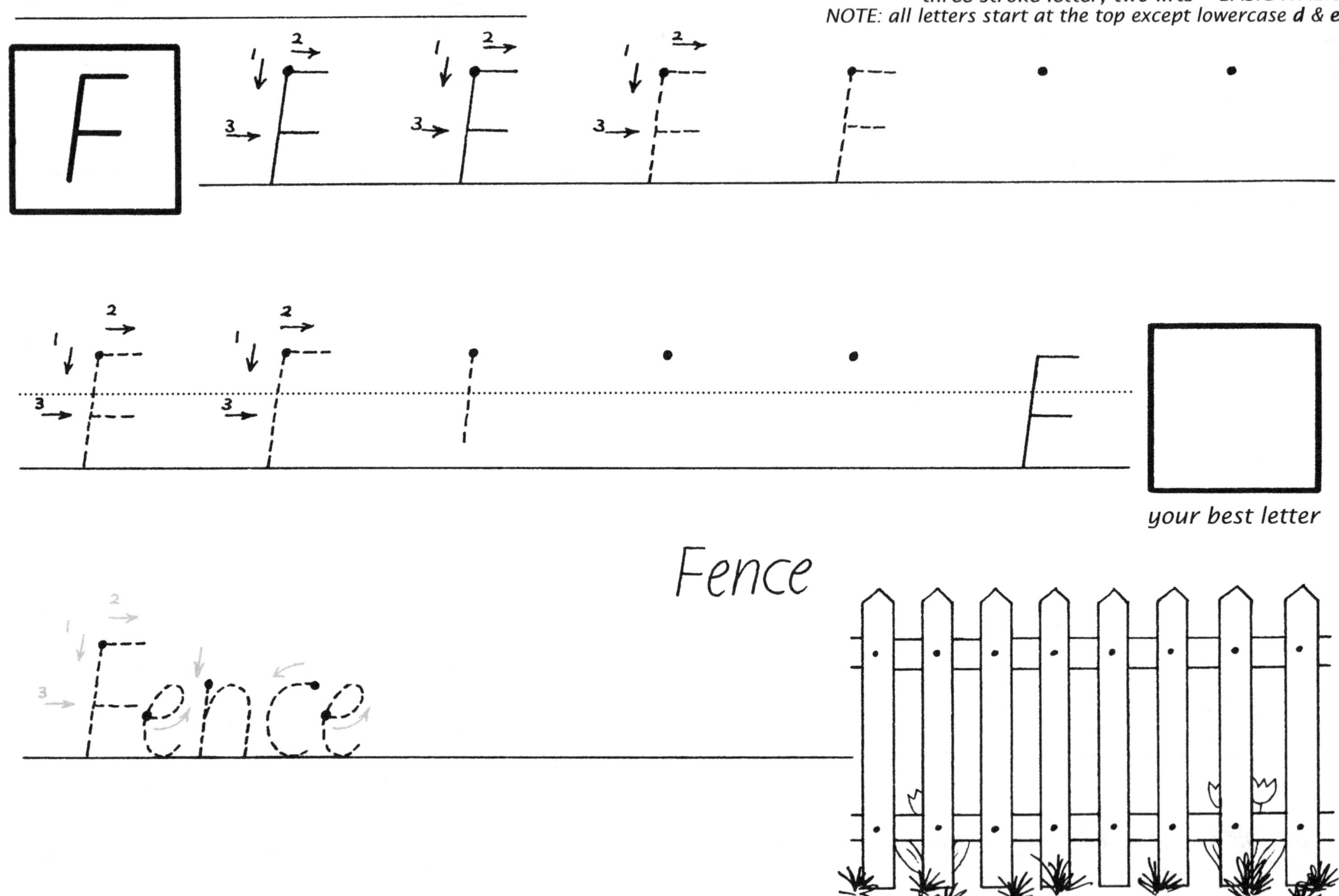

three stroke letter, two lifts · BASIC ITALIC
NOTE: all letters start at the top except lowercase d & e
F
your best letter
Fence
Fence

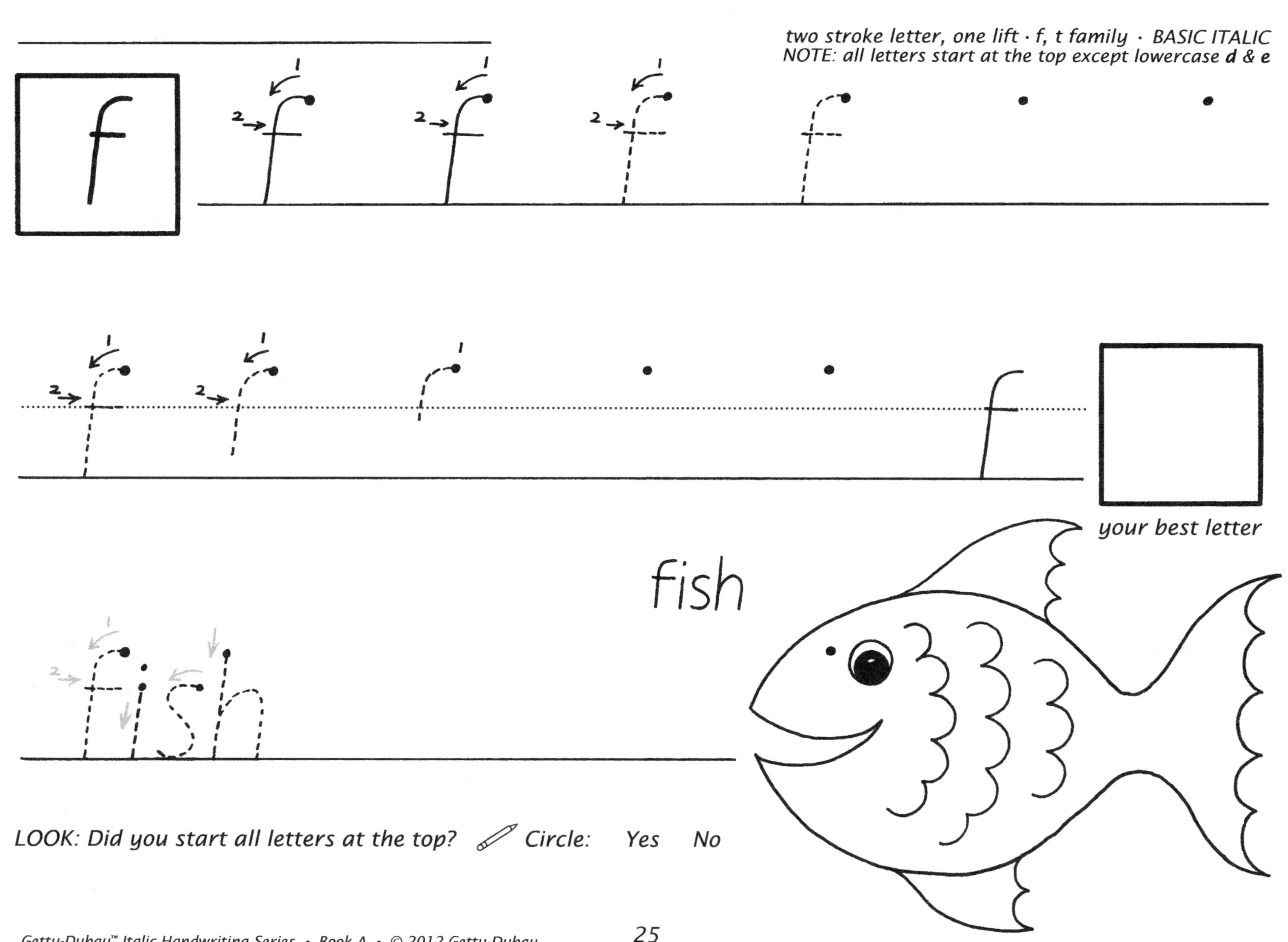

two stroke letter, one lift · f, t family · BASIC ITALIC
NOTE: all letters start at the top except lowercase d & e
1
2
f
your best letter
fish
fish
LOOK: Did you start all letters at the top?   Circle: Yes   No

your best letter

Sailboat

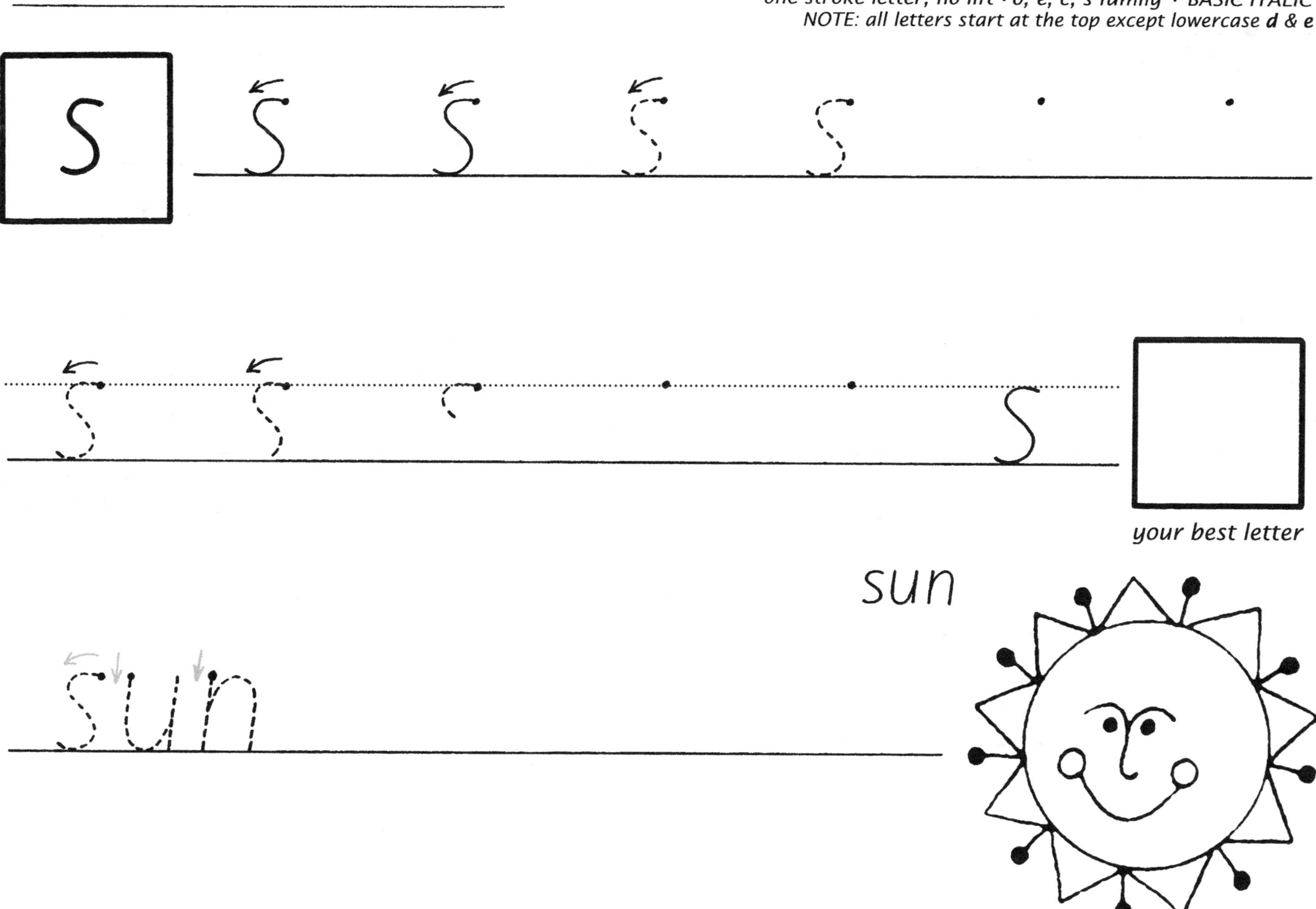

one stroke letter, no lift · o, e, c, s family · BASIC ITALIC
NOTE: all letters start at the top except lowercase d & e
your best letter
sun
sun

C

your best letter

Cow

LOOK: Did you trace each letter before writing your own?

Circle: Yes   No

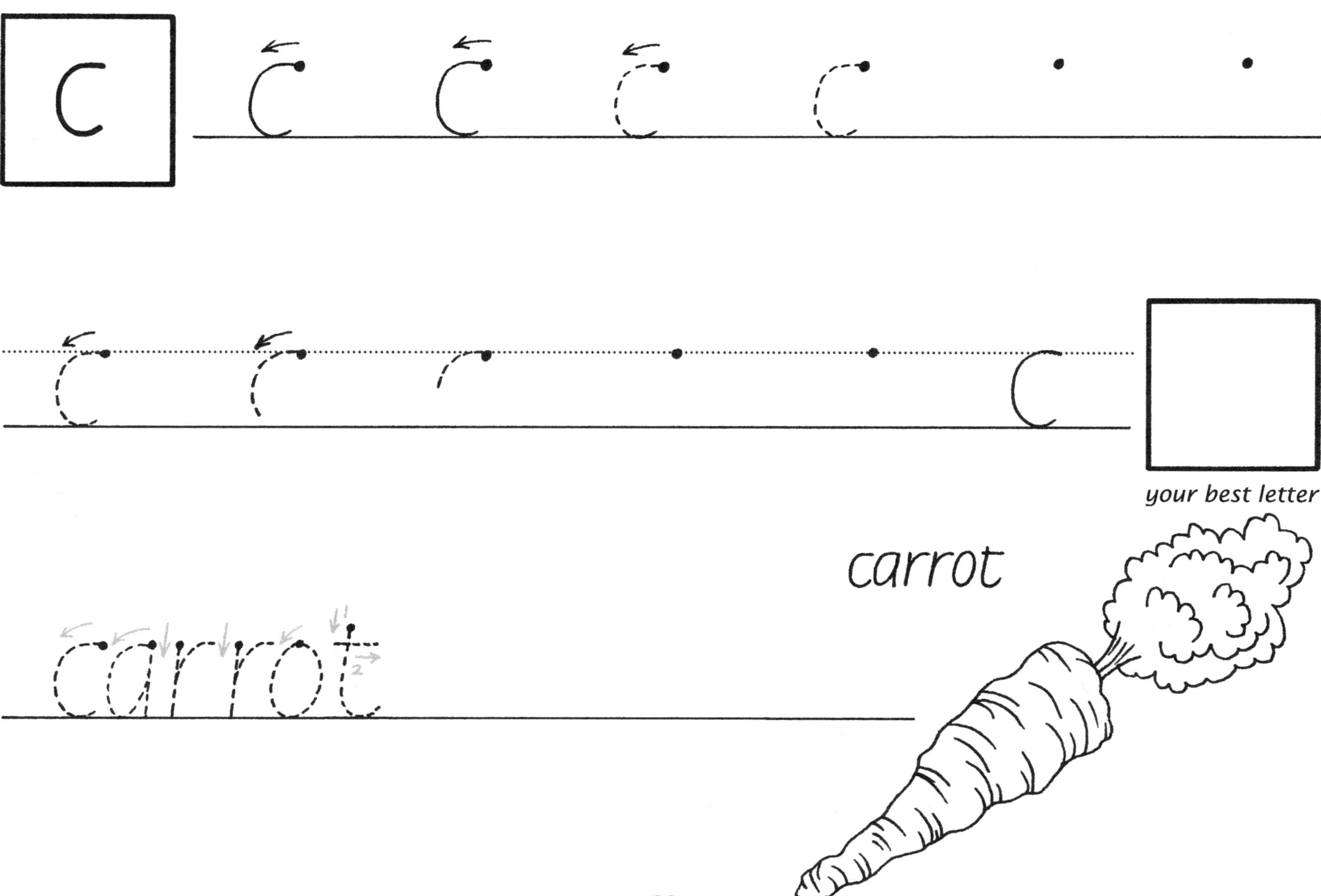

your best letter

carrot

your best letter

Egg

your best letter

LOOK: Did you trace each **e** before writing your own?

Circle: Yes   No

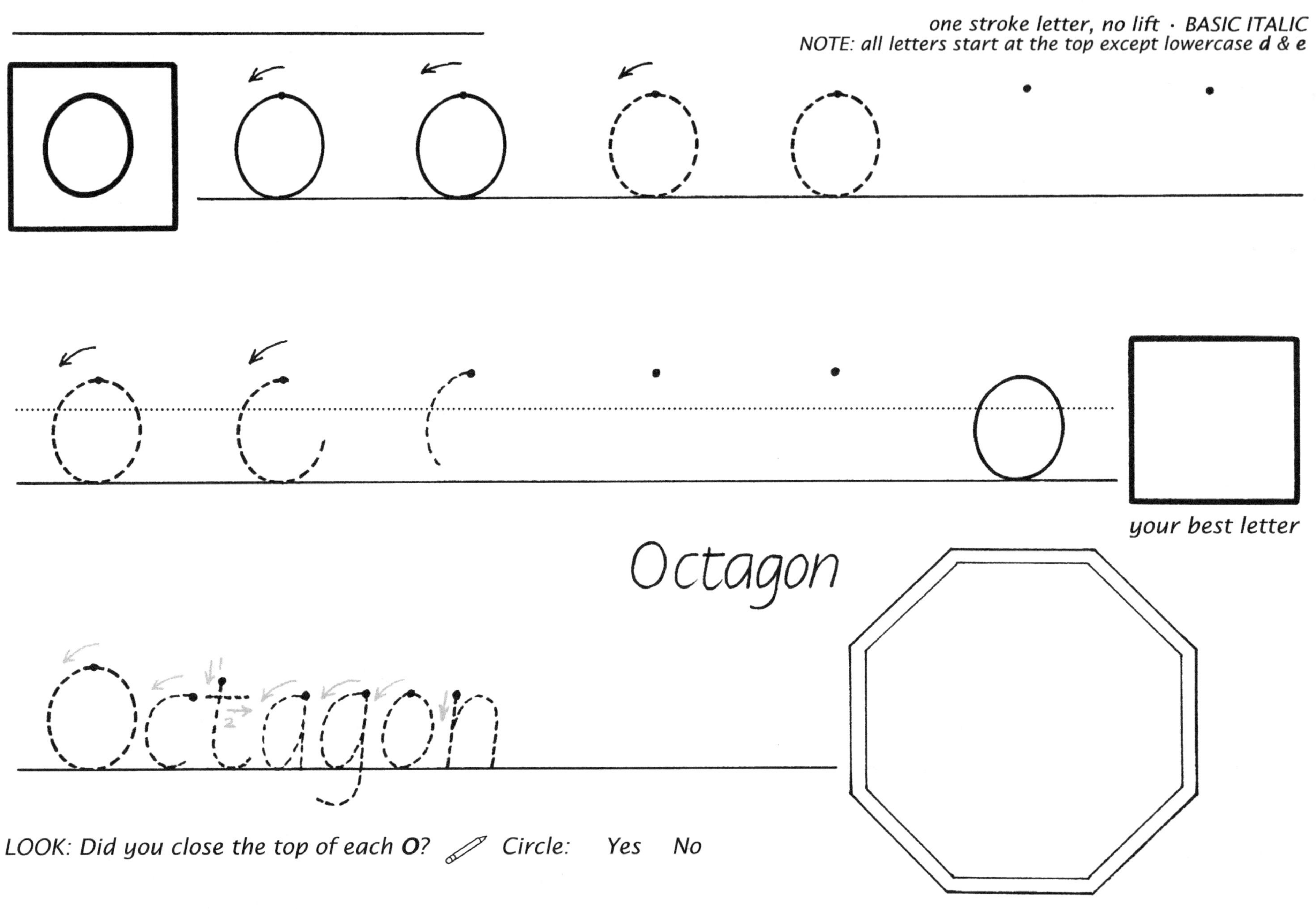

your best letter

Octagon

LOOK: Did you close the top of each **O**? Circle: Yes   No

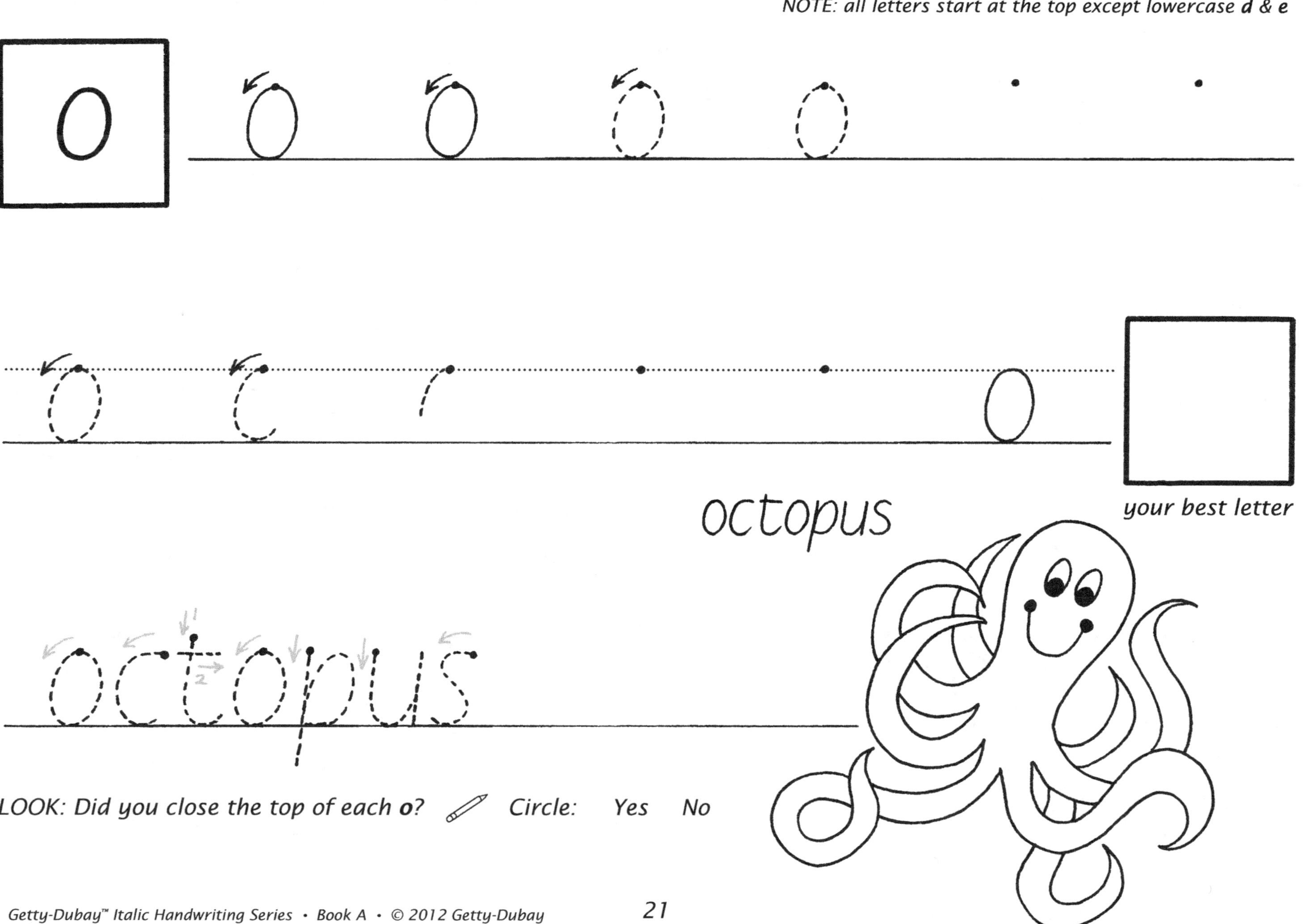

your best letter

LOOK: Did you close the top of each **o**? Circle: Yes   No

your best letter
Peacock

parrot

your best letter

B

Balloons

your best letter

Balloons

your best letter

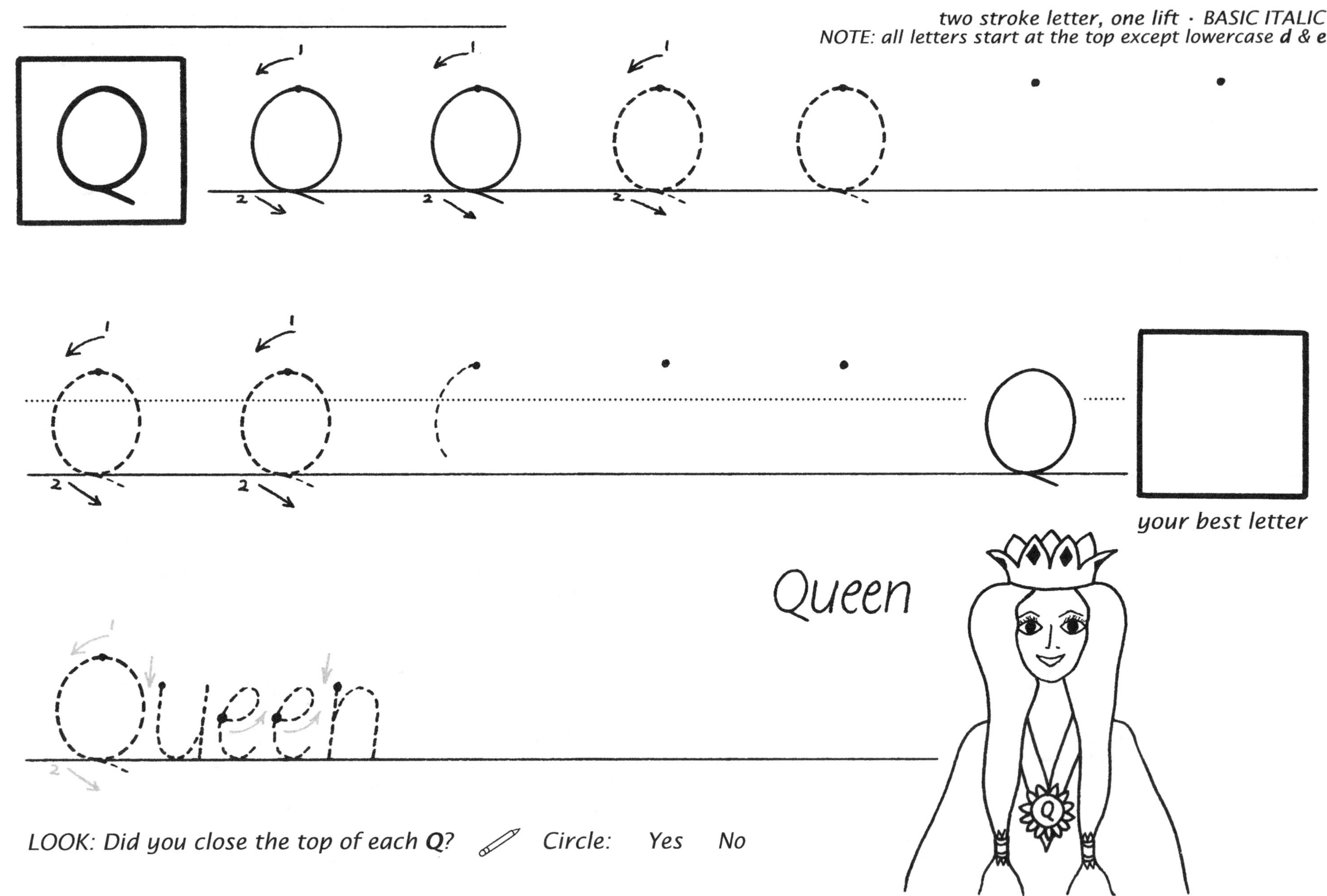

your best letter
Queen
LOOK: Did you close the top of each Q?   Circle: Yes   No

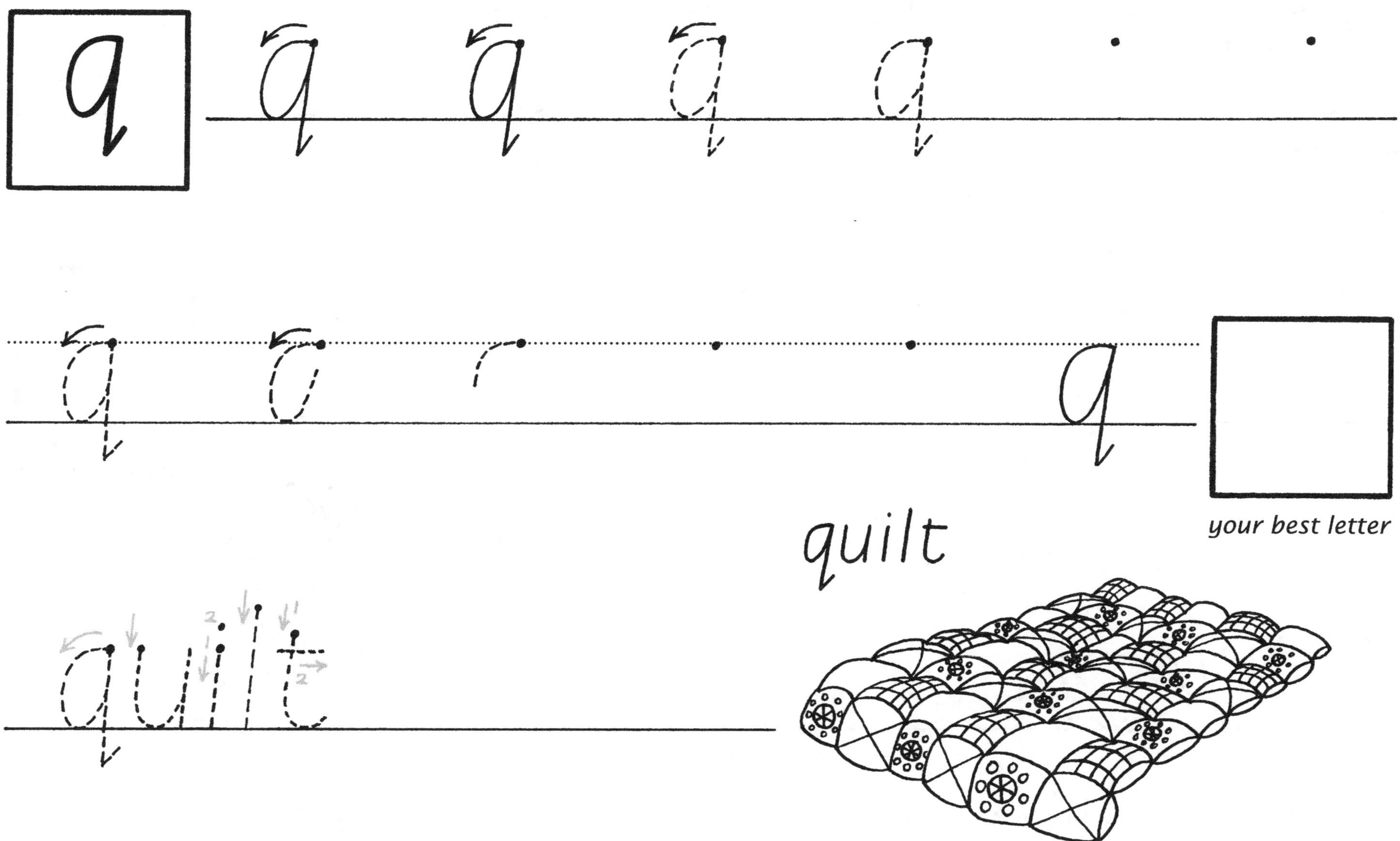

quilt

your best letter

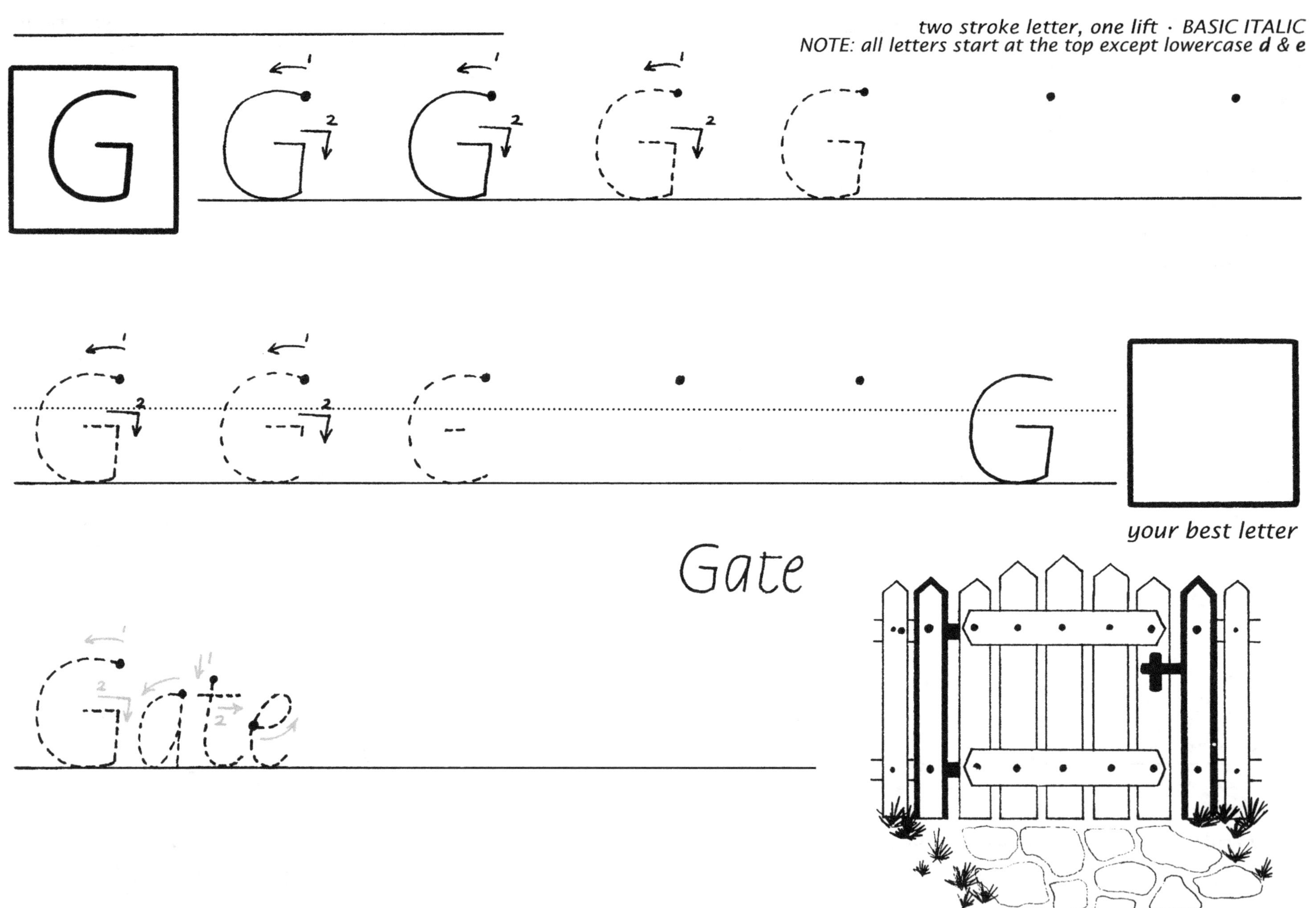

G
G
Gate
your best letter
Gate

your best letter

goat

LOOK: Did you trace each letter before writing your own?   Circle: Yes   No

your best letter
Dinosaur
Dinosaur

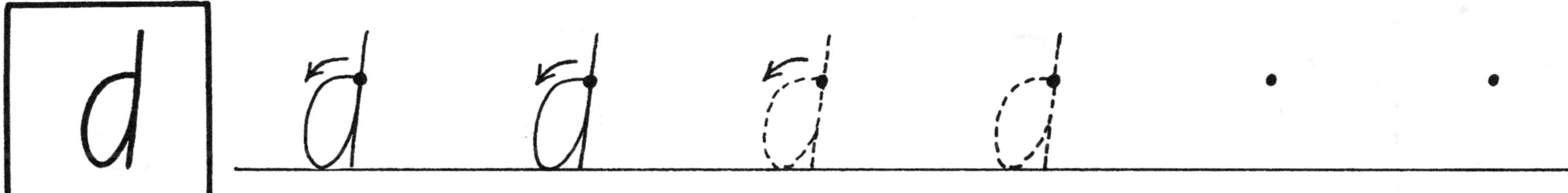

your best letter

dog

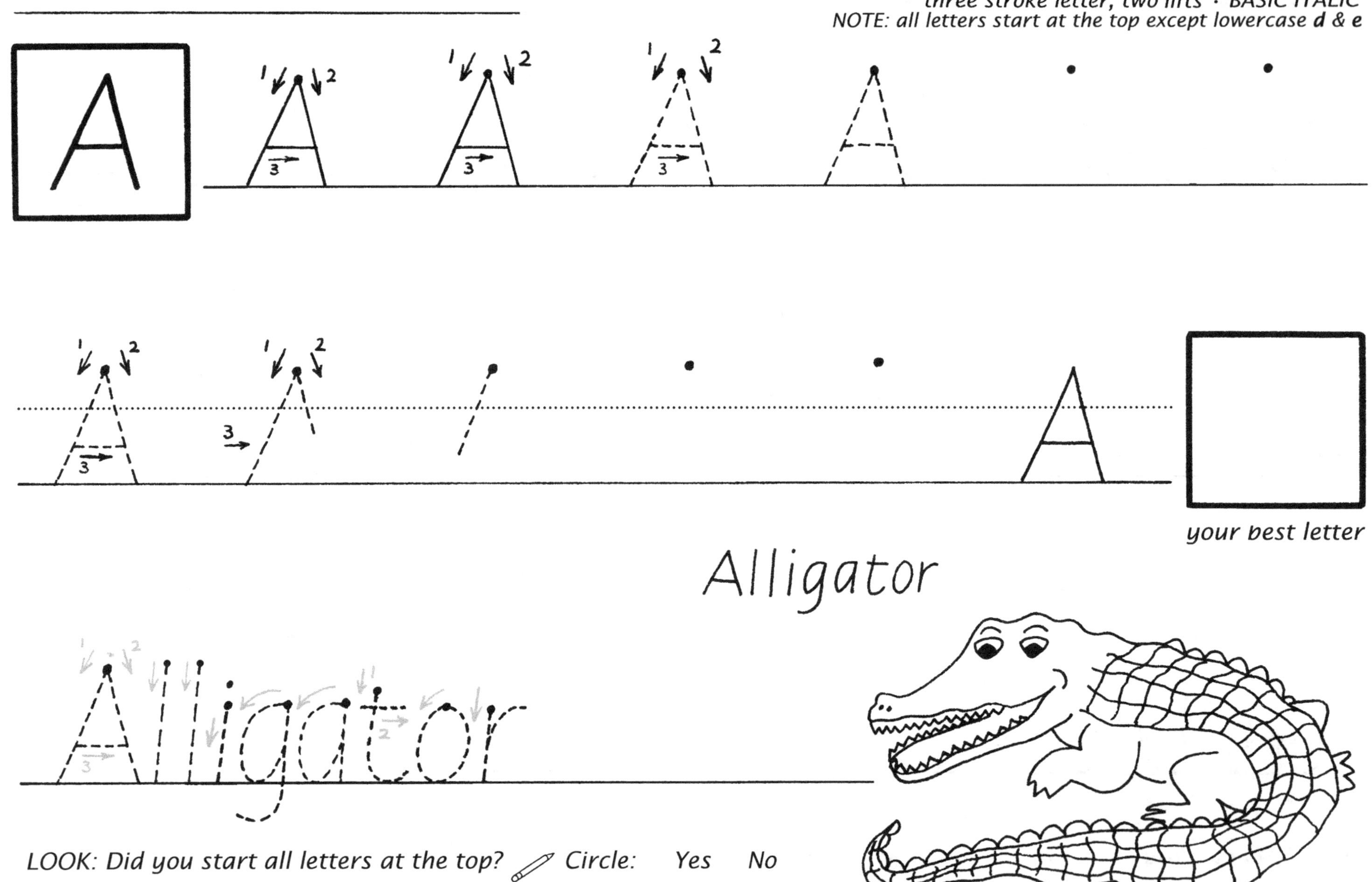

your best letter

Alligator

LOOK: Did you start all letters at the top? Circle: Yes   No

LOOK: Did you close each **a** at the top?   Circle: Yes   No

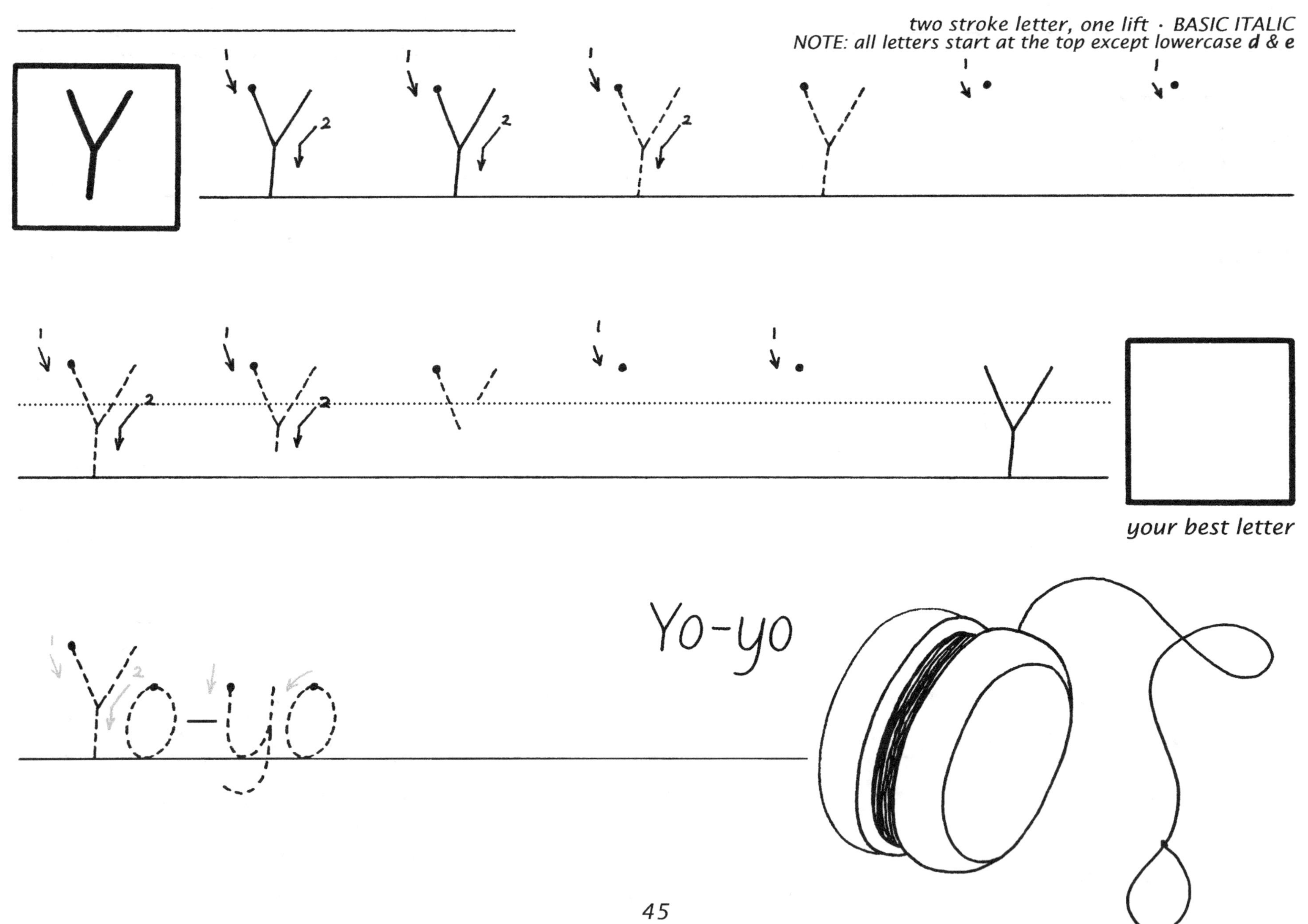

Getty-Dubay™ Italic Handwriting Series · Book A · © 2012 Getty-Dubay

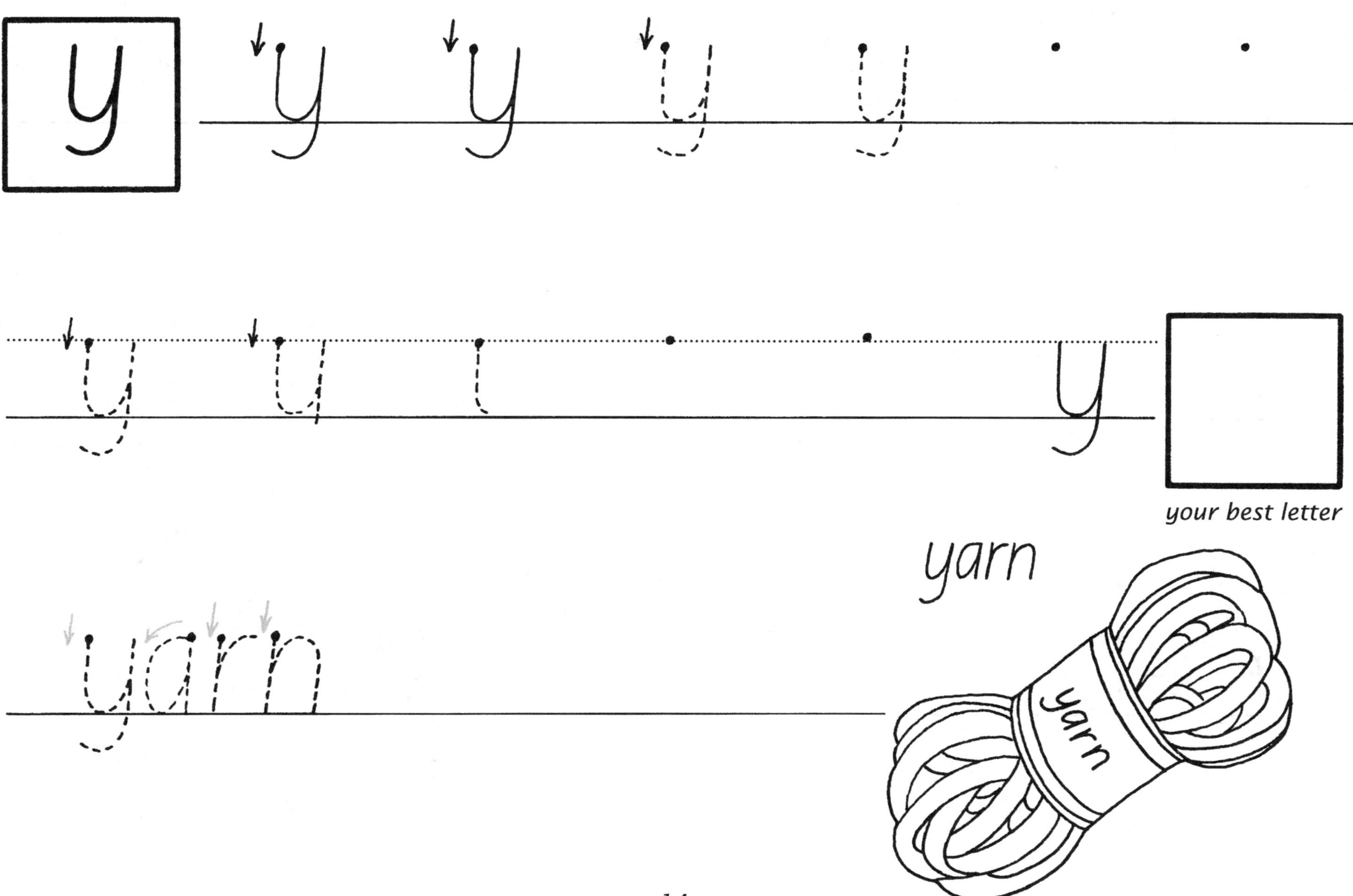

your best letter

yarn

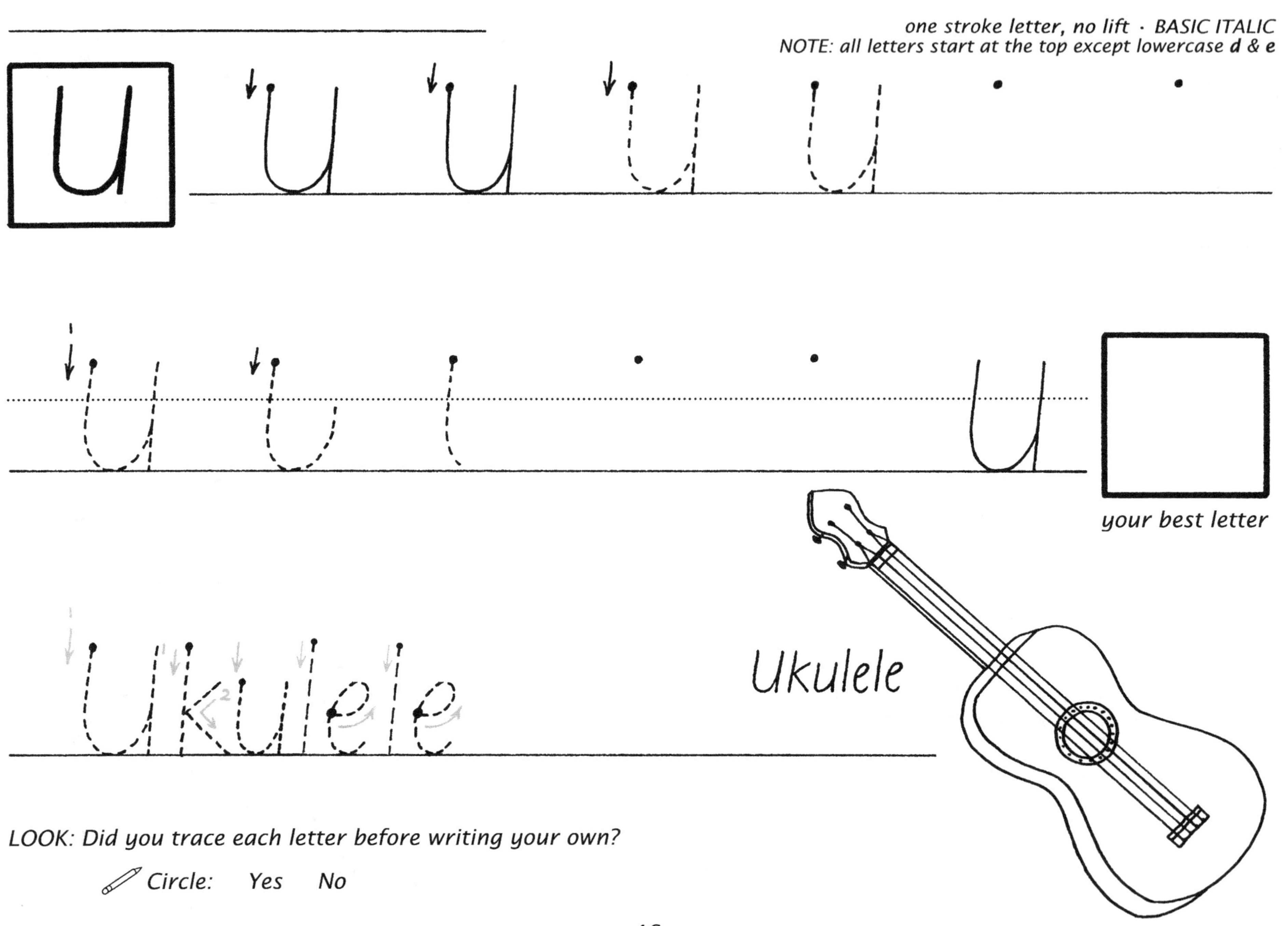

your best letter

LOOK: Did you trace each letter before writing your own?

Circle: Yes   No

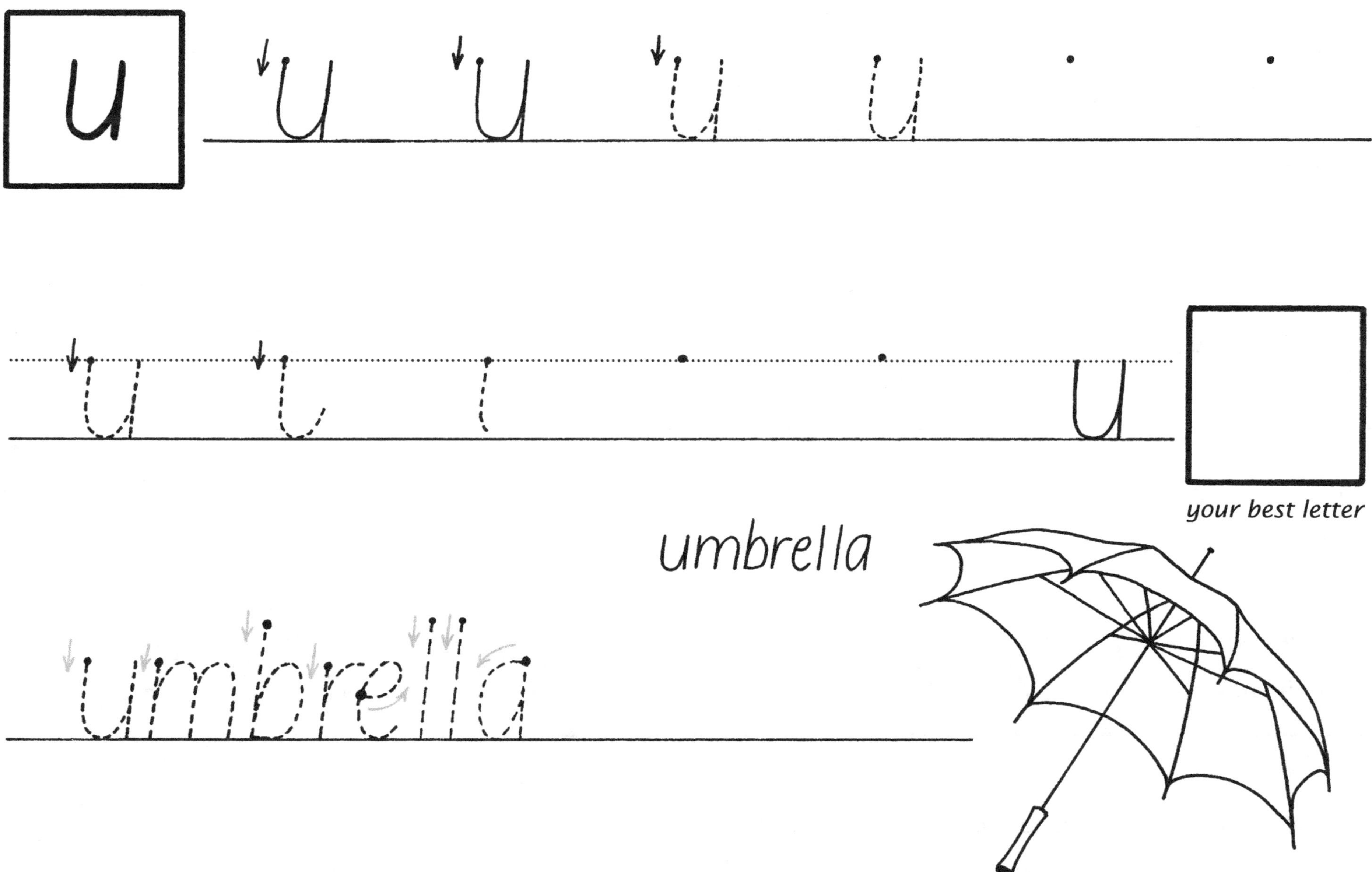

u

your best letter

umbrella

umbrella

three stroke letter, two lifts · BASIC ITALIC
NOTE: all letters start at the top except lowercase *d* & *e*

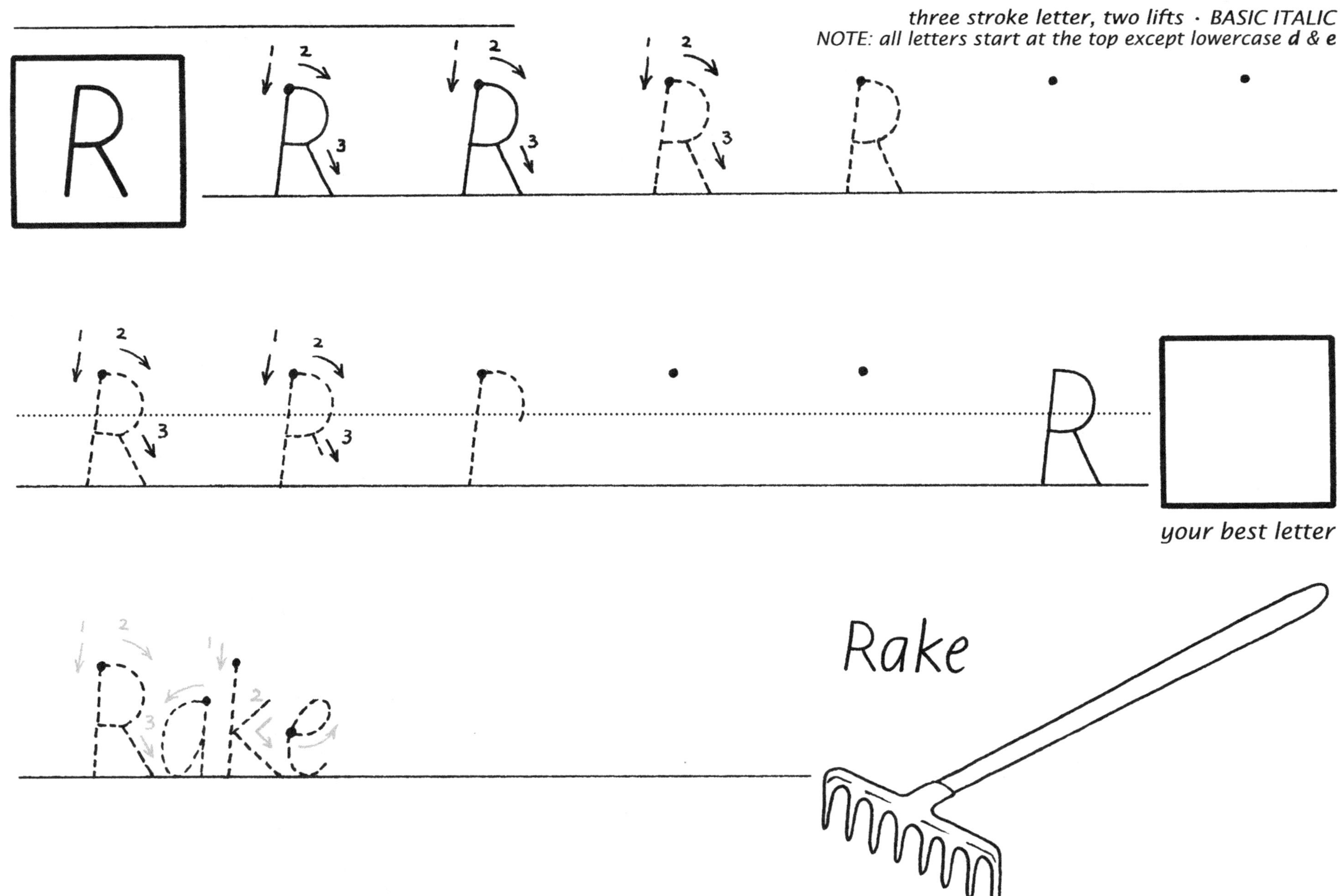

your best letter
Rake

your best letter

rabbit

LOOK: Did you start each letter at the top? ✎ Circle: Yes   No

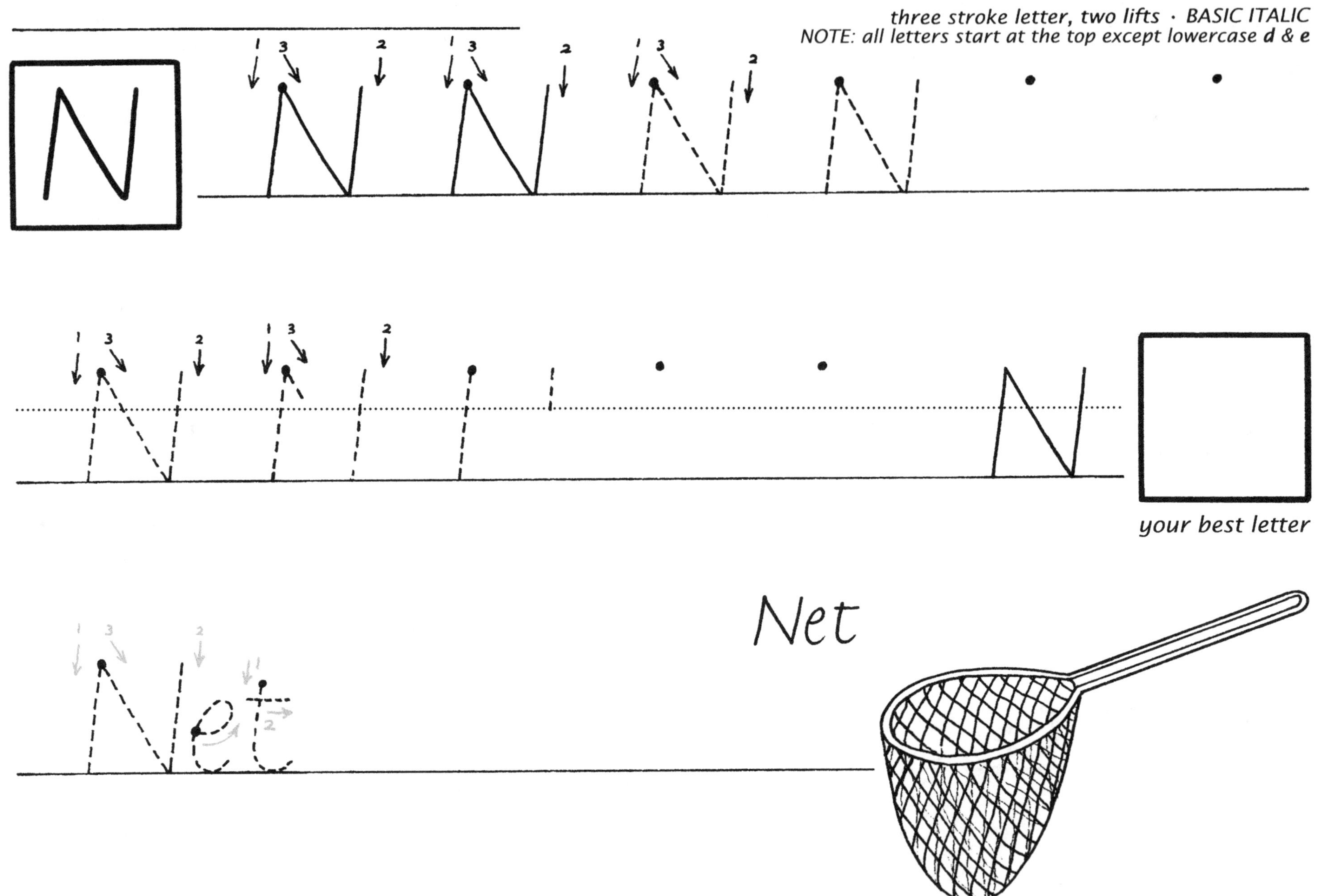

your best letter

Net

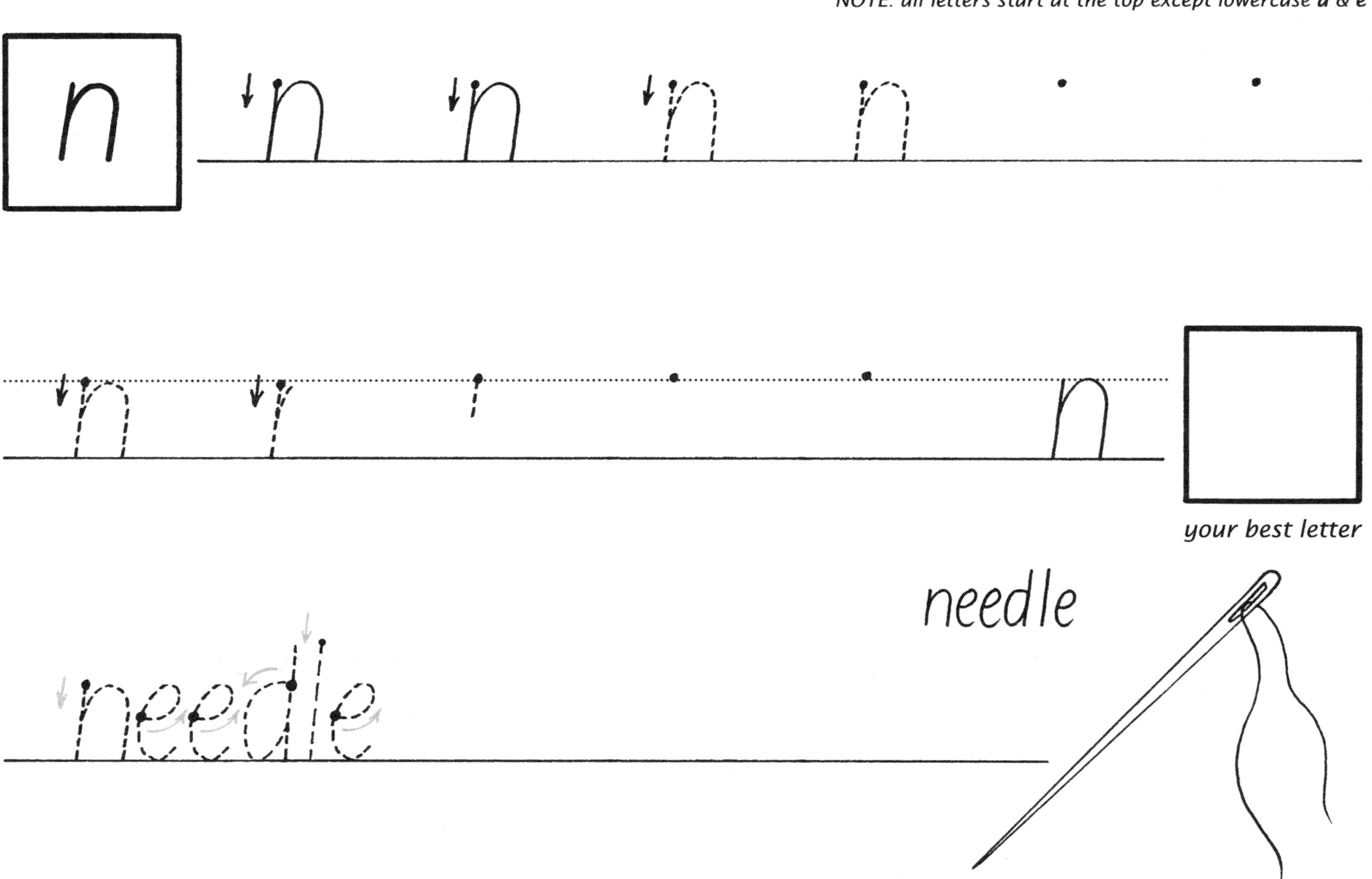

n
your best letter
needle
needle

M

Mittens

your best letter

Mittens

LOOK: Did you start all letters at the top? ✏ Circle: Yes   No

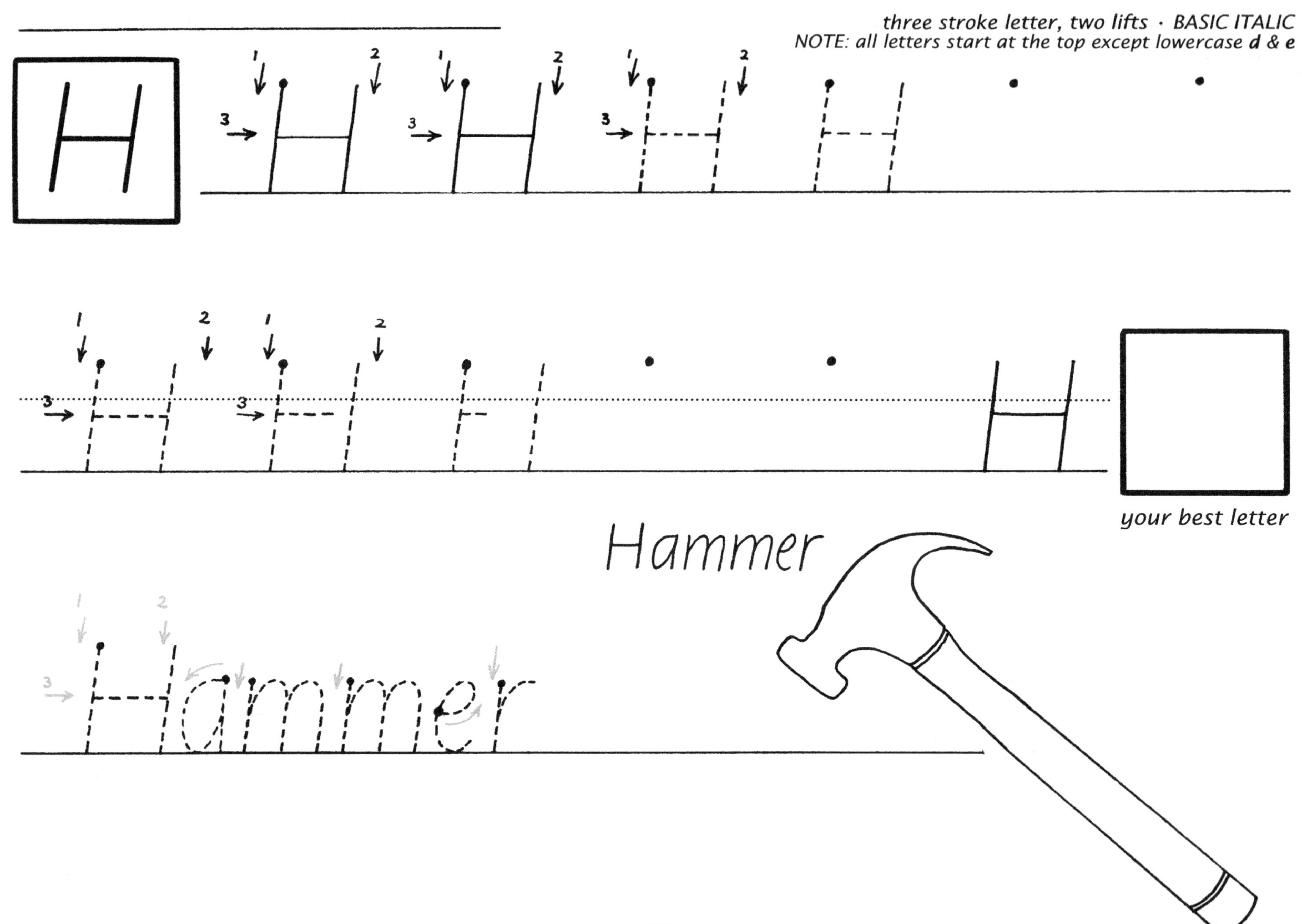

your best letter

Hammer

your best letter

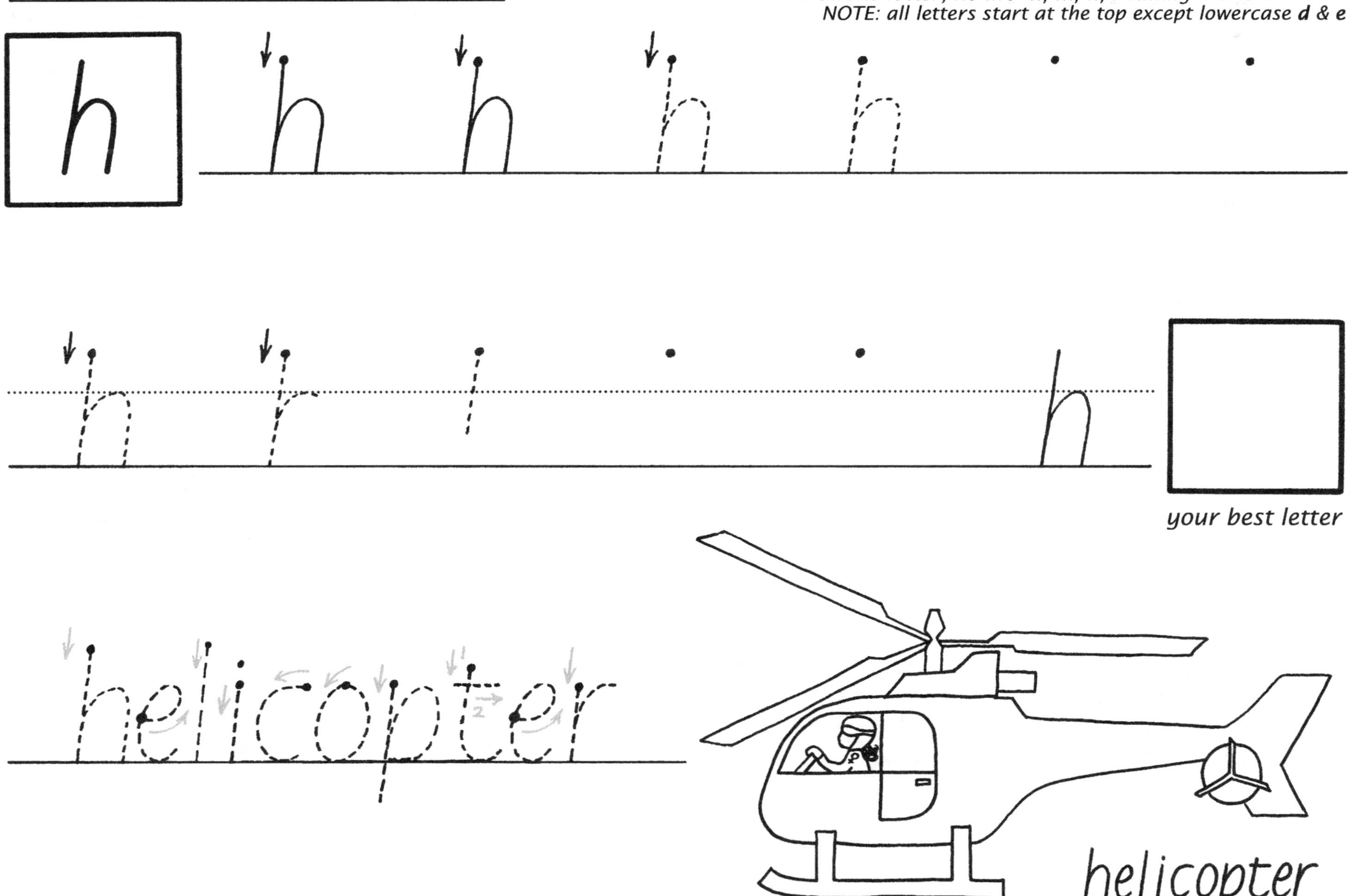

helicopter

Zipper

your best letter

Zipper

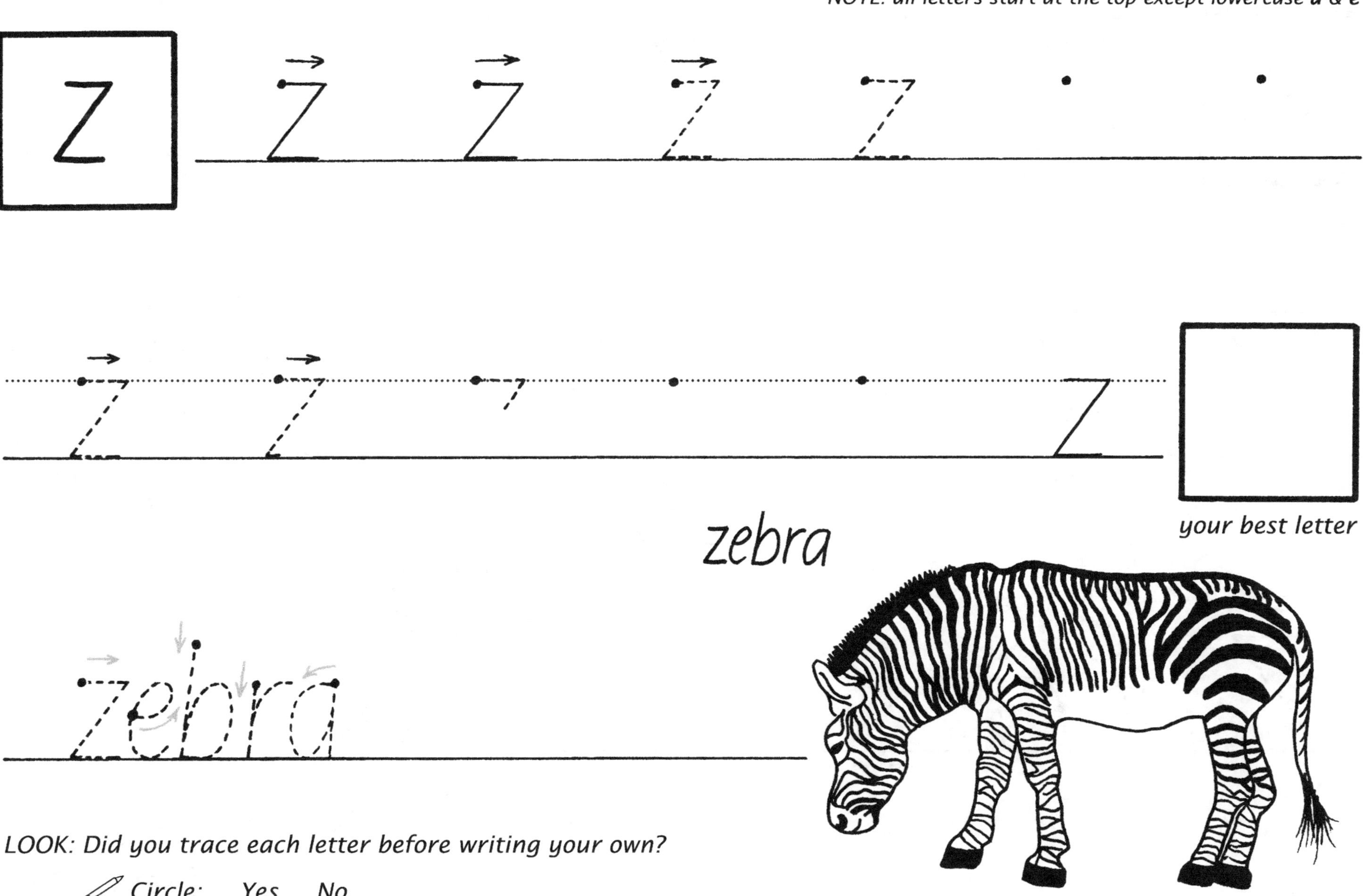

LOOK: Did you trace each letter before writing your own?

Circle: Yes   No

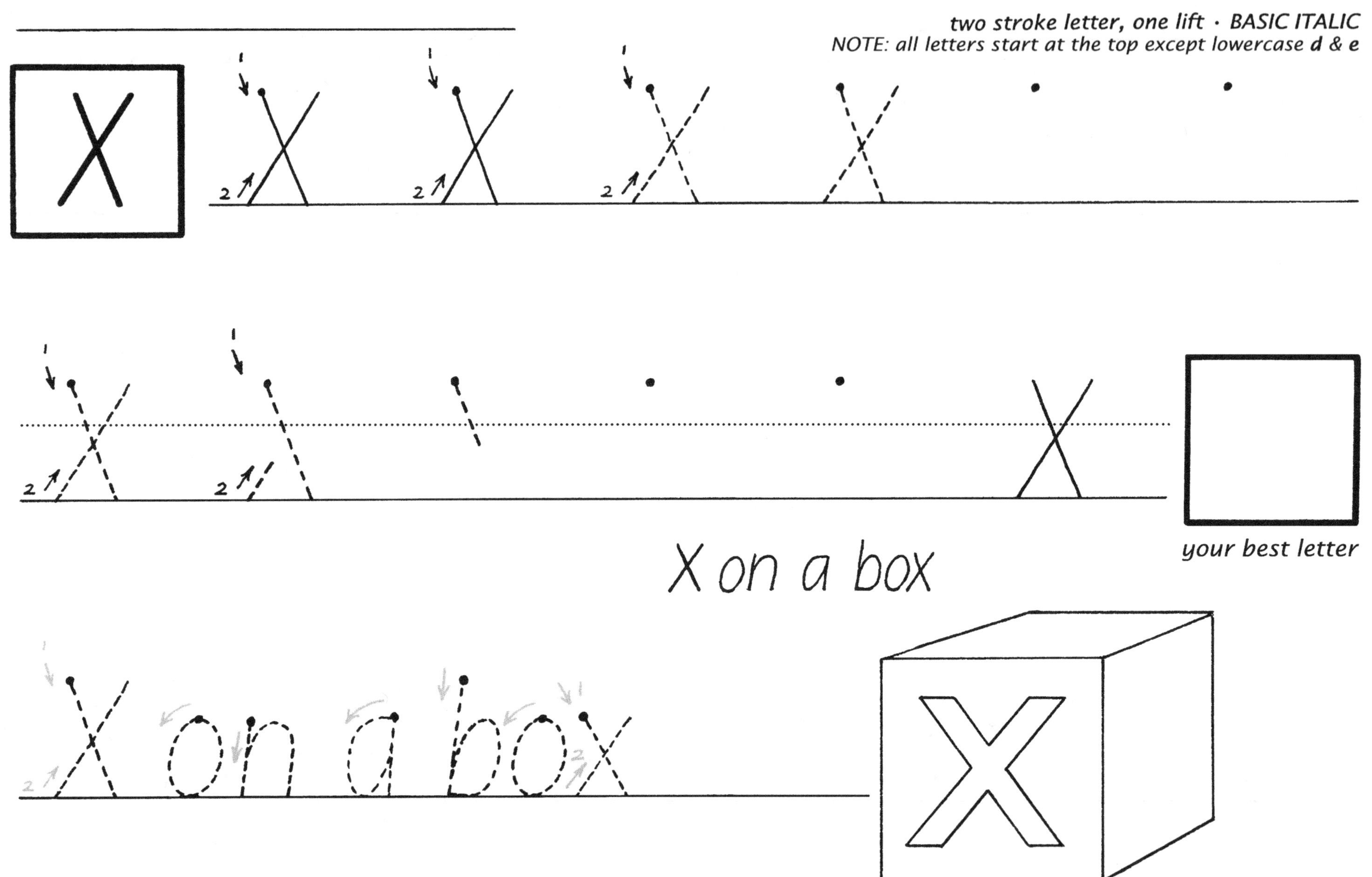

your best letter

X on a box

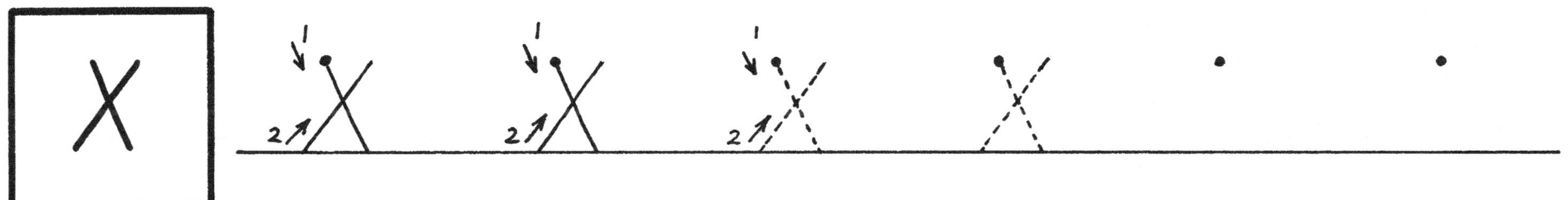

x in a box

your best letter

x in a box

your best letter

Watch

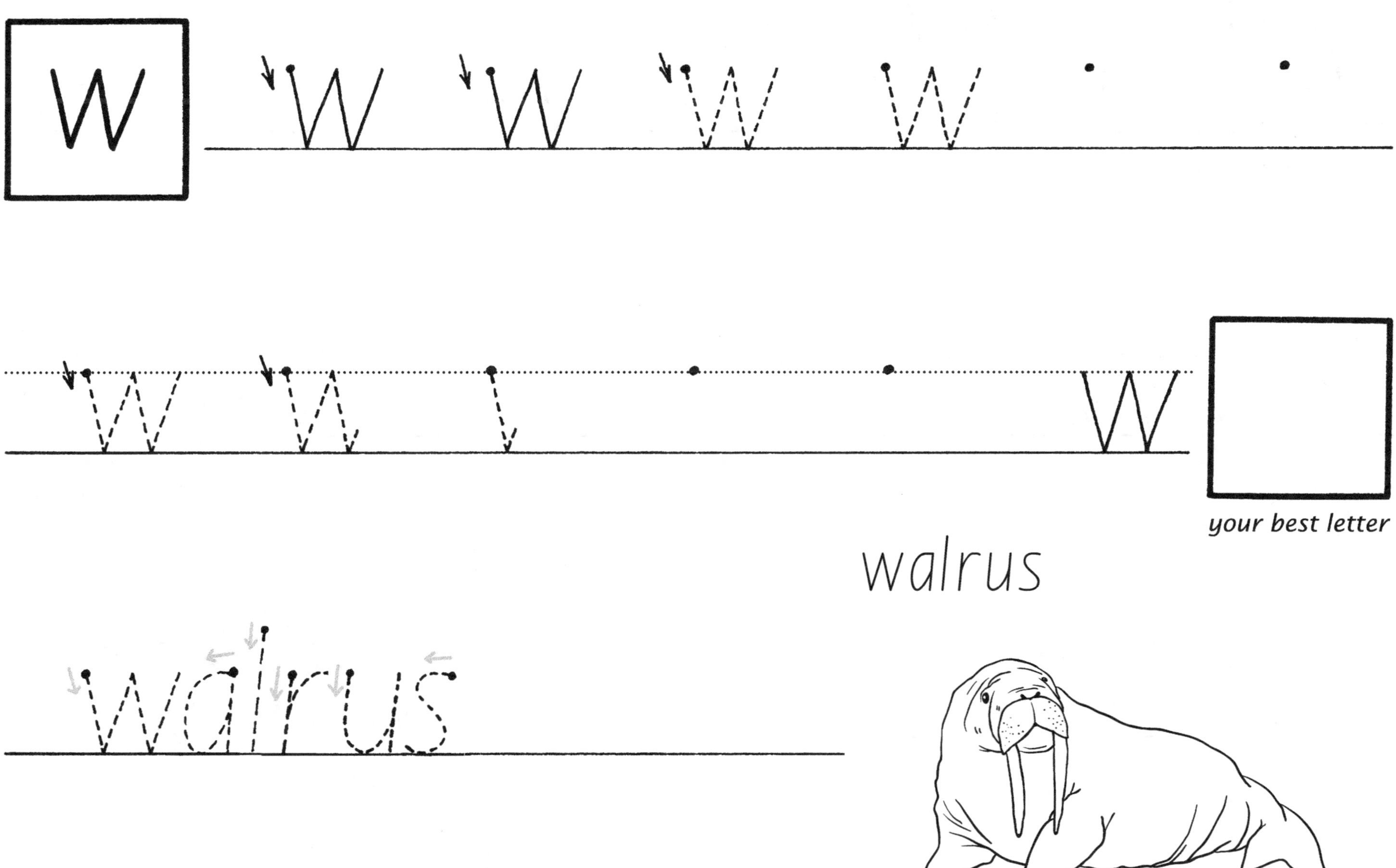

your best letter

walrus

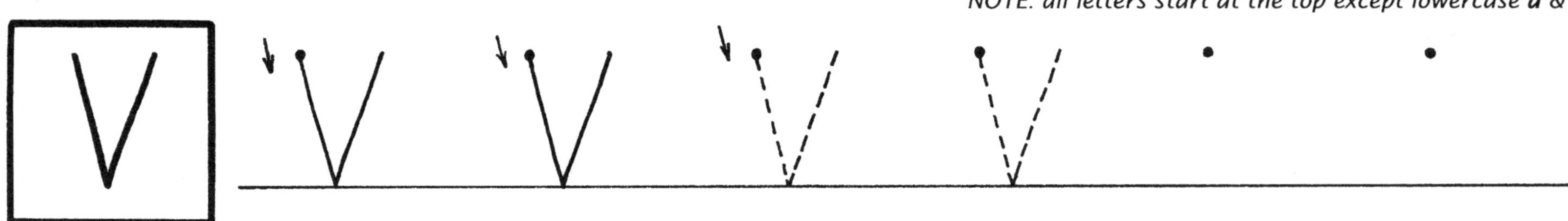

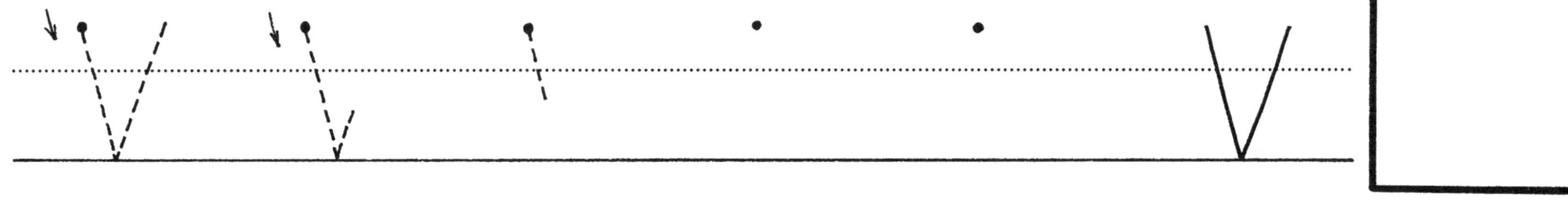

your best letter

Valentine

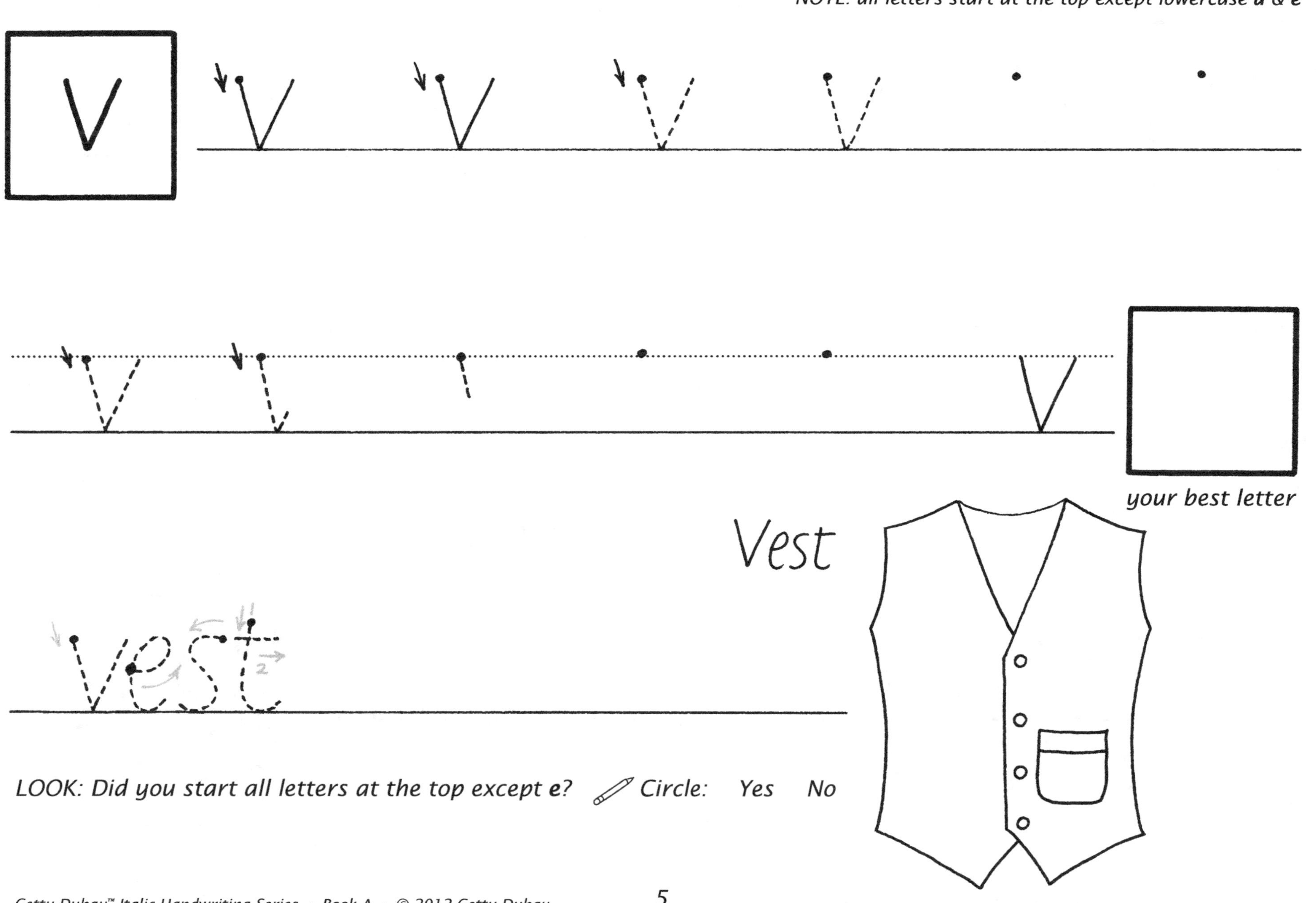

your best letter

Vest

LOOK: Did you start all letters at the top except *e*?   Circle: Yes   No

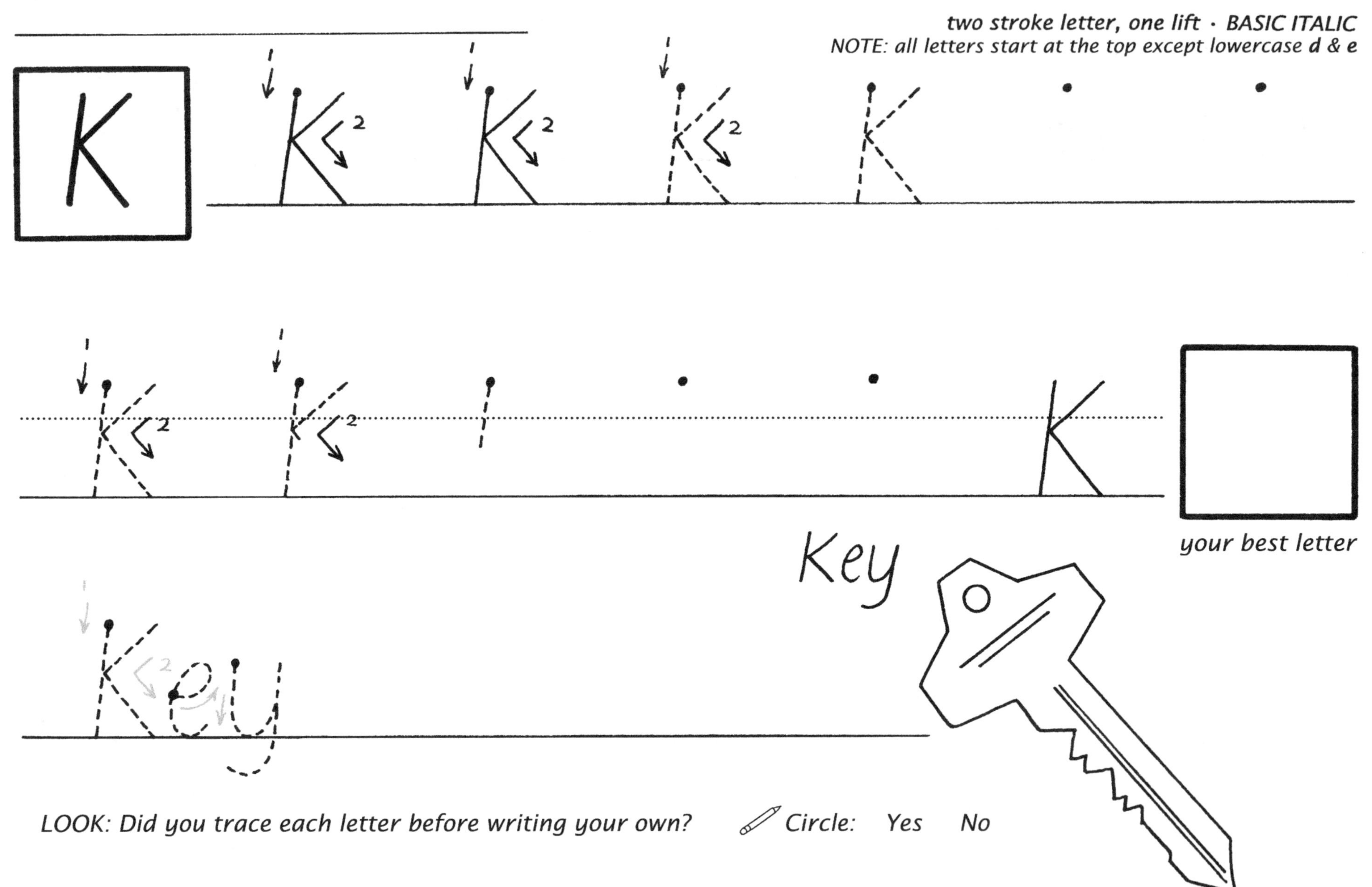

Key

your best letter

LOOK: Did you trace each letter before writing your own?   Circle: Yes   No

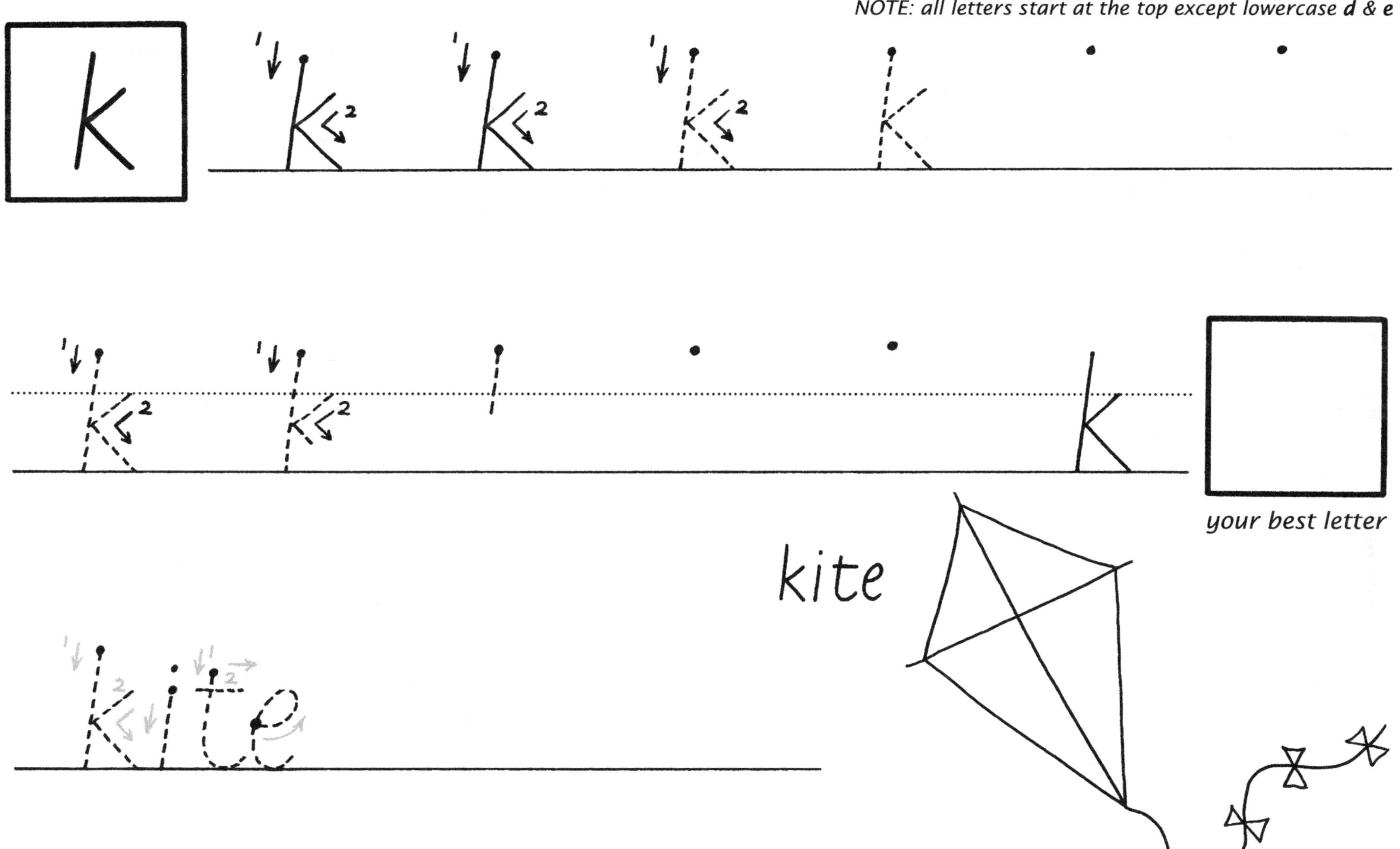

k
kite
your best letter

your best letter

Lock

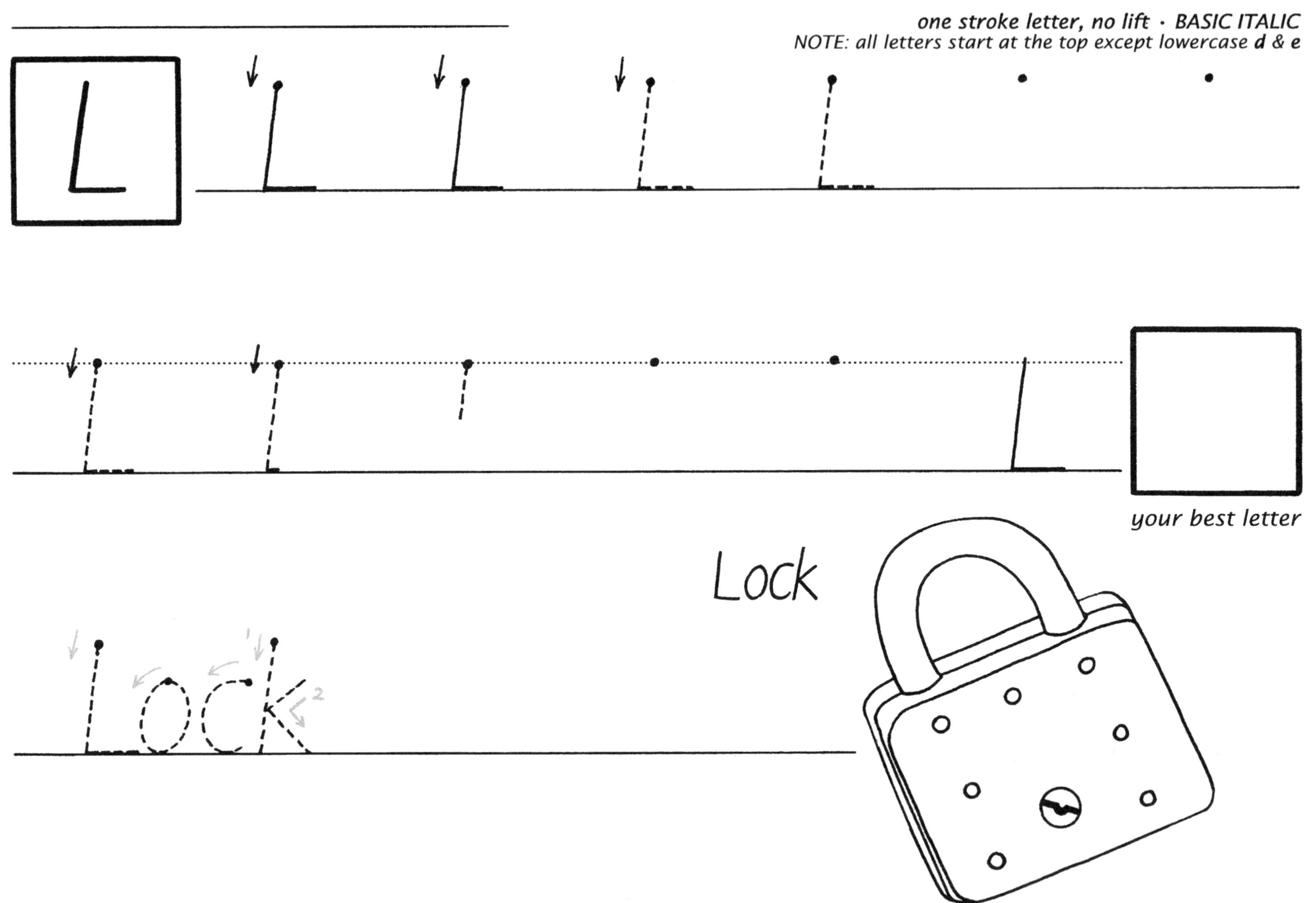

your best letter

lamb

lamb

J

your best letter

Jack-in-the-box

Jack-in-the-box

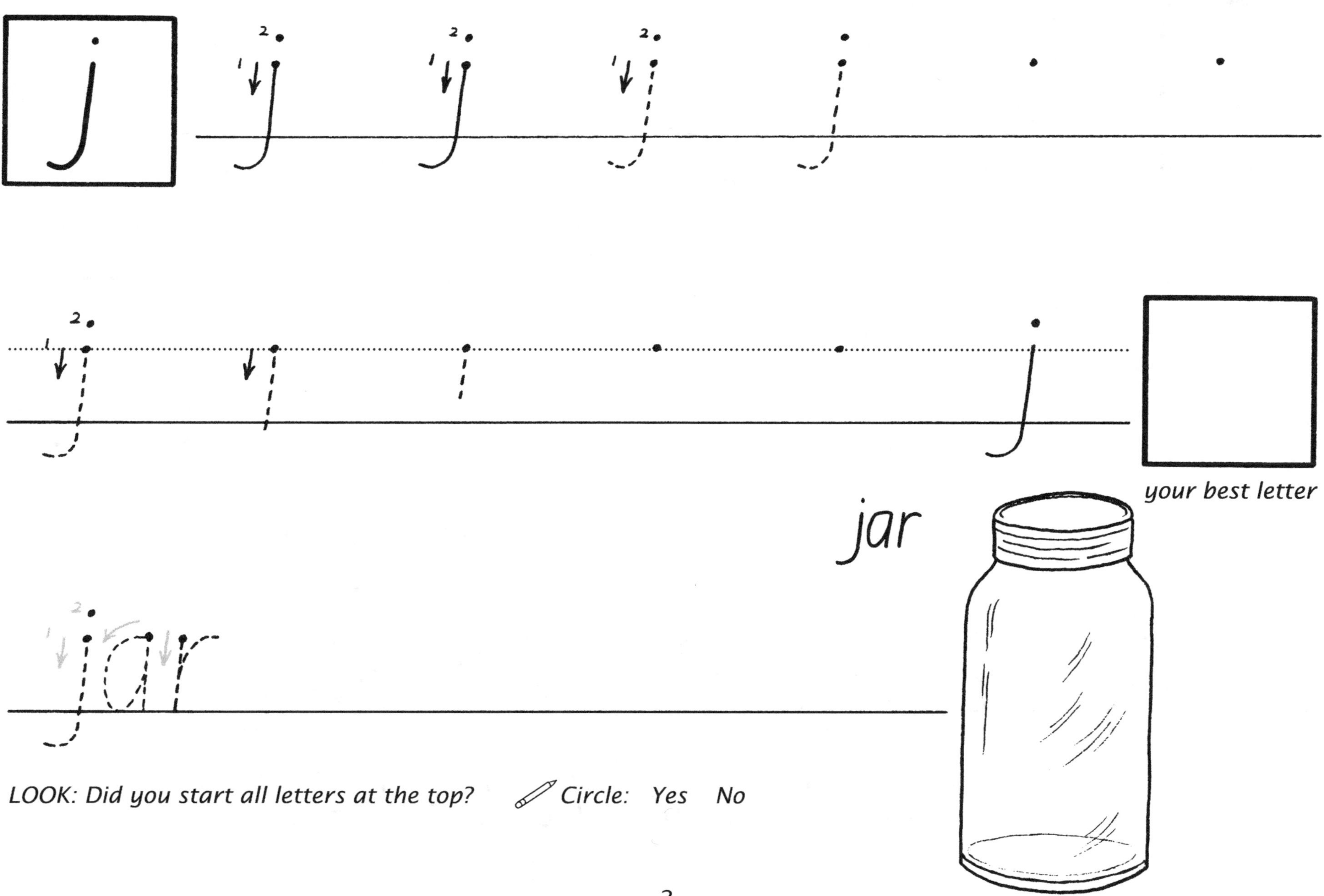

LOOK: Did you start all letters at the top?   Circle: Yes   No

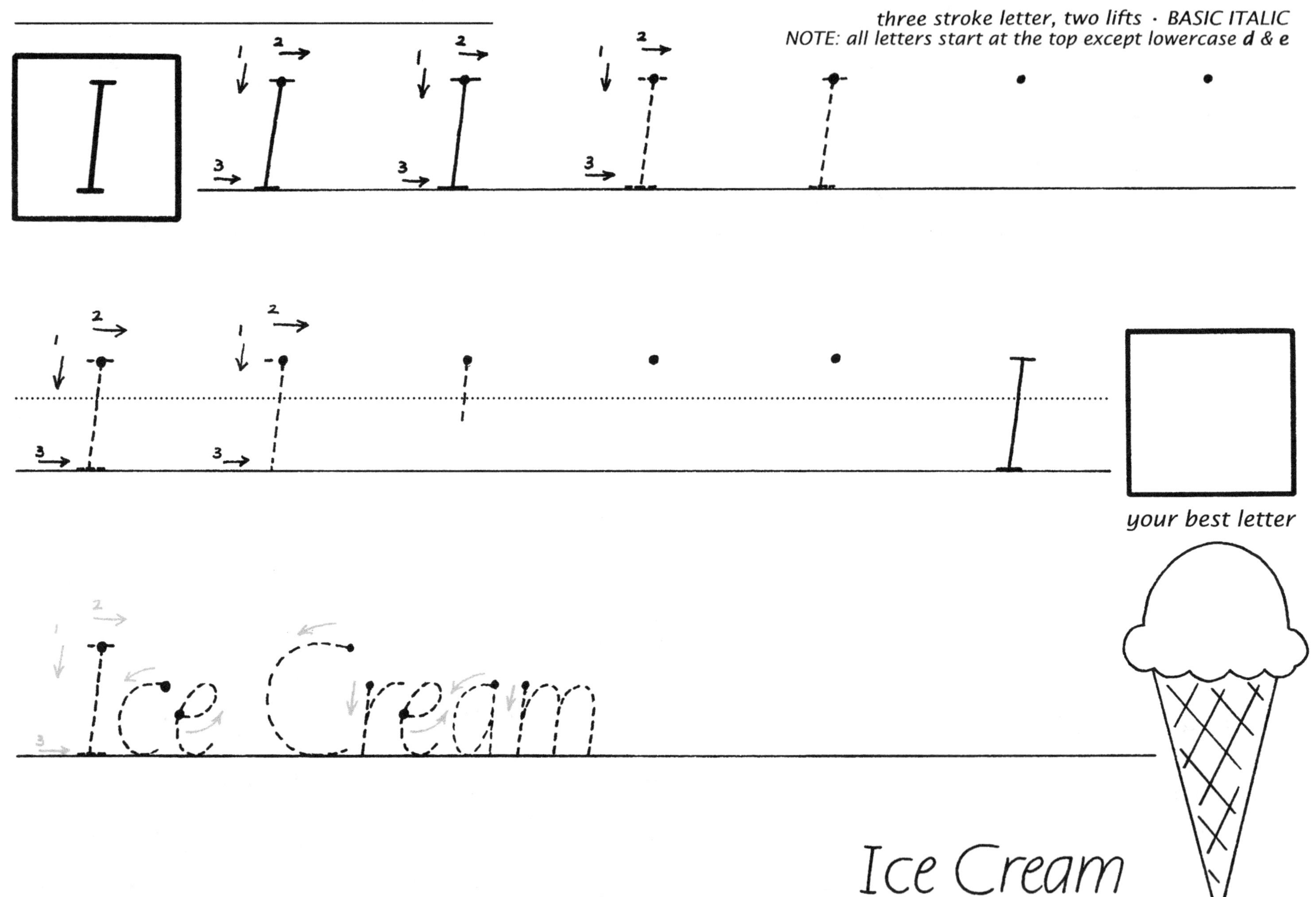

your best letter

Ice Cream

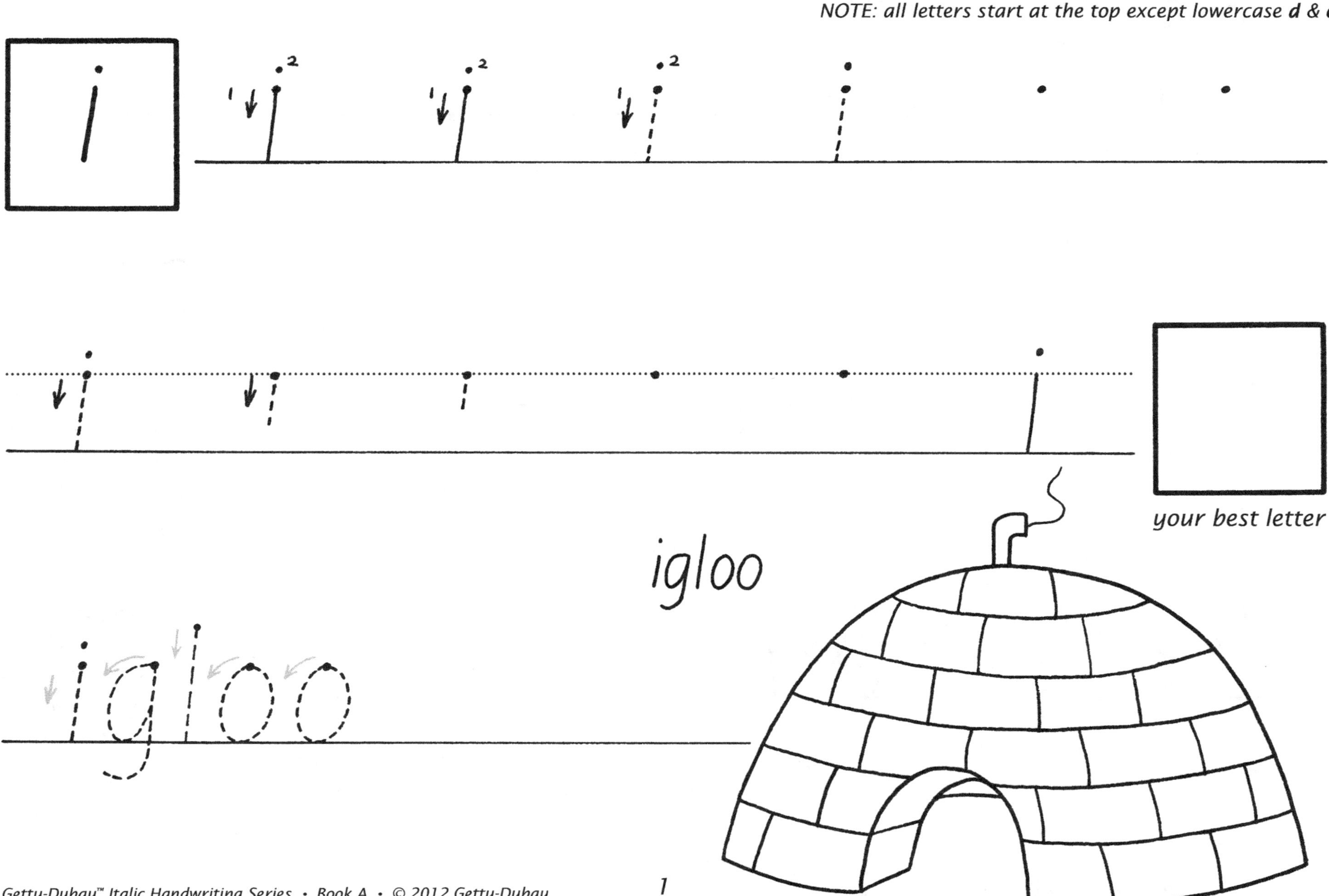

your best letter

igloo

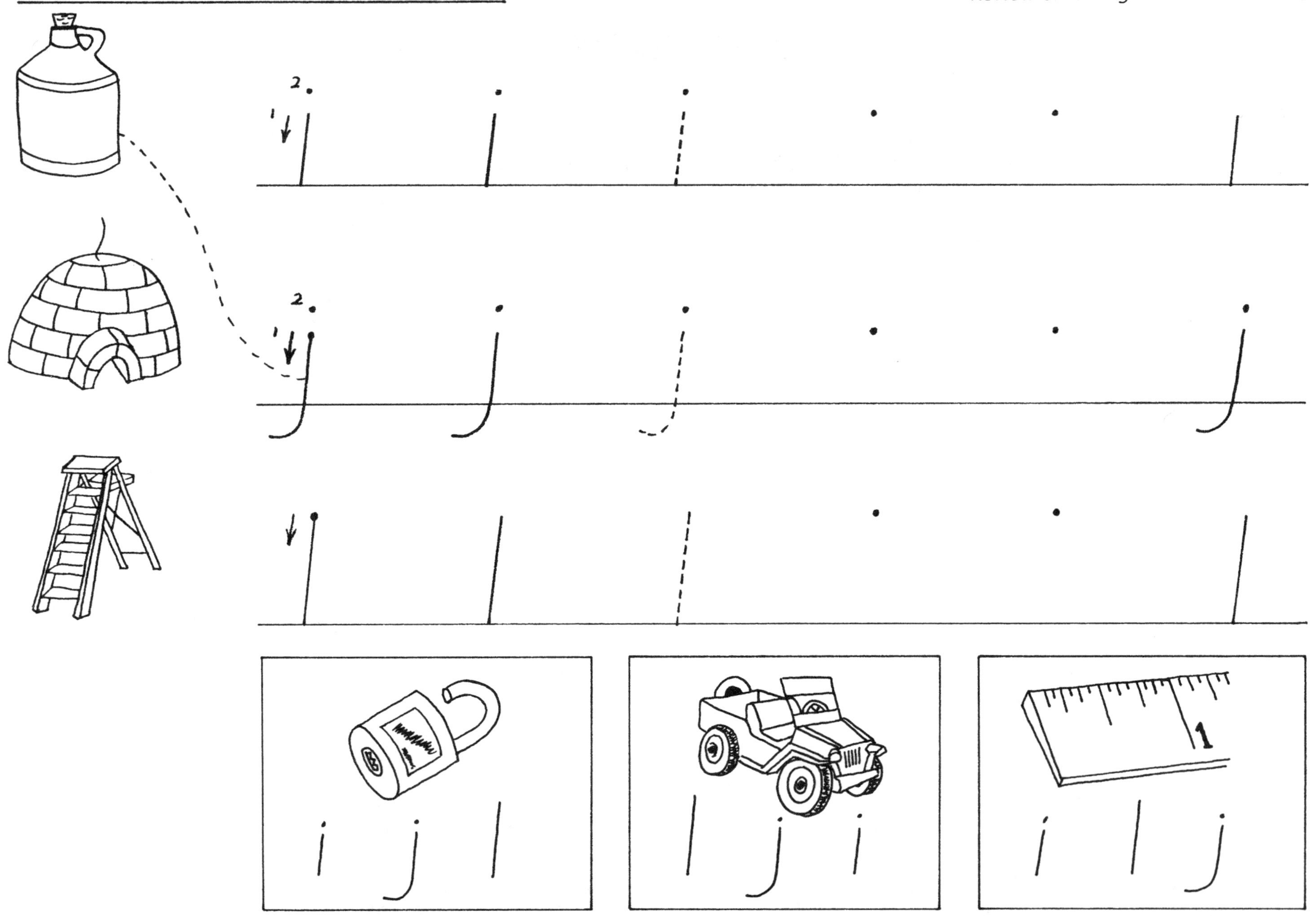

TOP THREE LINES: Ask the student to draw a line from the picture
to the letter that stands for the correct beginning sound.

BOTTOM THREE BOXES: Ask the student to circle the letter that
stands for the beginning sound of the picture.

BASIC SHAPES

Before the student begins writing in BOOK A, the authors recommend that the student practice the following shapes on unlined paper, one shape at a time. Allow the student to write each shape any size at first. Later, ask the student to write very large and very small forms of that same shape. We suggest the student also practice these shapes on a chalkboard and/or in cornmeal. (See INSTRUCTION MANUAL, "*Activity*," pp. 35 & 41.)

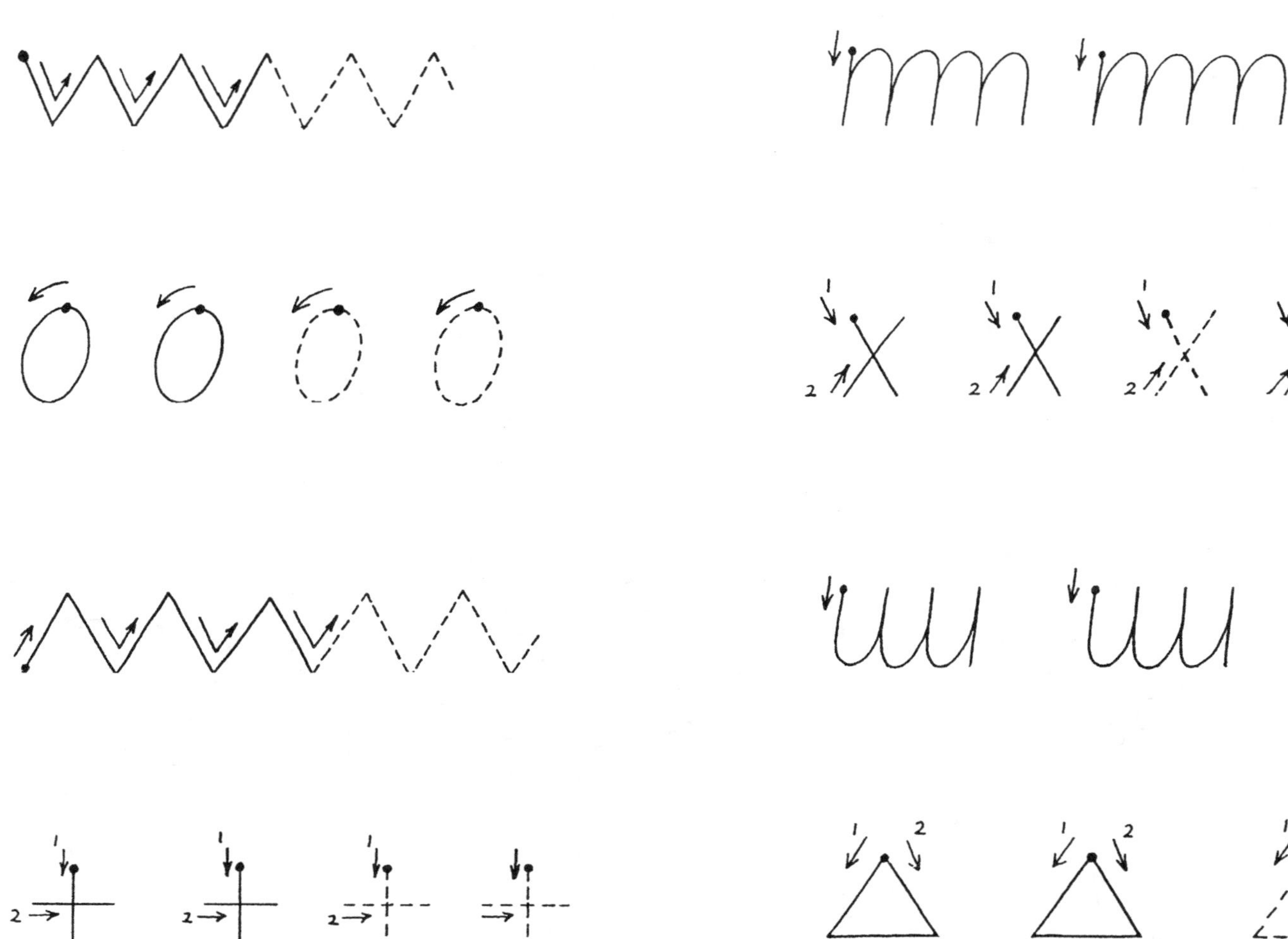

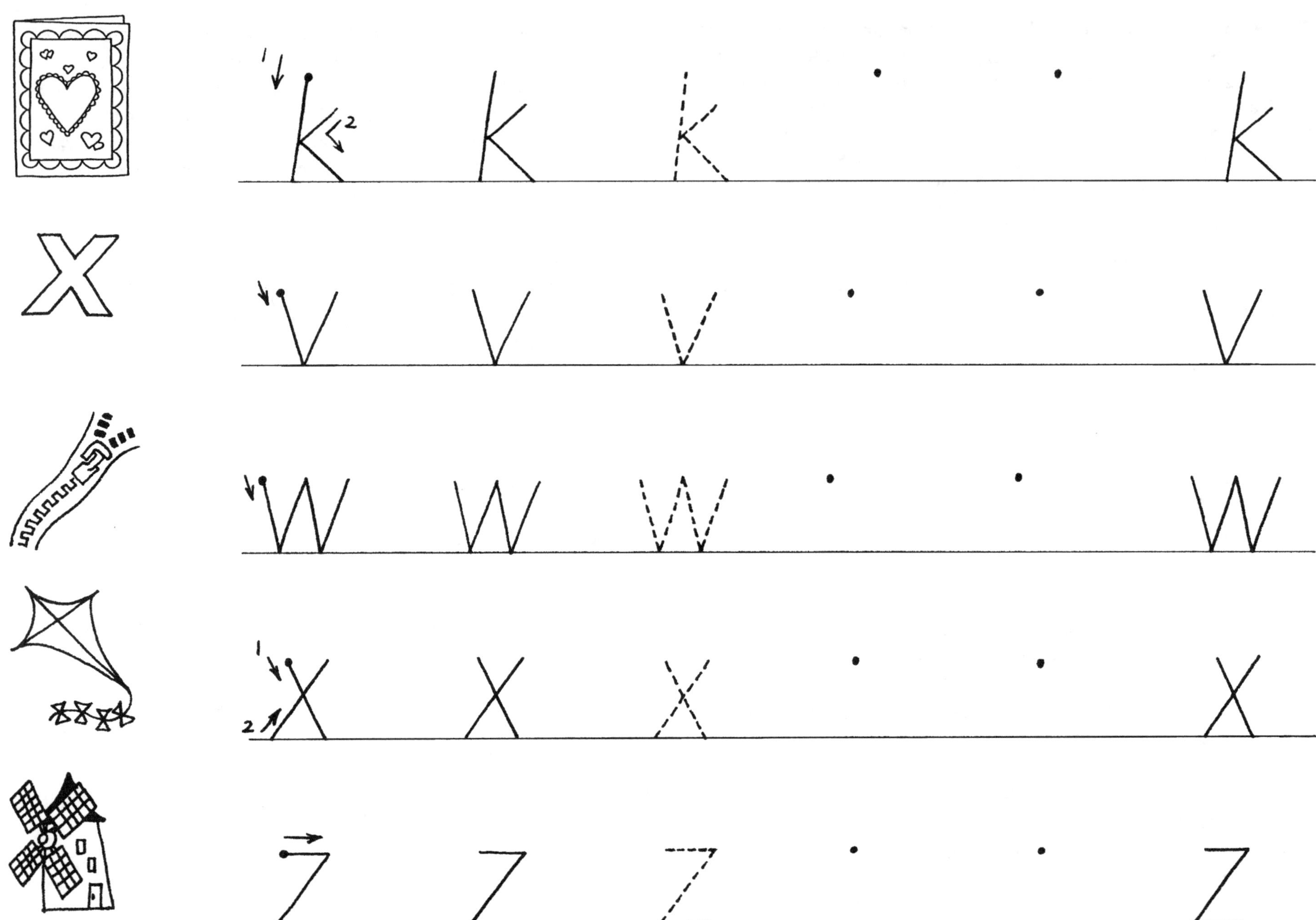

Ask the student to draw a line from the picture to the letter
that stands for the correct beginning sound.

THE BEGINNING WRITER

Learning how to write involves much more than learning to write letters. It is a sophisticated, complex process involving learning letterforms, learning how to space within and between words, and learning how to organize writing on a page. Research indicates that there exists an almost perfect correlation between measures evaluating the children's *awareness* of their fingers and the ability to *use* their fingers in precise manual skills.

Ways to determine manual ability

To assist young students increase awareness of their hands and fingers, and to help you, the teacher, evaluate students' manual skills, have your students perform these tasks:

1. Direct the students to touch each of their fingers to their thumb, in order, from the first to the little finger. (By the age of six years, most children should be able to complete this exercise using one or both hands at a time.)

2. Have the students connect two dots that are spaced approximately eight inches apart on a page. (Most children of five years can accomplish this. However, if the student draws beyond the second dot or draws an unusually shaky line when nearing the second dot, it may indicate potential deficiencies in handwriting skills.)

Ways to improve kinesthetic perception of the hands

1. Unstructured clay modeling facilitates a student's perception of his or her hands. Encourage the student to manipulate the clay in every possible way—squeezing, flattening, poking, making shapes, etc.

2. To heighten the student's perception of shape, use a box in which a variety of small objects are placed for the student to feel but not see.

   a. Ask the student to reach in the box and find an unseen object that matches the one he or she is looking at.

   b. Direct the student to locate in the box an object that you or another student has described.

   c. Ask the student to find two objects with similar characteristics—two fuzzy objects, two heavy objects, two small objects, etc.

3. Draw several circles on a sheet of paper. To determine the student's ability to aim the finger and hand and also to point, have the student place dots in the circles with a pencil, pen, or crayon. Vary the difficulty of this task by increasing or decreasing the size of the circles or increasing the rate at which the dots are made. (The student must be able to point at a given or imaginary point in order to begin the stroke of a letter.)

Ways to confirm hand-eye tracking skills

The ability to control continuous hand movements while drawing lines of varying difficulty is basic to handwriting. If you are able to detect problems as the student completes the following tasks and are able to obtain appropriate assistance for the student, subsequent difficulties may be avoided.

1. Demonstrate drawing parallel lines. Then direct the student to draw parallel lines of a given length, first at a relaxed pace then at a faster one.

2. Direct the student to draw two curved lines equal in distance from one another. Later require more difficult shapes that combine straight lines, angles, and/or curves.

3. Direct the student to connect numbered dots on a sheet of paper that require horizontal, vertical and lateral movements. Place the paper in front of the student, close to the dominant hand. Later, space the dots further apart and require the student to cross the midline of his or her body. This latter task may cause the neurologically challenged student some difficulty.

The above evaluative tasks may be of help in assisting the learning of handwriting and in discovering deficiencies.

(See INSTRUCTION MANUAL, p. 13, for more suggestions concerning the beginning writer.)

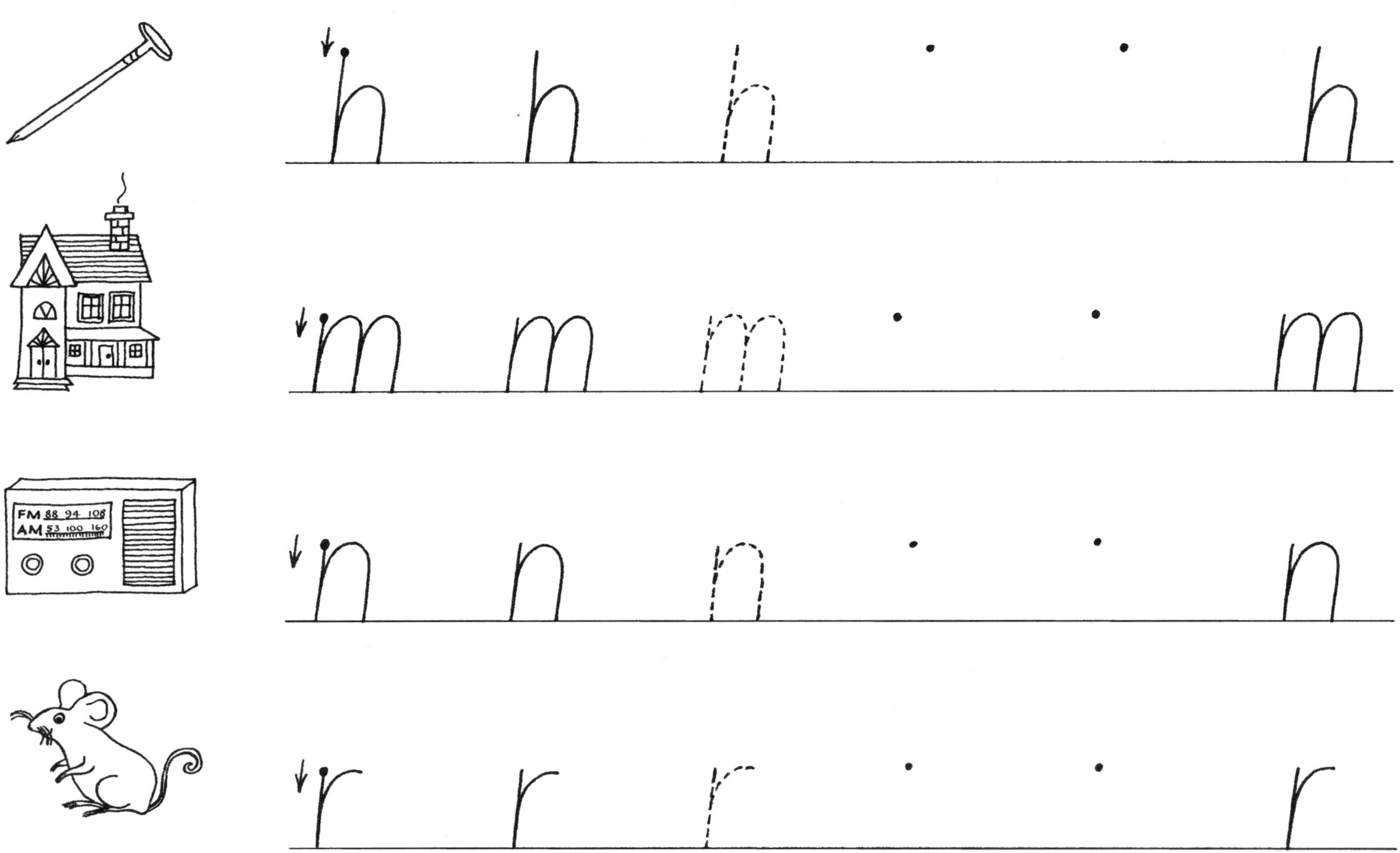

Ask the student to draw a line from the picture to the letter
that stands for the correct beginning sound.

GETTY-DUBAY™ ITALIC HANDWRITING SERIES
BASIC ITALIC ALPHABET

All letters written in one stroke unless otherwise indicated.   *All letters start at the top except lowercase **d** and **e**.*

A a   B b   C c   D d   E e   F f   G g

or

alternate 2-stroke e

H h   I i   J j   K k   L l   M m

or   or

N n   O o   P p   Q q   R r   S s   T t

or   or

U u   V v   W w   X x   Y y   Z z

0 1 2 3 4 5 6 7 8 9

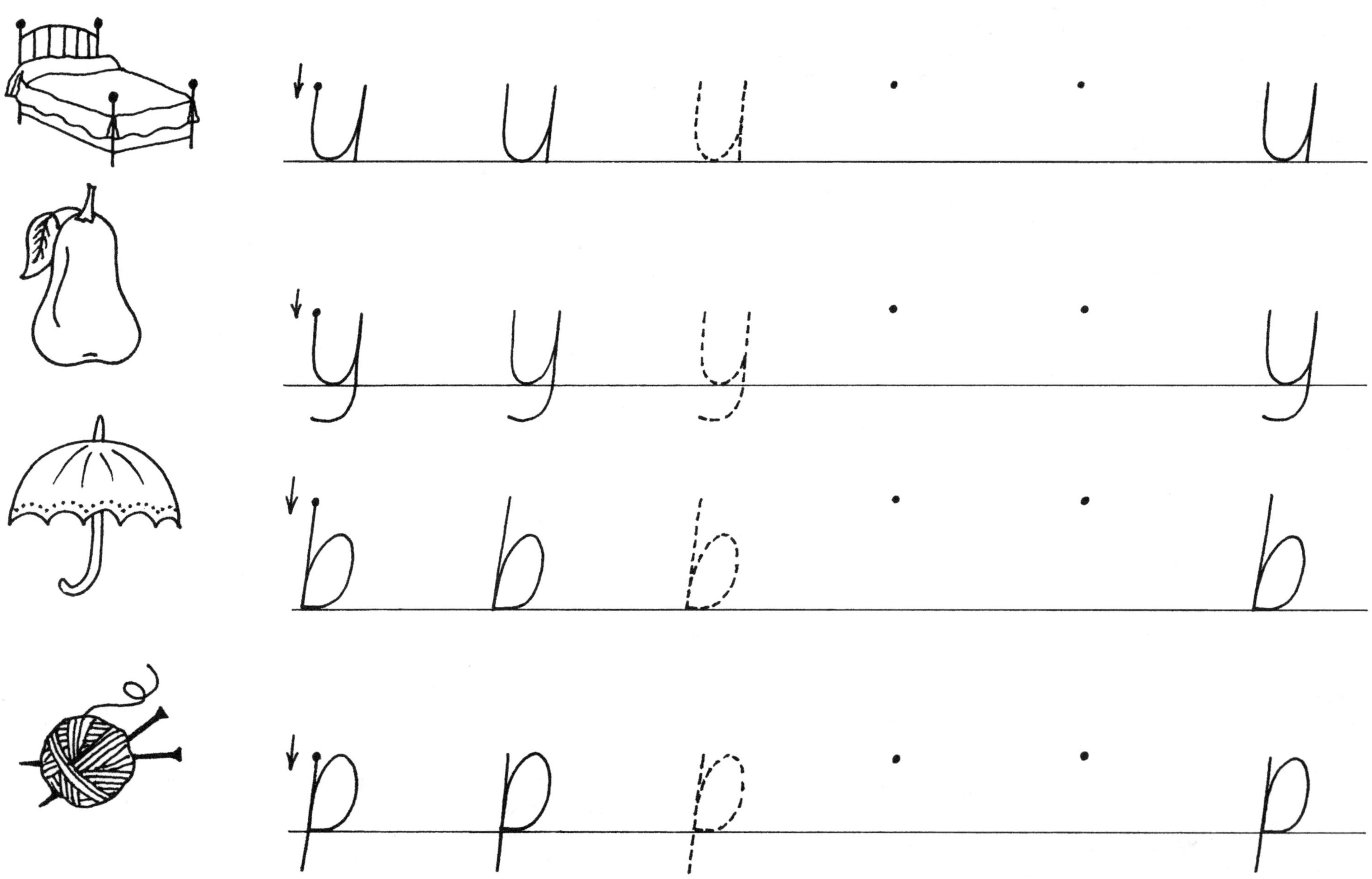

Ask the student to draw a line from the picture to the letter
that stands for the correct beginning sound.

GETTY-DUBAY™ HANDWRITING REMINDERS

PENCIL HOLD

Hold the pencil with the thumb and index finger, resting it on the middle finger. Rest the shaft of the pencil near the large knuckle. Hold the tool firmly and avoid pinching. To relax the hand, tap index finger on the pencil three times. Avoid "thumb wrap" and a "death grip".

PAPER POSITION

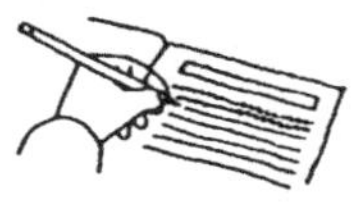

LEFT-HANDED: If the left-handed student writes with the wrist below the writing line, turn paper clockwise so it is slanted to the right, as illustrated.

If the left-handed student writes with a hook, with the wrist above the writing line, turn the paper counter-clockwise so it is slanted to the left, as illustrated. (Similar to right-handed position)

RIGHT-HANDED: If the student is right-handed, turn paper counter-clockwise so it is slanted to the left, as illustrated.

POSTURE

Rest feet flat on the floor and keep back comfortably straight without slumping. Rest forearms on writing surface. The student

holds workbook or paper with the nonwriting hand so that the writing area is centered in the front of the student.

PRACTICE PAPER

Book A—Use unlined or lined paper together with workbooks.

MATERIALS

The *Getty-Dubay™ Italic Handwriting Series* workbooks, BOOKS A-G, and the INSTRUCTION MANUAL constitute a step-by-step program. Related materials consist of:

1. BLACKLINE MASTERS/WORKSHEETS - half sheets for introduction to, or review of, workbook pages.
2. CLASSROOM WALL CHARTS - basic & cursive italic.
3. DESK STRIPS - basic & cursive italic.

VOCABULARY

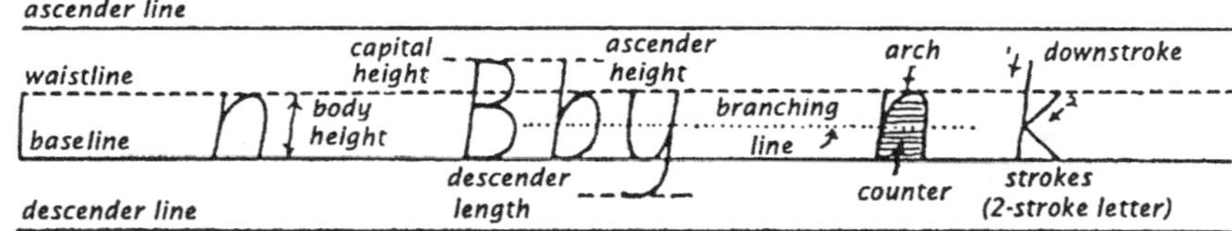

DIRECT INSTRUCTION

Several sessions of direct instruction each week are essential for a successful program. BOOK A – 5 to 10 minute sessions a day are recommended, see INSTRUCTION MANUAL, pp. 18-19

- SHAPE & STROKE SEQUENCE – teach basic italic in letter family groups, or according to the reading program in grade 1.
- SLOPE – encourage a consistent letter slope. Vertical letters (0° slope) may be the easiest to teach to beginning writers.
- SIZE – At first, allow students to write letters any size they wish on unlined paper, then introduce the workbook. A recommended progression through this book is one letter (lowercase and/or capital) per week.

SPACING

When young students are writing words, at first have them leave a space about the width of their two small fingers between words. As they become more proficient, they can leave less space.

ASSESSMENT

The *Getty-Dubay™ Italic Handwriting Series* provides a self-assessment process, LOOK, PLAN, PRACTICE, to enable the student to monitor progress. LOOK, step 1 of this process begins on some of the student pages in BOOK A. Assessment is the key to improving handwriting; in this book we introduce the first of three steps in the LOOK, PLAN, PRACTICE self-assessment process. The students look at their own writing and answer any questions on the page. The pencil indicates the student is to make a written response, generally by circling "yes" or "no". The teacher may encourage students to award themselves a star or a smiling face at the top of the page when they notice self-improvement.

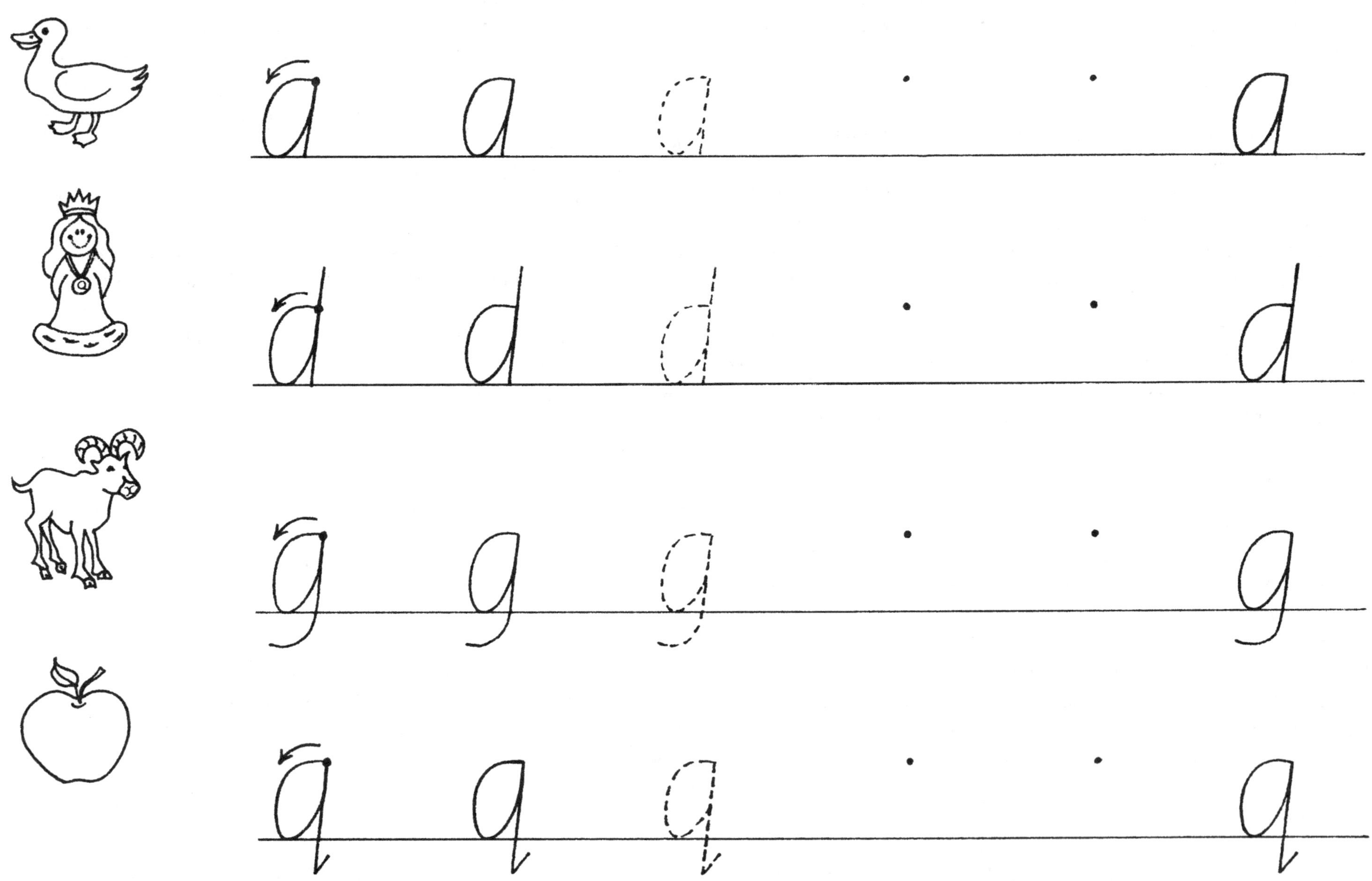

Ask the student to draw a line from the picture to the letter
that stands for the correct beginning sound.

INTRODUCTION

This is the first of seven workbooks providing instruction in basic italic handwriting. It is designed for the beginning student of handwriting and is recommended for preschool, kindergarten and/or early first grade (5 to 7 years of age).

The twenty-six lowercase letters and the twenty-six capitals are introduced one letter per page. Letters are arranged in the order of lowercase families, which group letters with similar strokes together and progress from simple to more complex forms. The matching capital letter occurs on the reverse of each lowercase page allowing introduction of both lowercase and capital together if preferred.

Each page is designed for the student to trace the models provided, write letters at the given dots, and to write a "best" letter in the empty box on each alphabet page. The standard writing tool is the pencil although other writing instruments such as the fiber tip pen may be used. When students are ready, they should trace the word describing the illustration on each letter page, following the dots and arrows.

It is essential that the instructor provide an understanding of the dot and the arrow to assist the writer in completing the pages successfully. The self-assessment method used in the *Getty-Dubay*™ *Italic Handwriting Series* enables students to monitor their individual progress. Step 1, LOOK, of the three-step LOOK, PLAN, PRACTICE format, is incorporated on 21 of the student pages. Students are asked to "LOOK" at their writing and affirm what is best. On the 21 pages with "LOOK" questions, students should circle their chosen answers. See INSTRUCTION MANUAL, PP. 13, 18 & 19.

The *Getty-Dubay*™ *Italic Handwriting Series* INSTRUCTION MANUAL is to be used in conjunction with this workbook. Explanations and in-depth descriptions of lowercase letters, capitals, joins, and numerals are presented in the manual, emphasizing shape, strokes, size, slope and spacing of the letters. Also included in the manual are: a rationale for italic handwriting, techniques for teaching and assessing handwriting, sequence of skills, handwriting activities, and a brief history of our alphabet.

BOOK B, basic italic, follows this workbook and is designed for the beginning reader. In the third book, BOOK C, basic italic letterforms are reinforced and cursive italic is introduced. BOOKS D, E, F, and G provide a complete basic italic and cursive italic handwriting program. BOOKS B, C, and/or D may also be suitable for the person learning English as a second language.

The format of this book was chosen to accommodate both the left- and right-handed writer. When open, the book fits easily on a small desk, and the writer is not encumbered with an additional page to the left or right. From day one, use a Getty-Dubay™ basic italic desk strip as a reminder. Blackline masters are designed for supplementary practice and are available for each workbook in the series. See www.handwritingsuccess.com for these supplementary materials.

You can guide children toward the challenge and delight in the writing process by reading to them, modeling handwriting, providing writing materials, and especially by building enthusiasm for the letters of our alphabet and for the written word.

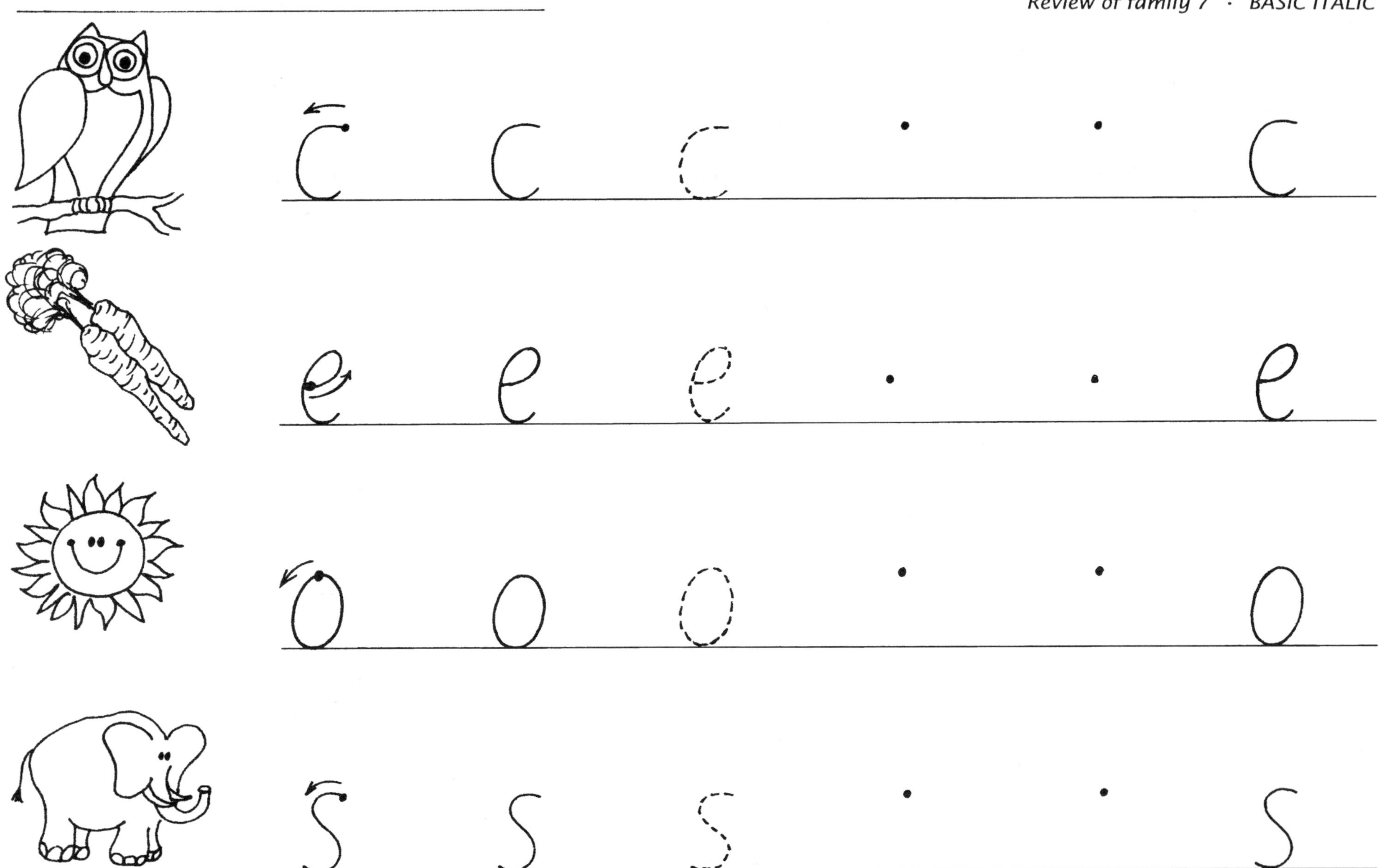

Ask the student to draw a line from the picture to the letter
that stands for the correct beginning sound.

CONTENTS

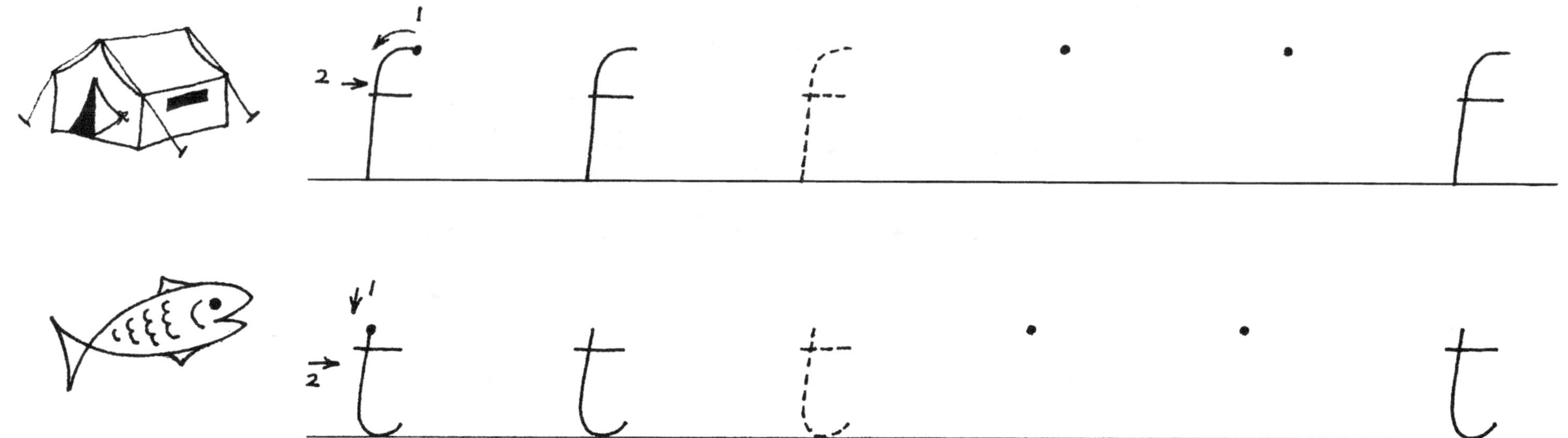

b c l

m k y

s n e

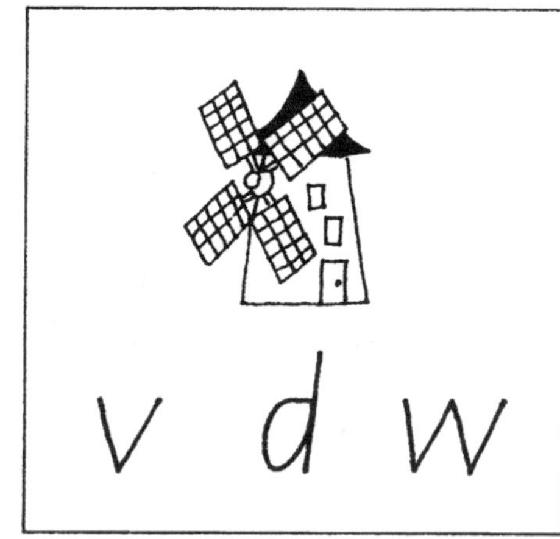

v d w

TOP TWO LINES: Ask the student to draw a line from the picture to the letter that stands for the correct beginning sound.

BOTTOM FOUR SQUARES: Ask the student to circle the letter that stands for the beginning sound of the picture.

by

Barbara Getty & Inga Dubay

GETTY-DUBAY™ ITALIC HANDWRITING SERIES

BOOK A ▪ Basic Italic
14 mm body height

BOOK B ▪ Basic Italic
11 mm body height, 9 mm

BOOK C ▪ Basic & Cursive Italic
9 mm, 6 mm body height   Introduction to Cursive Italic

BOOK D ▪ Basic & Cursive Italic
6 mm, 5 mm body height

BOOK E ▪ Basic & Cursive Italic
6 mm, 5 mm, 4 mm body height

BOOK F ▪ Basic & Cursive Italic
6 mm, 5 mm, 4 mm body height

BOOK G ▪ Basic & Cursive Italic
5 mm, 4 mm body height

INSTRUCTION MANUAL

BOOK A ▪ INTERNATIONAL EDITION
Copyright 2012 by Barbara M. Getty and Inga S. Dubay
ISBN 978-0-9827762-7-8

FOURTH EDITION
Copyright 2012 by Barbara M. Getty and Inga S. Dubay
THIRD EDITION
Copyright 1999 by Barbara M. Getty and Inga S. Dubay
SECOND EDITION
Copyright 1986 by Barbara M. Getty and Inga S. Dubay
REVISED EDITION
Copyright 1980 by Barbara M. Getty and Inga S. Dubay
FIRST EDITION
Copyright 1979 by Barbara M. Getty and Inga S. Dubay

All rights reserved. This text may not be reproduced in whole or in part without the express written permission of the copyright holder.

Published by Handwriting Success, LLC,
Portland, Oregon USA

www.handwritingsuccess.com

Printed at various locations around the world by IngramSpark.

Cover Design: Sinda Markham
Front cover picture: Flowers of the sunflower family in the Ochoco National Forest, Oregon, USA
Back cover pictures: Columbine flower, Golden-mantled squirrel

www.ingramcontent.com/pod-product-compliance
Lightning Source LLC
Chambersburg PA
CBHW081423210726
48464CB00020B/1370

one stroke numeral · no lift

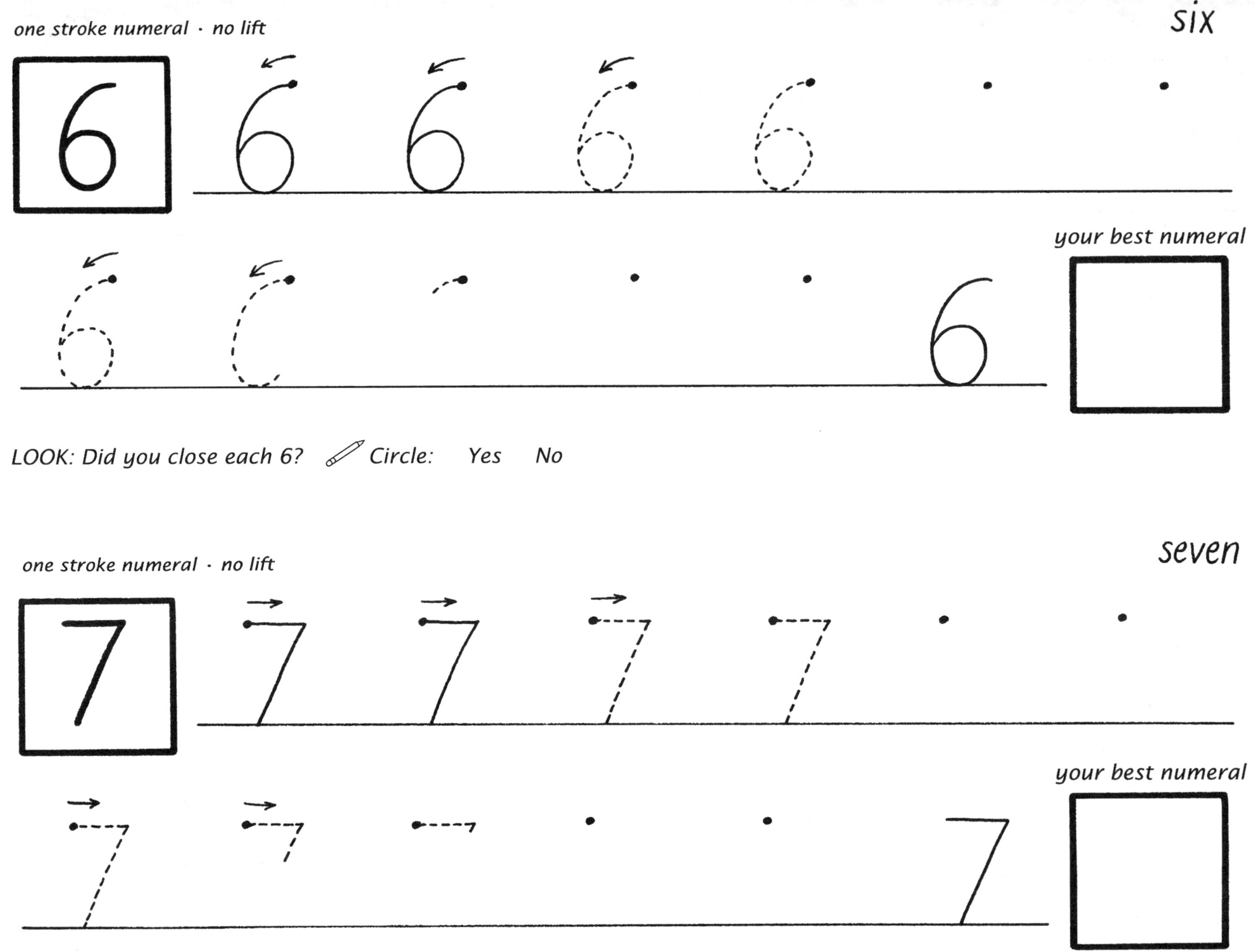

your best numeral

LOOK: Did you close each 6?　Circle:　Yes　No

one stroke numeral · no lift

your best numeral

four

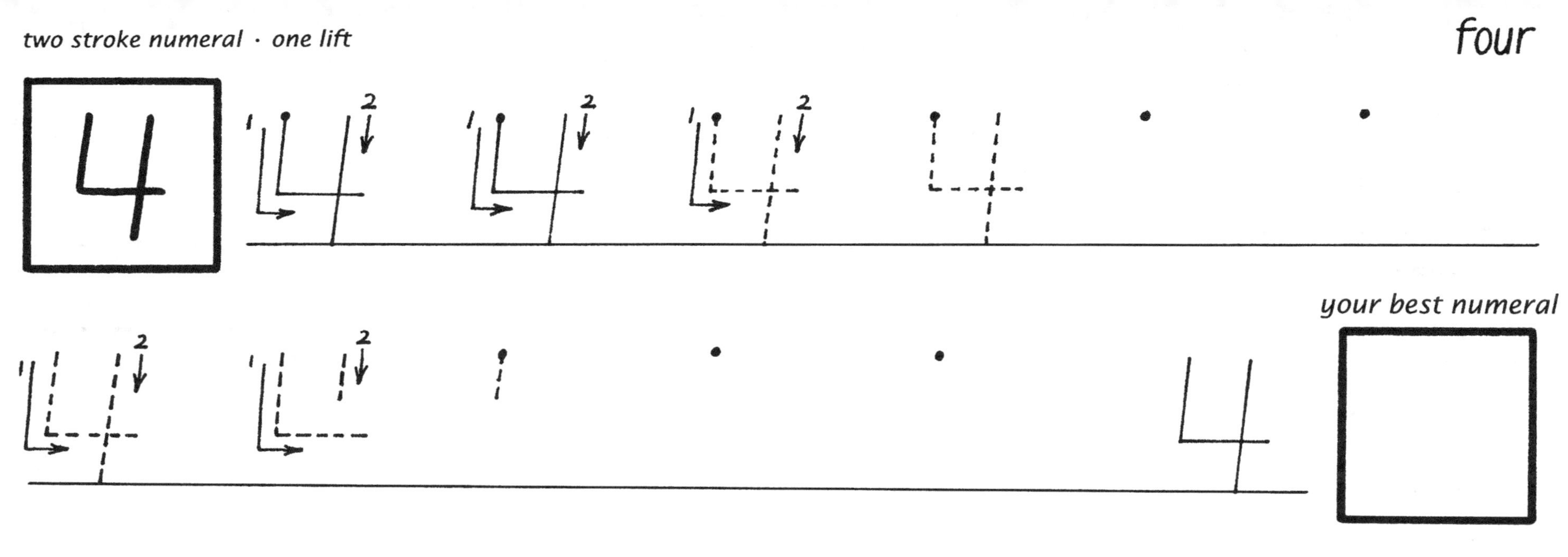

your best numeral

five

your best numeral

one stroke numeral · no lift

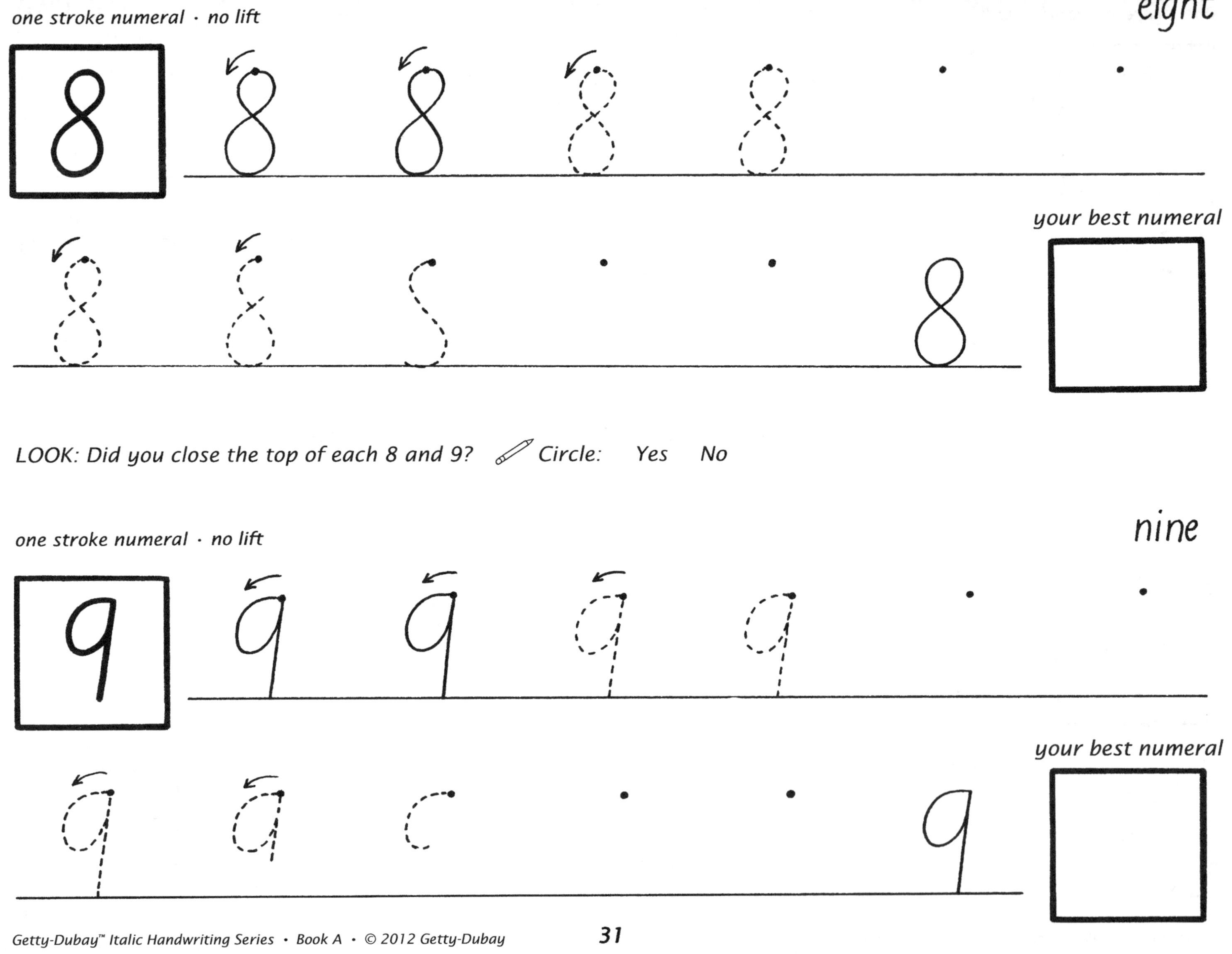

your best numeral

LOOK: Did you close the top of each 8 and 9? Circle: Yes   No

one stroke numeral · no lift

nine

your best numeral

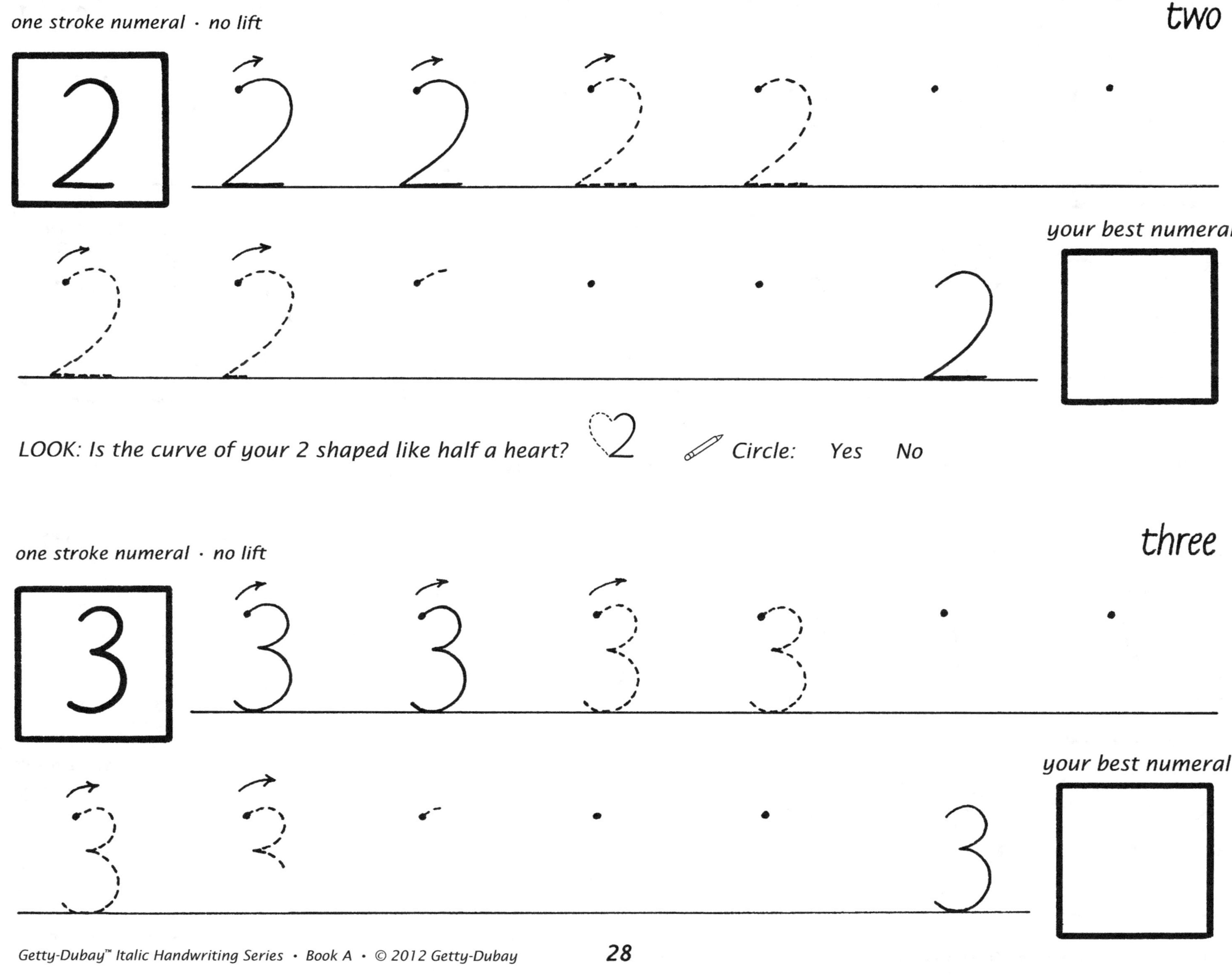

one stroke numeral · no lift
two
your best numeral
LOOK: Is the curve of your 2 shaped like half a heart?   Circle: Yes   No
one stroke numeral · no lift
three
your best numeral

6 3 1

9 2 5

7 0 4

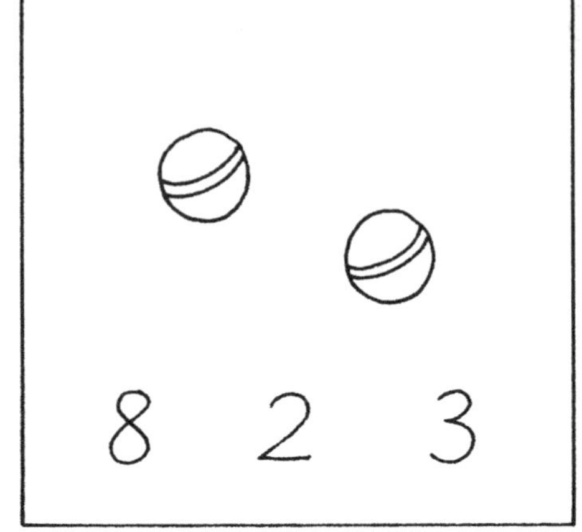

8 2 3

3 4 2

9 5 6

7 1 6

2 8 6

Ask the student to circle the numeral
that stands for the number of objects in the box.

zero

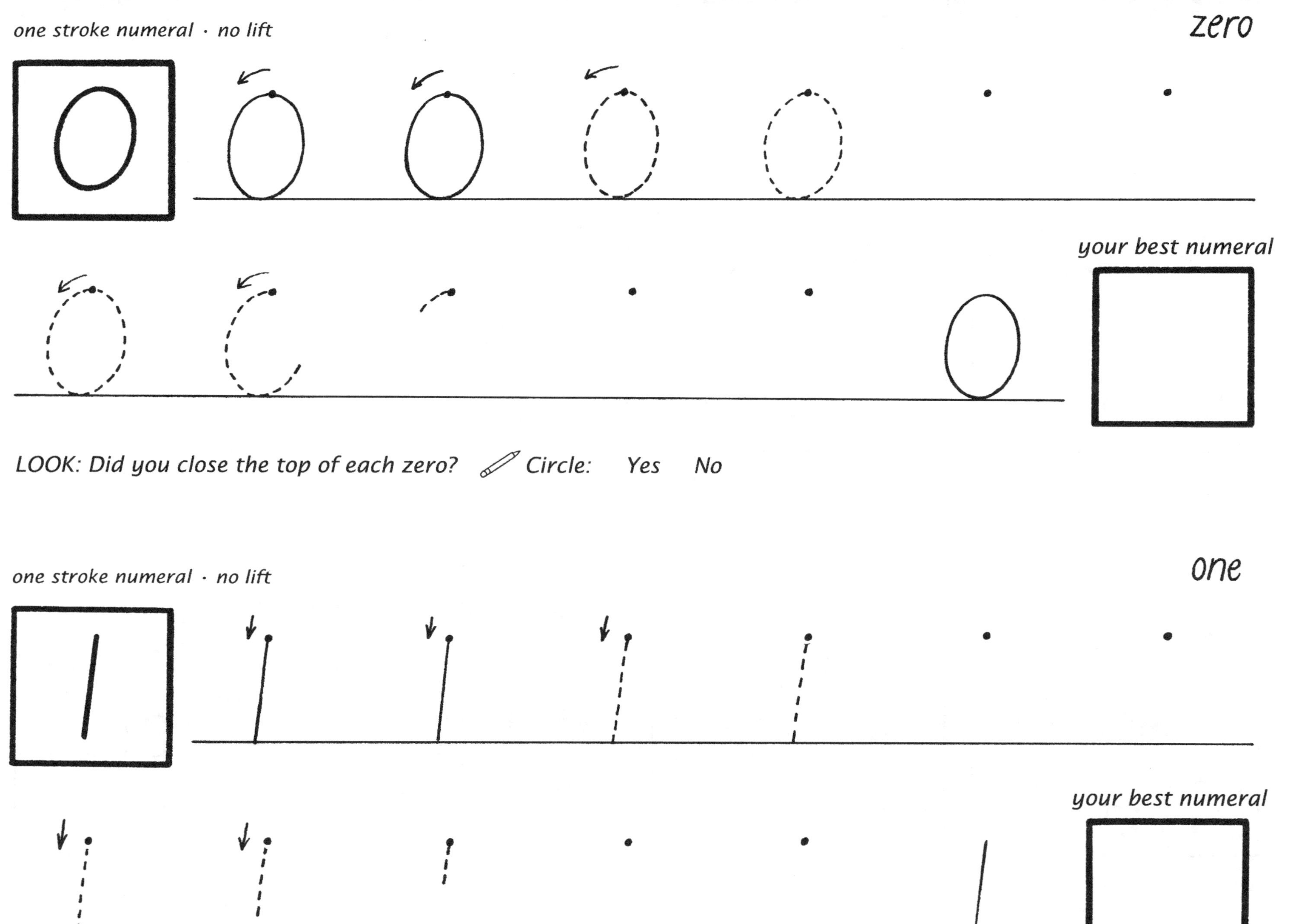

LOOK: Did you close the top of each zero?   Circle: Yes   No

one stroke numeral · no lift

one

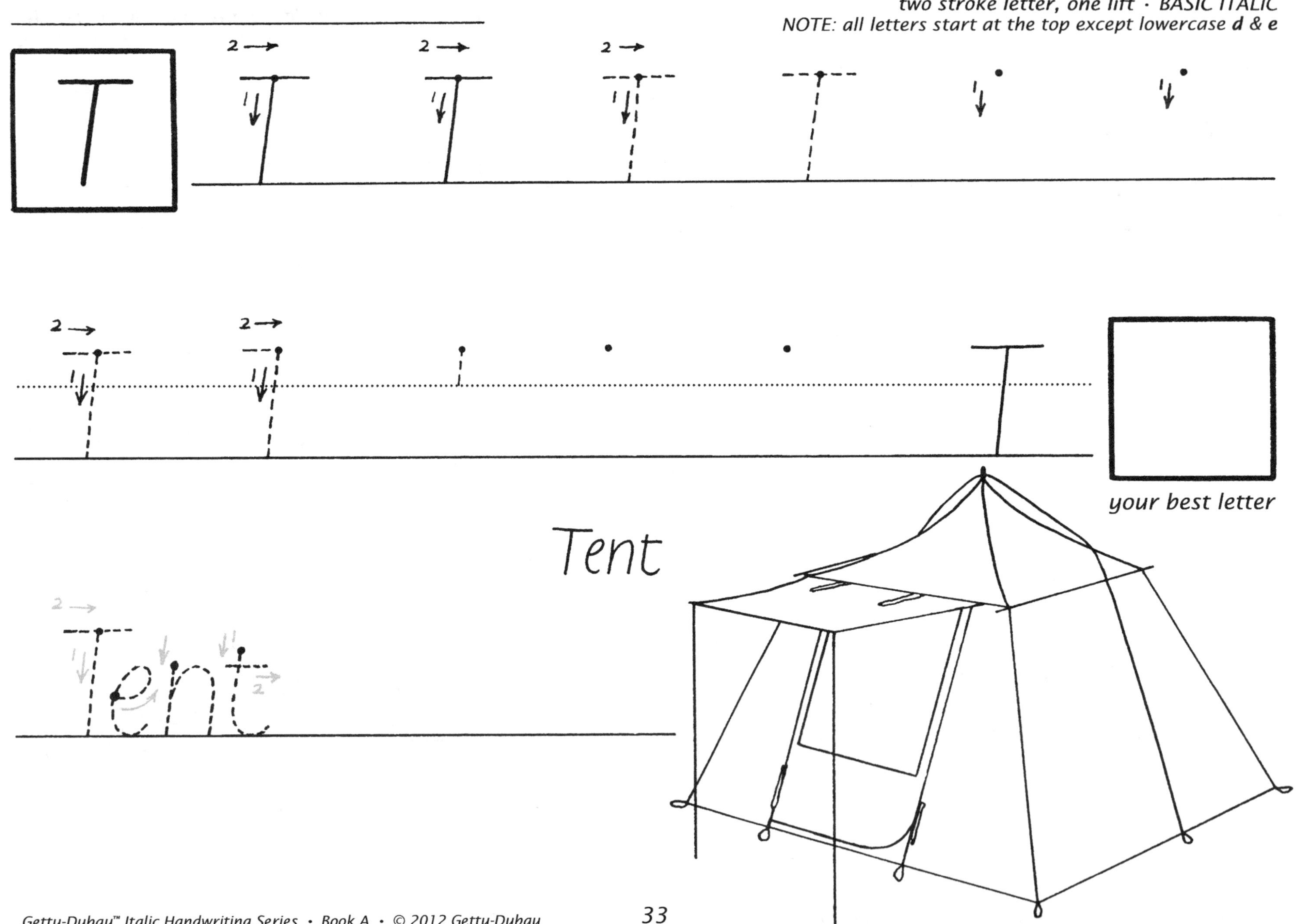

T
2
2
2
2
your best letter
Tent
Tent

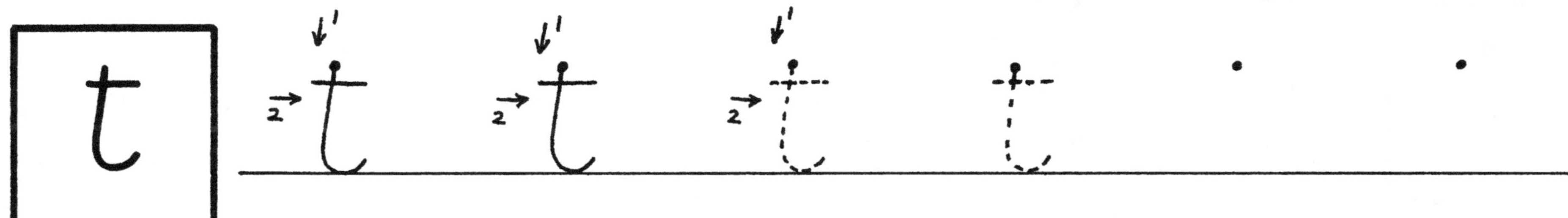

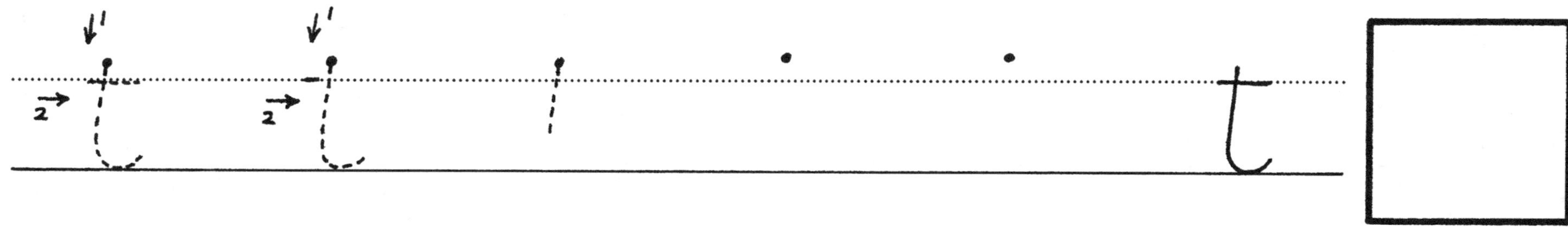

your best letter

turkey

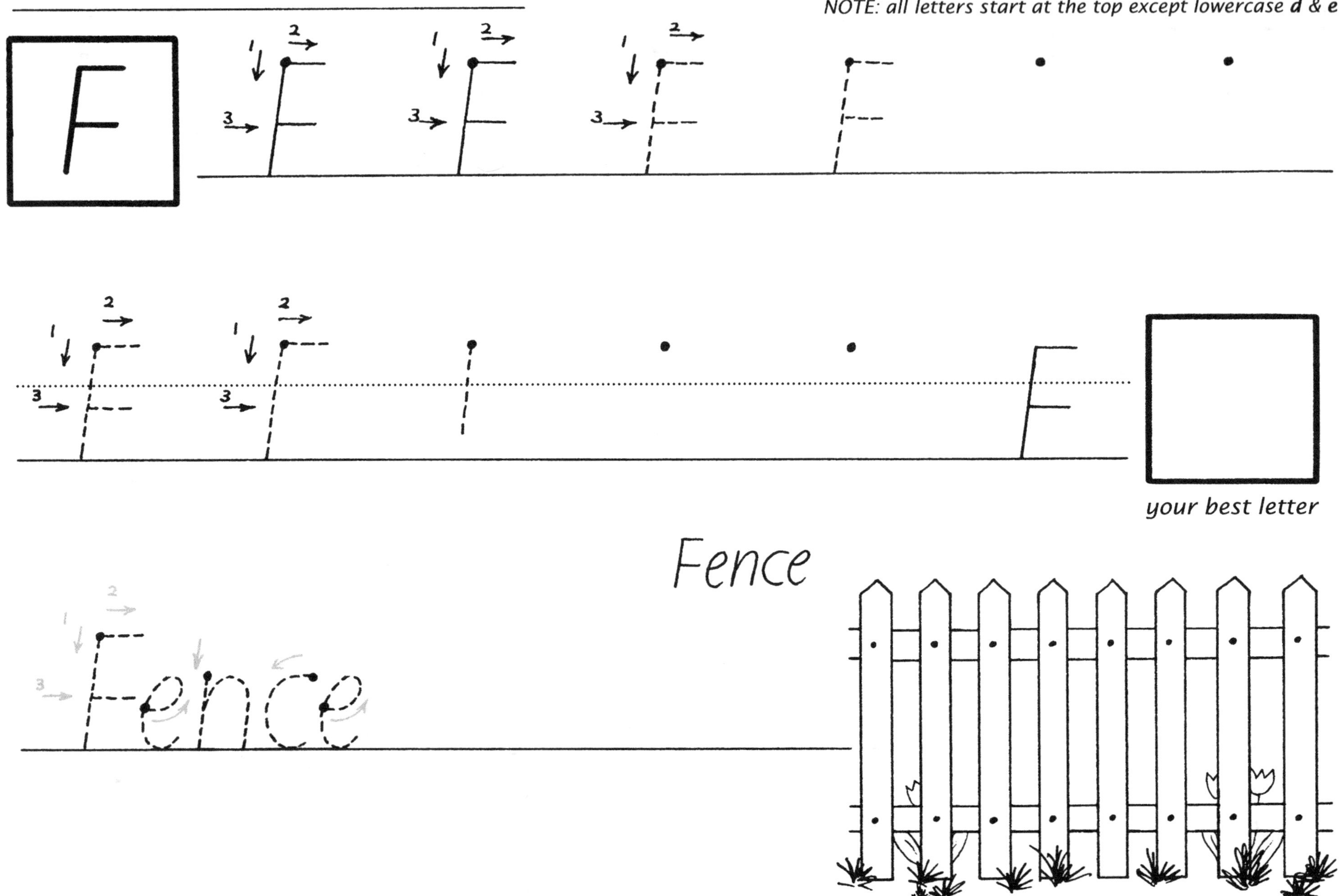

F
your best letter
Fence

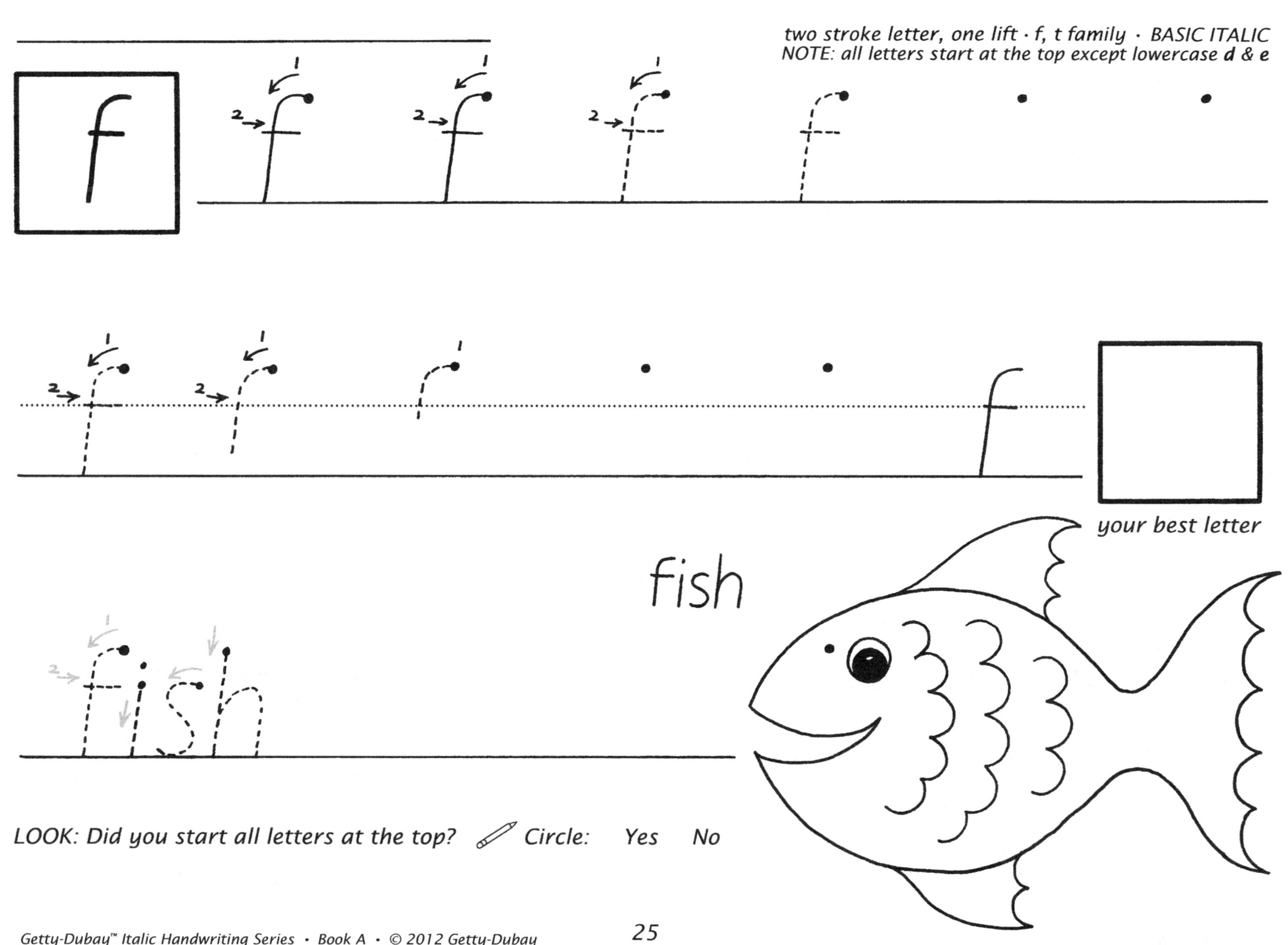

two stroke letter, one lift · f, t family · BASIC ITALIC
NOTE: all letters start at the top except lowercase d & e
f
your best letter
fish
fish
LOOK: Did you start all letters at the top?   Circle: Yes   No

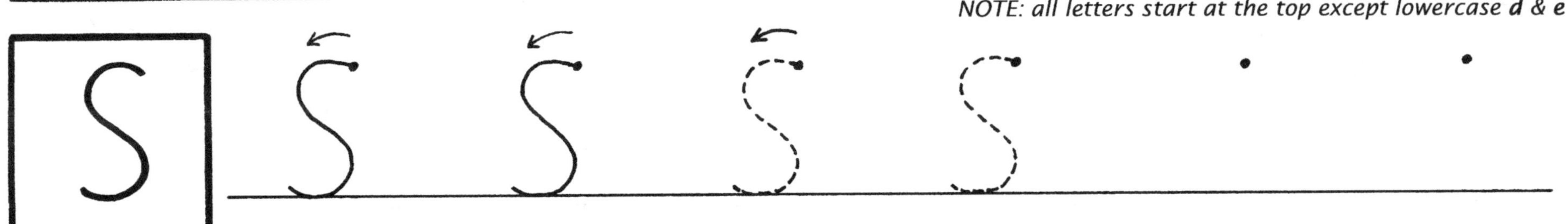

your best letter

Sailboat

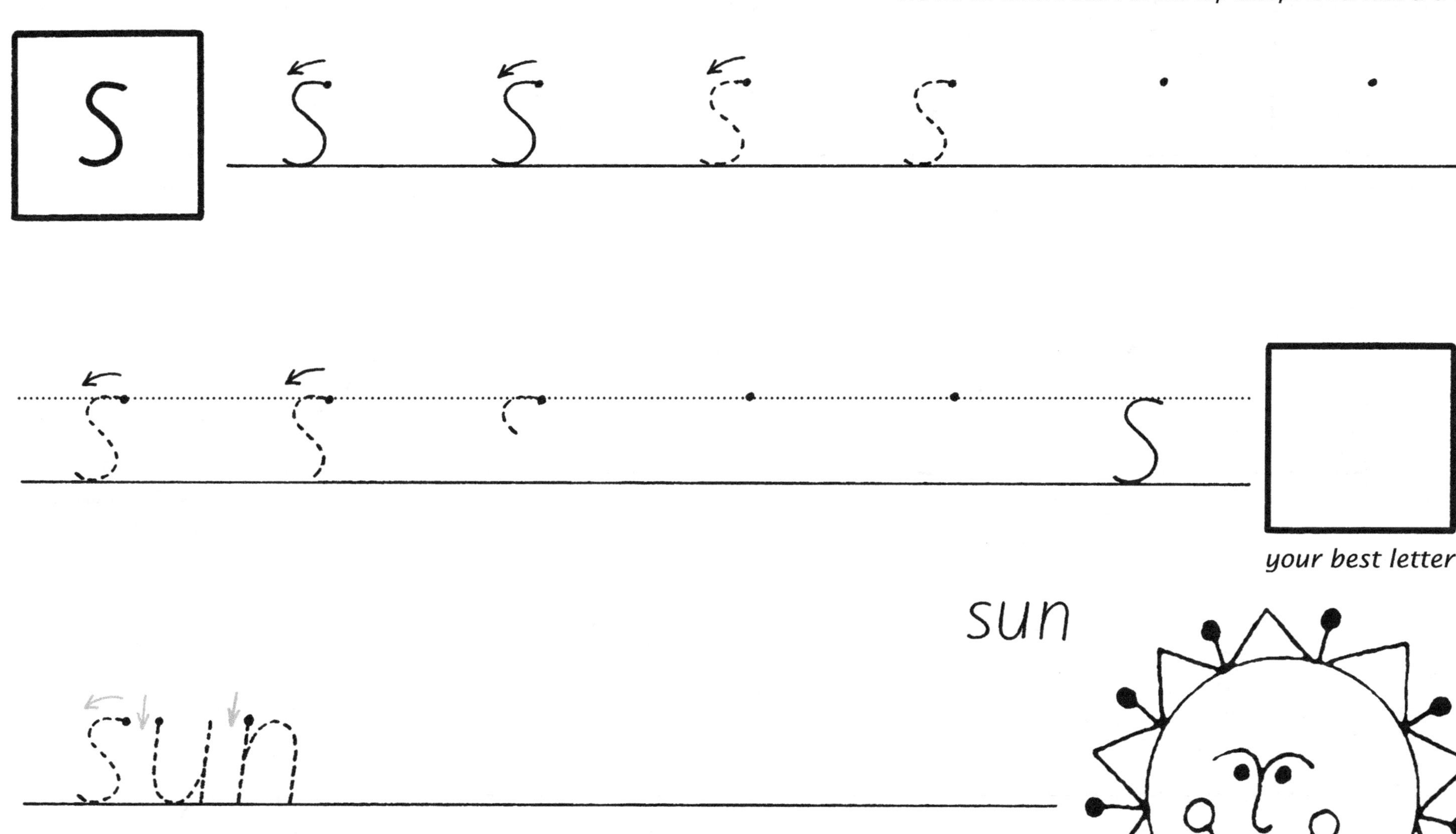

your best letter

sun

your best letter

Cow

LOOK: Did you trace each letter before writing your own?

Circle: Yes   No

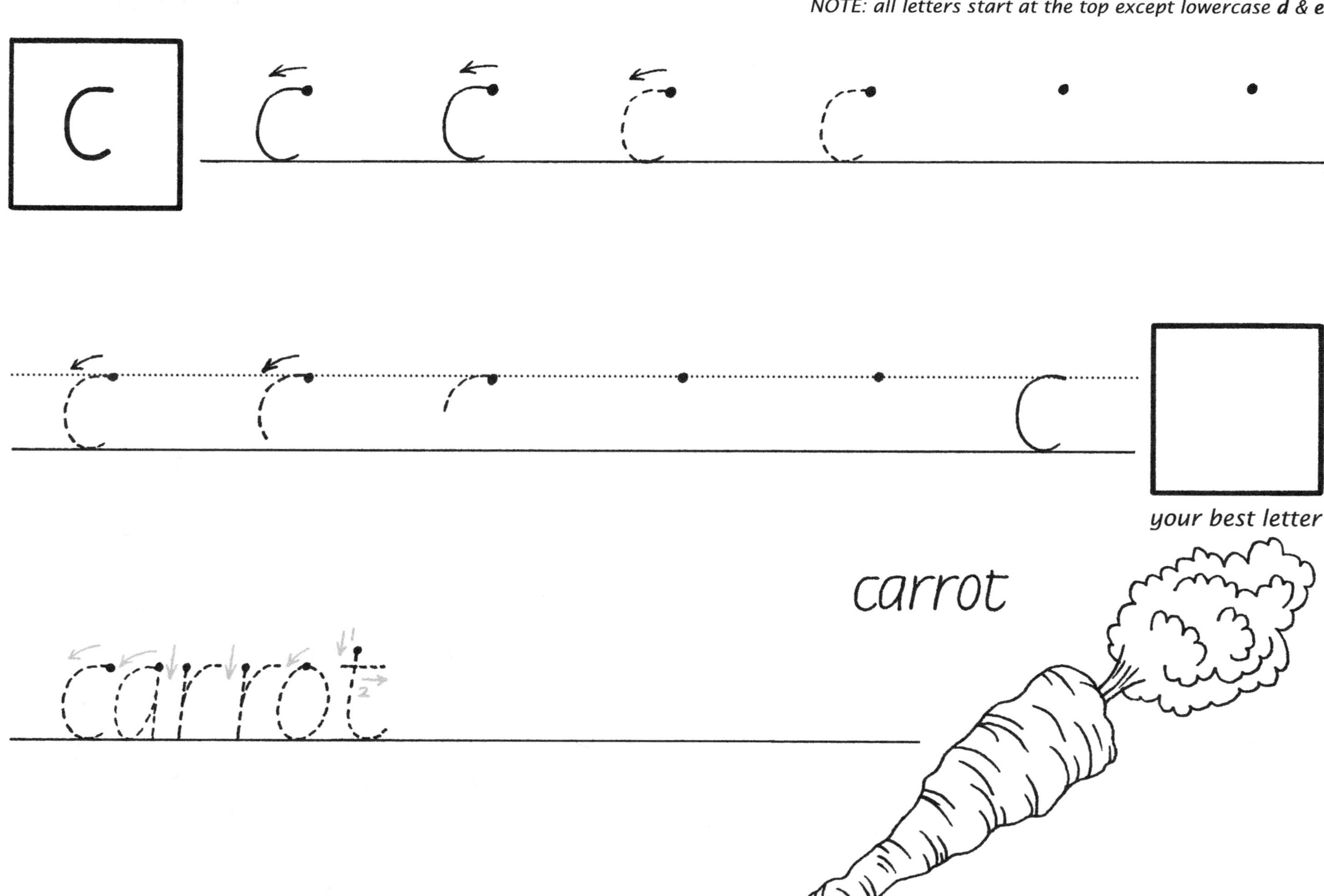

C
your best letter
carrot
carrot

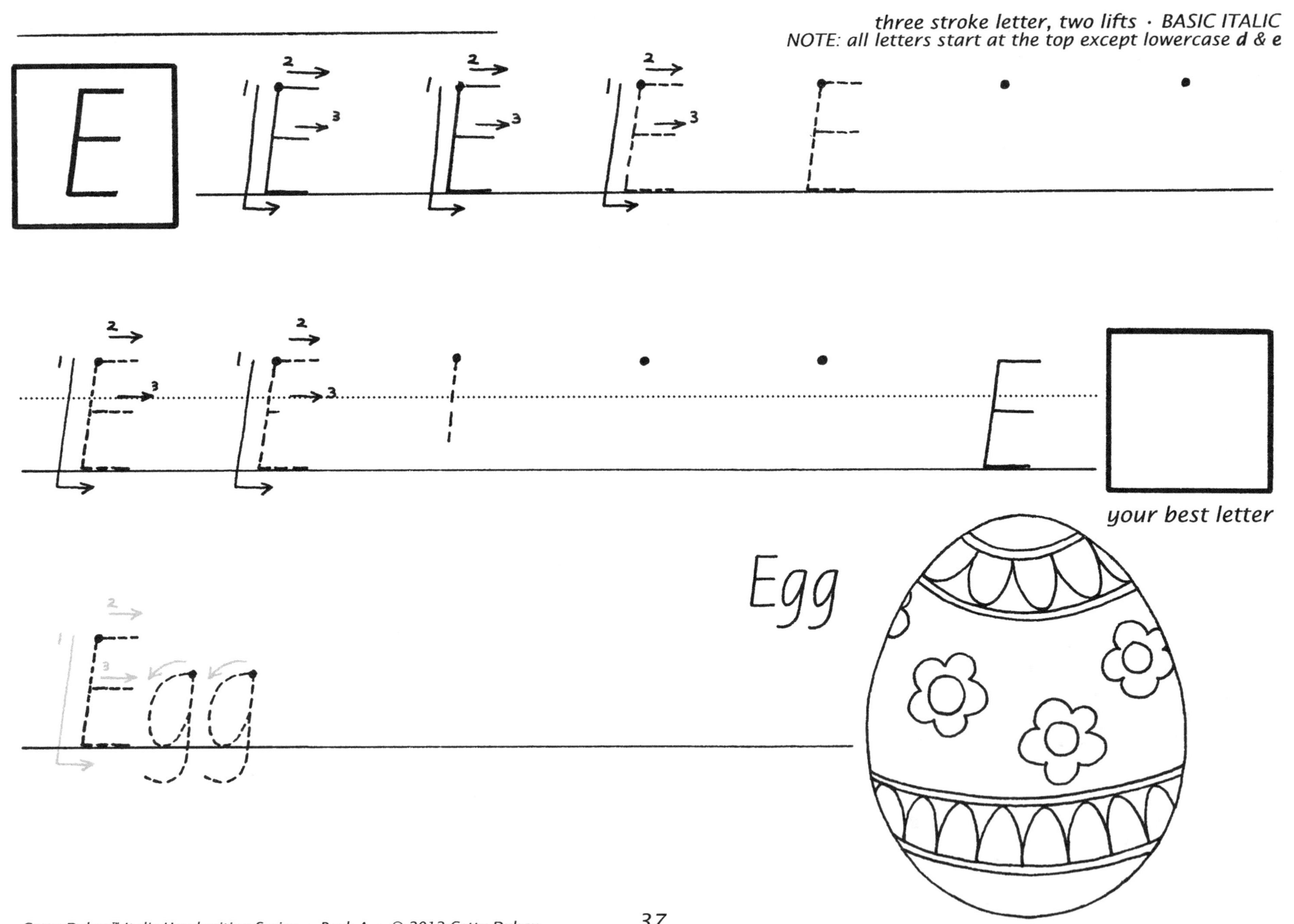

your best letter

Egg

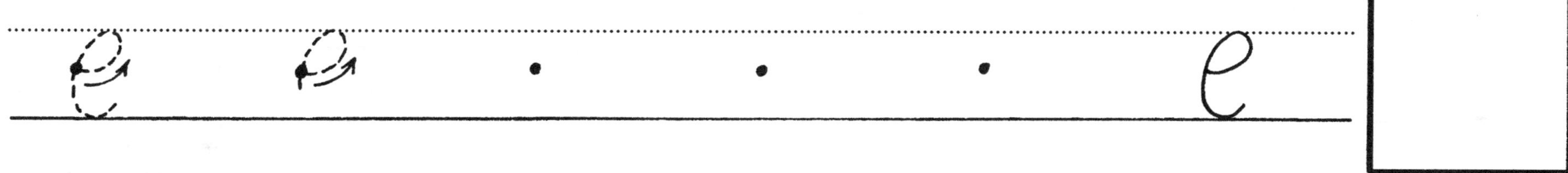

your best letter

elephant

LOOK: Did you trace each **e** before writing your own?

Circle: Yes   No

your best letter

Octagon

LOOK: Did you close the top of each **O**? ✐ Circle: Yes No

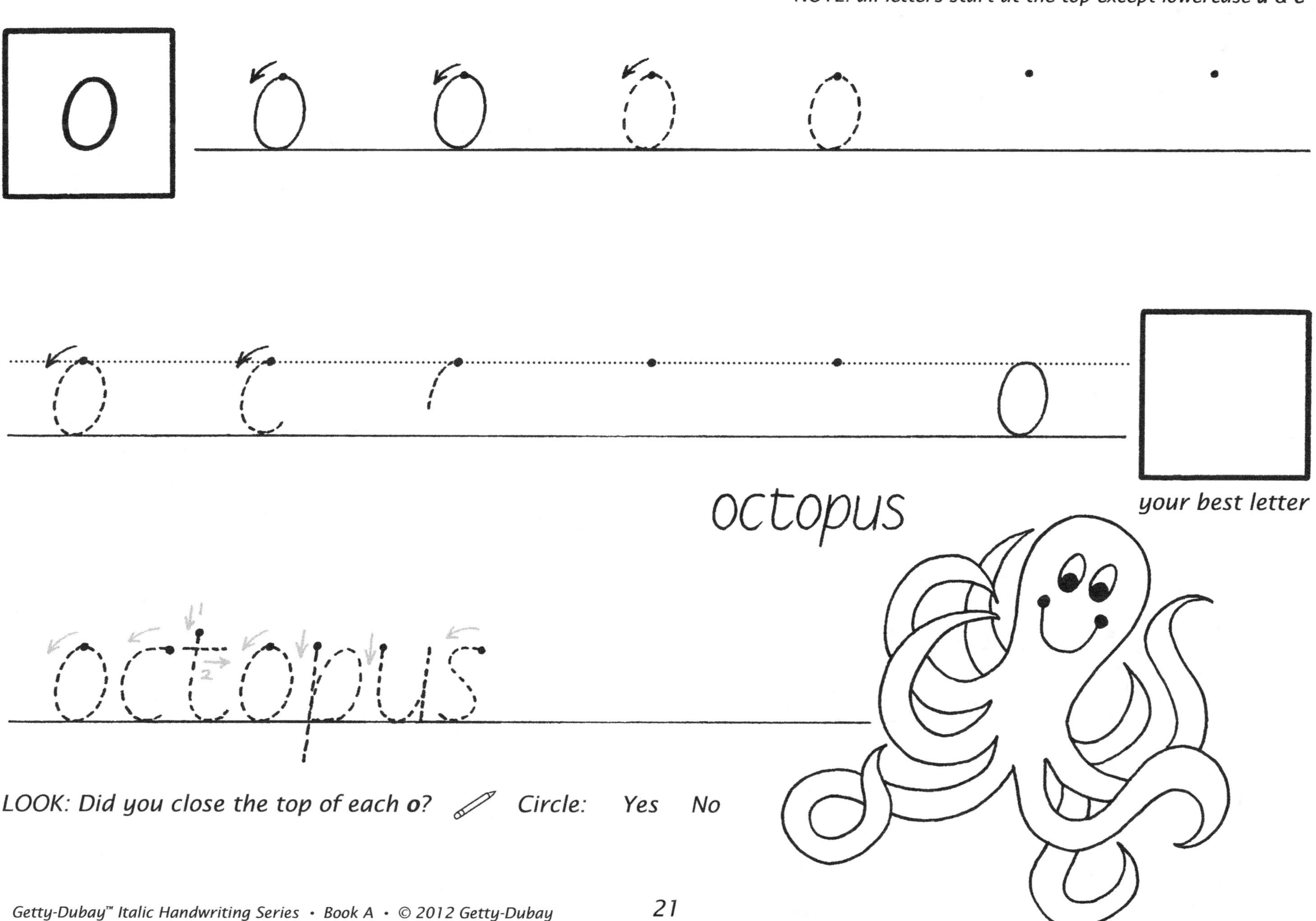

octopus

your best letter

LOOK: Did you close the top of each **o**? Circle: Yes No

P

your best letter

Peacock

Peacock

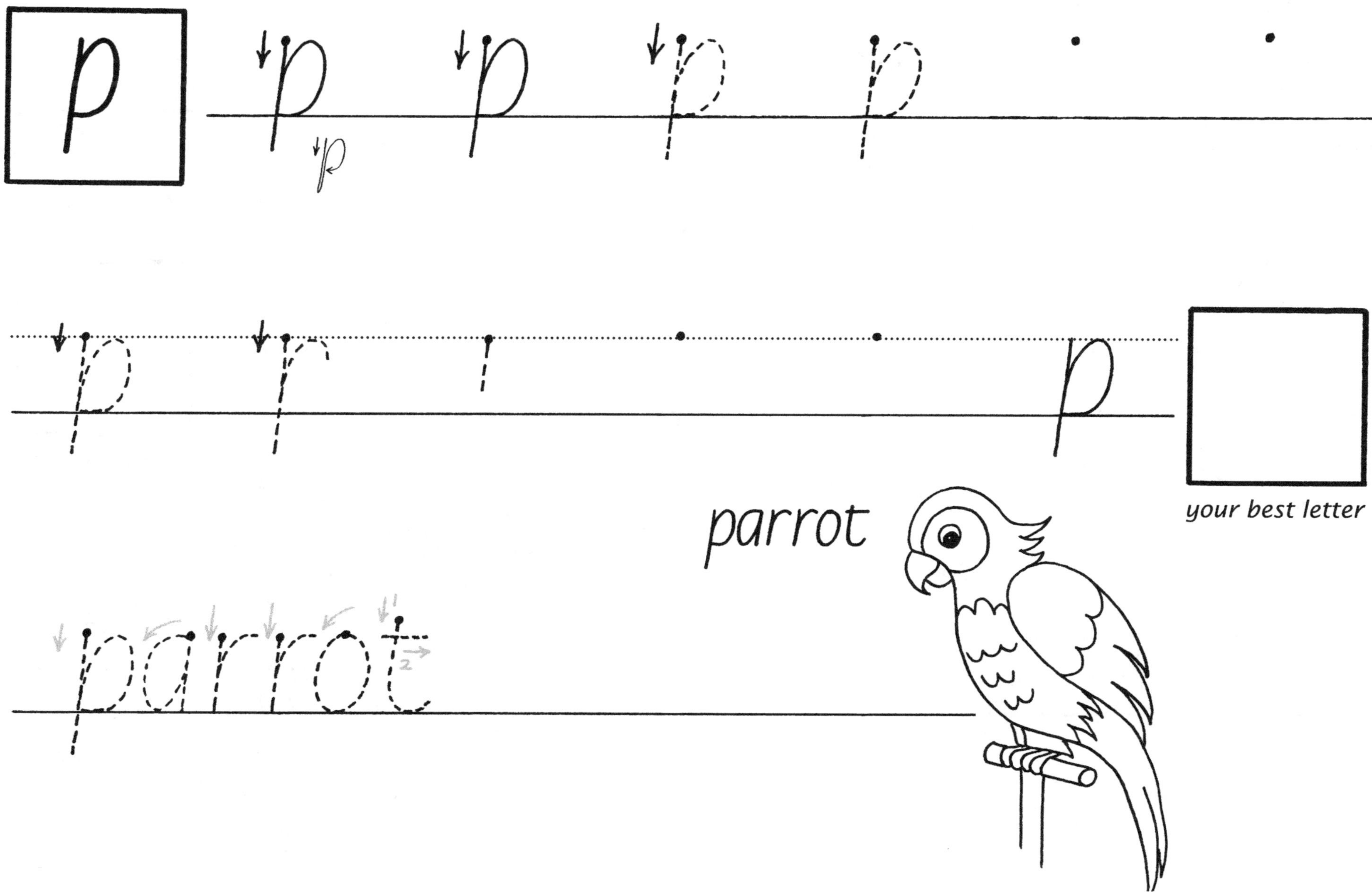

parrot

Balloons

your best letter

your best letter

butterfly

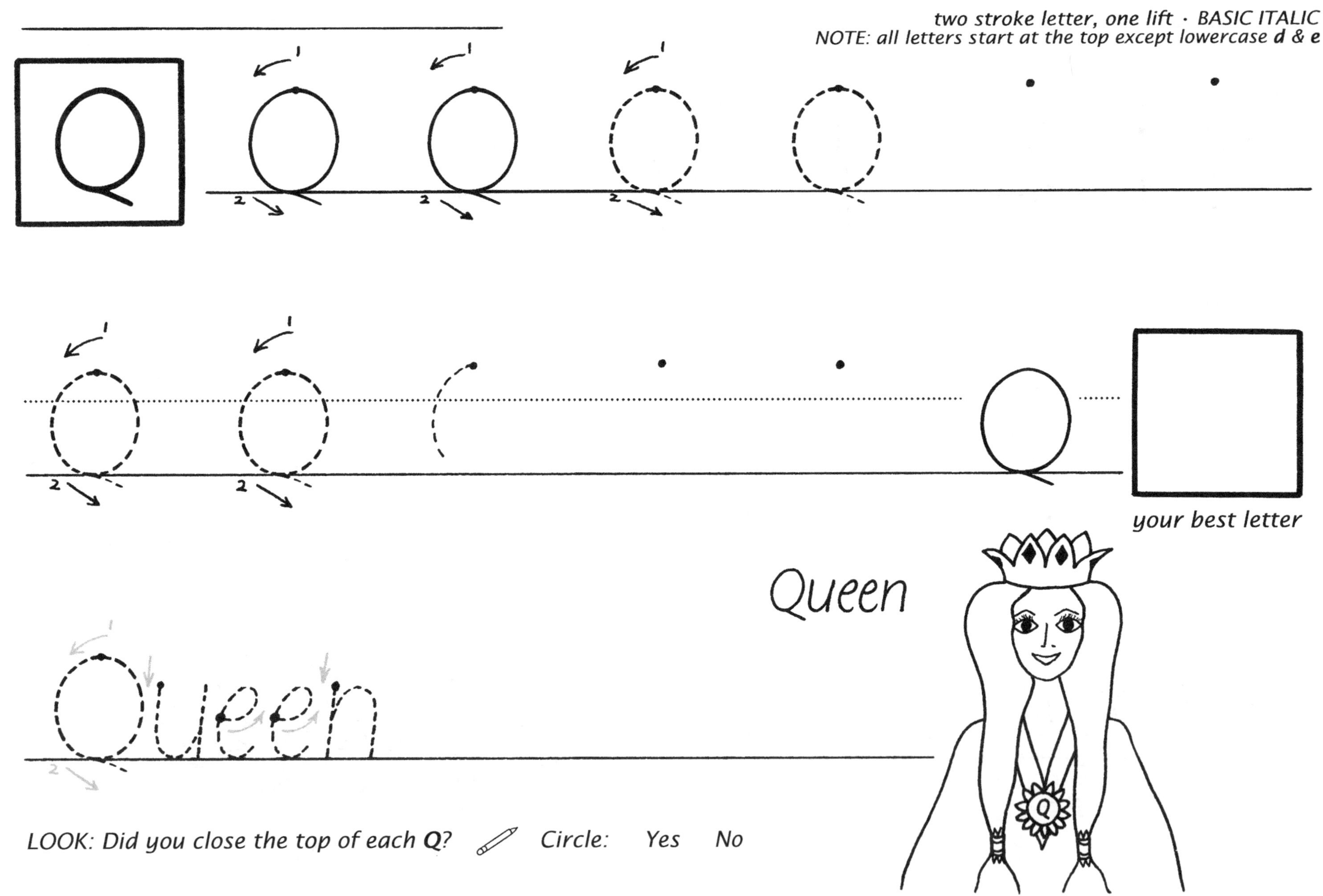

your best letter

Queen

LOOK: Did you close the top of each Q?   Circle: Yes   No

q

quilt

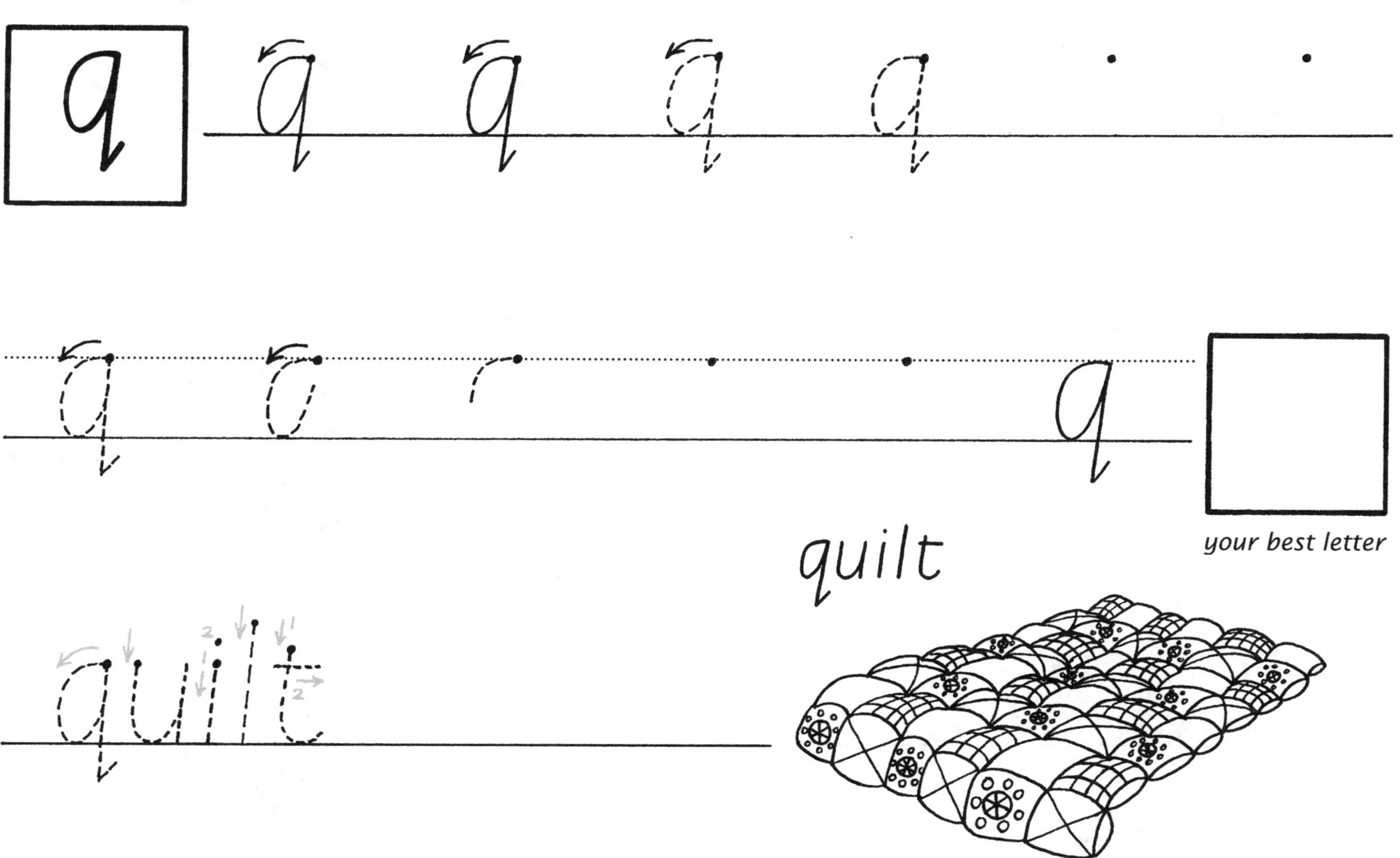

your best letter

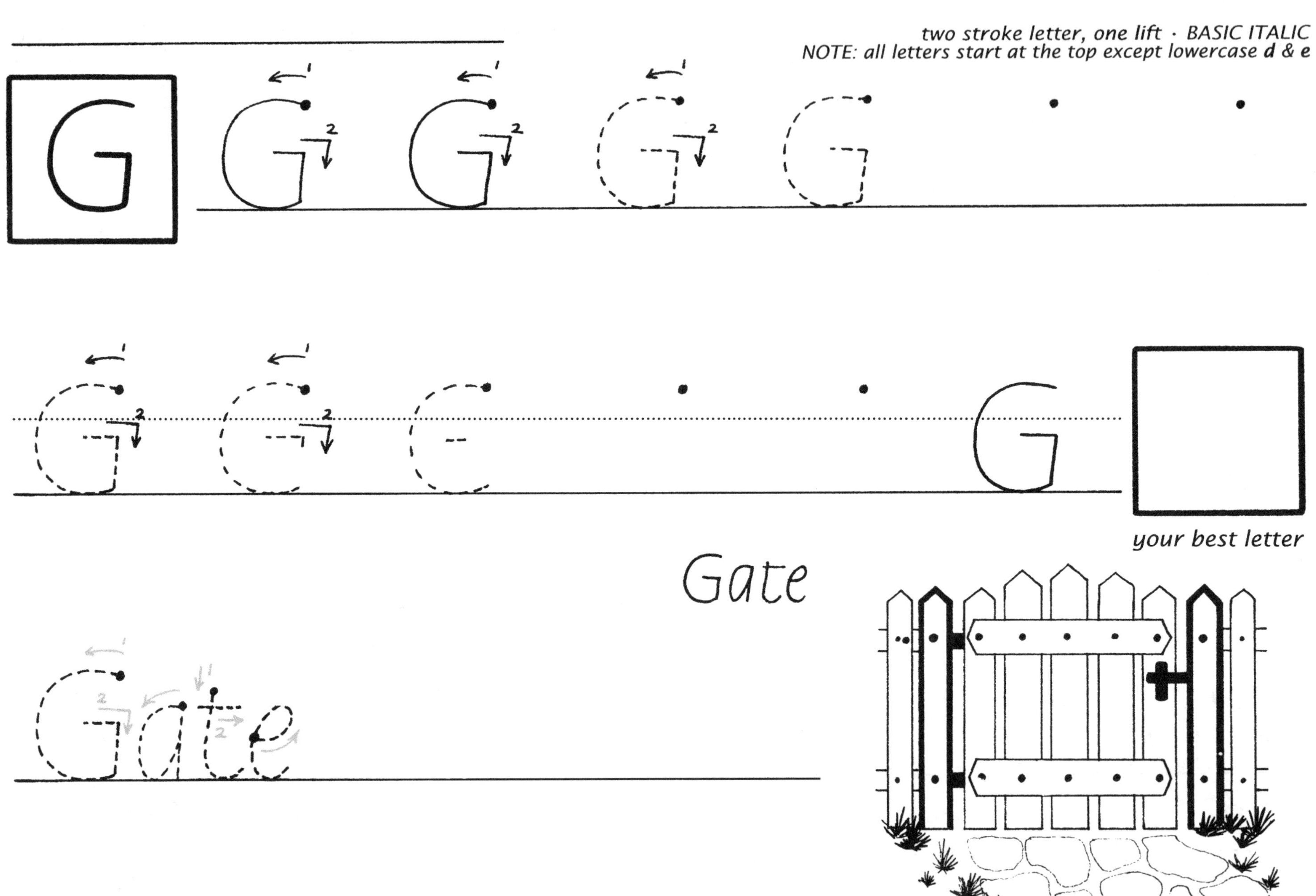

your best letter

Gate

your best letter

goat

LOOK: Did you trace each letter before writing your own? Circle: Yes   No

Dinosaur
your best letter
Dinosaur

your best letter

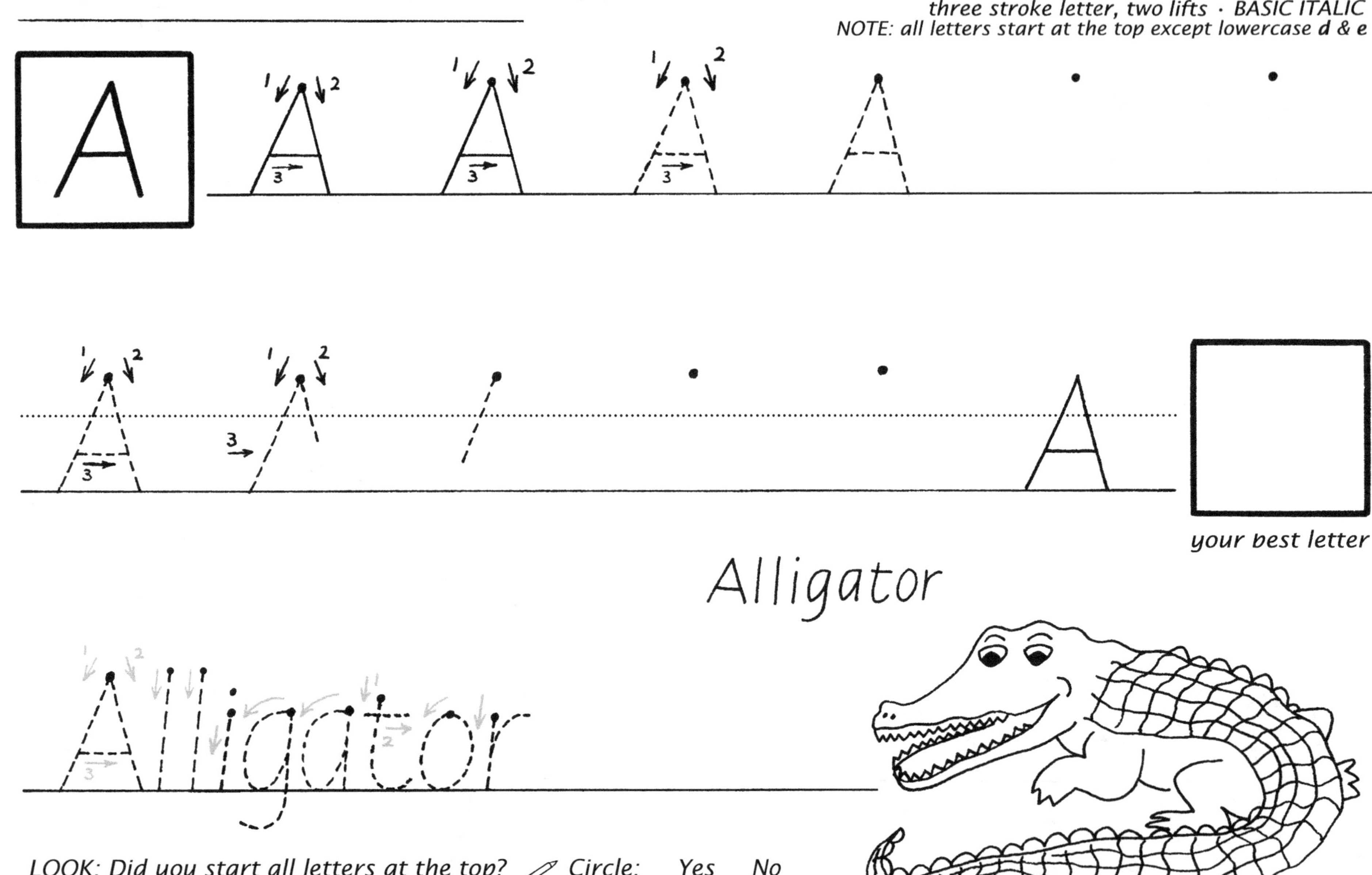

your best letter

Alligator

LOOK: Did you start all letters at the top? Circle: Yes   No

your best letter

apple

LOOK: Did you close each **a** at the top? Circle: Yes No

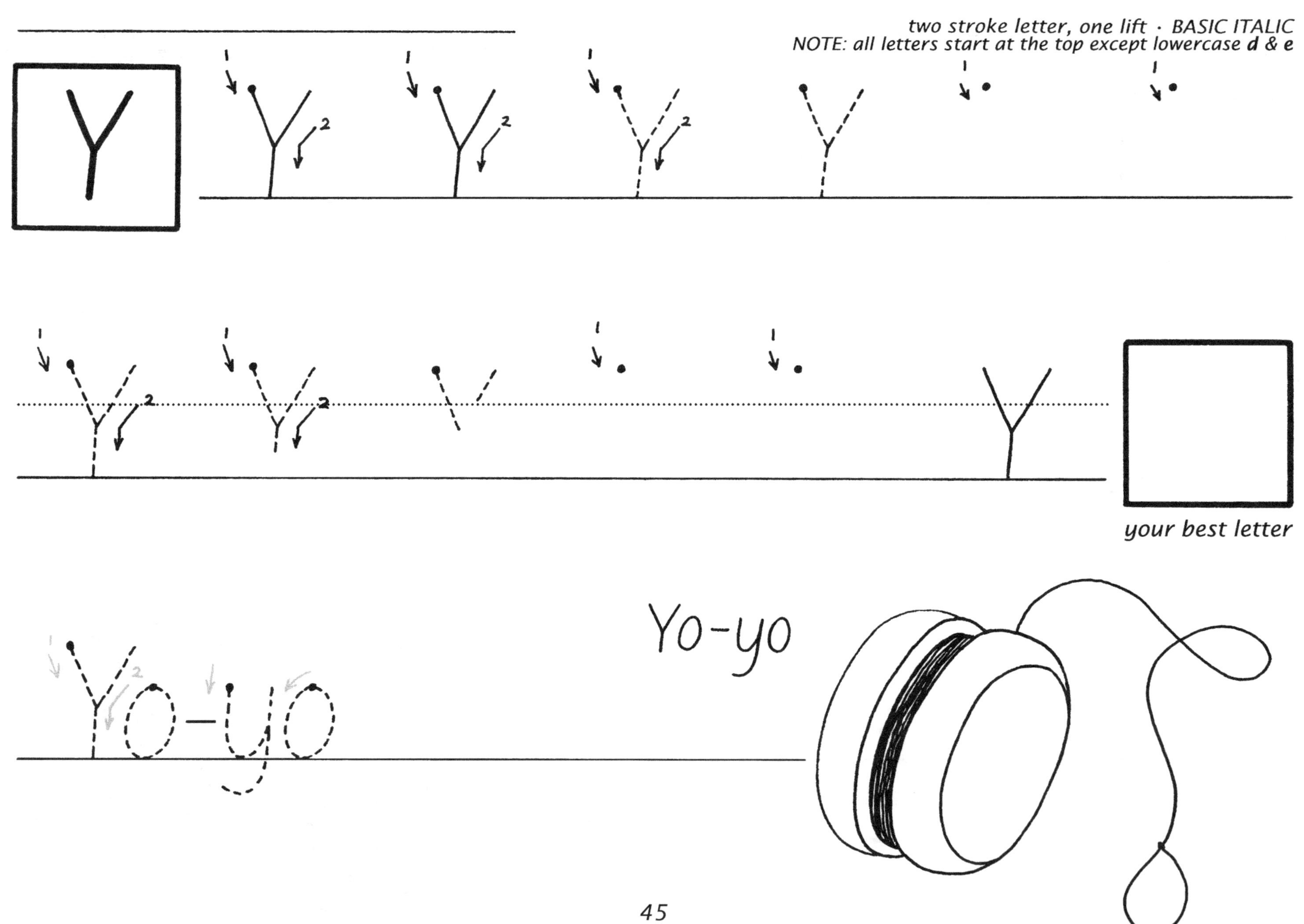

Getty-Dubay™ Italic Handwriting Series · Book A · © 2012 Getty-Dubay

your best letter

yarn

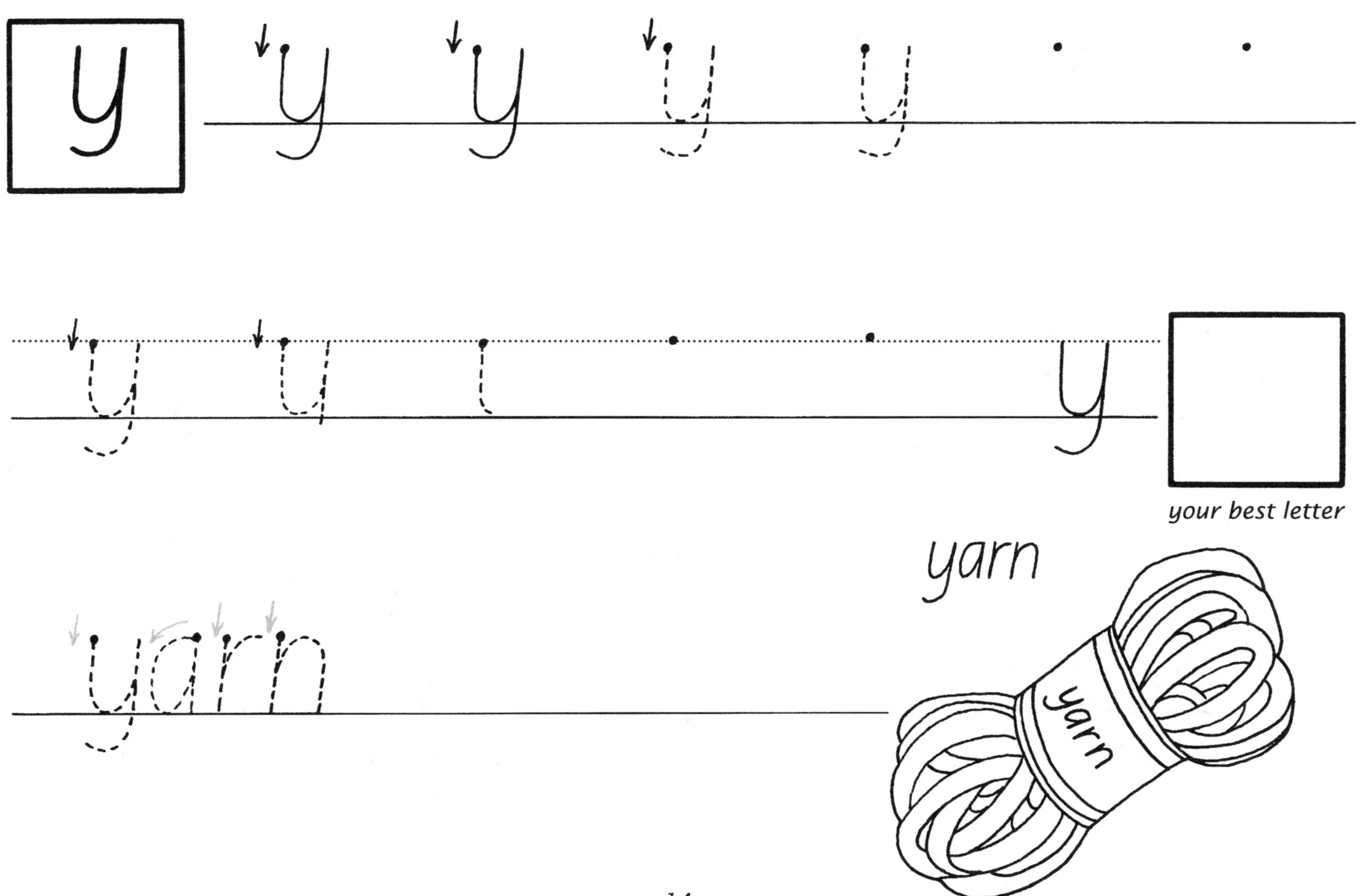

your best letter

Ukulele

LOOK: Did you trace each letter before writing your own?

Circle: Yes   No

u
your best letter
umbrella
umbrella

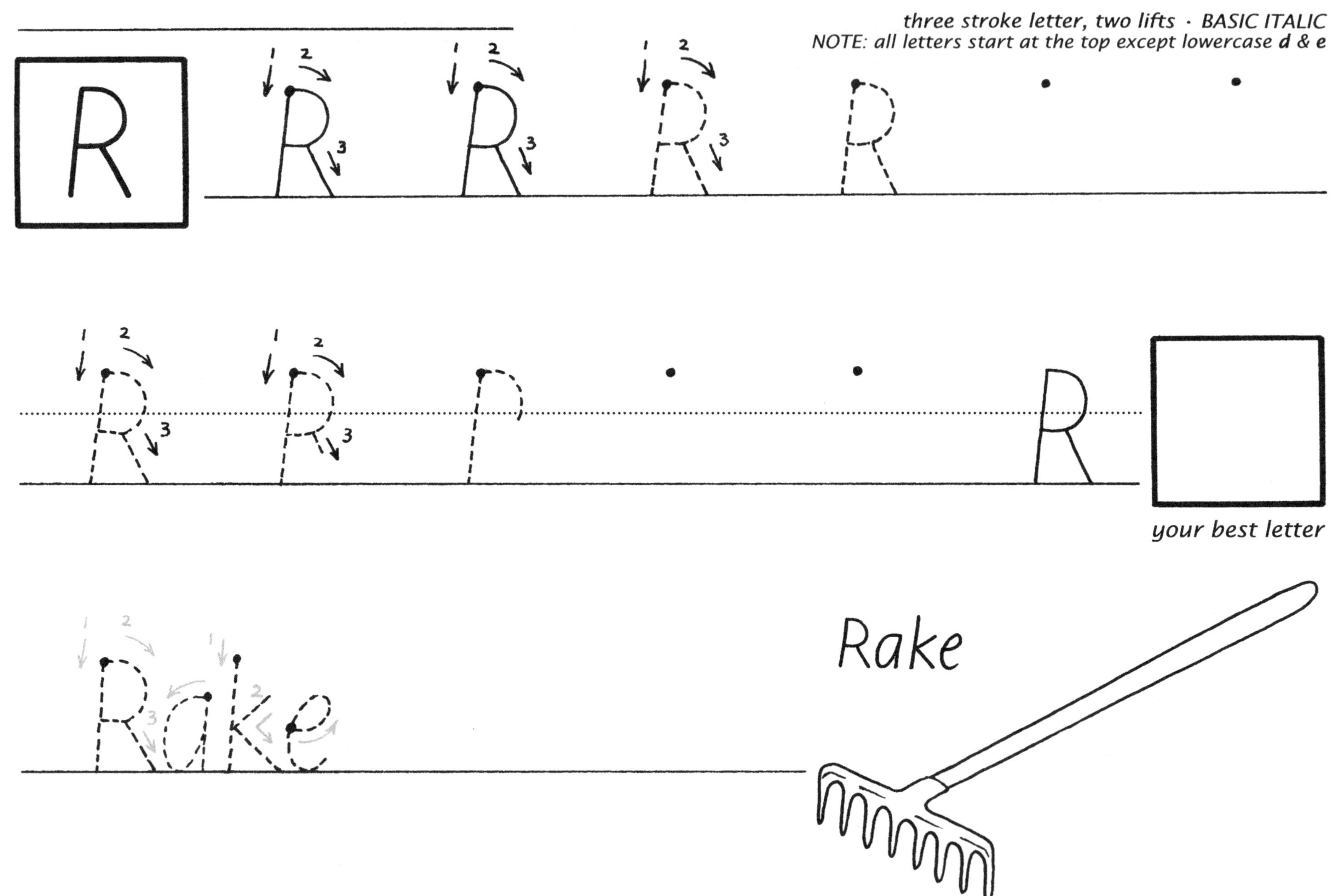

three stroke letter, two lifts · BASIC ITALIC
NOTE: all letters start at the top except lowercase d & e
your best letter
Rake

your best letter

rabbit

LOOK: Did you start each letter at the top?   Circle: Yes   No

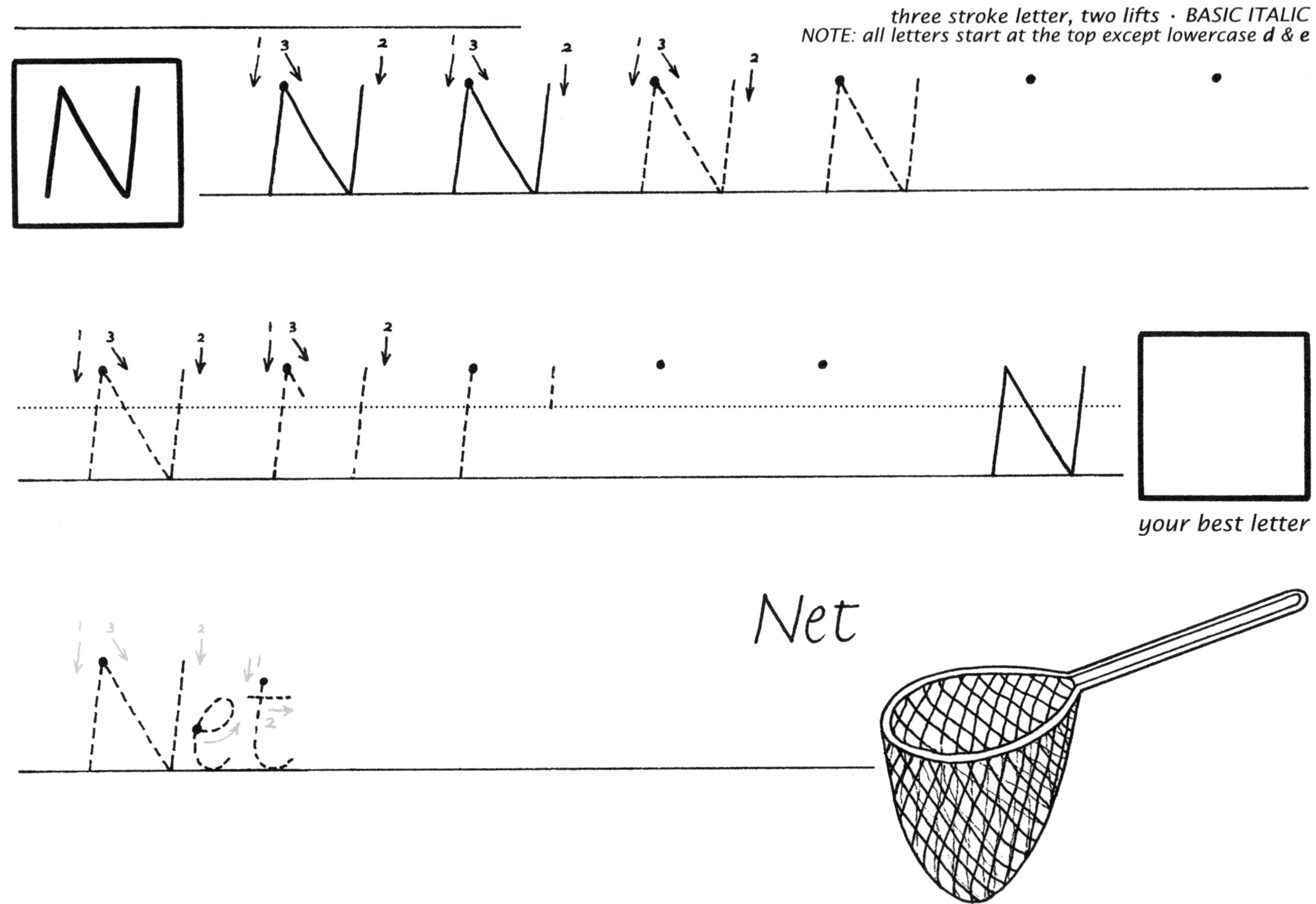

your best letter

Net

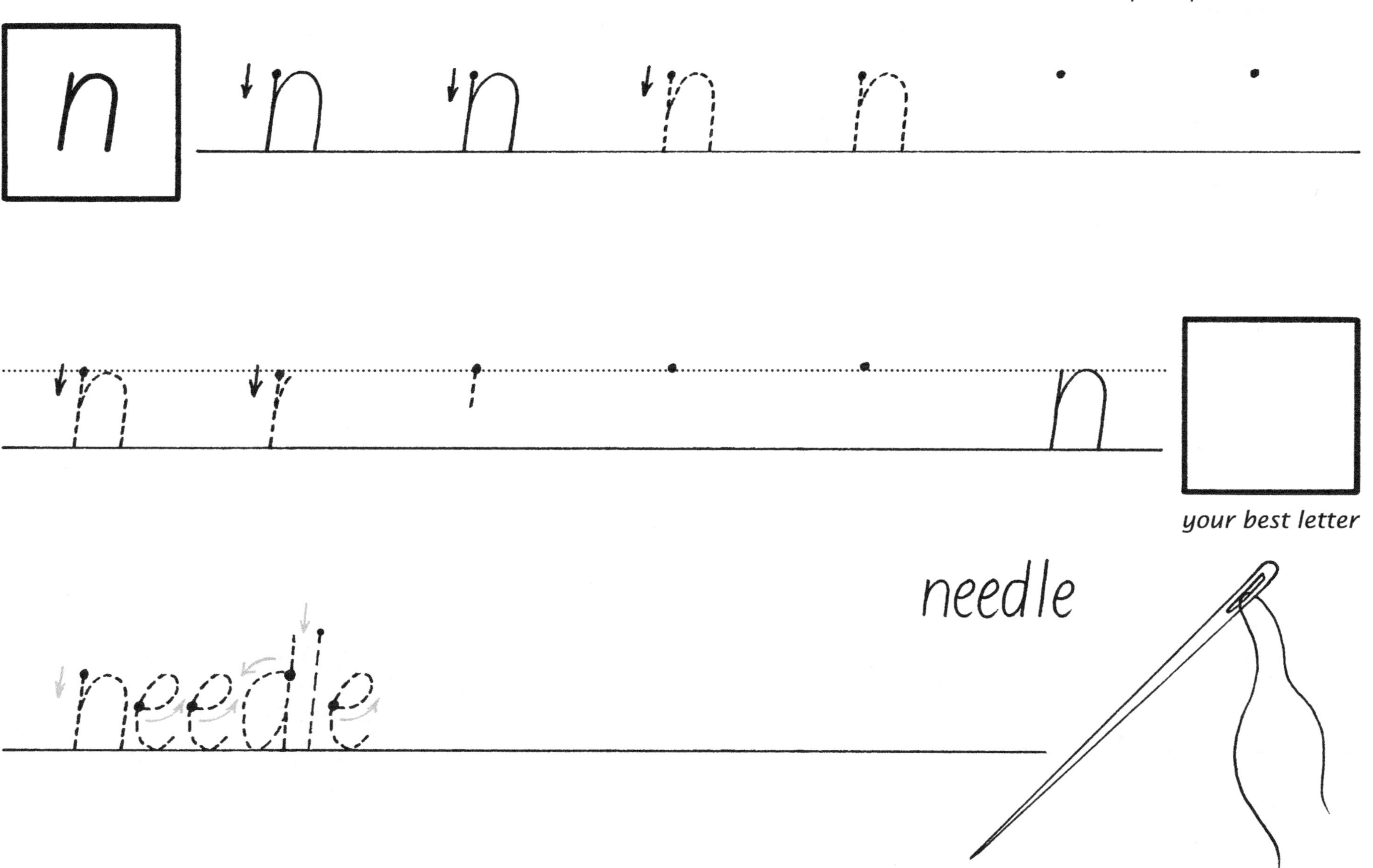

your best letter

needle

M M M M M M

M M I I M

your best letter

Mittens

Mittens

m

m m m m · ·

m r r · ·

m

your best letter

mouse

mouse

LOOK: Did you start all letters at the top?   Circle: Yes   No

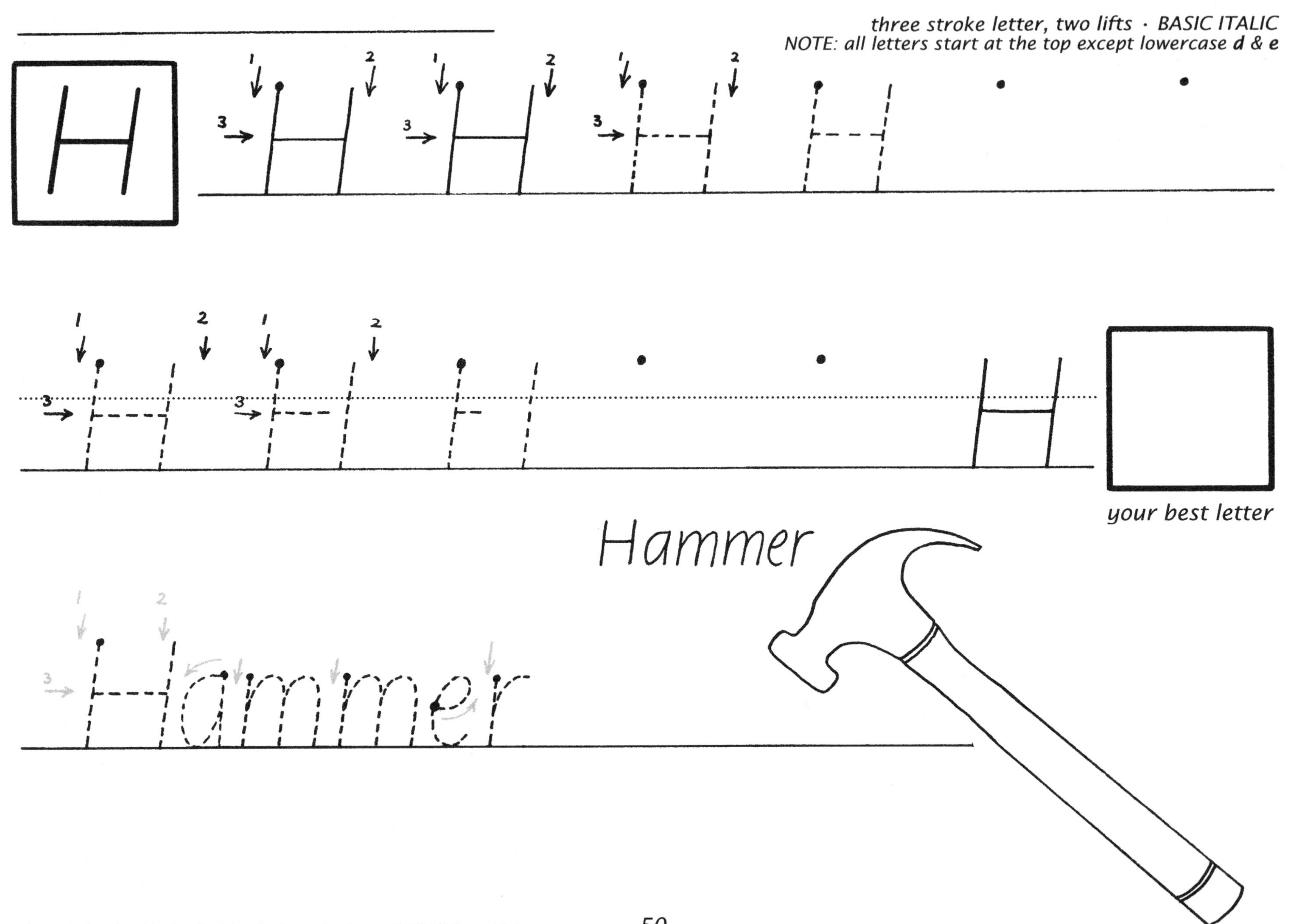

your best letter

Hammer

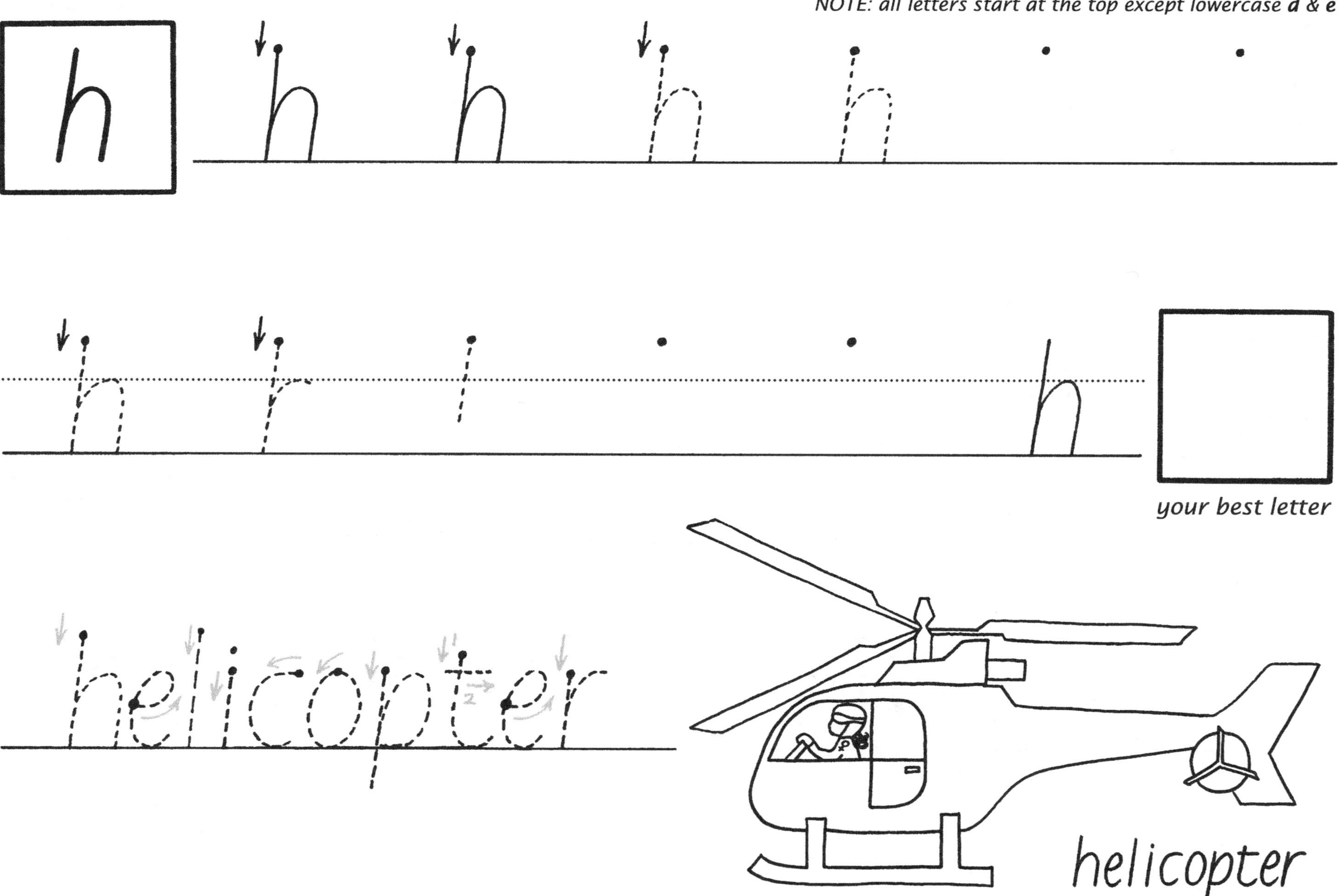

your best letter

helicopter

your best letter

Zipper

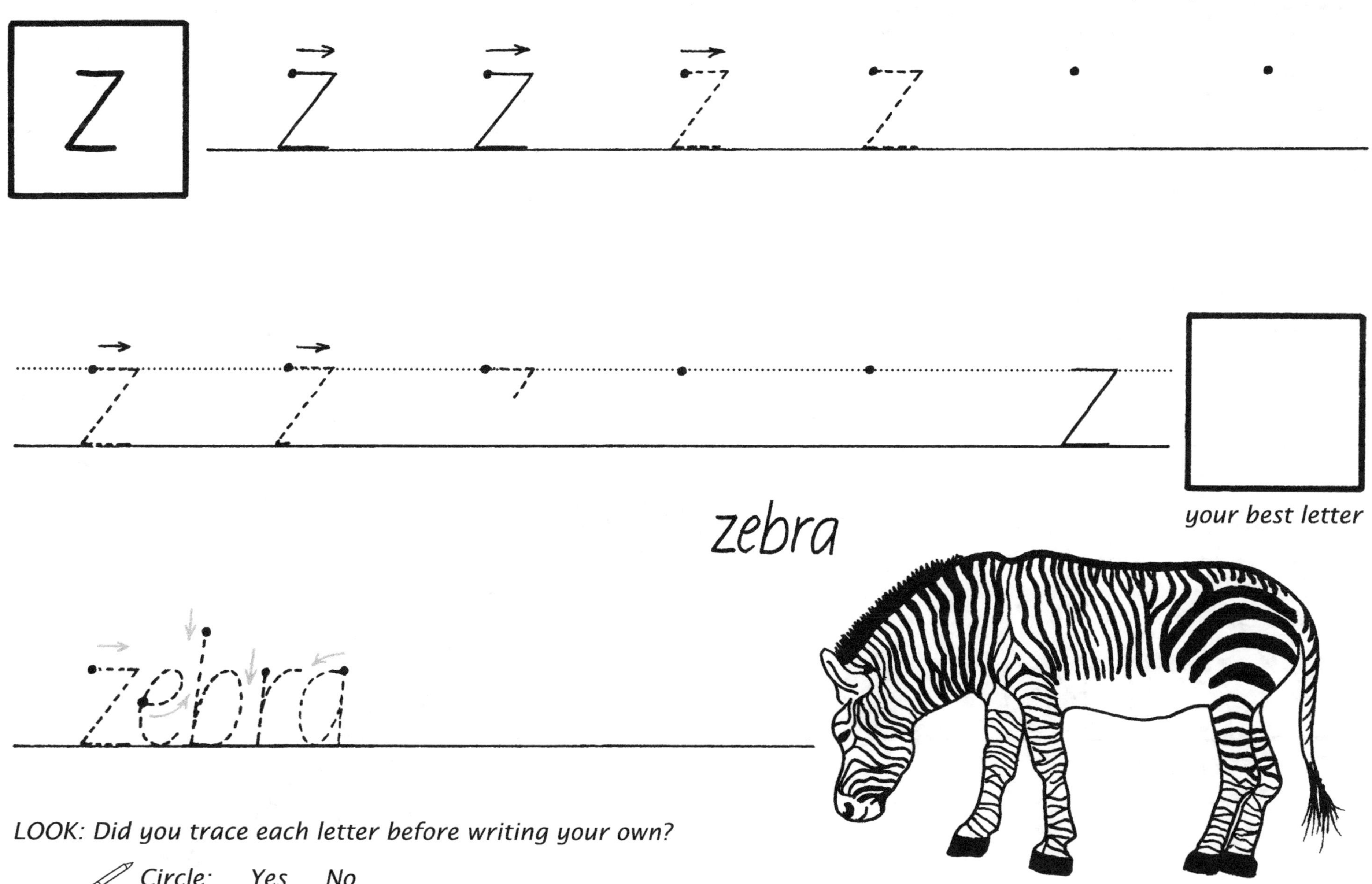

zebra

your best letter

LOOK: Did you trace each letter before writing your own?

Circle: Yes   No

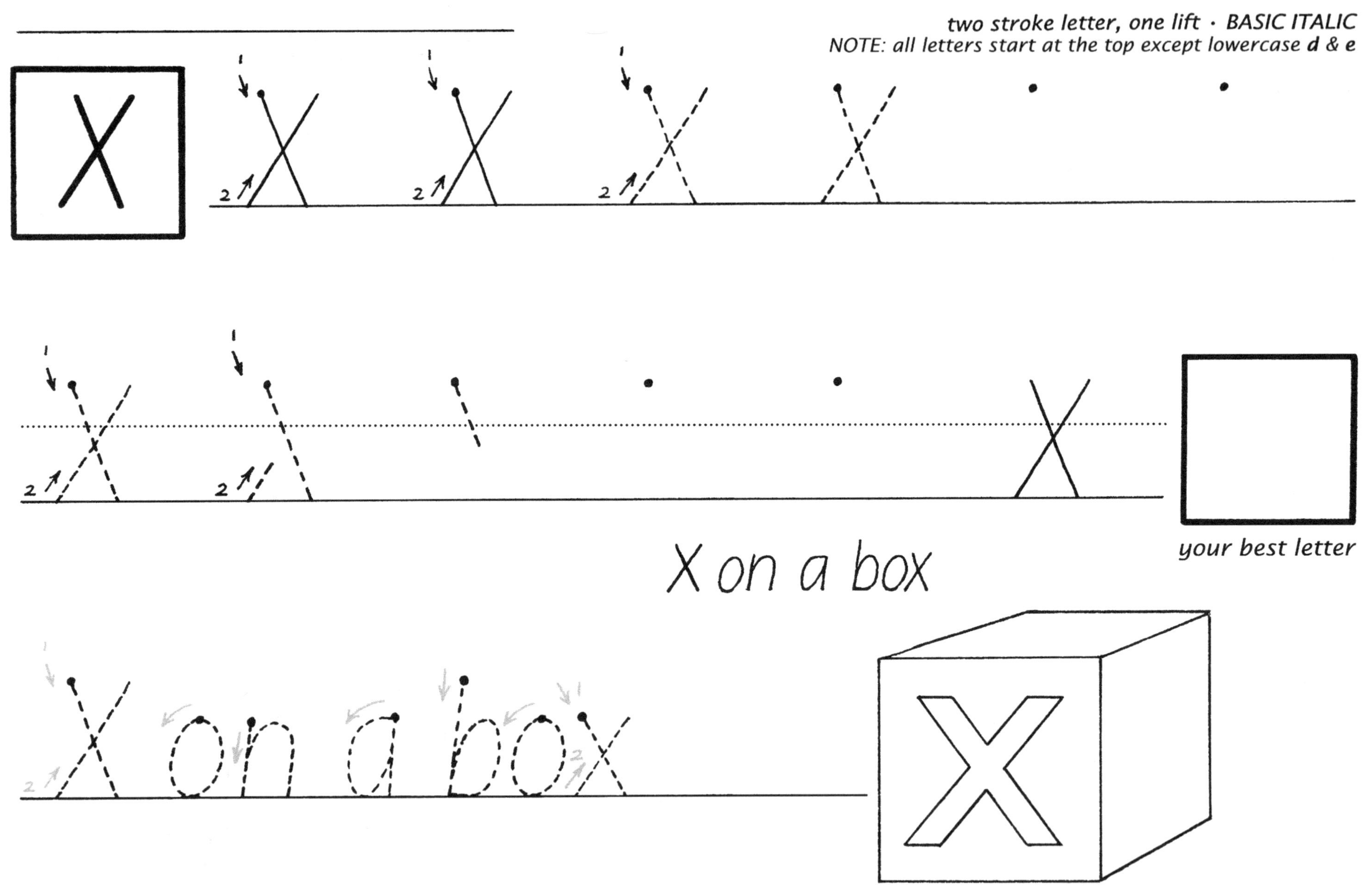

X on a box
your best letter
X on a box

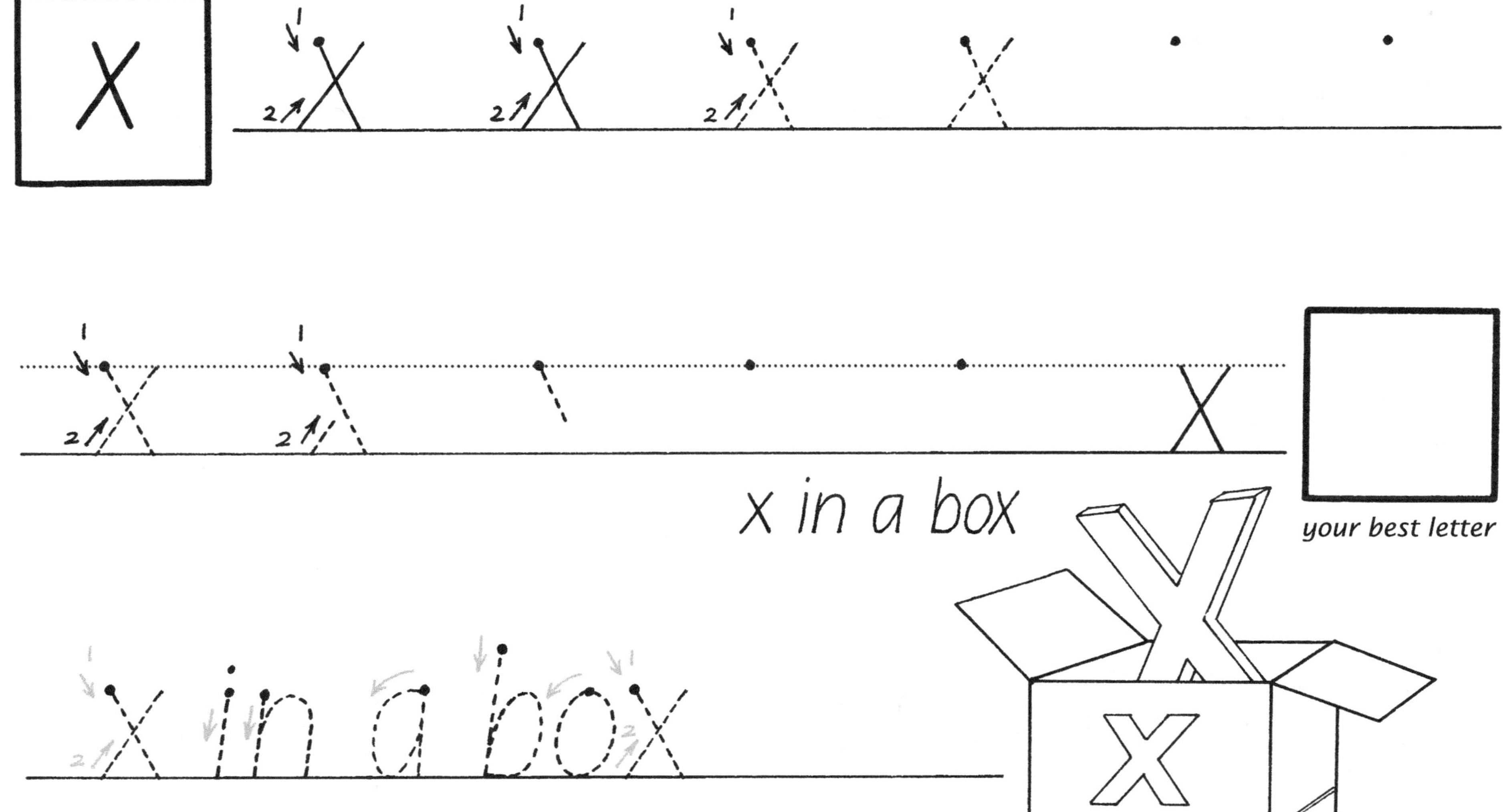

x in a box
your best letter
x in a box

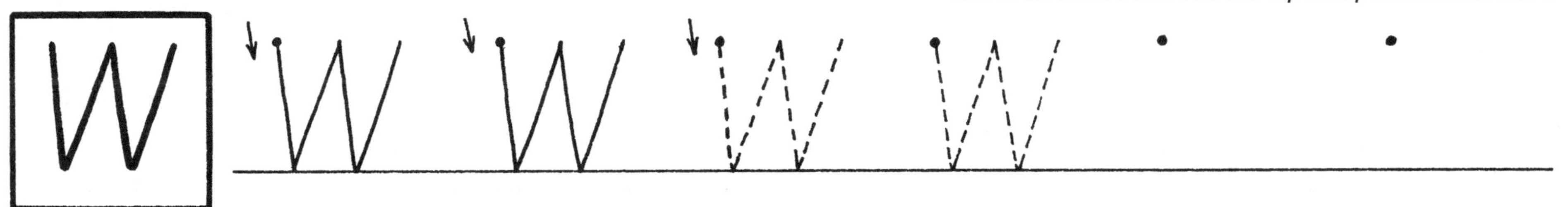

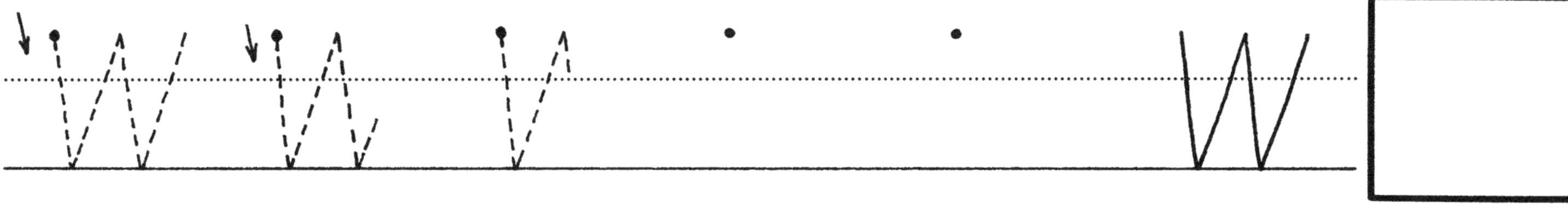

your best letter

Watch

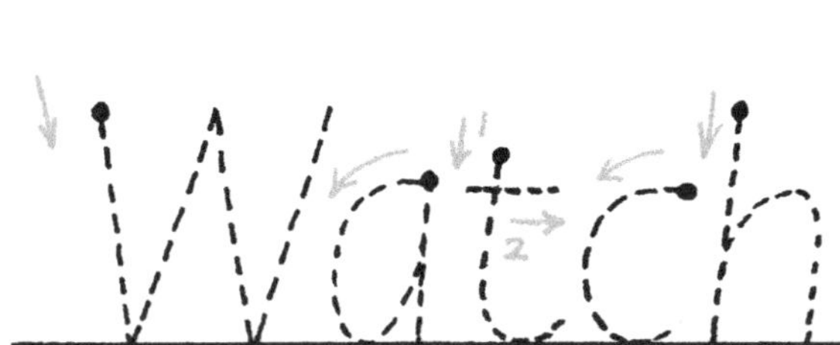

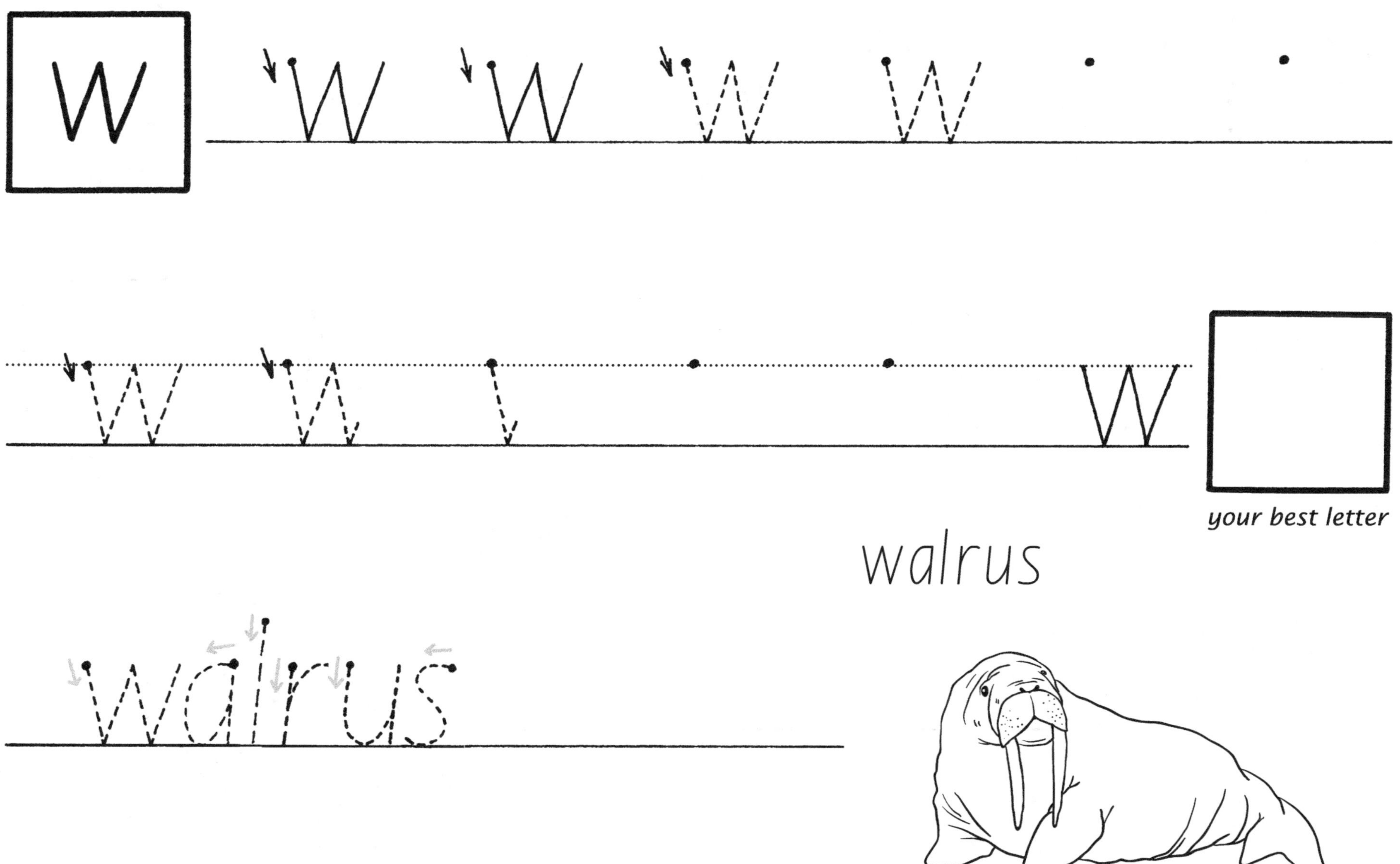

your best letter

walrus

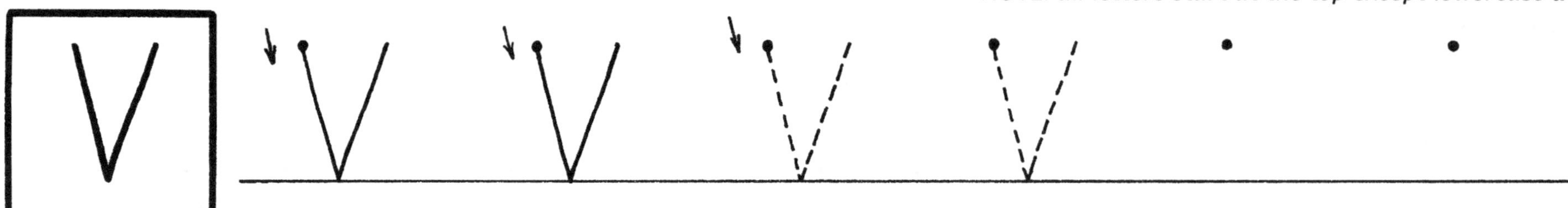

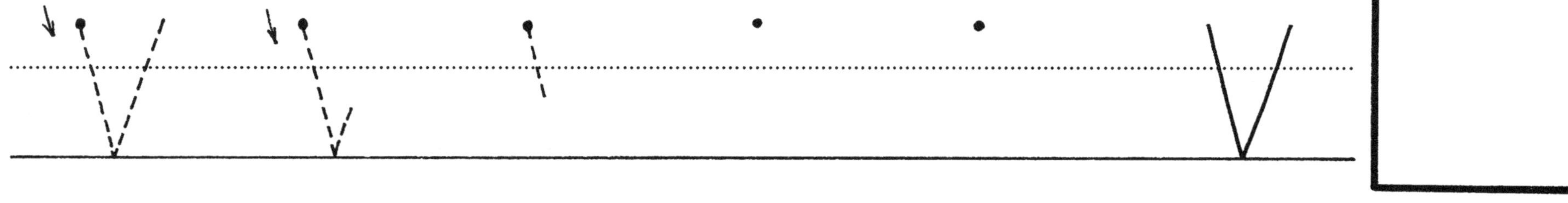

your best letter

Valentine

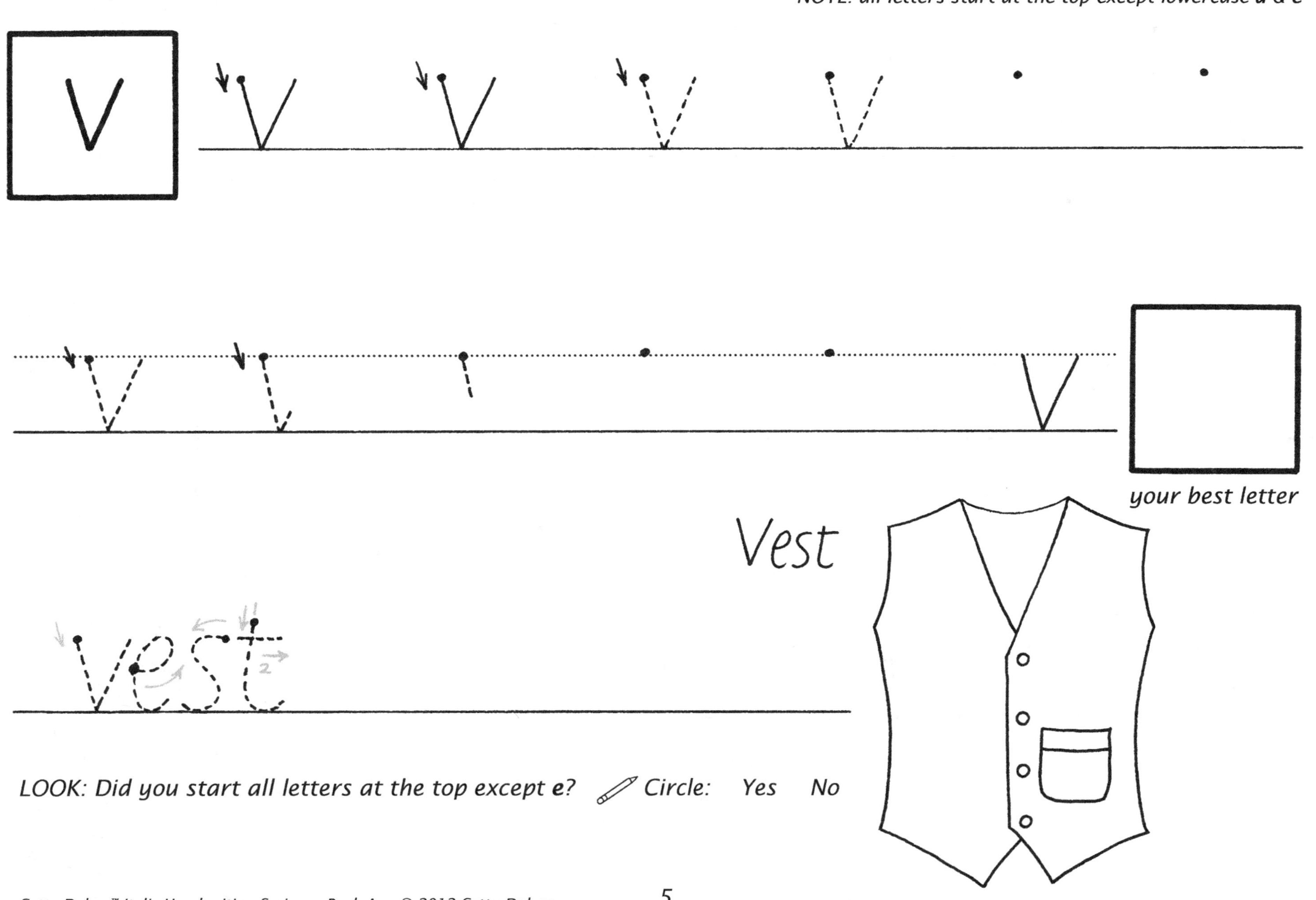

your best letter

Vest

LOOK: Did you start all letters at the top except **e**? ✏ Circle: Yes   No

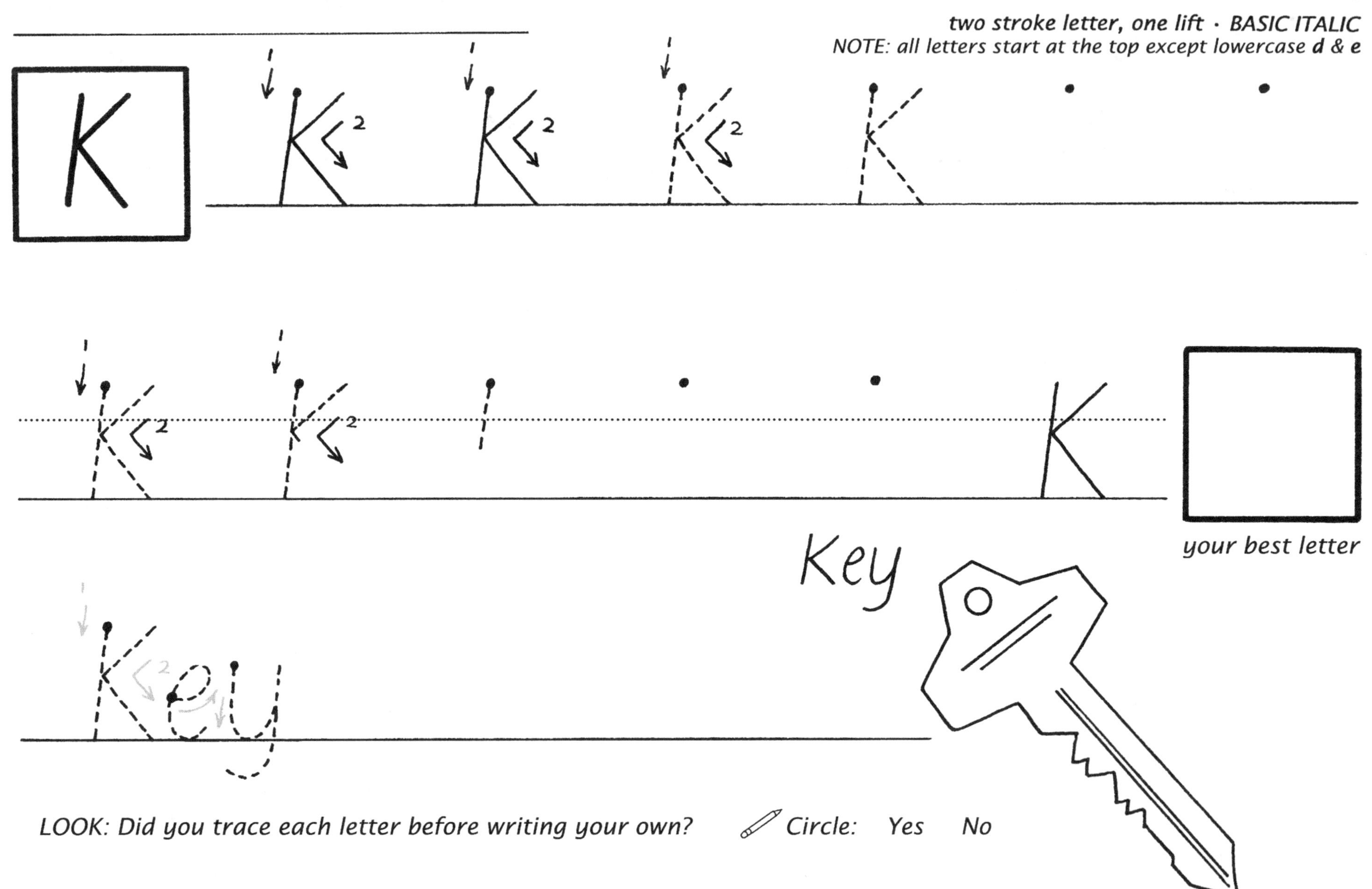

LOOK: Did you trace each letter before writing your own?   Circle: Yes   No

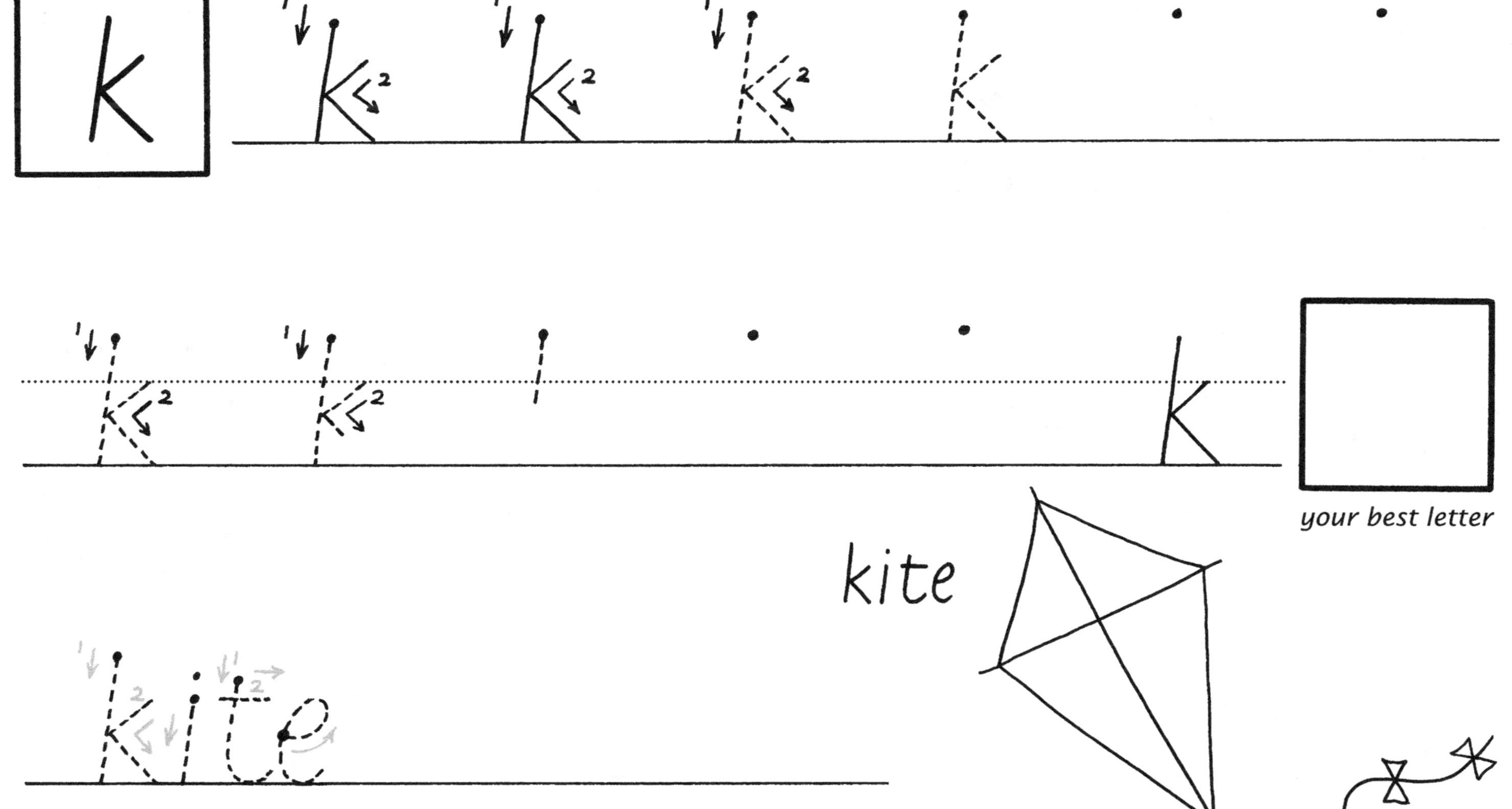

your best letter
kite
kite

your best letter

Lock

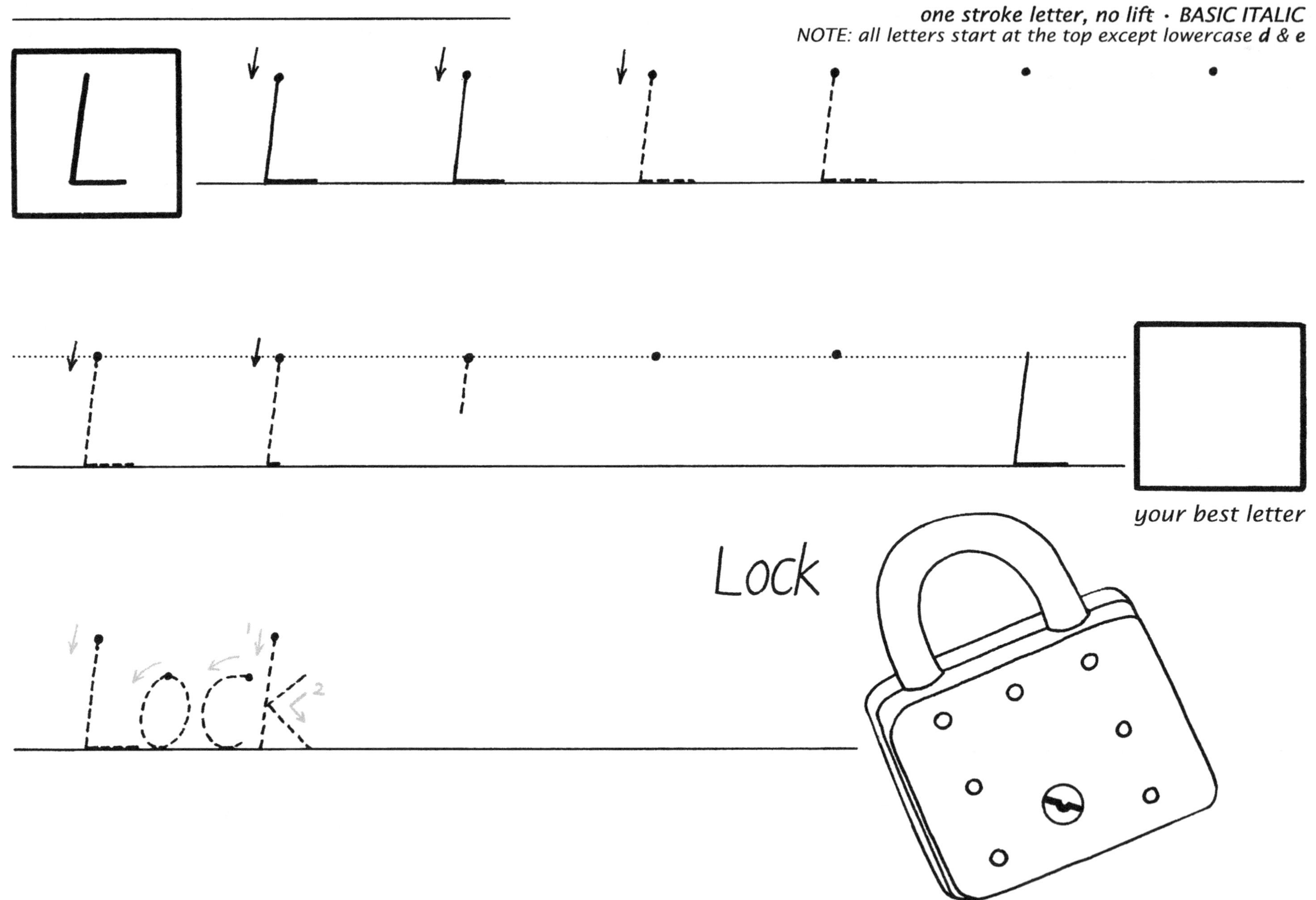

your best letter

lamb

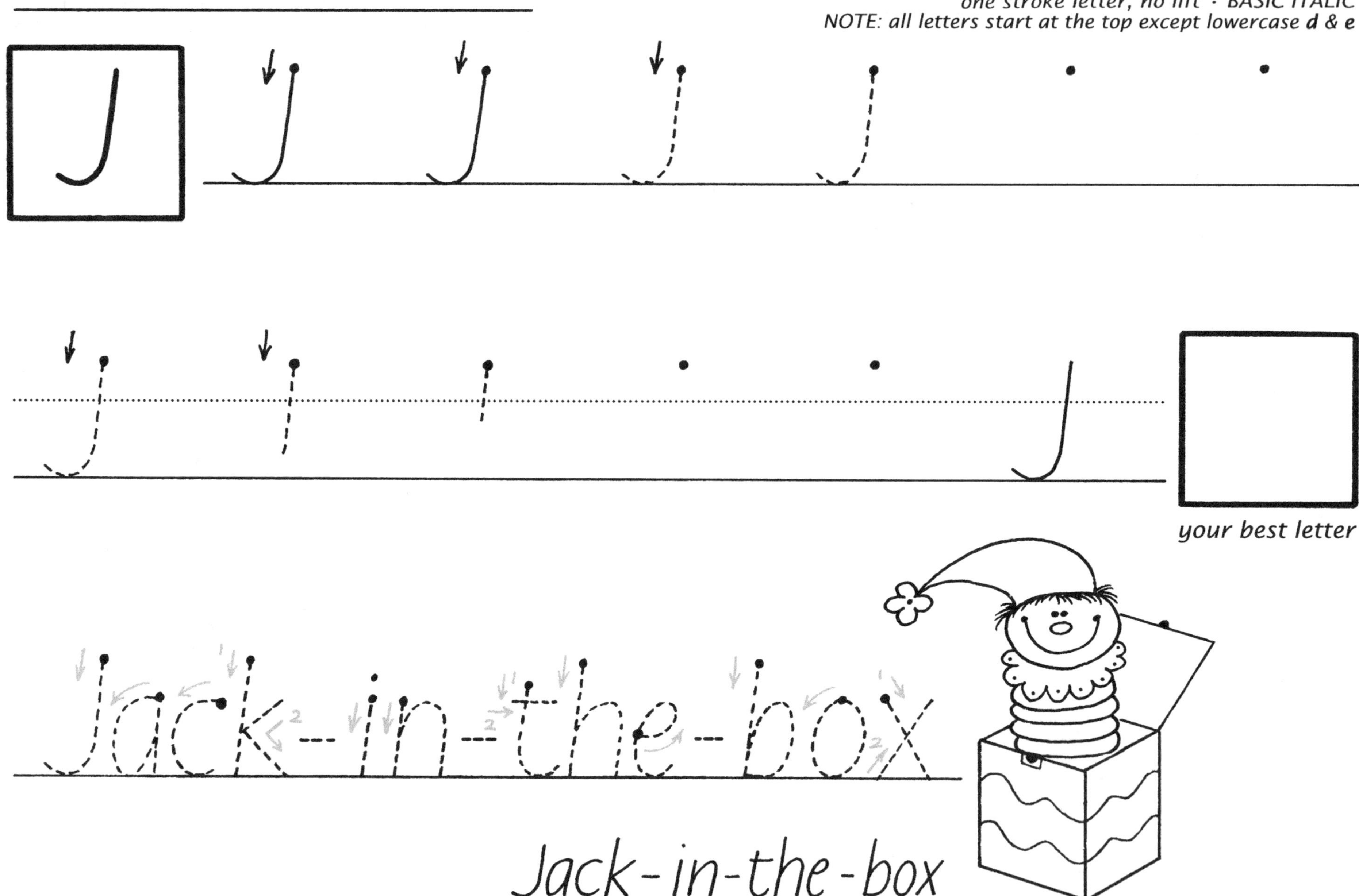

your best letter

Jack-in-the-box

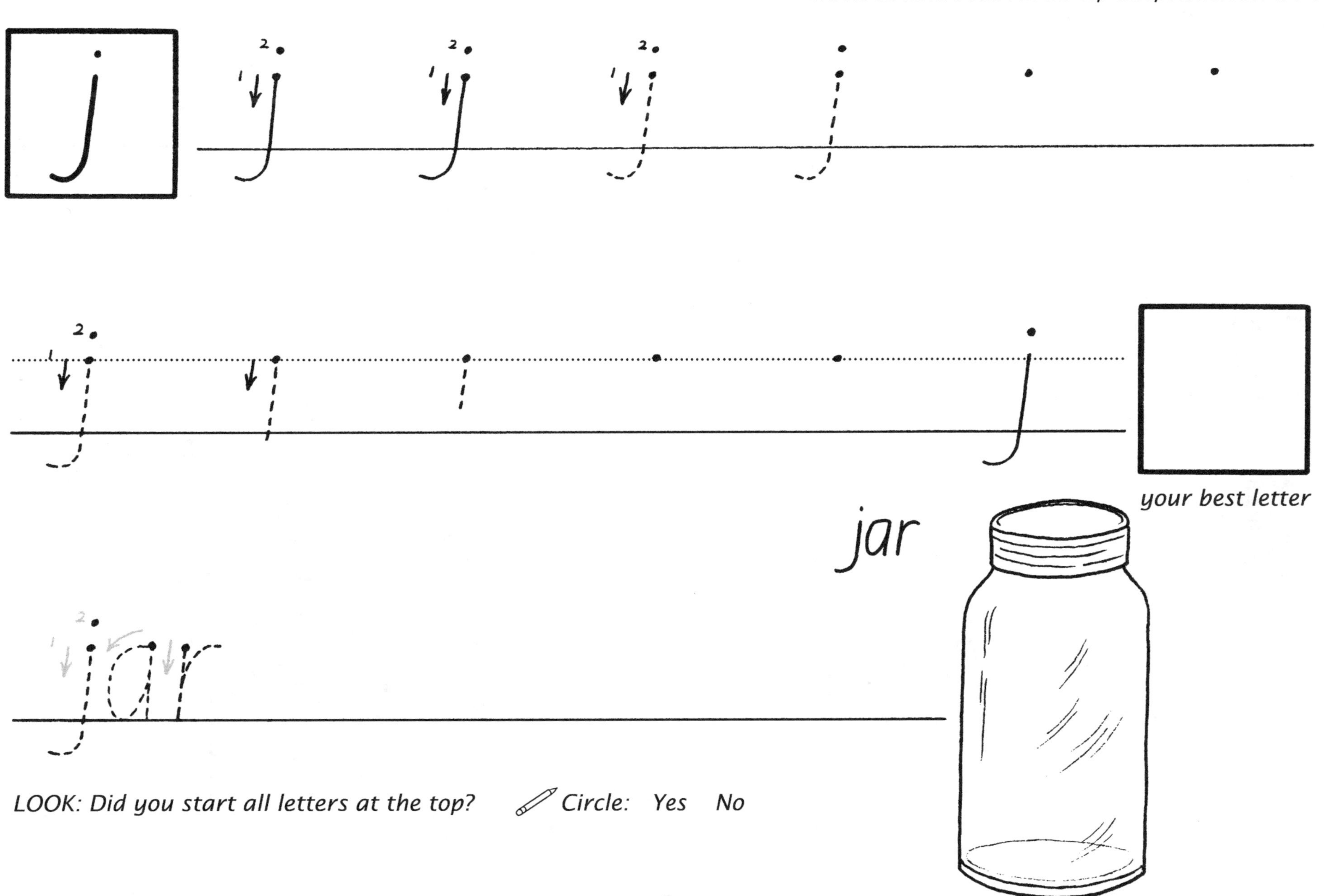

your best letter

jar

LOOK: Did you start all letters at the top?   Circle: Yes   No

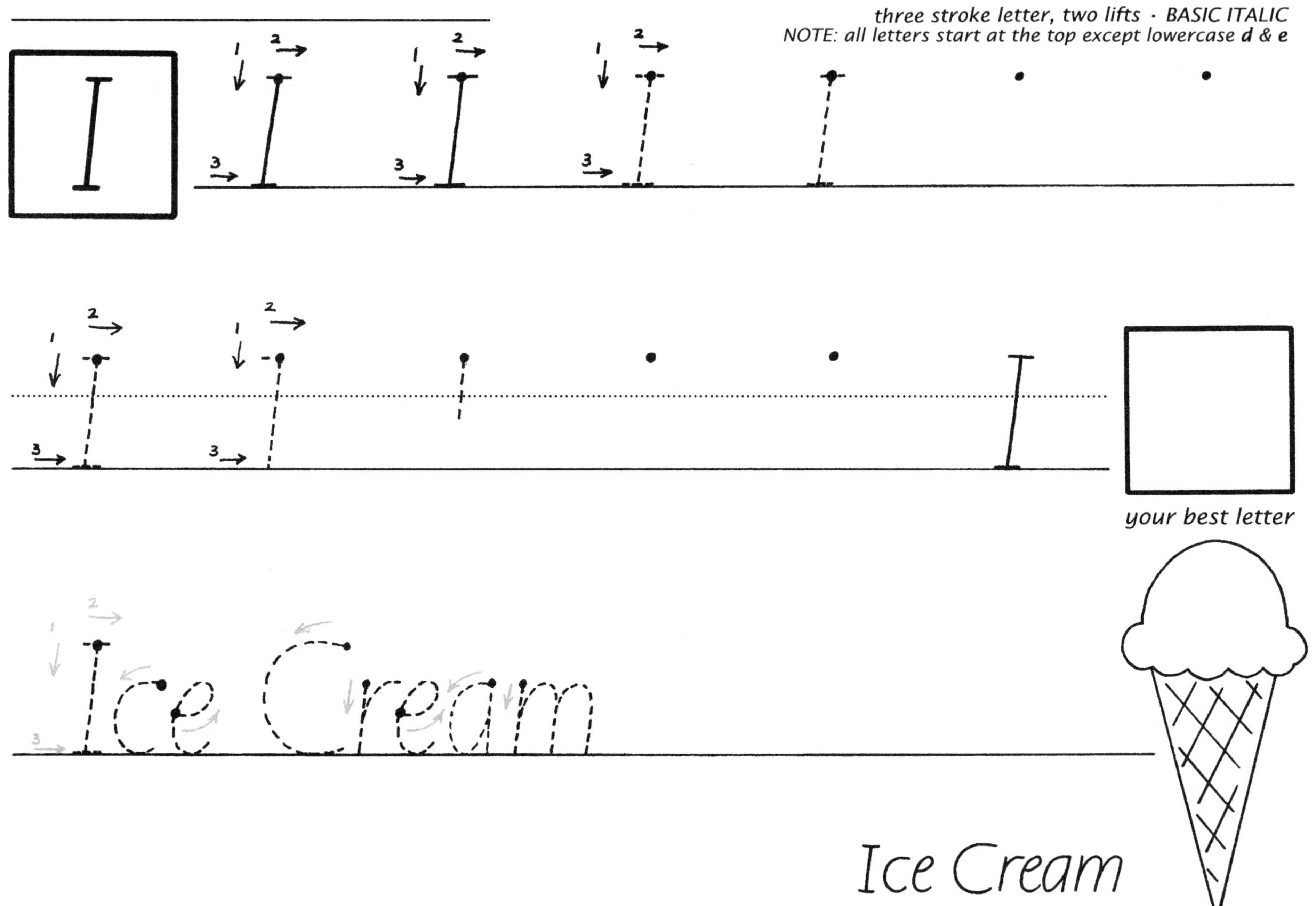

three stroke letter, two lifts · BASIC ITALIC
NOTE: all letters start at the top except lowercase d & e
your best letter
Ice Cream

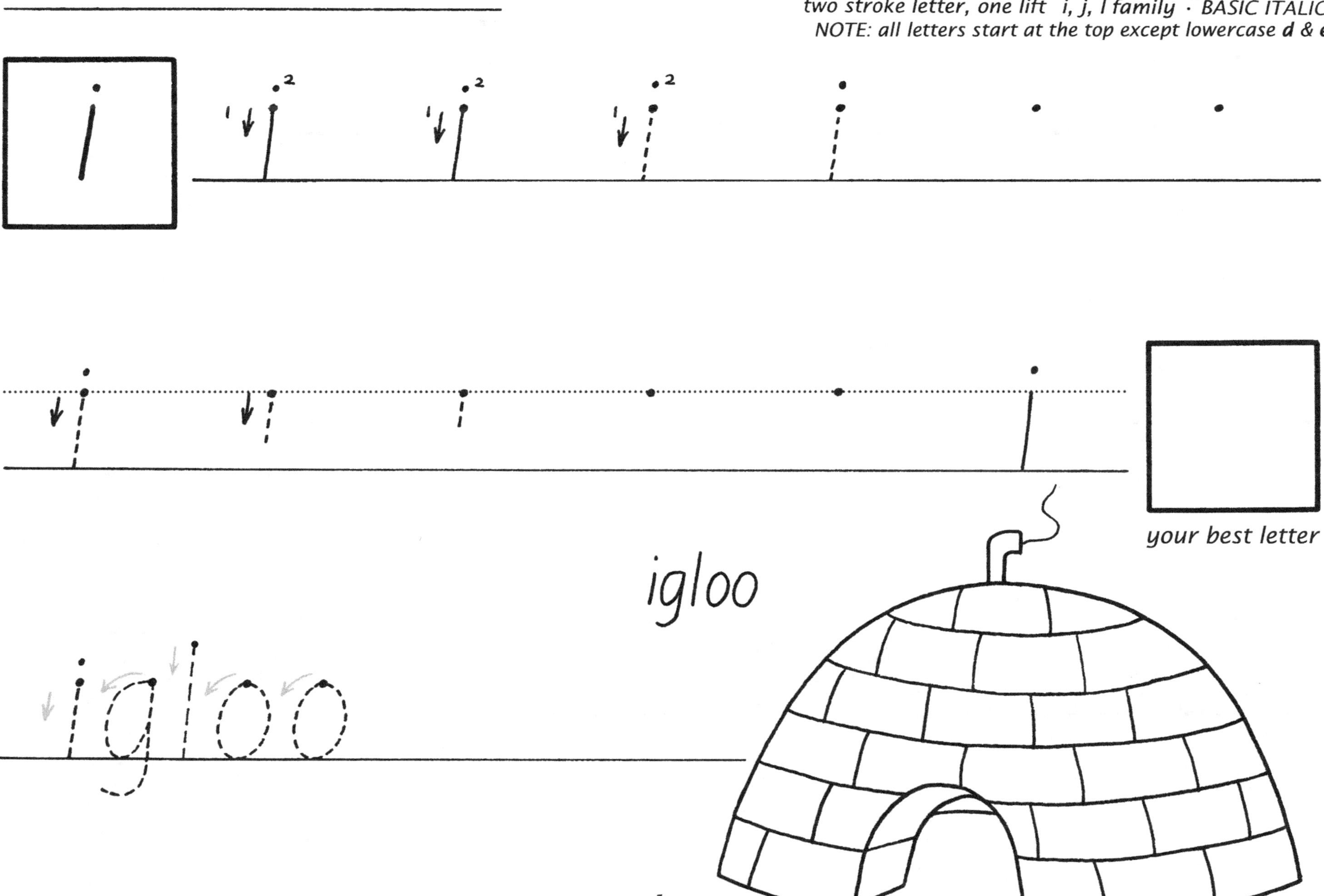

your best letter

igloo

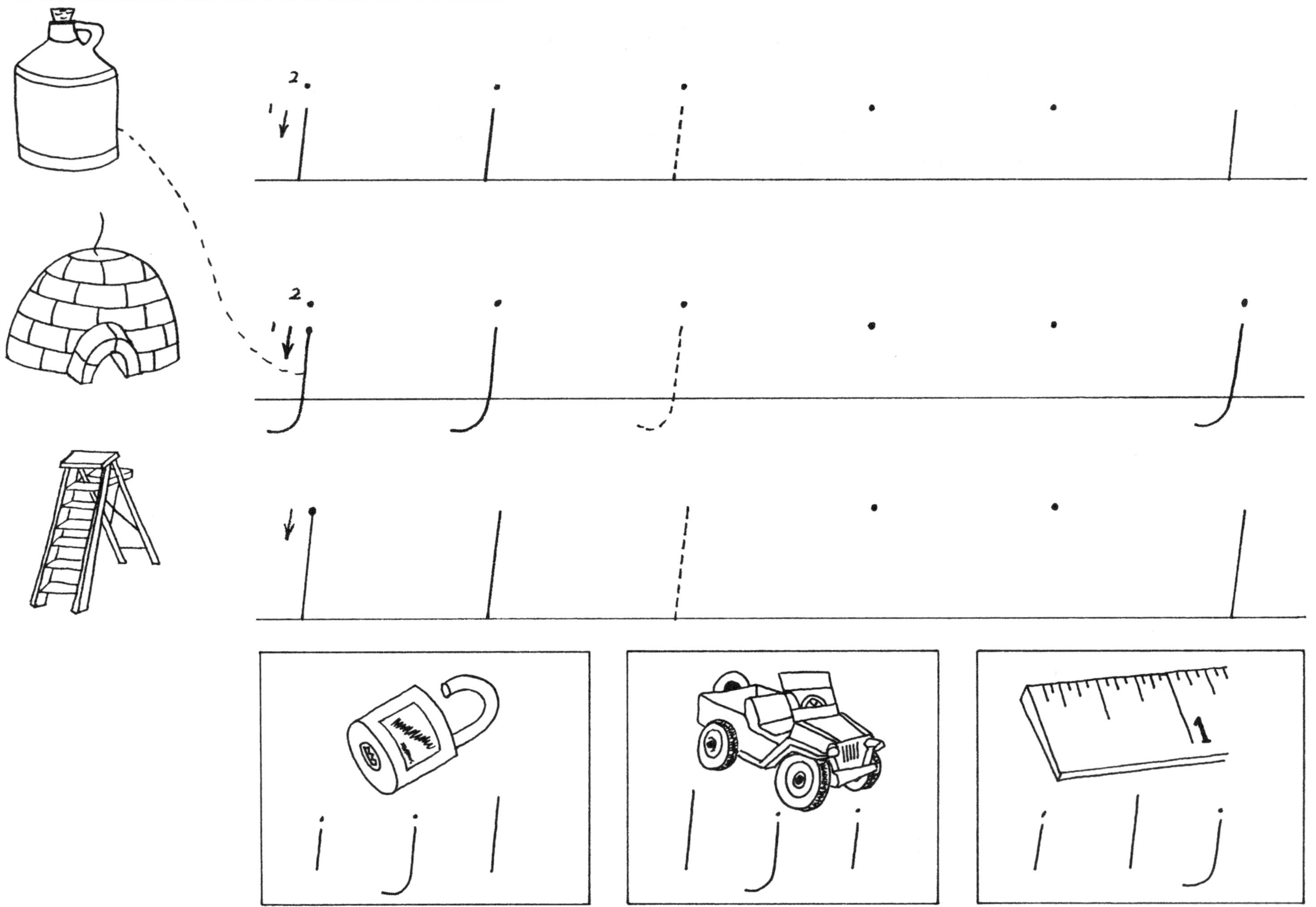

TOP THREE LINES: *Ask the student to draw a line from the picture to the letter that stands for the correct beginning sound.*

BOTTOM THREE BOXES: **Ask the student to circle the letter that stands for the beginning sound of the picture.**

BASIC SHAPES

Before the student begins writing in BOOK A, the authors recommend that the student practice the following shapes on unlined paper, one shape at a time. Allow the student to write each shape any size at first. Later, ask the student to write very large and very small forms of that same shape. We suggest the student also practice these shapes on a chalkboard and/or in cornmeal. (See INSTRUCTION MANUAL, "*Activity*," pp. 35 & 41.)

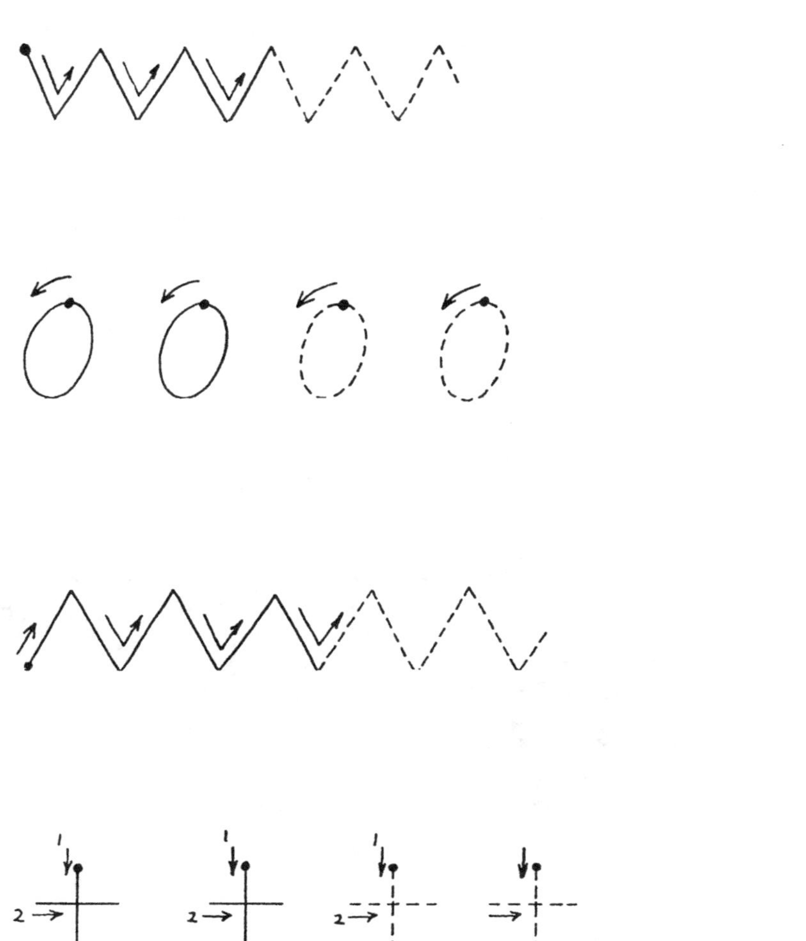

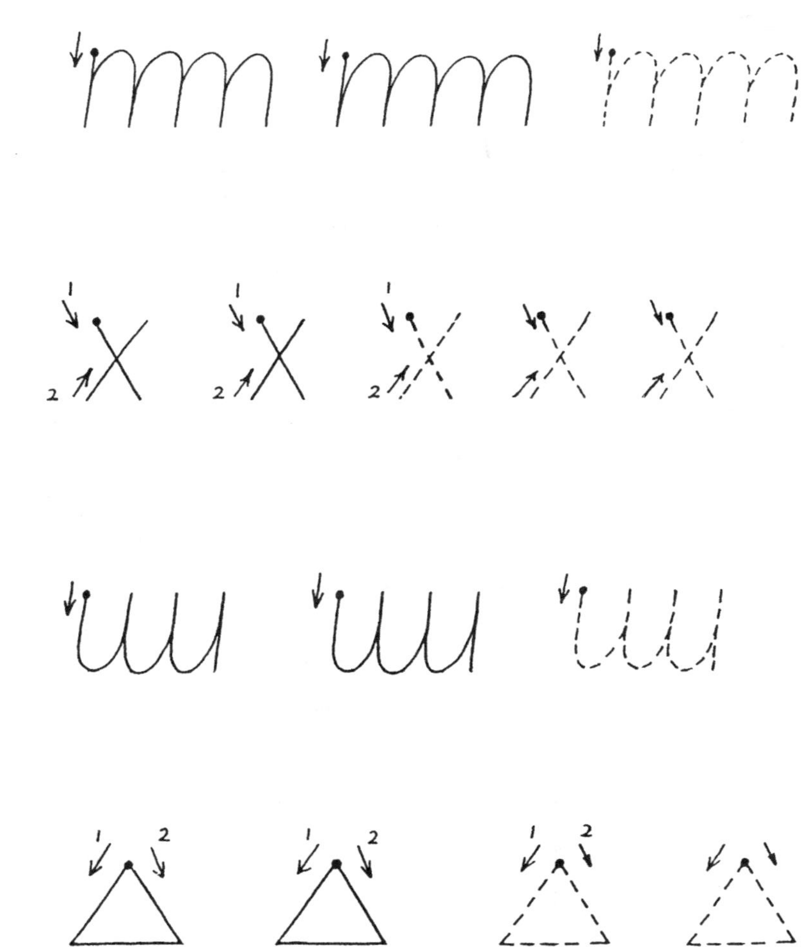

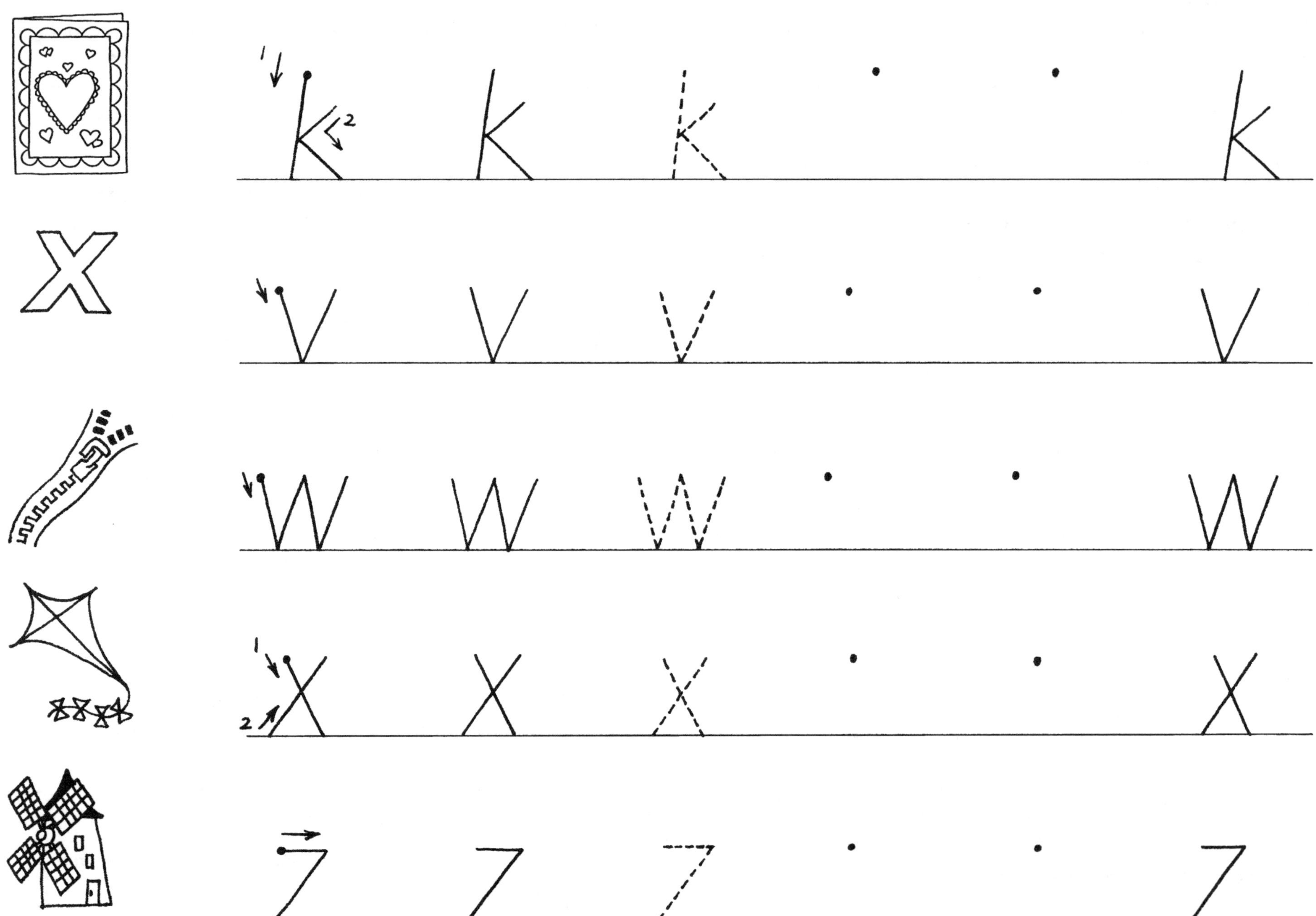

Ask the student to draw a line from the picture to the letter
that stands for the correct beginning sound.

Learning how to write involves much more than learning to write letters. It is a sophisticated, complex process involving learning letterforms, learning how to space within and between words, and learning how to organize writing on a page. Research indicates that there exists an almost perfect correlation between measures evaluating the children's *awareness* of their fingers and the ability to *use* their fingers in precise manual skills.

Ways to determine manual ability

To assist young students increase awareness of their hands and fingers, and to help you, the teacher, evaluate students' manual skills, have your students perform these tasks:

1. Direct the students to touch each of their fingers to their thumb, in order, from the first to the little finger. (By the age of six years, most children should be able to complete this exercise using one or both hands at a time.)

2. Have the students connect two dots that are spaced approximately eight inches apart on a page. (Most children of five years can accomplish this. However, if the student draws beyond the second dot or draws an unusually shaky line when nearing the second dot, it may indicate potential deficiencies in handwriting skills.)

Ways to improve kinesthetic perception of the hands

1. Unstructured clay modeling facilitates a student's perception of his or her hands. Encourage the student to manipulate the clay in every possible way—squeezing, flattening, poking, making shapes, etc.

2. To heighten the student's perception of shape, use a box in which a variety of small objects are placed for the student to feel but not see.

   a. Ask the student to reach in the box and find an unseen object that matches the one he or she is looking at.

   b. Direct the student to locate in the box an object that you or another student has described.

   c. Ask the student to find two objects with similar characteristics—two fuzzy objects, two heavy objects, two small objects, etc.

3. Draw several circles on a sheet of paper. To determine the student's ability to aim the finger and hand and also to point, have the student place dots in the circles with a pencil, pen, or crayon. Vary the difficulty of this task by increasing or decreasing the size of the circles or increasing the rate at which the dots are made. (The student must be able to point at a given or imaginary point in order to begin the stroke of a letter.)

Ways to confirm hand-eye tracking skills

The ability to control continuous hand movements while drawing lines of varying difficulty is basic to handwriting. If you are able to detect problems as the student completes the following tasks and are able to obtain appropriate assistance for the student, subsequent difficulties may be avoided.

1. Demonstrate drawing parallel lines. Then direct the student to draw parallel lines of a given length, first at a relaxed pace then at a faster one.

2. Direct the student to draw two curved lines equal in distance from one another. Later require more difficult shapes that combine straight lines, angles, and/or curves.

3. Direct the student to connect numbered dots on a sheet of paper that require horizontal, vertical and lateral movements. Place the paper in front of the student, close to the dominant hand. Later, space the dots further apart and require the student to cross the midline of his or her body. This latter task may cause the neuro-logically challenged student some difficulty.

The above evaluative tasks may be of help in assisting the learning of handwriting and in discovering deficiencies.

(See INSTRUCTION MANUAL, p. 13, for more suggestions concerning the beginning writer.)

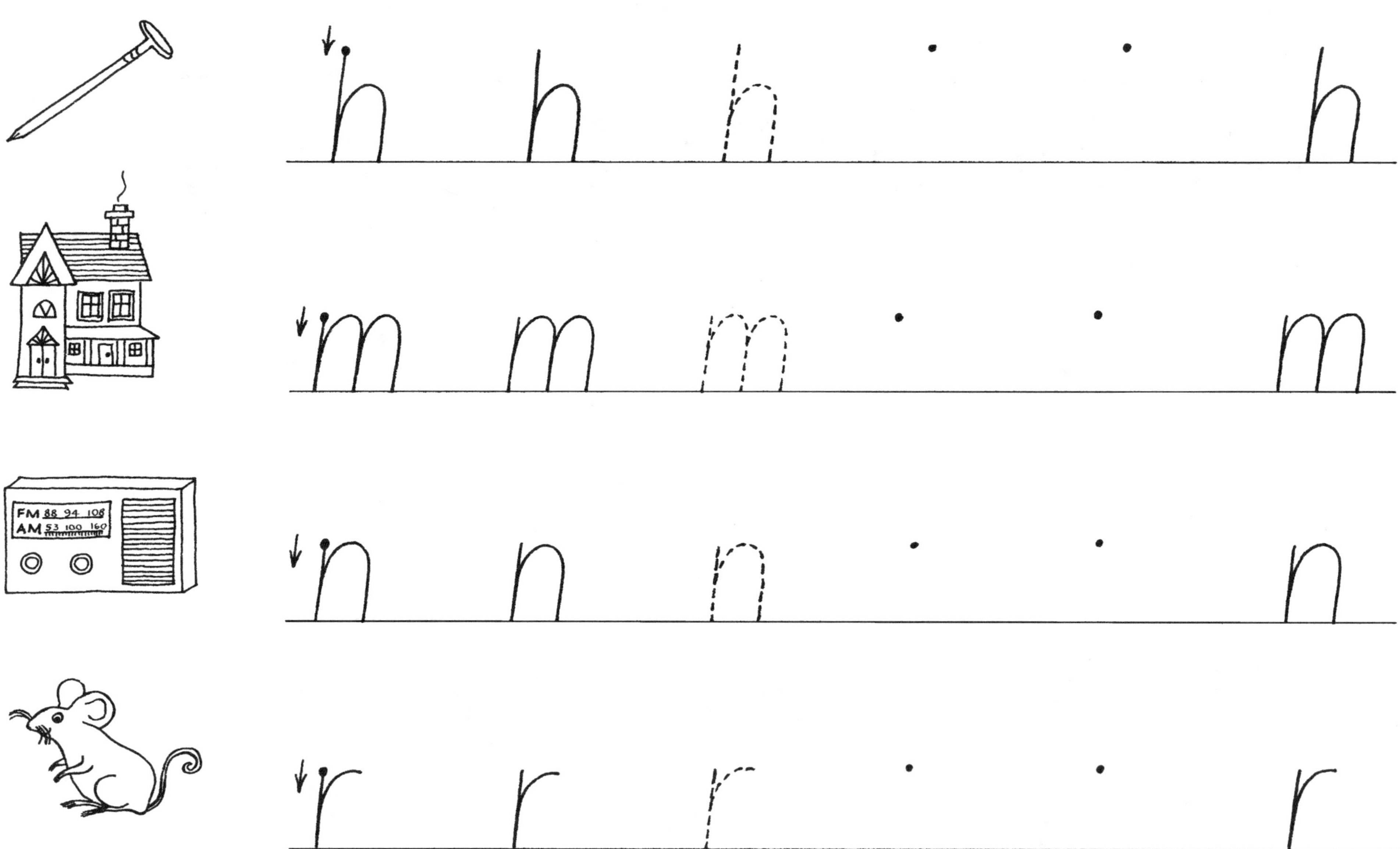

Ask the student to draw a line from the picture to the letter
that stands for the correct beginning sound.

All letters written in one stroke unless otherwise indicated. *All letters start at the top except lowercase **d** and **e**.*

Aa Bb Cc Dd Ee Ff Gg

or

alternate
2-stroke e

Hh Ii Jj Kk Ll Mm

or

Nn Oo Pp Qq Rr Ss Tt

or

or

Uu Vv Ww Xx Yy Zz

0 1 2 3 4 5 6 7 8 9

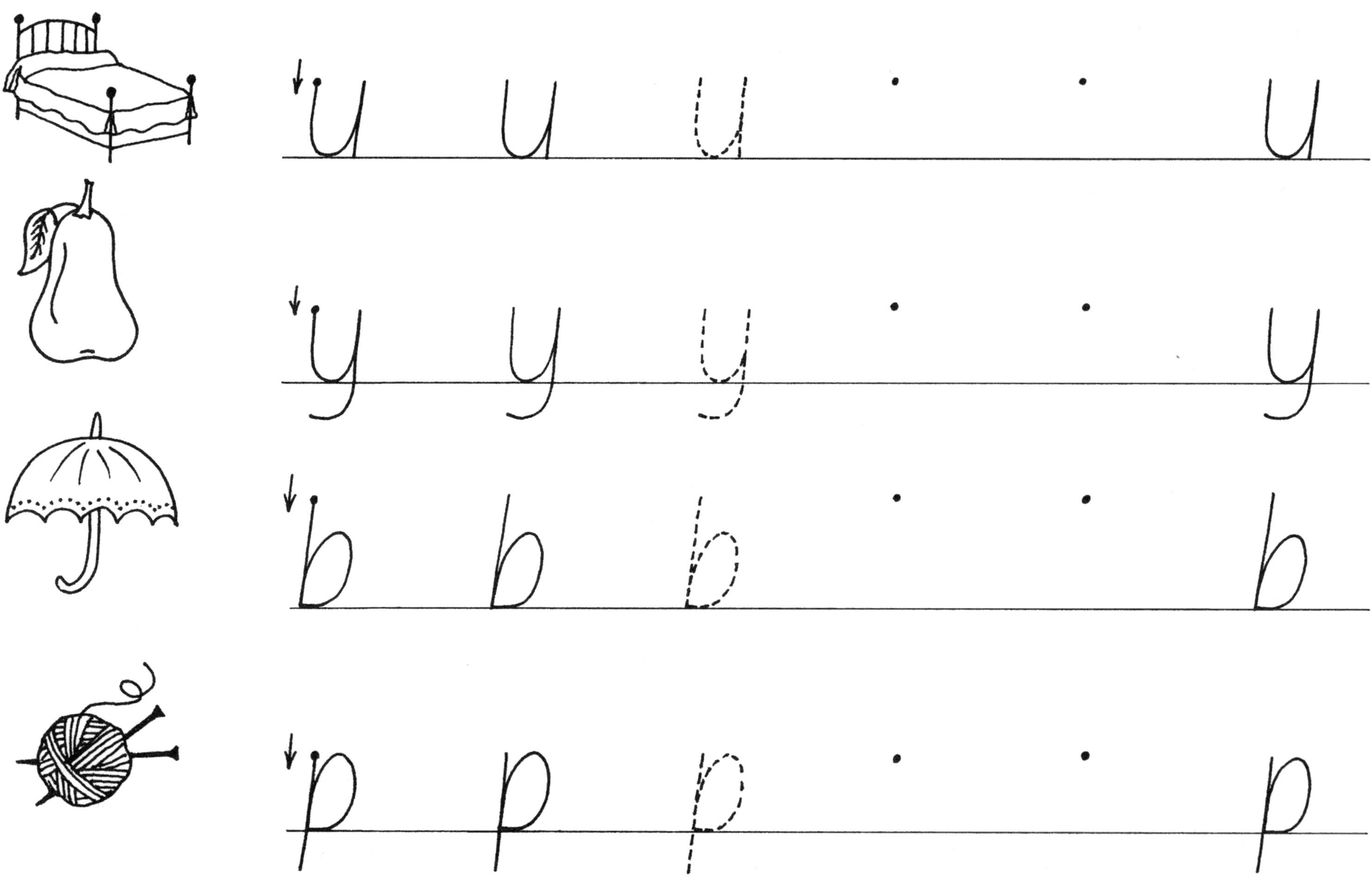

Ask the student to draw a line from the picture to the letter
that stands for the correct beginning sound.

GETTY-DUBAY™ HANDWRITING REMINDERS

PENCIL HOLD

Hold the pencil with the thumb and index finger, resting it on the middle finger. Rest the shaft of the pencil near the large knuckle. Hold the tool firmly and avoid pinching. To relax the hand, tap index finger on the pencil three times. Avoid "thumb wrap" and a "death grip".

PAPER POSITION

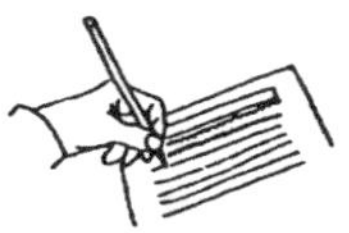

LEFT-HANDED: If the left-handed student writes with the wrist below the writing line, turn paper clockwise so it is slanted to the right, as illustrated.

If the left-handed student writes with a hook, with the wrist above the writing line, turn the paper counter-clockwise so it is slanted to the left, as illustrated. (Similar to right-handed position)

RIGHT-HANDED: If the student is right-handed, turn paper counter-clockwise so it is slanted to the left, as illustrated.

POSTURE

Rest feet flat on the floor and keep back comfortably straight without slumping. Rest forearms on writing surface. The student holds workbook or paper with the nonwriting hand so that the writing area is centered in the front of the student.

PRACTICE PAPER

Book A—Use unlined or lined paper together with workbooks.

MATERIALS

The *Getty-Dubay™ Italic Handwriting Series* workbooks, BOOKS A-G, and the INSTRUCTION MANUAL constitute a step-by-step program. Related materials consist of:

1. BLACKLINE MASTERS/WORKSHEETS - half sheets for introduction to, or review of, workbook pages.
2. CLASSROOM WALL CHARTS - basic & cursive italic.
3. DESK STRIPS - basic & cursive italic.

VOCABULARY

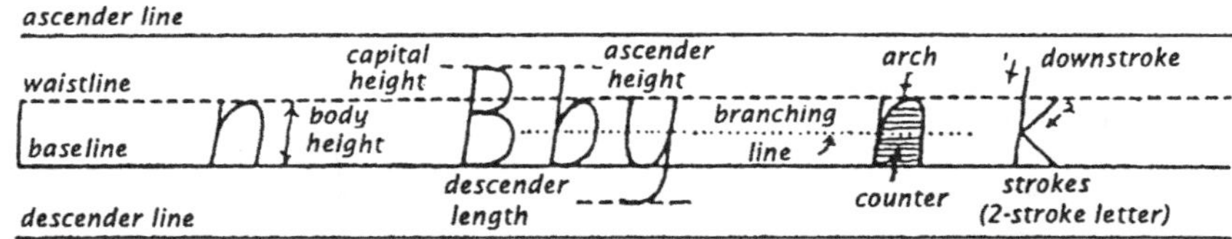

DIRECT INSTRUCTION

Several sessions of direct instruction each week are essential for a successful program. BOOK A – 5 to 10 minute sessions a day are recommended, see INSTRUCTION MANUAL, pp. 18-19

- SHAPE & STROKE SEQUENCE – teach basic italic in letter family groups, or according to the reading program in grade 1.
- SLOPE – encourage a consistent letter slope. Vertical letters (0° slope) may be the easiest to teach to beginning writers.
- SIZE – At first, allow students to write letters any size they wish on unlined paper, then introduce the workbook. A recommended progression through this book is one letter (lowercase and/or capital) per week.

SPACING

When young students are writing words, at first have them leave a space about the width of their two small fingers between words. As they become more proficient, they can leave less space.

ASSESSMENT

The *Getty-Dubay™ Italic Handwriting Series* provides a self-assessment process, LOOK, PLAN, PRACTICE, to enable the student to monitor progress. LOOK, step 1 of this process begins on some of the student pages in BOOK A. Assessment is the key to improving handwriting; in this book we introduce the first of three steps in the LOOK, PLAN, PRACTICE self-assessment process. The students look at their own writing and answer any questions on the page. The pencil indicates the student is to make a written response, generally by circling "yes" or "no". The teacher may encourage students to award themselves a star or a smiling face at the top of the page when they notice self-improvement.

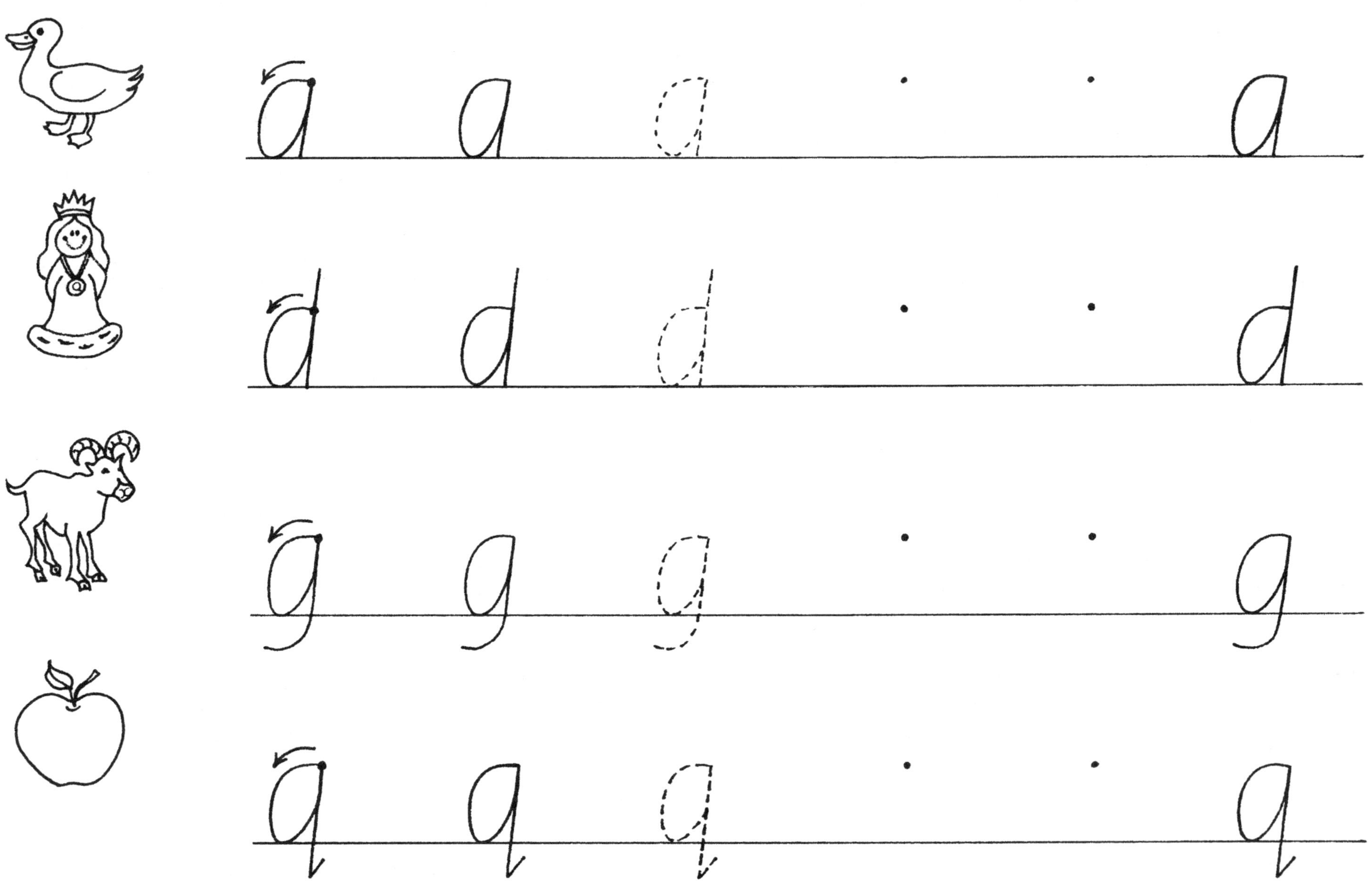

Ask the student to draw a line from the picture to the letter
that stands for the correct beginning sound.

Getty-Dubay™ Italic Handwriting Series · Book A · © 2012 Getty-Dubay

INTRODUCTION

This is the first of seven workbooks providing instruction in basic italic handwriting. It is designed for the beginning student of handwriting and is recommended for preschool, kindergarten and/or early first grade (5 to 7 years of age).

The twenty-six lowercase letters and the twenty-six capitals are introduced one letter per page. Letters are arranged in the order of lowercase families, which group letters with similar strokes together and progress from simple to more complex forms. The matching capital letter occurs on the reverse of each lowercase page allowing introduction of both lowercase and capital together if preferred.

Each page is designed for the student to trace the models provided, write letters at the given dots, and to write a "best" letter in the empty box on each alphabet page. The standard writing tool is the pencil although other writing instruments such as the fiber tip pen may be used. When students are ready, they should trace the word describing the illustration on each letter page, following the dots and arrows.

It is essential that the instructor provide an understanding of the dot and the arrow to assist the writer in completing the pages successfully. The self-assessment method used in the *Getty-Dubay™ Italic Handwriting Series* enables students to monitor their individual progress. Step 1, LOOK, of the three-step LOOK, PLAN, PRACTICE format, is incorporated on 21 of the student pages. Students are asked to "LOOK" at their writing and affirm what is best. On the 21 pages with "LOOK" questions, students should circle their chosen answers. See INSTRUCTION MANUAL, PP. 13, 18 & 19.

The *Getty-Dubay™ Italic Handwriting Series* INSTRUCTION MANUAL is to be used in conjunction with this workbook. Explanations and in-depth descriptions of lowercase letters, capitals, joins, and numerals are presented in the manual, emphasizing shape, strokes, size, slope and spacing of the letters. Also included in the manual are: a rationale for italic handwriting, techniques for teaching and assessing handwriting, sequence of skills, handwriting activities, and a brief history of our alphabet.

BOOK B, basic italic, follows this workbook and is designed for the beginning reader. In the third book, BOOK C, basic italic letterforms are reinforced and cursive italic is introduced. BOOKS D, E, F, and G provide a complete basic italic and cursive italic handwriting program. BOOKS B, C, and/or D may also be suitable for the person learning English as a second language.

The format of this book was chosen to accommodate both the left- and right-handed writer. When open, the book fits easily on a small desk, and the writer is not encumbered with an additional page to the left or right. From day one, use a Getty-Dubay™ basic italic desk strip as a reminder. Blackline masters are designed for supplementary practice and are available for each workbook in the series. See www.handwritingsuccess.com for these supplementary materials.

You can guide children toward the challenge and delight in the writing process by reading to them, modeling handwriting, providing writing materials, and especially by building enthusiasm for the letters of our alphabet and for the written word.

·abcdefghijklmnopqrstuvwxyz·

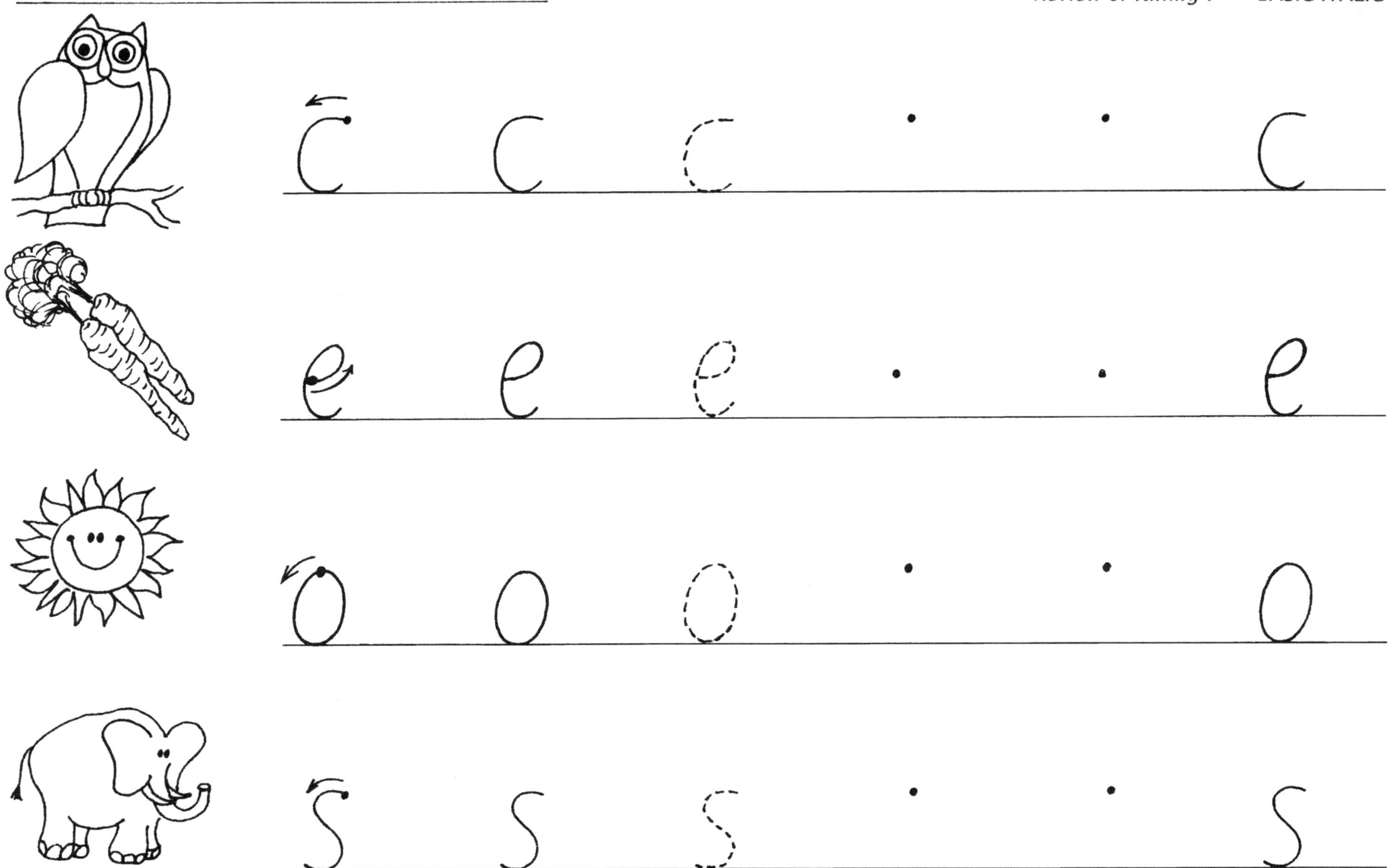

Ask the student to draw a line from the picture to the letter
that stands for the correct beginning sound.

CONTENTS

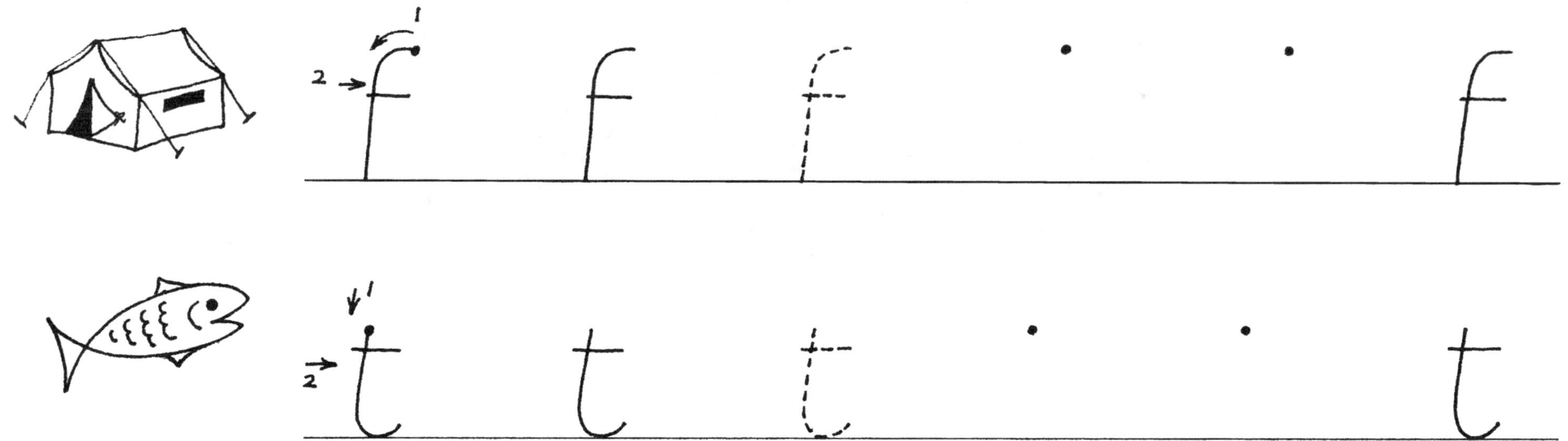

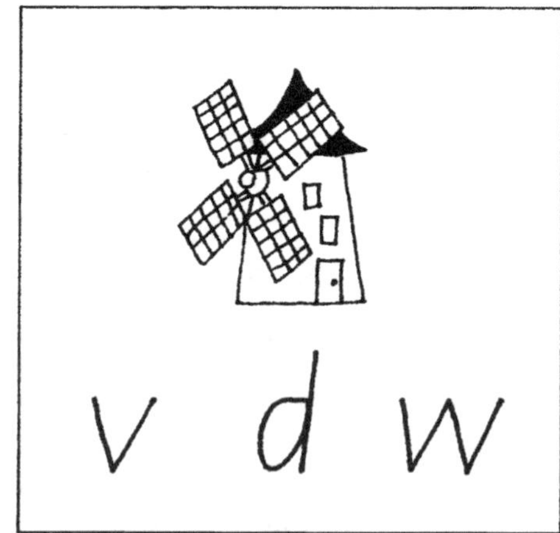

TOP TWO LINES: Ask the student to draw a line from the picture to the letter that stands for the correct beginning sound.

BOTTOM FOUR SQUARES: Ask the student to circle the letter that stands for the beginning sound of the picture.

by

Barbara Getty & Inga Dubay

GETTY-DUBAY™ ITALIC HANDWRITING SERIES

BOOK A ▪ Basic Italic
14 mm body height

BOOK B ▪ Basic Italic
11 mm body height, 9 mm

BOOK C ▪ Basic & Cursive Italic
9 mm, 6 mm body height   Introduction to Cursive Italic

BOOK D ▪ Basic & Cursive Italic
6 mm, 5 mm body height

BOOK E ▪ Basic & Cursive Italic
6 mm, 5 mm, 4 mm body height

BOOK F ▪ Basic & Cursive Italic
6 mm, 5 mm, 4 mm body height

BOOK G ▪ Basic & Cursive Italic
5 mm, 4 mm body height

INSTRUCTION MANUAL

BOOK A ▪ INTERNATIONAL EDITION
Copyright 2012 by Barbara M. Getty and Inga S. Dubay
ISBN 978-0-9827762-7-8

FOURTH EDITION
Copyright 2012 by Barbara M. Getty and Inga S. Dubay
THIRD EDITION
Copyright 1999 by Barbara M. Getty and Inga S. Dubay
SECOND EDITION
Copyright 1986 by Barbara M. Getty and Inga S. Dubay
REVISED EDITION
Copyright 1980 by Barbara M. Getty and Inga S. Dubay
FIRST EDITION
Copyright 1979 by Barbara M. Getty and Inga S. Dubay

All rights reserved. This text may not be reproduced in whole or in part without the express written permission of the copyright holder.

Published by Handwriting Success, LLC,
Portland, Oregon USA

www.handwritingsuccess.com

Printed at various locations around the world by IngramSpark.

Cover Design: Sinda Markham
Front cover picture: Flowers of the sunflower family in the Ochoco National Forest, Oregon, USA
Back cover pictures: Columbine flower, Golden-mantled squirrel

www.ingramcontent.com/pod-product-compliance
Lightning Source LLC
Chambersburg PA
CBHW081423210726
48464CB00020B/1370

* 9 7 8 0 9 8 2 7 7 6 2 7 8 *

one stroke numeral · no lift

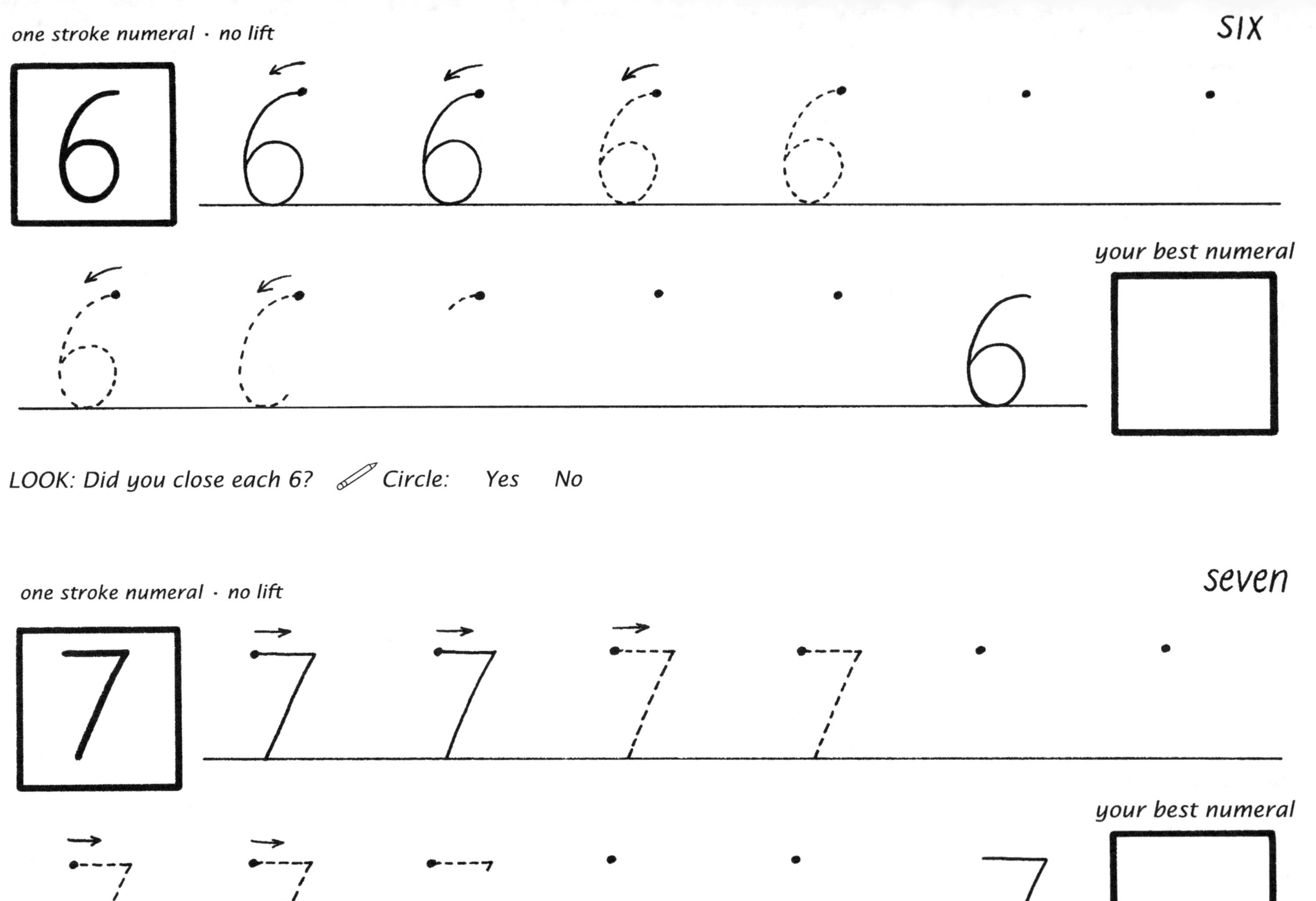

your best numeral

LOOK: Did you close each 6? Circle: Yes   No

seven

one stroke numeral · no lift

your best numeral

four

your best numeral

five

your best numeral

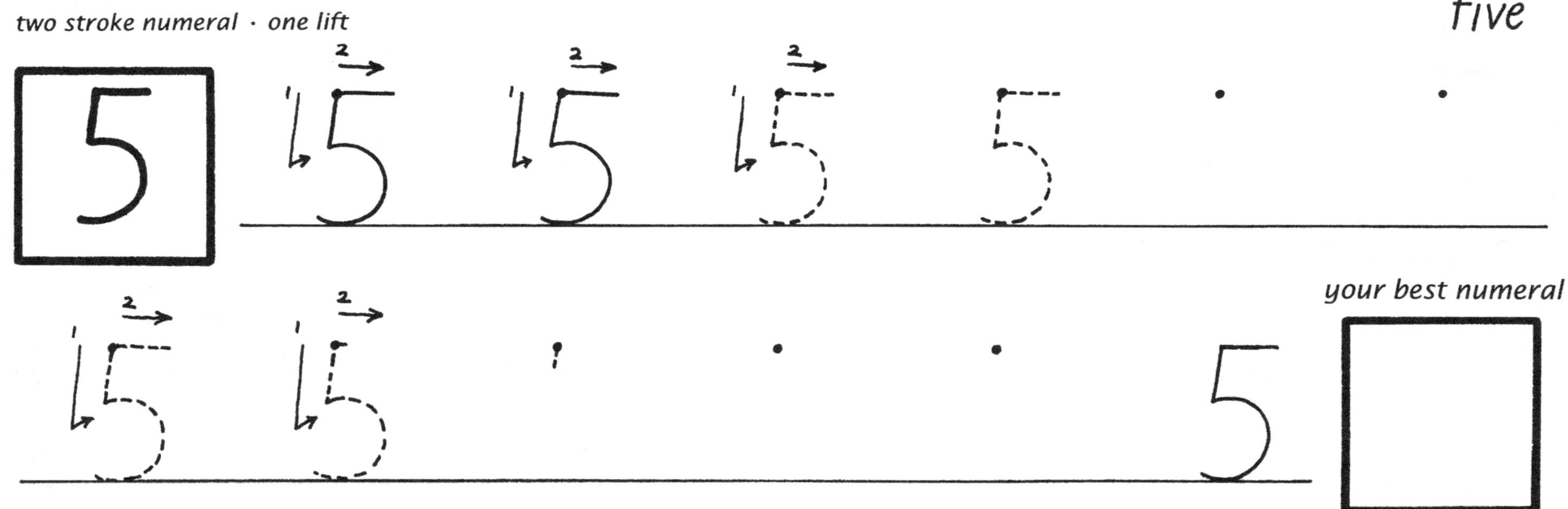

eight

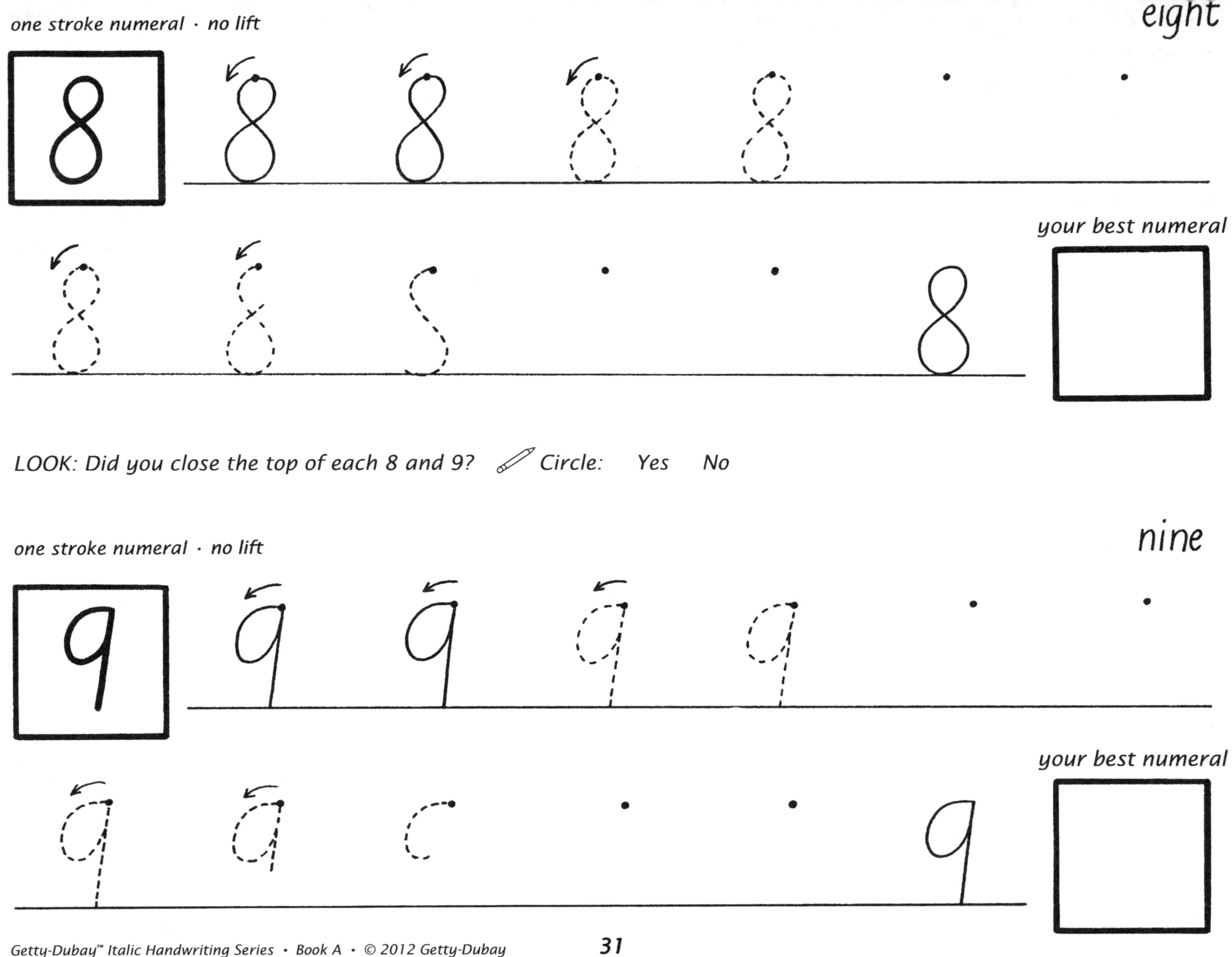

your best numeral

LOOK: Did you close the top of each 8 and 9?   Circle: Yes   No

one stroke numeral · no lift

nine

your best numeral

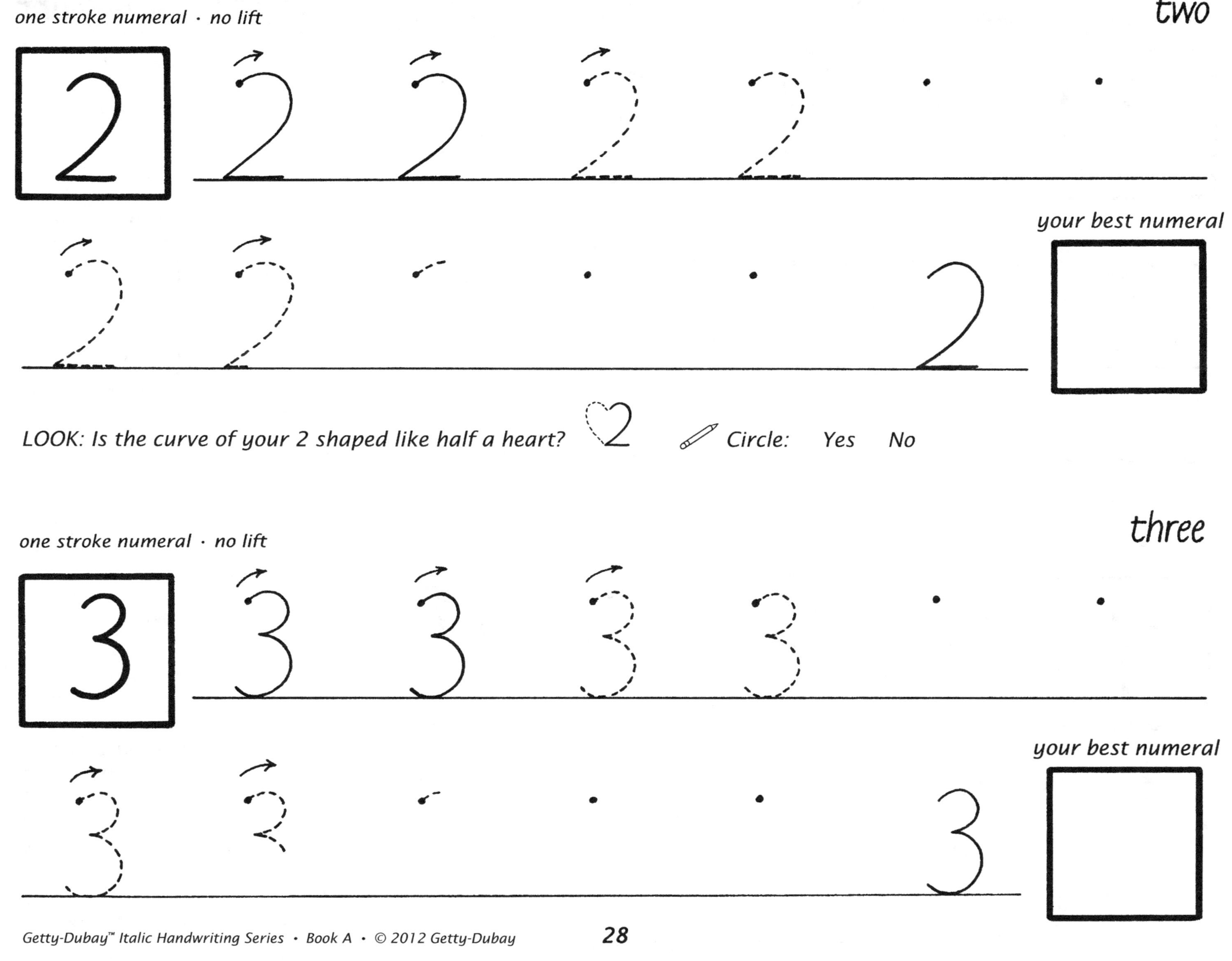

one stroke numeral · no lift
two
your best numeral
LOOK: Is the curve of your 2 shaped like half a heart?   Circle: Yes   No
one stroke numeral · no lift
three
your best numeral

6 3 1

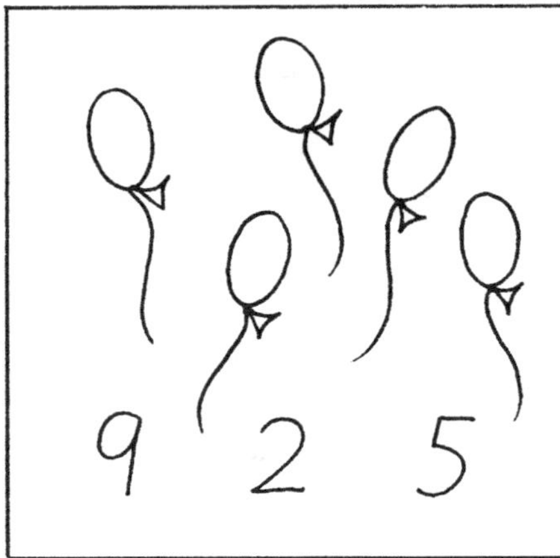

9 2 5

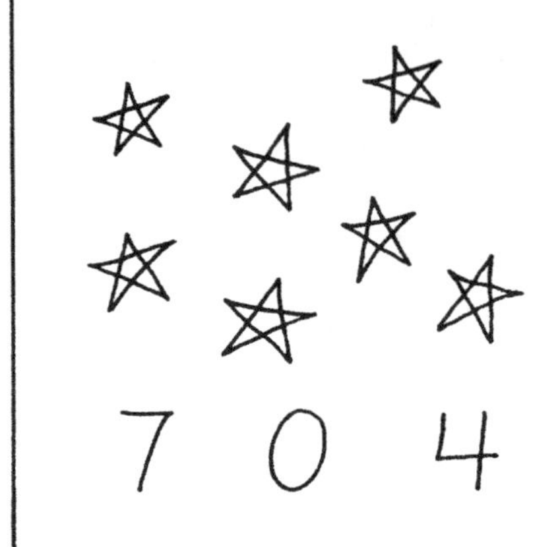

7 0 4

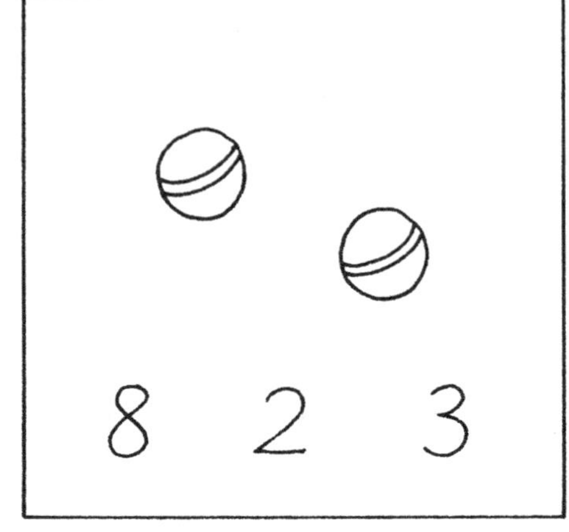

8 2 3

3 4 2

9 5 6

7 1 6

2 8 6

*Ask the student to circle the numeral
that stands for the number of objects in the box.*

one stroke numeral · no lift

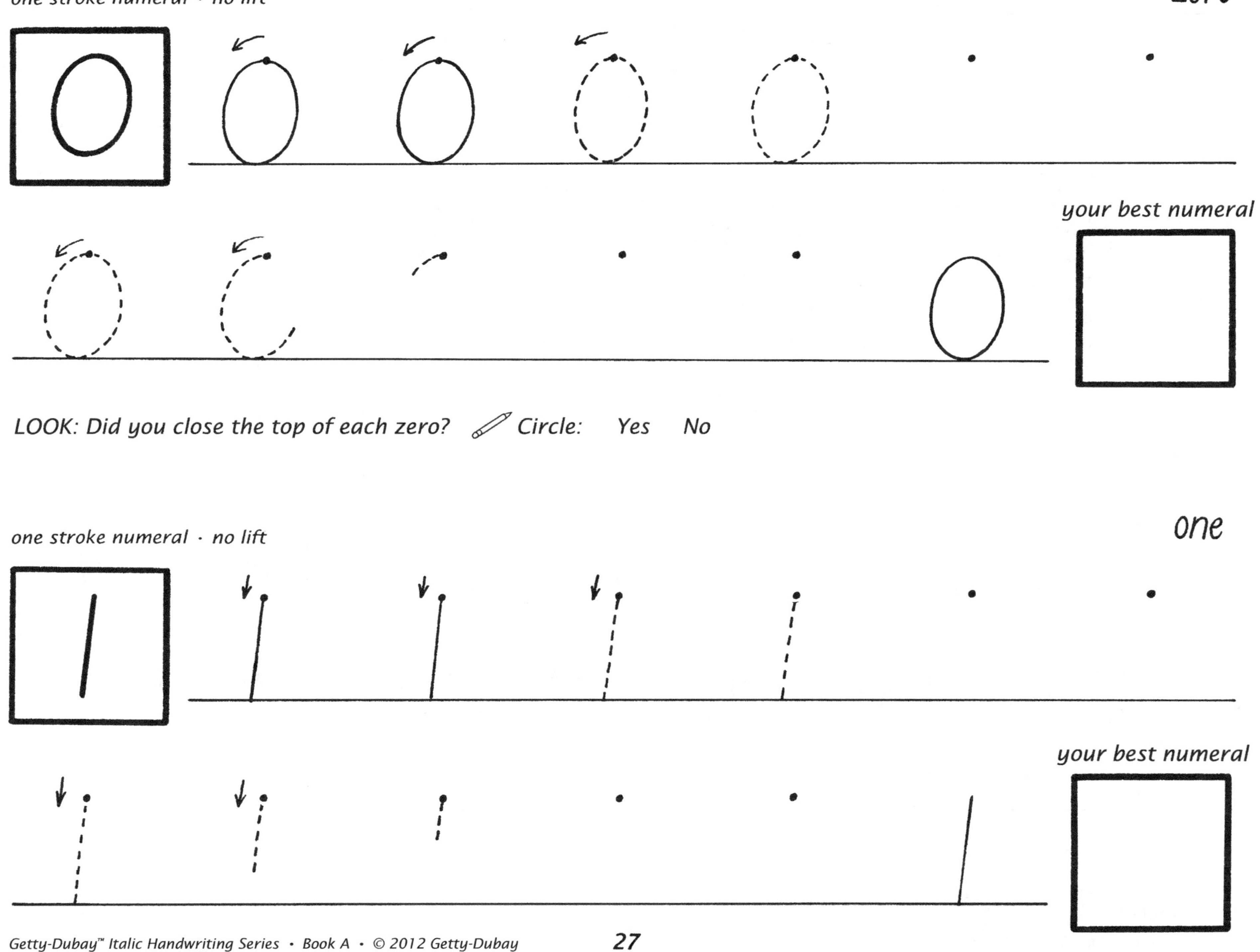

your best numeral

LOOK: Did you close the top of each zero? Circle: Yes   No

one stroke numeral · no lift

one

your best numeral

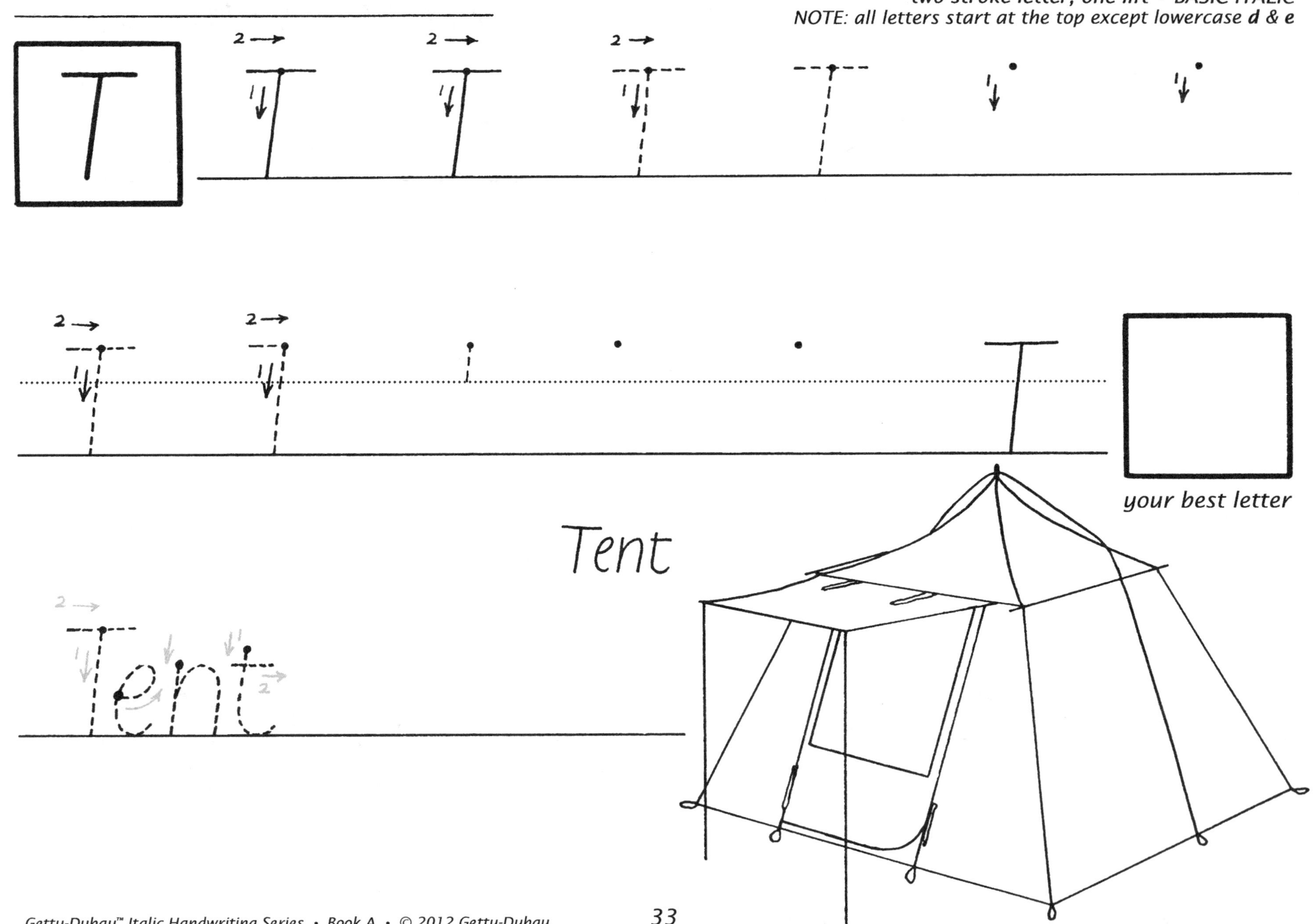

Tent

your best letter

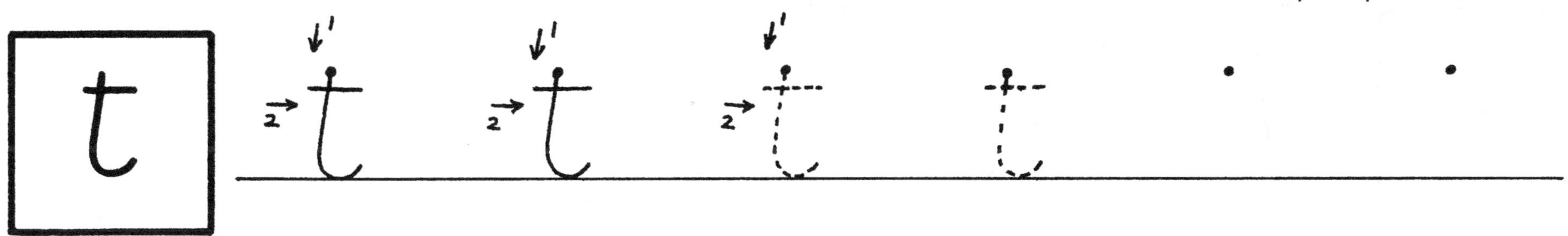

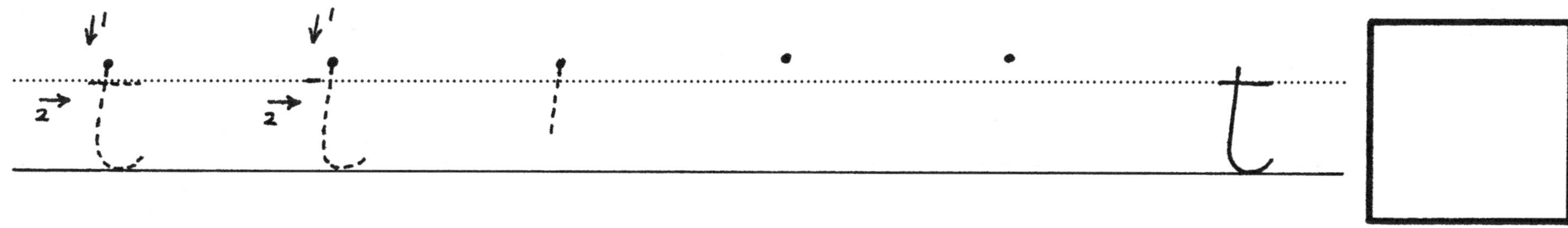

your best letter

turkey

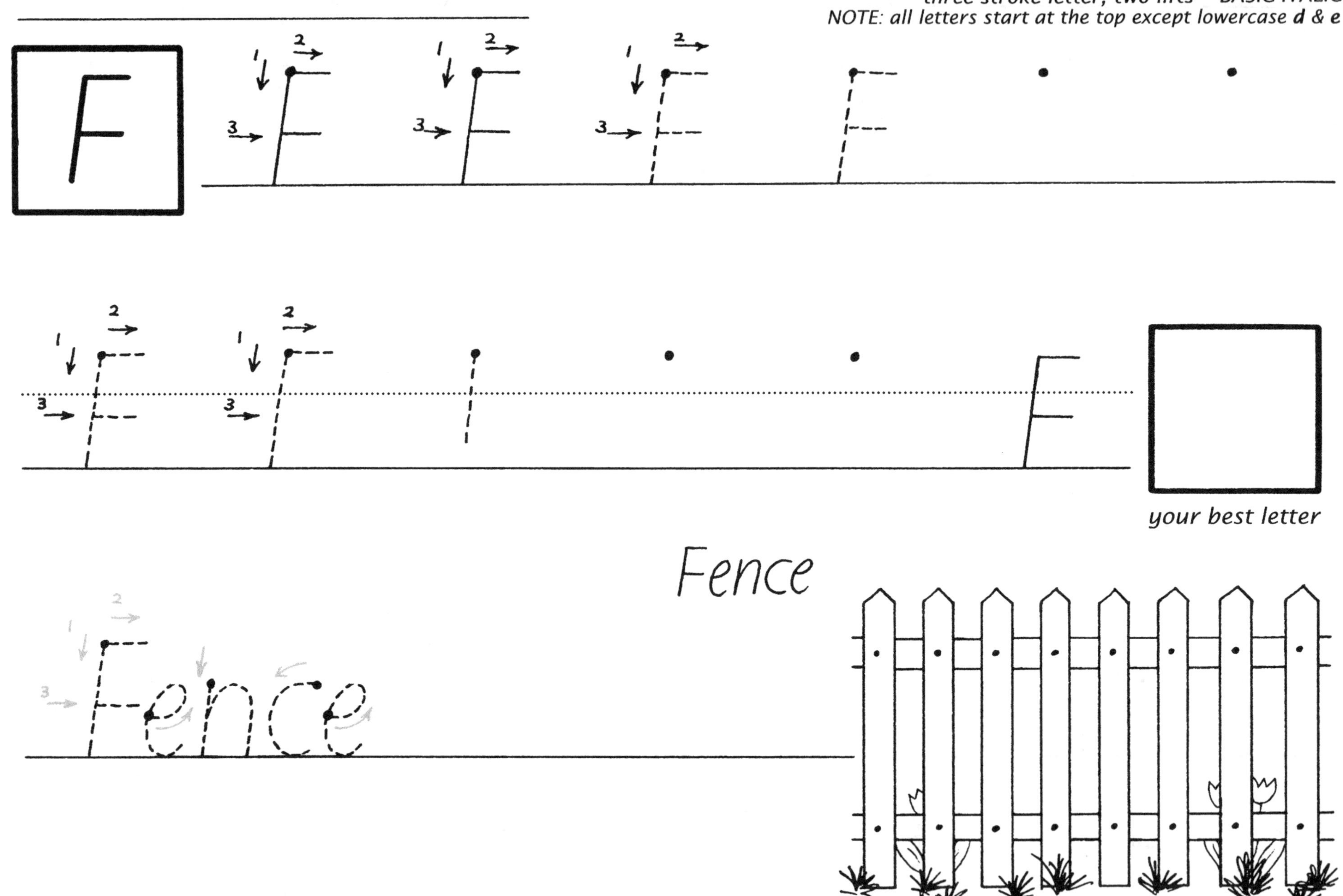

your best letter

Fence

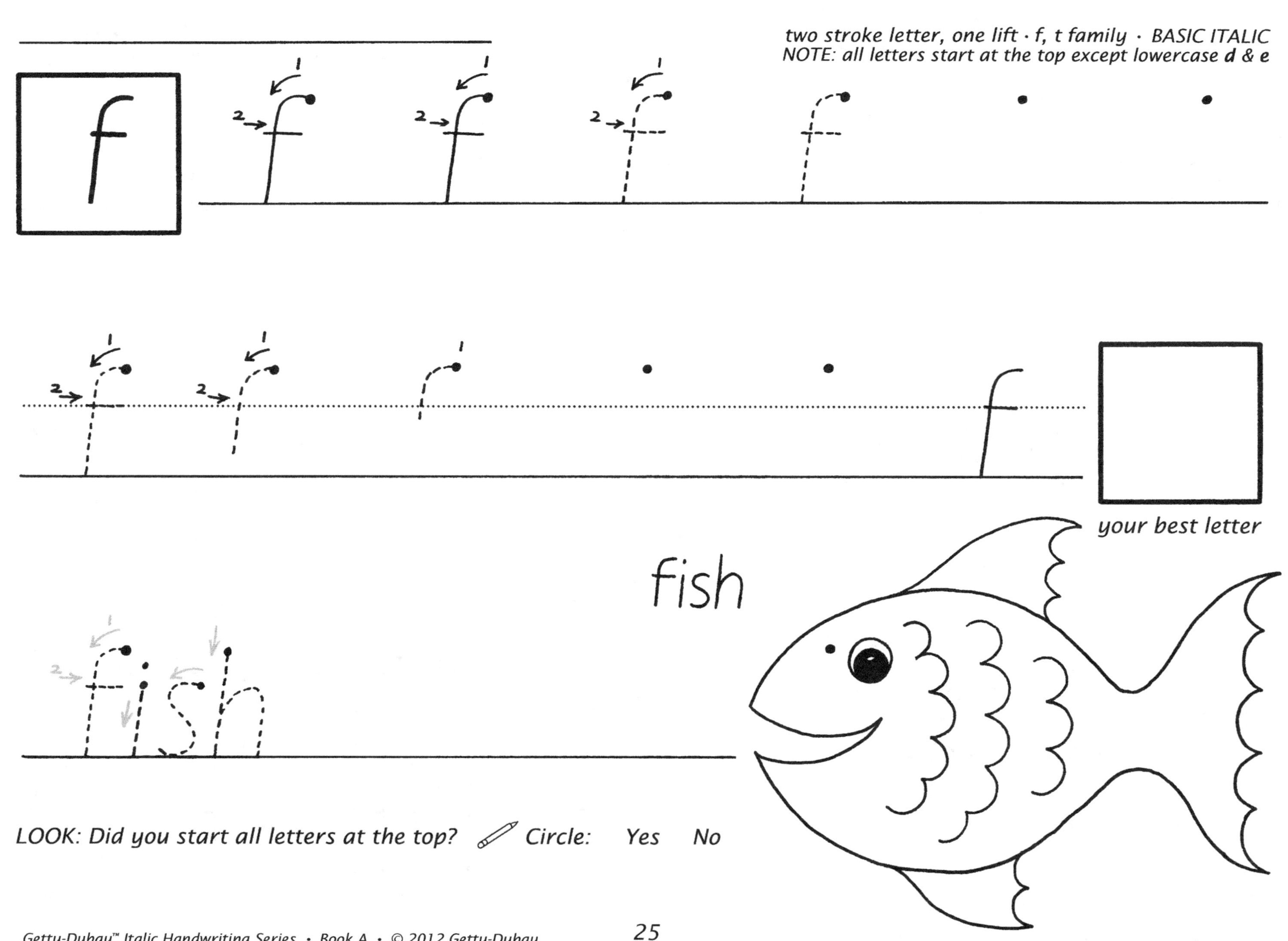

two stroke letter, one lift · f, t family · BASIC ITALIC
NOTE: all letters start at the top except lowercase d & e
f
your best letter
fish
fish
LOOK: Did you start all letters at the top?   Circle: Yes   No

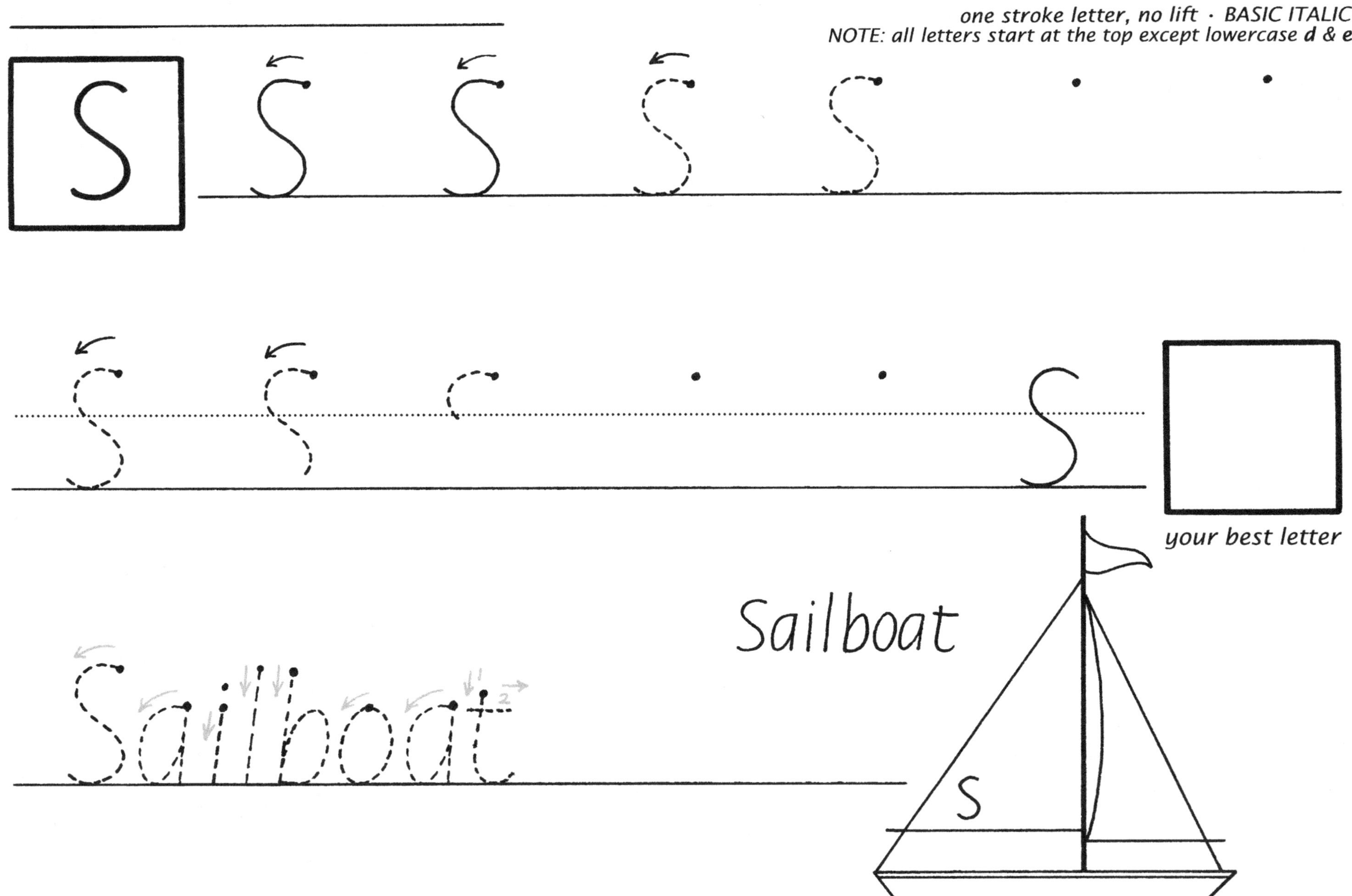
your best letter
Sailboat
S

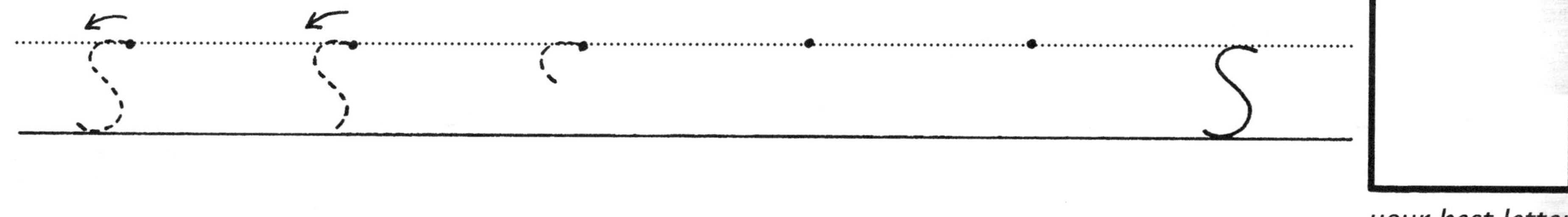

your best letter

sun

your best letter
Cow
LOOK: Did you trace each letter before writing your own?
Circle: Yes   No

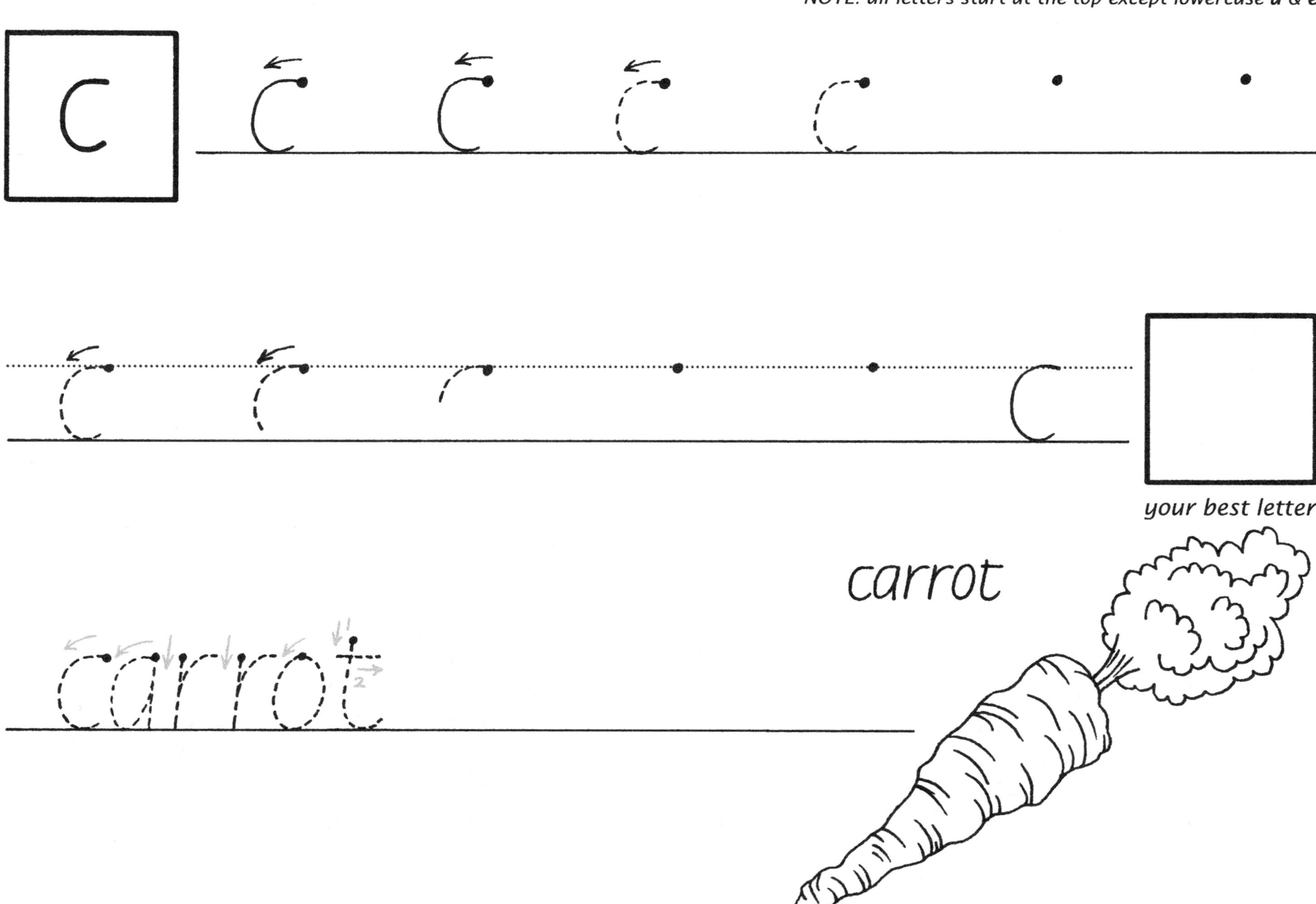

your best letter

carrot

E

2 3 1

2 3 1

2 3 1

2 1

2 3 1

2 1

your best letter

Egg

Egg

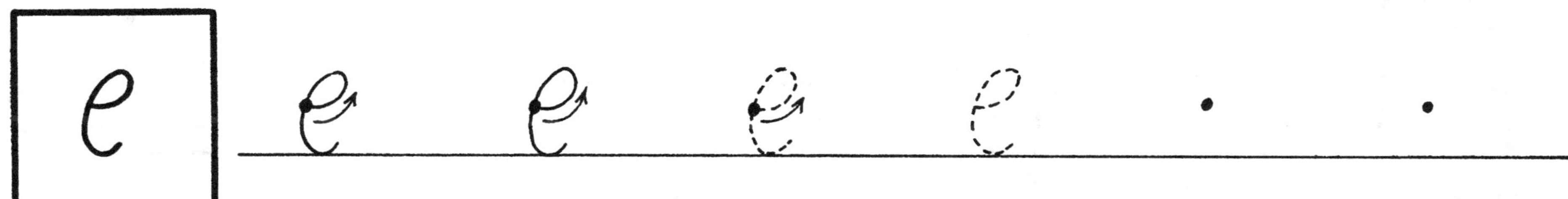

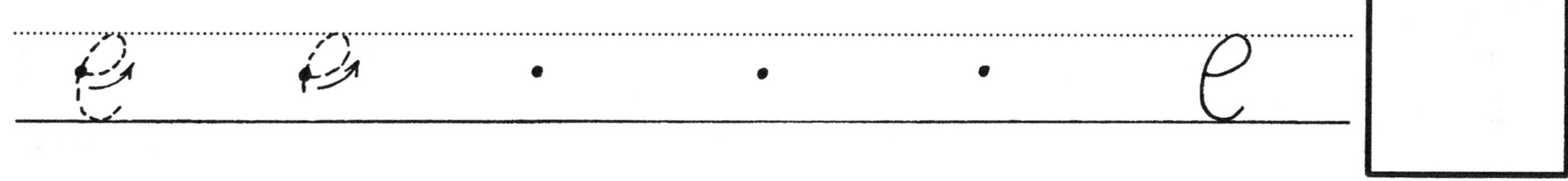

your best letter

elephant

LOOK: Did you trace each **e** before writing your own?

Circle: Yes   No

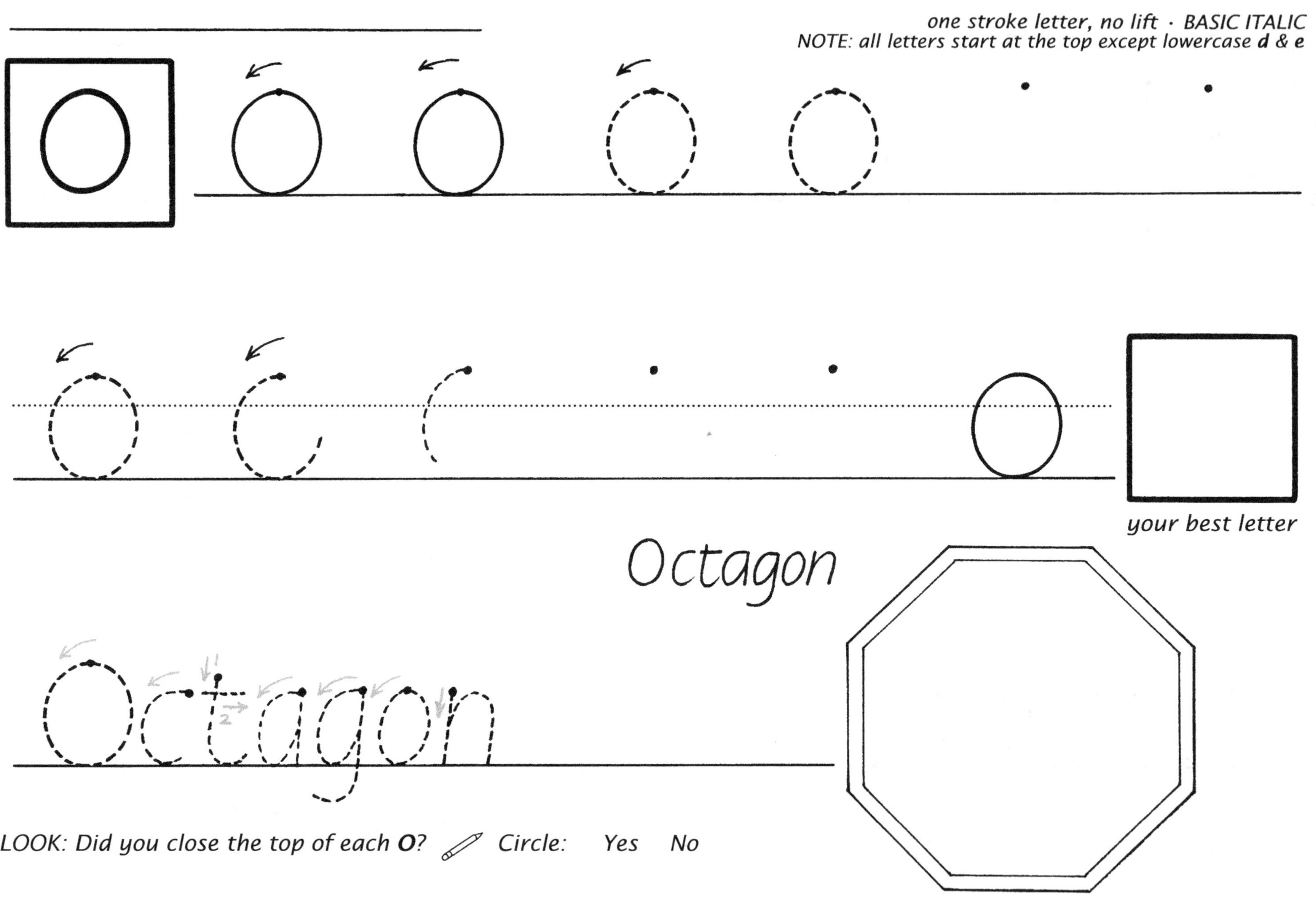

LOOK: Did you close the top of each **O**?   Circle: Yes   No

octopus

your best letter

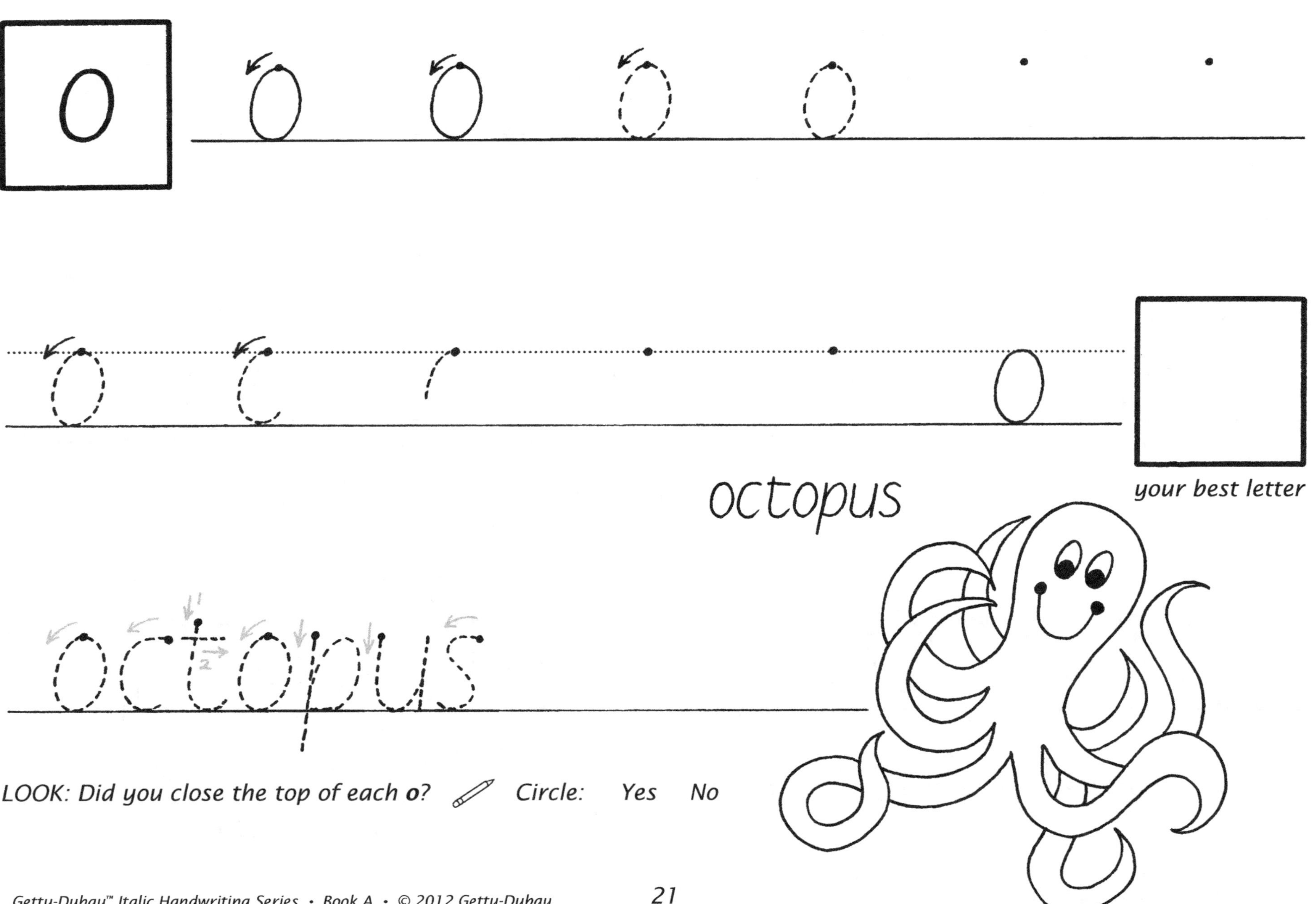

LOOK: Did you close the top of each **o**? Circle: Yes   No

your best letter

Peacock

parrot

your best letter

B B B B B

B P i B

your best letter

Balloons

Balloons

your best letter

butterfly

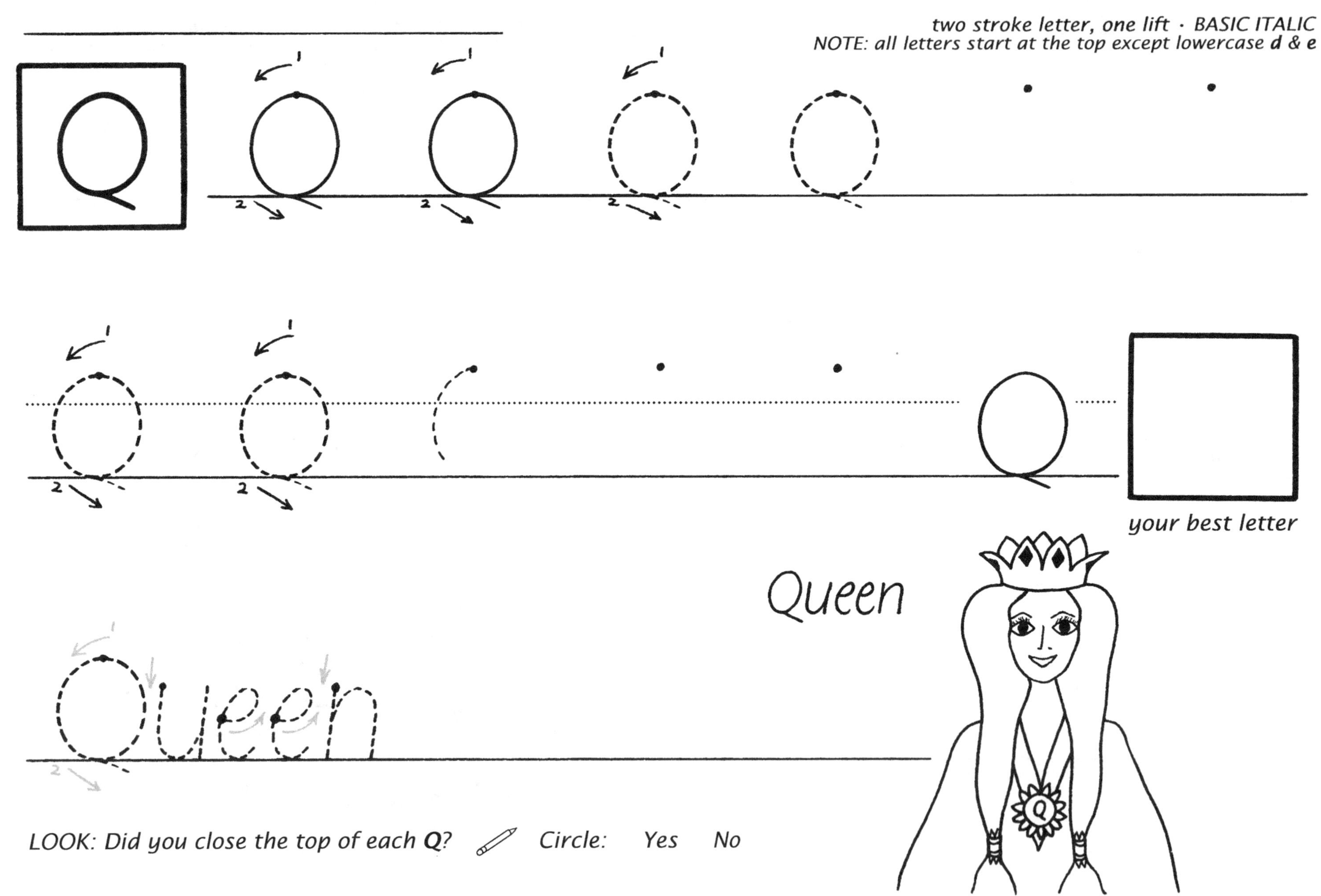

your best letter

Queen

LOOK: Did you close the top of each **Q**?   Circle: Yes   No

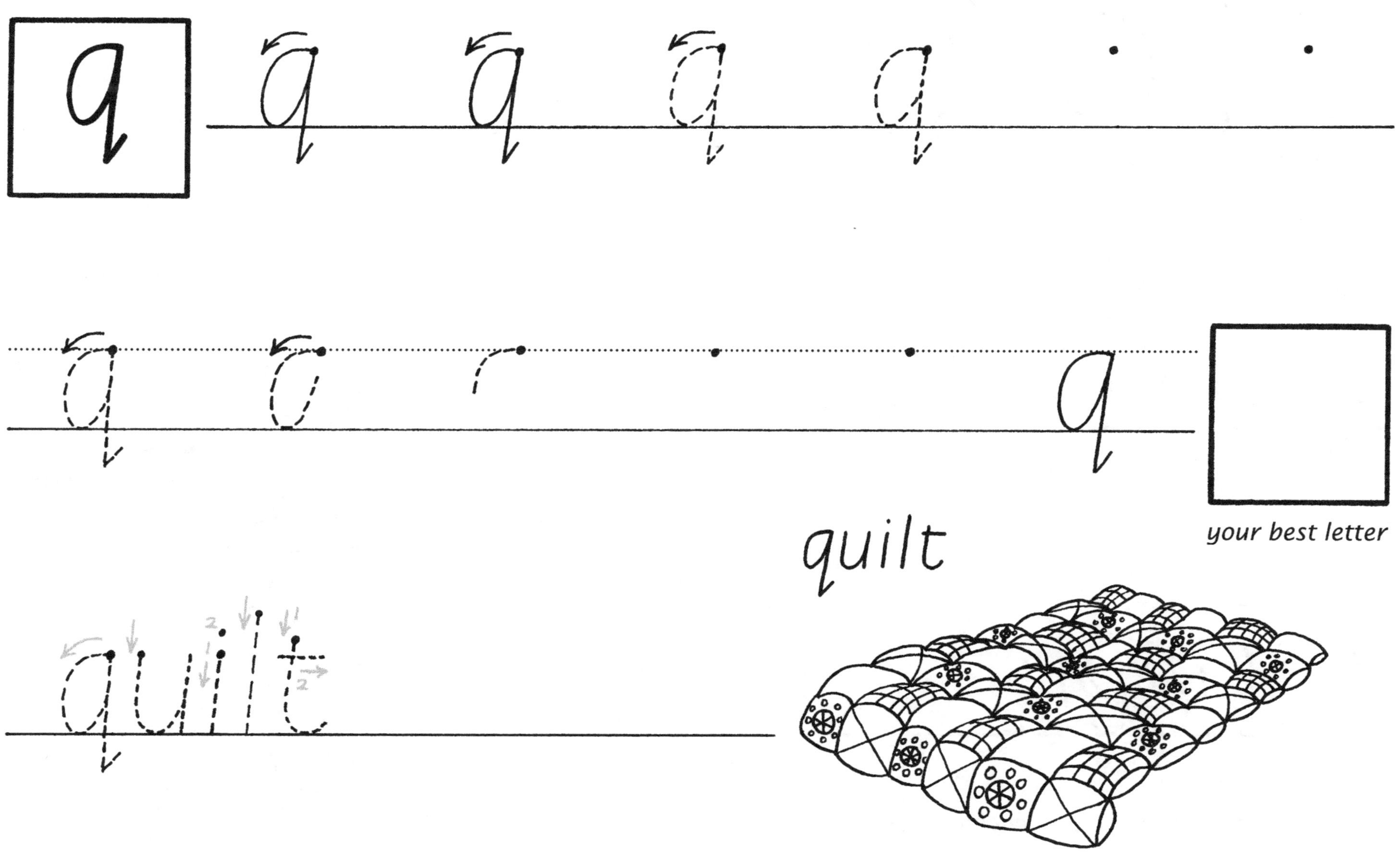

your best letter

quilt

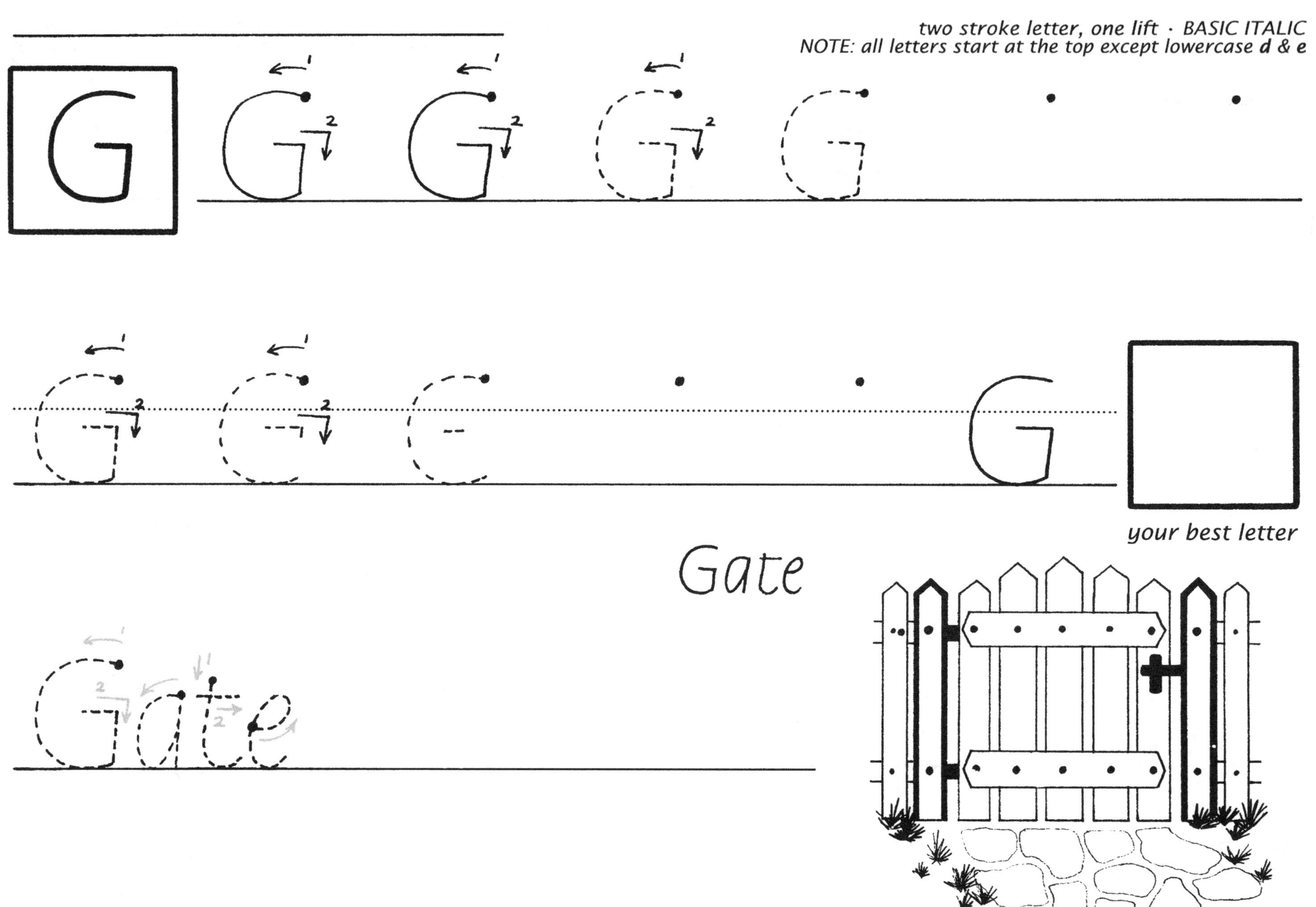

your best letter

Gate

your best letter

goat

LOOK: Did you trace each letter before writing your own? ✎ Circle: Yes   No

Dinosaur
your best letter
Dinosaur

your best letter
dog

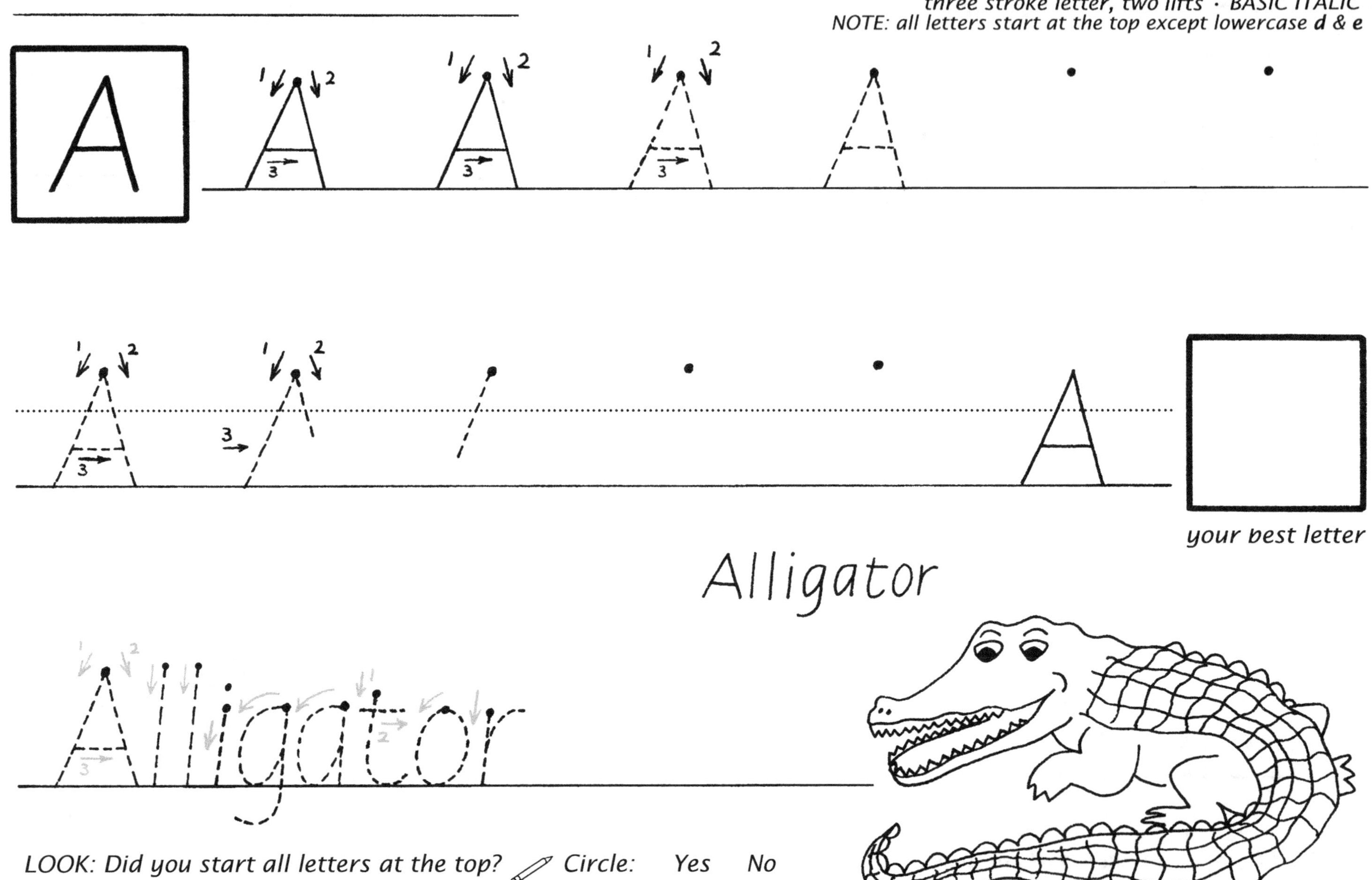

your best letter

Alligator

LOOK: Did you start all letters at the top? Circle: Yes   No

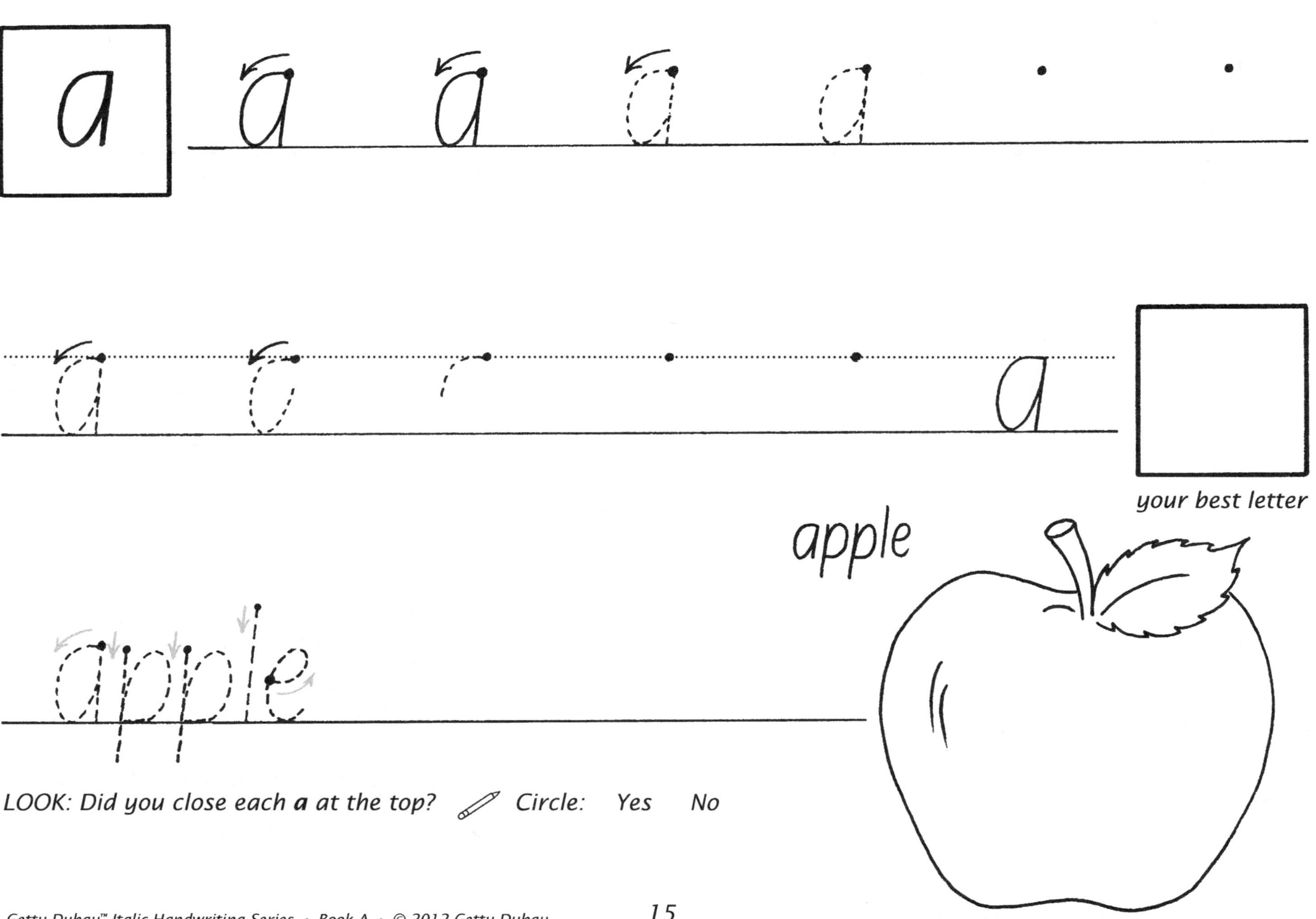
your best letter
apple
apple
LOOK: Did you close each **a** at the top?   Circle: Yes   No

two stroke letter, one lift · BASIC ITALIC
NOTE: all letters start at the top except lowercase *d* & *e*

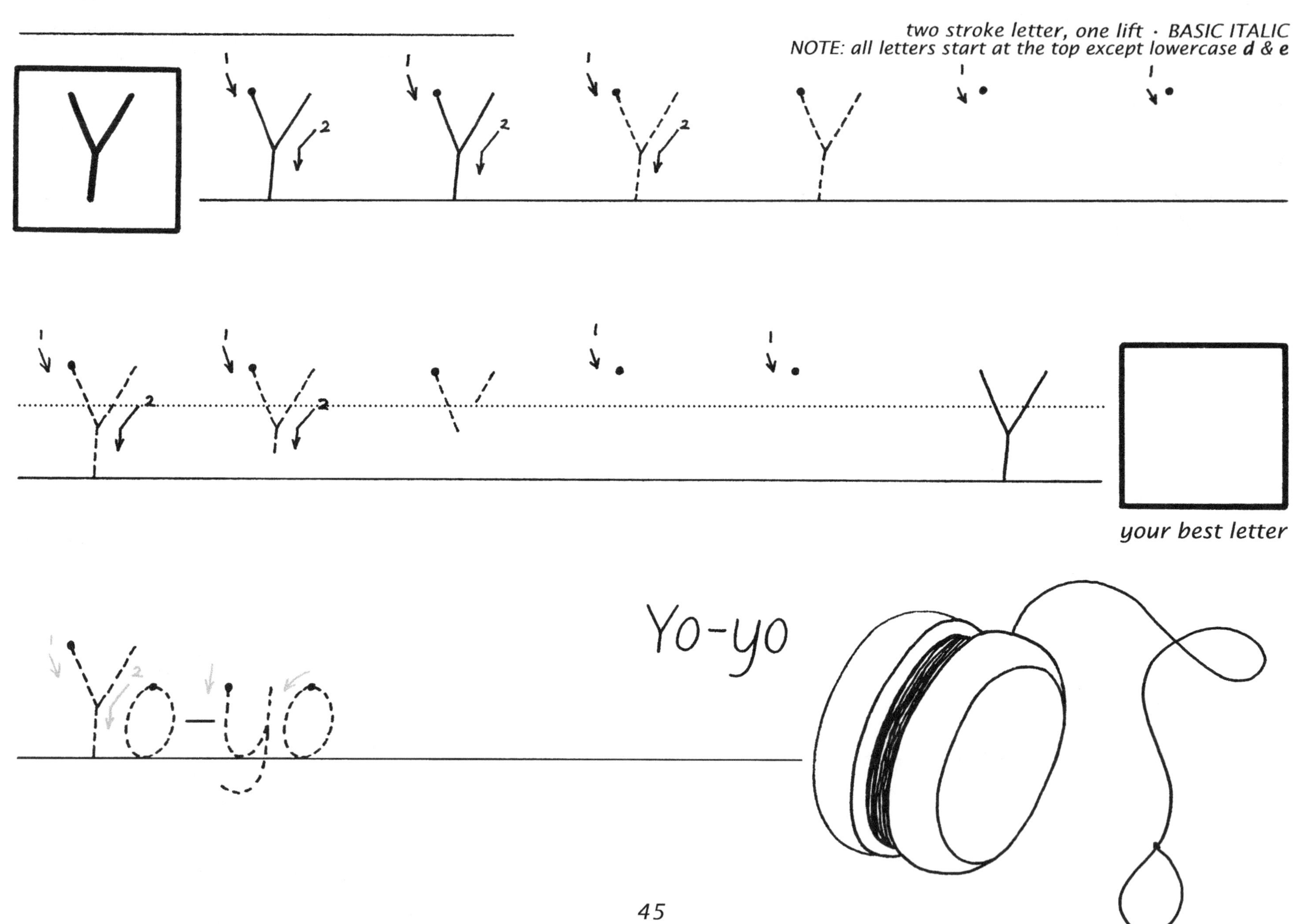

your best letter

Yo-yo

Getty-Dubay™ Italic Handwriting Series · Book A · © 2012 Getty-Dubay

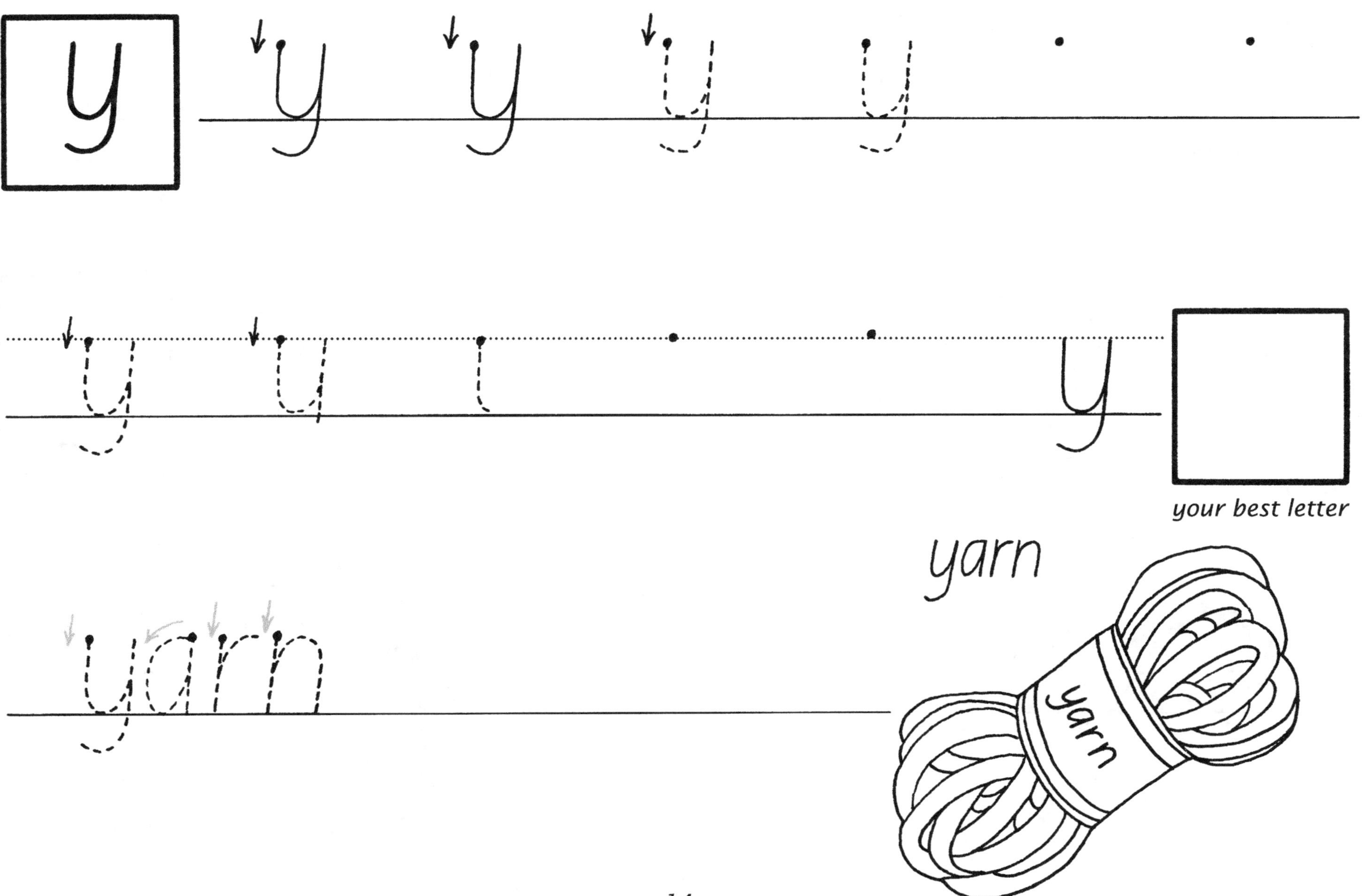

your best letter
yarn

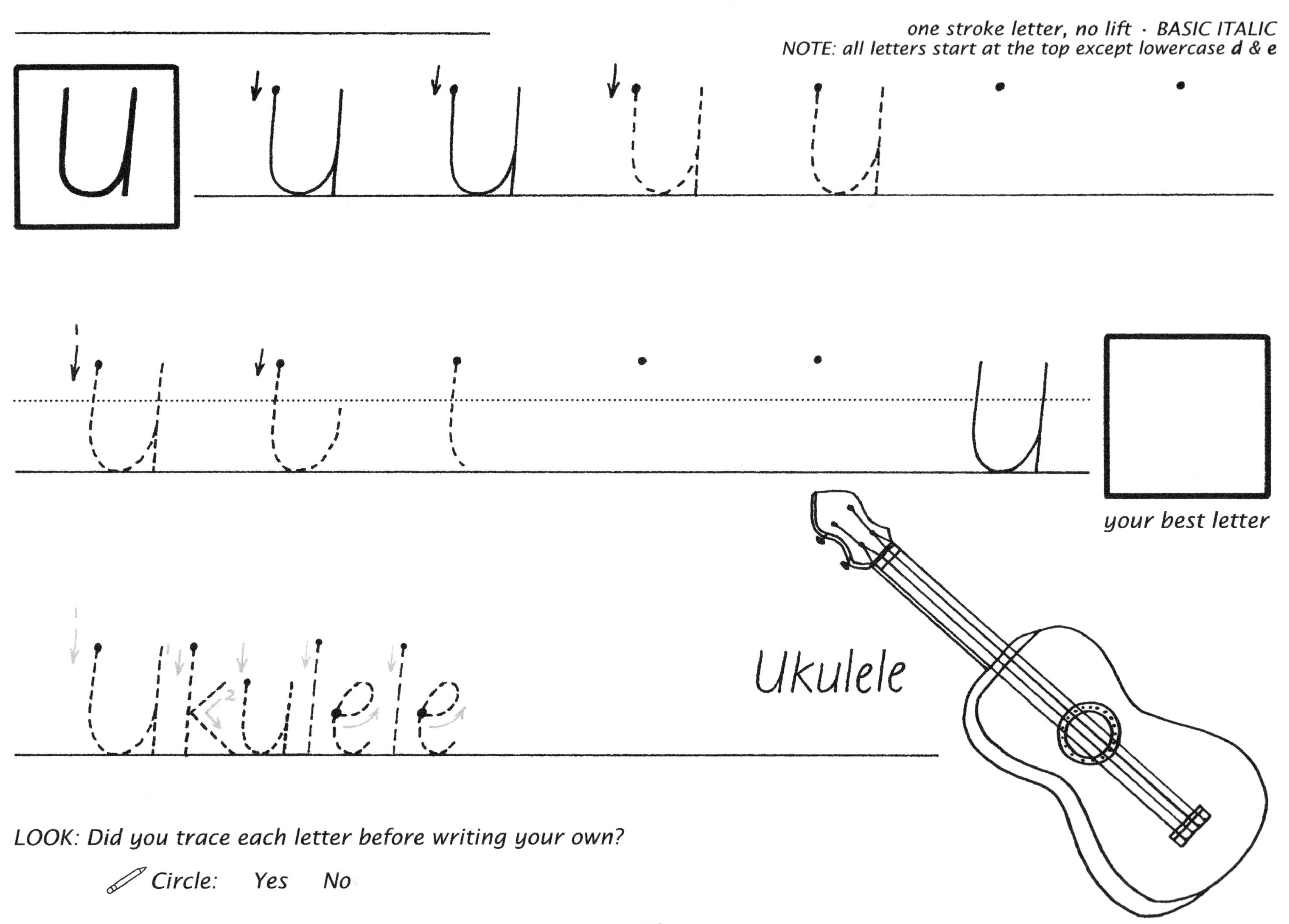

one stroke letter, no lift · BASIC ITALIC
NOTE: all letters start at the top except lowercase d & e
your best letter
Ukulele
LOOK: Did you trace each letter before writing your own?
Circle: Yes   No

u

your best letter

umbrella

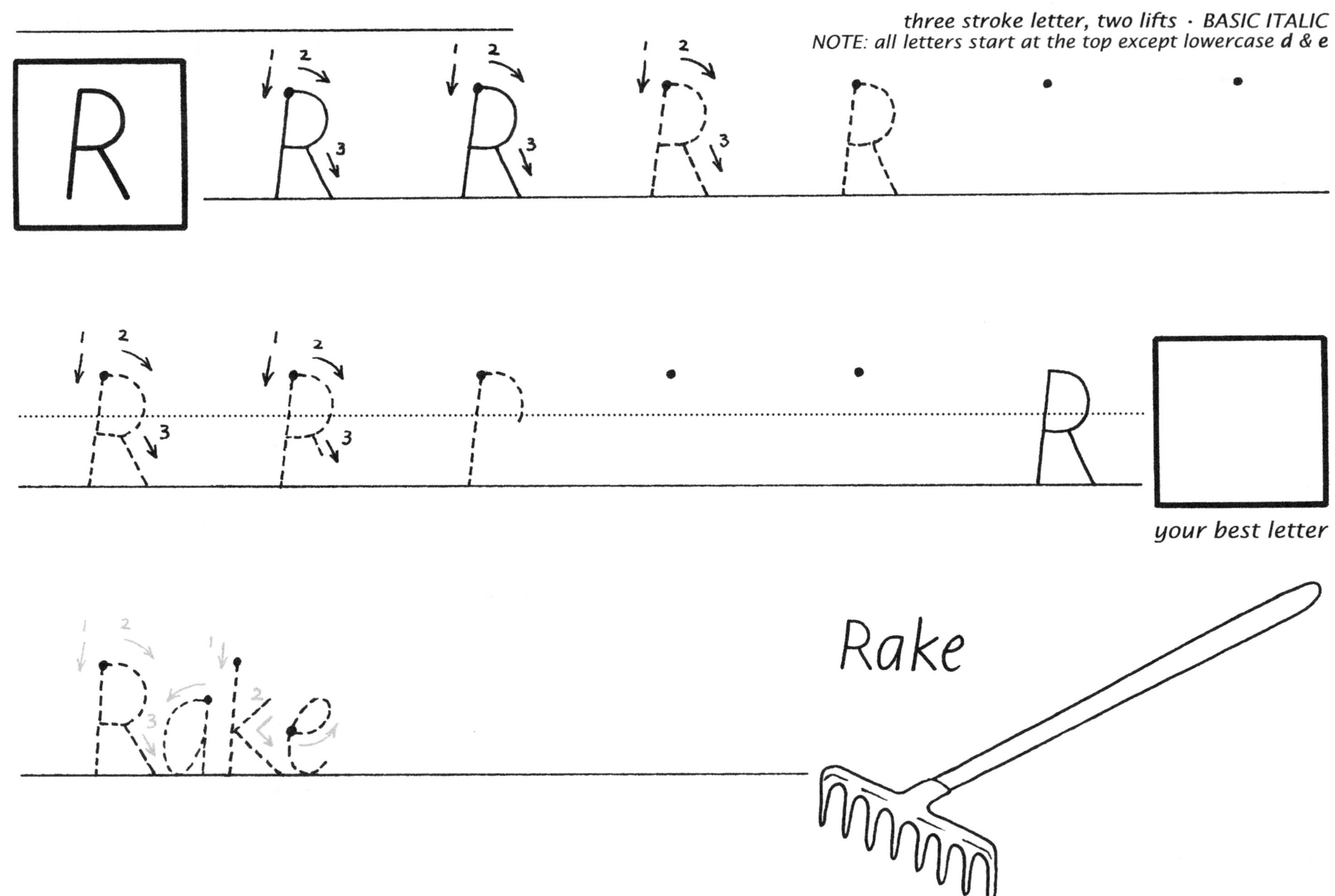

your best letter
Rake

your best letter

rabbit

LOOK: Did you start each letter at the top?   Circle: Yes   No

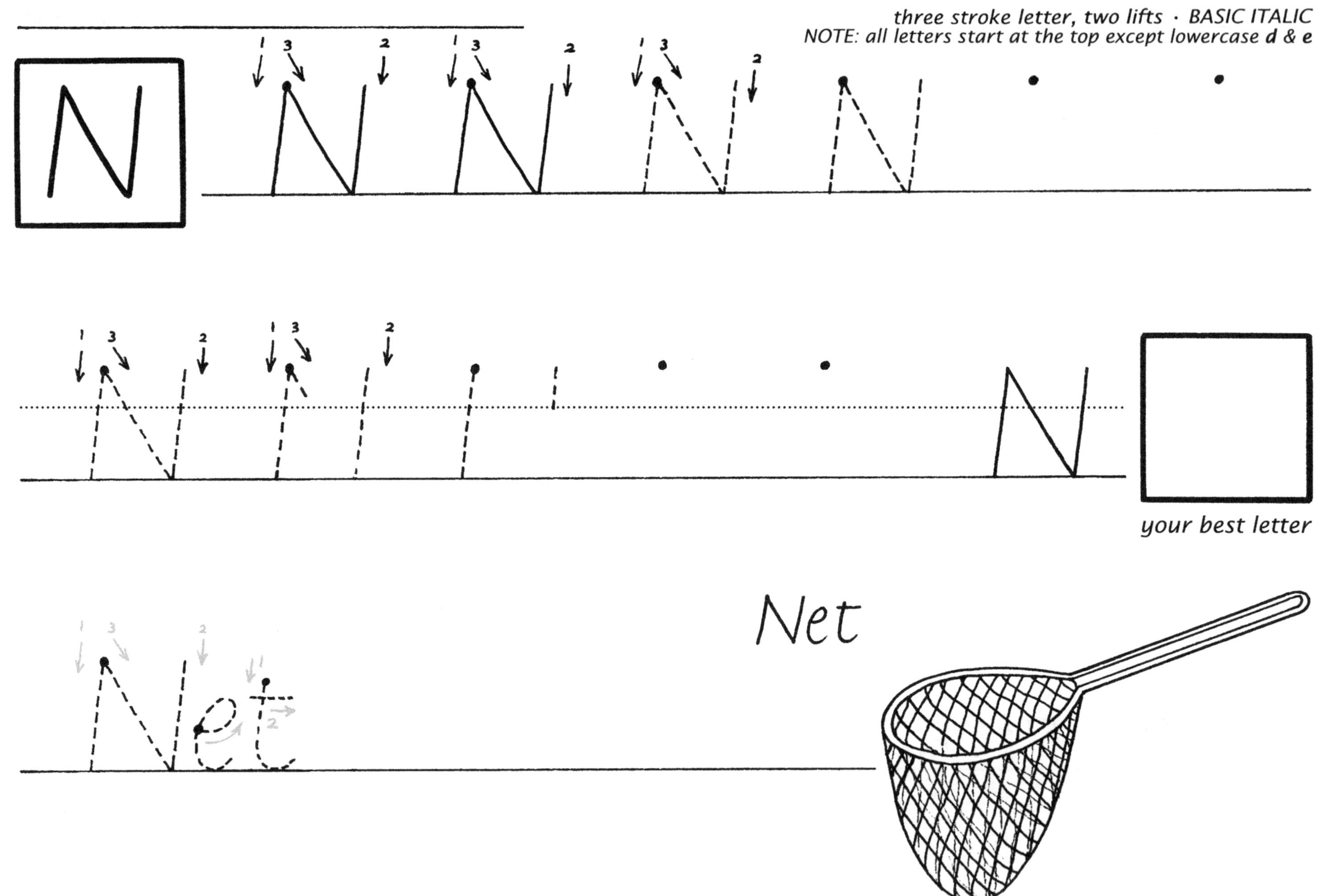

three stroke letter, two lifts · BASIC ITALIC
NOTE: all letters start at the top except lowercase d & e
your best letter
Net

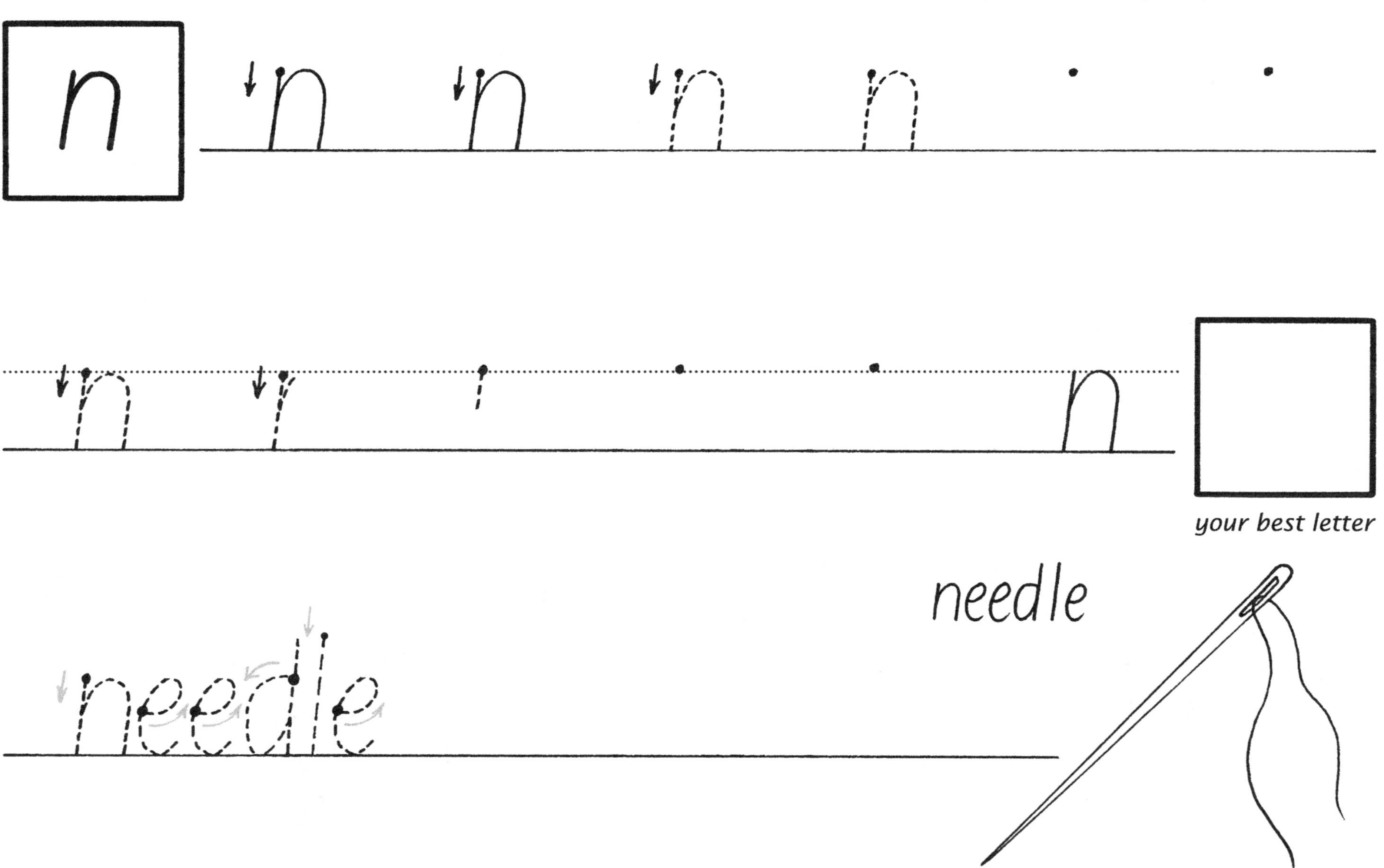

your best letter

needle

your best letter

Mittens

your best letter

LOOK: Did you start all letters at the top?   Circle: Yes   No

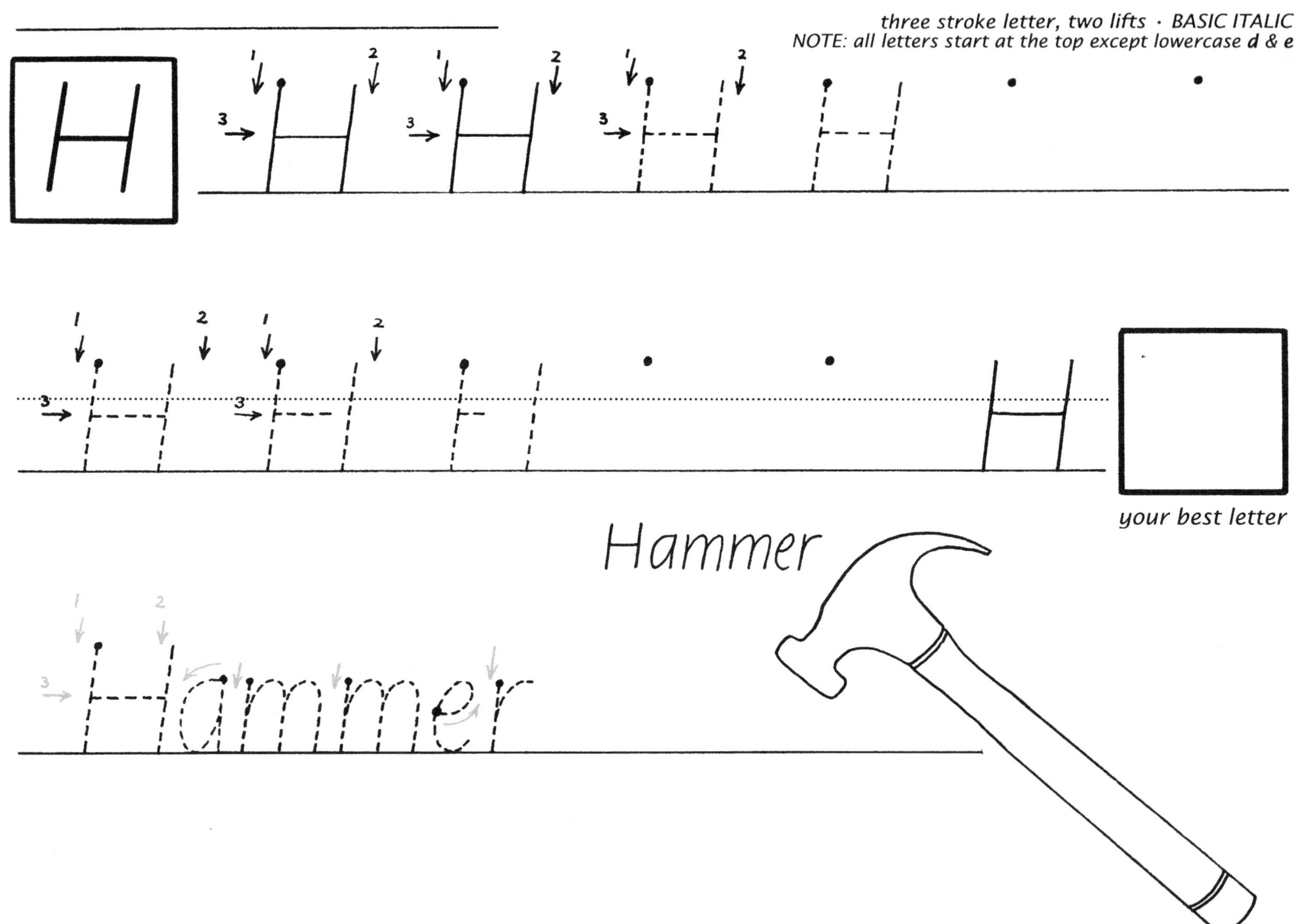
your best letter
Hammer
Hammer

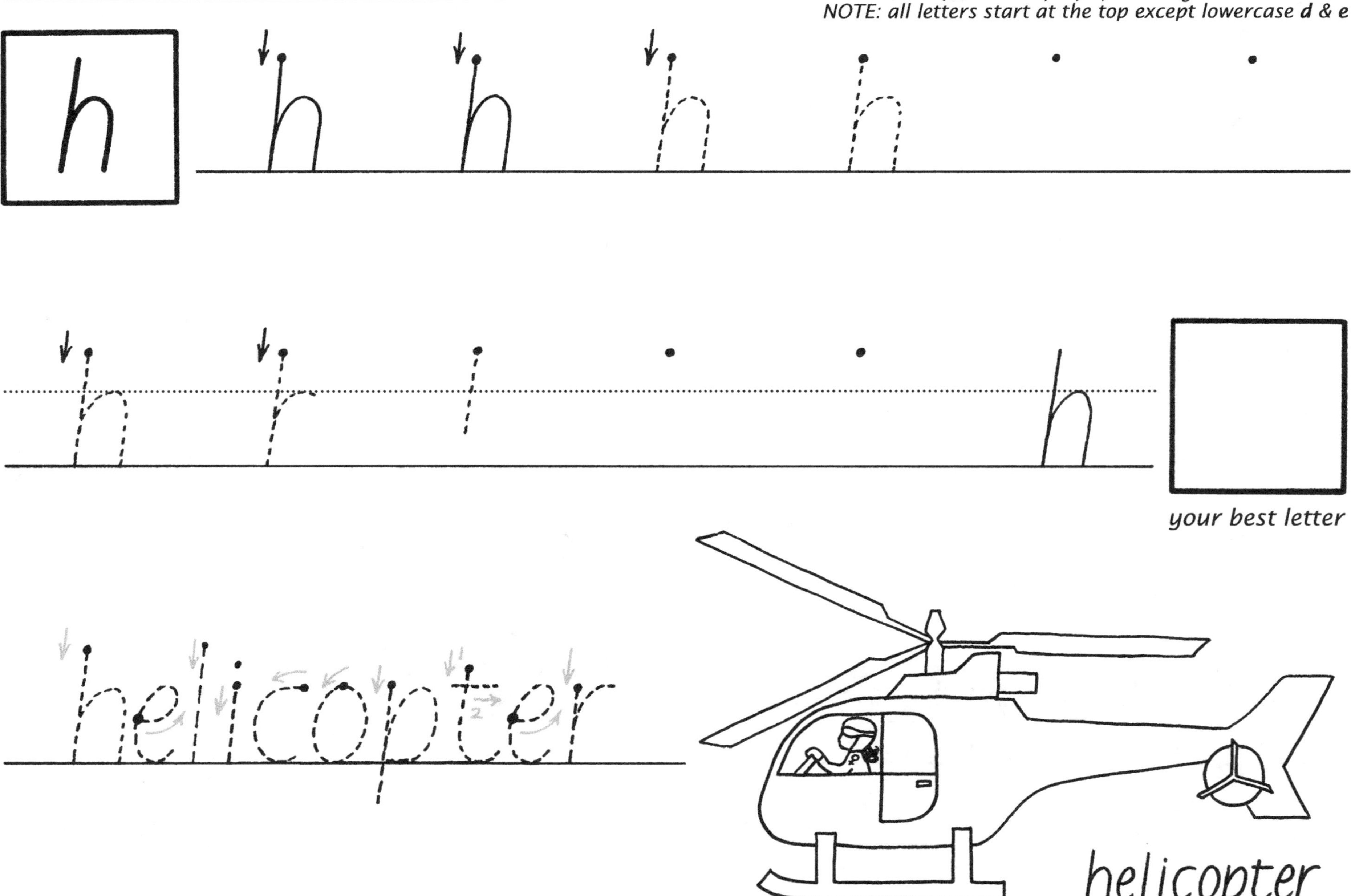

your best letter

helicopter

Z

your best letter

Zipper

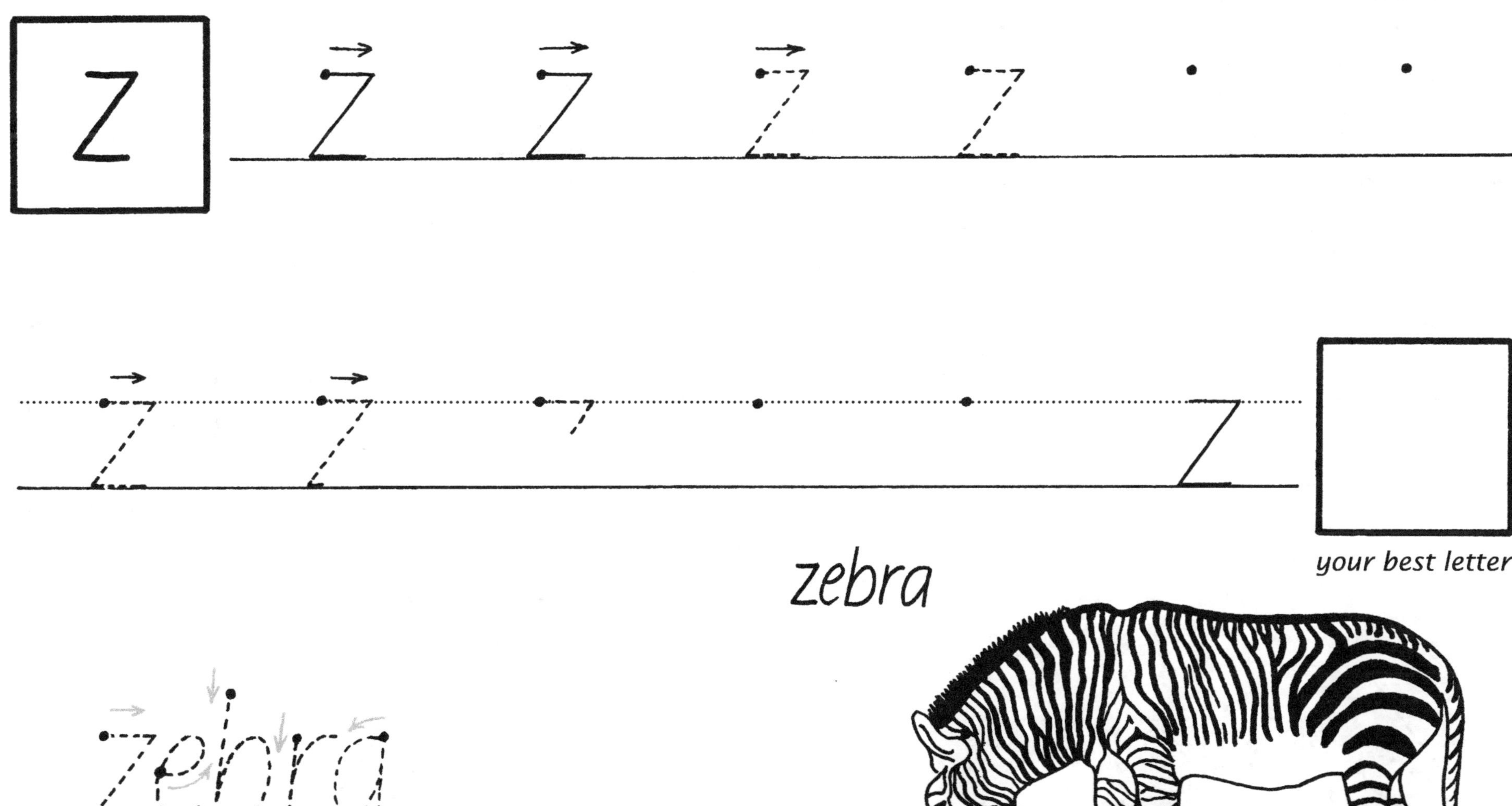

your best letter

zebra

LOOK: Did you trace each letter before writing your own?

Circle: Yes   No

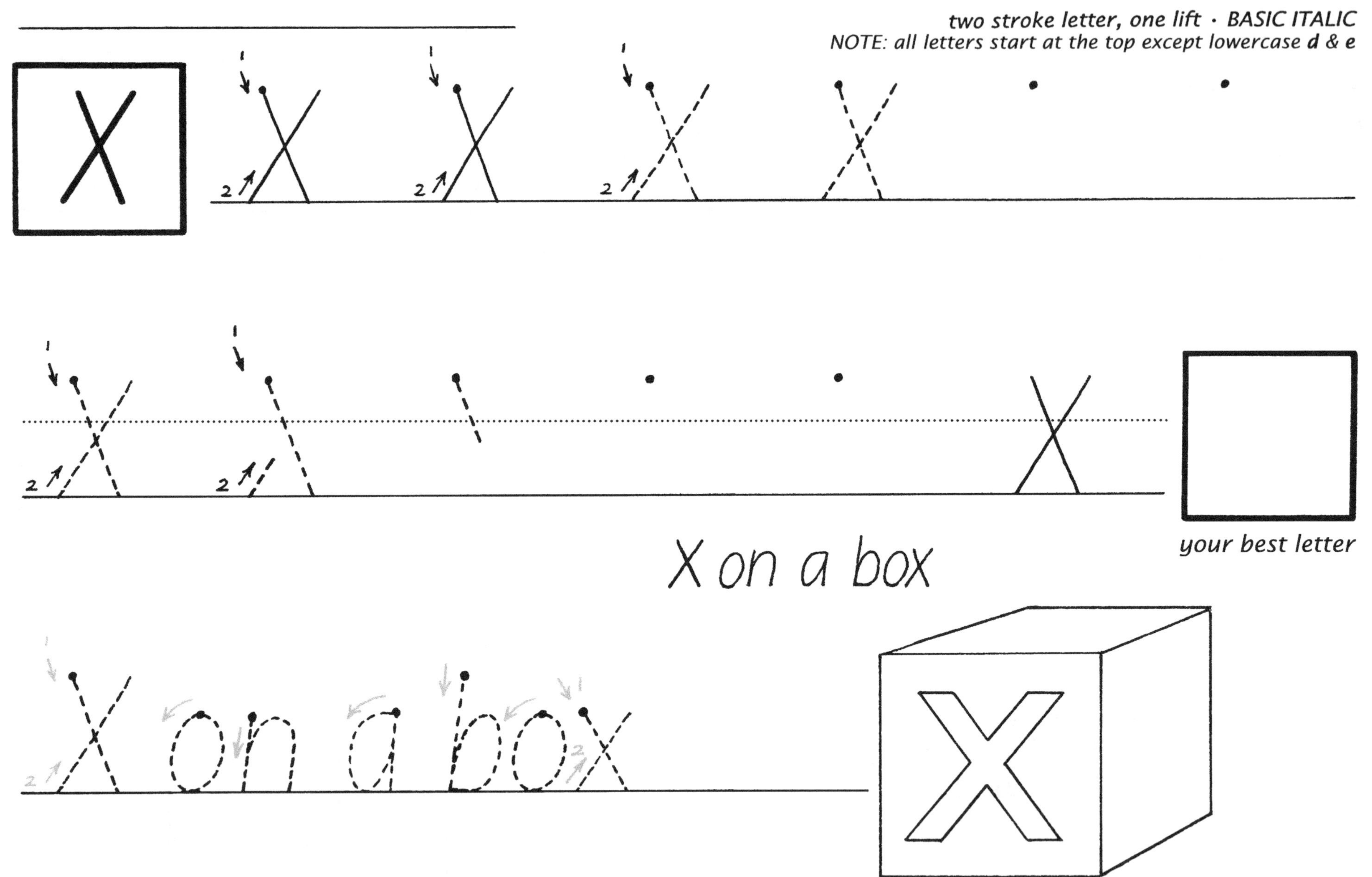

your best letter

X on a box

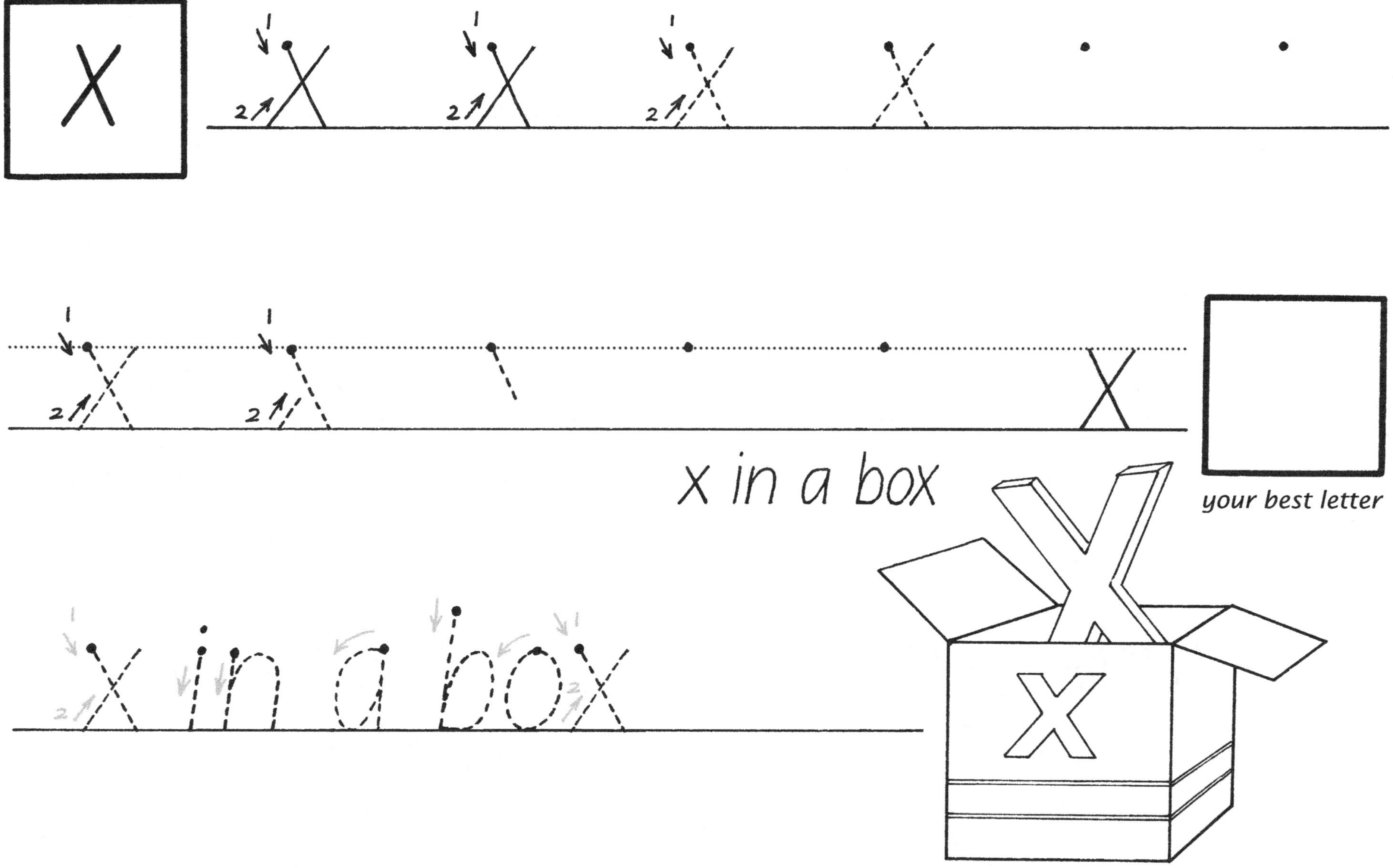

x in a box
your best letter
x in a box

W W W W W W · ·

w w w · · W

your best letter

Watch

your best letter

walrus

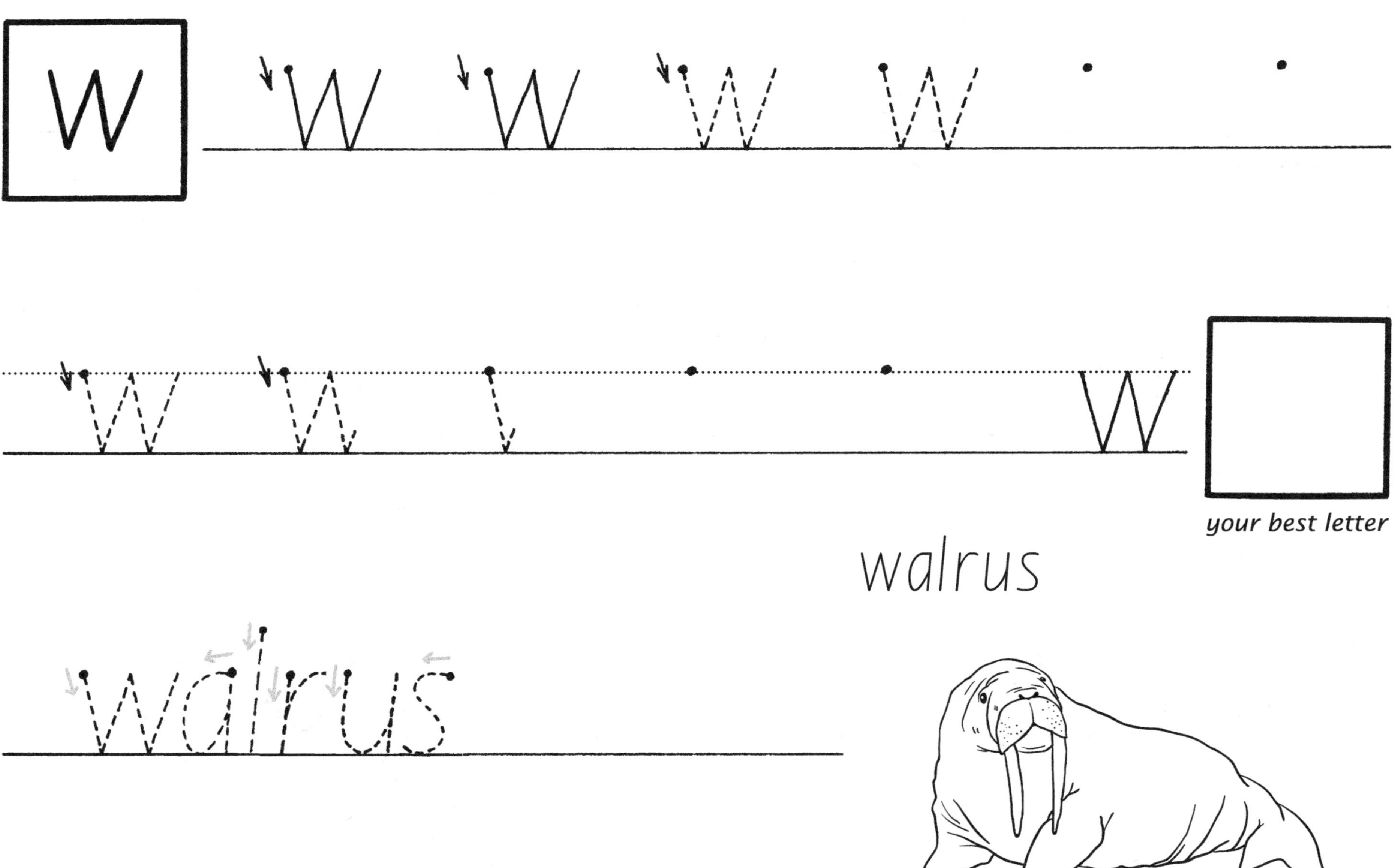

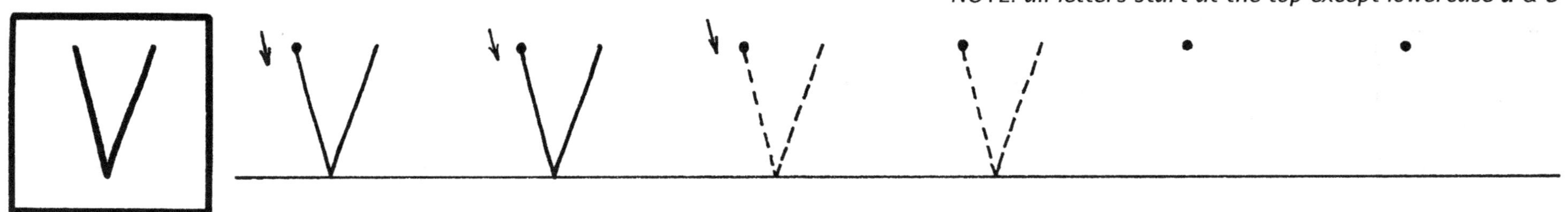

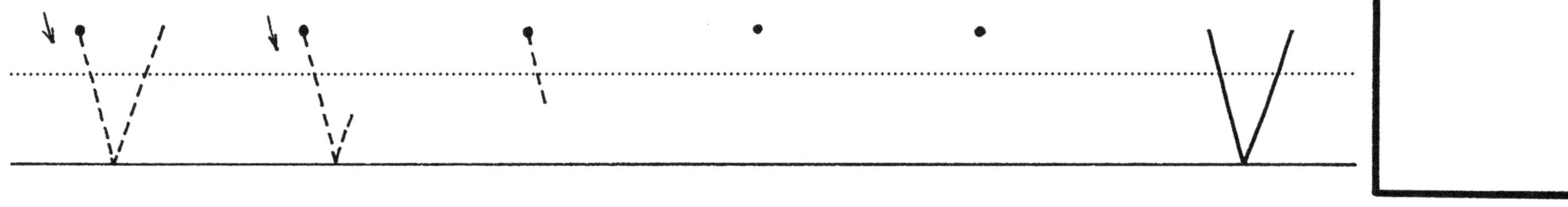

your best letter

Valentine

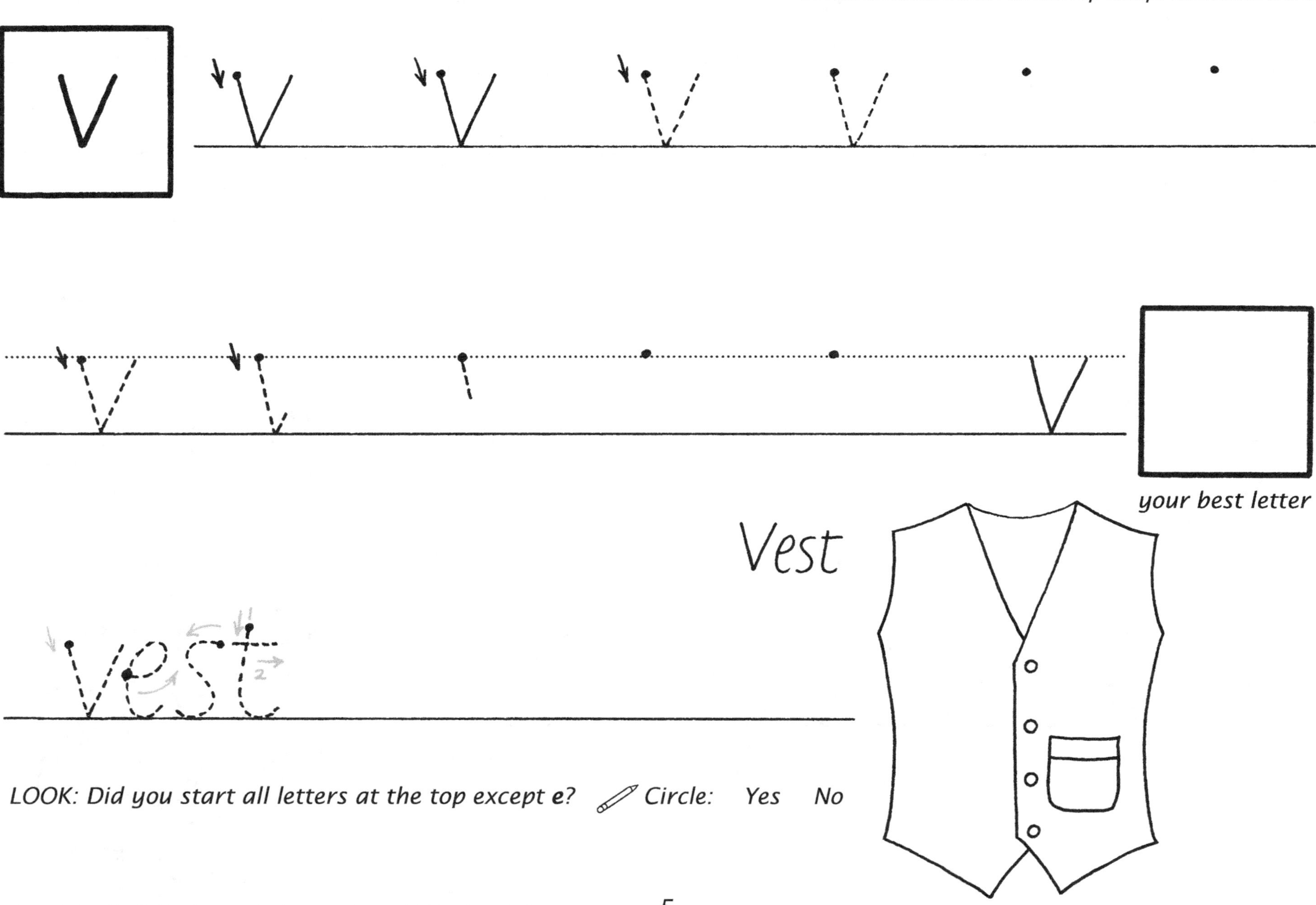

your best letter

Vest

LOOK: Did you start all letters at the top except *e*? Circle: Yes   No

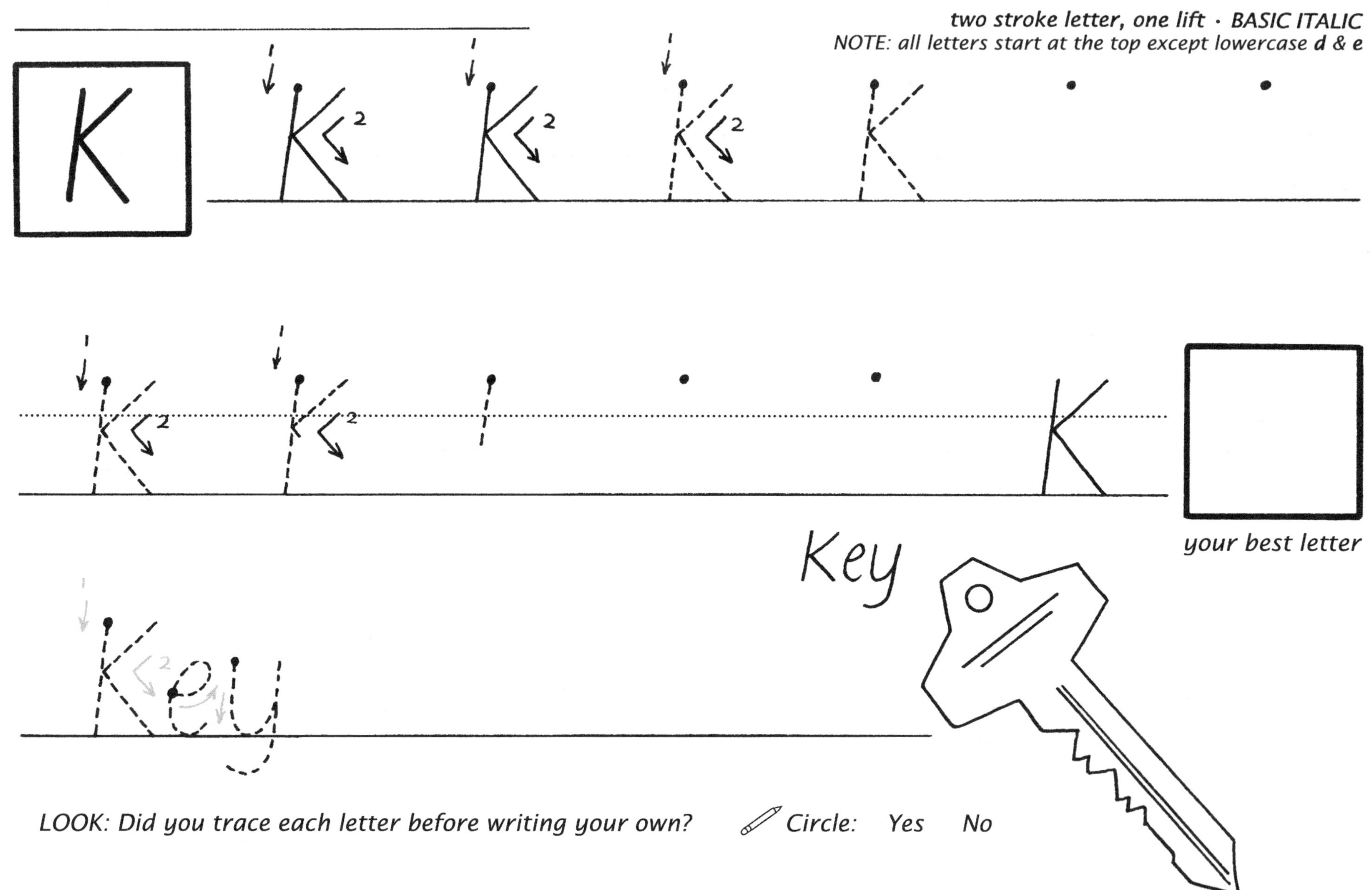

LOOK: Did you trace each letter before writing your own?   Circle: Yes   No

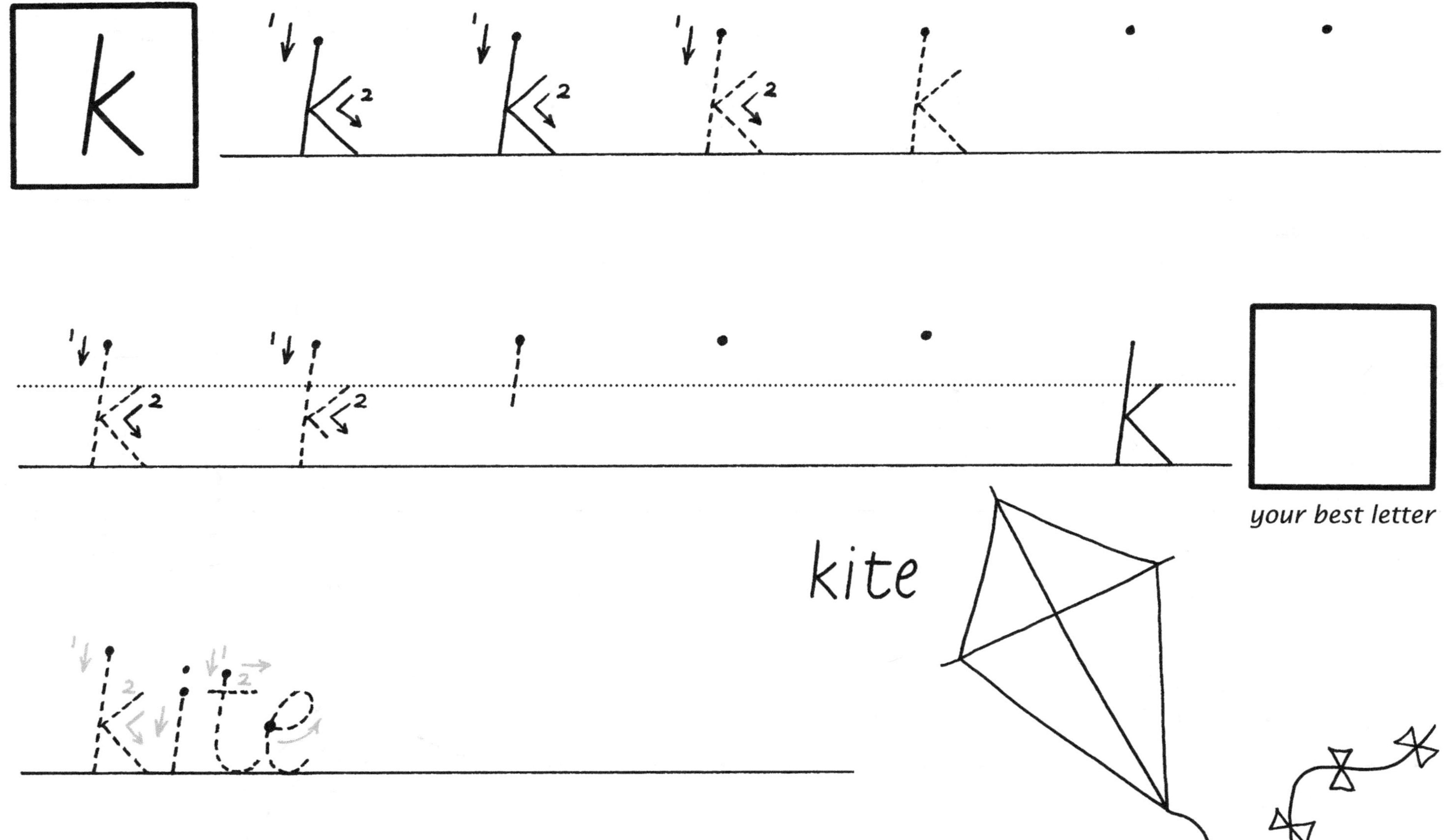

k
your best letter
kite
kite

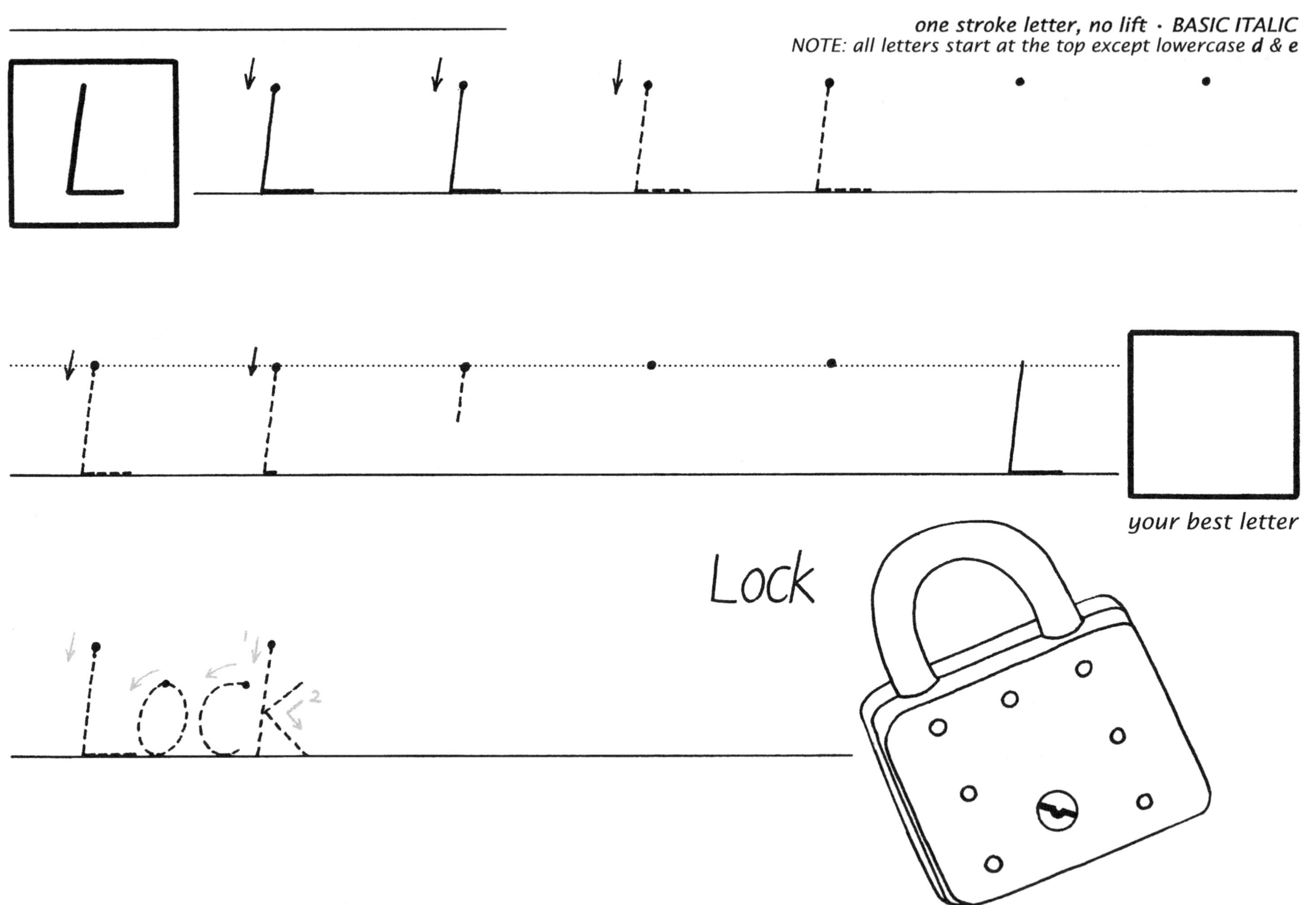

your best letter

Lock

your best letter

lamb

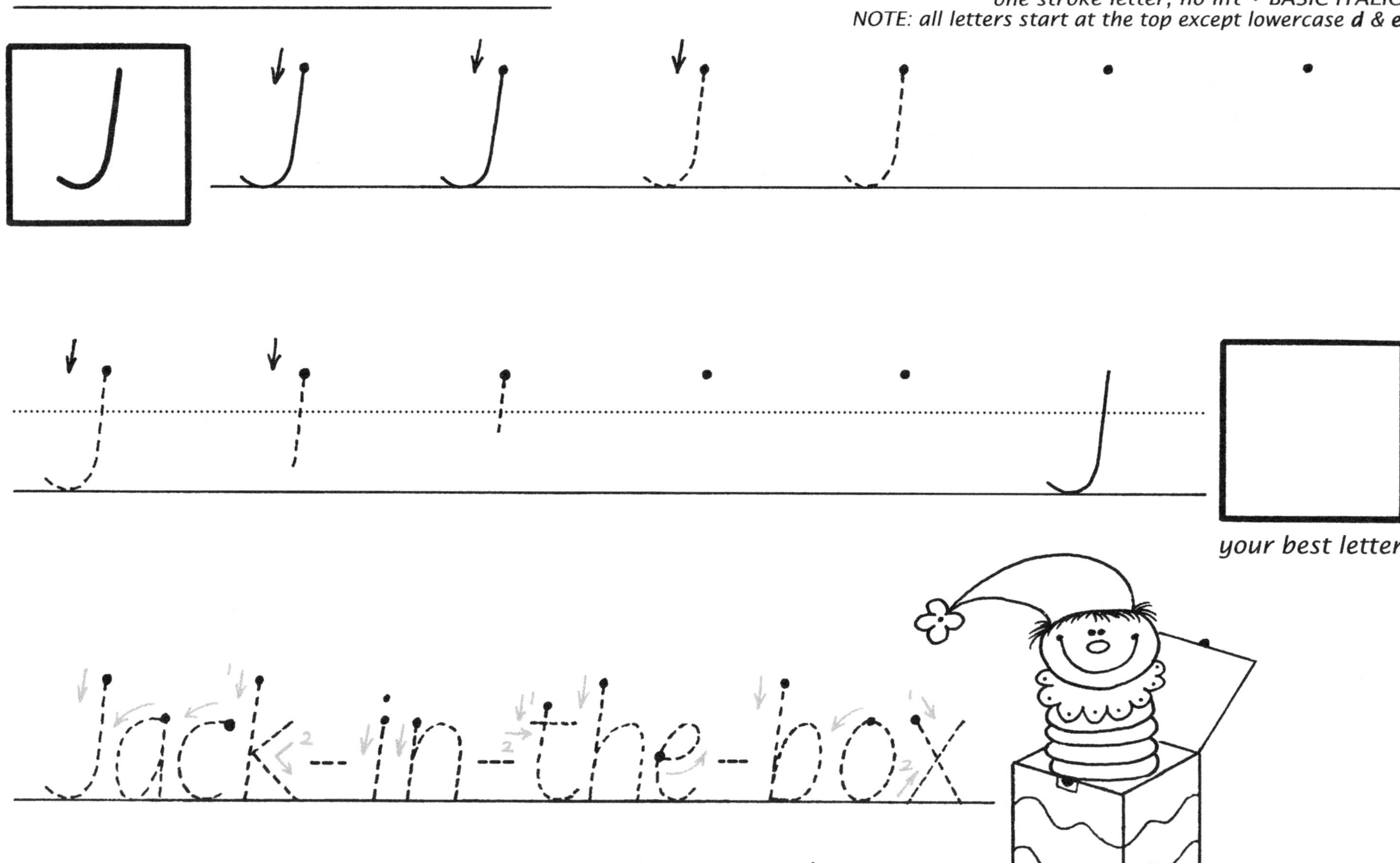

your best letter

Jack-in-the-box

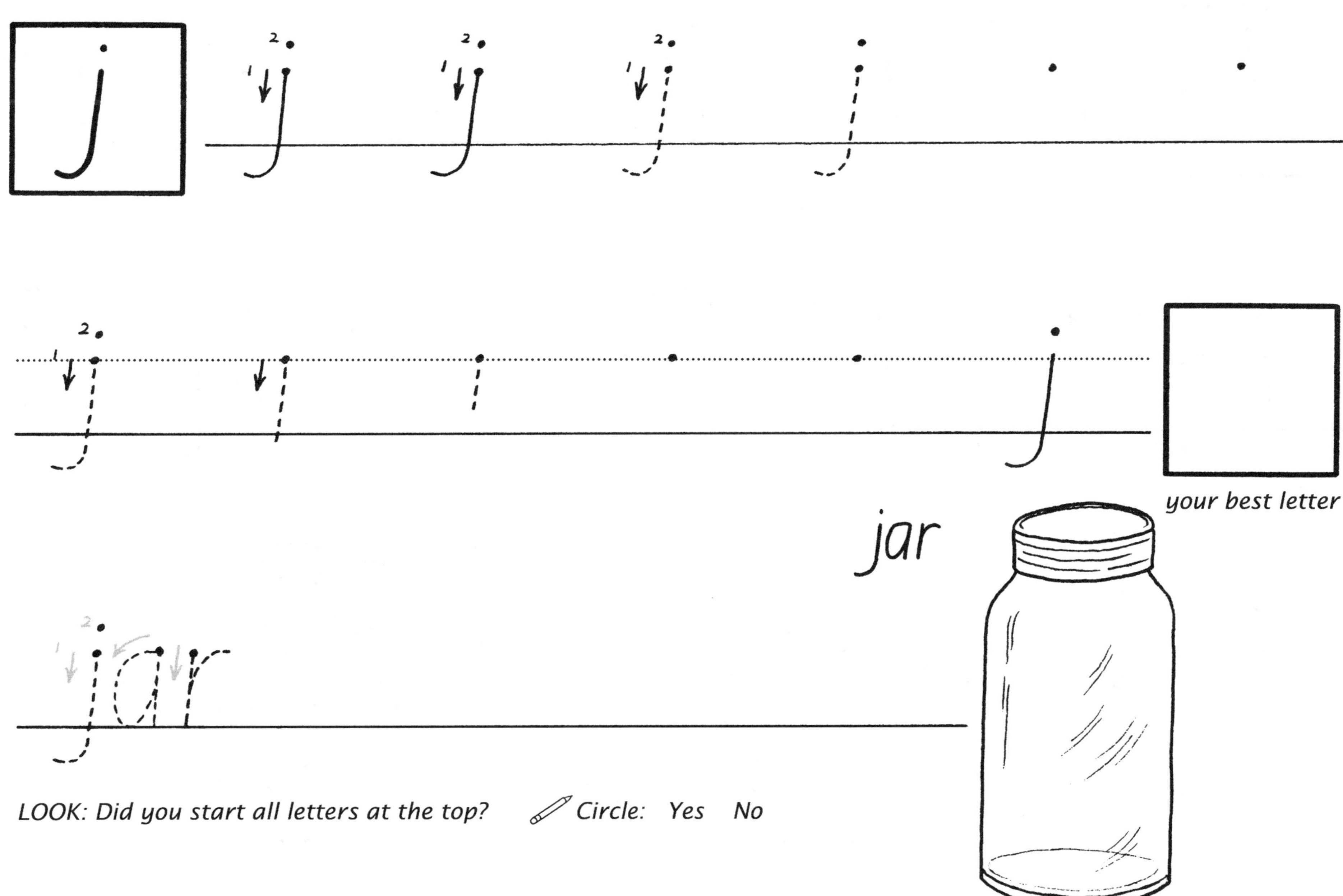

your best letter

jar

LOOK: Did you start all letters at the top?   Circle: Yes   No

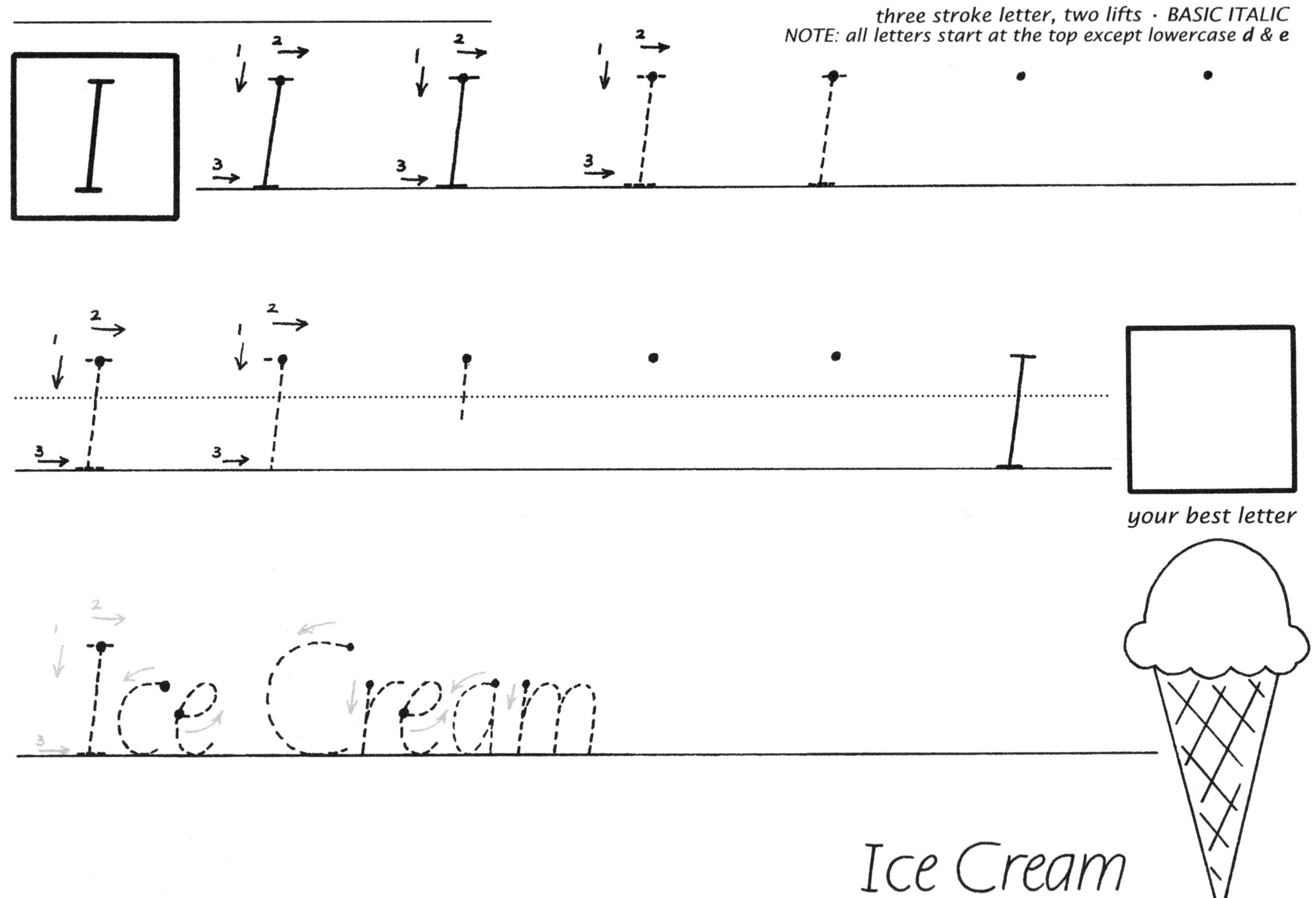

three stroke letter, two lifts · BASIC ITALIC
NOTE: all letters start at the top except lowercase d & e
your best letter
Ice Cream

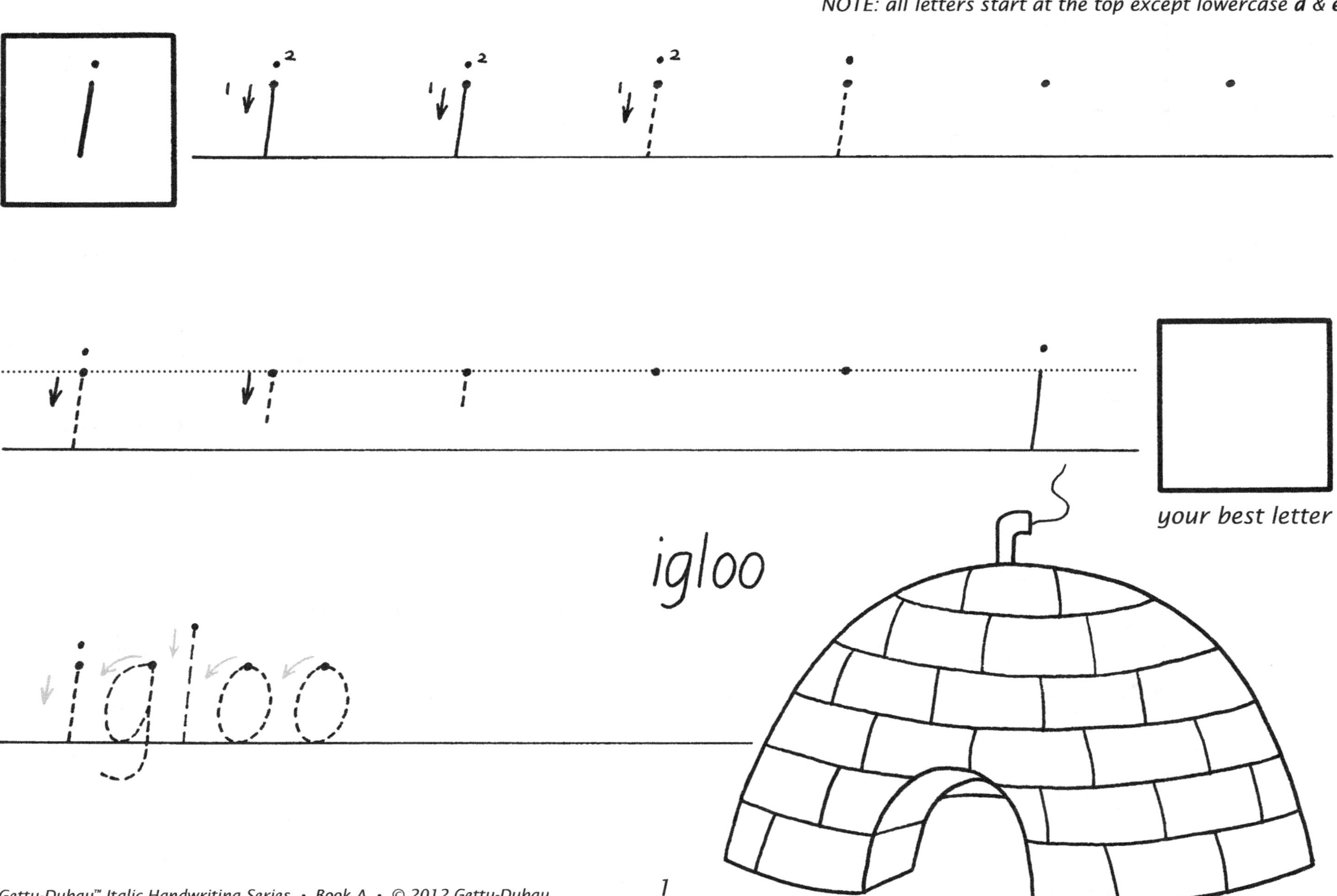

i
1 2
1 2
1 2
your best letter
igloo
igloo

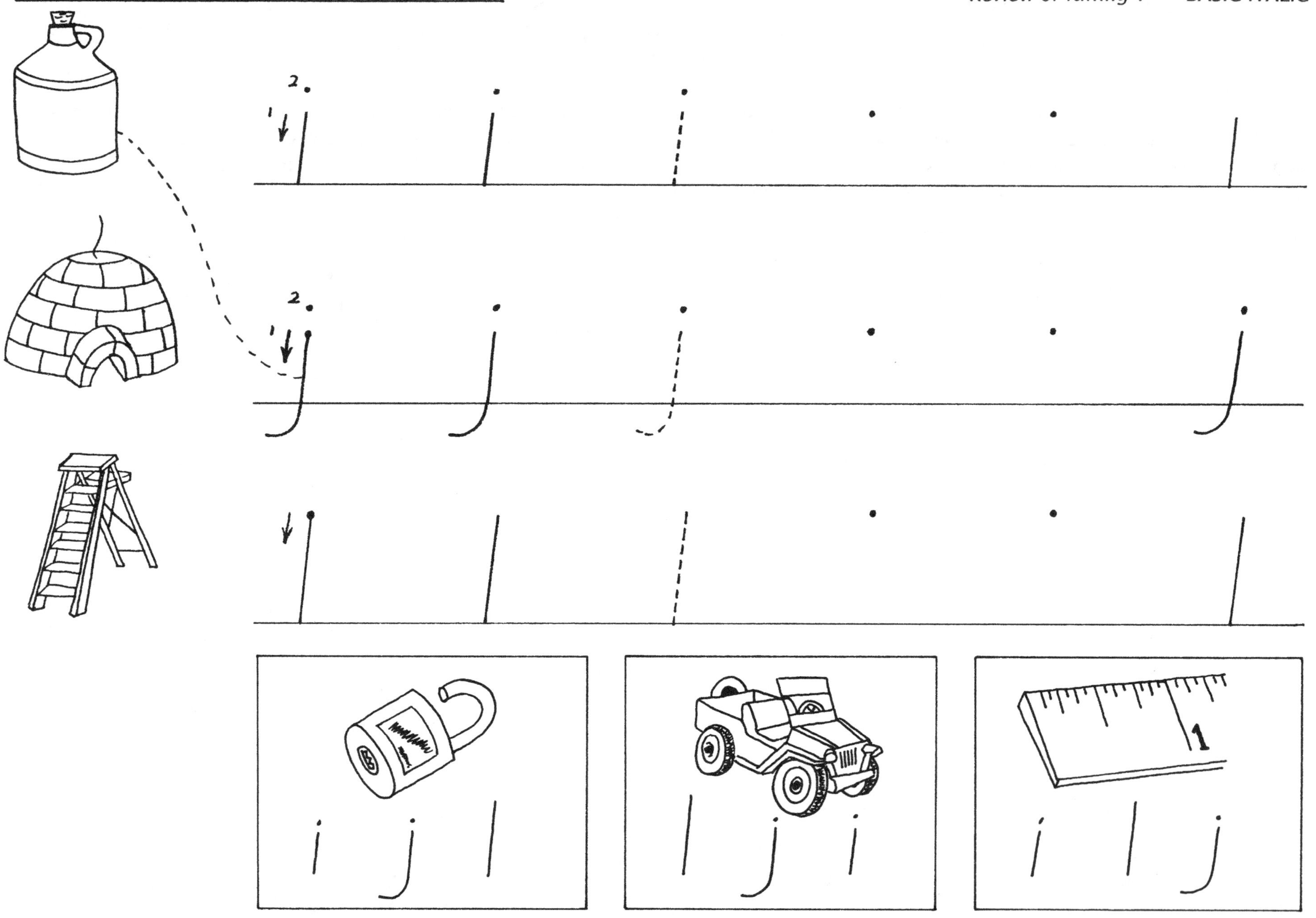

TOP THREE LINES: *Ask the student to draw a line from the picture to the letter that stands for the correct beginning sound.*

BOTTOM THREE BOXES: *Ask the student to circle the letter that stands for the beginning sound of the picture.*

BASIC SHAPES

Before the student begins writing in BOOK A, the authors recommend that the student practice the following shapes on unlined paper, one shape at a time. Allow the student to write each shape any size at first. Later, ask the student to write very large and very small forms of that same shape. We suggest the student also practice these shapes on a chalkboard and/or in cornmeal. (See INSTRUCTION MANUAL, "*Activity*," pp. 35 & 41.)

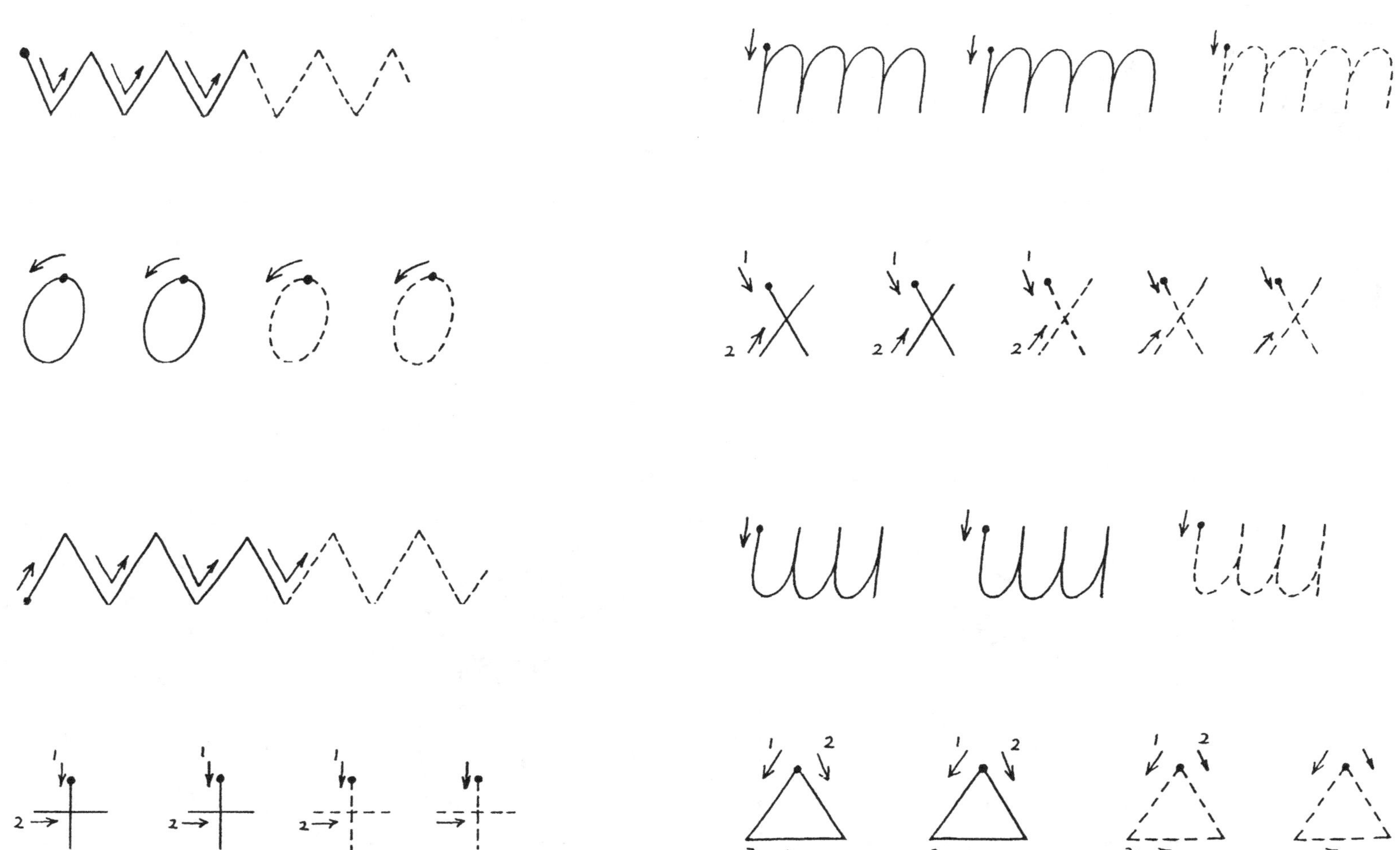

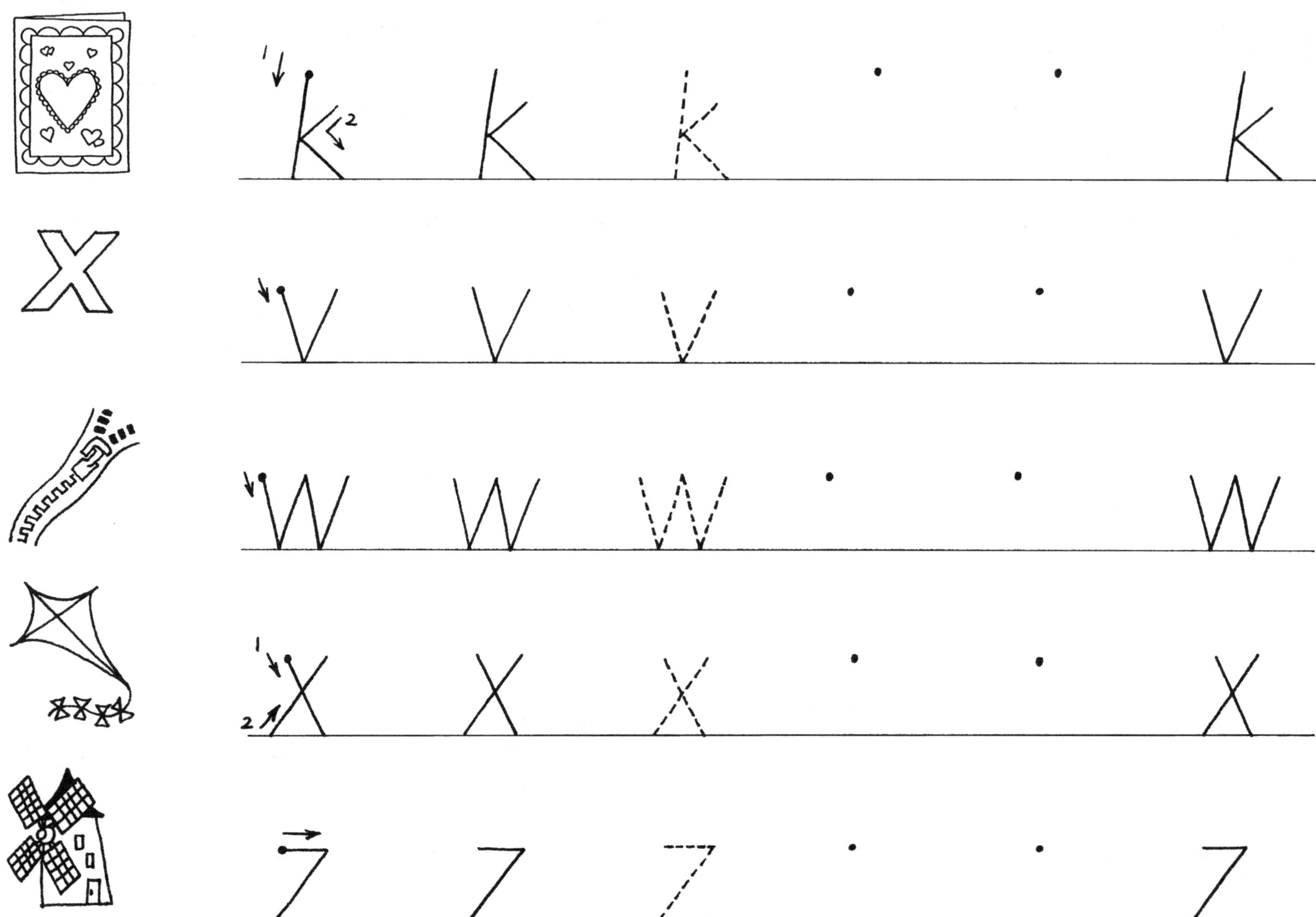

*Ask the student to draw a line from the picture to the letter
that stands for the correct beginning sound.*

Getty-Dubay™ Italic Handwriting Series · Book A · © 2012 Getty-Dubay

60

THE BEGINNING WRITER

Learning how to write involves much more than learning to write letters. It is a sophisticated, complex process involving learning letterforms, learning how to space within and between words, and learning how to organize writing on a page. Research indicates that there exists an almost perfect correlation between measures evaluating the children's *awareness* of their fingers and the ability to *use* their fingers in precise manual skills.

Ways to determine manual ability

To assist young students increase awareness of their hands and fingers, and to help you, the teacher, evaluate students' manual skills, have your students perform these tasks:

1. Direct the students to touch each of their fingers to their thumb, in order, from the first to the little finger. (By the age of six years, most children should be able to complete this exercise using one or both hands at a time.)

2. Have the students connect two dots that are spaced approximately eight inches apart on a page. (Most children of five years can accomplish this. However, if the student draws beyond the second dot or draws an unusually shaky line when nearing the second dot, it may indicate potential deficiencies in handwriting skills.)

Ways to improve kinesthetic perception of the hands

1. Unstructured clay modeling facilitates a student's perception of his or her hands. Encourage the student to manipulate the clay in every possible way—squeezing, flattening, poking, making shapes, etc.

2. To heighten the student's perception of shape, use a box in which a variety of small objects are placed for the student to feel but not see.

   a. Ask the student to reach in the box and find an unseen object that matches the one he or she is looking at.

   b. Direct the student to locate in the box an object that you or another student has described.

   c. Ask the student to find two objects with similar characteristics— two fuzzy objects, two heavy objects, two small objects, etc.

3. Draw several circles on a sheet of paper. To determine the student's ability to aim the finger and hand and also to point, have the student place dots in the circles with a pencil, pen, or crayon. Vary the difficulty of this task by increasing or decreasing the size of the circles or increasing the rate at which the dots are made. (The student must be able to point at a given or imaginary point in order to begin the stroke of a letter.)

Ways to confirm hand-eye tracking skills

The ability to control continuous hand movements while drawing lines of varying difficulty is basic to handwriting. If you are able to detect problems as the student completes the following tasks and are able to obtain appropriate assistance for the student, subsequent difficulties may be avoided.

1. Demonstrate drawing parallel lines. Then direct the student to draw parallel lines of a given length, first at a relaxed pace then at a faster one.

2. Direct the student to draw two curved lines equal in distance from one another. Later require more difficult shapes that combine straight lines, angles, and/or curves.

3. Direct the student to connect numbered dots on a sheet of paper that require horizontal, vertical and lateral movements. Place the paper in front of the student, close to the dominant hand. Later, space the dots further apart and require the student to cross the midline of his or her body. This latter task may cause the neuro-logically challenged student some difficulty.

The above evaluative tasks may be of help in assisting the learning of handwriting and in discovering deficiencies.

(See INSTRUCTION MANUAL, p. 13, for more suggestions concerning the beginning writer.)

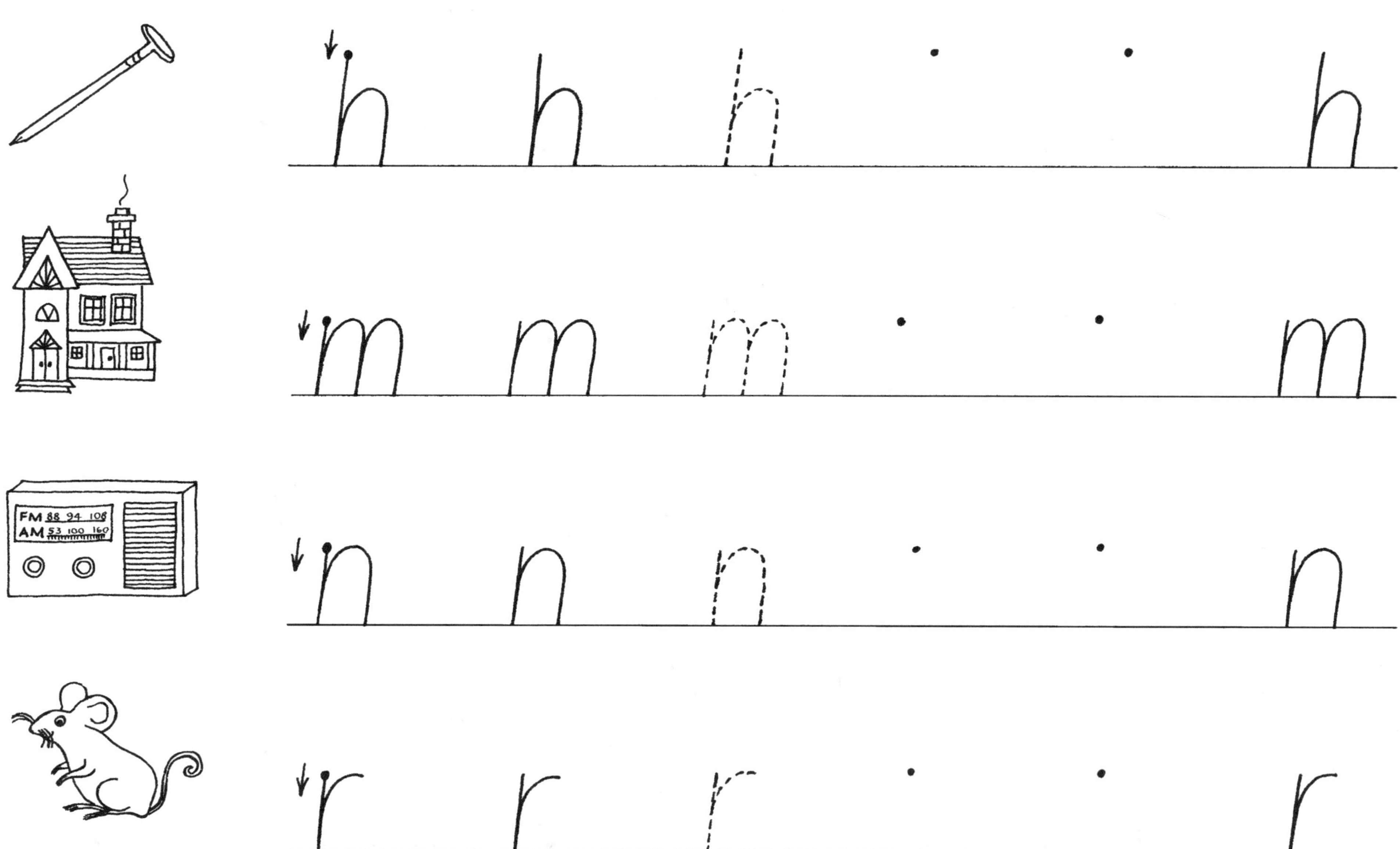

Ask the student to draw a line from the picture to the letter
that stands for the correct beginning sound.

GETTY-DUBAY™ ITALIC HANDWRITING SERIES
BASIC ITALIC ALPHABET

All letters written in one stroke unless otherwise indicated. *All letters start at the top except lowercase **d** and **e**.*

Aa Bb Cc Dd Ee Ff Gg

or

alternate
2-stroke e

Hh Ii Jj Kk Ll Mm

or

Nn Oo Pp Qq Rr Ss Tt

or

Uu Vv Ww Xx Yy Zz

0 1 2 3 4 5 6 7 8 9

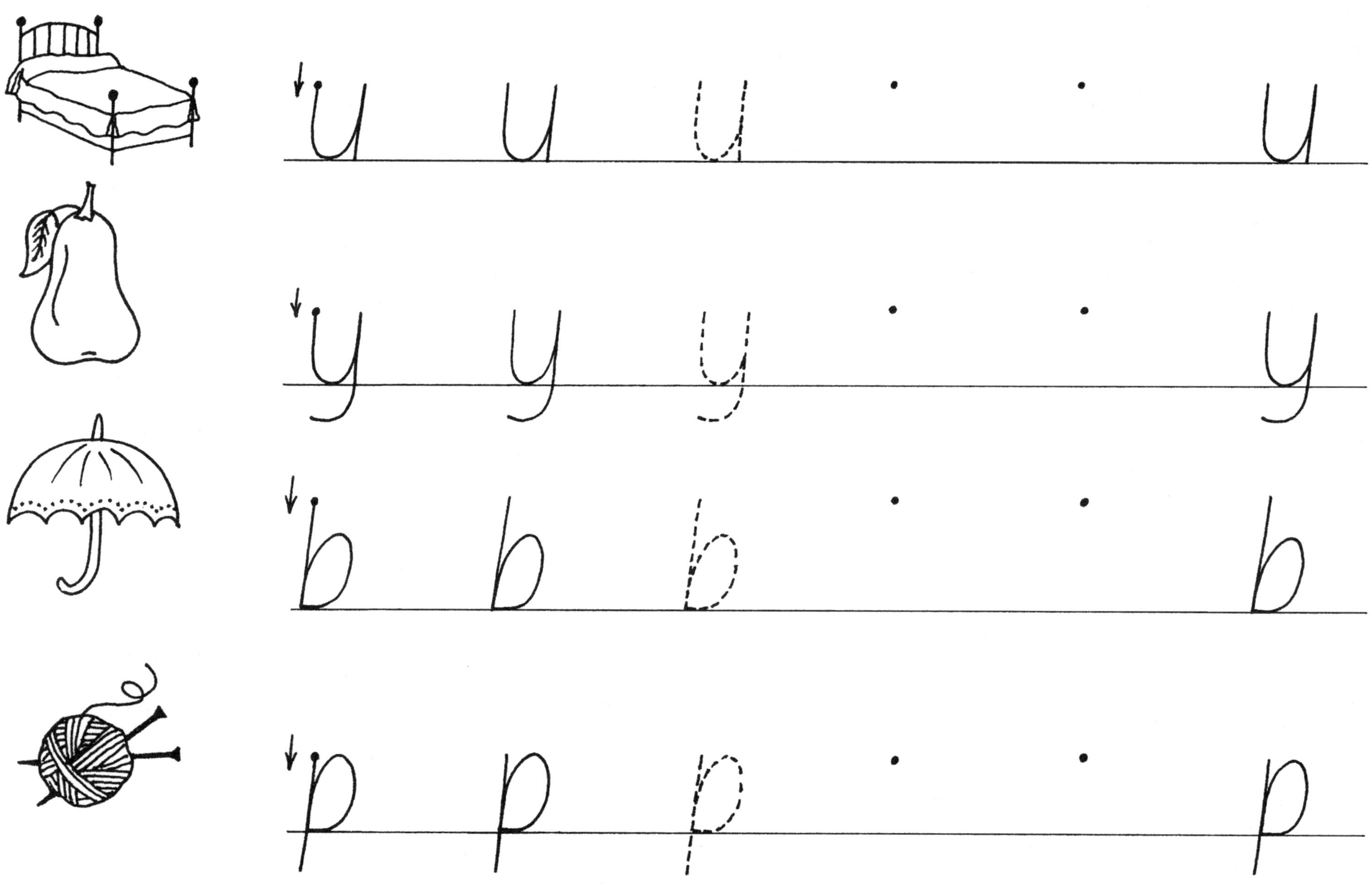

Ask the student to draw a line from the picture to the letter
that stands for the correct beginning sound.

GETTY-DUBAY™ HANDWRITING REMINDERS

PENCIL HOLD

Hold the pencil with the thumb and index finger, resting it on the middle finger. Rest the shaft of the pencil near the large knuckle. Hold the tool firmly and avoid pinching. To relax the hand, tap index finger on the pencil three times. Avoid "thumb wrap" and a "death grip".

PAPER POSITION

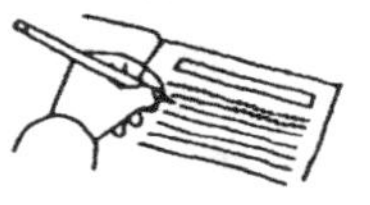

LEFT-HANDED: If the left-handed student writes with the wrist below the writing line, turn paper clockwise so it is slanted to the right, as illustrated.
If the left-handed student writes with a hook, with the wrist above the writing line, turn the paper counter-clockwise so it is slanted to the left, as illustrated. (Similar to right-handed position)

RIGHT-HANDED: If the student is right-handed, turn paper counter-clockwise so it is slanted to the left, as illustrated.

POSTURE

Rest feet flat on the floor and keep back comfortably straight without slumping. Rest forearms on writing surface. The student holds workbook or paper with the nonwriting hand so that the writing area is centered in the front of the student.

PRACTICE PAPER

Book A—Use unlined or lined paper together with workbooks.

MATERIALS

The *Getty-Dubay™ Italic Handwriting Series* workbooks, BOOKS A-G, and the INSTRUCTION MANUAL constitute a step-by-step program. Related materials consist of:

1. BLACKLINE MASTERS/WORKSHEETS - half sheets for introduction to, or review of, workbook pages.
2. CLASSROOM WALL CHARTS - basic & cursive italic.
3. DESK STRIPS - basic & cursive italic.

VOCABULARY

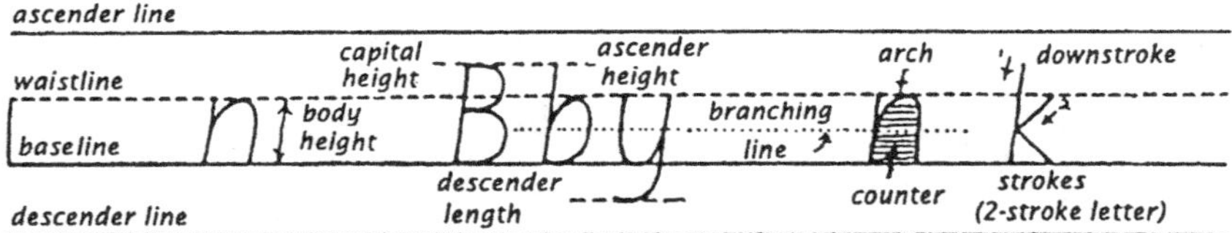

DIRECT INSTRUCTION

Several sessions of direct instruction each week are essential for a successful program. BOOK A – 5 to 10 minute sessions a day are recommended, see INSTRUCTION MANUAL, pp. 18-19

- SHAPE & STROKE SEQUENCE – teach basic italic in letter family groups, or according to the reading program in grade 1.
- SLOPE – encourage a consistent letter slope. Vertical letters (0° slope) may be the easiest to teach to beginning writers.
- SIZE – At first, allow students to write letters any size they wish on unlined paper, then introduce the workbook. A recommended progression through this book is one letter (lowercase and/or capital) per week.

SPACING

When young students are writing words, at first have them leave a space about the width of their two small fingers between words. As they become more proficient, they can leave less space.

ASSESSMENT

The *Getty-Dubay™ Italic Handwriting Series* provides a self-assessment process, LOOK, PLAN, PRACTICE, to enable the student to monitor progress. LOOK, step 1 of this process begins on some of the student pages in BOOK A. Assessment is the key to improving handwriting; in this book we introduce the first of three steps in the LOOK, PLAN, PRACTICE self-assessment process. The students look at their own writing and answer any questions on the page. The pencil indicates the student is to make a written response, generally by circling "yes" or "no". The teacher may encourage students to award themselves a star or a smiling face at the top of the page when they notice self-improvement.

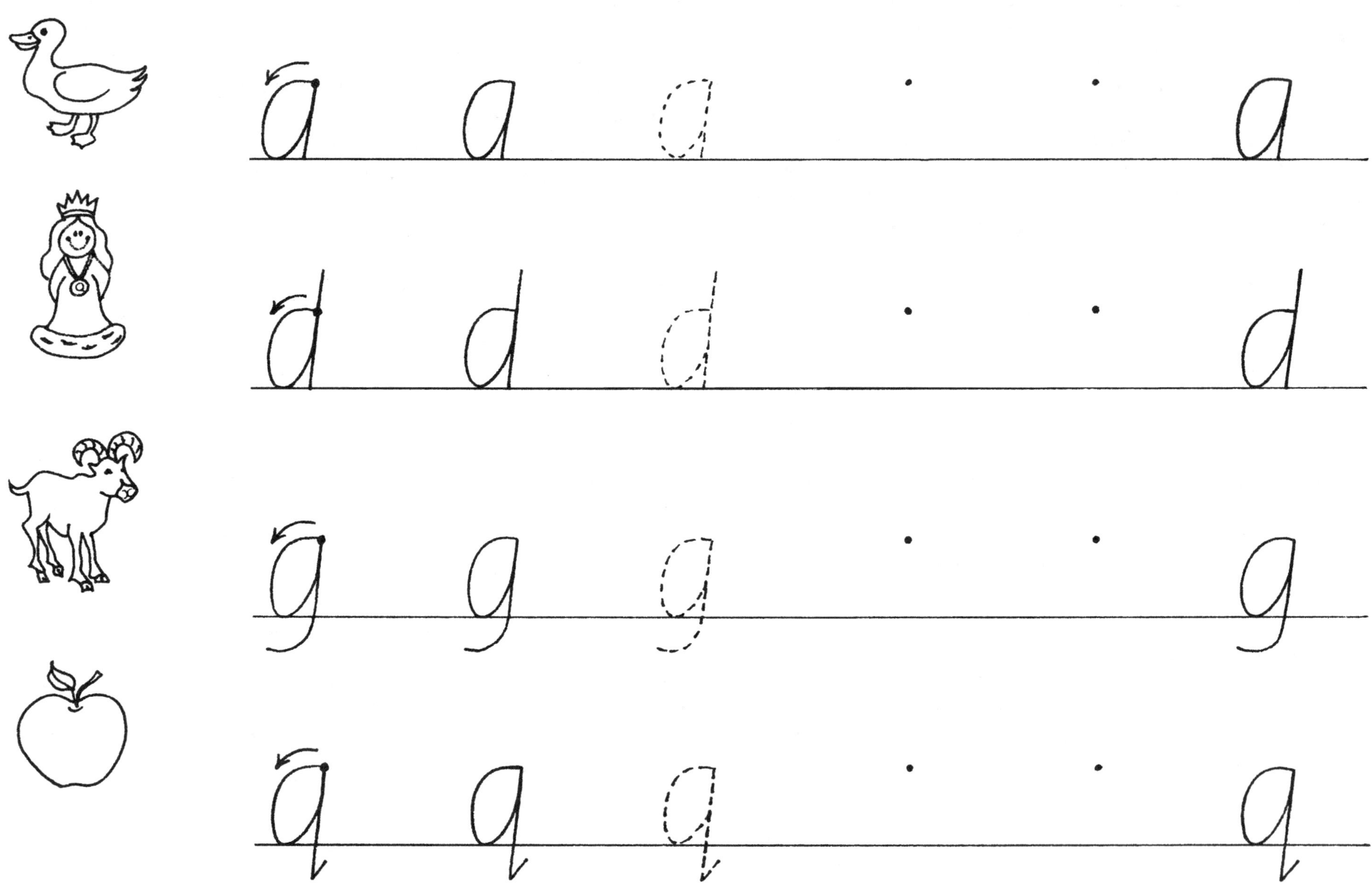

Ask the student to draw a line from the picture to the letter
that stands for the correct beginning sound.

INTRODUCTION

This is the first of seven workbooks providing instruction in basic italic handwriting. It is designed for the beginning student of handwriting and is recommended for preschool, kindergarten and/or early first grade (5 to 7 years of age).

The twenty-six lowercase letters and the twenty-six capitals are introduced one letter per page. Letters are arranged in the order of lowercase families, which group letters with similar strokes together and progress from simple to more complex forms. The matching capital letter occurs on the reverse of each lowercase page allowing introduction of both lowercase and capital together if preferred.

Each page is designed for the student to trace the models provided, write letters at the given dots, and to write a "best" letter in the empty box on each alphabet page. The standard writing tool is the pencil although other writing instruments such as the fiber tip pen may be used. When students are ready, they should trace the word describing the illustration on each letter page, following the dots and arrows.

It is essential that the instructor provide an understanding of the dot and the arrow to assist the writer in completing the pages successfully. The self-assessment method used in the *Getty-Dubay™ Italic Handwriting Series* enables students to monitor their individual progress. Step 1, LOOK, of the three-step LOOK, PLAN, PRACTICE format, is incorporated on 21 of the student pages. Students are asked to "LOOK" at their writing and affirm what is best. On the 21 pages with "LOOK" questions, students should circle their chosen answers. See INSTRUCTION MANUAL, PP. 13, 18 & 19.

The *Getty-Dubay™ Italic Handwriting Series* INSTRUCTION MANUAL is to be used in conjunction with this workbook. Explanations and in-depth descriptions of lowercase letters, capitals, joins, and numerals are presented in the manual, emphasizing shape, strokes, size, slope and spacing of the letters. Also included in the manual are: a rationale for italic handwriting, techniques for teaching and assessing handwriting, sequence of skills, handwriting activities, and a brief history of our alphabet.

BOOK B, basic italic, follows this workbook and is designed for the beginning reader. In the third book, BOOK C, basic italic letterforms are reinforced and cursive italic is introduced. BOOKS D, E, F, and G provide a complete basic italic and cursive italic handwriting program. BOOKS B, C, and/or D may also be suitable for the person learning English as a second language.

The format of this book was chosen to accommodate both the left- and right-handed writer. When open, the book fits easily on a small desk, and the writer is not encumbered with an additional page to the left or right. From day one, use a Getty-Dubay™ basic italic desk strip as a reminder. Blackline masters are designed for supplementary practice and are available for each workbook in the series. See www.handwritingsuccess.com for these supplementary materials.

You can guide children toward the challenge and delight in the writing process by reading to them, modeling handwriting, providing writing materials, and especially by building enthusiasm for the letters of our alphabet and for the written word.

·abcdefghijklmnopqrstuvwxyz·

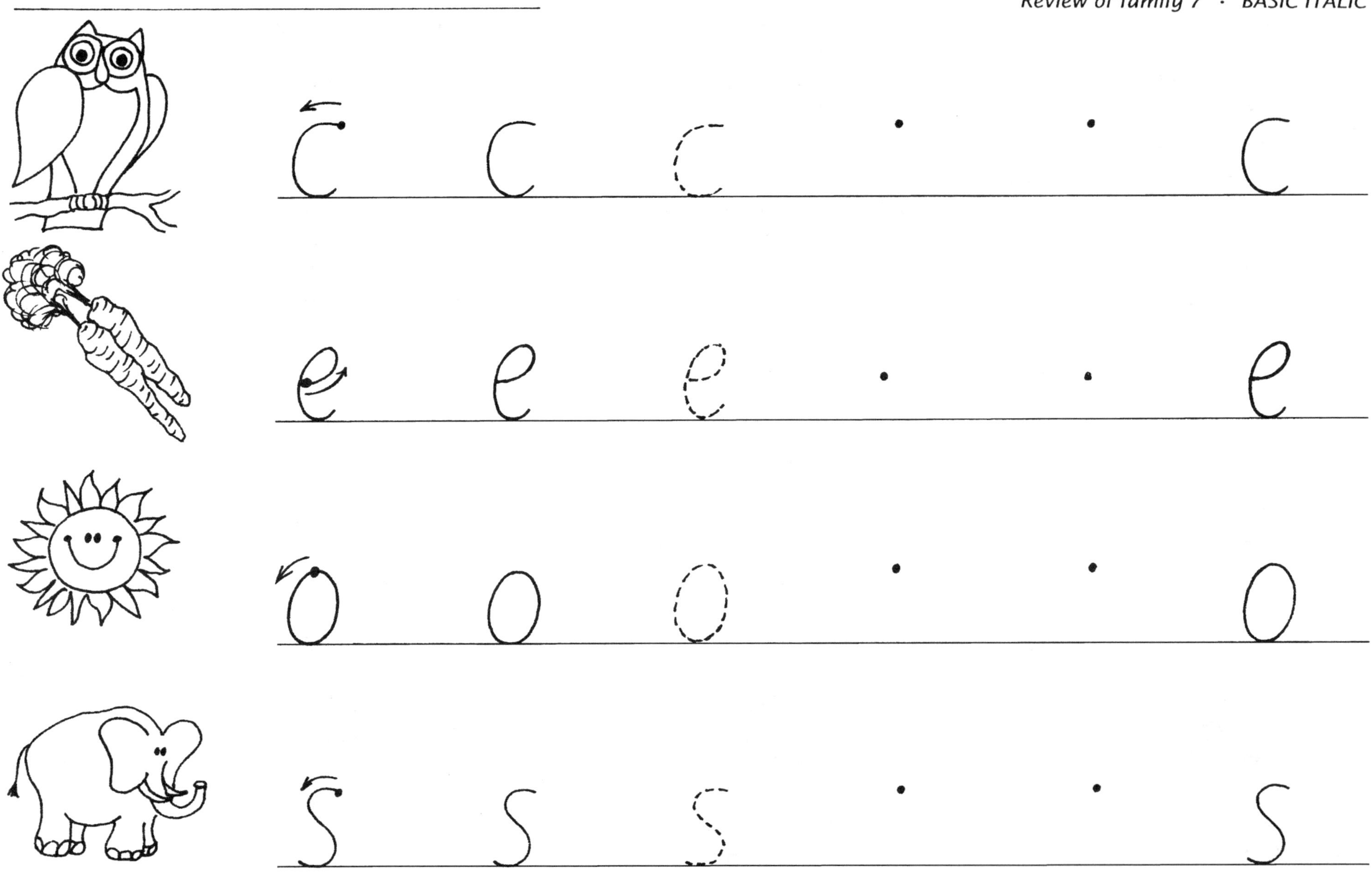

*Ask the student to draw a line from the picture to the letter
that stands for the correct beginning sound.*

CONTENTS

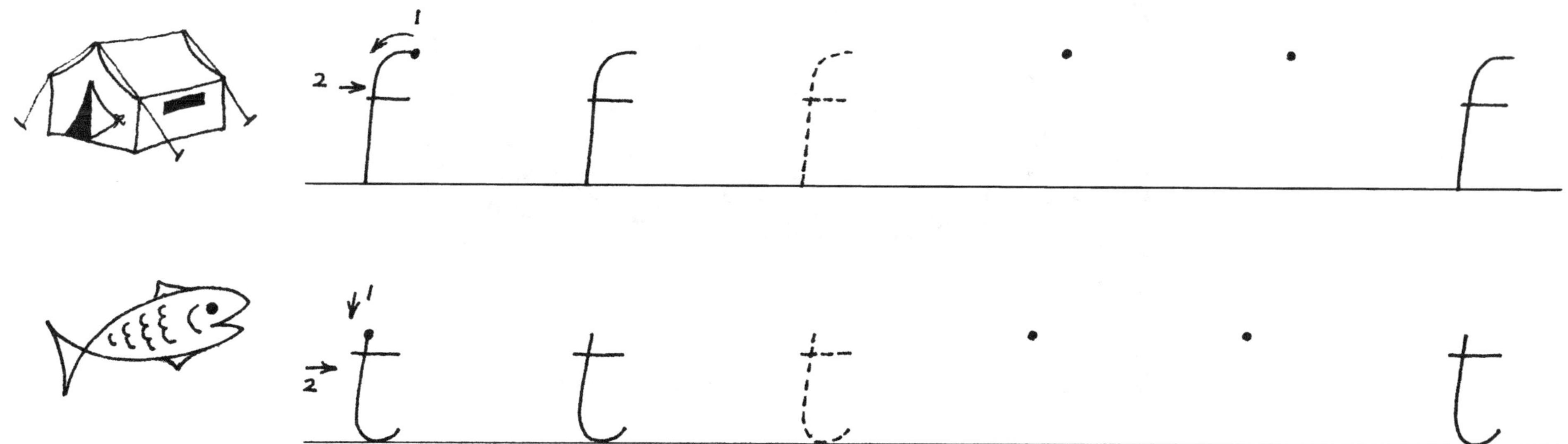

TOP TWO LINES: Ask the student to draw a line from the picture to the letter that stands for the correct beginning sound.

BOTTOM FOUR SQUARES: Ask the student to circle the letter that stands for the beginning sound of the picture.

by

Barbara Getty & Inga Dubay

GETTY-DUBAY™ ITALIC HANDWRITING SERIES

BOOK A ▪ Basic Italic
14 mm body height

BOOK B ▪ Basic Italic
11 mm body height, 9 mm

BOOK C ▪ Basic & Cursive Italic
9 mm, 6 mm body height   Introduction to Cursive Italic

BOOK D ▪ Basic & Cursive Italic
6 mm, 5 mm body height

BOOK E ▪ Basic & Cursive Italic
6 mm, 5 mm, 4 mm body height

BOOK F ▪ Basic & Cursive Italic
6 mm, 5 mm, 4 mm body height

BOOK G ▪ Basic & Cursive Italic
5 mm, 4 mm body height

INSTRUCTION MANUAL

BOOK A ▪ INTERNATIONAL EDITION

Copyright 2012 by Barbara M. Getty and Inga S. Dubay
ISBN 978-0-9827762-7-8

FOURTH EDITION
Copyright 2012 by Barbara M. Getty and Inga S. Dubay
THIRD EDITION
Copyright 1999 by Barbara M. Getty and Inga S. Dubay
SECOND EDITION
Copyright 1986 by Barbara M. Getty and Inga S. Dubay
REVISED EDITION
Copyright 1980 by Barbara M. Getty and Inga S. Dubay
FIRST EDITION
Copyright 1979 by Barbara M. Getty and Inga S. Dubay

All rights reserved. This text may not be reproduced in whole or in part without the express written permission of the copyright holder.

Published by Handwriting Success, LLC,
Portland, Oregon USA

www.handwritingsuccess.com

Printed at various locations around the world by IngramSpark.

Cover Design: Sinda Markham
Front cover picture: Flowers of the sunflower family in the Ochoco National Forest, Oregon, USA
Back cover pictures: Columbine flower, Golden-mantled squirrel